S0-AZQ-101

Noble
gases

| | | | | | | | VIIA | 2   4.0026
He
s²
Helium |

	IIIA	IVA	VA	VIA	VIIA	
	5 10.811 **B** s²2s²2p¹ Boron	6 12.0111 **C** s²2s²2p² Carbon	7 14.0067 **N** s²2s²2p³ Nitrogen	8 15.9994 **O** s²2s²2p⁴ Oxygen	9 18.9984 **F** s²2s²2p⁵ Fluorine	10 20.183 **Ne** s²2s²2p⁶ Neon
	13 26.9815 **Al** [Ne]3s²3p¹ Aluminum	14 28.086 **Si** [Ne]3s²3p² Silicon	15 30.9738 **P** [Ne]3s²3p³ Phosphorus	16 32.064 **S** [Ne]3s²3p⁴ Sulfur	17 35.453 **Cl** [Ne]3s²3p⁵ Chlorine	18 39.948 **Ar** [Ne]3s²3p⁶ Argon

VIII	IB	IIB	IIIA	IVA	VA	VIA	VIIA	
28 58.71 **Ni** [Ar]3d⁸4s² Nickel	29 63.54 **Cu** [Ar]3d¹⁰4s¹ Copper	30 65.37 **Zn** [Ar]3d¹⁰4s² Zinc	31 69.72 **Ga** [Ar]3d¹⁰4s²4p¹ Gallium	32 72.59 **Ge** [Ar]3d¹⁰4s²4p² Germanium	33 74.992 **As** [Ar]3d¹⁰4s²4p³ Arsenic	34 78.96 **Se** [Ar]3d¹⁰4s²4p⁴ Selenium	35 79.909 **Br** [Ar]3d¹⁰4s²4p⁵ Bromine	36 83.80 **Kr** [Ar]3d¹⁰4s²4p⁶ Krypton
46 106.4 **Pd** [Kr]4d¹⁰5s⁰ Palladium	47 107.870 **Ag** [Kr]4d¹⁰5s¹ Silver	48 112.40 **Cd** [Kr]4d¹⁰5s² Cadmium	49 114.82 **In** [Kr]4d¹⁰5s²5p¹ Indium	50 118.69 **Sn** [Kr]4d¹⁰5s²5p² Tin	51 121.75 **Sb** [Kr]4d¹⁰5s²5p³ Antimony	52 127.60 **Te** [Kr]4d¹⁰5s²5p⁴ Tellurium	53 126.904 **I** [Kr]4d¹⁰5s²5p⁵ Iodine	54 131.30 **Xe** [Kr]4d¹⁰5s²5p⁶ Xenon
78 195.09 **Pt** [Xe]4f¹⁴5d⁹6s⁰ Platinum	79 196.967 **Au** [Xe]4f¹⁴5d¹⁰6s¹ Gold	80 200.59 **Hg** [Xe]4f¹⁴5d¹⁰6s² Mercury	81 204.37 **Tl** [Xe]4f¹⁴5d¹⁰6s²6p¹ Thallium	82 207.19 **Pb** [Xe]4f¹⁴5d¹⁰6s²6p² Lead	83 208.980 **Bi** [Xe]4f¹⁴5d¹⁰6s²6p³ Bismuth	84 (210) **Po** [Xe]4f¹⁴5d¹⁰6s²6p⁴ Polonium	85 (210) **At** [Xe]4f¹⁴5d¹⁰6s²6p⁵ Astatine	86 (222) **Rn** [Xe]4f¹⁴5d¹⁰6s²6p⁶ Radon

63 151.96 **Eu** [Xe]4f⁷5d⁰6s² Europium	64 157.25 **Gd** [Xe]4f⁷5d¹6s² Gadolinium	65 158.924 **Tb** [Xe]4f⁹5d⁰6s² Terbium	66 162.50 **Dy** [Xe]4f¹⁰5d⁰6s² Dysprosium	67 164.930 **Ho** [Xe]4f¹¹5d⁰6s² Holmium	68 167.26 **Er** [Xe]4f¹²5d⁰6s² Erbium	69 168.934 **Tm** [Xe]4f¹³5d⁰6s² Thulium	70 173.04 **Yb** [Xe]4f¹⁴5d⁰6s² Ytterbium	71 174.97 **Lu** [Xe]4f¹⁴5d¹6s² Lutetium
95 (243) **Am** [Rn]5f⁷6d⁰7s² Americium	96 (247) **Cm** [Rn]5f⁷6d¹7s² Curium	97 (247) **Bk** [Rn]5f⁷6d²7s² Berkelium	98 (251) **Cf** [Rn]5f⁹6d¹7s² Californium	99 (254) **Es** Einsteinium	100 (253) **Fm** Fermium	101 (256) **Md** Mendelevium	102 (254) **No** Nobelium	103 (257) **Lw** Lawrencium

Tables

LINEAR MEASURE

12 inches (in.) = 1 foot (ft.)
3 feet = 1 yard (yd.)
$5\frac{1}{2}$ yards, or $16\frac{1}{2}$ feet = 1 rod (rd.)
320 rods, 1760 yards, or 5280 feet = 1 mile (mi.)

SQUARE MEASURE

144 square inches (sq. in.) = 1 square foot (sq. ft.)
9 square feet = 1 square yard (sq. yd.)
$30\frac{1}{4}$ square yards = 1 square rod (sq. rd.)
160 square rods, or 43,560 square feet = 1 acre (A.)
640 acres = 1 square mile (sq. mi.)

CUBIC MEASURE

1728 cubic inches (cu. in.) = 1 cubic foot (cu. ft.)
27 cubic feet = 1 cubic yard (cu. yd.)

LIQUID MEASURE

2 pints (pt.) = 1 quart (qt.)
4 quarts, or 8 pints = 1 gallon (gal.)
$31\frac{1}{2}$ gallons = 1 barrel (bbl.)

DRY MEASURE

2 pints = 1 quart
8 quarts = 1 peck (pk.)
4 pecks = 1 bushel (bu.)

METRIC LINEAR MEASURE

10 millimeters (mm.) = 1 centimeter (cm.)
10 centimeters = 1 decimeter (dm.)
10 decimeters = 1 meter (m.)
1000 meters = 1 kilometer (km.)

METRIC EQUIVALENTS

1 inch = 2.54 centimeters
1 yard = 0.9144 meter
1 mile = 1.609 kilometers
1 centimeter = 0.39 inch
1 meter = 39.37 inches, or 1.1 yard
1 kilometer = 0.62 mile

1 gram (g.) = 0.03528 ounce (oz.)
1 ounce = 28.35 grams
1 kilogram (kg.) = 2.205 pounds (lb.)
1 pound = 0.454 kilogram
1 liter (l.) = 1.057 quarts
1 quart = 0.946 liter

COMMON EQUIVALENTS (APPROXIMATE)

1 bu. = 2150 cu. in., or $1\frac{1}{4}$ cu. ft.
1 gal. = 231 cu. in.
1 cu. ft. = $7\frac{1}{2}$ gal.
1 cu. ft. water = 62.5 lb.
1 gal. water = $8\frac{1}{3}$ lb.
1 cu. ft. ice = $57\frac{1}{2}$ lb.

1 bbl. flour = 196 lb.
1 cord (4-foot wood) = 128 cu. ft.
1 T. hay = 500 cu. ft.
1 T. hard coal = 35 cu. ft.
1 T. soft coal = 42 cu. ft.
$\pi = 3.1416$

7101013104

Chemistry: A Study of Matter

Ex Libris

NAME _____

ADDRESS _____

CITY _____

WE BUY & SELL

USED BOOKS

HIGHEST PRICES PAID ALL YEAR FOR BOOKS IN GOOD CONDITION

Southworth's

HAMMOND
INDIANAPOLIS
MICHIGAN CITY

Extension **RMAKERS**

Bookstores

"Statewide Service to Purdue Students"

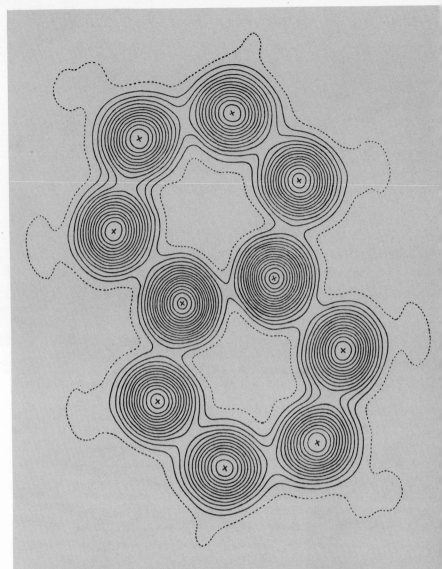

A BLAISDELL BOOK IN THE PURE AND APPLIED SCIENCES

Chemistry

ALFRED B. GARRETT

W. T. LIPPINCOTT

FRANK HENRY VERHOEK

The Ohio State University

A Study of Matter

Blaisdell Publishing Company
A Division of Ginn and Company

Waltham, Massachusetts | Toronto | London

COPYRIGHT © 1968 BY BLAISDELL PUBLISHING COMPANY
A DIVISION OF GINN AND COMPANY
ALL RIGHTS RESERVED. NO PART OF THE MATERIAL COVERED BY
THIS COPYRIGHT MAY BE PRODUCED IN ANY FORM OR BY ANY
MEANS OF REPRODUCTION
LIBRARY OF CONGRESS CATALOG CARD NUMBER: 67–11447
PRINTED IN THE UNITED STATES OF AMERICA

Preface

General chemistry includes a great variety of interrelated topics that may be studied in depth or in breadth. For this text the authors have selected topics which are the basis of much of the thought and activity of modern chemists. These topics are discussed rigorously in an open-ended manner and integrated or connected with underlying principles of structure, energy, and reactivity, thus establishing a solid foundation in the study of chemistry. Once the student has acquired such a foundation, he can build on it with the further readings listed at the end of each chapter or with advanced courses in chemistry.

Some of the great scientific ideas discussed are a challenging, maturing extension of those presented in the new programs of CHEMS and CBA as well as of PSSC and BSCS; however, other topics represent material which teachers have been accustomed to find only in more advanced texts.

Among the topics treated are: atomic and molecular structure, energy states in atoms and molecules, the solid state, intermolecular attractive forces, introductory thermodynamics, introductory chemical kinetics, coordination chemistry, some chemistry of representative metals and of nonmetals, organic chemistry including some polymer chemistry and some physical organic chemistry, and introductory biochemistry.

The chapters are written as essays on each topic, building from the simple to the complex, with some chapters divided into sections of different degrees of difficulty. Each chapter presents descriptive chemistry carefully interwoven with principles.

Certain enriching material supplementing the text discussion appears throughout the book in a special type face; this material includes historical developments, elaboration and refinement of definitions, extended descriptions of experiments and equipment, and some illustrative examples. Epigraphs at the beginning of the chapters commemorate important discoveries and people in the history of chemistry. Each chapter concludes with a summary, a list of special terms, a reading list, and questions and problems for the student.

The text is arranged so that the teacher can select any of a variety of sequences of topics. For teachers wishing to emphasize introductory physical chemistry the sequence of Chapters 1–15 and 20–25 is recommended; for those favoring a principles-oriented course in descriptive inorganic chemistry, the sequence of Chapters 1–21 and 26–28 is suggested; for those wishing to prepare students for more biologically directed curricula, the sequence of Chapters 1–14, 20–24, and 29–33 might be appropriate. Rarely would the entire book be covered in a single course.

The text is designed for the student in the first course in college chemistry. A background in high school chemistry is assumed, but the diligent student should succeed without it. The book is written for all, including the best in the class. The authors have made a special effort, in developing the difficult areas, to keep the background and the intellectual maturity of the student in mind. The mathematics required is a good understanding of algebra and a sound, thorough comprehension of arithmetic.

The authors wish to acknowledge with grateful appreciation the assistance of their colleagues in the Department of Chemistry at The Ohio State University, including Professors P. G. Gassman, R. E. Gerkin, P. M. Harris, D. Horton, D. Meek, R. J. Ouellette, S. Shore, and A. Wojcicki.

To the forerunners of this text—McPherson and Henderson; McPherson, Henderson, Fernelius, and Mack; and Mack, Garrett, Haskins, and Verhoek, we bow in appreciation. In view of the many curriculum changes and new discoveries in science we have determined that this version should present entirely new material.

The authors invite you to explore these ideas with them in their venture to understand and interpret the universe.

A.B.G.
W.T.L.
F.H.V.

Contents

Chemistry: A Study of Matter

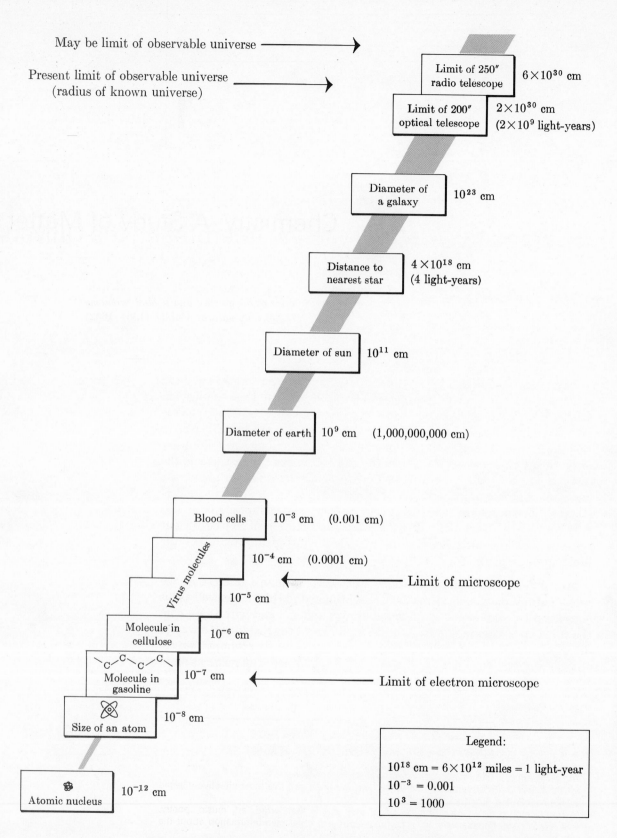

Figure 1.1 Range in sizes and distances of objects in the universe.

Chemistry: An Approach to Interpreting the Universe

*Let us remember, please, that the search for the constitution
of the world is one of the greatest and noblest problems
presented by nature.* Galileo (1564–1642)

Today we can describe with considerable confidence the composition and
structure, not only of the very tiny objects in the universe—molecules,
atoms, and atomic nuclei—but also of the great massive bodies such as the
moons, the planets, the stars, and even the galaxies. We can describe as
well the kinds of changes or reactions that occur not only in the laboratory
or on the earth's surface but also in the sun and in the farthest star in the
farthest galaxy. The story of man's search for information about the
structure and composition of the stuff in the universe and for an understanding of the changes in energy, structure, and composition of this
stuff and his studies on the types of forces and motion of objects in our
universe comprise an impressive part of the world's great literature—the
literature of science.

Man's Early Attempts. Earliest history records man's interest in the
many natural phenomena such as fire, lightning, and thunder as well as his
concern with common things like air, water, and soil and with the moon,
the sun, and the stars. For thousands of years he struggled to find a way to
describe them in terms of simpler substances. In his early attempts, superstitions and black magic played a major role. Folk lore and religious dicta

---

● ● ● OBJECTIVES OF MAN THE INTELLECTUAL

In the Sciences : An interpretation of the material universe.
In the Social Sciences and Humanities : The way man can live most effectively in the
universe he learns to interpret.
In the Communicative Arts (mathematics, oral and written word, art, music, poetry,
drama, etc.): An effective method of communicating to other men information about the
reality he discovers in other searches.

were often dominant. For hundreds of years many people lived under the beliefs that—

The earth was the center of the universe.
The four elements were fire, air, earth, and water.
A philosopher's stone could change base metals to gold.
Life developed by spontaneous generation.

As knowledge about the universe gradually was distilled and refined, the quest to know the universe gradually became known as *science*.

Science Develops. The collection of facts and theories about the natural phenomena and objects in the universe is the body of knowledge now called science. The feature that distinguishes today's search for knowledge of the universe from the procedure of the early days is the tough-minded attitude of the scientist—his requirement that conclusions or theories be subjected to experimentation or testing before they are accepted. This unique process establishes the validity of a theory. It is one of the important steps in the scientific method; this method is often summarized in the following terms: observation, classification, theorizing, and testing.

The Science of Chemistry. The body of information that describes the structure and composition of the material in the universe together with the changes in structure and composition and the energy relations involved in these changes is known as *chemistry*. The beginnings of chemistry go

Figure 1.2 A seventeenth-century chemistry laboratory. *(Photograph courtesy of the Fisher Scientific Company.)*

● ● ●   SOME ASPECTS OF THE SCIENTIFIC METHOD

1. Being informed.   3. Being creative.   5. Being flexible.
2. Being organized.   4. Being objective.

Figure 1.3 A modern laboratory. Laboratories now require excellent equipment for exact measurements, analysis of small quantities of material, and handling of chemicals to prevent contamination. *(Photograph courtesy of the Fisher Scientific Company.)*

back to the arts and crafts of ancient times, in which man developed practical technologies for the smelting and alloying of metals, the making of glass, the production of charcoal and lime, etc. Association of the metallic arts with the Egyptian priesthood gave rise to the mysticism and obscurity of the period of alchemy. Alchemy was developed by Arabic cultures between A.D. 600 and 1000 and transmitted to the then Western world toward the end of that time. Its practitioners were largely concerned with the transmutation of base metals into gold, and they flourished until the early eighteenth century, having in the meantime given rise to a school which emphasized the role of chemistry in the cure of disease (the iatrochemists). The alchemists discovered a great many chemical facts in their search for transmutation processes. Dependence upon the immutable results of experiments, rather than the mystical pronouncements of authorities, became the accepted basis for discussion, and with the discoveries (in 1774) of oxygen by Joseph Priestley and of the true nature of combustion by Antoine Lavoisier, chemistry began to be the modern science that has been developing up to the present day.

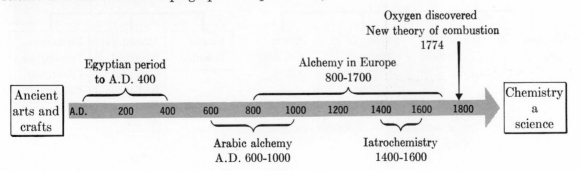

Figure 1.4 Time scale for the development of chemistry.

Some of the Procedures and Language of Chemistry

How to Organize the Search for the Truth about the Universe. The problem of understanding the universe is a huge one. Many years of toil and study were required before the method of tackling the problem became clear. The method finally chosen is that used in approaching any big problem, that is, *simplification by classification.*

The Two Entities of the Universe. Careful observation of the world around us indicates the two great entities, *matter* and *energy.* Matter is anything that has mass (or weight) and occupies space. The things or substances that can be observed such as rocks, water, soil, machines, trees, etc., are examples of matter as well as some things that cannot be seen but can be detected such as air and other gases, or particles too small to see such as atoms, ions, molecules, electrons, protons, or neutrons. Energy is the ability to do work. It may also be defined as heat or anything transformable into heat. Some familiar forms are mechanical, electrical, radiant, and chemical energy.

Some Further Classifications in the Study of Matter. The study of matter can be further organized by the use of several different classifications: homogeneous and heterogeneous substances, for example, or solids, liquids, and gases. The classification chosen depends upon the convenience desired or the particular phenomenon being studied. Several different classifications are indicated in Figure 1.5. In the study of chemistry each of these classifications is used.

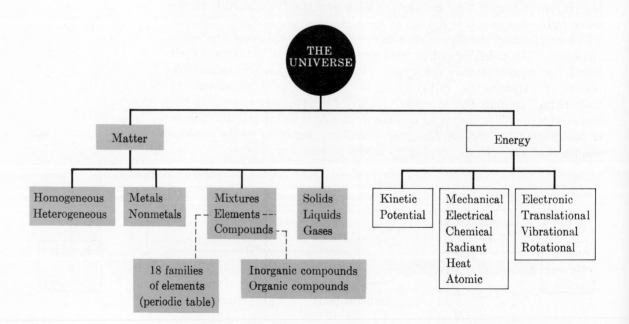

Figure 1.5 Simplification by classification.

Homogeneous and Heterogeneous Substances. The term *substance* is used for any form of matter. If the substance appears to be uniform throughout, it is called a *homogeneous* substance; for example, sugar, water, alcohol, or a solution. Any homogeneous system of material is called a *phase.* If a substance is not uniform throughout but is of such a nature that we can distinguish two or more parts (phases) which are themselves homogeneous, it is called *heterogeneous*; for example, salt and pepper mixture, sandstone, or muddy water.

Metals and Nonmetals. Metals are substances that have a metallic luster, are malleable and ductile, and are good conductors of heat and electricity. Nonmetals are poor conductors of heat and electricity, and are neither malleable nor ductile.

	Metals	*Nonmetals*
Examples	Iron, copper, gold, tin	Sulfur, carbon, iodine, phosphorus

Solids, Liquids, and Gases. These are called the physical states of matter. They are also called the solid, liquid, and gaseous phases. Theoretically, every substance can exist in these three states. Actually, all substances can be solidified, but some substances decompose when they are heated in an attempt to change them to a liquid or to a gas. For example, sugar decomposes before it vaporizes; limestone decomposes at ordinary pressures when the temperature is raised.

Mixtures, Elements, and Compounds. For the chemist, these are perhaps the most useful classifications of substances. *Mixtures* contain two or more substances; they may be homogeneous or heterogeneous, but they can always be separated by physical processes. For example, a solution of sugar and water is a homogeneous mixture; the sugar can be separated from the water by simply evaporating the water. Iron and sulfur is a heterogeneous mixture; the sulfur can be dissolved preferentially with carbon disulfide or the iron can be removed from sulfur with a magnet.

Careful study has shown that the universe is made of about 100 substances called *elements*, from which all other substances (compounds and mixtures) are made. Examples of elements are copper, iron, lead, hydrogen, oxygen, and chlorine. A considerable part of the subject matter of chemistry involves the study of elements and the compounds and mixtures they form.

Elements combine or react with each other to form new substances called *compounds*; for example, the elements hydrogen and oxygen combine to form the compound water. The elements combined in compounds cannot be separated by physical means; thus they differ from mixtures. Furthermore, each compound always contains the same elements in the same ratio by weight. There are about two million different compounds known today and millions more probably exist.

Are solutions compounds or mixtures? Much of the time chemists work with solutions rather than pure elements or compounds. Air is a solution of gases; the ocean water is a solution of salts in water. Solutions are homogeneous and hence are similar to compounds in this respect, but the

Periodic table

	IA	IIA	IIIB	IVB	VB	VIB	VIIB		VIII		IB	IIB	IIIA	IVA	VA	VIA	VIIA	O
1	1 Hydrogen **H**																	2 Helium **He**
2	3 Lithium **Li**	4 Beryllium **Be**											5 Boron **B**	6 Carbon **C**	7 Nitrogen **N**	8 Oxygen **O**	9 Fluorine **F**	10 Neon **Ne**
3	11 Sodium **Na**	12 Magnesium **Mg**											13 Aluminum **Al**	14 Silicon **Si**	15 Phosphorus **P**	16 Sulfur **S**	17 Chlorine **Cl**	18 Argon **Ar**
4	19 Potassium **K**	20 Calcium **Ca**	21 Scandium **Sc**	22 Titanium **Ti**	23 Vanadium **V**	24 Chromium **Cr**	25 Manganese **Mn**	26 Iron **Fe**	27 Cobalt **Co**	28 Nickel **Ni**	29 Copper **Cu**	30 Zinc **Zn**	31 Gallium **Ga**	32 Germanium **Ge**	33 Arsenic **As**	34 Selenium **Se**	35 Bromine **Br**	36 Krypton **Kr**
5	37 Rubidium **Rb**	38 Strontium **Sr**	39 Yttrium **Y**	40 Zirconium **Zr**	41 Niobium **Nb**	42 Molybdenum **Mo**	43 Technetium **Tc**	44 Ruthenium **Ru**	45 Rhodium **Rh**	46 Palladium **Pd**	47 Silver **Ag**	48 Cadmium **Cd**	49 Indium **In**	50 Tin **Sn**	51 Antimony **Sb**	52 Tellurium **Te**	53 Iodine **I**	54 Xenon **Xe**
6	55 Cesium **Cs**	56 Barium **Ba**	57–71 Series of Lanthanide Elements	72 Hafnium **Hf**	73 Tantalum **Ta**	74 Tungsten **W**	75 Rhenium **Re**	76 Osmium **Os**	77 Iridium **Ir**	78 Platinum **Pt**	79 Gold **Au**	80 Mercury **Hg**	81 Thallium **Tl**	82 Lead **Pb**	83 Bismuth **Bi**	84 Polonium **Po**	85 Astatine **At**	86 Radon **Rn**
7	87 Francium **Fr**	88 Radium **Ra**	89–103 Series of Actinide Elements															

Series of Lanthanide Elements	57 Lanthanum **La**	58 Cerium **Ce**	59 Praseodymium **Pr**	60 Neodymium **Nd**	61 Promethium **Pm**	62 Samarium **Sm**	63 Europium **Eu**	64 Gadolinium **Gd**	65 Terbium **Tb**	66 Dysprosium **Dy**	67 Holmium **Ho**	68 Erbium **Er**	69 Thulium **Tm**	70 Ytterbium **Yb**	71 Lutetium **Lu**
Series of Actinide Elements	89 Actinium **Ac**	90 Thorium **Th**	91 Protactinium **Pa**	92 Uranium **U**	93 Neptunium **Np**	94 Plutonium **Pu**	95 Americium **Am**	96 Curium **Cm**	97 Berkelium **Bk**	98 Californium **Cf**	99 Einsteinium **Es**	100 Fermium **Fm**	101 Mendelevium **Md**	102 Nobelium **No**	103 Lawrentium **Lw**

Figure 1.6 Periodic table.

composition of solutions can be varied often over a wide range. Hence a solution cannot be considered to be a compound. A solution is defined as a homogeneous mixture. The composition of a solution is described in terms of the amount of dissolved substance (called the *solute*) and the amount of the *solvent*. (See Chap. 14.)

Classification of the Elements. The problem of learning about the elements is further simplified by classifying them into families; all the elements in a family have *similar* properties. This classification is called the periodic table (Figure 1.6). Thus the study of the elementary substances in the entire universe resolves itself into the much more simple problem of learning about the various families of elements and the compounds they form.

Chemical and Physical Properties. In order to identify a substance, we describe it in terms of its characteristics or *properties*. For convenience a distinction is sometimes made between physical properties and chemical properties, although a definitive distinction between these is somewhat difficult to establish. Among physical properties are included such characteristics as color, hardness, solubility, odor, boiling point, freezing point, and vapor pressure. Among chemical properties are included such characteristics as heat of combustion, stability (toward decomposition), or reactivity. Some of these properties are illustrated in Table 1.1.

Substance	Physical Properties	Chemical Properties
Helium	Gas, low boiling point	Inert
Water	Liquid at 25°C, colorless	Stable at 25°C; reacts with some metals
Sulfur	Solid, yellow, brittle	Stable at 25°C; burns in oxygen, releasing energy
Iron	Solid, metallic luster, high density	Rusts readily; burns in oxygen, releasing energy

Table 1.1 Typical Physical and Chemical Properties of Several Substances

Chemical Changes. Those changes in which a new substance or new substances are formed are called *chemical changes*. For example: Iron rusts; in this change a new substance, rust or iron oxide, is formed. Carbon burns; in this change a new substance, carbon dioxide, is formed. Nitroglycerine explodes; in this reaction new substances, nitrogen, carbon dioxide, water, and other gases, are formed. Water is electrolyzed; in this change oxygen and hydrogen are formed. An energy change also accompanies a chemical change. As a result, there is a difference in the chemical energy of the reactants and products. If the new substance is made of two or more elements in chemical combination, we call it a *compound*. For example, carbon dioxide is a compound of carbon and oxygen. Compounds have definite composition by weight.

Physical Changes. Those changes which involve a change in the form or state of a substance but do not involve the production of a new substance are called *physical changes*. For example: Water boils; in this change no new substance is formed, but water changes from the liquid state to the gaseous state. Sulfur melts; solid sulfur is changed to liquid sulfur.

Atoms Are Building Blocks of Elements. For several hundred years philosophers debated the question of whether matter is continuous stuff or is discontinuous and hence made of particles. As early as 400 B.C. the Greek philosopher Democritus found it helpful to assume that matter is made of particles (which he called atoms). But it remained just a philosophical question until 1803 when an English schoolteacher, John Dalton, gathered enough data from experiments on the solubility of different gases in liquids and the definite amounts of elements that combine with each other to lead him to make certain assumptions in order to explain his observations. Today we have gathered still more evidence to support these assumptions of Dalton. Furthermore, we can describe with confidence the structure and composition of atoms. We define an element as a substance made of one type of atom only.

A summary of the main points of the atomic theory as accepted today is as follows:

1. All matter is made up of unit particles called *atoms*.
2. The atoms of a particular element have the same mass, or at least an average mass characteristic of the element; atoms of different elements have different average masses.
3. In chemical reactions whole atoms, never fractions of atoms, combine or separate, or change places.
4. When atoms combine with other atoms, they do so in one or more whole-number ratios which are usually small.

Names and Symbols for Elements. The privilege of naming an element is that of the discoverer. Most of the elements are given English names, but some were given names in Latin; for example, silver was called *argentum* and iron *ferrum*. Abbreviations of the names of elements are called *chemical symbols*; for example, hydrogen is H, oxygen is O, silver is Ag, and iron is Fe. In the atomic theory each symbol represents one atom of the element. Thus, H represents one atom of hydrogen, 2H represents two atoms of hydrogen, H_2 represents a molecule of hydrogen containing two atoms, and H_2O represents a molecule of water containing two atoms of hydrogen and one atom of oxygen.

Three Basic Laws Explained by Assuming the Existence of Atoms. *1. Law of Conservation of Matter and Energy.* One of the questions that bothered

---

● ● ●   DALTON'S THEORY AS ORIGINALLY STATED

1. Matter is made of minute pellets (or atoms) and definite numbers of these units combine or separate in reactions.
2. The ultimate particles of a pure substance are alike in size and weight.
3. The simple atoms of an elementary substance are indivisible, and can neither be created nor destroyed.
4. The "compound atoms" (molecules) of a chemical compound are formed by the union of two or more elementary atoms.
5. Combination between atoms takes place in the simplest possible ratios.

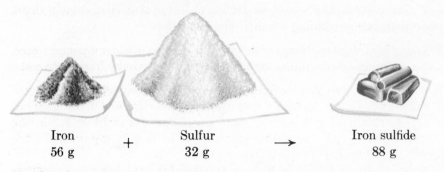

Iron   +   Sulfur   →   Iron sulfide
56 g   32 g   88 g

Figure 1.7 Definite quantities of substances involved in the chemical reaction, iron + sulfur → iron sulfide.

the early scientists was whether matter is lost or destroyed when substances combine or decompose. What happens to wood when it burns? What happens to sugar when it dissolves? What happens to the energy in coal when the coal burns?

Many careful experiments in which the weights of the reactants were compared with the weights of the products of reactions showed no detectable loss of weight when the reactions occurred. These results are expressed in a formal *law of conservation of mass: Matter is neither created nor destroyed in chemical processes.*

Other similar experiments on the transformations of energy led scientists to believe that a similar conservation law exists for energy: Energy is neither lost nor destroyed, but may be transformed from one form to another.

Today it is known that in nuclear changes, such as those which occur in radioactive transformations, matter can be converted to energy and energy to matter, but neither is lost. In chemical changes, however, our interpretation is that atoms combine with each other, or rearrange in different combinations; hence they are not destroyed but appear in new forms and arrangements without measurable change in mass.

2. Law of Definite Composition. Another observation of the early scientists was that a given weight of an element always combines with definite weights of other elements. For example, it is found that

> 1.000 g of oxygen combines with 1.125 g of aluminum.
> 1.008 g of hydrogen combines with 16.03 g of sulfur.
> 1.008 g of hydrogen combines with 35.45 g of chlorine.

Finding results of this sort generally true, the scientists expressed the *law of definite composition: In chemical compounds, the several elements are always combined in definite proportions by weight* (Figure 1.7).

How can this be explained? Dalton's theory, that elements are made of atoms, provides an answer. Dalton reasoned in this manner: The atoms of a given element all have the same mass, but this mass is different from the masses of atoms of other elements. Reaction of one element with another takes place between the atoms of each element. Hence, if a specified number of atoms of the one element always combines with a specified number of atoms of the other element, then a specified mass of the first element must always combine with a specified mass of the second. Hence, the elements should have definite combining weights, and the product formed will always have a definite composition.

3. Law of Multiple Proportions. It was observed that some elements have more than one combining weight. For example,

1.008 g of hydrogen combines with 8.000 g of oxygen in the compound water. 1.008 g of hydrogen combines with 16.000 g of oxygen in hydrogen peroxide.

It was further noted that *the ratios of the weights of the second element* (oxygen in the example given) *combined with a fixed weight of the first* (hydrogen) *can always be expressed as a ratio of small whole numbers* (8:16 or 1:2 in the example given). The preceding sentence is, in fact, a statement of the formal law of multiple proportions.

Again, Dalton's theory of atoms was helpful in explaining this observation. We need only to assume that the same atoms can combine in more than one ratio. For example, in water, *one* atom of oxygen combines with two atoms of hydrogen

$$
\begin{array}{c}
H \\
\quad \diagdown \\
\qquad O \\
\quad \diagup \\
H
\end{array}
$$

while in hydrogen peroxide, two atoms of oxygen combine with two of hydrogen

$$
\begin{array}{c}
H \\
\ \diagdown \\
\quad O\!-\!O \\
\qquad\ \diagdown \\
\qquad\quad H
\end{array}
$$

Twice as much oxygen combines with the same weight of hydrogen in hydrogen peroxide as in water, and the two-to-one ratio of the combining weights of oxygen is explained.

Atomic Weights, Formulas, and Equations. The atomic theory and the laws of chemical combination led chemists to the formulation of a scale of relative atomic weights, to the use of the chemical formula, and to the concept of the chemical equation. Formulas and equations each convey both qualitative and quantitative information. They state not only what is present or what substances react, but also the relative amounts of each element present, or how much of one reactant will react with a given weight of another. Weight relations in formulas and equations will be discussed in Chap. 3.

Chemistry and Other Disciplines

Chemistry and the Other Sciences. Chemistry has a close relationship to the other sciences because of the application of the study of chemical change and the structure of matter to every other science. Consequently, it is important to remember that the division between the sciences is not sharp. Today all sciences overlap each other, and oftentimes the same subject matter is to be found in several sciences.

Chemistry and Technology. Science and technology are related in that one (science) is the process of study, search, and discovery, and the other (technology) is the application of the results of that study or that discovery for some practical purpose. Sometimes the relationship is a very close one such as that between chemistry and chemical engineering, or chemistry and disease prevention (water purification, pest control, and food preservation), or research on the synthesis of rocket fuels and the launching of rockets.

Chemistry and an Enlightened World. The results of the search for an understanding of the universe have enlightened man in a satisfying and exciting manner as to the nature of his world. Many of his old fears and superstitions have been removed, and a new dimension has been added, a new method of learning about the universe—the method of science.

Enlightenment has come not only from learning about the universe but also from applying this knowledge to a more comfortable and interesting life in this world man is beginning to learn so much about.

Today's knowledge can be traced back to the time when man first learned to write, about 7,000 years ago—a span of time which becomes more remarkably significant if we think of it as 100 consecutive life spans of 70 years each. The great contributions of chemistry have come in the very recent part of this span and represent about three of these consecutive 70-year life spans.

SOME SPECIAL TERMS

Matter
homogeneous
heterogeneous
states of matter
solids
liquids
gases

Energy
kinetic energy
potential energy
heat
light
conservation of energy

Properties of matter
physical
chemical

Elements
metals
nonmetals

Laws of chemical combination
law of conservation of mass
law of definite composition
law of multiple proportions

Atoms
atomic theory
atomic masses
ions
molecules

Equations
symbols
formulas

● ● ●

Today the magnificent achievements, the horrendous dangers, and the golden promise of science and technology are in the minds and hearts of men everywhere, as perhaps never before. . . . That science and technology have brought profound physical changes is among the most significant and self-evident facts of our generation. Disease and premature death ; indecent conditions of shelter ; hunger and malnutrition ; exhausting labor under horrible conditions—these ancient curses science and technology have helped to ameliorate in large areas of the world. And only the barest beginning has been made. We all need to remind ourselves from time to time of what a magnificent humane contribution these physical changes have made, and continue to make to mankind.—David Lilienthal.

QUESTIONS AND PROBLEMS

1. Give examples of each of the following: (a) a substance, (b) several physical properties, (c) several chemical properties, (d) a property that might be considered either chemical or physical, (e) several physical and several chemical changes, (f) a substance of low density, (g) a substance of high density.

2. Do you know anything that occupies space and has no mass, or that has mass and occupies no space?

3. Describe the interconversion of kinetic and potential energy in: (a) a waterfall, (b) a burning torch, (c) a bouncing ball, (d) the condensing of steam, (e) the melting of ice.

4. (a) Why should chemistry be concerned with energy changes? (b) Show by examples how energy may be obtained more easily from some materials than from others. (c) What commonplace substances are important sources of energy?

5. Distinguish between temperature and heat, using an example.

6. Distinguish between laws and theories in science. Comment critically on the statement, "It is impossible to prove either a law or a theory in science."

7. Account for each of the following facts in terms of the law of conservation of mass: (a) A candle burns and the material composing it entirely disappears. (b) A piece of iron burns and the resulting product weighs more than the original iron. (c) The material of an atomic bomb "explodes" and the resulting material weighs slightly less than the original.

8. Design an experiment to: (a) test any (or all) postulates in the atomic theory, (b) illustrate the law of definite composition, (c) measure the heat evolved in the burning of a match.

9. Design an experiment or experiments that will reveal whether the following are mixtures or pure substances: air, water, a nickel, natural gas, gasoline, ink, dry ice.

10. State how you would separate into its components: (a) a mixture of sugar and sand, (b) a mixture of sand and water, (c) a mixture of ethyl alcohol and water, (d) a mixture of iron filings and sand, (e) a mixture of salt and sugar.

11. Give the phases present in each of the following: (a) a sealed container half-filled with a slush of water and ice, (b) a slice of bread, (c) this page of the book, (d) a milkshake.

12. (a) How could the weight of a cannon ball be changed without changing its mass? (b) Could its mass be changed without changing its weight?

13. How might an astronaut in a spacecraft in orbit determine the mass of an object within the spacecraft?

14. What properties distinguish water from other colorless liquids?

15. What properties distinguish solid white salts like sodium chloride and potassium chloride from one another?

16. State the units in which each of the following is measured: (a) mass, (b) length, (c) density, (d) heat, (e) light, (f) concentration, (g) temperature.

17. Calculate your weight in (a) kilograms, (b) grams.

18. Calculate the length of your arm in (a) meters, (b) centimeters.

19. Convert: (a) 1 liter to quarts, (b) 1 pint to cubic centimeters, (c) 1 ounce to grams.

20. At what temperature do the centigrade and Fahrenheit temperature scales give the same reading?

21. (a) A cube of aluminum weighs 21.616 g. The density of aluminum at 20°C is 2.7 g/cc. What is the length of the cube edge? (b) How much would a cube of gold (density at 20°C 19.3 g/cc) of the same size weigh?

22. The cube of aluminum in Problem 21 contains 5.06×10^{22} atoms. What is the diameter of a single aluminum atom, assuming that the atoms are touching each other?

23. One gram of matter, if completely transformed into energy, would produce 2.15×10^{13} cal. How many tons of coal would be required to furnish this amount of heat if 1 g of the coal, when burned, produced 7,400 cal?

REFERENCES

CHEMICAL BOND APPROACH PROJECT. *Chemical Systems.* New York: McGraw-Hill, 1964.

CHEMICAL EDUCATION MATERIAL STUDY. *Chemistry: An Experimental Approach.* San Francisco: Freeman, 1963.

DAMPIER, W. C., and M. DAMPIER (eds.). *Readings in the Literature of Science.* New York: Harper, 1959.

GARRETT, A. B. *The Flash of Genius.* Princeton: Van Nostrand, 1963.

LEICESTER, H. M., and H. S. KLICKSTEIN. *A Source Book in Chemistry, 1400–1900.* New York: McGraw-Hill, 1952.

PART ONE

ATOMS, MOLECULES, AND IONS

2

Atoms: Their Composition and Size

I have chosen the word atom to signify those ultimate particles, in preference to particle, molecule, or any other diminutive term, because I believe it to be more expressive; it includes in itself the notion of indivisible, which the other terms do not. . . . All the changes we can produce, consist in separating particles that are in a state of cohesion or combination, and joining those that were previously at a distance. John Dalton (1766–1844)

The atomic age really began with Dalton's formulation of the atomic theory at the beginning of the nineteenth century (Chap. 1). For the next hundred years chemists were busy testing the theory. In convincing themselves of its validity, they further explored the important laws of chemical combination, they determined the combining weights of the elements and the formulas for many compounds, and they developed a scale of relative atomic weights.

Nearly all of the tests of the atomic theory involved experiments with matter in bulk, and required some very clever and ingenious methods of reasoning, at which chemists became especially skilled. However, as the concept of atoms became more and more real, and as chemists depended on the use of the concept of atoms to explain many phenomena, it became important to know more about the nature and structure of atoms. Soon it was obvious to many scientists that a profitable approach to the study of atomic structure would involve some of the techniques of the physicist in addition to those of the chemist. Such techniques included work with spectroscopes, electrical measuring devices, and cathode-ray tubes designed to examine much smaller samples of matter than it was possible to study with standard chemical techniques.

The results of using physical techniques in unraveling the difficult problem of atomic structure were so successful that today chemists are able to explain many chemical phenomena in terms of the structure of the atoms or ions present and of the forces acting among these particles. The use by chemists of physical as well as standard chemical techniques has progressed to such a point that there is no longer a sharp distinction between chemistry and physics (Figure 2.1).

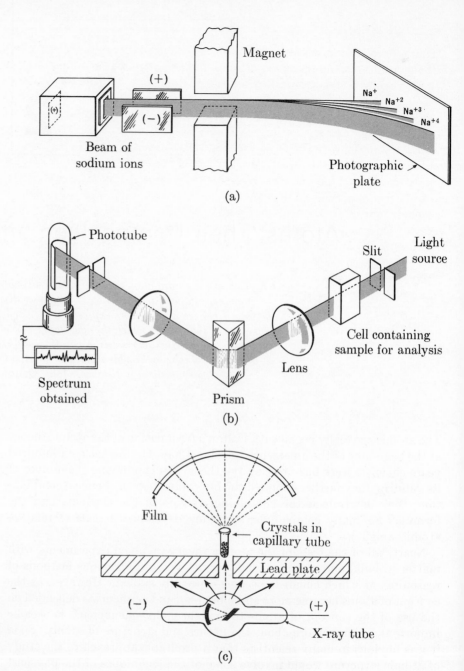

Figure 2.1 Apparatus used by both chemists and physicists : (a) Diagram of a mass spectrometer, used for separating isotopes and for measuring atomic masses. (b) Diagram of a spectrometer, used for measuring absorption spectra of atoms and molecules. (c) Diagram of an X-ray apparatus, used to elucidate structure of crystals (an early use of X-rays was the determination of nuclear charge).

In this chapter we shall trace the development of the theory of atomic structure brought about by the use of physical techniques, starting at the close of the nineteenth century.

Development of the Theory of Atomic Structure

During nearly all of the nineteenth century, chemists and physicists were content to look upon the atoms of the elements as hard, elastic, round, dense, unchanging particles. About 1900 they became aware that the characteristic properties and behavior of the elements could be interpreted if the atoms were not simple particles, but structured—each kind of atom must possess a structure characteristic of that kind, and the properties of each element are a consequence of the particular structures of its atoms.

The problem of determining the structures of atoms, however, was an enormous one. Even the largest atoms are about a thousand times too small to be seen with the most powerful microscope. This means, of course, that we cannot make direct observations of the structure of atoms and so must resort to inference and deduction from data obtained from a variety of indirect experiments. Such inference and deduction lead us to imagine a particular internal structure for an atom, and if predictions on the basis of our imagined structure agree with experiment, we dignify our imagined structure by calling it a *theory*. Working out an acceptable theory of the structure of the atom has been one of the most absorbing problems of physics and chemistry during the present century. The task is by no means completed, and our present theory is constantly growing and improving. However, the experimental facts of atomic behavior are clearly consistent with our modern concepts of atomic structure, and, in that sense, the theory is correct (Figure 2.2).

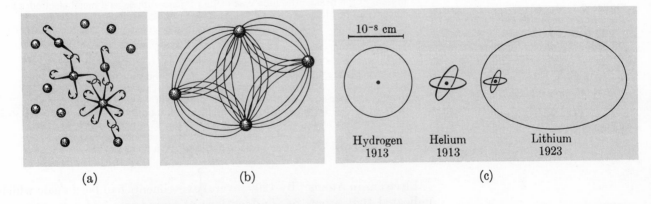

(a)   (b)   (c)

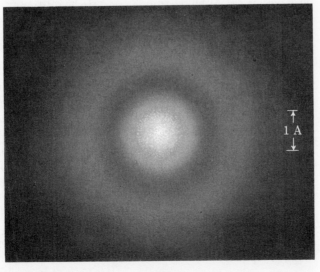

(d)

Figure 2.2 Evolving concept of atomic structure : (a) Lucretius' atoms. (b) Newton's atoms. (c) Bohr's atoms. (d) Modern construct of a lithium atom.

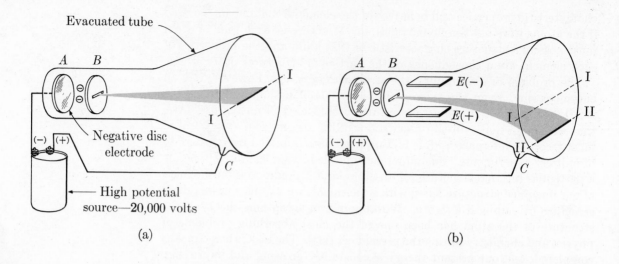

Figure 2.3 Experiments with cathode-ray tubes : (a) A beam of cathode rays is produced with the help of a slit in the disc. (b) The beam is deflected by an electric field ; the direction of deflection indicates that negative electrical charges are present in the beam. The tube was made of glass with several metal electrodes sealed into the glass. A source of high voltage was connected to the electrodes *A* and *C* such that *A* was charged negatively with respect to *C*. The disc *B* contained a small slit. When the tube was partially evacuated and the voltage applied between *A* and *C*, the characteristic cathode radiation was observed on the screen at the end of the tube opposite the slit. The screen was fashioned like that of a television picture tube ; it was coated with a compound such as zinc sulfide which would fluoresce when struck by the cathode ray. Thus the passage of the ray through the tube could be followed by the position of the streak of light at the end of the tube. Normally the ray caused a bright streak at position I. When a potential difference was produced between the two plates *E* which parallel the normal direction of flow of the cathode rays, the rays were attracted toward the positive plate as indicated by the new position of the streak at point II.

Electrons in Atoms. By 1900 several experiments had been made which indicated that atoms or combinations of atoms acquired a negative or positive electrical charge under certain conditions. Michael Faraday, in 1833, had observed that various forms of matter in the molten state or in aqueous solution conduct an electric current and undergo a chemical change as a result of the passage of current through them. He reasoned that in order to explain these results he would have to assume that electrical charges were associated with atoms and molecules.

As a result of Faraday's work with electricity, George Stoney concluded, in 1881, that there must be an *elementary unit of electricity*, and he introduced the term *electron* to designate this unit.

In 1879 Sir William Crookes performed a series of experiments in which electricity was passed through gases in tubes at low pressure. He noticed unusual radiation (or rays) from the negative electrode which became known as *cathode rays*.

Later Joseph J. Thomson studied extensively the nature of the electrical discharge which could be made to occur in gases at low pressure in a cathode-ray tube such as that shown in Figure 2.3. The observed deflections of the cathode ray were just those to be expected for a beam of negatively charged particles. In 1897, after twenty years of work with these rays, Thomson announced to the Royal Society his conclusion, "Cathode rays are primordial corpuscles (particles) of negative electricity."

If they were negatively charged particles, then how big a charge did they carry? Thomson was not able to determine this, but he was able to measure the ratio of charge to mass, e/m. He accomplished this by measuring the magnetic field strength necessary to return the spot to position I after deflection to II by a measured electric field (Figure 2.4). The value he obtained was close to the recent accurate value of $e/m = 1.76 \times 10^8$ coul*/g. Thomson found, as he changed the nature of the metal electrodes

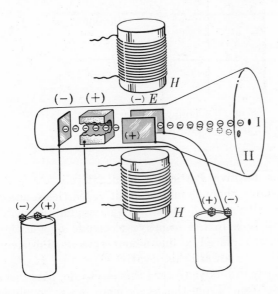

Figure 2.4 J. J. Thomson's apparatus for measuring ratio of charge-to-mass of cathode-ray particles (electrons). The narrow cathode beam was first deflected by the electrostatic field at E between H-H and then brought back to its original position by a magnetic field. Knowing the magnetic and electrostatic field strengths, the ratio of e/m was calculated.

(Al, Fe, Pt) or the type of residual gas left in the partially evacuated tube (CO_2, H_2, air), that the value of the e/m ratio for the particles produced remained unchanged. This was a severe test of his suggestion that these rays were all alike even though they were produced in different tubes with different electrodes and different gases. He concluded that he was dealing with a *common fundamental particle*, obtainable from all matter. This negatively charged particle, originally called the cathode ray, must be the *unit* of electricity, the existence of which had already been postulated by Stoney, and named by him the electron.

---

* A coulomb (coul) is a unit of electric charge.

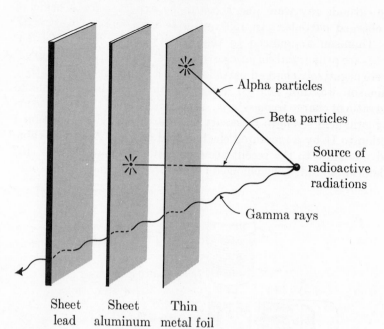

Alpha particles

Beta particles

Source of
radioactive
radiations

Gamma rays

Figure 2.5 The relative penetrating power of alpha, beta, and gamma radiations.

Sheet
lead

Sheet
aluminum

Thin
metal foil

Evidence for Positive Particles. If negatively charged particles of matter exist, surely there should be positive particles, since matter as a whole is electrically neutral. A test of this assumption was obtained by placing a small hole in the negative electrode of a cathode-ray tube, behind which was placed a fluorescent screen. Positive particles, if present, should move toward this negative electrode. It was observed that particles evidently did move toward this electrode, pass through the hole, and strike the screen. From this experiment it was concluded that there were positively charged particles present in a discharge tube.

Further experiments showed these *positive rays* or particles to have the following characteristics:

1. The ratio of charge-to-mass (e/m) was found to be several thousand times *smaller* than the value of e/m for electrons (note that the larger the value of m, the smaller the value of the ratio e/m).
2. The value of e/m was *dependent* on the nature of the residual gas in the tube.

To explain these data it was necessary to assume that these particles, unlike the cathode-ray particles, varied in mass depending on the nature of the gas. The reasonable hypothesis was made that these positively charged particles were formed in the tube from neutral atoms or molecules, probably as a result of collisions between electrons and atoms, or molecules, of the gas in the tube. If such a collision could knock an electron from the neutral substance, a positive particle would be left behind. This would then be drawn toward the negative electrode, and if moving in the right direction, would pass through the hole and hit the fluorescent screen.

Evidence for Positive and Negative Particles from Radioactivity. While physicists were studying cathode rays, some chemists were studying the interesting phenomenon of fluorescence. Henri Becquerel, a French scientist, was attempting in 1896 to convert sunlight into a deeply penetrating radiation by causing the sunlight to produce fluorescence of uranium compounds. His experimental procedure was to lay a piece of uranium ore on a wrapped photographic plate and expose the uranium to sunlight. When the photographic plate under the uranium was developed, he found it streaked. But when he repeated the experiment without exposing the uranium to sunlight, he found the plate was again streaked. The sunlight evidently had nothing to do with it at all! "We must assume," he concluded, "that radiations from a yet undiscovered element cause the streaks."

A young Polish girl, Marie Sklodowska, had come to his laboratory, and he asked her to work on the problem. In the course of her work, she and her husband, Pierre Curie, isolated from uranium ore a compound of a new element which they named *polonium*, after Madame Curie's native country, Poland. Later she isolated a compound of the element *radium*.

These two elements emitted radiations that had a much greater effect on photographic plates than the original uranium ore. These radiations were made of three different rays (Figure 2.5 and Table 2.1).

Rays	Characteristics
Alpha rays—positive particles, with $e/m = 4.82 \times 10^4$ coul/g	He^{+2} ions
Beta rays—negative particles, with $e/m = 1.76 \times 10^8$ coul/g	Electrons
Gamma rays—electromagnetic rays of shorter wavelength than light rays, able to penetrate matter even more deeply than X-rays	Similar to light but very deeply penetrating, even more so than most X-rays

Table 2.1 Types of Radiation

Hence we have further evidence that matter is made of positive and negative particles. Further studies showed that the positive alpha particles are emitted by many of the heavy elements from uranium to lead.

Determining the Charge and the Mass of Electrons. Thomson could determine from his experiments neither the mass nor the charge of the electron alone, but only the ratio e/m. It remained for an American scientist, Robert Millikan, to devise an ingenious experiment to measure the charge on the electron; he studied the rate of fall of electrically charged oil drops (that is, drops which had acquired one or more electrons or lost one or more electrons) suspended between charged plates (Figure 2.6). From these data he calculated the charge on the oil drops; he found that this charge was always equal to, or was some multiple of, a definite unit charge (1.6020×10^{-19} coul). He concluded that the unit charge was the charge on the electron, and he explained his observations by assuming that the droplets picked up one or more electrons or lost one or more electrons. After Millikan's success in determining the charge on the electron, he used Thomson's values for the ratio of the charge to the mass, $e/m = 1.76 \times 10^8$ coul/g, and calculated the mass.

$$\frac{e}{m} = 1.76 \times 10^{-8} \text{ coul/g}$$

$$e = 1.60 \times 10^{-19} \text{ coul}$$

$$m = \frac{e}{e/m} \frac{1.60 \times 10^{-19} \text{ coul}}{1.76 \times 10^{-8} \text{ coul/g}} = 9.11 \times 10^{-28} \text{ g, mass of the electron}$$

The electron, then, is assumed to be a *particle* of negative electricity of definite charge and mass which is a universal constituent of matter and which in suitable multiples makes up all negative charges.

The Nature of the Nucleus

Rutherford's Metal Foil Experiment. In 1911, Ernest Rutherford and his students, Hans Geiger and Ernest Marsden, performed the classic experiments which established the size and density of the nucleus. They bombarded atoms in gases as well as in metal films with alpha particles in an experiment similar to that described in Figure 2.7. They used very thin films of metal foil fabricated from very malleable metals, such as gold, silver, copper, and platinum; the films were prepared to have a thickness of about 1,000 atoms or about 1×10^{-5} cm. This film was placed in the path of a beam of alpha particles. Behind the foil was placed a screen, C, coated with zinc sulfide which would scintillate when struck with an alpha particle. Another zinc sulfide screen, D, was placed at the side of the path to detect alpha particles that might be highly deflected.

It was found that most of the alpha particles passed through the foil and struck screen C, undeflected in their paths. This result showed that the atoms of the metals were mostly free space, not occupied by massive particles which might hinder the passage of the alpha particles.

On careful study they discovered that a few of the particles were deflected on passage through the film and were seen as bright spots of light as they impinged on the sides of the screen. Furthermore, they found that one

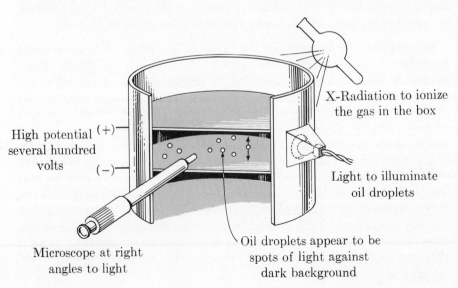

Figure 2.6 Diagram of apparatus used by Robert A. Millikan.

High potential $(+)$ several hundred volts $(-)$

X-Radiation to ionize the gas in the box

Light to illuminate oil droplets

Microscope at right angles to light

Oil droplets appear to be spots of light against dark background alpha particle in 10,000 or so seemed to undergo a collision with some very dense solid matter and be deflected backwards from the metal foil, striking screen D.

Rutherford interpreted these results to indicate that the atom contains a *small, heavy nucleus*. He reasoned that the nucleus must carry a positive charge which caused the alpha particles (He^{+2}) to be strongly repelled. With this assumption and a measurement of the number of particles which were deflected per unit time as a function of the angle of deflection, Rutherford estimated the number of charges on the nucleus of the several metal atoms.

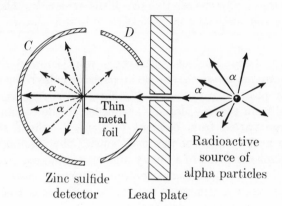

Figure 2.7   Ernest Rutherford's metal foil experiment. Approximately one in ten thousand alpha (α) particles bounced back from the metal foil, providing evidence for the existence of a heavy, compact, positively charged atomic nucleus.

From earlier experiments and from many later ones it was also possible to estimate that the diameter of atoms is approximately 10^{-8} cm. From Rutherford's experiments it was possible to calculate the diameter of the nucleus to be about 10^{-12} cm, or 10,000 times smaller than the diameter of the atom.

Atomic Numbers.   About the time that these scattering experiments were in progress several groups of physicists discovered methods of measuring the wavelengths of X-rays, the new type of radiation discovered by Roentgen only several years earlier (1895). Rutherford knew that X-rays could be produced by bombarding metals with rapidly moving electrons, so he proposed to a member of his research group, H. G. J. Moseley, that they plan a series of experiments with X-rays to try to determine the charge on the nucleus. They proposed to bombard a series of metal targets in X-ray tubes and to examine the wavelengths of the X-rays emitted.

● ● ●

Rutherford said when considering the results of his experiments: "It was quite the most incredible event that has ever happened to me in my life. It was almost as incredible as if you fired a 15 inch shell at a piece of tissue paper and it came back and hit you. On consideration I realized that this scattering backwards must be the result of a single collision, and when I made calculations I saw that it was impossible to get anything of that order of magnitude unless you took a system in which the greater part of the mass of the atom was concentrated in a minute nucleus. *It was then that I had the idea of an atom with a minute massive centre carrying a charge.*"

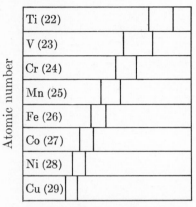

Figure 2.8 Results of H. G. J. Moseley's experiments. The wavelengths of certain X-rays emitted from metals decreased systematically as the nuclear charge increased. From these experiments Moseley obtained values for the charge on atomic nuclei. These values are known as the atomic number.

Moseley found that the X-ray wavelengths of different metals were reproducible and were characteristic of the particular metal used. But more than this, he found that a simple mathematical relationship existed between the wavelength of the X-ray and a whole number which is equal to about one-half the relative atomic weight of the metal. Moseley noted that these whole numbers (*or atomic numbers*) were nearly identical to the estimated nuclear charges in Rutherford's experiments with metal foils. He then concluded that the atomic number was the charge on the nucleus, in units of the electronic charge, 1.60×10^{-19} coul (Figure 2.8). For scientists this was a major breakthrough in the area of atomic structure, for now not only did they know the relative size of the nucleus but they had an exact measure of the nuclear charge. After this the picture unfolded rapidly.

Building Blocks of the Nucleus. Millikan's work showed that there existed a minimum negative charge on a particle called the electron; experiments with positive rays indicated that heavy positive particles could be obtained from atoms. Moseley's work led to the conclusion that the nuclear charge varied from element to element. Since atoms are neutral and since hydrogen is the lightest element, the presumption was that hydrogen atoms consisted of a heavy nucleus containing one positive particle (named the *proton*) and one electron. Atoms of other elements were imagined to contain a number of protons comparable to their nuclear charge and an equal number of electrons.

Measurements of e/m for hydrogen in positive-ray tubes give 9.4×10^4 coul/g. The mass of the proton then is calculated to be 1.67×10^{-24} g, about 1,837 times the mass of the electron (9.1×10^{-28} g). Other atomic nuclei should have masses equal to their nuclear charge times the mass of the proton.

That this picture is incomplete became evident when the e/m value for the helium nucleus was measured in an improved positive-ray tube. Moseley's work indicated that the nuclear charge on helium was $+2$; but the mass of the helium nucleus calculated from its e/m value was 6.68×10^{-24} g, or *four* times that of the hydrogen nucleus instead of *two* times. How could this be? Could there be more than two protons in the helium nucleus? If not, how could the larger mass be accounted for? This spurred a search for the existence of a third particle.

Evidence for a Third Fundamental Particle—The Neutron. Before the particle accelerators, such as cyclotrons, were invented, scientists were limited in their use of "atomic bullets" to bombardments with alpha particles from natural radioactive materials. Such alpha particles have very high velocities and hence energies high enough to penetrate the nuclei of some elements, be captured by these nuclei, and combine with them forming excited unstable nuclei.

When alpha particles were used to bombard beryllium, boron, or other light elements, a "very penetrating" radiation was observed. This new radiation did not have the set of unique characteristics of any of the then-known radiation. Alpha, beta, and gamma rays have varying efficiencies of penetration of matter as shown in Figure 2.5. Alpha particles and beta particles can penetrate only thin films of matter. Most gamma rays penetrate considerably farther, but at most only a few inches of solid objects. However, the "very penetrating radiation" observed by Curie and Joliot from the bombardment of light elements passed readily through a thickness of several feet of solid matter. The origin and nature of the radiation was not clear for several years. For a time it was considered to be extremely short wavelength electromagnetic radiation, similar to gamma rays.

An English scientist, James Chadwick, in 1932, made an important observation which led to a better understanding of the nature of the "rays"; he observed that hydrogen-containing compounds (water, paraffin, etc.) were particularly effective in reducing the energy until the radiation stopped. Application of the simple principles of colliding particles shows that the most efficient interchange of energy between colliding particles occurs when the particles have the same mass. In view of this fact, Chadwick suggested that the "very penetrating radiation" was not really radiation but neutral solid particles which had about the mass of the proton; he called the particle the *neutron*. Its high penetration of matter could be understood since the neutral particle would not be affected by the strong electric forces on approach to the regions of the atom rich in electrons or protons. Only "hits" on the massive center of the atoms could cause the particle to be deflected. Chadwick was able to calculate the mass of the neutron from the energy and direction of the recoil of protons produced on impact of neutrons with hydrogen atoms (Figure 2.9). Accurate data from recent experiments show that the mass of the neutron is 1.676×10^{-24} g, or about the mass of the proton.

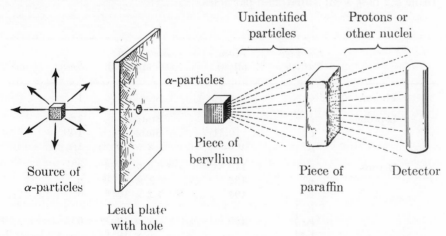

Figure 2.9 Chadwick's experiments leading to the discovery of the neutron. The alpha (α) particles striking the beryllium give rise to unidentified particles which are allowed to bombard paraffin. Protons are then ejected from the paraffin. Knowing the momentum of the ejected proton, it is possible to estimate the masses of the unidentified particles, the neutrons.

Today, the nuclear reactor is direct evidence of the existence of neutrons, for its operation depends upon the production and utilization of neutrons (Chap. 25).

The existence of neutrons provides the explanation for the unexpected mass of the helium nucleus mentioned in the last section. The fourfold greater mass of the helium nucleus than that of the hydrogen nucleus, but only twofold greater charge than that of the hydrogen nucleus, is explained if it contains two protons and two neutrons. The two protons give it the charge of two positive units and its two neutrons add weight but no charge. The discrepancy in the observed weight, 6.65×10^{-24} g, compared to the value 6.69×10^{-24} g calculated from the sum of the masses of two protons and two neutrons, represents one of the examples of the conversion of mass to energy in nuclear changes mentioned in Chap. 1. The loss of mass appears as the energy released as the four particles fuse the compact helium nucleus (Chap. 25).

The neutron is extremely small in size, about 10^{-12} cm or 1/10,000 the diameter of the hydrogen atom, the smallest of the atoms. Since it has the mass of a hydrogen atom concentrated in a volume about 1/1,000,000,000,000 the volume of the hydrogen atom, it has an exceptionally high density. If a thimbleful of neutrons could be collected and packed like marbles in a box, it would be found that the thimbleful of neutrons would weigh approximately 200,000,000 tons.

Other Particles in the Nucleus. It is an oversimplification to describe the nucleus only in terms of the protons and neutrons. Today, about 30 different particles have been identified among the products when atoms are bombarded by very high-energy particles. As bombarding particles of higher and higher energies are used, the number of fragments increases. Each has a very fleeting lifetime, but each is probably important to the understanding of the details of nuclear construction of the atoms. The neutrino, positron, mesons, and pions are examples of these identified particles. However, our present purposes are aimed at an understanding of the chemical reactions of atoms, ions, and molecules; hence particles in the nucleus other than protons and neutrons need not concern us further here. Table 2.2 lists some subatomic particles.

Table 2.2 Some Subatomic Particles

	Kind of Particle	Mass (Mev)	Mean Life (sec, approx.)	Spin
Photon	γ	0	Stable	1
Leptons	ν	0	Stable	1/2
	$e^{\mp}$	0.51	Stable	1/2
	$\mu^{\mp}$	105.7	2×10^{-6}	1/2
Mesons	π^+	140	π^{+2} 2.6×10^{-8}	0
	π^0	135	2×10^{-16}	0
	$K^{\mp}$	494	K^+ 1.2×10^{-8}	0
	K^0 ⎫			
	K^1 ⎬	498	1×10^{-10}	0
	K^2 ⎭		6×10^{-8}	
Baryons	p	938	Stable	1/2
	n	940	1×10^3	1/2
	λ	1115	2.5×10^{-10}	1/2
	Σ^+	1189	0.8×10^{-10}	1/2
	Σ^-	1197	1.6×10^{-10}	1/2
	Σ^0	1193	$< 0.1 \times 10^{-10}$	1/2
	Ξ^-	1318	1×10^{-10}	?
	Ξ^0	1311	1.5×10^{-10}	?

Note: 1 a.m.u. = 1.66×10^{-24} g $\equiv$ 931.2 Mev.
    1 e.m.u. $\equiv$ 0.51 Mev.

The Components of the Atom. The model of the atom that emerged after Rutherford's work on bombarding metal foil and Chadwick's work on identifying the neutron consisted of a nucleus, composed of protons and neutrons, surrounded by electrons. Atoms of various elements were pictured as differing from one another in the number of protons, neutrons, and electrons present. The atom is neutral; hence, the number of electrons

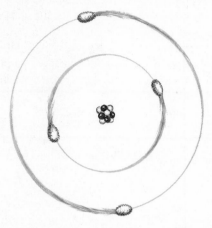

Figure 2.10 An early model of a beryllium atom showing four protons and five neutrons in the nucleus and four electrons orbiting the nucleus. This model with its orbiting electrons is inconsistent with much experimental evidence.

in the atom is equal to the number of protons in the nucleus (Figure 2.10). Since protons and neutrons were known to be about 1,837 times heavier than electrons, the mass of the atom is very nearly equal to the sum of the masses of the neutrons and protons present.

Chemical Atomic Weights

The elegant experiments and imaginative reasoning that led to a model of the arrangement of electrons outside the nucleus will be presented in Chap. 4. The remainder of this chapter will be devoted to the methods currently used for the determination of atomic weights.

Exact Atomic Masses. By 1860 chemists had developed a generally accepted scale of *relative* atomic weights based on very careful determinations of the combining weights of elements and the formulas of compounds.* This early scale of relative weights was of great use to chemists for many years; a present-day version is shown in Figure 2.11.

Once the essential electrical nature of the atoms had been established, it became evident that experiments similar to those which had been used to establish this could be used to determine the masses of atoms. Thomson's positive-ray experiments had shown that the masses of the positive-ray particles were characteristic for each gas in the positive-ray tube, and this ability of the positive-ray apparatus to determine masses was put to use by F. W. Aston in his design of a mass spectrograph. This original instrument has been modified until today the masses of positive ions can be determined with great precision (Figure 2.12).

---

* For a discussion of the methods and reasoning used, see a recent history of chemistry.

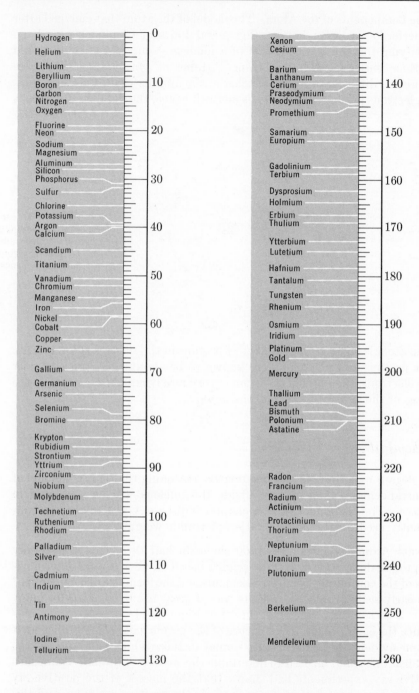

Figure 2.11 Scale of atomic weights. (Adapted from *Chemical Systems* by Chemical Bond Approach Project. Copyright 1964 by Earlham College Press, Inc. Published by Webster Division, McGraw-Hill.)

The masses of atoms obtained from mass spectrographic data are all of the order of 10^{-24} g. Examples are given in Table 2.3.

Isotopes. In some of his earliest experiments with the mass spectrometer, Aston observed that the element neon formed ions of three different masses. He interpreted this as an indication that neon contained atoms of three different masses.

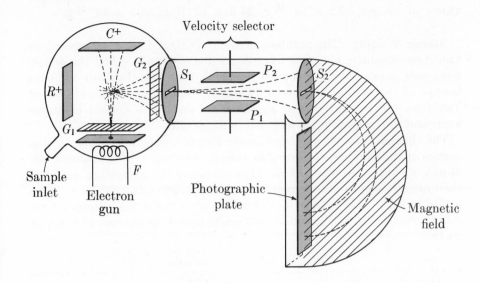

Figure 2.12 Diagram showing features of a mass spectrometer. Electrons, produced at the hot filament F, pass through a slit and are accelerated by an electric field between grid G_1 and the collector plate C^+. Positive ions, produced by collisions of electrons with the sample gas, are accelerated by an electronic field between the repulsion plate R^+ and grid G_2. Passing through slit S_1, they enter the velocity selector, passing through an electric field between plates P_1 and P_2 and a magnetic field perpendicular to the plane of the paper. The two fields are arranged so that deflection of ions by the electric field is opposed by the magnetic field; for adjusted field strengths this means that only ions having identical velocities pass through slit S_2; all others miss the opening. The selected ions then pass into another magnetic field, where they undergo a circular deflection of radius proportional to their ratio of mass to charge.

For two ions of the same charge, the heavier will experience the smaller amount of bending in the magnetic field, and the heavier will strike a detector at a point different from that struck by the lighter one. The distance between the two positions is a measure of the difference in the masses of the two ions. The intensity of the current produced when the detector is at the point where the heavier ions strike, compared to its intensity at the point where the lighter ions strike, measures the relative number of ions of the two different masses. In the mass spectrometer, therefore, we may not only measure exactly the relative masses of the positive ions in the beam, but also their relative numbers.

The existence of atoms of the same element with different masses had been discovered earlier in the identification of the elements formed in radioactive disintegrations. Numbers of these elements could be grouped together on the basis of their similarity in chemical properties, and appeared to be chemically identical, even though their formation by losses of alpha and beta particles indicated that their atomic weights must be different. Frederick Soddy, in 1913, was the first to suggest that these were in fact atoms of the same element, even though they had different atomic weights, and he coined the name isotopes for these different-weight atoms.

Aston's work confirmed the existence of isotopes for nonradioactive elements as well. Later work has shown that nearly all of the naturally

Table 2.3 Masses of Some Atoms (in grams)

Atom	Mass (g)
^{1}H	1.67×10^{-24}
^{4}He	6.65×10^{-24}
^{9}Be	14.97×10^{-24}
^{12}C	20.04×10^{-24}
^{23}Na	38.19×10^{-24}
^{27}Al	44.81×10^{-24}
^{19}F	37.3×10^{-24}

occurring elements consist of two or more isotopes. Thus, neon has isotopic atoms of masses 33.2×10^{-24} g, 34.9×10^{-24} g, 36.5×10^{-24} g.

Atomic Weights. The numbers given in Table 2.3 are inconvenient to use. Consequently, chemists have devised a new unit, called the *atomic mass unit* (a.m.u.); this is defined in such a way that the most common isotope of carbon has a mass of 12 a.m.u. When the atomic masses of Table 2.3 are converted into atomic mass units, the masses of atoms expressed in these units are as given in Table 2.4.

The chemical atomic weight of an element is a weighted average of the masses of the isotopes, expressed in atomic mass units. For example, the atomic weight of neon is 20.183. (The masses of the isotopes of neon and their abundances as determined from mass spectrometric data are shown in Table 2.5.) This is in close agreement with the value obtained from measurement of properties of the naturally occurring mixture of isotopes, 20.183.

Table 2.4 Masses of Some Atoms (in atomic mass units)

Atom	Mass (a.m.u.)
^{9}Be	9.012
^{19}F	18.998
^{23}Na	22.990
^{27}Al	26.982
^{31}P	30.974
^{45}Sc	44.956
^{55}Mn	54.938
^{59}Co	58.933

Table 2.5 Masses and Relative Abundances of Neon Isotopes

Mass Number of Isotope	Mass (g)	Abundance (per cent)	Contribution to Atomic Weight (a.m.u)
20	33.2×10^{-24}	90.92	18.187
21	34.9×10^{-24}	0.26	0.055
22	36.5×10^{-24}	8.82	1.941
			20.183

In general, the atomic weight values obtained by mass spectrometry are more precise than those obtained by chemical methods. We may use with confidence the values of the chemical atomic weights listed in the table on the inside back cover. These represent the average atomic weights, in atomic mass units, of the isotopic atoms of each element as fixed by the relative abundance of their isotopes in nature (Figure 2.13).

Composition of the Nuclei of Isotopes. How can atoms of the same element have different masses? Each of these atoms must have the same number of electrons, since the number (and arrangement) of electrons, as we shall see in Chap. 5, determine the chemical behavior of atoms. Each must contain the same number of protons, since the atoms are neutral. The mass difference must be accounted for by different numbers of neutrons in the nucleus. Thus each neon atom contains 10 protons, but 10, 11, or 12 neutrons. The sum of the number of protons plus the number of neutrons gives the mass number of the isotope, equal to the mass of the atom in atomic mass units, rounded off to the nearest whole number. To specify the particular isotope of an element, we write the nuclear charge (= number of protons), as a subscript before the symbol of the atom, and the mass number (= number of protons *plus* number of neutrons) as a superscript at the left. Thus, the symbol $^{21}_{10}$Ne indicates that particular isotope of neon which has 11 neutrons. This isotope has a mass of 20.994 a.m.u.

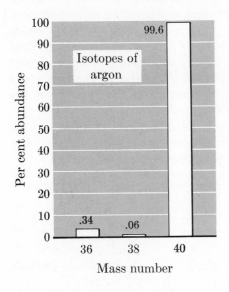
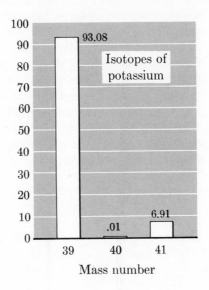

Figure 2.13 The relative abundance of the isotopes of argon and potassium.

Atoms, Molecules, and Ions. The types of combinations of protons, neutrons, and electrons in atoms and molecules will be described in Chaps. 4, 5, and 6, but we shall point out here the information that an atom has the same number of electrons as protons and, hence, is electrically neutral; the same is also true of molecules. However, some atoms and molecules can gain one or more extra electrons or lose one or more and, hence, become electrically charged. Such atoms and molecules are called *ions*. Examples of some ions are:

Ag^+	silver ion	NO_3^-	nitrate ion	SO_4^{-2}	sulfate ion
Cl^-	chloride ion	NH_4^+	ammonium ion	CO_3^{-2}	carbonate ion

SUMMARY

From the evidence cited we conclude that there are at least three fundamental particles of which matter is composed: the *electron*, a negatively charged particle of mass 0.0005486 a.m.u.; the *proton*, a positively charged particle, equal in magnitude of charge but opposite in sign to that of the electron, and of mass 1.0073 a.m.u.; and the *neutron*, an electrically neutral particle of mass 1.0087 a.m.u.

The heavier particles—protons and neutrons—are found in the nucleus, a small dense region at the center of the atom. Around this central positive nucleus the electrons are distributed; the manner of this arrangement will be our early major concern. The atom is electrically neutral and hence contains the same number of protons as electrons.

In the lighter elements there are roughly equal numbers of protons and neutrons in the nucleus. For example, helium has two neutrons and two protons; lithium has three protons, and either three or four neutrons in its stable isotopes; beryllium has four protons and five neutrons; boron has five protons and five or six neutrons; carbon has six protons and six or seven neutrons; nitrogen has seven protons and seven or eight neutrons; oxygen has eight protons and eight, nine, or ten neutrons in its stable isotopes, etc. In the heavier elements there is an increased proportion of neutrons over protons; thus, in the uranium atom there are 92 protons and 142, 143, or 146 neutrons in the isotopes found in nature. The sum of the number of protons and the number of neutrons in the atom gives the approximate mass of the isotope.*

Exact atomic masses and the relative abundances of isotopes may be determined in the mass spectrograph or in the mass spectrometer. The weighted value of the atomic masses is known as the *atomic weight*.

SOME SPECIAL TERMS

Electron	Positive rays	Atomic nucleus
cathode ray	ion beams	radioactivity
cathode-ray tube	mass spectrograph	alpha and beta particles
charge-to-mass ratio	mass spectrometer	gamma rays
oil-drop experiment	protons	metal foil experiments
charge on electron	atomic masses	X-rays
mass of electron	isotopes	atomic numbers
	atomic weights	subatomic particles

QUESTIONS AND PROBLEMS

1. Give experimental evidence which indicates that (a) the nucleus is made up of several components, (b) the atom is porous, (c) the nucleus is positively charged, (d) the nucleus occupies a small volume, (e) the electrons are outside the nucleus, (f) many elements have isotopes.
2. What is the composition of the nucleus of each of the following atoms: (a) titanium: element 22, mass 48 a.m.u.; (b) arsenic: element 33, mass 75 a.m.u.; (c) indium: element 49, mass 115 a.m.u.; (d) cesium: element 55, mass 133 a.m.u.?
3. What is the composition of the nuclei of the isotopes of (a) potassium (element 19) having masses of 39 and 41 a.m.u., respectively; (b) strontium (element 38) having masses of 86, 87, and 88 a.m.u., respectively.
4. For each of the following particles give the sign of the charge, the magnitude of the charge, and the mass: (a) proton, (b) electron, (c) lithium atom, (d) chloride ion, (e) magnesium ion, (f) alpha particle, (g) magnesium nucleus, (h) potassium nucleus.
5. Summarize the information attainable from experiments with cathode-ray tubes. Classify this information as qualitative or quantitative.
6. Describe the motion of an electron beam moving transversely (a) between two parallel plates, one charged negatively, the other charged positively; (b) between the pole pieces of a magnet.

---

* Actually the sum of the weights of the protons and neutrons in a nucleus is always greater than the measured mass of the nucleus, as indicated for helium in Chap. 25; this difference in mass is called the *mass defect* and is related to the binding of the nuclear particles in the atom. This is discussed in Chap. 25.

7. Assuming that the kinetic energy of electrons in a cathode-ray beam is given by $V \times e$, where V is the accelerating voltage of the cathode tube and e is the charge on the electron, calculate the kinetic energy of an electron in a cathode tube operating at 4,000 volts.

8. In the oil-drop experiment, state whether similar results could have been obtained had (a) light instead of X-rays been used to ionize the air; (b) helium instead of air been used in the chamber; (c) a magnetic field been used instead of the electrostatic field to deflect the charged drop. Why or why not?

9. Values for the ratio of charge-to-mass for two isotopes of hydrogen obtained from the mass spectrometer are 4.7×10^4 and 3.1×10^4 coul/g, respectively. Recalling that the charge on the electron is 1.60×10^{-19} coul, calculate the mass in grams of each of these isotopes. What are their masses in a.m.u.?

10. Calculate the atomic weight of each of the following elements from the data provided:

Isotope	Mass (a.m.u.)	Abundance (per cent)
^{6}Li	6.0151	7.40
^{7}Li	7.0160	92.60
^{28}Si	27.977	92.3
^{29}Si	28.976	4.6
^{30}Si	29.974	3.1

11. Using the atomic weights given on the inside back cover, calculate the weight in grams of each of the atoms of the following monoisotopic elements: bismuth, gold, thulium, praseodymium, cesium, iodine.

12. Do atoms exist? Explain your answer.

REFERENCES

Aston, F. W. "Isotopes and Atomic Weights," in W. C. Dampier and Margaret Dampier (eds.), *Readings in the Literature of Science*. New York: Harper, 1959.

Garrett, A. B. *The Flash of Genius*. Princeton: Van Nostrand, 1963.

Kay, W. A. "Recollections of Rutherford," in D. E. Gershenson and D. A. Greenberg, *The Natural Philosopher*, Vol. *1*. Waltham, Mass.: Blaisdell, 1963.

Roller, D., and D. H. D. Roller. "The Development of the Concept of Electrical Charge," in *Harvard Case Histories in Experimental Science*, Case 8. Cambridge: Harvard University Press, 1954.

3

Moles; Symbols, Formulas, and Equations

*When you can measure what you are speaking about and express it
in numbers, you know something about it. . . .*

Lord Kelvin (1824–1907)

Some of the fundamental concepts that chemists use as they pursue their objective of understanding the universe were introduced in Chap. 1. A few of these are:

1. Matter is made of atoms.
2. The weights and numbers of atoms can be determined in a given weight of an element.
3. Symbols are used to designate elements.
4. Formulas are used to designate compounds.
5. Equations are used to indicate chemical changes.

Information about the components of atoms and the method of determining the weights of atoms were explored more thoroughly in Chap. 2. Now we are ready to explore the meaning and use of symbols, formulas, and equations which make up the language of chemistry and the weight relationships which they record.

Historical: Relative Atomic Weight. In recent years (since 1919) we have learned how to determine the masses of single atoms with the mass spectrograph. These are very small numbers ranging from 1.67×10^{-24} g for the hydrogen atom to 39.5×10^{-23} g for the atom (isotope) of uranium most commonly found in nature. However, previous to that time chemists devised an ingenious method of simple numbers that indicated how much heavier or lighter one atom is than another. Up to 1905 hydrogen was the standard and given the weight 1.000.

After 1905 oxygen of nature was used as the chemical standard and assigned an atomic weight of 16.0000. When the isotopes of oxygen were discovered in 1929 and it was learned that natural oxygen was a mixture of three isotopes having masses of approximately 16, 17, and 18 a.m.u., the physicists defined an atomic mass scale in terms of the oxygen 16 isotope. Meanwhile the chemists retained as the base of their scale the average mass of naturally occurring oxygen atoms designated as 16.0000. This resulted in slightly different atomic weight scales for the two groups, but the differences were of the order of one part in 10,000 or less. Finally, in 1961, chemists and physicists worked out an international agreement to define carbon isotope of mass 12 as the standard. With this came the definition of atomic mass unit currently in use—i.e., $\frac{1}{12}$ the mass of carbon isotope 12, or 1.66×10^{-24} g.

When speaking of individual atoms or small groups of atoms, we express atomic weights usually in atomic mass units; thus, for example, the weight of an oxygen 16 isotope is referred to as 16 a.m.u. A number of grams of an element equal to the number of atomic mass units in its atomic weight (e.g., 16 g of oxygen) is known as the gram-atomic weight, and is a convenient quantity for use in the laboratory.

The Avogadro Number; the Mole

Now the question arises: "What is the relationship between the weights of individual atoms in grams and the gram-atomic weight (g-at. wt.)?" In other words: "How many atoms are in one gram-atomic weight?"

We can find the answer to this question by dividing the gram-atomic weights of several elements by the measured mass of one atom of those elements. This is shown in Table 3.1.

Table 3.1 Calculations of the Avogadro Number

For hydrogen: $\dfrac{1.008 \text{ g}}{1 \text{ g-at. wt.}} \times \dfrac{1 \text{ atom}}{1.674 \times 10^{-24} \text{ g}} = 6.02 \times 10^{23}$ atoms in one g-at. wt. of hydrogen.

For helium: $\dfrac{4.003 \text{ g}}{1 \text{ g-at. wt.}} \times \dfrac{1 \text{ atom}}{6.65 \times 10^{-24} \text{ g}} = 6.02 \times 10^{23}$ atoms in one g-at. wt. of helium.

For oxygen: $\dfrac{16.00 \text{ g}}{1 \text{ g-at. wt.}} \times \dfrac{1 \text{ atom}}{26.6 \times 10^{-24} \text{ g}} = 6.02 \times 10^{23}$ atoms in one g-at. wt. of oxygen.

Hence we see that the atomic weight in grams is the weight of 6.02×10^{23} atoms; this is called a gram-mole or simply a *mole* of an element. The number of atoms in a mole is called the *Avogadro number*.

Chemists now use the word mole to refer to the Avogadro number of particles of any chemical species. Thus, 1 g-at. wt. (4 g) of helium is often referred to as a mole of helium; 2 g of helium constitutes one-half mole, while 10 g of helium is 2.5 moles. A mole of water is 6.02×10^{23} water molecules (which weighs 18 g); a mole of chloride ions is 6.02×10^{23} ions and weighs 35.5 g (Figure 3.1).

Chemical Symbols

Symbols have been used as a chemical shorthand since the advent of alchemy. Modern symbols are derived from or are abbreviations of the accepted names of elements. The symbol of an element is used to represent or signify any or all of the following:

1. The name of that element.
2. The presence of that element in a compound. The formula HCl indicates that this substance is composed of the elements hydrogen and chlorine.
3. *One atom* of the element or a weight of the element equivalent to the weight of one atom. The symbol F may indicate one atom of fluorine or 19 a.m.u. of fluorine or 31.55×10^{-24} g of fluorine.
4. *One mole* of the element—i.e., 6.02×10^{23} atoms of the element.
5. A *symbol weight* of the element in any weight units; thus it may represent one gram-atomic weight, one pound-atomic weight, one ton-atomic weight, or a weight in any units numerically equivalent to the atomic weight in atomic mass units. The symbol Al may represent 26.98 a.m.u. of aluminum, 26.98 g of aluminum, 26.98 lb of aluminum, or 26.98 tons of aluminum, etc.

It is usually obvious from the context just which of the above interpretations of the symbol is intended.

Chemical Formulas

The formula of a substance is a symbolic representation of its composition. Several kinds of formulas are in common use. The choice of a particular kind of formula depends upon the ideas the chemist wishes to convey.

All types of formulas illustrate quantitatively the fundamental characteristic of pure substances—i.e., that they have a definite composition. Thus the formula NO_2 states that the composition of this substance is fixed at the ratio of two atoms of oxygen for each atom of nitrogen. Expressing

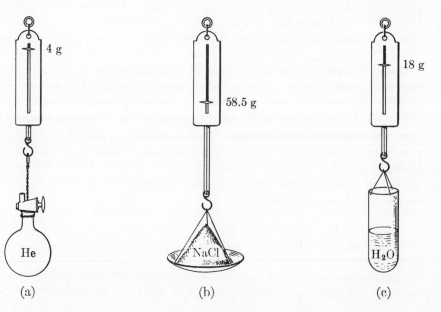

Figure 3.1 Weights (in grams) of one mole of several substances. (a) Helium, 6.02×10^{23} atoms. (b) Sodium chloride, 6.02×10^{23} chloride ions (35.5 g) plus 6.02×10^{23} sodium ions (23 g). (c) Water, 6.02×10^{23} molecules.

(a)   (b)   (c)

this in another way, we might state that for every mole of nitrogen atoms there are 2 moles of oxygen atoms present in this compound. Stated in terms of weights of materials there are 14 g of nitrogen for every 32 g of oxygen or, in terms of per cent by weight:

$$\text{Per cent nitrogen present} = \frac{14}{32 + 14} \times 100 = 30\%$$

$$\text{Per cent oxygen present} = \frac{32}{32 + 14} \times 100 = 70\%$$

Three types of formulas are of particular interest at this point:

1. The *empirical* (or simplest) *formula*, which gives the symbols for the elements present and indicates the simplest whole-number ratio of the respective atoms in the substance under consideration.
   Examples: CH, $HgCl$, NO_2, P_2O_5, CO_2
2. *The molecular formula*, which gives the actual number and kinds of atoms in one molecule of the substance under consideration.
   Examples: C_2H_2, C_6H_6, Hg_2Cl_2, N_2O_4, P_4O_{10}, CO_2
3. The *structural formula*, which gives the relative arrangements of atoms in space and may indicate the types of chemical bonds connecting the atoms.
   Examples:

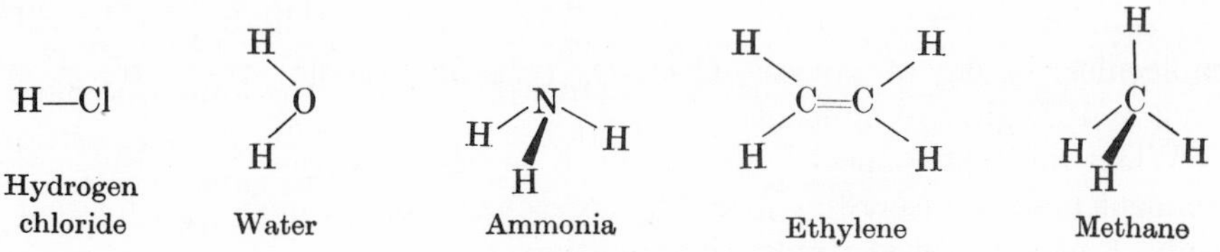

Hydrogen chloride   Water   Ammonia   Ethylene   Methane

Before discussing the methods used to determine each type of formula it might be desirable to look at the conventions chemists have adopted for measuring bulk quantities of substances which are represented by formulas.

Gram-Molecular Weights—Moles of Molecules. Just as it was convenient to use the gram-atomic weight of an element as the standard measure for atoms in bulk, so it has become useful to use the gram-molecular weight (or gram-formula weight) as a standard measure for molecules in bulk. The gram-molecular weight, then, is the weight in grams of a substance numerically equal to the weight of one molecule of the substance in atomic mass units. The molecular weight of a substance is obtained from the molecular formula by adding the weights of all atoms present in the molecule. The molecular weight of nitrogen dioxide is 46 a.m.u. (resulting from contributions of 14 a.m.u. for the nitrogen atom and 2×16 or 32 a.m.u. for the two oxygen atoms). The gram-molecular weights of carbon dioxide, sulfur dioxide, and hydrogen chloride are 44 g, 64 g, and 36.5 g, respectively.

The number of molecules in one gram-molecular weight of a substance may be calculated by dividing the gram-molecular weight by the average weight of one molecule of the substance. Thus for nitrogen dioxide (NO_2),

$$\frac{46\,g}{1\,\text{g-mol. wt.}} \times \frac{1\,\text{molecule}}{7.64 \times 10^{-23}\,g} = 6.02 \times 10^{23}\,\text{molecules in 1 g-mol. wt.}$$

Can you suggest another way to arrive at this answer?

Since the gram-molecular weight of a substance contains the Avogadro number of molecules, it has become the practice to refer to this quantity as a mole of the material under consideration. Thus, 46 g of nitrogen dioxide is referred to as a mole of nitrogen dioxide, 23 g is $\frac{1}{2}$ mole, and 230 g is 5 moles.

One apparent anomaly arises in considering the mole concept in connection with elements which normally appear as molecules; the familiar O_2 molecule is an example. When a chemist speaks about a mole of oxygen, he may mean 6.02×10^{23} *atoms* of oxygen (16 g) or he may mean 6.02×10^{23} molecules of oxygen (32 g). Since the stable form of oxygen at room conditions is the molecular form, O_2, the expression a mole of oxygen *usually* means 6.02×10^{23} *molecules* of oxygen. To avoid confusion, however, most chemists will refer to a *mole of oxygen atoms* or to a *mole of oxygen molecules*, as the case may be.

The number of molecules present in a given sample of a molecular substance may be determined by a simple calculation involving the gram-molecular weight. Thus in 11 g of carbon dioxide ($\frac{11}{44}$ or $\frac{1}{4}$ g-mol. wt. or mole) there are $\frac{1}{4} \times 6.02 \times 10^{23}$ molecules; in 7.3 g of hydrogen chloride ($\frac{7.3}{36.5}$ or $\frac{1}{5}$ g-mol. wt. or mole) there are $\frac{1}{5} \times 6.02 \times 10^{23}$ hydrogen chloride molecules; in 6 g of glucose, $C_6H_{12}O_6$ ($\frac{6}{180}$ or $\frac{1}{30}$ mole), there are $\frac{1}{30} \times 6.02 \times 10^{23}$ glucose molecules.

When molecular species are involved in chemical reactions, the mole concept makes it easy to choose the correct number of molecules for reaction. Consider, for example, the equation

$$2SO_2 + O_2 \longrightarrow 2SO_3$$

This indicates that two molecules of sulfur dioxide are needed for every oxygen molecule that reacts, and an experimenter might use 2 moles (128 g) of sulfur dioxide with 1 mole (32 g) of oxygen molecules and be certain he had the correct ratio of numbers of molecules for the reaction. However, he might also use 1 mole of sulfur dioxide with $\frac{1}{2}$ mole of oxygen molecules, or $\frac{1}{5}$ mole of sulfur dioxide and $\frac{1}{10}$ mole of oxygen molecules, or any of an unlimited number of combinations provided only that the ratio of the number of moles of sulfur dioxide to the number of moles of oxygen molecules is 2:1.

PROBLEM. ■ If 2 g of sulfur dioxide is converted to sulfur trioxide, what weight of oxygen is consumed and what weight of sulfur trioxide is formed?

SOLUTION

2 g of sulfur dioxide constitutes $\frac{2}{64}$ or $\frac{1}{32}$ mole. Since the ratio of moles of SO_2 to moles of O_2 is 2:1, $\frac{1}{64}$ mole O_2 is consumed. The weight of $\frac{1}{64}$ mole of O_2 is $\frac{1}{64} \times 32\,g\,O_2/\text{mole}$ or $\frac{1}{2}\,g\,O_2$. The weight of sulfur trioxide formed is 2.5 g consisting of a contribution of 2 g from the SO_2 and 0.5 g from the molecular oxygen.

Gram-Formula Weights—Moles of Simplest Formula Units. Chap. 5 will show that many compounds, such as sodium chloride, are composed of *ions* rather than of simple molecules. Other compounds, such as silicon dioxide, are made of *macro*molecules, molecules which are very large, and often as large as the crystals of the substance. It is evident that ionic and macromolecular compounds cannot be adequately represented by molecular formulas. Instead, the *simplest* formula usually is used to represent these substances. The question then arises, What shall be the standard measure for these substances in bulk? Chemists have agreed to use the gram-formula weight as the standard, and they have defined this as the weight in grams of the substance numerically equivalent to the weight of the atoms in the simplest formula expressed in atomic mass units. Thus in sodium chloride, NaCl, the formula weight is 58.5 a.m.u., resulting from contribution of 23.0 a.m.u. from the sodium ion and 35.5 a.m.u. from the chloride ion. One gram-formula weight or weight of 1 mole of sodium chloride has a mass of 58.5 g and may be regarded as containing 6.02×10^{23} of the simplest formula units—i.e., 6.02×10^{23} units, each composed of one sodium ion and one chloride ion. A gram-formula weight, or the weight of 1 mole of calcium fluoride, CaF_2, has a mass of 78 g and may be regarded as containing 6.02×10^{23} units, each composed of one calcium ion and two fluoride ions. A gram-formula weight of silicon dioxide is 60.1 g, and may be regarded as containing 6.02×10^{23} units, each composed of one silicon atom and two oxygen atoms present in a macromolecular structure.

Determination of Formulas. All chemical formulas must, of course, agree with the result of experimental data. The kinds of data necessary to determine the three types of formulas discussed above will be summarized in the following paragraphs.

Simplest Formulas. The experiments required to determine the simplest formula must tell us the simplest whole number ratio of the respective atoms in the substance under consideration. But these experiments are most often performed on samples large enough to be weighed—i.e., on bulk quantities of the substance. If we could determine the simplest ratio of *moles* of the respective elements in the substance, we would then know the simplest ratio of atoms.

The simplest ratio of moles of the respective elements may be obtained from the number of grams of the respective elements in a given sample of the compound. For example, a certain sample of silver oxide was found to contain 1.7271 g of silver and 0.1281 g of oxygen.

$$\text{Number of moles of silver present in the sample} = 1.7271 \text{ g of silver} \times \frac{1 \text{ mole silver}}{107.9 \text{ g silver}}$$

$$= 0.016 \text{ mole of silver}$$

$$\text{Number of moles of oxygen present in the sample} = 0.1281 \text{ g of oxygen} \times \frac{1 \text{ mole oxygen atoms}}{16 \text{ g oxygen}}$$

$$= 0.008 \text{ mole of oxygen atoms}$$

The ratio of moles of silver atoms to moles of oxygen atoms is 0.016/0.008 or 2:1. Thus the simplest formula is Ag_2O.

PROBLEM. ■ The compound methyl formate is found by experiment to contain 40.00% carbon, 6.71% hydrogen, and 53.28% oxygen. Calculate the simplest formula.

SOLUTION

In 100 g of methyl formate there are 40.00 g of carbon, 6.71 g of hydrogen, and 53.28 g of oxygen.

Moles of carbon in 100 g of methyl formate
$$= 40.00 \text{ g carbon} \times \frac{1.00 \text{ mole carbon atoms}}{12.01 \text{ g carbon}}$$
$$= 3.33 \text{ moles carbon}$$

Moles of hydrogen in 100 g of methyl formate
$$= 6.71 \text{ g hydrogen} \times \frac{1.00 \text{ mole hydrogen atoms}}{1.008 \text{ g hydrogen}}$$
$$= 6.66 \text{ moles hydrogen atoms}$$

Moles of oxygen in 100 g of methyl formate
$$= 53.28 \text{ g oxygen} \times \frac{1.00 \text{ mole oxygen atoms}}{16.00 \text{ g oxygen}}$$
$$= 3.33 \text{ moles oxygen atoms}$$

The ratio of moles of C:H:O is 3.33/6.66/3.33 or 1:2:1 and the simplest formula becomes CH_2O.

Molecular Formulas. The molecular formula indicates the number and kind of atoms in one molecule of the substance under consideration. It may be the simplest formula or a multiple of the simplest formula. Once the simplest formula has been obtained, the molecular formula may be determined, provided the molecular weight is known. To do this, several methods are available, such as:

1. Use of the mass spectrometer. In the mass spectrometer the weights of molecules, as well as of atoms, may be obtained with high precision.

2. Measurement of vapor density. A mole of gas at 0°C and 760 mm pressure (standard conditions of temperature and pressure) occupies approximately 22.4 liters. The gram-molecular weight of gases and volatile liquids may be determined by measuring the density of the gas or vaporized liquid and calculating the weight of 22.4 liters of the gas or vapor at standard temperature and pressure (Chap. 12).

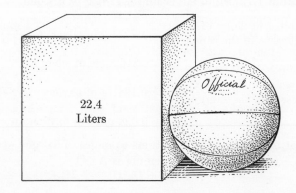

Figure 3.2 Comparison of the gram-molecular volume of a gas at standard conditions with a standard basketball.

3. Determination of the depression of the freezing point or elevation of the boiling point of a solvent caused by the presence of a solute. One mole of a molecular solute such as sugar dissolved in 1,000 g of water will lower the freezing point of water 1.86°C. By dissolving a weighed sample of a molecular solute in a known weight of water and measuring the freezing point of the solution, it is possible to calculate the weight of the solute which, when dissolved in 1,000 g of water, will lower the freezing point 1.86°C. This is the gram-molecular weight of the solute.

Since the methods of determining molecular weights will be presented later (Chaps. 12 and 14), the following example will suffice to illustrate the determination of the molecular formula from the simplest formula.

PROBLEM. ■ The simplest formula for methyl formate has been found to be CH_2O (see problem, page 42). The molecular weight of this compound has been found to be 60 a.m.u. by the freezing-point depression method. What is the molecular formula?

SOLUTION

The molecular weight must be a multiple of the weight of the simplest formula unit—i.e., CH_2O. Since the weight of CH_2O is 30 a.m.u., it is evident that the molecular weight is twice this, which corresponds to the molecular formula $C_2H_4O_2$.

Structural Formulas. One modern method used to determine the arrangement of the atoms within a molecule or an ion is to study the pattern given by X-rays directed toward a sample of the substance under consideration. Microwave spectroscopy also is used for this purpose (Chap. 12). Before the chemists knew the process of determining a structure by the use of these methods, they had devised an ingenious method of deducing structural formulas by complicated sequences of chemical reactions called "proofs of structure." Some of the most brilliant reasoning and sequences of experiments in all chemistry were devised to prove the structures of important organic compounds. Even today structural formulas are often developed by the "proof of structure" technique. An example of this method will be given in Chap. 10.

Chemical Equations

A chemical equation is simply a sentence written with chemical symbols and formulas; it represents facts which are already known from experiment; it indicates with symbols and formulas the rearrangement of atoms, ions, and/or molecules which occurs during a chemical reaction; it is a record, in chemical notation, of what chemical species and what relative amounts of them enter into the reaction and what species and what relative amounts are formed. Consider, for example, the reaction of hydrogen with oxygen to form water (Figure 3.3):

In words:

   2 molecules of hydrogen react with 1 molecule of oxygen to form
      2 molecules of water.

In equation form:

$$2H_2(g) + O_2(g) \longrightarrow 2H_2O(l)$$

Note that the reactants (the materials consumed) are placed on the left-hand side and the products (the materials produced) are placed on the right-hand side of the chemical equation. The letters (*s*), (*l*), or (*g*) are sometimes used to indicate *solid*, *liquid*, or *gaseous* phase. The numbers placed before the formulas are called coefficients. The arrow indicates the direction of predominant change.

It must be emphasized that an equation is a statement of *facts learned by experiment*. In other words, we cannot attempt by equation writing to find out what the products of a chemical reaction are, or what their formulas are; but having discovered these products in actual experiments, we can record the facts in an equation.

Modern chemists usually use *net equations*—equations which specify only the chemical species consumed and the species formed in the chemical reaction. Occasionally they use equations to show a series of intermediate compounds that often are formed in the process of the reaction, or an *over-all equation* to show all the reactants and products in which they are interested.

In words:

> A solution of silver nitrate (containing Ag^+ and NO_3^-) is poured into a solution of sodium chloride (containing Na^+ and Cl^-) and a white *precipitate* of silver chloride (AgCl) appears.

In equation form:

Over-all equation: $AgNO_3(aq) + NaCl(aq) \longrightarrow AgCl(s) + NaNO_3(aq)$

Net equation: $Ag^+(aq) + Cl^-(aq) \longrightarrow AgCl(s)$

The net equation indicates that the product of the reaction, silver chloride, was formed by the reaction of silver ions with chloride ions. No statement is made about the presence or the fate of the sodium and nitrate ions which are present in the reaction mixture. Since these ions remain unchanged during the reaction, they are not included in the net equation. An abbreviation (*aq*) often is used to indicate that the species is in water (aqueous) solution.

Writing and Balancing Equations. When the chemical reaction is known, the *first* step in writing and balancing an equation for that reaction is to write the correct formulas for the reactants and products. This involves symbols and *subscripts* only.

All atoms entering into the reaction must be accounted for in the

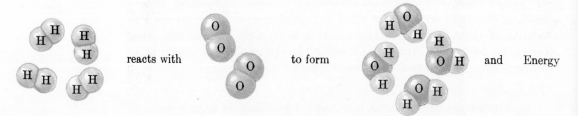

Figure 3.3 Reactants and products in the formation of water from hydrogen and oxygen.

products of that reaction; this is a requirement of the law of conservation of mass. The *second* step in balancing an equation is to balance the equation with respect to atoms. This merely involves making the numbers of each kind of atom the same on both sides of the equation by changing the coefficients only, but without changing the formulas of the species reacting or the species formed. Atoms may be bonded in the products to atoms which are different from those to which they were bonded in the reactants; they may also exist as a different ionic species in the products than in the reactants; but their number must remain constant.

PROBLEM 1. ■ Write the equation for the reaction of mercuric oxide decomposition.

SOLUTION
The expression for the chemical fact that mercuric oxide decomposes to give mercury and oxygen is first written as follows:

$$HgO \longrightarrow Hg + O_2$$

This is not a balanced equation because there are two oxygen atoms on the right-hand side and only one on the left-hand side. To balance the expression (and make an equation of it) one cannot change the formula for mercuric oxide* to HgO_2, for this would be contrary to the results of the experiments used to determine the formula. However, by doubling the amount of mercuric oxide in the expression we obtain the equation

$$2HgO \longrightarrow 2Hg + O_2$$

Note that in doubling the amount of mercuric oxide we have doubled the number of mercury atoms on the left in the expression. This means we must double the number of mercury atoms on the right. This equation indicates that two formula units of mercuric oxide decompose to give two atoms of mercury and one oxygen molecule.

PROBLEM 2. ■ Write the equation for the reaction of potassium chlorate decomposition (Figure 3.4).

SOLUTION
The expression for the decomposition of potassium chlorate to give potassium chloride and oxygen is initially written as follows:

$$KClO_3 \longrightarrow KCl + O_2$$

The next step required to make this into an equation is to note that the three oxygen atoms on the left might be regarded as being transformed into one and one-half oxygen molecules on the right.
The equation then becomes:

$$KClO_3 \longrightarrow KCl + 1\tfrac{1}{2}O_2$$

Since many students find it difficult to think of fractions of molecules, both sides of the equation can be multiplied by two, giving the equally correct and perhaps more common equation for the decomposition of potassium chlorate:

$$2KClO_3 \longrightarrow 2KCl + 3O_2$$

---

* According to the official method of nomenclature the oxide of mercury (HgO), commonly called mercuric oxide, is named mercury(II) oxide.

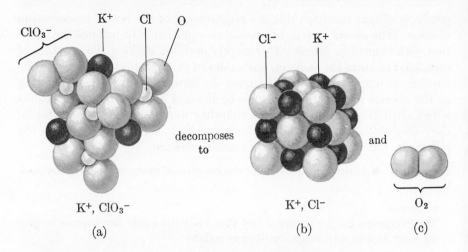

Figure 3.4 An intimate look at the reaction $2KClO_3 \rightarrow 2KCl + 3O_2$. (a) The probable arrangement of K^+ and ClO_3^- ions in a fragment of a potassium chlorate crystal. Note the ClO_3^- clusters. (b) The probable arrangement of K^+ and Cl^- ions in a fragment of a potassium chloride crystal. (c) An oxygen molecule.

Note that the difficulty of fraction of molecules does not arise if the equation is interpreted in terms of moles; it is clear to say that 1 mole of $KClO_3$ decomposes to produce 1 mole of KCl and $1\frac{1}{2}$ moles of oxygen.

To be correct, an equation must be balanced with respect to electrical charges as well as with respect to mass, as shown in Problem 3.

PROBLEM 3. ■ Write the equation for the reaction of a piece of metallic zinc with a solution of iron trichloride.*

SOLUTION
The equation might be represented by:

$$Zn(s) + Fe^{+3}(aq) \longrightarrow Zn^{+2}(aq) + Fe(s)$$

While this expression is balanced with respect to mass, it is not balanced with respect to charge. The correct equation is:

$$3Zn(s) + 2Fe^{+3}(aq) \longrightarrow 3Zn^{+2}(aq) + 2Fe(s)$$

where the number of electrical charges on each side of the equation is $+6$ and the masses of iron and zinc are the same on each side of the equation.

Very often the charge is balanced in the process of balancing mass (Problem 4).

PROBLEM 4. ■ Write the equation for the reaction of the dichromate ion with hydroxide ions in aqueous solution, which gives rise to the chromate ion and water.

SOLUTION
First write

$$Cr_2O_7^{-2}(aq) + OH^-(aq) \longrightarrow CrO_4^{-2}(aq) + H_2O$$

---

* According to the official rules of nomenclature this chloride of iron ($FeCl_3$) may be named iron trichloride, ferric chloride, or iron(III) chloride.

In balancing the masses one obtains:

$$Cr_2O_7{}^{-2}(aq) + 2OH^-(aq) \longrightarrow 2CrO_4{}^{-2}(aq) + H_2O$$

which is also balanced with respect to charge.

Facility in balancing equations comes largely from practice. Most simple equations can be balanced by inspection which usually involves working back and forth from one side of the expression to the other, changing the coefficients preceding the formulas until the expression is balanced with respect to both mass and charge. In Appendix E a more systematic but longer method of balancing equations will be presented. This method will prove useful for complex reactions.

Additional Information Shown in Chemical Equations. Chemical equations may be written to show not only the reactants and products but also some conditions of the experiment.

1. Chemists sometimes indicate on the arrow the optimum conditions or the use of a catalyst for the reaction—e.g.,

$$2KClO_3 \xrightarrow[200°C]{MnO_2} 2KCl + 3O_2$$

The information on the arrow states that the reaction takes place in the presence of manganese dioxide, which speeds up the reaction (hence a *catalyst*), and that the temperature at which the reaction occurs is 200°C.

2. The heat liberated or absorbed may be indicated in the equation as:

$$2H_2(g) + O_2(g) \longrightarrow 2H_2O(g) + \text{energy (116 kcal)}$$

This equation must now be read: When 2 moles of hydrogen gas reacts with 1 mole of oxygen gas to give 2 moles of water vapor, 116 kilocalories (kcal) of heat is liberated (Figure 3.3).

Some Limitations of Many Equations. Most equations do not indicate a number of important facts about a reaction. These include:

1. The equation gives no information about the path by which the reactants were converted to products. The equation $2H_2 + O_2 \rightarrow 2H_2O$ does *not* imply that two molecules of hydrogen collide with a molecule of oxygen whereupon two molecules of water are formed. We now know that the actual path of this reaction involves a series of processes.

2. The equation gives no information about the reaction rate or even whether the reaction will occur in a finite time. The reaction of hydrogen with oxygen indicated above will not take place at an appreciable rate at room temperature unless set off by a spark or catalyzed (Chap. 16); then the reaction probably will proceed with explosive violence.

3. The equation gives no information whether a reaction is complete or, if incomplete, of the extent of the reaction. Chemists have good reason to believe that the reactants never completely disappear in a reaction mixture. In many reactions the concentrations of reactants left when the reaction has "run its course" may be extremely small and the reaction is said to have proceeded to completion. In many other reactions the concentrations of reactants are appreciable when the reaction has "run its

course." An example of the latter case is the reaction shown by the equation

$$N_2 + 3H_2 \longrightarrow 2NH_3$$

Reactions that do not go to completion are usually represented by equations using a double arrow, which indicates that both forward and reverse reactions occur and a state of equilibrium develops:

$$N_2 + 3H_2 \rightleftharpoons 2NH_3$$

At 400°C the position of equilibrium lies rather strongly to the left, which means that if this reaction were allowed to "run its course" in a closed reactor the concentrations of reactants at this time would be considerably greater than the concentrations of products.

Note that the quantities of substances present at equilibrium can be readily calculated from the quantities of starting materials if the amount of one of the substances present when the reaction has run its course can be measured.

It is necessary to realize these limitations in order to comprehend fully the relation between equations and the reactions they represent.

Predicting Products in Chemical Reactions. While it is true that the experimental facts must be known before an equation can be written, it is the function of the theoretical framework of chemistry to provide a basis for predicting reliably the products of chemical reactions. If the theory were highly developed or if the behavior of chemical substances were well enough known, it should be possible to predict the products for any reaction. It would then be unnecessary to remember the results of experiments in order to write equations. But the theory of chemistry is far from this goal at the present time. For this reason the student will find many reactions whose products he can readily predict from his knowledge of theory, and many other reactions whose products he will have to remember from having carried out the reaction or having read the accounts of others who have done so.

Chemical Calculations. In discussing the balancing of equations, the emphasis was placed on the numbers of *atoms*, *molecules*, or *ions* involved in the reaction. However, the equations can equally well represent changes not alone of atoms but also of matter in bulk. To make the transition from the molecular scale to bulk scale one needs only to recall that symbols or formulas may represent one chemical species or a mole (or a pound-mole or a ton-mole) of this species. In this way an equation might simultaneously represent both a molecular-size view and a macro-size view of the reaction. For example, the equation

$$4Li + O_2 \longrightarrow 2Li_2O$$

may be regarded as simultaneously stating both of the following:

1. If 4 atoms of lithium reacts* with oxygen, 1 molecule of oxygen will be consumed and 2 formula units of lithium oxide will be formed.

---

* By custom in chemical literature the singular form of the verb is used for a quantity of material whether it be a quantity amounting to one unit or more than one unit.

2. If 4 moles of lithium atoms reacts with oxygen, 1 mole of oxygen molecules will be consumed and 2 moles of lithium oxide will be formed.

Since moles may be converted to weight, the equation may be regarded as stating the weight relationships in the reaction. Thus, if 27.8 g (or 4 moles) of lithium reacts with oxygen, 32.0 g (or 1 mole) of oxygen will be consumed and 59.8 g (or 2 moles) of lithium oxide will be formed. Of course, if 6.94 g (1 mole) of lithium were used, only 8.00 g ($\frac{1}{4}$ mole) of oxygen would be consumed and 14.94 g ($\frac{1}{2}$ mole) of lithium oxide would be formed.

The following problems illustrate weight relationships in chemical equations:

PROBLEM 1. ■ What weight of carbon dioxide is produced when 640 g of methane burns? How much oxygen will be consumed and how much water will be formed?

SOLUTION
One first needs a correctly written and balanced equation. It is:

$$CH_4 + 2O_2 \longrightarrow CO_2 + 2H_2O$$

From the equation the mole relation between the material given and that desired can be obtained if we assume the reaction goes to completion. In this case the relation is: for every mole of methane burned, 1 mole of carbon dioxide will be produced.

The problem states that 640 g or

$$\left(640 \text{ g} \times \frac{1 \text{ mole } CH_4}{16 \text{ g } CH_4}\right)$$

or 40 moles of methane is to be burned.

Evidently then 40 moles of carbon dioxide will be formed; or

$$\left(40 \text{ moles} \times \frac{44 \text{ g } CO_2}{1 \text{ mole } CO_2}\right)$$

or 1,760 g of carbon dioxide is formed.

To find the weight of oxygen required, the relation between methane (the material given) and oxygen (that desired) is obtained from the equation; it is: for every mole of methane burned, 2 moles of oxygen is consumed.

Since 40 moles of methane is to be burned, evidently 80 moles or

$$\left(80 \text{ moles} \times \frac{32 \text{ g } O_2}{1 \text{ mole } O_2}\right)$$

or 2,560 g of oxygen will be consumed.

To find the weight of water formed, the equation gives the relation: for every mole of methane burned, 2 moles of water forms. Since 40 moles of methane is to be burned, evidently 80 moles or

$$\left(80 \text{ moles} \times \frac{18 \text{ g } H_2O}{1 \text{ mole } H_2O}\right)$$

or 1,440 g of water will be formed (Figure 3.5).

The equation says:

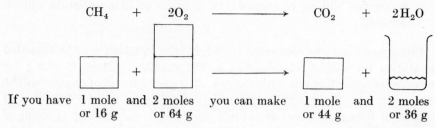

If you have   1 mole   and   2 moles   you can make   1 mole   and   2 moles
         or 16 g   or 64 g   or 44 g   or 36 g

The problem:

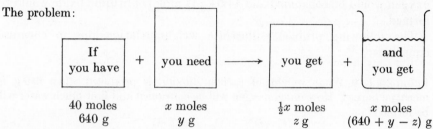

   40 moles x moles $\frac{1}{2}x$ moles x moles
    640 g y g z g $(640 + y - z)$ g

Figure 3.5 Interpretation of a chemical equation in terms of moles and grams of reactants and products.

PROBLEM 2. ■ How many grams of iron can be produced when 6.54 g of zinc is placed in a saturated solution of iron trichloride?

SOLUTION

The balanced equation for the reaction is:

$$3Zn + 2Fe^{+3} \longrightarrow 3Zn^{+2} + 2Fe$$

Assuming the reaction goes to completion we need first to find the relation between zinc and iron from the equation; it is: for each 3 moles of zinc which reacts, 2 moles of iron will be formed. With this information the problem can be solved in a manner analogous to that used in Problem 1. The problem states that 6.54 g of zinc is to be consumed. This is

$$\frac{6.54 \text{ g}}{65.4 \text{ g/mole Zn}}$$

or 0.100 mole Zn.

The equation states that for every 3 moles of zinc which is consumed, 2 moles of iron will be formed.

The number of moles of iron that can be formed from 0.100 mole of zinc is

$$\text{Moles of iron} = 0.100 \text{ mole of zinc} \times \frac{2 \text{ moles of iron}}{3 \text{ moles of zinc}} = 0.067$$

The number of grams of iron formed then is

$$\text{Grams of iron} = 0.067 \text{ mole of iron} \times \frac{55.8 \text{ g of iron}}{1 \text{ mole of iron}} = 3.74$$

These steps can be shortened to one relation as follows:

$$\text{Grams of iron formed} = \frac{\text{grams of zinc consumed}}{\text{grams of zinc per mole}} \times \frac{\text{moles of iron}}{\text{moles of zinc from eq.}}$$

$$\times \frac{\text{grams of iron}}{\text{moles of iron}}$$

$$\text{Grams of iron formed} = \left(6.54 \text{ g of zinc} \times \frac{1 \text{ mole of zinc}}{65.4 \text{ g of zinc}}\right)$$

$$\times \left(\frac{2 \text{ moles of iron}}{3 \text{ moles of zinc from eq.}}\right) \times \frac{55.9 \text{ g of iron}}{1 \text{ mole of iron}}$$

$$= 3.74$$

Note the three steps: (a) conversion of grams zinc to moles zinc, (b) use of relation in the equation which tells how many moles of iron can be produced from a given number of moles of zinc, (c) conversion of the moles of iron to grams of iron. These appear in order in the arithmetical equation and in such a way that all units except the grams of iron may be canceled in the equation.

PROBLEM 3. ■ How many grams of sulfur trioxide can be prepared from 24 g of sulfur dioxide and 8 g of oxygen?

SOLUTION
The equation is

$$2SO_2 + O_2 \longrightarrow 2SO_3$$

The equation indicates that the ratio of sulfur dioxide to oxygen is 2 moles to 1 mole. Since the weights of both reactants are given, it is desirable to check to see if these weights are in the proper ratio for the reaction or if one reactant is in short supply.
The number of moles of SO_2 available is

$$24 \text{ g } SO_2 \times \frac{1 \text{ mole } SO_2}{64 \text{ g } SO_2} = \frac{3}{8} \text{ mole } SO_2$$

The number of moles of O_2 available is

$$8 \text{ g } O_2 \times \frac{1 \text{ mole } O_2}{32 \text{ g } O_2} = \frac{1}{4} \text{ mole } O_2$$

For complete reaction $\frac{1}{4}$ mole of O_2 would require

$$\frac{1}{4} \text{ mole } O_2 \times \frac{2 \text{ moles } SO_2}{1 \text{ mole } O_2} = \frac{1}{2} \text{ mole of } SO_2$$

But only $\frac{3}{8}$ mole of SO_2 is available. Here sulfur dioxide is in short supply, and when this has reacted oxygen will be left over.
The problem now becomes: how much SO_3 can be prepared from $\frac{3}{8}$ mole SO_2 and excess oxygen? From the equation we see that $\frac{3}{8}$ mole of SO_3 can be made from $\frac{3}{8}$ mole of SO_2.

$\therefore$ The mass of SO_3 prepared will be $\frac{3}{8}$ mole $SO_3 \times \dfrac{80 \text{ g } SO_3}{1 \text{ mole } SO_3} = 30 \text{ g}$

PROBLEM 4. ■ As an example of the calculation of the quantities present in an incomplete reaction consider the following: An experimenter mixes 1.0 mole of nitrogen and 3.0 moles of hydrogen in a reactor under such conditions that at equilibrium, 0.9 mole of nitrogen remains unreacted. Calculate the quantities of hydrogen and ammonia present.

SOLUTION
The chemical equation is

$$N_2 + 3H_2 \longrightarrow 2NH_3$$

Moles of nitrogen reacted = 1.0 mole $-$ 0.9 mole = 0.1 mole N_2
at start   at end

Moles of hydrogen reacted = 0.1 mole N_2 $\times$ $\dfrac{3 \text{ moles } H_2}{1 \text{ mole } N_2}$ = 0.3 mole H_2

The ratio 3 moles H_2 to 1 mole N_2 is obtained from the chemical equation.

Moles of hydrogen
left unreacted = 3.0 moles $-$ 0.3 mole = 2.7 moles H_2
at start   reacted

Moles of ammonia formed = 0.1 mole N_2 $\times$ $\dfrac{2 \text{ moles } NH_3}{1 \text{ mole } N_2}$ = 0.2 mole NH_3

The final mixture obtained from the reaction of 1.0 mole of nitrogen and 3.0 moles of hydrogen under the particular conditions of incomplete reaction used in the experiment thus contains 0.9 mole N_2, 2.7 moles H_2, and 0.2 mole NH_3.

In 1811 the Italian chemist Amedeo Avogadro stated a principle verified often since then, that equal volumes of different gases at the same temperature and pressure contain the same number of molecules. This has important consequences in reactions of gases as illustrated in Figure 3.6 and in the following problem.

Figure 3.6 Relative volumes of hydrogen, oxygen, and water vapor observed in the reaction of hydrogen and oxygen to form gaseous water.

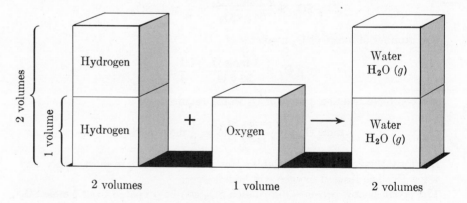

Problem 5. ■ It is desired to carry out the reaction

$$2C_2H_6(g) + 7O_2(g) \longrightarrow 4CO_2(g) + 6H_2O(g)$$

A flask containing 3 liters of ethane under a pressure of one atmosphere and at 25°C is available, and it is desired to supply exactly the correct amount of oxygen to oxidize the ethane. How much oxygen is required?

SOLUTION
According to Avogadro's hypothesis 3 liters of oxygen at 25°C and 1 atm pressure contains the same number of oxygen molecules as there are ethane molecules in the 3-liter flask of ethane at the same temperature and pressure. The equation shows, however, that $3\frac{1}{2}$ times as many oxygen as ethane molecules are needed, so we need $3 \times 3\frac{1}{2} = 10\frac{1}{2}$ liters of oxygen measured at 1 atm and 25°C to do the job.

SUMMARY

In this chapter the relation was established between the mass of a sample of matter and the number of atoms, molecules, or ions present therein. In addition, both the qualitative and quantitative meanings of chemical symbols, formulas, and equations were developed. The concept of the mole (6.02×10^{23} particles) was introduced as a useful unit for chemical arithmetic and in comparisons between chemical species.

SOME SPECIAL TERMS

Atomic weights
  relative atomic weight
  gram-atomic weight
  gram-molecular weight
  gram-formula weight

Chemical formulas
  empirical formula
  molecular formula
  structural formula
  chemical symbol

Chemical equations
  net equation
  over-all equation
  balanced equation

Moles
  gram-mole
  pound-mole
  ton-mole
  Avogadro number

QUESTIONS AND PROBLEMS

1. Distinguish between: (a) atomic weight and gram-atomic weight, (b) mass of one atom and atomic weight, (c) gram-molecular weight and gram-formula weight, (d) empirical formula and molecular formula, (e) gram-mole and pound-mole, (f) over-all equation and net equation.
2. In 1811 chemists spoke of "Avogadro's hypothesis," but today they speak of Avogadro's law. How can this change in terms be justified?
3. How many atoms are present in each of the following: (a) 9 g of aluminum, (b) 64 g of oxygen, (c) 10 g of calcium, (d) 10.7 g of silver, (e) 11 g of carbon dioxide, (f) 126 g of hydrogen nitrate (HNO_3)?
4. How many molecules are present in each of the following: (a) 8.0 g of oxygen, (b) 7.6 g of fluorine, (c) 64 g of methane (CH_4), (d) 1.52 g of carbon disulfide (CS_2), (e) 126 g of hydrogen nitrate (HNO_3)?
5. What is the weight in grams of 1.2×10^{24} atoms of each of the following: (a) helium, (b) lithium, (c) nitrogen, (d) neon, (e) iron, (f) lead?
6. How many moles of atoms and how many moles of molecules are present in 100-g samples of each of the following: (a) Cl_2, (b) I_2, (c) S_8, (d) P_4, (e) C_2H_6, (f) $SiCl_4$?
7. What is the weight in grams of (a) 0.2 mole of $KClO_3$, (b) 12 moles of sucrose ($C_{12}H_{22}O_{11}$), (c) 5 moles of Na_2HPO_4, (d) 3 moles of dichromate ions ($Cr_2O_7^{-2}$), (e) 1×10^{-5} mole of NH_4^+ ions?
8. How many sodium ions are present in each of the following: (a) 2 moles of Na_3PO_4, (b) 5.8 g of NaCl, (c) a mixture containing 14.2 g of Na_2SO_4 and 2.9 g of NaCl?
9. Using the data provided, calculate empirical formulas for the compounds indicated: (a) an oxide of nitrogen, a sample of which contains 6.35 g of

nitrogen and 3.65 g of oxygen; (b) an oxide of copper, one gram of which contains 0.7989 g of copper; (c) an oxide of carbon that contains 42.85 per cent carbon; (d) a compound of potassium, chlorine, and oxygen containing $K = 31.97\%$, $O = 39.34\%$; (e) a compound of hydrogen, carbon, and nitrogen containing: $H = 3.70\%$, $C = 44.44\%$, $N = 51.85\%$.

10. It is found that 15.5 g of phosphorus combines with 12 g of oxygen to form a compound whose molecular weight is 220. What is the molecular formula of the compound?

11. Chloroform is a colorless liquid having a molecular weight of approximately 110. Analysis shows that it contains 10.05% carbon, 0.84% hydrogen, 89.10% chlorine. Calculate the molecular formula for this compound.

12. Calculate the number of particles in a pound-mole.

13. This question refers to the equation $2NO_2 + 7H_2 \rightarrow 2NH_3 + 4H_2O$ which for the purposes of this problem we shall assume proceeds to completion:
    (a) How many moles of NH_3 can be produced from 1 mole of NO_2 and excess H_2? How many grams of NH_3 is this?
    (b) How many moles of NH_3 will be produced from 1 mole of H_2 and excess NO_2? What weight of water is produced?
    (c) How many moles of NH_3 and of water will be produced from 3 moles of NO_2 and 12 moles of H_2?
    (d) How many grams of NO_2 and H_2 must be taken to produce 604 g of NH_3?

14. (a) Write a balanced equation for the reaction of methanol (CH_3OH) with oxygen to give carbon dioxide and water.
    (b) Calculate the number of grams, the number of moles, and the number of molecules of carbon dioxide produced when 9.6 g of methanol is oxidized with excess oxygen.

15. When 1.5 g of a gaseous compound of carbon and hydrogen was burned, there were formed 4.4 g of carbon dioxide and 2.7 g of water. If the molecular weight of the compound of carbon and hydrogen is 30, write a (balanced) chemical equation for the burning process.

16. How many grams of hydrogen will be liberated when 5.0 g of zinc is added to a solution containing 60 g of H_2SO_4?

17. How many moles and how many grams of sodium carbonate are needed to prepare 220 g of carbon dioxide by the action of hydrochloric acid on sodium carbonate $Na_2CO_3 + 2HCl \rightarrow 2NaCl + H_2O + CO_2$?

18. Native sulfur ore containing some rock impurities is used to make sulfuric acid. The reactions are:

$$S + O_2 \longrightarrow SO_2$$

$$2SO_2 + O_2 \longrightarrow 2SO_3$$

$$SO_3 + H_2O \longrightarrow H_2SO_4$$

From 10 g of the ore, 29.4 g of sulfuric acid was obtained. What is the per cent of sulfur in the ore?

19. (a) How many grams each of carbon dioxide and water can be obtained when 200 g of heptane (C_7H_{16}) is burned in the presence of 30 moles of oxygen gas? (b) Which starting material remains unreacted? How much of it?

20. Current market prices for zinc and iron are 12 and 5 cents per pound, respectively. Which metal would be the cheapest to use in the preparation of hydrogen by the reaction $M + H_2SO_4 \rightarrow MSO_4 + H_2$?

REFERENCES

AVOGADRO, A. "Essay on the Manner of Determining the Relative Masses of Elementary Molecules and the Proportions in Which They Enter into These Compounds," in W. C. Dampier and Margaret Dampier (eds.), *Readings in the Literature of Science*. New York: Harper, 1959, p. 105.

KIEFFER, W. F. *The Mole Concept in Chemistry*. New York: Reinhold, 1962.

NASH, L. *Stoichiometry*. Reading, Mass.: Addison-Wesley, 1966.

4

The Electron Configuration of Atoms

*You cannot mark an electron, you cannot paint it in red. Indeed,
you must not even think of it as marked when you do your
counting. . . . A wave on the other hand can easily be imprinted
with an individual structure by which it can be recognized beyond
doubt.*   Erwin Schrödinger (1887–1961)

Where Are the Electrons in the Atom? There is convincing evidence
from experiments with alpha-particle bombardment that the heavy
fundamental particles, the protons and the neutrons, are concentrated in a
very small nucleus in the center of the atom (Chap. 2). But since the
diameter of the atom is about ten thousand times that of the nucleus, we
must assume that the electrons are arranged in some fashion in the
relatively vast space between the nucleus and the outer sphere of influence
which characterizes the volume of the atom.

The Role of Electrons in Determining the Effective Size of the Atom.
Since the atoms of which all matter is made are mostly space, one may
wonder why one object doesn't easily penetrate another or how we can
hammer a nail and not have the nail pass right through the hammer head.
To explain this we must assume that the outer surfaces of all atoms contain
electrons, and the close approach of one object to another requires the
electrons of one object to come near to those of the other. The approach
continues until the strong repulsive force of the similarly charged electrons
becomes dominant. By virtue of these electronic repulsions an object
appears to be solid (even though we now know it is very porous) when
struck with another piece of matter.

Only the neutral particles are free from these electrostatic repulsive
forces; hence neutrons can pass through matter in a fashion which reflects
its true openness.

It is our plan to consider here some of the experimental evidence and
theoretical considerations which point to the detailed arrangements of the
electrons in the atoms. Through a knowledge of this arrangement we shall

find a valuable key to the chemical reactions of atoms, their combining capacity, and the spatial arrangement of atoms in molecules.

A Theory for the Arrangement of Electrons in Atoms

Following his bombardment studies, Rutherford postulated that moving electrons, attracted by the nucleus of the atom, may be circling it in orbits just as the planets of the solar system move about the sun. This idea was appealing but it raised the important question of what keeps the electrons in their orbits—for the theory of electrodynamics insists that moving electrons would spiral into the nucleus and the atom would collapse. In answering this question physicists opened a Pandora's box of serious problems for classical physics. The first clues to the answer were found in studies of the light emitted from excited atoms.

Light Emission by Atoms. Early in the history of chemistry it was observed that when elements were heated in a flame (and later when they were excited in an electric discharge tube) colors of light were seen which were characteristic of the material used. For example, discharge tubes containing neon gas at low pressure (as in a neon sign) glow red, sodium vapor emits yellow light, mercury provides a greenish glow, etc. Color is associated with the wave properties of light. The wavelengths for the various colors of the visible spectrum are given in Table 4.1. Examination

Table 4.1 Wavelengths Associated with Various Colors of Visible Light

Color	Wavelength Range (Angstroms)
Red	7,500 to 6,100
Orange	6,100 to 5,900
Yellow	5,900 to 5,700
Green	5,700 to 5,000
Blue	5,000 to 4,500
Violet	4,500 to 4,000

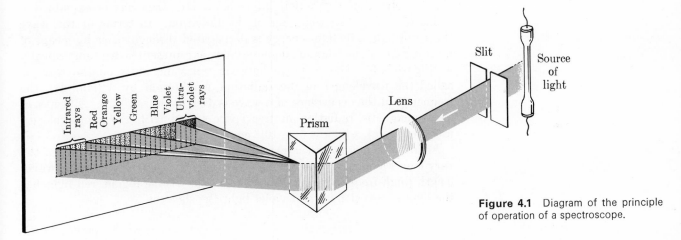

Figure 4.1 Diagram of the principle of operation of a spectroscope.

of the light from a single element, such as hydrogen, in a spectroscope (Figure 4.1) shows that not one color (or wavelength) of light is emitted by hydrogen, but that several different wavelengths are present in the visible region and many more in the ultraviolet and infrared regions. Other elements behave in similar fashion with each element giving a unique pattern of wavelengths (or lines) known as its emission spectrum. The emission spectra in the visible region are given for several elements in Figure 4.2.

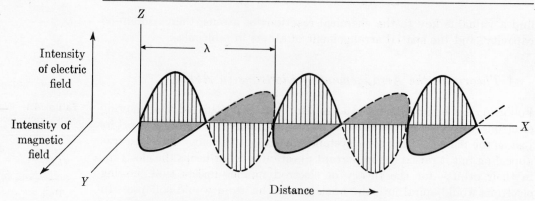

Figure 4.3 Light is propagated through space by means of waves which have both an electric and a magnetic component.

To understand how a study of atomic spectra led to an improved theory for the arrangement of electrons in atoms, it will be necessary to review briefly the nature of light and its origin.

The Nature of Light. We know that light is one form of energy; we can feel the warming effect of the sun's rays on our bodies; we can concentrate the rays of the sun with a lens and heat a piece of paper until it catches fire. Light energy is a form of electromagnetic radiation similar to radio waves, gamma rays, etc. All of these forms of radiation exhibit certain properties such as refraction, diffraction, interference, etc., that may be explained in terms of a wavelike character of the radiation. In terms of the wave theory of light, the light energy is propagated through space by means of wave motion of electric and magnetic fields, as represented diagrammatically in Figure 4.3. The distance between repeating units on the wave is called the wavelength of the radiation, symbolized by λ (lambda); the frequency of the occurrence of a wave is designated as ν (nu). All types of electromagnetic radiation in free space travel with the same velocity (denoted by c), which is 3×10^{10} cm/sec.

Figure 4.4 illustrates the range of electromagnetic radiations from the very long wavelength (low-frequency) radio waves to the very short wavelength (high-frequency) gamma rays. In the visible region, red light has the longest wavelength and violet light the shortest.

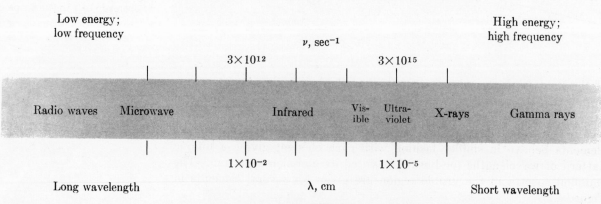

Figure 4.4 Range of electromagnetic radiations.

EMISSION SPECTRA

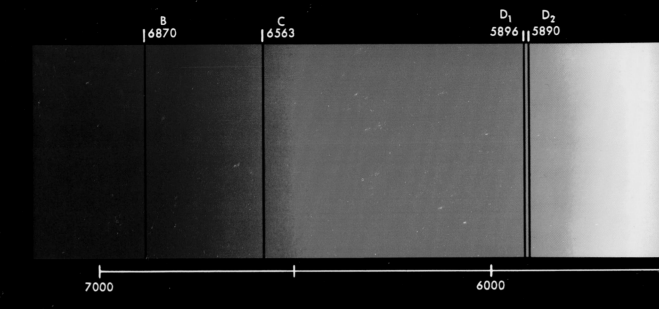

Figure 4.2(a) A continuous spectrum and three bright-line spectra in the visible region. The spectrum of an incandescent solid shows a continuous gradation of colors ranging from red to violet similar to the spectrum of the sun shown in the upper band. The other three bands represent the bright-line spectra seen when atoms of hydrogen, helium, and mercury are vaporized in a flame or an electric arc and observed in a spectroscope. The image of the spectroscope slit appears at wavelengths characteristic of the light-emitting elements; the numbers record wavelengths in angstrom units. The black lines in the continuous spectrum are seen when the sun is observed in a spectroscope, and are produced because the vapors of cool gases around the sun absorb some of its light. They are called the Fraunhofer lines, after their discoverer. Note that two of them occur at the same wavelengths as two of the lines in the emission spectrum of hydrogen, showing the presence of hydrogen atoms between the earth and the emitting surface of the sun.

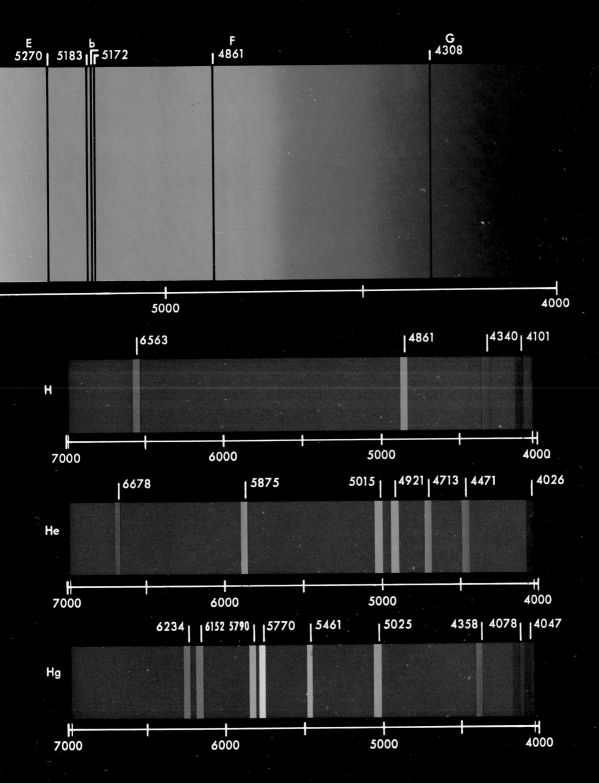

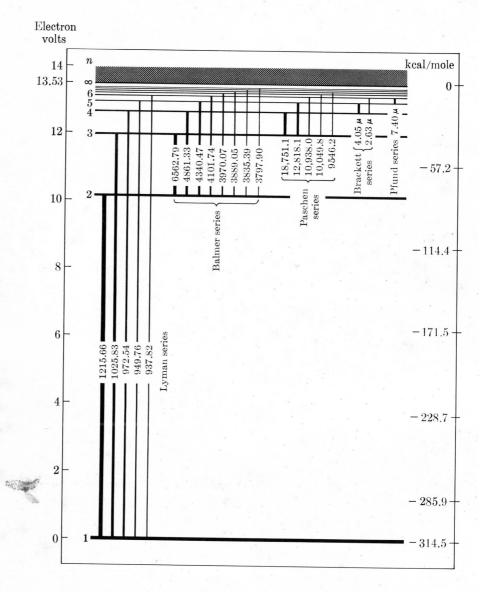

Figure 4.2(b) Energy levels in the hydrogen atom assigned on the basis of the emission spectrum of hydrogen. Wavelengths of spectral lines are given in angstroms unless otherwise noted.

Light Comes in Bundles. *Quantum Theory.* Although the wave theory is useful in the description of many of the properties of light, it does not explain certain observations involving light such as the interaction of light with metal surfaces (photoelectric effect) and the radiation emitted from hot objects (blackbody radiation). To explain blackbody radiation, the physicist Max Planck, in 1900, postulated that light carried its energy in definite amounts or "quanta." He assumed that the energy of a light wave had to be an integral number of quanta where the energy of each quantum is given by the equation

$$E = h\nu$$

where E is the energy of one quantum; ν is the frequency of the light wave; h, known as Planck's constant, has a value of 6.62×10^{-27} erg-sec. When this value is used for h, the energy of the quantum will be in ergs.*

In 1905 Einstein successfully applied Planck's quantum theory to the photoelectric effect. In doing so he made the further assumption that a single molecule or atom absorbs or emits only a single quantum of light at one time. Einstein also substituted the term *photon* for quantum, and the two terms have been used since.

The success of the quantum theory in explaining two important but previously puzzling phenomena of physics established it as a useful and powerful tool.

Since the frequency of the light wave is related to its wavelength by the equation $\nu = c/\lambda$, where c is the velocity of light and λ the wavelength, the energy of a quantum of light is related to the wavelength by the equation

$$E = h\frac{c}{\lambda}$$

This equation indicates that the shorter the wavelength of light the greater the energy of its quanta. This means, for example, that a quantum of red light carries less energy than a quantum of green light.

In accepting the quantum theory, scientists were forced to regard light as having both particle and wave properties, and photons were said to be "particle-waves." Although this view of light at first seemed cumbersome, it successfully explained a great variety of experimental facts which defied explanation in terms of the older wave theory of light. One group of these experimental facts is the spectra of the elements, which were interpreted by Bohr by means of this new theory.

The Spectrum of the Hydrogen Atom. The visible emission spectrum of hydrogen *atoms* consists of a characteristic group of lines spaced between the violet and red regions of the visible spectrum (Figure 4.2). In terms of the quantum theory, each of these lines is the result of millions of photons of a single wavelength striking the eye or the photographic plate of the spectrometer. Moreover, since an atom may emit only one photon at a time, it is evident that many atoms are giving off identical photons

---

* An erg is an energy unit (Appendix A).

simultaneously as the spectrum is being observed. From this it follows that:

1. A hydrogen atom may lose only discrete quantities of energy—i.e., those corresponding to the energies of the photons in its spectral lines (and no others).
2. The ability to emit only discrete quantities or packets of energy is a property of the hydrogen atom.

The only reasonable explanation for these observations is that the *internal energy content of atoms changes only in steps* (and not continuously). The successive internal energies which an atom may possess are called its *energy levels*.

In 1913 Niels Bohr showed the connection between Rutherford's planetary model of the hydrogen atom and the energy level concept. He suggested that:

1. The electron can exist only in certain orbits.
2. The energy levels of the atom arise because the electron possesses a fixed but different energy in each of the successive orbits.
3. Photons are emitted or absorbed when an electron moves from one energy level (orbit) to another. The energy of the photon is the difference between the energies of the electron in the energy levels involved in the transition; the wavelength of the photon is related to its energy by the Planck equation,

$$E_{\text{photon}} = E_{\text{level } X} - E_{\text{level } Y} = h\nu = h\frac{c}{\lambda}$$

The spectrum of hydrogen then results from electron transitions between energy levels as shown in Figure 4.5. In this figure the horizontal lines represent the internal energy of the hydrogen atom when the electron is in the successive orbits and the arrows (a) represent the transitions between energy levels resulting in the liberation of photons which appear as lines in the spectrum (b).

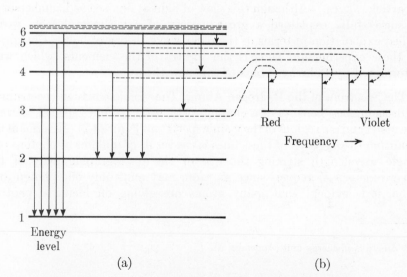

Figure 4.5 Origin of the visible spectrum of hydrogen.

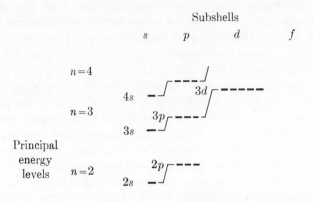

Figure 4.6 Subshell energy levels for elements 1 through 20.

The success of the Rutherford-Bohr theory depended largely on the effectiveness with which it defined the energy levels for hydrogen and predicted the wavelengths of spectral lines—not only those observed previously but many which were to be discovered later.

Subshells. Advocates of the Rutherford-Bohr theory encountered a series of failures when they used it to predict the spectra of elements other than hydrogen. Moreover, as the research in spectra continued, additional spectral lines were observed. The spectra of sodium and potassium atoms, for example, though somewhat similar to the spectrum of hydrogen, require for their interpretation the introduction of more energy levels. These were fitted into the model by assuming that the main orbits or principal energy levels, n, are composed of a series of *subshells*, which are given the symbols s, p, d, and f, as shown in Figure 4.6. *The first principal energy level (shell) contains only one subshell, an s level; the second principal energy level contains two subshells called s and p levels; the third shell contains three subshells; an s, p, and d, and so on.* But even this modification of the Rutherford-Bohr model could not account for all the observations of the spectroscopists.

Orbitals. When an atom is excited in a magnetic field, some of the spectral lines are found to separate or split and appear as several lines. To explain such line-splitting it was assumed that each subshell contains a group of energy levels, often called orbitals.

In the absence of interaction with other atoms or with external electrical or magnetic fields, all of the orbitals in a given group are in the same energy level. Interaction with or application of a field causes the orbitals to appear in several new energy levels; the appearance of these new levels permits new energy transitions and hence additional lines in the spectrum. Studies of this line-splitting led to the conclusion: *The s subshell has just one orbital; the p subshell has three orbitals; the d subshell has five orbitals; and the f subshell has seven.*

Spinning Electrons. Very careful measurements of the spectra of sodium and potassium, the atoms of which have single unpaired electrons, showed that some of the lines were doublets—that is, two lines of nearly, but not exactly, equal wavelength. To explain the existence of these doublets it was assumed that electrons behave like spinning tops, some spinning in one direction and others in the opposite direction. The spinning electrons would act like small magnets, and the interaction of these magnets with the electrons moving in orbits would produce the effect of additional energy levels. This assumption was verified by experimental evidence from a beam of sodium atoms in a magnetic field. Using an apparatus such as that described in Figure 4.7, Otto Stern and W. Gerlach (1922) observed that the beam was divided by the magnetic field, at high temperatures of the oven (A), into two beams, indicating that there are two, and only two, different kinds of magnets in the beam. This was interpreted to mean that the single valence electrons on the sodium atoms are spinning in either of two directions. In half of the atoms the spin is in one direction, in the other half it is in the opposite direction, and the applied magnetic field sorts the atoms into these two different kinds. The magnetic effects of the other ten electrons within the sodium atom just cancel each other, since five of them spin one way and five the other.

Quantum Numbers to Describe the Energy of Electrons in Atoms. The atomic model derived to fit the above observations is founded on the idea that the internal energy content of atoms changes only in steps. As indicated earlier, the successive internal energies which an atom may

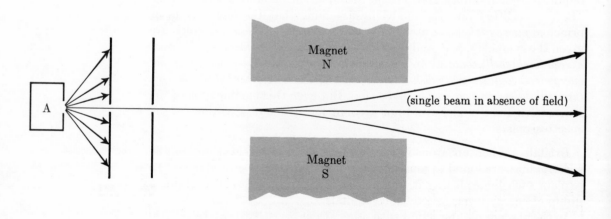

Figure 4.7 Diagram illustrating the Stern-Gerlach experiment. Vaporized metal atoms such as those of silver or sodium emerge from a heated oven (A) and move toward a screen with a hole in it. A beam of atoms moves through the hole and into the magnetic field where the beam is split into two equivalent beams. Physicists interpreted this to mean that the unpaired electron in each of these atoms behaves just like a spinning top which can spin in either of two directions corresponding perhaps to a clockwise and a counterclockwise spin.

A. *Original Bohr Theory*	B. *Modified Bohr Theory*	C. *Modern Bohr Theory, sometimes known as Atomic Orbital Theory*
Assumes main energy levels, n, often designated K, L, M, N, or 1, 2, 3, 4.	Assumes the main levels contain sublevels designated s, p, d, f.	Assumes the sublevels are composed of orbitals which for each sublevel are equivalent in energy; each orbital may contain a pair of electrons spinning in opposite directions.

$n = 3$	$3d$ $3p$ $3s$	↑↓ ↑↓ ↑↓ ↑↓ ↑↓ $3d$ ↑↓ ↑↓ ↑↓ $3p$ ↑↓ $3s$
$n = 2$	$2p$ $2s$	↑↓ ↑↓ ↑↓ $2p$ ↑↓ $2s$
$n = 1$	$1s$	↑↓ $1s$

Figure 4.8 Development of electronic energy level patterns for atoms, showing how the energy level pattern for electrons in atoms developed as a result of spectroscopic studies, starting with the original Bohr theory and proceeding to the atomic orbital theory.

possess are called its *energy levels*. Spectroscopists describe each energy level by a set of numbers called *quantum numbers*. These are:

1. The principal (or shell) energy levels—represented by the principal quantum number n.
2. Within each shell there is a series of subshell energy levels known as s, p, d, or f and represented by the subshell quantum number l.
3. Within each subshell there is a series of orbital energy levels represented by the magnetic quantum number m.
4. Within each orbital the electron may have either of two possible spin orientations represented by the spin quantum number s.

The particular energy level occupied by each electron in an atom can be specified in terms of these four quantum numbers. The four quantum numbers identify the energy level of the electron just as the postal zip code identifies geographical locations. The relations among quantum numbers are given on page 66.

The Wave Nature of Electrons (The Electron-Cloud Model of the Atom)

Wave Nature of Electrons. The postulates of the quantum theory endowed light, in its description as photons, with a particle nature, although most of the phenomena dealing with light previously had been described in terms of waves. It was natural that some scientists should consider the converse and suggest that electrons, which since Thomson's discovery had been presumed to be particles, might be described in terms of waves. This was first seriously proposed in 1924 by de Broglie, who suggested that with each particle there must be associated a wave of wavelength given by $\lambda = h/mv$, where m is the mass, v the velocity of the particle, and h Planck's constant. Experimental proof of the wave nature of electrons came in 1926, when C. J. Davisson and L. H. Germer showed that a beam of electrons striking a nickel crystal gave a diffraction pattern, just as if a beam of X-rays had been allowed to strike the crystal [Figure 2.1(c)], and quite different from the pattern to be expected when a beam of particles strikes a target.

Particle-Wave Probability. This discovery put the electron and the photon in the same class, for both behave as particles *and* waves. Moreover, from their studies of photons physicists had learned two important facts:

1. The particle-waves of small mass cannot both be located and their velocity determined precisely at the same time, as we are accustomed to do

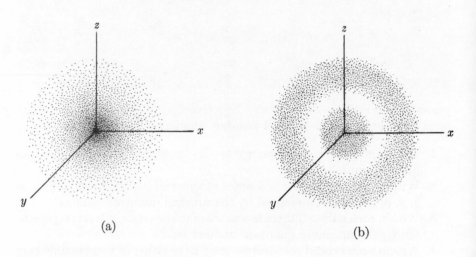

(a)   (b)

Figure 4.9 Probability representations for electrons in atoms : (a) Plot of high probability points for a 1s electron. A 1s electron can be found anywhere from near the nucleus to a great distance away but it is most likely to be found approximately 10^{-8} cm from the nucleus. (b) An electron-cloud picture of the 2s orbital.

● ● ●   USE OF MODELS

One of the main contributions of Bohr was to devise a model for the atom and demonstrate by the aid of the model that he could account for spectral lines in terms of energy levels within the atom.

However, models, like analogies, are scarcely ever perfect. Even today the chemist is uncertain what the atom looks like, and he does not yet have an atomic model that satisfies him. But he is thoroughly convinced that there are various energy levels in atoms and he uses his imperfect models to explain the appearance of the variety of spectral lines that result from electron transitions between various energy states. To do this he uses two quite different models and different types of calculations. We have called these models the *modified Bohr model* and the *electron-cloud model.*

A startling result of work with these two models is that they give almost identical answers in the calculation of the energy levels of atoms in spite of their radically different nature and the entirely different type of mathematics used to make the calculations.

with larger bodies. For example, we can know both the position and the speed of a ship at sea, a football in flight, or a satellite. However, Werner Heisenberg concluded that it is impossible for us to know both the precise position and the exact velocity of a photon or an electron at the same time. If we know the velocity of an electron quite accurately, we shall then know its energy accurately, but we cannot know its position precisely. Since energy levels are especially important in our view of the atom we shall seek to determine the energy of the electron in the atom, but in so doing we cannot know the precise position of the electron.

2. When the position of a particle-wave cannot be determined precisely, the mathematics of wave behavior can be used to describe the probability of the particle-wave being in a certain place.

For these reasons modern descriptions of the atom include precise statements about the energies of electrons and refer always to the probability of the electron's being in a certain region (Figure 4.9).

The Wave Function. The probability or chance of finding a particle-wave (electron) in a certain region in space is related to the intensity of the wave in that region times the size of the region. If we could calculate the intensity (charge density) of the electron wave in the neighborhood of a nucleus, we could outline the region in which the electron is most likely to be found.

The behavior of a wave can be described in mathematical terms by the wave function denoted by the symbol ψ; the intensity of the electron wave is related to the square of the wave function, ψ^2. The square of the function, ψ^2, at any point, is related to the probability of finding the electron at that point. The magnitude of ψ can be calculated for electrons in the

---

● ● ●   THE MEANING OF THE WAVE FUNCTION

Because of its particle-wave nature, an electron in the field of an atomic nucleus may be thought of as a wave. One way to describe wave behavior is in terms of the disturbance the wave creates at various points in space. In the case of a water wave, for example, this disturbance is measured by the height of the wave ; for electromagnetic radiation, it is the strength of the electrical or magnetic field associated with the wave.

Since the disturbance changes from point to point along the path of propagation of the wave, it often is convenient to express the over-all picture of this disturbance in mathematical terms. The mathematical quantity called the wave function ψ is the mathematical description of the wave in terms of the disturbance it creates at different points in space.

The mathematical form of the wave function for an electron in an atom is obtained by solving the Schrödinger wave equation. But realistic solutions to the wave equation are possible only if the electron (and the atom) has certain energy values—i.e., the system may exist only in certain energy states.

The solutions found give ψ in terms of several variables, one of which is the distance from the nucleus, r, but the mathematical dependence on the variables is different for each energy state. Once these solutions have been found, it is possible to calculate ψ for each energy state at any point outside the nucleus. This value will be the amplitude of the wave at that point.

In studies of the wave nature of electromagnetic radiation, the intensity of the radiation often is more important and useful than the amplitude of the wave. In light, intensity is related to the square of the amplitude. It is this which is related to the probability of finding a photon at a given point. Similarly, with the electron, ψ^2 is considered a measure of the intensity (or charge density) of the electron wave. It measures the probability of finding an electron at the point for which ψ^2 has been calculated.

neighborhood of nuclei and other electrons by solving a complex mathematical equation developed by Erwin Schrödinger in 1925 (see Appendix C). In order to obtain a valid solution, the potential energy of interaction between nuclei and electrons, and between electrons and electrons, must be known as a function of the positions of the particles. It is found that a solution to the Schrödinger equation is possible, under conditions which correspond to physical reality, only for particular values of the total energy of the system of particles. The values of the energy for which a solution is possible depend in turn upon the values of three integers, which again are known as quantum numbers, in fact the same quantum numbers as used in the modified Bohr theory.

In effect, then, the mathematical treatment of the electron as a charged particle-wave in the field of the nucleus produces a model of the atom as a system of energy levels. In order to characterize the energy state (or level) of any electron it is necessary to specify its magnetic quantum number m, subshell quantum number l, and principal quantum number n.

Electron Spin; The Pauli Principle. The interpretation of spectra on the basis of the Bohr model of the atom required a fourth quantum number (called the spin quantum number) in order to explain spectra more completely. Thus, it was postulated that each electron was itself a small magnet, interpreted as resulting from the spinning of the electron. This motion was also quantized, and the energy was characterized by values of spin quantum numbers $+\frac{1}{2}$ and $-\frac{1}{2}$. Careful study has shown that *no two electrons in an atom can have the same four quantum numbers*. This statement, first presented in 1925, is known as the *Pauli exclusion principle*.

In the wave theory the concept of electron spin must also be introduced, and finds some theoretical confirmation when the Schrödinger equation is solved taking into account the demands of relativity theory. Thus the existence of four quantum numbers receives a reasonable explanation.

All of this adds up to an overwhelming confirmation of the atom's energy-level pattern developed by spectroscopists. In addition, it provides a reliable mathematical tool for extending the concept of energy levels to areas of chemistry and physics widely removed from spectroscopy.

Relationships Among the Quantum Numbers. The three quantum numbers obtained from solution of Schrödinger's equation are found to be related to each other, and they correspond directly to those discovered by the spectroscopists. The principal quantum number, n, can have any integral value other than zero. For any chosen value of n, a subshell

Table 4.2   Relationships Among Quantum Numbers and Electronic Energy Levels

n	1	2				3								
l	0(s)	0(s)	1(p)			0(s)	1(p)			2(d)				
m	0	0	-1	0	$+1$	0	-1	0	$+1$	-2	-1	0	$+1$	$+2$
Symbol for Energy Level	$1s$	$2s$	$2p_y$	$2p_z$	$2p_x$	$3s$	$3p_y$	$3p_z$	$3p_x$	$3d_{xy}$	$3d_{yz}$	$3d_{z^2}$	$3d_{xz}$	$3d_{x^2-y^2}$

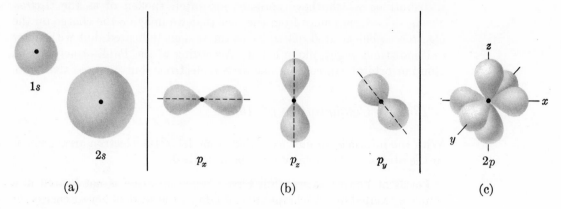

Figure 4.10 Orbital shapes. (a) *s* orbitals are spherically symmetrical. (b) *p* orbitals are distorted ellipsoids with two lobes which join at the nucleus : p_x orbitals extend along the *x* axis ; p_y orbitals extend along the *y* axis ; and p_z orbitals extend along the *z* axis of an arbitrarily chosen system of coordinates. (c) The three perpendicular 2*p* orbitals with a common origin as they might be imagined to appear in the atom.

quantum number, l, sometimes called the azimuthal quantum number, can have integral values from 0 to a maximum of $n - 1$. For any chosen values of n and l, the magnetic quantum number, m, can have positive or negative integral values from $-l$ to $+l$, including zero. Each combination of the three quantum numbers specifies an energy level, so that we may say that an electron is in the energy level characterized by the values $n = 2$, $l = 1$, $m = +1$, for example, or by the values $n = 2$, $l = 0$, $m = 0$, and so on. The relationships among the quantum numbers for $n = 1$, 2, and 3 are shown in Table 4.2. If a sufficient number of electrons is available, each of the energy levels listed in the lowest line of the table can be occupied by two electrons, of opposite spin, according to the Pauli principle (Figure 4.8 C).

Electron Clouds: Regions of Highest Probability. Let us now look at some energy levels in an atom and discover, if we can, the regions in space where electrons in each of these states spend most of their time. Each energy level, such as those described by combinations of quantum numbers in Table 4.2, is known as an *orbital* and may be represented by a wave function ψ. A value for ψ can be obtained for any point in space and the square of this value specifies the probability of finding an electron (having the energy characteristic of that orbital) at that point. Pictorial representations of the region of highest probability for a given orbital—e.g., the surface which encloses, say, 90 per cent of the charge distribution, can be worked out from a locus of the high-probability points. Figure 4.10 is a photograph of some orbital shapes. It is important to note that *all s orbitals (states for which the l quantum number is 0) are spherical and that all p orbitals (states for which the l quantum number is 1) consist of egg-shaped lobes and that the p orbitals of the same principal quantum number are mutually perpendicular to each other.*

Since these diagrams represent the distribution of electron charge, the distributions which they represent are often spoken of as the *electron clouds*. The term comes from the fact that we imagine the charge on the electron to be smeared out to cover the regions indicated, but with fuzzy and indistinct edges, like a cloud. According to the Pauli principle each cloud or orbital can contain one or two electrons, but no more than two.

Electron Configuration of Atoms

With the information now available, a model of the electron arrangement in the atoms of the elements can be described.

Levels of Lowest Energy Fill First. When an atom is not heated in a flame or excited in a discharge tube, it adopts the state of lowest energy, or the "ground state". In such a state the electrons of the atom are in the lowest energy levels allowed to them by the Pauli exclusion principle. For atoms with more than two electrons, however, it is not possible to put all the electrons into the energy state corresponding to $n = 1$, since this is forbidden by the Pauli principle. Hence the normal state of the lithium atom (three electrons) will have two electrons in the state $n = 1$, and one in the state $n = 2$. If we examine each element in turn, allowing the nuclear charge to increase by one unit from one element to the next, we can determine the arrangement of electrons in the energy levels by assigning them always to the lowest levels permitted by the exclusion principle. Examination of the spectra of successive elements permits us to identify the energy levels of each experimentally. The order of increasing energy as a function of the quantum numbers of the energy level is given for the light elements in Figure 4.11. This order changes as the atomic number changes according to Figure 4.12.

The right-hand column in Figure 4.11 gives the total number of electrons possible in each designated subshell energy level (l), counted by allowing integral m values from $-l$ to $+l$ and values of the spin quantum number of

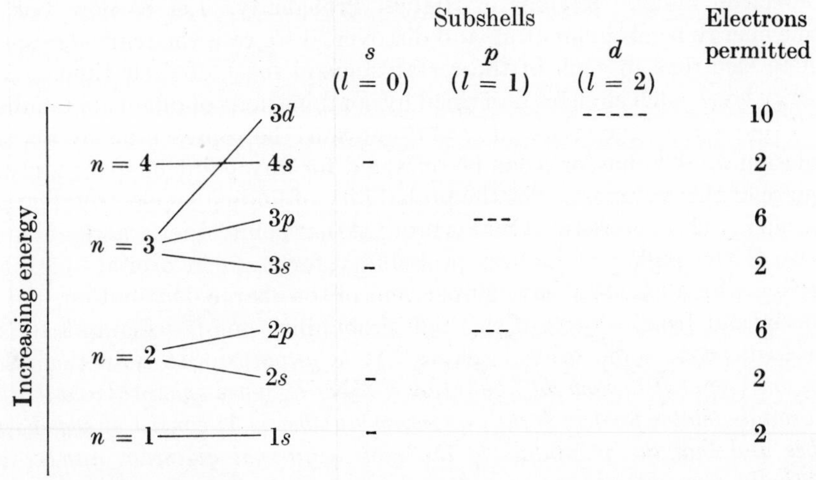

Figure 4.11 Order of increasing energy in the ground states of light elements. The orbitals corresponding to the same values of *l* are included together, since, in general, these have the same energy in the absence of an electrostatic or magnetic field.

	Subshells			Electrons permitted
	s ($l=0$)	p ($l=1$)	d ($l=2$)	
3d			-----	10
$n=4$ —— 4s	-			2
3p		---		6
$n=3$ —— 3s	-			2
2p		---		6
$n=2$ —— 2s	-			2
$n=1$ —— 1s	-			2

Increasing energy

$+\frac{1}{2}$ and $-\frac{1}{2}$ for each m value. The symbols (s, p, d, f) give the conventional designation as energy levels, listing the principal quantum number $n = 1$, 2, 3, etc., and the letter designation for $l = 0, 1, 2$, etc. (the s, p, d, f sub-shells).

Atoms of Elements from Hydrogen to Calcium. Figure 4.11 enables us, starting with the lightest element, hydrogen, to write down the electron configuration of the ground state for the atoms of each successive element. Hydrogen will have its single electron in the $1s$ level. There can be two electrons in the $1s$ level ($s = +\frac{1}{2}, -\frac{1}{2}$), and helium adopts this configuration ($1s^2$). Lithium can have two of its three electrons in the $1s$ level without violating the Pauli principle, but the third must go into the next lowest level, which Figure 4.11 shows to be $2s$. Again a total of two electrons can enter this level, which is filled at beryllium (four electrons). The fifth electron of boron must now go to the next lowest level, the $2p$ level. Since for this level m may have values $-1, 0, +1$ and s may have values $+\frac{1}{2}$ and $-\frac{1}{2}$, a total of six electrons may appear here, and as additional electrons are added in the atoms from carbon (6) to neon (10), these six places are filled. The electron configurations in the ground states of the first ten elements are thus those given in Table 4.3.

Table 4.3 Electron Configurations of the First Ten Elements

Element	Atomic Number	Configuration
H	1	$1s^1$
He	2	$1s^2$
Li	3	$1s^2\, 2s^1$
Be	4	$1s^2\, 2s^2$
B	5	$1s^2\, 2s^2\, 2p^1$
C	6	$1s^2\, 2s^2\, 2p^2$
N	7	$1s^2\, 2s^2\, 2p^3$
O	8	$1s^2\, 2s^2\, 2p^4$
F	9	$1s^2\, 2s^2\, 2p^5$
Ne	10	$1s^2\, 2s^2\, 2p^6$

A question arises as to whether the two $2p$ electrons of carbon are in the same p orbital, with $s = +\frac{1}{2}$ and $s = -\frac{1}{2}$, or in different p orbitals with s for both equal to $+\frac{1}{2}$ (or both $-\frac{1}{2}$). From the shape of the charge distributions of the p orbitals shown in Figure 4.10, it is evident that if one electron is in each of two orbitals, they can get farther away from each other than if they are both in the same orbital. Since electrons repel each other, the former is the state of lower energy, and the atom adopts the former configuration, with the two spin quantum numbers the same. Similarly, the three $2p$ electrons in nitrogen occupy three different p-orbitals and have the same spin quantum numbers. In oxygen, however, the fourth p electron must pair with an electron of opposite spin quantum number in one of the p orbitals. A detailed description of the electron configurations of the elements carbon through neon might then be given in Table 4.4, where the p orbitals along the x and y axes (p_x and p_y), have arbitrarily been designated as the ones which the $2p$ electrons of carbon occupy. It is

Table 4.4 Electron Configurations of Atoms of the Elements Carbon Through Neon

C	$1s^2\, 2s^2\, 2p^1{}_x\, 2p^1{}_y$
N	$1s^2\, 2s^2\, 2p^1{}_x\, 2p^1{}_y\, 2p^1{}_z$
O	$1s^2\, 2s^2\, 2p^2{}_x\, 2p^1{}_y\, 2p^1{}_z$
F	$1s^2\, 2s^2\, 2p^2{}_x\, 2p^2{}_y\, 2p^1{}_z$
Ne	$1s^2\, 2s^2\, 2p^2{}_x\, 2p^2{}_y\, 2p^2{}_z$

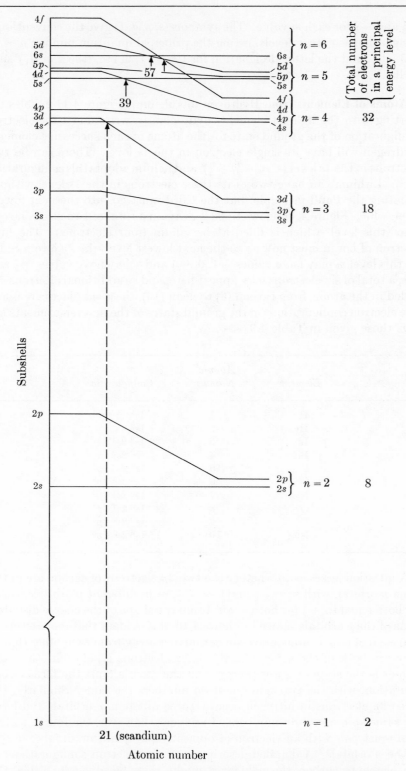

Figure 4.12 The relative values of the energy levels of atoms. Note the shift in the relative value of the 3*d* and 4*s* energy levels starting with element 21 where the 3*d* level drops below the 4*s* level. A similar shift occurs in the other transition series at the points indicated by the other arrows.

a general rule (Hund's rule) that electrons in different orbitals of the same subshell maintain identical spin quantum numbers wherever possible.

Electron Configurations of Elements from Sodium to Potassium. Returning now to electron configurations of the elements beyond neon we note that the eleventh electron to be added to form the sodium atom cannot appear in the $2p$ level, since this would require two electrons to have the same four quantum numbers, and it must go to the $3s$ level. The electron configuration of the sodium atom is thus $1s^2\,2s^2\,2p^6\,3s^1$, so that sodium is like lithium in having its electron of highest energy in an s level. This is related to the chemical similarity of sodium and lithium. Beyond sodium the $3s$ and $3p$ orbitals fill as before, as shown in Table 4.5.

Table 4.5 Electron Configurations of Atoms of the Elements Sodium Through Argon

Element	Atomic Number	Configuration
Na	11	$1s^2\,2s^2\,2p^6\,3s^1$
Mg	12	$1s^2\,2s^2\,2p^6\,3s^2$
Al	13	$1s^2\,2s^2\,2p^6\,3s^2\,3p^1$
Si	14	$1s^2\,2s^2\,2p^6\,3s^2\,3p^2$
P	15	$1s^2\,2s^2\,2p^6\,3s^2\,3p^3$
S	16	$1s^2\,2s^2\,2p^6\,3s^2\,3p^4$
Cl	17	$1s^2\,2s^2\,2p^6\,3s^2\,3p^5$
Ar	18	$1s^2\,2s^2\,2p^6\,3s^2\,3p^6$

With argon (atomic number 18) the $3p$ orbitals are filled, so the next element, potassium (atomic number 19), has one electron in the energy level lying immediately above the $3p$ level (Figure 4.11). This is the $4s$ orbital and the configuration for potassium is

$$_{19}\mathrm{K} \qquad 1s^2\,2s^2\,2p^6\,3s^2\,3p^6\,4s^1$$

Calcium (atomic number 20) has two $4s$ electrons, thereby filling this orbital.

$$_{20}\mathrm{Ca} \qquad 1s^2\,2s^2\,2p^6\,3s^2\,3p^6\,4s^2$$

Atoms of Elements Beyond Calcium. With element 21 (scandium) a new phenomenon appears as electrons are added to the atom (see Figure 4.12). If we visualize electrons being added one by one around the nucleus of scandium, the first 18 electrons will fill the $1s$, $2s$, $2p$, $3s$, and $3p$ levels in that order, but the nineteenth electron will go into one of the $3d$ orbitals rather than the $4s$ because, when the nuclear charge is 21 and there are 19 electrons, the $3d$ level is below the $4s$ level, as is shown by the spectrum of Sc^{+2}. The electron configuration of this ion is

$$_{21}\mathrm{Sc}^{+2} \qquad 1s^2\,2s^2\,2p^6\,3s^2\,3p^6\,3d^1\,4s^0$$

This one electron in the $3d$ level now alters the relative positions of the $3d$ and the $4s$ levels so that the last two electrons, the twentieth and twenty-first, go into the $4s$ level rather than into any of the other $3d$ orbitals, producing the neutral atom

$$_{21}\mathrm{Sc} \qquad 1s^2\,2s^2\,2p^6\,3s^2\,3p^6\,3d^1\,4s^2$$

Hence, upon ionization by removal of electrons, the two $4s$ electrons are removed first, then the $3d$ electron comes off.

In the case of element 22 (titanium), the nineteenth and twentieth electrons go into $3d$ orbitals:

$$_{22}\text{Ti}^{+2} \qquad 1s^2\, 2s^2\, 2p^6\, 3s^2\, 3p^6\, 3d^2\, 4s^0$$

This causes the energy of additional electrons in the $4s$ level to be lower than they would be in other $3d$ levels, and hence the last two electrons, the twenty-first and twenty-second, go into the $4s$ level:

$$_{22}\text{Ti} \qquad 1s^2\, 2s^2\, 2p^6\, 3s^2\, 3p^6\, 3d^2\, 4s^2$$

This type of shifting of the relative positions of the d and s orbitals is found in each of the series of elements 21–29; 39–47; 57, 72–79, which are called *transition elements* (Figure 4.12). A similar shifting of d and f orbitals is found in the series 58–71, called the *lanthanide series*, and in 89–103, called the *actinide series*. In the atoms of elements in these series inner f electron orbitals as well as inner d orbitals fill before any more electrons are added in levels beyond the outer s level, as shown in Table 4.6. In each of these elements, however, the most loosely bound electrons are the outer s electrons, as a result of the rearrangement of the relative values of the orbital energies as the nuclear charge increases.

Other Evidence for Electron Configurations

The Rutherford-Bohr model of the atom, with its modifications developed by the work of a generation of spectroscopists, and the more comprehensive and unified electron-cloud model are in remarkably good agreement concerning the energy level pattern for electrons in atoms. There are, however, two other sources which provide additional confirming evidence for this pattern. These are the periodic classification of elements and the table of ionization potentials.

Periodic Relations Among the Elements. In 1868 Dmitri Mendeleev in Russia observed that the physical and chemical properties of the elements appeared to be periodic functions of their atomic weights, and suggested a classification of the elements based on this periodicity. (By a *periodic function* we mean that some quantity changes in a cyclic fashion, returning to a similar value after a definite period, while another quantity changes in a uniform fashion. A familiar example is given by the periodic changes in the phases of the moon, which occur while the time changes in uniform fashion during the year.) Mendeleev's classification was known as a periodic table of the elements. H. G. J. Moseley later (1912) showed that the periodicity was a function of the atomic number rather than of atomic weight, and from this emerged the periodic law: *The physical and chemical properties of the elements are periodic functions of their atomic numbers.* Figure 1.6 shows this periodic arrangement; the elements in each column have similar properties.

This chart is a dramatic reflection of the pattern of electron configuration in atoms. In the first horizontal row there are two elements corresponding to the places available for electrons in the $1s$ orbitals, often known, from their position in the Bohr model, as electrons in the first shell. In the second row there are eight elements arranged in groups of

Table 4.6 Electron Configurations of Atoms of the Elements

Atomic Number (Z)	Element	MAIN SHELLS AND SUBSHELLS 1	2		3			4				5		
		s	s	p	s	p	d	s	p	d	f	s	p	d
1	H	1												
2	He	2												
3	Li	2	1											
4	Be	2	2											
5	B	2	2	1										
6	C	2	2	2										
7	N	2	2	3										
8	O	2	2	4										
9	F	2	2	5										
10	Ne	2	2	6										
11	Na	2	2	6	1									
12	Mg	2	2	6	2									
13	Al	2	2	6	2	1								
14	Si	2	2	6	2	2								
15	P	2	2	6	2	3								
16	S	2	2	6	2	4								
17	Cl	2	2	6	2	5								
18	Ar	2	2	6	2	6								
19	K	2	2	6	2	6		1						
20	Ca	2	2	6	2	6		2						
21	Sc	2	2	6	2	6	1	2						
22	Ti	2	2	6	2	6	2	2						
23	V	2	2	6	2	6	3	2						
24	Cr	2	2	6	2	6	5	1						
25	Mn	2	2	6	2	6	5	2						
26	Fe	2	2	6	2	6	6	2						
27	Co	2	2	6	2	6	7	2						
28	Ni	2	2	6	2	6	8	2						
29	Cu	2	2	6	2	6	10	1						
30	Zn	2	2	6	2	6	10	2						
31	Ga	2	2	6	2	6	10	2	1					
32	Ge	2	2	6	2	6	10	2	2					
33	As	2	2	6	2	6	10	2	3					
34	Se	2	2	6	2	6	10	2	4					
35	Br	2	2	6	2	6	10	2	5					
36	Kr	2	2	6	2	6	10	2	6					
37	Rb	2	2	6	2	6	10	2	6			1		
38	Sr	2	2	6	2	6	10	2	6			2		
39	Y	2	2	6	2	6	10	2	6	1		2		
40	Zr	2	2	6	2	6	10	2	6	2		2		
41	Nb	2	2	6	2	6	10	2	6	4		1		
42	Mo	2	2	6	2	6	10	2	6	5		1		
43	Tc	2	2	6	2	6	10	2	6	6		1		
44	Ru	2	2	6	2	6	10	2	6	7		1		
45	Rh	2	2	6	2	6	10	2	6	8		1		

Table 4.6 Continued

		MAIN SHELLS AND SUBSHELLS						
		1	2	3	4	5	6	7
Atomic Number (Z)	Element	s	s p	s p d	s p d f	s p d f	s p d f	s
46	Pd	2	2 6	2 6 10	2 6 10			
47	Ag	2	2 6	2 6 10	2 6 10	1		
48	Cd	2	2 6	2 6 10	2 6 10	2		
49	In	2	2 6	2 6 10	2 6 10	2 1		
50	Sn	2	2 6	2 6 10	2 6 10	2 2		
51	Sb	2	2 6	2 6 10	2 6 10	2 3		
52	Te	2	2 6	2 6 10	2 6 10	2 4		
53	I	2	2 6	2 6 10	2 6 10	2 5		
54	Xe	2	2 6	2 6 10	2 6 10	2 6		
55	Cs	2	2 6	2 6 10	2 6 10	2 6	1	
56	Ba	2	2 6	2 6 10	2 6 10	2 6	2	
57	La	2	2 6	2 6 10	2 6 10	2 6 1	2	
58	Ce	2	2 6	2 6 10	2 6 10 2	2 6	2	
59	Pr	2	2 6	2 6 10	2 6 10 3	2 6	2	
60	Nd	2	2 6	2 6 10	2 6 10 4	2 6	2	
61	Pm	2	2 6	2 6 10	2 6 10 5	2 6	2	
62	Sm	2	2 6	2 6 10	2 6 10 6	2 6	2	
63	Eu	2	2 6	2 6 10	2 6 10 7	2 6	2	
64	Gd	2	2 6	2 6 10	2 6 10 7	2 6 1	2	
65	Tb	2	2 6	2 6 10	2 6 10 9	2 6	2	
66	Dy	2	2 6	2 6 10	2 6 10 10	2 6	2	
67	Ho	2	2 6	2 6 10	2 6 10 11	2 6	2	
68	Er	2	2 6	2 6 10	2 6 10 12	2 6	2	
69	Tm	2	2 6	2 6 10	2 6 10 13	2 6	2	
70	Yb	2	2 6	2 6 10	2 6 10 14	2 6	2	
71	Lu	2	2 6	2 6 10	2 6 10 14	2 6 1	2	
72	Hf	2	2 6	2 6 10	2 6 10 14	2 6 2	2	
73	Ta	2	2 6	2 6 10	2 6 10 14	2 6 3	2	
74	W	2	2 6	2 6 10	2 6 10 14	2 6 4	2	
75	Re	2	2 6	2 6 10	2 6 10 14	2 6 5	2	
76	Os	2	2 6	2 6 10	2 6 10 14	2 6 6	2	
77	Ir	2	2 6	2 6 10	2 6 10 14	2 6 7	2	
78	Pt	2	2 6	2 6 10	2 6 10 14	2 6 9	1	
79	Au	2	2 6	2 6 10	2 6 10 14	2 6 10	1	
80	Hg	2	2 6	2 6 10	2 6 10 14	2 6 10	2	
81	Tl	2	2 6	2 6 10	2 6 10 14	2 6 10	2 1	
82	Pb	2	2 6	2 6 10	2 6 10 14	2 6 10	2 2	
83	Bi	2	2 6	2 6 10	2 6 10 14	2 6 10	2 3	
84	Po	2	2 6	2 6 10	2 6 10 14	2 6 10	2 4	
85	At	2	2 6	2 6 10	2 6 10 14	2 6 10	2 5	
86	Rn	2	2 6	2 6 10	2 6 10 14	2 6 10	2 6	
87	Fr	2	2 6	2 6 10	2 6 10 14	2 6 10	2 6	1
88	Ra	2	2 6	2 6 10	2 6 10 14	2 6 10	2 6	2
89	Ac	2	2 6	2 6 10	2 6 10 14	2 6 10	2 6 1	2
90	Th	2	2 6	2 6 10	2 6 10 14	2 6 10	2 6 2	2
91	Pa	2	2 6	2 6 10	2 6 10 14	2 6 10 2	2 6 1	2
92	U	2	2 6	2 6 10	2 6 10 14	2 6 10 3	2 6 1	2

Table 4.6 Continued

Atomic Number (Z)	Element	1	2		3			4				5				6				7
		s	s	p	s	p	d	s	p	d	f	s	p	d	f	s	p	d	f	s
93	Np	2	2	6	2	6	10	2	6	10	14	2	6	10	4	2	6	1		2
94	Pu	2	2	6	2	6	10	2	6	10	14	2	6	10	5	2	6	1		2
95	Am	2	2	6	2	6	10	2	6	10	14	2	6	10	7	2	6			2
96	Cm	2	2	6	2	6	10	2	6	10	14	2	6	10	7	2	6	1		2
97	Bk	2	2	6	2	6	10	2	6	10	14	2	6	10	8	2	6	1		2
98	Cf	2	2	6	2	6	10	2	6	10	14	2	6	10	9	2	6	1		2
99	Es	2	2	6	2	6	10	2	6	10	14	2	6	10	10	2	6	1		2
100	Fm	2	2	6	2	6	10	2	6	10	14	2	6	10	11	2	6	1		2
101	Md	2	2	6	2	6	10	2	6	10	14	2	6	10	12	2	6	1		2
102	No	2	2	6	2	6	10	2	6	10	14	2	6	10	14	2	6			2
103	Lw	2	2	6	2	6	10	2	6	10	14	2	6	10	14	2	6	1		2

two and six respectively. The group of two corresponds to the number of places available in the $2s$ orbitals; the group of six corresponds to the number of places in the $2p$ orbitals. These constitute the eight "electrons in the second shell," divided into two subshells of two and six. In the third row there are again eight elements in groups of two and six, corresponding to the $3s$ and $3p$ orbitals. The fourth row contains eighteen elements in three groups of two, ten, and six elements, matching the $4s$, $3d$, and $4p$ orbitals. In potassium and calcium, confirming the spectral data, the $4s$ orbitals are filled before the $3d$ orbitals. The remainder of the table completes the pattern for the arrangement of electrons in atoms (Chap. 11).

The Table of Ionization Energies. A second source of supporting data for the validity of our present theory of atomic structure is obtained from the table of ionization energies of atoms (Table 4.7).

The energy necessary to remove an electron from an atom or an ion in the gaseous state is known as the *ionization energy*. Figure 4.13 shows one type of apparatus that can be used to measure this quantity. Since in this apparatus the quantity actually measured is the potential in volts necessary to pull electrons from the atoms, the ionization energy is the product of the charge on the electron by the *ionization potential*, and is commonly expressed in electron volts. The ionization energy is often loosely (but

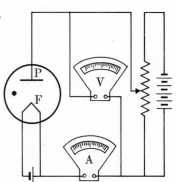

Figure 4.13 Diagram of apparatus for determining ionization potentials. Electrons from the filament F are accelerated toward the positively charged plate P and in transit some of them collide with the atoms of the gas in the tube. If the electrons have sufficient energy they will ionize the gaseous atoms by knocking off electrons. By increasing the voltage difference between the plate and the filament, the energy of the bombarding electrons may be increased at will so any gas can be ionized. Eventually all electrons find their way to the plate and contribute to the current passing through the ammeter (A). As the voltage (V) is increased systematically, there appear sudden increases in current as the bombarding electrons acquire sufficient energy to ionize the gas thereby producing many more electrons. The voltage at these points is an ionization potential.

improperly) called the ionization potential, since the numerical values of the two are the same when the former is expressed in electron volts and the latter in volts.

When the first electron is removed from the neutral atom,

$$M + \text{energy } (E_1) \longrightarrow M^+ + e^-$$

the minimum energy required, E_1, is called the *first* ionization energy. The minimum energy, E_2, to remove the second electron from the singly ionized atom

$$M^+ + \text{energy } (E_2) \longrightarrow M^{+2} + e^-$$

is termed the *second ionization energy*. The third ionization energy refers to the minimum energy to remove the third electron from the doubly charged atom:

$$M^{+2} + \text{energy } (E_3) \longrightarrow M^{+3} + e^-$$

Table 4.7 Ionization Energies (in kcal/mole)

Element	First	Second	Third	Fourth	Fifth	Sixth	Seventh	Eighth
H	313							
He	567	1254						
Li	124	1743	2822					
Be	215	420	3547					
B	191	579	874	5978	7843			
C	260	562	1103	1468	9037	11240		
N	325	683	1097	1784	2256	11660	15300	
O	314	809	1271	1781	2624	3170	16960	
F	402	806	1444	2009	2633	3606	4244	
Ne	495							
Na	118	1090						
Mg	176	346	1847					
Al	138	434	656	2766				
Si	188	377	772	1040	3838			
P	253	453	695	1184	1499			
S	239	539	808	1090	1670	2020		
Cl	299	549	920	1255	1563	2232	2622	
Ar	362							
K	100	733						
Ca	141	274	1180					

Table 4.7 summarizes the ionization energies for the atoms of the first 20 elements. Some interesting variations in the numerical values of these energies are evident.

1. Note that the energy to remove the first electron from helium is approximately twice that needed to remove the single electron from hydrogen, while the second electron in helium requires about twice the energy of the first.

2. The first electron is removed from lithium rather easily, compared with that for hydrogen or helium; the second electron in lithium requires an abnormally large energy to remove it.

3. To remove the first electron in beryllium requires only slightly more energy than that of lithium, while to remove the second electron in beryllium requires about twice the energy of the first but much less than the second electron in lithium.

4. With boron, a discontinuity in the ionization energy data occurs between the third and fourth ionization energy; with carbon, a marked jump occurs between the fourth and fifth ionization energy; with nitrogen, a jump occurs between the fifth and the sixth, etc.

5. Sodium, like lithium, shows a discontinuity between the first and second ionization energies; magnesium, like beryllium, shows one between the second and third; aluminum, like boron, shows one between the third and the fourth, etc.

6. Potassium shows again a low energy for removal of the first electron and a sharp rise for the removal of subsequent electrons in the fashion of lithium and sodium. Calcium, like magnesium and beryllium, shows a break in the ionization energy data after the second electron is removed.

These discontinuities are marked, in Table 4.7, by the stepped lines, which show again the build-up of the electron configurations in terms of the main shells. Comparison of the data for sodium through argon, for example, with the configurations given in Table 4.5 shows that it is relatively easier to remove the first, second, third, etc., electrons from the $3s$ and $3p$ levels than to break into the $2s$ and $2p$ levels. Hence when the first electron has been removed from sodium, a large increase in energy is needed to remove a second, which must come from the $2p$ level. It is not too difficult to remove two electrons from magnesium, since these are in the $3s$ level, but again a great increase is necessary to break into the shell of quantum number 2. In a similar way the distribution of electrons in levels of different energies can be verified for other atoms in the table.

The energy levels of the subshells also appear in the ionization energy data. For example, the first ionization energy of boron is less than that of beryllium because the $2p$ orbital of boron holds the electron less tightly than the two electrons of beryllium are held in the $2s$ orbital.

Similarly, Table 4.7 shows the stability of the half-filled shells. According to Hund's rule the three $2p$ electrons in nitrogen are each in a different orbital, whereas the fourth $2p$ electron in oxygen must be paired. The decrease in the first ionization energy in going from nitrogen to oxygen indicates that it is easier to remove an electron from the pair than it is to break into the stable configuration of three unpaired electrons in the half-filled subshell of nitrogen.

SUMMARY

This chapter summarizes the accumulated evidence and thinking of scientists as related to electron configurations of atoms. It emphasizes how many sources, both experimental and theoretical and both qualitative and quantitative, have been used in developing a consistent pattern. It also shows how a successful, simple theory evolved and how that theory was modified and adjusted to embrace more complicated atoms. It develops the current view of the electron not as a ball revolving around the nucleus but as a particle-wave with a specified energy having a certain probability of being in a given region in the space outside the nucleus.

SOME SPECIAL TERMS

Nature of light
wavelength
frequency
energy
quantum theory
photon
Planck equation
Spectrum
Spectroscopy

Energy levels in atoms
Rutherford-Bohr theory
shells, subshells, orbitals
electron spin
Pauli principle
Wave nature of electrons
particle-wave duality
particle-wave probability
wave function

quantum numbers
uncertainty principle
Electron-cloud model
orbital shapes
s, p, d, f
Electron configurations
periodic relations among
elements
ionization energies
lasers

QUESTIONS AND PROBLEMS

1. Summarize the quantum theory of light.
2. Distinguish between emission and absorption spectra of elements.
3. Calculate the energy associated with a mole of each of the following types of photons: (a) red photons of wavelength 6,700 A; (b) yellow photons of wavelength 5,800 A; (c) violet photons of 4,500 A; (d) X-ray photons of wavelength 1.54 A.
4. Account for the presence of *discrete lines* in atomic spectra.
5. Offer an explanation for the fact that the spectrum of atomic hydrogen consists of a series of lines even though the hydrogen atom has only one electron.
6. What experimentally controlled factors might give rise to an increase or a decrease in (a) the number of lines in the hydrogen spectrum; (b) in the intensity of the lines in the hydrogen spectrum?
7. Cite experimental evidence for the existence of energy levels in atoms.
8. Discuss the major shortcomings of the Rutherford-Bohr theory.
9. Explain in terms of an energy-level picture why elements 1 (hydrogen) and 3 (lithium) are highly reactive whereas element 2 (helium) is inert.

● ● ●   LASERS—LIGHT AMPLIFICATION BY STIMULATED
EMISSION OF RADIATION

The theory of lasers and masers (microwave amplification) derives directly from the theory of energy emission of atomic systems as electrons drop from higher to lower energy levels. In the ordinary process the dropping is random; hence, the waves, while of the same frequency (and the same wavelength), are not in phase.

By application of intense external radiation, energy is absorbed in such a way as to cause the atoms to emit their energy in *unison* with all waves in phase, reinforcing each other they may even bump into other atoms, and force them to join in this reinforcement process which can produce a powerful amplification.

Many uses of lasers and masers are being explored. These include such a variety of possibilities as amplification of weak signals from satellites or distant galaxies, production of very accurate atomic clocks, transmission of telephone and television programs, and production of cutting devices even for metals.

10. According to Bohr the energy of each orbit in the hydrogen atom is given by the equation $E = \dfrac{2\pi^2 m e^4}{h^2 n^2}$, where m, e, h, and n are, respectively, the mass of the electron, charge on the electron, velocity of light (cm/sec), Planck's constant, and the principal quantum number. (a) Using this equation calculate the energy of each of the first two orbits for hydrogen— i.e., when $n = 1$ and $n = 2$—and calculate the difference in energy between these states. (b) Calculate also the energy of each of the first two orbits in the helium ion He$^+$. To do this multiply the energy for each orbit in the hydrogen atom by Z^2 where Z is the nuclear charge on helium. Compare the energies of the first and second orbits in He$^+$ with those in hydrogen.

11. What is the maximum number of electrons that can be accommodated in (a) all orbits with $n = 4$; (b) all the $4f$ orbitals; (c) all the $5g$ orbitals?

12. (a) List all the elements that have an s orbital containing only one electron. (b) List all the elements that have a single electron in a p subshell. (c) List all the elements that have three electrons in d orbitals. (d) List all the elements that have five electrons in f subshells.

13. Write electron configurations for all the elements (a) in Group V of the periodic table; (b) in the first transition series ($_{21}$Sc–$_{30}$Zn).

14. (a) Which group in the periodic table contains elements with the highest ionization energies? (b) Which period contains elements with the highest ionization energies?

15. The quantum numbers for the electrons in the outer shells of several atoms are given below. Identify the atoms.

(a) n	l	m	s	(b) n	l	m	s	(c) n	l	m	s
2	0	0	$-\frac{1}{2}$	2	0	0	$-\frac{1}{2}$	3	0	0	$-\frac{1}{2}$
2	0	0	$+\frac{1}{2}$	2	0	0	$+\frac{1}{2}$	3	0	0	$+\frac{1}{2}$
				2	1	-1	$-\frac{1}{2}$	3	1	-1	$-\frac{1}{2}$
								3	1	0	$-\frac{1}{2}$
								3	1	$+1$	$-\frac{1}{2}$

16. Account for the fact that the ionization energies of boron and oxygen are less than those of their immediate neighbors—i.e., of the next higher and the next lower elements, respectively.

17. What evidence is there for the idea that electrons have wave properties?

18. Show that you know what is meant by each of the following: (a) wave function, (b) electron cloud, (c) ψ^2, (d) probability distribution of an electron in an atom.

19. Draw a picture of what you think the electron clouds of the outermost electrons in each of these atoms look like: (a) helium, (b) lithium, (c) boron, (d) nitrogen, (e) neon.

20. Compare and contrast the models of the atom as viewed by Dalton, by Rutherford and Bohr, and by modern quantum mechanics.

REFERENCES

GAMOW, G. *The Atom and Its Nucleus.* Englewood Cliffs, N.J.: Prentice-Hall, 1961.

GARRETT, A. B. *The Flash of Genius.* Princeton: Van Nostrand, 1962.

KLEIN, M. J. "Einstein's First Paper on Quanta," in D. E. Gersheuson and D. A. Greenberg (eds.), *The Natural Philosopher*, Vol. 2. Waltham, Mass.: Blaisdell, 1963.

SCHRÖDINGER, E. "What Is Matter?" *Scientific American* Reprint 241. San Francisco: Freeman, 1963.

5

Chemical Bonds

If then we consider the nonpolar molecule as one in which the electrons belonging to the individual atom are held by such constraints that they do not move far from their normal positions, while in the polar molecule [ionic substance] the electrons, being more mobile, so move as to separate the molecule into positive and negative parts, then all the distinguishing properties of the two types of compounds become necessary consequences of this assumption. G. N. Lewis (1875–1946)

While persistent experimenters and theoreticians were painstakingly working out the detailed structure of the atom, other groups of scientists were trying to find out how atoms are held together in the myriads of substances found in the world. In the course of their examination of this problem, they were led to recognize three types of chemical bonds: (a) covalent, (b) electrovalent, and (c) metallic.

Nature of Combining Forces of Atoms. It is well known that a particle bearing an electric charge exerts a force, known as an electrostatic force, on other charged particles in its vicinity. Since atoms are made of negatively and positively charged particles, we might expect to find that the combining forces involved in chemical combination are electrostatic, and that they arise from the opposite electrical charges on nuclei and electrons. It is true that both nuclei and electrons show magnetic characteristics also, which we describe in terms of their spins, but the evidence is that with rare exceptions magnetic forces have little to do with holding atoms to each other. We shall find, then, that *the forces between atoms are those between charged particles, attractive between charges of opposite sign, repulsive between charges of like sign, and obeying Coulomb's law.* Coulomb's law states that the electrostatic force between two charged bodies is proportional to the product of the charges and inversely proportional to the square of the distance between them. Oppositely charged bodies tend to get as close together as possible, whereas like-charged bodies tend to get as far away from each other as possible. The force of attraction or repulsion decreases sharply as the charged bodies are separated. In mathematical form, Coulomb's law may be stated

$$F = \text{a constant} \times \frac{e_1 e_2}{r^2}$$

where F is the force acting between bodies bearing charges e_1 and e_2 and at a distance r from one another.

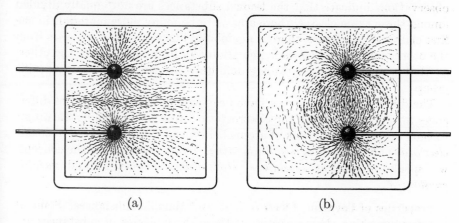

(a)   (b)

Figure 5.1 Nature of combining forces in atoms. Drawings of photographs showing the force field between two charged rods. Two rods of same charge (a) and two rods of opposite but equal charge (b). The photographs were made by floating plant seeds on oil and placing charged rods on the oil surface. The seeds in the vicinity of the rod acquire equal and opposite charges at each end and tend to line up in the electrical field around the charged rod. When two rods are present, the interaction of the two electrostatic fields is indicated by the arrangement of the seeds. Since atoms contain electrons and protons, the combining forces between them are electrostatic in nature.

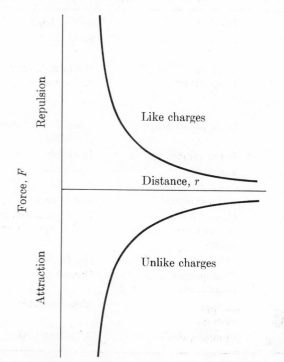

Figure 5.2 The attractive force between charged particles decreases rapidly as the particles (and their charges) are separated.

Classification of Substances by Bond Type. If we try to classify or group different chemical substances on the basis of their properties we seem at first to get only baffling confusion. Patient examination in a search for gross similarities, however, shows that three general types of substances emerge. Some substances are (a) soft and of low melting point; others are (b) hard and of high melting point; and still others (c) have a metallic luster, not generally shown by either of the other two kinds. Further observations indicate that the known substances are not equally divided among these three classes; there appear to be many more materials in the first class. Furthermore, there is no definite line separating one class from the other; rather the classes merge gradually from one class to the other, so that some substances cannot definitely be assigned to any specific group.

The differences in properties have been explained as the result of differences in the way in which the electrostatic forces act in holding the atoms to each other, and we speak of atoms held to each other by *covalent bonds*, *electrovalent bonding*, and *metallic binding*. By an extension of the concept, we speak of *covalent substances*, *electrovalent substances*, and *metallic substances*.

Properties of Covalent, Electrovalent, and Metallic Substances. Some of the distinguishing characteristics of these three classes of substances are listed in Figure 5.3 and Table 5.1. The covalent substances, in addition

Table 5.1 Properties of Substances Compared

Properties	Small-Molecule Covalent Substance	Network Covalent Substance	Electrovalent Substance	Metallic Substance
Hardness	Soft	Hard	Hard	Soft or hard
State at room temperature	Gas, liquid, or solid	Solid	Solid	Solid
Melting point	Within 200°C above or below room temperature	Very high	Well above room temperature	Room temperature and above
Boiling point	Short liquid range (100°C)	Very high	Long liquid range	Long liquid range (1500°C)
Solubility in water	Usually insoluble	Insoluble	Often soluble	Insoluble
Solubility in oils	Usually soluble	Insoluble	Insoluble	Insoluble
Conductivity for electricity	Nonconducting	Nonconducting	Conducts when melted or in solution	Conducts in solid and in melt
Chemical reaction on conduction	Nonconducting	Nonconducting	Chemical reaction occurs when current passes	No chemical reaction on passage of current
Conductivity for heat	Insulator	Insulator	Insulator	Conductor
Opacity	Transparent	Transparent	Transparent or translucent	Opaque
Reflectivity				Metallic luster
Typical Example	Methane, CH_4	Quartz $(SiO_2)_x$, Diamond, C_x	Sodium Chloride, NaCl	Aluminum, Al

to being soft and low melting, are nonconductors of electricity, are usually insoluble in water, and are liquids only within a short range of temperature. Electrovalent substances are those which are hard and brittle, have high melting points and a long liquid range, are nonconductors except when melted, and undergo chemical reaction when an electric current passes through them. Metallic substances are those which have the metallic properties which all of us recognize, such as metallic luster and good conduction of electricity and heat. There are exceptions to these characteristics, however. While covalent substances as a class tend to be insoluble in water, some (such as sugar and alcohol) are water-soluble. While metals as a class are solids of high melting point; one (mercury) is a liquid, and several others melt a little above room temperature. Nevertheless, there is enough divergence among the three groups to show that the separation into these three classes is a useful classification.

There is a fourth class of substances, small in number and including such extremely hard and high-melting-point materials as diamond and silicon carbide (carborundum). These substances consist of huge *networks* of atoms held together by covalent bonds. The result is that the entire crystal may be a single structure.

Let us now seek the explanation for the different properties of these classes.

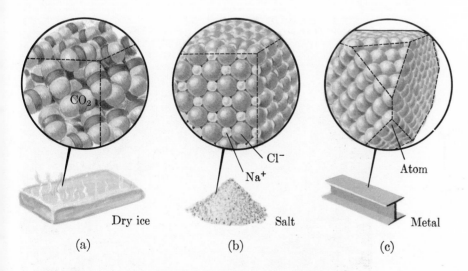

Figure 5.3 Classification of substances by bond type. (a) Covalent substances: soft, low-melting, nonconductors of electricity, short liquid range. Examples: Dry ice, wax, mothballs. (b) Ionic substances: hard and brittle, high-melting, long liquid range. Examples: salts (NaCl, CaSO₄). (c) Metallic substances: metallic luster, good conductors of heat and electricity. Examples: copper, iron, sodium.

Relation of Structural Units to Properties. In order to explain such properties as hardness, boiling point, and electrical conductivity of the three classes of substances, we must make some hypotheses about the structural units and binding in each.

Hardness and rigidity we might expect to be associated with an extended structure, in which all particles are tied to other particles by inflexible linkages, as in the steel skeleton of a skyscraper. Softness and fluidity could arise from unlinked particles, as in a collection of glass beads in a dish, which may be easily penetrated by an inserted pencil and will pour like a liquid. Electrical conductivity requires charged particles, and these must be able to move when other electric forces are applied. Charged particles which were unable to move could also produce inflexibility. If the electrical forces could be satisfied, for example, by only one particular arrangement of particles of opposite charge, any stress which tended to change this arrangement would be resisted if it tended to bring particles of like charge closer together. Inflexibility in such a solid at low temperatures might change to conductivity in the liquid melt at higher temperatures if the forces resisting change in the solid are overcome in the liquid so that the charged particles are unlinked and free to move. The unlinking of particles is carried to an extreme in gases, where the particles are widely separated from each other; hence we interpret boiling as the result of the addition of energy to separate the particles of a liquid. More energy is needed for this separation (higher boiling point) when the attracting forces, which hold the particles together in the liquid, are large.

These concepts can give reasonable explanations of the properties of the three classes. Small-molecule covalent compounds are of the unlinked-particle type (softness); they are made of small neutral molecules which are

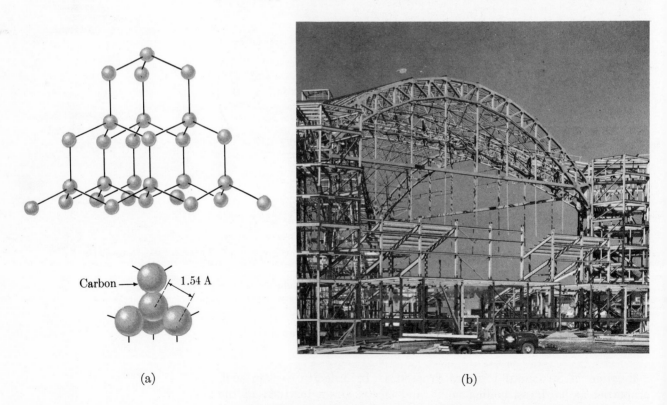

Carbon →   1.54 A

(a)

(b)

Figure 5.4 Rigidity is associated with extended structures in which the atoms are connected in three dimensional networks. An analogy is the steel network structure of a large building. (a) Network of carbon atoms in the diamond crystal. (b) Steel network structure gives rigidity and strength. (*Photograph courtesy of the Department of Photography, The Ohio State University.*)

Figure 5.5 CO_2 crystal. Softness and flexibility are associated with weakly linked particles. Covalent substances are made of molecules held to each other with relatively weak binding forces. Note the CO_2 molecules in the structure.

Figure 5.6 NaCl crystal. Hardness and high melting point are associated with strongly linked particles. Ionic substances are made of ions held to each other with strong electrostatic forces between the charged particles. Note that there are Na^+ ions and Cl^- ions in the lattice, but no NaCl molecules appear.

Figure 5.7 Metal crystal. Electrical conductivity is associated with extended structures containing easy-to-move electrons. Atoms of a pure metal are all of the same size and usually arranged so as to pack the largest number in the smallest space.

held to each other only by weak forces of attraction (low boiling points). Electrovalent compounds are of the second inflexible type mentioned; they are made of charged particles (called ions), both positive and negative, held firmly in a tight arrangement in the solid, but freed to move in the liquid or, when dissolved, to become carriers of an electric current (conductivity in the melt and in solution). Metals have free current carriers even in the solid state; we guess that these may be free electrons, since the passage of the current does not produce any chemical change in the metal.

What Property Determines How Atoms Combine? The structural units suggested above in explanation of the observed properties all have the same fundamental units, namely atoms, which exist in one case as *combined atoms in molecules*, in another as *ions*, and in the third case, as *atoms*. We must look then for some characteristics of atoms which permit them (a) to combine to form the molecules characteristic of covalent compounds, or (b) to form the ions characteristic of electrovalent compounds, or (c) to form metallic solids with free electrons. Ordinarily we do not find atoms of the same element appearing in more than two of these three types of substances.

To find the answer to this we must look for differences in the structure and properties of atoms—that is, in the *number* of electrons contained in the atom, the *energy levels* occupied in the atom's normal energy state, and the *ionization energy*—as a guide to the preferred types of behavior. Perhaps it would be helpful first to examine the number ratios in which atoms of one element combine with another, particularly among the elements of lower atomic number.

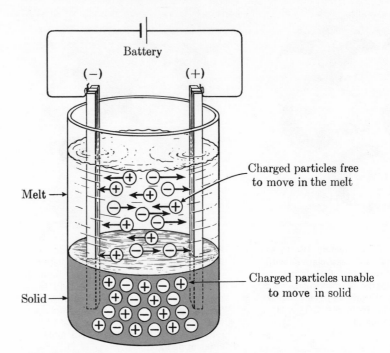

Battery

Figure 5.8 Diagram of a partially melted solid (ionic) in which two electrodes are inserted. The ionic solid is a nonconductor of electricity, but, when melted, this substance becomes a good conductor because of the freedom of the ions to move toward the electrodes.

Charged particles free to move in the melt

Melt →

Charged particles unable to move in solid

Solid →

Atomic Ratios in Compounds. Consider first the formulas of some compounds of hydrogen with one other element (Table 5.2). Remember that each formula has been determined by careful examination and represents the natural combining ratio of the atoms. Note that in these the number of hydrogen atoms combined with other atoms is 1, 2, 3, or 4. When we observe that the hydrogen atom has a single $1s$ electron, we guess that the atom ratios arise from the fact that hydrogen has *one* electron while the other atoms have 1, 2, 3, or 4 electrons to use in bonding. This is confirmed by examination of lithium and sodium compounds. Like hydrogen they have one electron in the outermost shell, and form compounds in which there is not more than one atom of the other element per atom of lithium or sodium: LiH, $LiCl$, Li_2O, $NaCl$, Na_2O.

When we move on to helium, with two electrons, we find that it does not combine chemically with other elements. However, other atoms with two electrons in the outer shell (beryllium, magnesium, calcium) do form compounds, and often in the ratio of 1:2, as in CaH_2, $BeCl_2$, and MgF_2.

Table 5.2 Atom Ratios in Several Substances

Compound	Ratio: $\dfrac{\textit{Atoms of Second Element}}{\textit{Atoms of Hydrogen}}$
H_2	1:1
HCl	1:1
H_2O	1:2
NH_3	1:3
LiH	1:1
CH_4	1:4
H_2O_2	1:1
N_2H_4	1:2

Except for helium, the two outer electrons, then, seem to be associated with a combining ratio of 2. However, the fact that the two electrons of helium do not lead to chemical combination is in agreement with the fact that the two $1s$ electrons in lithium and in beryllium apparently do not play any role in compound formation either, since only the outer electron in lithium (or the outer two in beryllium) seems to be involved. This is what one might expect from examination of the ionization energies (Chap. 4), from which it is evident that the $1s$ electrons in lithium and beryllium are held much more tightly than the $2s$ electron or electrons of those elements. This difference in the energies of $2s$ and $1s$ electrons appears to limit compound formation only to the less tightly bound electrons.

The outer or valence electrons of sodium, magnesium, and calcium do not overlie a shell of two electrons, but a shell of eight. Examination of the ionization energies again shows that large amounts of energy must be expended to break into the lower shell while relatively small amounts are needed to remove the outer electrons. Hence, compound formation is again limited to the less tightly bound electrons.

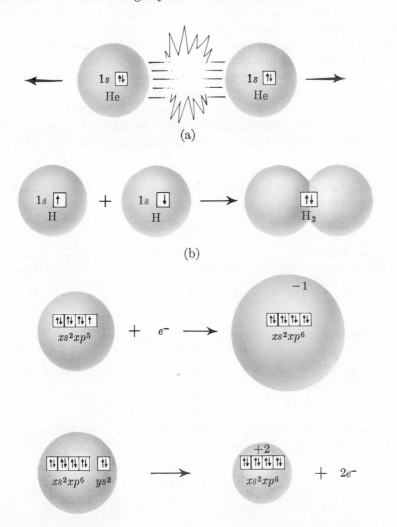

Figure 5.9 (a) Helium atoms with two $1s$ electrons are unreactive. (b) Hydrogen atoms with one electron form H_2 molecules.

Figure 5.10 Eight electrons in a shell often confer stability. This configuration may arise as a result of ionization processes, the atoms acquiring or losing electrons so as to present an outer shell of eight electrons. This configuration also may arise as a result of sharing pairs of electrons between two atoms as illustrated in Figure 5.11.

Further confirmation of the stability of the underlying shell of eight electrons is obtained by the observation that neon and argon, each with eight electrons in the outer shell, are inert, like helium, and normally form no compounds.

Figure 5.11 Atoms use outer-shell electrons in combining with other atoms. Here a pair of electrons is shared in the outer shells of both atoms as in F + F → F₂.

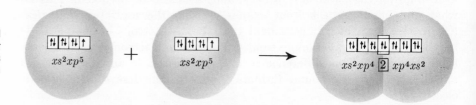

Stability and Noble Gas Configuration. From the above evidence we might conclude that (a) the number of atoms of a given element that one atom of another element can combine with depends upon the number of electrons in the outermost (valence) shell, and (b) a shell of two or eight represents a very stable configuration. The second part of this conclusion is correct; but the first part might lead us to predict that a chlorine atom, with seven electrons, might combine with seven other atoms. No such compounds of chlorine are known. In many of its common compounds, chlorine combines with one other atom, as in HCl, LiCl, and NaCl. If we note that hydrogen, lithium, and sodium are elements which have one usable electron per atom, then we suggest that a chlorine atom adds one electron to its seven to make eight in the outer shell, in order to arrive at the peculiar stability of the eight-in-the-shell configuration of argon. This point of view is confirmed on examination of the formulas H_2O, NH_3, and CH_4.

A chlorine atom with seven electrons	needs one from a hydrogen atom	to form an outer shell of eight.
$:\overset{..}{\underset{..}{Cl}}\cdot$	$\cdot H$	$:\overset{..}{\underset{..}{Cl}}:H$
An oxygen atom with six electrons	needs two from two hydrogen atoms	to form an outer shell of eight.
$:\overset{..}{\underset{.}{O}}\cdot$	$\cdot H$ $\cdot H$	$:\overset{..}{O}:H$ $\overset{..}{H}$
A nitrogen atom with five electrons	needs three from three hydrogen atoms	to form an outer shell of eight.
$\cdot \overset{..}{\underset{.}{N}}\cdot$	$\cdot H$ $\cdot H$ $\cdot H$	$H:\overset{..}{N}:H$ $\overset{..}{H}$
A carbon atom with four electrons	needs four from four hydrogen atoms	to form an outer shell of eight.
$\cdot \overset{.}{\underset{.}{C}}\cdot$	$\cdot H$ $\cdot H$ $\cdot H$ $\cdot H$	H $H:\overset{..}{C}:H$ $\overset{..}{H}$

In the atoms of chlorine and hydrogen in HCl, for example, if we permit each of the atoms held together by the pair of electrons to have a share in both of the electrons in the pair, chlorine not only has eight electrons, but hydrogen has two. Hydrogen has thus acquired the stable configuration— two-in-the-outer-shell—characteristic of helium. This stable two-electron configuration for hydrogen is also present in each of the other compounds.

From consideration of these compounds, then, one would conclude that one type of chemical combination arises from the tendency of atoms to acquire, by sharing valence electrons in pairs, the electron configuration of a noble gas, with two electrons (for light elements) or eight electrons in the outer shell. This is an empirical generalization, based simply on a consideration of the atom ratios in a few chemical compounds. It remains to be seen if the generalization covers all compounds and if there is a reasonable explanation for combinations occurring in this manner.

We must immediately conclude that it is doubtful if all compounds are formed in this manner. If they are, then their properties might be expected to be similar, whereas we have found three classes, indicating three different kinds of bonding. Some compounds in both the covalent and electrovalent classes satisfy these numerical values of two and eight valence electrons, so these numbers must be common to both these classes. Thus, of the compounds listed on page 86, LiH, LiCl, Na_2O, for example, have electrovalent properties, while HCl, H_2O, NH_3 and others have covalent properties. Nevertheless, we may examine the significance of the presence of a pair of electrons shared by two atoms in a molecule.

Electron-Dot or Lewis Formulas. Since atoms appear to become more stable by pairing electrons and acquiring either eight or two outer-shell electrons, it is oftentimes but not always possible to predict the number and type of covalent bonds which might be formed between several atoms in a molecule. To do this we need only to write the valence-shell electron configuration of each of the uncombined atoms, pair the electrons, and form as many covalent bonds as needed to give stable outer-shell configurations. For example, hypochlorous acid, HOCl, should contain two covalent bonds, one between the oxygen and hydrogen atoms, and one between the oxygen and chlorine atoms. These arise when a hydrogen atom H· and a chlorine atom ·C̈l: share one electron each with an oxygen atom, ·Ö·, to give H:Ö:C̈l:, a structure in which all electrons are paired and all atoms have acquired stable valence-shell electron configurations. Similarly, formaldehyde, H_2CO, may be written

$$H:C::\overset{\cdot\cdot}{\underset{\cdot\cdot}{O}}:$$
$$\overset{}{H}$$

Here, all electrons are paired and all atoms have stable valence electron configurations when the oxygen atom is doubly bonded and the hydrogen atoms are each singly bonded to the carbon atom. Formulas which include dots to represent valence electrons are known as Lewis formulas in recognition of the work of the American chemist G. N. Lewis who early conceived the idea of electron-pairing and valence-shell stability as an explanation for atom combination.

Other Lewis formulas are:

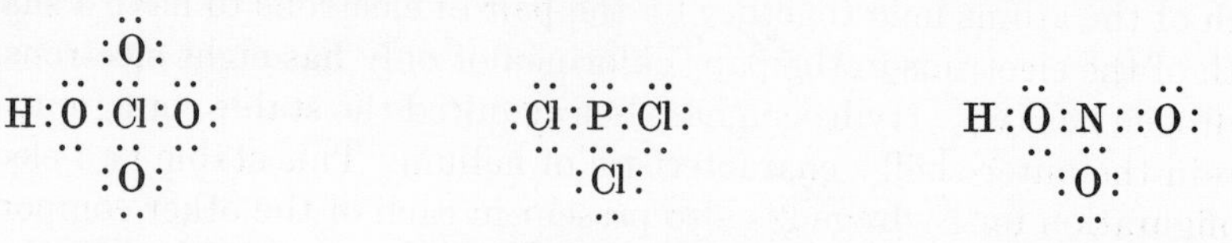

$$
\begin{array}{ccc}
\text{H:}\overset{..}{\underset{..}{\text{O}}}\text{:}\overset{..}{\underset{..}{\text{Cl}}}\text{:}\overset{..}{\underset{..}{\text{O}}}\text{:} &
\text{:}\overset{..}{\underset{..}{\text{Cl}}}\text{:}\underset{..}{\text{P}}\text{:}\overset{..}{\underset{..}{\text{Cl}}}\text{:} &
\text{H:}\overset{..}{\underset{..}{\text{O}}}\text{:N::}\overset{..}{\underset{..}{\text{O}}}\text{:}
\end{array}
$$

| Perchloric acid | Phosphorus trichloride | Nitric acid |

Covalent Bonds. Let us make the assumption that chemical combination occurs when an electron on one atom pairs off with an electron on another atom, which has the opposite spin. The electron clouds of the two electrons can then occupy the same space without violating the Pauli exclusion principle and can act as a binding force of negative electricity to hold the positively charged nuclei together. According to the picture of electron orbitals developed in Chap. 4, combination by pairing of unpaired electrons would then consist in an overlapping of an electron cloud from each of two atoms. Figure 5.12 represents such a process for p electrons of two chlorine atoms; the shape of the cloud changes as a result of combination. The corresponding electron-dot picture also is shown in Figure 5.12. Calculation shows that a combination of two electrons of opposite spin, one from each of two atoms, does form a configuration of lower energy than the energy of the separated atoms, and hence is a stable state. The bond thus formed is called a *covalent* bond. Covalent bonds are most often formed between the atoms of the nonmetallic elements.

Experimental confirmation of the pairing of electron spins in compound formation is found from magnetic measurements. Unpaired electrons give a type of magnetism called paramagnetism. Many atoms are paramagnetic, because they have unpaired electrons. When these electrons pair off with electrons of opposite spin, paramagnetism is no longer observed, but the compound shows a type of magnetism called diamagnetism. Covalent compounds are consistently diamagnetic (with few exceptions), showing that their electrons are paired (see Chap. 26).

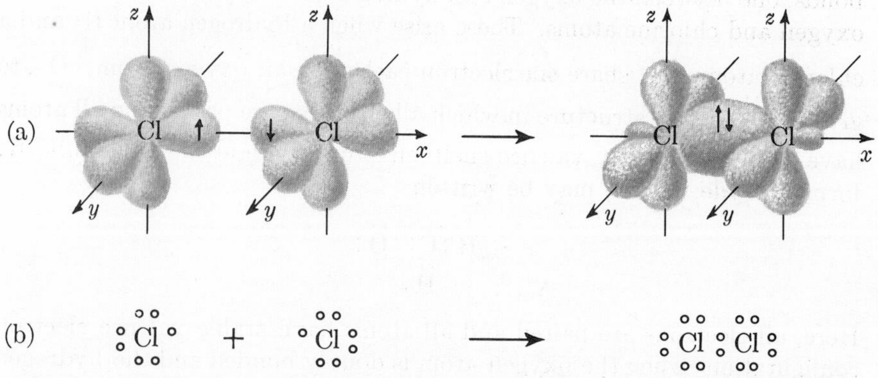

Figure 5.12 Covalent bond formation in chlorine molecules. (a) Electron-cloud picture showing overlapping of a half-filled p orbital from each atom to form the bond. (b) The Lewis or electron-dot formulas showing the valence electrons in the two atoms.

The significance of the two or eight valence-shell configuration in stable compounds is now seen to be simply that these numbers represent the maximum number of electrons which can be held in low-energy states in the lighter elements. Combination takes place until all of the unpaired electrons in the atoms have paired with electrons from other atoms, and these maxima are reached. The nitrogen atom, for example, has three unpaired electrons, and will form bonds with other atoms until these three are paired. If each of the other atoms brings one unpaired electron, as hydrogen does,

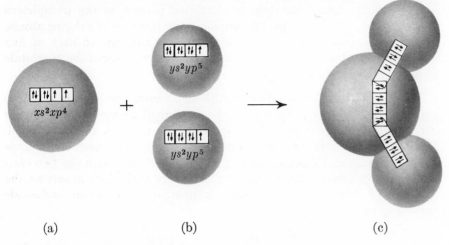

(a)   (b)   (c)

Figure 5.13 Illustration of the principle that combination takes place until all unpaired electrons are paired. (a) This atom has two unpaired electrons. (b) Each of these atoms has one unpaired electron. (c) Here all electrons are paired.

the formula of the compound will be in the atom ratio of $1:3$, as NH_3. In combination with itself, however, a nitrogen atom will pair its three unpaired electrons with the three on another nitrogen atom, to share three *pairs* between them as shown here :N:::N:. If the electrons of the three pairs are credited to both atoms, then each atom, again, has eight electrons in the outer shell.

Double and Triple Bonds. A bond such as that just shown for nitrogen, in which three pairs of electrons are shared, is called a *triple bond*, to distinguish it from a *single bond*, in which one pair of electrons is shared. Similarly, we speak of *double bonds*, in which two pairs are shared, as for example in carbon dioxide, CO_2, :Ö::C::Ö:. Again, it will be observed that each atom has eight electrons in its outer shell.

Exceptions to the Rule of Eight. Compound formation by pairing of unpaired electrons does not always produce eight electrons in the valence shell, however; consider, for example, boron compounds. In the boron atom there are three electrons in the valence shell. In the configurations in Table 4.3 two of these are shown paired in the s orbital and one unpaired in the p orbital. One might suppose then that boron should combine with one chlorine atom, to give a compound like this: B:Ċl:, in which all the electrons are paired, but only chlorine has eight in the outer shell. This compound has not been found. Apparently, under the forces of other atoms, the s electrons of the boron atom unpair, one of them being promoted to a p orbital, so that the atom behaves as if it had three unpaired electrons, and forms the compound BCl_3.

$$:Cl:B:Cl:$$
$$:Cl:$$

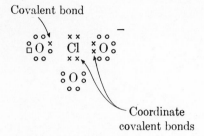

Covalent bond

Figure 5.14 The chlorate ion structure illustrating that two of the oxygen atoms are bonded by a coordinate covalent bond. Here the seven valence electrons on the chlorine atom are indicated by x; the valence electrons on oxygen are indicated by o for convenience. An additional electron □ contributing the negative charge also is shown; there is, of course, no difference between electrons, and one cannot distinguish those originally belonging to oxygen from those originally belonging to chlorine.

Note, however, that the boron atom has *less than eight* electrons in the outer shell; nevertheless, it reaches a moderately stable state with all its electrons paired.

In other compounds, *more than eight* electrons may be used in binding. In gaseous PCl_5, for example, the phosphorus atom has ten electrons in the valence shell. Again, the two $3s$ electrons, present in the phosphorus atom, $1s^2\ 2s^2\ 2p^6\ 3s^2\ 3p_x\ 3p_y\ 3p_z$, unpair in the presence of chlorine atoms, and the five unpaired electrons pair with one electron on each of five chlorine atoms. Presumably the phosphorus atom uses one of the $3d$ orbitals to accommodate the fifth pair of electrons.

The Coordinate Covalent Bond. Although boron compounds in which the boron atom has six electrons in the outer shell are stable, boron forms other compounds in which there are eight electrons in the outer shell. Since the boron atom has only three unpaired electrons, such compounds can only be formed if some other atom presents boron with the two electrons needed for the fourth pair. This occurs with such atoms as the nitrogen of ammonia, which forms compounds with boron trifluoride according to the following scheme:

$$\begin{array}{cccc}
\text{H} & :\overset{..}{\text{F}}: & & \overset{..}{\text{H}:\overset{..}{\text{F}}:} \\
\overset{..}{\text{H}:\overset{..}{\text{N}}:} + & \overset{..}{\text{B}:\overset{..}{\text{F}}:} & \longrightarrow & \text{H}:\overset{..}{\text{N}}:\text{B}:\overset{..}{\text{F}}: \\
\text{H} & :\overset{..}{\text{F}}: & & \overset{..}{\text{H}:\overset{..}{\text{F}}:}
\end{array}$$

The bond shown between the nitrogen atom and the boron atom, in which both electrons of the shared pair come originally from one of the bonded atoms, is called a *coordinate covalent bond*. In general, a coordinate covalent bond is a single bond similar in properties to the type of covalent bond in which one of the electrons of the bond came from each of the bonded atoms; it differs from the usual type only in the ancestry of its electrons. Coordinate covalent bonds are common, especially in ions containing several atoms such as sulfate ion, SO_4^{-2}, chlorate ion, ClO_3^{-}, and phosphate ion, PO_4^{-3}. In chlorate ion, for example, two of the oxygen atoms are linked to the chlorine atom by such a bond. (See Figure 5.14.)

Polar and Nonpolar Covalent Bonds. What would happen if the electrons in the shared pair were not shared equally between the two atoms held together by the bond, if one of the atoms had more than its share of the negative charge of the electron pair? This would mean that there would be more negative charge on one end of the bond; and since the molecule as a whole is electrically neutral, this would leave the other end positive, for the nuclear charge on the atom of that end would not be balanced by the number of electrons left to it. This would produce a bond which had two *poles*, a positive pole and a negative pole; it would be called a *polar covalent bond*. Such a bond is frequently represented by writing the signs δ^+ (delta plus) and δ^- (delta minus) over the charged atoms of the polar bond, thus $\overset{\delta+\ \ \delta-}{\text{H Cl}}$. Molecules having such polar covalent bonds are usually *dipoles* (two poles) or *dipolar molecules*.

Molecular polarity is measured experimentally in terms of a quantity called the *dipole moment*. The dipole moment is the product of the magnitude of the charge at one end of the dipole by the distance between the two

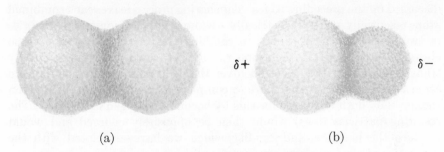

$\delta+$ $\delta-$

(a)   (b)

Figure 5.15 Nonpolar and polar covalent bonds. (a) In Br_2. A nonpolar bond; the electron cloud is symmetrical around both nuclei. Examples: H_2, Cl_2, F_2. (b) In BrF. A polar covalent bond; the electron cloud is unsymmetrical and more dense (dark shading) around one nucleus. Examples: HCl, BrF.

charges. The dipole moment of hydrogen chloride, for example, is 1.03×10^{-18} electrostatic unit-centimeter (e.s.u.-cm). Since the distance between the hydrogen and the chlorine nuclei is 1.27×10^{-8} cm, and the charge on the electron is 4.80×10^{-10} e.s.u.,* this datum tells us that on the average the chlorine atom, having the higher electron affinity, has an excess of negative charge on it, having attracted the electron cloud more strongly than the hydrogen atom did. Polar covalent bonds are said to possess some ionic character. Hydrogen chloride molecules, for example, have about 17 per cent ionic character calculated as follows:

If the bond were 100 per cent ionized, the dipole moment would be the product of a full charge (4.80×10^{-10} e.s.u.) and the internuclear distance (1.27×10^{-8} cm) or 6.10×10^{-18} e.s.u.-cm. The measured dipole moment is 1.03×10^{-18} e.s.u.-cm, so the bond is not 100 per cent ionic but

$$\frac{1.03 \times 10^{-18}}{6.10 \times 10^{-18}} \times 100 \text{ per cent ionized}$$

or 17 per cent ionized.

As a consequence of its dipolar character, a molecule having a dipole moment will tend to orient itself in the electric field between the plates of a condenser, so that the positive end is toward the negative plate and the negative end is toward the positive plate (Figure 5.16). It is this property which permits us to measure the dipole moment, since the effect of the oriented dipoles is to shield the one plate from the opposite charge on the other, thus changing, in an observable way, the electrical characteristics of the condenser.

Most covalent bonds have polar character. Perhaps the only nonpolar bonds are those between identical atoms as in H_2, Cl_2, and I_2. The carbon-hydrogen bonds in most organic compounds appear to be nonpolar.

Electrovalent Binding. The discussion relative to Table 5.2 has suggested that atoms combine with each other in such number ratios as to produce, among the elements in the first few rows of the periodic table at least, units in which each atom has eight (or two) electrons in its outer shell. The implications of this for covalent compounds, in which this stable configuration is reached by sharing electrons between two atoms, has been

---

* One electrostatic unit = 3.336×10^{-10} coul.

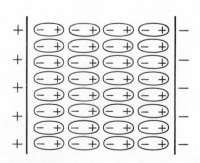

Figure 5.16 Orientations of dipoles in an electric field.

discussed on the preceding pages. The sharing process leaves each combined atom essentially neutral electrically. If, however, the ionization energies of two atoms which are about to combine are very different, it may be cheaper, energywise, for the atoms to "buy" this stable configuration by transferring an "extra" electron (over the eight-in-the-outer-shell) to an atom which needs only one more to complete its outer shell to eight, even though they both must pay for this by becoming charged electrically. The resulting particles (ions) would then be oppositely charged and would produce the hardness and rigidity which we have associated with the properties of electrovalent compounds.

Figure 5.17 Transfer of an electron from the outer shell of one atom to the outer shell of the other as in Na + Cl → NaCl.

The transfer of the "extra" electron may be illustrated by the following electron-dot picture of the formation of sodium chloride from sodium and chlorine atoms:

$$Na\cdot \ + \ \cdot \overset{\cdot\cdot}{\underset{\cdot\cdot}{Cl}}: \ \longrightarrow \ Na^+ \ + \ :\overset{\cdot\cdot}{\underset{\cdot\cdot}{Cl}}:^-$$

The sodium ion would be positive by one unit of electronic charge, since its charge of 11 protons in the nucleus is not balanced by the 10 electrons outside ($1s^2$, $2s^2$, $2p^6$) and the chlorine ion would be negative by one unit of electronic charge (17 protons, with 18 electrons). Again, both atoms (ions) have no unpaired electrons, and indeed, both have 8 electrons in the outer shell. In this case, however, the electrons are not shared. Rather, the sodium atom loses control of its valence electron which becomes the property of the chlorine atom and the pair of ions Na^+, Cl^- results. The "bond" so formed is that which results from the attraction of two oppositely charged particles for each other, and it is called an *electrovalent* or *ionic bond*. *Ionic bonds are most often formed between metals and nonmetals.*

There is a great difference, however, between a covalent bond and the ionic bond found in sodium chloride. In a covalent bond the two atoms in a bond are directly joined; they belong to each other. In sodium chloride, however, a chloride ion has no greater tendency to be paired with a particular sodium ion than with any other sodium ion at the same distance. As a consequence, when groups of ions are close together as in solid sodium chloride, the ions arrange themselves in such a way that every chloride ion is surrounded by as many sodium ions as can conveniently crowd around it without getting in each other's way (namely, six) and each sodium ion is similarly surrounded by six chloride ions, to give the three-dimensional array shown in Figure 5.6. This array of oppositely charged ions extends almost indefinitely in all three directions. Within the crystal there is *no* structural unit that we can point to and call a "sodium chloride molecule NaCl." On the contrary, *each* chloride ion belongs to the *six* sodium ions which are its nearest neighbors, and, to a lesser extent, to the other sodium ions farther away, and each sodium ion belongs similarly to many chloride ions. For this reason, even though we sometimes speak of an ionic bond, we cannot speak of any real bond between two specific ions; rather, we must speak of *electrovalent binding* as the type of force which holds ionic crystals together. The formula NaCl thus does not represent a molecule of sodium chloride, but represents the simplest ratio of Na^+ and Cl^- ions in the compound.

For atoms which differ from sodium in the number of electrons outside the noble gas shell of eight, and from chloride in the number of electrons short of a noble gas shell, we would expect a different number of electrons to be lost or gained, if ions are formed. This is in fact the case, and we observe ionic ratios such as in $Ca^{+2}2Cl^-$, in which a calcium atom has released two electrons to chlorine atoms, one electron going to each of two atoms, and in $Mg^{+2}O^{-2}$, in which the two electrons released by magnesium have gone to fill the second shell of a single oxygen atom from six to eight. Here again the crystal structure may be pictured as an infinite three-dimensional array of alternating positive and negative ions.

It must not be supposed that all simple ions have eight electrons in the outer shell. One common ion which does not is the zinc ion Zn^{+2} which has the electron configuration $1s^2\ 2s^2\ 2p^6\ 3s^2\ 3p^6\ 3d^{10}$, with eighteen electrons in the outer shell, and there are many others with more than eight among the transition elements. In the first twenty elements, however, the eight-in-the-outer-shell configuration for ions is commonly observed.

Some ions are charged particles containing several atoms which are themselves held together by covalent or coordinate covalent bonds. Thus, ions such as NH_4^+, ClO_3^-, SO_4^{-2}, etc., are well known. In the solid state these ions are present in crystal lattices or networks associated with ions of opposite charge in a fashion similar to that for simple ions such as the sodium and chloride ions.

Criterion for Bond Type. The Electronegativity Scale. Which pairs of elements will combine to form electrovalent compounds which will form polar covalent compounds and which, nonpolar covalent compounds? The type of compound formed will evidently be determined by the relative attraction of the two nuclei for electrons, as modified and screened by the inner shells of electrons. This modification and screening lead us to consider only the electrons in the outermost shell, the *valence electrons*, which are the ones concerned in chemical binding. Let us consider the possibility of combination of two atoms A and B, each of which has a single unpaired electron in its valence shell. If electrovalent binding occurs between A and B, one of the atoms must have a much greater ability than the other to attract the unpaired electron. If A and B form a nonpolar covalent bond, the two atoms must have nearly the same ability to attract electrons. Polar covalent bonds should arise when the two atoms have different electron-attracting abilities but not so widely different that an ionic bond is formed. If some measure of this electron-attracting power were available, the type of bond formed between any two atoms could be predicted.

A number of ways of estimating the relative electron-attracting power of atoms have been devised, and the values are recorded in what is known as a scale of *electronegativities* of the elements. Electronegativity might be defined as a measure of the attraction exerted by the atom upon electrons in its valence shell; this attraction is related to the type of bond the atom is capable of forming.

The type of binding formed—whether covalent, polar covalent, or electrovalent—thus depends upon the *electronegativity* of the atoms. From its relative nature one might suppose that each compound would have to be considered separately. Fortunately, however, there is sufficient regularity in the way in which atoms of a particular element interact with atoms of other elements to permit us to assign numerical values of electronegativity to those elements for which necessary data have been obtained. These numerical values express in a semiquantitative way the tendency of the atoms to appropriate the electrons available to take part in bonding. In this *electronegativity scale* the noble gases are assigned the value 0, and fluorine—the element the atoms of which have the greatest attraction for electrons—the value 4.0. The other elements then fall between these limits, as shown in Table 5.3.

The values are such that electrovalent compounds between two elements are represented by differences in electronegativity values for the two elements greater than approximately 1.7. In general covalent compounds have difference values less than 1.7, and the nearer the difference is to zero, the more nearly nonpolar is the covalent bond formed. For example, sodium chloride, an electrovalent compound, has an electronegativity difference 3.0 (for chlorine) $- 0.9$ (for sodium) $= 2.1$. This is greater than 1.7, and in accord with the electrovalent character of sodium chloride. Hydrogen chloride, a polar covalent compound, has an electronegativity difference 3.0 (for chlorine) $- 2.1$ (for hydrogen) $= 0.9$. This is less than 1.7, and in accord with the polar covalent character of hydrogen chloride. A chlorine molecule has a nonpolar covalent bond, as recorded by the difference $3.0 - 3.0 = 0$ for the electronegativity values. The electronegativity values make a useful tool for recording and predicting information about the character of binding.

Table 5.3 Electronegativity Values of the Elements (values given by Pauling for elements in their common oxidation states)

Li	Be											B	C	N	O	F
1.0	1.5											2.0	2.5	3.0	3.5	4.0
Na	Mg											Al	Si	P	S	Cl
0.9	1.2											1.5	1.8	2.1	2.5	3.0
K	Ca	Sc	Ti	V	Cr	Mn	Fe	Co	Ni	Cu	Zn	Ga	Ge	As	Se	Br
0.8	1.0	1.3	1.5	1.6	1.6	1.5	1.8	1.8	1.8	1.9	1.6	1.8	1.8	2.0	2.4	2.8
Rb	Sr	Y	Zr	Nb	Mo	Tc	Ru	Rh	Pd	Ag	Cd	In	Sn	Sb	Te	I
0.8	1.0	1.2	1.4	1.6	1.8	1.9	2.2	2.2	2.2	1.9	1.7	1.7	1.8	1.9	2.1	2.5
Cs	Ba	(rare	Hf	Ta	W	Re	Os	Ir	Pt	Au	Hg	Tl	Pb	Bi	Po	At
0.7	0.9	earths)	1.3	1.5	1.7	1.9	2.2	2.2	2.2	2.4	1.9	1.8	1.8	1.9	2.0	2.2
		1.1–1.2														
Fr	Ra	(actinides)														
0.7	0.9	1.1–1.7														

Compound	Electronegativity Difference	Ionic Character (per cent)
NaCl	2.1	100
HF	1.9	43
HCl	0.9	17
HBr	0.7	11
HI	0.4	5
HH	0	0

Table 5.4 Electronegativity Difference and Bond Type

Factors Influencing the Electronegativity. The electronegativity determines the tendency of atoms to attract electrons when forming compounds. The scale of values in Table 5.3 shows that this quality increases from left to right across any row in the periodic table, but decreases from top to bottom in any column. Can these changes be correlated with the structure of the atoms?

Across a row in the periodic table, the nuclear charge is increasing. This causes a greater attraction for the electrons in the atom, as indicated in the increase in ionization energies (Table 4.7). It also causes an increase in the tendency to attract the binding electrons in compounds, as indicated in the electronegativity.

Down a column in the periodic table, the nuclear charge is increasing also. That this does not cause a greater attraction for electrons is due to the fact that for every downward step there is added one additional shell of electrons under the shell of valence electrons. The screening effect of this added shell, protecting the outer electrons from the attractive force of the nucleus, more than compensates for the increased nuclear charge, and the net result is a lessening of the attractive force. This lessening shows again in the decrease in ionization energy from top to bottom in a column (see Table 11.3), which parallels the decrease in electronegativity.

Comparison of the Properties of Covalent and Electrovalent Compounds. *Covalent Compounds Made of Small Molecules.* Earlier we made the hypothesis that the typical covalent compounds of the first column of Table 5.1 were made of small neutral particles (molecules), and that only weak forces of attraction existed between these molecules. The assumption of weak forces between molecules explains the low boiling points and small liquid range, since these properties mean that it is easy to separate the molecules from each other, moving them from the close distances of solids and liquids to the large distances characteristic of gases. One reason for this is that nearly all of the charges—positive and negative—present in the atoms are satisfied in a single molecule. The electric forces acting outside the molecule, which could attract nuclei and electrons of atoms in other molecules, are very weak. Separation of the molecules from each other thus involves only these weak *van der Waals* forces of attraction of electrons and nuclei of atoms of one molecule for the nuclei and electrons of atoms in another molecule.

The presence of polar bonds and dipoles in a molecule often increases the tendency of molecules to stick to each other. The positive end of one molecule attracts the negative end of another. The positive end of the second attracts the negative end of another, and so on. The result is to increase the boiling point of a compound containing polar molecules, compared to that of similar compounds whose molecules are nonpolar, and to make it more soluble in water, which is also a polar compound.

Covalent Compounds Made of Large Molecules. A crystal of diamond or silicon dioxide may be one giant molecule of network type with all atoms bonded with covalent bonds (Figure 5.18).

No weak van der Waals forces are involved in holding this structure together as is the case in the collection of small covalent molecules; but rather all of the bonds are the strong covalent type. The rigidity of this structure can be destroyed only by breaking some of these bonds to make smaller fragments; hence, high temperatures are necessary in order to melt or vaporize such compounds. Many types of large-molecule covalent compounds exist and will be studied later; some of these are starch, cellulose, and proteins (Chap. 31).

Electrovalent Compounds. The properties of electrovalent compounds are those listed in Table 5.1. The rigid pattern of charged ions in the crystal, tightly interlocked by the electrostatic forces between the alternating particles of opposite charge, gives to these compounds properties which are quite different from those of covalent compounds. In covalent compounds of small molecules the molecules are only weakly bound to

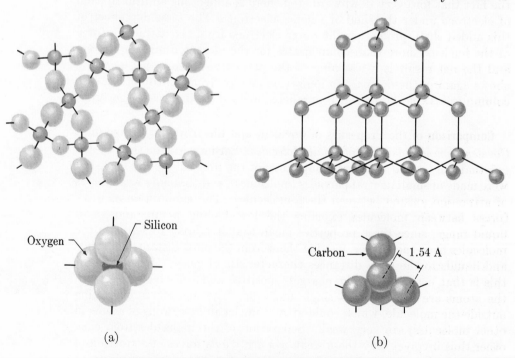

Oxygen   Silicon

Carbon →   1.54 A

(a)   (b)

Figure 5.18 Macromolecules. These are three-dimensional structures; a quartz crystal or a diamond is a three-dimensional network of atoms and is known as a macromolecule. (a) Structure of quartz. (b) Structure of diamond.

each other, and it is easy to separate one from another. In electrovalent compounds, however, the forces are equally strong between all particles in the crystal, and separation of one unit from another is a matter of extreme difficulty. Hence the melting points are high, and the crystals are hard. The attractive forces between charged ions persist in the melted material; it is difficult to separate the ions by boiling, and the liquid range is large. The ions are free to move in the melt, however, and, released from the rigid pattern of the crystal, they can, by their motion, carry electric charge across the melt, which, therefore, conducts electricity.

Metallic Binding. What holds the atoms of metals to each other? Certainly these forces must be different from those in covalent or electrovalent compounds; they produce not only the hard metals such as chromium, vanadium, and tungsten, but also the malleable metals such as copper and silver.

Perhaps the most unusual characteristic of a solid metal and the property which distinguishes a metal from other substances is its easy conductivity for electricity. We believe that this conductivity arises from the ease with which electrons can move through metals; a current in a wire is the result of the passage of electrons along the wire. No chemical change accompanies this passage. Hence, the movement of electrons does not result from ionization processes; the electrons are fed in at one end of the wire from a dynamo or battery, and return to the dynamo or battery, in the completed electrical circuit, at the other end of the wire. There must then be electrons in the metal of the wire which are not attached to specific atoms, which can be exchanged for other electrons from the dynamo, and which are free to travel through the wire. On investigation, we find that this freedom of motion which electrons have in metals also accounts for the high conductivity for heat and also for the luster shown by metals. The conductivity for heat, like the conductivity of electricity, is unique with metals; for example, one can hold a wooden stick in a flame without discomfort, but a metallic rod quickly transmits the heat to the hand.

Electron Structure of Metal Atoms. In reconciling this freedom of electrons in metals with the requirement that electrons be used in binding atoms together, we must note that none of the atoms of the metallic elements has more than a few electrons in the outermost shell. Among the first 20 elements, for example, the metals include only those listed in Table 5.5

In a pure metal, all atoms are alike. Having so few electrons, it is not

Element	Electron Configuration
Li	$1s^2\, 2s^1$
Be	$1s^2\, 2s^2$
Na	$1s^2\, 2s^2\, 2p^6\, 3s^1$
Mg	$1s^2\, 2s^2\, 2p^6\, 3s^2$
Al	$1s^2\, 2s^2\, 2p^6\, 3s^2\, 3p^1$
K	$1s^2\, 2s^2\, 2p^6\, 3s^2\, 3p^6\, 4s^1$
Ca	$1s^2\, 2s^2\, 2p^6\, 3s^2\, 3p^6\, 4s^2$

Table 5.5 Electron Configurations of Metals Among Elements 1 to 20

Figure 5.19 Electron cloud distortion in various types of bonds. (a) Very little distortion: ionic bond. (b) Distortion caused by interaction: covalent bond. (c) Distortion caused by interaction among many atoms: metallic bond.

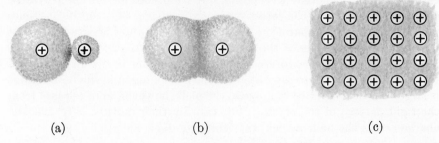

(a)   (b)   (c)

possible for the metal atoms to combine with each other in such a way as to produce the eight-in-the-outer-shell configuration of a noble gas. The nearest approach to eight could be made by aluminum, but not even this element can produce more than six electrons for each two atoms, either by sharing, or by transfer.

Electrons Shared by Several Metal Atoms: Community Sharing. An approach to the stability of the eight-in-the-outer-shell configuration can be made, however, if we assume that electrons can be shared among more than two atoms. This apparently occurs in metals, and the sharing is really on a grand scale. Each atom in a metal crystal contributes all its valence electrons to the community, retaining only a small share in them, but acquiring at the same time a small share in the electrons of all the other atoms. Since even a small bit of metal may contain as many as 10^{20} valence electrons, a small share may still add up to a considerable number.

Energy Levels in Metals. This grand sharing, however, must still operate within the restrictions of the Pauli exclusion principle. There must therefore be energy levels within the metal crystal, as there are in isolated atoms, and no more than two electrons may be in any one of those energy levels. A difference between the metal crystal and the isolated atom, however, is that the energy difference between one level and another in the metal is very small. It is easy for an electron to move from one level to another, provided that the level into which it is moving is not filled with its quota of two electrons. Further, each of these energy levels belongs to the crystal as a whole; the electron cloud which occupies it extends through the crystal as a whole, and is a part of the valence shell of each atom in the crystal. On the average, each atom has a sufficient share in the many electron clouds to satisfy its valence requirements. These electron clouds are at the same time satisfying the requirements of all the other atoms in the crystal, and the attraction of all the atoms for the super cloud of electron clouds gives rise to metallic binding.

Location of Valence Electrons in Different Types of Bonding. 1. *Covalent Binding: Localized Electrons and Directional Bonds.* A sharp distinction among the three types of binding is apparent when we examine the distribution of negative charge about the atomic nuclei. In a covalent molecule the negative charge of the two electrons of the bonding pair is *localized* between the two nuclei which are held together by the covalent *bond*. If such localized spots of negative charge are on the same atom, they will tend to repel each other; consequently, covalent bonds from the same atom are *directional*. This is implied in the spatial arrangement of the *p*-electron clouds on isolated atoms. Further, as we shall see in Chap. 6, when two or more atoms are attached by covalent bonds to another atom, lines drawn from these atoms to the central atom make definite and determinable angles with each other. In methane, CH_4, for example, each C—H bond lies at an angle of 109° 28′ from each other C—H bond.

The localized and directional characteristics of the covalent bond are maintained, no matter whether the molecule is free, as in a gas, or held (by van der Waals forces) to other molecules in a solid at low temperature. Later (Chap. 6) we shall learn the electron configurations which produce linear, triangular, tetrahedral, and octahedral structures.

2. *Electrovalent Binding: Localized Electrons and Nondirectional Bonds.* In an electrovalent substance negative charge is still *localized* on the negative ions, but the forces between the ions are *nondirectional*. The ions behave like charged spheres, positive and negative, and the attractions and repulsions are dependent only upon the distances between the charges and not upon the direction from one charge to another. In a crystal of an electrovalent substance, therefore, the arrangement of ions depends upon two general factors: (a) the way in which the ions pack together in such a ratio that the solid as a whole is neutral; and (b) the need to keep positive and negative ions as far away as possible from other ions of like charge, but as close as possible to ions of opposite charge. (In some cases the relative sizes also is a factor.) No one ion has any particular attachment to any other specified ion, however, and if we add enough energy to melt the crystal, the ions are free to move about, exchanging partners promiscuously under the influence of the heat motion. Chemists are not yet sure what happens when an electrovalent solid is vaporized. Near the boiling point the vapor appears to consist of fragments of the crystal containing varying numbers of pairs of ions. At higher temperatures (or very low pressure) these may break down into single pairs of ions, covalent molecules, or free atoms of the two elements.

3. *Metallic Binding: Nonlocalized Electrons and Nondirectional Bonds.* A metal differs from both of the other two types by having the negative charge *nonlocalized*, and spread throughout the crystal. This situation has been likened to a diffuse "sea" of negative charge bathing the positive units which are left when the valence electrons leave to become a part of the sea. The electrostatic forces between these positive units are again *nondirectional*, and the atoms dispose themselves in a regular array determined by the way in which they can be packed so as to be as far apart from every other atom as possible, yet closely grouped to share in the negative charge which surrounds them. Since, in a pure metal, all atoms are alike, the structural grouping is almost always that which would be reached by packing spheres together with as many points of contact between the spheres as possible (Chap. 15).

When a metal is melted, the nonlocalized, nondirectional properties of the binding are maintained. The evidence for this is that the metallic properties of luster and conductivity are retained in the melt. On vaporization, most of the metals separate into single atoms; a few which have an unpaired electron in the outer shell combine to form diatomic covalent molecules, such as Li_2. These are unstable and readily break down into single atoms at higher temperatures.

Type of Bond and Ease of Deformation of Solids. Perhaps one of the properties of the three types of solids easiest to interpret in terms of binding is the difference in the way in which they behave under stress. A metal is characterized by the fact that it can be forged into varied shapes, or drawn into wire. The ease of forging means that the units of the structures move easily with respect to each other; the ease of drawing means that the units maintain their cohesion even while changing position. This is easily understood on the basis of the concept of metallic binding just developed. In the metal, all the positive units are alike, and moving a group of them with respect to the others makes little change in the energy of the whole. Contrast this with the behavior of an electrovalent compound if we should try to change the position of one of the ions. Motion of, say, a positive ion, in whatever direction, must bring it closer to another positive ion. Such motion is opposed by the repulsion of the second ion, and it turns out to be energetically easier for the crystal to break apart than to suffer deformation. In a crystal of a nonpolar covalent substance, the forces holding the molecules together are so small that they may move over each other with relative ease. These substances cannot be drawn, however, because application of even a small force will pull the crystal apart.

SUMMARY

In this chapter we have examined the nature of the forces binding atoms together in the various types of known substances. We have found that atoms combine by sharing pairs of electrons (covalent bonds), by transfer of electrons (electrostatic binding), or by community sharing of electrons (metallic binding). We have seen that the combining power of an atom is related to the number of electrons in its valence shell and that light atoms combine until they acquire a stable configuration of eight, or in some cases, two, outer-shell electrons. The concept of electronegativity was introduced and was used as a criterion for predicting the kind of binding to be expected between atoms. Finally, the properties of substances were related to the kind of binding present.

SOME SPECIAL TERMS

Combining forces of atoms	Atom ratios in compounds
Types of binding	Stability and noble gas configuration
covalent	Lewis formulas
electrovalent	Coordinate covalent bonds
metallic	Polar and nonpolar covalent bonds

Types of substances	Dipole moment
covalent	Electronegativity
electrovalent	Localized and nonlocalized binding
metallic	Paramagnetic
network structures	Diamagnetic

QUESTIONS AND PROBLEMS

1. Element A is a good conductor of electricity; element B is a nonconductor. A and B are both solids. Predict which element probably (a) is the most malleable, (b) is the better heat conductor, (c) has the greater number of valence electrons, (d) has the higher ionization energy, and (e) is brittle.

2. Offer an explanation for the fact that the elements in Group V of the periodic table—nitrogen, phosphorus, arsenic, antimony and bismuth—change in properties from distinctly covalent substances to distinctly metallic substances in proceeding from nitrogen to bismuth.

3. Several elements, including tin and antimony, exist in either a metallic or a nonmetallic form, depending on the temperature. Which form is expected to be stable at the lower temperatures? Why?

4. Mixtures of many molten metals solidify on cooling to form solid solutions. Is this consistent or inconsistent with our ideas on metallic binding?

5. Compare the electrical conductivity of copper, melting point (m.p.) 1083°C, sodium chloride, m.p. 808°C, and naphthalene, C_8H_{10}, m.p. 80°C, at room temperature and at 1000°C.

6. Classify each of the following as covalent, electrovalent, or metallic on the basis of the properties indicated: (a) This is a white solid which melts at 772°C to give a transparent liquid which conducts electricity. (b) This is a silver-white solid which melts at 98°C to give a silvery liquid. Both the solid and liquid are good conductors of heat. (c) This is a yellow solid melting at 113°C to give a clear yellow liquid. Both liquid and solid are poor conductors. (d) This is a dark metallic-appearing solid which sublimes readily, giving a purple vapor. It is a poor conductor of heat and electricity.

7. Which of the substances, magnesium fluoride or sulfur hexafluoride, is expected to have: (a) the lowest melting point, (b) the best heat conductivity, (c) the best ductility, (d) a tendency to be brittle, (e) the highest melting point?

8. Using electron-dot structures write formulas for the following: (a) Cl_2, (b) HF, (c) ClBr, (d) NF_3, (e) CCl_4, (f) CO_2, (g) NO_2, (h) Li_3N, (i) $CaCl_2$, (j) $KClO_3$, (k) H_2SO_4, (l) SF_6, and (m) $XeOF_4$.

9. Offer an explanation for the trend in dipole moments μ among the following: CH_4 $\mu = 0$, CO $\mu = 0.12$, HI $\mu = 0.38$, HCl $\mu = 1.03$.

10. Offer an explanation for the fact that neither methane, CH_4, nor carbon tetrachloride, CCl_4, has a dipole moment, whereas methyl chloride, CH_3Cl, has an appreciable dipole moment.

11. Write electron-dot formulas for each of the following: (a) HNO_3, (b) N_2O_5, (c) Cl_2O_7, (d) HCN, (e) HNO_2, (f) H_2NNH_2, and (g) CS_2.

12. Comment on each of the following statements: (a) The greater the difference in electronegativities of two atoms, the stronger is the bond between them. (b) It is possible to state with assurance that chemical bonds between atoms are either electrovalent or covalent. (c) Covalent bonds are more likely to occur between atoms of nearly the same electronegativity than between atoms of widely different electronegativities.

REFERENCES

GEHMAN, W. G. "Standard Ionic Crystal Structures," *J. Chem. Educ., 40* (1963), p. 61.

PAULING, L. *The Nature of the Chemical Bond.* Third edition. Ithaca: Cornell University Press, 1960.

VERHOEK, F. H. "What Is a Metal?" *Chemistry, 37* (1964), p. 6.

VON HIPPEL, A. R. "Molecular Designing of Materials," *Science, 138* (1962), p. 91.

6

Molecular Structure and Intermolecular Forces of Attraction

We shall say that there is a chemical bond between two atoms or groups of atoms in case that the forces acting between them are such as to lead to the formation of an aggregate with sufficient stability to make it convenient for the chemist to consider an independent molecular species. Linus Pauling (1901—)

The studies of covalent, electrovalent, and metallic binding have led to several especially interesting and useful concepts of attractive forces between atoms. These concepts have enabled chemists to account for the properties of many known substances and to devise methods to synthesize many previously undiscovered materials having properties that could be predicted prior to their syntheses.

Because of its great power in correlating and predicting the properties of matter, the theory of chemical bonding will be developed in more detail in this chapter, with particular emphasis on the nature of the covalent bond and the shapes of molecules.

Molecules are here defined* as *particles consisting of two or more atoms held together by covalent bonds*. These species may be neutral such as CH_4, C_2H_5OH, H_2, H_2O; or they may be charged such as sulfate ion, SO_4^{-2}, where the four oxygen atoms are viewed as being bonded covalently to the sulfur atom, or ammonium ion, NH_4^+, where four hydrogen atoms are covalently bonded to the nitrogen atom.

Nature of the Covalent Bond. The idea that a pair of electrons shared by two atoms constitutes a covalent bond was discussed in Chap. 5. The strong interaction between atoms which occurs when orbitals containing single electrons from two atoms overlap results in an attractive or binding

---

* The term *molecule* was originally used by chemists in connection with the kinetic-molecular theory of gases where, in that context, it was defined as the smallest independently existing particle in the gas. In recent years many chemists have found it convenient to use the newer definition given above. This newer definition is somewhat more limited than the older one used in the kinetic theory, but more definitive.

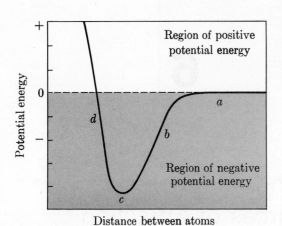

Potential energy

Region of positive potential energy

0

d

b

a

Region of negative potential energy

c

Distance between atoms

Figure 6.1 A plot of potential energy of a pair of atoms which form a diatomic molecule as a function of distance between atoms. At point *a* the atoms are widely separated and are not interacting. We say that the potential energy in this region is zero. At point *b* the bonding orbitals of the atoms are overlapping somewhat, the bond starts to form, and the potential energy drops, but the atoms have not yet reached the equilibrium bond distance. At *c* the bond has formed. Overlapping is a maximum, the potential energy is the lowest, and the distance between atoms is the equilibrium bond distance. Starting from the internuclear distance *c*, energy must be added, in order to reach any other point on the curve. At *d* the atomic separation is less than the bond distance, and the potential energy rises because of repulsion between the two nuclei. At all points of negative potential energy on the curve the net attractive force of the two atoms for one another is greater than the repulsive forces acting to separate the atoms.

force between the atoms if the electrons have opposite spins. When the chemical bond forms, energy is released, and we say that the bonded atoms have a lower potential energy than the unbonded (free) atoms. This is illustrated in Figure 6.1.

Many scientists believe that this binding force arises because the electron charge becomes highly concentrated in the region between the atomic nuclei with the result that the positively charged nuclei are attracted toward the negative electronic charge between them (Figure 6.2). It is reasonable to expect that the magnitude of the force between the electronic charge and the two nuclei will depend upon the charges on the nuclei, the distances between the nuclei, and on the other atoms or groups of atoms that are bonded to the atoms in question. Chemists have measured the energy needed to break a covalent bond, the *covalent bond energy* (Table 6.1), and have determined the distance between nuclei held by a covalent bond, the *covalent bond distance*.

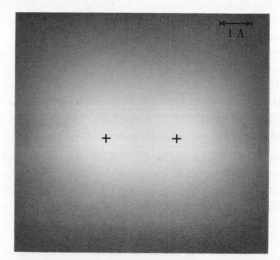

Figure 6.2 Illustrating the concentration of electronic charge between two nuclei which gives rise to the attractive force in the covalent bond.

Bond Energies and Bond Distances. Some covalent bond energies and covalent bond distances are given in Table 6.1 and Figure 6.3. Note the very high bond energies for bonds having bond distance less than one Angstrom unit (A). Compare these covalent bond energies with the energy binding water molecules to each other in liquid water (9,700 cal/mole), and with the ionic bond energy (181,000 cal/mole) necessary to break all bonding in the ionic solid sodium chloride.

Chemists often make use of bond energies to aid in predicting whether or not a given reaction will occur. This will be discussed in Chap. 20.

Molecular Structure

Orientation of Covalent Bonds in Space: Stereochemistry. That molecules have definite shapes was deduced by organic chemists about the middle of the nineteenth century from studies of the number and kind of products obtained in a variety of chemical reactions. More recently such techniques as molecular spectroscopy, X-ray and electron diffraction, and electron microscopy have confirmed this deduction and have provided precise information regarding molecular shape. As an illustration of this precision it is reported, on the basis of molecular spectroscopy studies, that the shape of the water molecule is triangular and that the angle

is 104.5°. Table 6.2 gives the shapes of some simple molecules.

As the knowledge of molecular shapes developed, those chemists interested in chemical binding attempted to extend the theory of the covalent bond to account for the reported shapes and bond angles. They realized that the molecular shape must be the result of orientation of the covalent bonds in definite directions in space. They reasoned that the shape was controlled by a "central" atom which was bonded to two or more

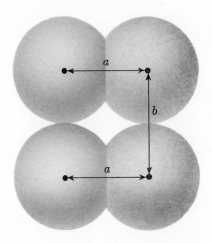

Figure 6.3 Two types of internuclear distances in covalent substances: *a*, covalent bond distance, and *b*, van der Waals distance. The covalent radius is $\frac{1}{2}a$; the van der Waals radius is $\frac{1}{2}b$ in molecules composed of similar atoms.

Table 6.1 Some Bond Energies and Bond Distances

Bond	Bond Energy (kcal/mole of bonds)	Bond Distance (A)
H—H	103	0.75
H—O (in water)	110	0.96
H—C (in hydrocarbons)	98	1.09
H—N (in ammonia)	93	1.01
I—I	35	2.66
F—F	36	1.42
H—F	135	0.92
H—I	71	1.62
N≡N	225 (for total of 3 bonds)	1.10
N=N	100 (for total of 2 bonds)	1.23
N—N	38	1.47
C—C	82	1.54

Note: The bond energy is the average energy required, per mole of bonds, to break all the bonds of the type indicated, in gaseous molecules.

other atoms. Their reasoning and method of predicting can be illustrated in the following specific cases:

Case I. Hydrogen Sulfide, H_2S—A central atom combined with two other atoms. From molecular spectroscopy studies, it is known that the atoms in this molecule do not lie in a straight line but that the molecule is triangular having an H—S—H bond angle of 92°. Why should this molecule be triangular? And is there reason to expect a 92° angle between the two covalent bonds on the sulfur atom?

Table 6.2 Shapes of Some Simple Molecules

Molecule	Shape	Bond Angles
Water, H_2O	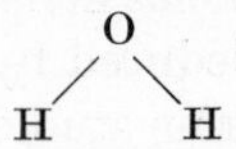 O / \\ H H	104.5°
Fluorine oxide, F_2O	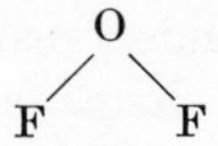 O / \\ F F	101.5°
Hydrogen sulfide, H_2S	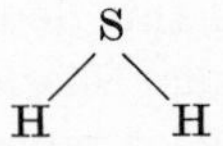 S / \\ H H	92.2°
Hydrogen selenide, H_2Se	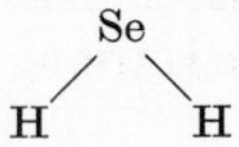 Se / \\ H H	91°
Hydrogen telluride, H_2Te	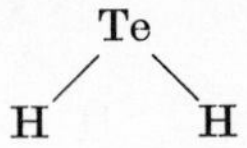 Te / \\ H H	89.5°
Ammonia, NH_3	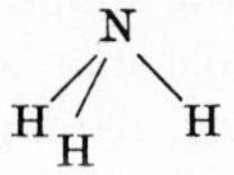 N // \\ H H H	106.75°
Phosphine, PH_3	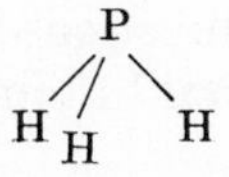 P // \\ H H H	91.6°
Stibine, SbH_3	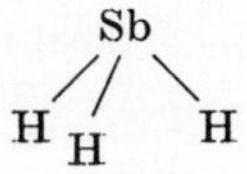 Sb // \\ H H H	91.5°
Nitrogen trifluoride, NF_3	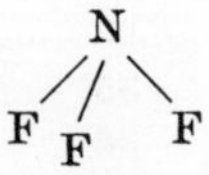 N // \\ F F F	102.2°
Methane, CH_4	H | C // \\ H H H	109.5°

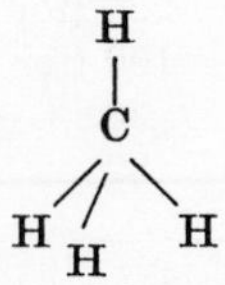

To answer these questions we might well ask another question: What electron clouds (orbitals) on the sulfur atom are used to form the two covalent bonds with hydrogen? Examination of the electron configuration of an unreacted sulfur atom reveals that there are two $3p$ orbitals which are only half-filled, i.e., which contain only one electron each. These must be the electron clouds used in forming the two covalent bonds with the two hydrogen atoms. Moreover, we believe that p orbitals are oriented at approximately right angles to one another in space (see Chap. 4). Hence it seems reasonable to expect that the two covalent bonds directed from a sulfur atom are oriented at approximately right angles to one another as shown in Figure 6.4.

If the molecular shape is due to the space orientation of the bonding orbitals on the central atom, we would predict that water, hydrogen selenide, H_2Se, and hydrogen telluride, H_2Te, all should be triangular molecules. The "central" atom in each of these compounds—oxygen, selenium, and tellurium—has two half-filled valence shell p orbitals oriented at right angles to each other and available for bonding. The data of Table 6.2 confirm the prediction that the molecules are triangular. However, the bond angle in the water molecule is somewhat larger than that in the other H_2X molecules listed. No doubt this is related to the fact that the oxygen atom is much smaller than the sulfur, selenium, and tellurium atoms so that there should be more repulsion among valence electrons in this atom than in the other atoms in the group. This repulsion could result in an increase in the bond angle.

The fact that all of the H_2X molecules listed above are triangular constitutes significant support for the idea that *the space orientation of covalent bonds depends upon the orbitals used in bond formation.*

Case II. Ammonia, NH_3—*A central atom combined with three other atoms.* Further support for this idea of orientation of bonds comes from an examination of the shapes of other simple molecules. A typical example is the ammonia molecule, NH_3. Here there are three covalent bonds directed from the nitrogen atom to the hydrogen atoms. The orbitals used by the nitrogen atoms must be the three half-filled $2p$ orbitals. Since these orbitals are all oriented at right angles, the shape of the ammonia molecule is expected to be pyramidal with the nitrogen at the apex and the three hydrogen atoms forming the corners of the base of the pyramid as shown in Figure 6.5. Experimental evidence from several sources shows that this is correct; the ammonia molecule is pyramidal in accordance with the concept of space orientation of covalent bonds. Here, as in the case of water, the bond angles are somewhat greater than 90°, undoubtedly because of the small size of the nitrogen atom. (However, see p. 112.)

The shapes of many simple molecules can be accurately predicted by simply writing the electron-dot formula for the molecule, identifying the orbitals used in forming the covalent bonds, and recalling how those orbitals are oriented in space. Thus the molecules Cl_2O, F_2O, SCl_2, $SeCl_2$, and $TeBr_2$, in which oxygen, sulfur, selenium, and tellurium use two p orbitals, are all angular like water; the molecules NCl_3, PH_3, AsH_3, and PCl_3 are all pyramidal like ammonia because the "central" atom uses three p orbitals to form bonds.

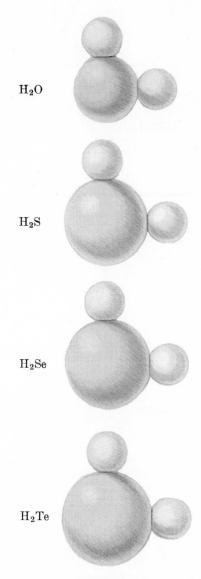

H_2O

H_2S

H_2Se

H_2Te

Figure 6.4 Angular molecules of the hydrides of oxygen family elements.

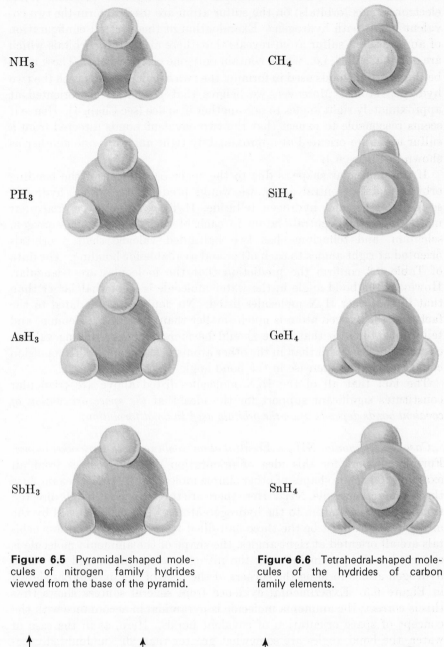

NH₃

CH₄

PH₃

SiH₄

AsH₃

GeH₄

SbH₃

SnH₄

Figure 6.5 Pyramidal-shaped molecules of nitrogen family hydrides viewed from the base of the pyramid.

Figure 6.6 Tetrahedral-shaped molecules of the hydrides of carbon family elements.

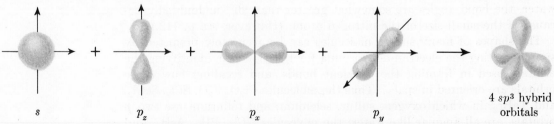

s + p_z + p_x + p_y →   4 sp^3 hybrid orbitals

Figure 6.7 Formation of sp^3 hybrid orbitals.

Not all molecules containing three atoms bonded to a "central" atom are pyramidal. Boron trifluoride, BF_3, is planar; the boron atom in this molecule uses s and p orbitals. This will be discussed in the following sections.

Case III. Methane, CH_4—A central atom combined with four other atoms; hybridization. An important extension of the concept of space orientation of covalent bonds is necessary to account for the shape of molecules in which a central atom is bonded to *four* other atoms. Examples include CH_4, $SiCl_4$, SO_4^{-2}, and NH_4^+. In all of these examples the central atom is found by experiment to be at the center of a tetrahedron with the four surrounding atoms located at the corners of the tetrahedron as shown in Figure 6.6. In all of these species the central atom apparently uses one s and three p orbitals to form the four covalent bonds. The s orbital is spherically shaped, and there is no preferred direction for a bond formed from it; however, we would guess that a group attached to it would avoid the other groups attached to the p orbitals, so that a molecule such as NH_4^+ would correspond to the ammonia pyramid with a fourth hydrogen attached at the top. Since the bonding orbitals are of two kinds, we would expect the energy of the bond using the s orbital to be different from those using the three p orbitals, and the fourth hydrogen to be closer to the nitrogen than the other three. This appears *not* to be the case; all four bonds have the same energy, are of equal length, and are oriented at equal angles in space so that the four hydrogen atoms lie at the corners of a regular tetrahedron!

To account for equal energies and equal lengths of the four bonds it has been postulated that when one s and the three p orbitals are used to form single covalent bonds from the same atom, an *orbital mixing*, called *hybridization*, occurs such that the four atomic orbitals are converted to four new or hybrid orbitals. These new hybrid orbitals are called sp^3 *hybrids* to imply that each new orbital is a mixture of portions from one s and three p orbitals. (Figure 6.7.) The four hybrid orbitals are thought of as being oriented from the central atom toward the corners of a regular tetrahedron. When covalent bonds are formed with these orbitals, the molecular shape becomes the characteristic tetrahedron such as that found in methane, CH_4, or in sulfate ion, SO_4^{-2}. In cases such as these, where four identical atoms are bound, all four bonds have the same length and the same energy. In most molecular species involving a central atom surrounded by four other atoms the structure is tetrahedral; a few square planar structures also are known, e.g., $PtCl_4^{-2}$, $Ni(CN)_4^{-2}$.

Orbital mixing (hybridization) can be used to explain the space orientation of bonds in a great many cases in which the "central" atom uses more than one kind of orbital in forming bonds, e.g., when s and p orbitals or s, p, and d orbitals are used.

Case IV. Other Types of Hybridization. The covalent bonds in many boron atoms are believed to involve hybrid orbitals from the boron atom. Since boron atoms contain three valence electrons and often form compounds in which three covalent bonds are directed from boron, it seems reasonable to imagine that one s and two p orbitals on the boron atoms are involved in bond formation. To do this an electron must be "promoted" from the s to an empty p orbital. This gives the atom an electron configuration in which single electrons are present in the s and in each of two of the p orbitals. This promotion requires energy, but much more energy is released when the bonds form. We now imagine that as the bonds form, the s and the two p orbitals hybridize, forming three new sp^2 hybrid orbitals. The net result of promotion plus hybridization and bonding is a more stable system than the original configuration. Since boron compounds of the type BX_3 are known to be planar with angles of approximately 120° between the atoms bonded to boron, the indication is that sp^2 hybrid orbitals are oriented in the same plane with angles of 120° between them as shown in Figure 6.8. Certain compounds of carbon probably have sp^2 hybrid orbitals. Examples of this type will be discussed in the section on multiple bonding, below.

Compounds of beryllium of the type BeX_2 are linear and undoubtedly involve sp hybrid orbitals from the beryllium atoms. Here, the beryllium atom must "promote" an electron from the s to a p orbital thus creating two half-filled orbitals which might hybridize to give sp hybrid orbitals. Other examples of sp hybrids are known. In all cases these hybrids appear to be oriented at 180° from one another as shown in Figure 6.9.

Returning briefly to the structure of water and ammonia, we recall explaining the shapes of these molecules—angular for water and pyramidal for ammonia—in terms of the use of half-filled p orbitals (two on the oxygen atom and three on the nitrogen atom) in forming the bonds. However, we noted that the bond angles in both cases were considerably larger than

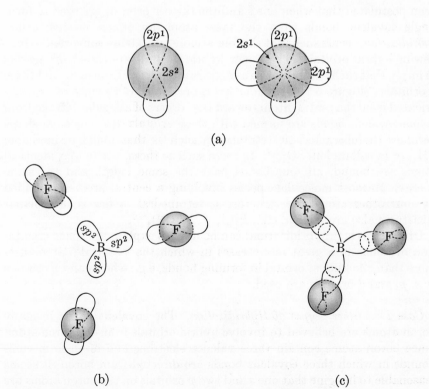

Figure 6.8 Imagined steps in formation of bonds in BF_3: (a) Promotion of electron from $2s$ to p orbital in B atom. (b) Hybridization of s and p orbitals on B accompanies the formation of the B—F bonds. (c) A p orbital on each F atom overlaps with an sp^2 hybrid orbital on the B atom.

(a)

(b)   (c)

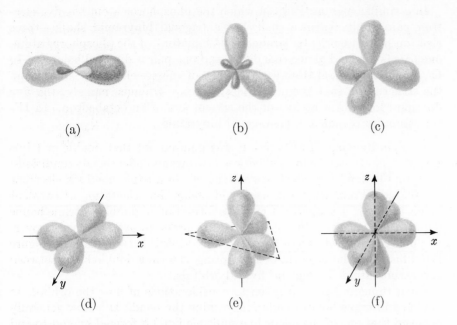

(a)   (b)   (c)

(d)   (e)   (f)

Figure 6.9 Types of hybrid orbitals: (a) sp linear, (b) sp^2 trigonal planar, (c) sp^3 tetrahedral, (d) dsp^2 planar, (e) dsp^3 trigonal bipyramid, and (f) d^2sp^3 octahedral.

the 90° expected for mutually perpendicular p orbitals. In fact, these bond angles, 105° for water and 107° for ammonia, are closer to the tetrahedral angle (109°) than to 90°. Many chemists believe that the valence orbitals on the nitrogen and oxygen atoms in these molecules, whether used in bonds or not used, are hybridized. Looking at the Lewis formulas for water and ammonia we note that both oxygen and nitrogen have eight electrons (four pairs) in their valence shells—enough to form sp^3 hybrid orbitals. Hybridization here would involve the use of bonded electron pairs (two for water, three for ammonia) and nonbonded or lone pairs of electrons (two for water, one for ammonia). In the light of this discussion we shall commonly refer to water and ammonia as containing sp^3 hybrid orbitals.

Other types of hybridization are recognized (Figure 6.9) and will be introduced when needed. For the present, it is important to remember that (a) *sp hybrid orbitals are oriented at* 180° *from one another*; (b) *sp*^{2} *hybrid orbitals are oriented in one plane with angles of* 120° *between them*; and (c) *sp*^{3} *hybrid orbitals are tetrahedrally oriented.*

A Symmetry Criterion for Molecular Shape. For molecules containing a central atom surrounded by two or more other atoms, the molecular shape often can be predicted by determining the number of electron pairs in the valence shell of the central atom and then imagining that the orbitals containing these electron pairs arrange themselves in the most symmetrical fashion possible around the central atom. The atoms bonded to the central atom would of course be bonded to these symmetrically arranged orbitals. Thus, in SF_6 for example, the sulfur atom has six pairs of electrons in its valence shell. These, when arranged symmetrically, will be directed toward the corners of an octahedron—four pairs pointing toward a square lying in a plane around the S atom, one pair directed above and one pair directed below this plane. The result is the octahedral structure.

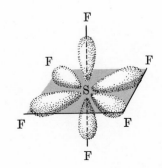

In a similar manner PCl_5, in which the phosphorus atom has five elec- tron pairs in its valence shell, has a trigonal bipyramid shape—three electron pairs are oriented around the "equator" of the phosphorus atom, one pair is directed above this plane, and one pair is directed below it. In IF_5, we find a central atom with six pairs of valence electrons. Once again the structure is that predicted on symmetry grounds, namely, the five fluorine atoms form at five of the six corners of an octahedron. In IF_7 the structure is that of a pentagonal bipyramid.

Multiple Bonding. In Chap. 5 it was pointed out that double or triple covalent bonds may be formed between two atoms under certain conditions. In a double bond four electrons are shared; in a triple bond six electrons are shared. From what has been said about the orientation of covalent bonds in space, it is apparent that the formation of double or triple bonds requires distortion of the bond angles in order to get appreciable over- lapping (Chap. 5) of two or three pairs of orbitals between nuclei. Figure 6.10 illustrates the problem of attempting to form a double bond between two carbon atoms having sp^3 hybrid orbitals.

Much thought has been given to considerations of how the orbitals in double and triple bonds overlap in forming the bond. It is now generally believed that one of the bonds in a multiple bond is formed by end-to-end overlap of the atomic orbitals and the remaining bonds are formed by sideways overlap of the orbitals as shown in Figure 6.11.

A covalent bond formed by end-to-end overlap of orbitals is called a *sigma* (σ) *bond* while those formed by sideways overlap are called *pi* (π) *bonds*. Figure 6.12 illustrates the σ and π bonding in formaldehyde, H_2CO, and in cyanide ion, CN^-. These species contain double and triple bonds, respectively.

The bond distance in double and triple bonds is less than that of the corresponding single bond, and the bond energy for multiple bonds is greater than that for the corresponding single bond. This is illustrated in Table 6.1, where the N—N, N=N, and N≡N bond distances are given as 1.47, 1.23, and 1.10 A, respectively; and the N—N bond energy is cited as 38,000 cal/mole compared with 225,000 cal/mole for N≡N.

Figure 6.10 Illustrating the problem in attempting to form a double bond with sp^3 hybrid orbitals.

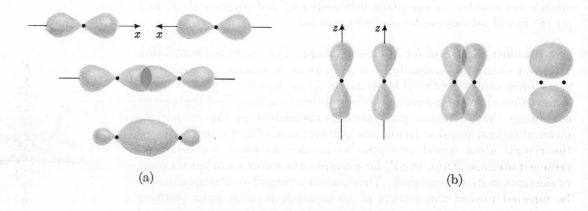

(a)   (b)

Figure 6.11 Electron clouds and sigma and pi bonds : (a) *Sigma bond* formed by end-to-end overlap of two atomic orbitals. (b) *Pi bond* formed by sideways overlap of two *p* atomic orbitals.

The reactivity of many compounds containing multiple bonds is greater than that of many compounds containing single bonds, due mainly to the π bonds present because the electrons in many π bonds are more accessible to an attacking reagent than are those in most σ bonds. However, there are notable exceptions to this π bond reactivity including the nitrogen molecule, N_2.

Structures of Simple Molecules Containing Multiple Bonds. To illustrate the principles just discussed for predicting the molecular shapes and type of bonding of several simple molecules let us consider, as examples, the molecules of formaldehyde, H_2CO, acetylene, C_2H_2, and propylene, C_3H_6.

Formaldehyde. The electron-dot formula for formaldehyde is

$$\begin{array}{c} H \\ \ddot{\text{H}}:\ddot{\text{C}}::\ddot{\text{O}}: \end{array}$$

Here the carbon atom is bonded to three other atoms with a double bond between the carbon and oxygen atoms. The molecule is known to be planar.

The planar structure and the fact that three atoms are bonded to the carbon atom suggest that the carbon atom is using three sp^2 hybrid orbitals to form three σ bonds, one with each of the hydrogen atoms and one with the oxygen atom. The fourth orbital on the carbon (presumably an unhybridized p orbital) is used to form the π bond with oxygen. The oxygen atom uses one of its p orbitals to form the σ bond and a second p orbital to form the π bond with carbon. Each hydrogen atom uses its s orbital to form a σ bond with an sp^2 hybrid orbital on carbon.

Acetylene. The electron-dot formula for acetylene is

$$\text{H:C:::C:H}$$

Each carbon atom is bonded to two other atoms. A triple bond connects the carbon atoms. The molecule is linear.

The linear structure and the fact that each carbon atom is bonded to two other atoms suggest that sp hybrid orbitals are being used in the σ

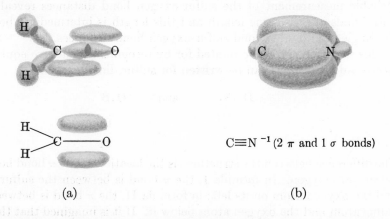

$$C\equiv N^{-1}\ (2\ \pi\ \text{and}\ 1\ \sigma\ \text{bonds})$$

(a)   (b)

Figure 6.12 σ and π bonding in formaldehyde and cyanide ions : (a) Formaldehyde. (b) Cyanide ion.

H—C≡C—H

Figure 6.13 Bonding in acetylene.

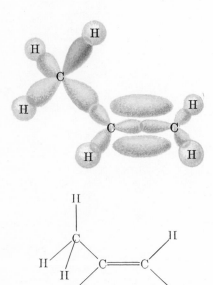

Figure 6.14 Shape and bonding in propylene.

bonds connecting the carbon atoms to one another and to the hydrogen atoms. The two π bonds arise from unhybridized p orbitals on both carbon atoms. The hydrogen atoms use s orbitals to form the σ bonds with carbon. (See Figure 6.13.)

Propylene. The electron-dot formula for propylene is

$$\begin{array}{ccc} & H & H \\ & \cdot\cdot & \cdot\cdot \\ H:C::C:C:H \\ & \cdot\cdot & \cdot\cdot \\ & H & H \end{array}$$

Two of the carbon atoms are bonded to three other atoms; the third carbon atom is bonded to four other atoms. Each of the two carbon atoms bonded to only three other atoms is using three orbitals to form σ bonds and one orbital to form a π bond. If the π bond is formed from an unhybridized p orbital, the σ bonds must be formed from sp^2 hybrid orbitals. Since sp^2 hybrid orbitals are oriented in a plane and at 120° from one another, this suggests that the two carbon atoms and the four atoms bonded to them lie in the same plane, restricted from rotating by the π bond. The third carbon atom uses sp^3 hybrid orbitals to form σ bonds to both carbon and hydrogen atoms. The bond angles of this carbon atom are 109.5°. All hydrogen atoms use s orbitals to form σ bonds.

The over-all shape of this molecule then is a planar structure consisting of two carbon and three hydrogen atoms bonded to a tetrahedron made up of a carbon atom bonded to another carbon atom and three hydrogen atoms. This is illustrated in Figure 6.14.

Resonance: Delocalized π Bonding. Many covalent molecules containing multiple bonds cannot be presented adequately by an electron-dot formula. An example is the sulfur dioxide molecule which is sometimes represented by the formula

$$\begin{array}{c} \cdot\cdot \quad \cdot\cdot \\ \ddot{S}::\ddot{O}: \\ \cdot\cdot \\ :\ddot{O}: \\ \cdot\cdot \end{array}$$

This formula implies that the molecule contains one oxygen atom singly bonded to sulfur and a second oxygen atom doubly bonded to sulfur. Reliable measurement of the sulfur-oxygen bond distances reveals that both bonds are the same length and this length is intermediate between the single- and double-bond sulfur-oxygen bond distances.

This situation can be accounted for by recognizing that two equivalent electron-dot formulas can be written for sulfur dioxide, namely,

$$\begin{array}{ccc} \cdot\cdot \quad \cdot\cdot & & \cdot\cdot \quad \cdot\cdot \\ :\ddot{O}::\ddot{S} & \text{and} & :\ddot{O}:\ddot{S} \\ \cdot\cdot & & \cdot\cdot \quad \cdot\cdot \\ :\ddot{O}: & & \ddot{O}: \\ \cdot\cdot & & \cdot\cdot \\ \text{I} & & \text{II} \end{array}$$

The difference between the structures is the location of the π bond between sulfur and oxygen. In formula I, the π bond is between the sulfur atom and the oxygen atom on its left; in formula II, the π bond is between the sulfur atom and the oxygen atom below it. If it is imagined that the true structure of this molecule is neither that represented by formula I nor that represented by formula II but is some structure intermediate between

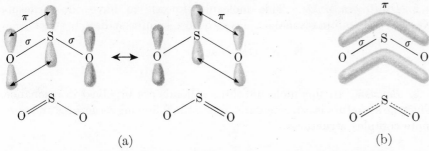

Figure 6.15 Delocalization of π bonds in SO_2: (a) Localized structures. (b) Delocalized structure.

(a)   (b)

the two, the observation of equal bond lengths and bond energies can be accounted for. This situation whereby the actual structure of a molecule is intermediate between two (or more) structures differing only in the positions of the electrons is known as *resonance,* and the several electronic formulas that represent the structure are known as *resonance hybrids.*

Perhaps the simplest view of the bonding in structures exhibiting resonance is to imagine that the electrons in the π bonds are not localized between two atoms but are able to interact with more than two atoms.* This interaction is known as *delocalization* and arises because of overlapping of the orbitals used to form π bonds between two atoms with orbitals from adjacent atoms; it is illustrated in Figure 6.15.

Examples of other molecules which we describe in terms of the resonance concept are:

1. *Sulfur trioxide.* Here the actual structure is believed to be intermediate among

$$
\begin{array}{ccc}
:\!\overset{..}{\underset{..}{O}}\!: & :\!\overset{..}{O} & :\!\overset{..}{\underset{..}{O}}\!: \\
:\!\overset{..}{\underset{..}{O}}\!:\!:\!S & \text{and} \quad :\!\overset{..}{\underset{..}{O}}\!:\!\overset{..}{\underset{..}{S}} \quad \text{and} & :\!\overset{..}{\underset{..}{O}}\!:\!\overset{..}{S} \\
:\!\overset{..}{\underset{..}{O}}\!: & :\!\overset{..}{\underset{..}{O}}\!: & :\!\overset{..}{\underset{..}{O}}
\end{array}
$$

••• CONDITIONS FOR RESONANCE

Resonance is said to exist only when an alteration of one electronic formula to give another is possible without a change in the positions of the atomic nuclei. To decide whether or not resonance exists in a structure the following criteria may be applied.

1. Can two or more acceptable Lewis-type electronic formulas differing only in the positions of paired electrons be written for the structure?
2. Do the several electronic formulas contain the same number of paired electrons (usually no unpaired electrons)?
3. Do the several electronic formulas contain the same number of shared electrons?

   Example : $:\!\overset{..}{\underset{..}{Cl}}\!:\!\overset{..}{\underset{..}{Cl}}\!:$ and $:\!\overset{..}{\underset{..}{Cl}}\!:\!:\!\overset{..}{\underset{..}{Cl}}$ cannot be considered equivalent structures because they contain different numbers of shared electrons. Sometimes resonance hybrids with different numbers of shared electrons are written, but these are usually considered of less importance than those having the same number of shared electrons.

---

* The true structure is not an equilibrium mixture of the two nor of a system oscillating between the two, but a unique one that our graphic art cannot represent by the dot formula or by the bond formula.

2. *Dinitrogen oxide*. This molecule, known to have the structure N—N—O, exhibits resonance. Its structure is intermediate between

$$:\ddot{N}::N::\ddot{O}: \quad \text{and} \quad \ddot{N}:::N:\ddot{O}:$$

I   II

3. *Benzene*. In this molecule three π bonds are involved in resonance. The true structure is intermediate among the following structures and some more complex structures.

I   and   II

In benzene, the delocalization of electrons in the π bonds is extensive so that the electron clouds representing them are fused into a ring covering all six carbon atoms as shown in Figure 6.16.

Molecules exhibiting resonance are much more stable than we would predict them to be if their true structure were that represented by any one of the resonance forms. For example, the multiple bonds in benzene are much less reactive than in ethylene, $CH_2{=}CH_2$, in which the π bonds are not delocalized.

Molecular Orbitals. The theoretical treatment of covalent bonding forces involves the postulate that in order to have bonding between two atoms the atomic orbitals and nuclei of the atoms in question must interact such that electrons from both atoms are attracted simultaneously to both nuclei. In mathematical terms this means that as the bond forms, the wave functions for the orbitals on the two atoms must overlap.

Two theories relative to the nature of the orbitals present in molecules have been profitably developed. The first, known as the valence bond theory, starts with *atoms* and their atomic orbitals and assumes that when a covalent bond is formed, a pair of atomic orbitals overlap such that each

Figure 6.16 Bonding and structure in benzene: (a) Localized structures and formulas. (b) Delocalized structure and formula.

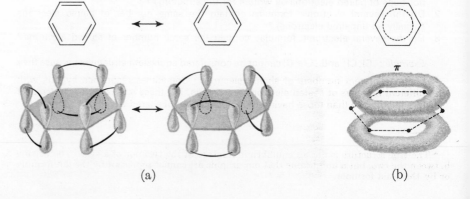

(a)   (b)

electron in the bond is attracted to both nuclei. In this theory the atomic orbitals retain their identities in the covalent bond. The second theory, known as the molecular orbital theory, assumes the initial existence of *molecules*. These molecules consist of nuclei located at distances similar to those in the final molecule, and electrons subject to the influence of the nuclei. The arrangement and energies of the electrons are then described in terms of *molecular orbitals*. In the molecular orbitals the electrons are interacting with more than one nucleus.

Each molecular orbital has a characteristic energy and electrons occupy these oribitals in accordance with the same rules as those used to build atoms in Chap. 4; that is, the electrons fill the lowest energy levels first; orbitals of the same energy will be occupied by one electron each before a second electron is added to any one of the equal-energy orbitals. The Pauli exclusion principle prohibits the appearance of more than two electrons in any one orbital. The number of orbitals in the molecule formed from two atoms must be the same as the number of orbitals originally present in the valence shells of the two atoms, and the number of electrons distributed among the molecular orbitals must be the same as the number originally present in the two atoms.

A complete determination of the molecular orbitals would require the solution of the Schrödinger equation for the system of two nuclei (or more) and their electrons. This has never been done because of formidable mathematical obstacles. A mathematically more tractable approximate procedure is to postulate that the molecular orbitals are linear combinations of atomic orbitals. This is known as the LCAO treatment. For example, if ψ_A and ψ_B are the interacting atomic orbital wave functions for atoms A and B, a linear combination of ψ_A and ψ_B would produce two molecular orbitals—one by an addition of the two wave functions and a second by subtraction of the two wave functions. Since these molecular orbitals might not be the result of equal contributions from the two wave functions, weighting factors for each wave function are included. Thus a mathematical expression for the two molecular orbitals arising when ψ_A and ψ_B interact is

$$\psi_{MO_I} = a\psi_A + b\psi_B$$

$$\psi_{MO_{II}} = c\psi_A - d\psi_B$$

where the constants a, b, c, and d are weighting factors representing the fractions of ψ_A and ψ_B which must be used to give the best representations of the molecular orbitals ψ_{MO_I} and $\psi_{MO_{II}}$. If A and B are atoms of the same element, a, b, c, and d, all are equal in magnitude.

In terms of electron density the MO_I above gives a high concentration of electron charge between nuclei and is called a bonding molecular orbital, while MO_{II} gives a very low concentration of electron charge between nuclei and is known as an antibonding molecular orbital. The bonding molecular orbital lies lower in energy than the antibonding molecular orbital.

Both bonding and antibonding molecular orbitals may be either σ or π orbitals. As noted earlier, σ orbitals are cylindrical around an axis connecting the nuclei; π orbitals are not cylindrical around this axis.

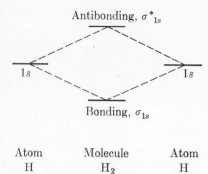

Figure 6.17 Atomic and molecular energy levels in H atoms and in the H₂ molecule.

Molecular Orbitals in Hydrogen-like Systems. If two atoms with $1s$ electrons combine, two molecular orbitals might be formed as shown in Figure 6.17. The σ_{1s} or bonding molecular orbital lies lower in energy than the σ_{1s}^{*} antibonding molecular orbital. Each of these molecular orbitals can hold two electrons, and in the hydrogen molecule, the two electrons reside in the orbital of lowest energy—the bonding orbital, σ_{1s}; hence a stable molecule is formed. If, however, an attempt is made to form a diatomic helium molecule He_2, four electrons must be fitted into the molecular orbitals. Two electrons are expected to go to σ_{1s} and two to the antibonding orbital of high energy σ_{1s}^{*}. Filling the antibonding orbital nullifies the effect of the filled bonding orbital. The net result is that no bond is formed and hence He_2 does not exist. The hydrogen molecule $H_2{}^{+}$ is expected to have its one electron in a bonding molecular orbital and hence to have some stability. This species is known to exist; its binding energy is 61 kcal/mole—a relatively high bond energy.

Second Period Diatomic Molecules. In a more complex molecule such as O_2, bonding involves the p orbitals of the atom as well as s orbitals; p orbitals are mutually perpendicular to each other. It is convenient to consider the x axis as the axis through the centers of the two oxygen atoms about to be joined, so that we designate the p orbital along that axis as p_x, while the orbitals p_y and p_z are perpendicular to that axis.† Thus the orbitals in the oxygen atoms about to form a molecule can be considered to be oriented as in Figure 6.18, which also shows the spherical $2s$ orbitals. (The *filled* $1s$ orbitals are buried in the core or kernel of the oxygen atoms, and probably play only a minor role in bonding or antibonding.) As the atoms are brought together, the s orbitals can overlap, forming σ_s and σ_s^{*} molecular orbitals; the p_x orbitals also overlap, forming another set of σ molecular orbitals of different energy, σ_{p_x} and $\sigma_{p_x}^{*}$. The p_y orbitals and the p_z orbitals, however, overlap only "side-to-side" (Figure 6.11), and form a quite different set of molecular orbitals known as the π_{p_y} and π_{p_z} and $\pi_{p_y}^{*}$ and $\pi_{p_z}^{*}$. The energies of the molecular orbitals, and their relation to the atomic orbitals from which they came, are shown in Figure 6.19.

The molecular orbitals π_{2p_y} and π_{2p_z} have lower energies than the atomic orbitals p_y and p_z from which they came. The atomic orbitals p_y and p_z have the same energies (they are physically indistinguishable since the

Figure 6.18 Coordinates chosen for p orbitals of the oxygen molecule.

† Some authors prefer to choose the z-axis as the axis through the atom centers.

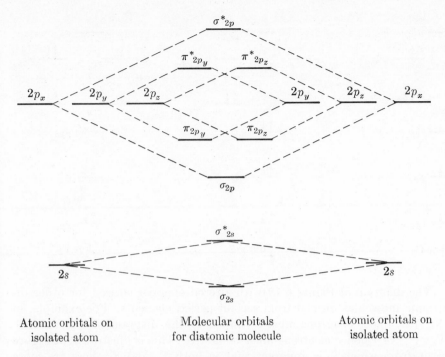

Figure 6.19 A molecular orbital diagram for a diatomic molecule similar to oxygen.

only identification they have is that the y and z axes are perpendicular to the central axis of the molecule and to each other, but the labels y and z are purely arbitrary), and the π_{2p_y} and π_{2p_z} molecular orbitals into which they coalesce also are of equal energy. Similarly the high-energy antibonding orbitals $\pi^*_{2p_y}$ and $\pi^*_{2p_z}$ have the same energy.

Into the molecular orbitals in the center of Figure 6.19 there must now be placed the 12 valence electrons of the two oxygen atoms. They fill the lowest energy levels first, so two each enter the σ_{2s}, σ^*_{2s}, σ_{2p_x}, π_{2p_y}, and π_{2p_z}. This accounts for 10 of the 12. The two remaining electrons enter the $\pi^*_{2p_y}$ and $\pi^*_{2p_z}$ orbitals, remaining unpaired in spins in accordance with Hund's rule (page 71). The increase in energy in filling two electrons into the antibonding σ^*_{2s} orbital almost exactly offsets the decrease in energy when two electrons sink into the bonding σ_{2s} orbital, and the net bonding effect for those two orbitals is very small. Similarly the energy requirements to place two electrons in the π^*_{2p} orbitals nullifies the bonding effect of one of the pairs in the π_{2p} orbitals. The molecule thus contains one clear σ bond (the σ_{2p}) and a net of one π bond, to give to the oxygen molecule what amounts to double-bond (one σ bond plus one π bond) character. The electron configuration of oxygen can be sketched as shown in Figure 6.20, where the arrows represent electrons with parallel ($\uparrow\uparrow$), or antiparallel ($\uparrow\downarrow$), spins. The formation of the oxygen molecule can be written as

$$O[1s^2\,2s^2\,2p^4] + O[1s^2\,2s^2\,2p^4]$$
$$\rightarrow O_2[(1s^2)(1s^2)(\sigma_{2s})^2(\sigma^*_{2s})^2(\sigma_{2p_x})^2(\pi_{2p_y})^2(\pi_{2p_z})^2(\pi^*_{2p_y})^1(\pi^*_{2p_z})^1]$$

where the identification of the $1s$ electrons of the atom cores with their individual atoms is indicated by retaining for them the notations of atomic orbitals.

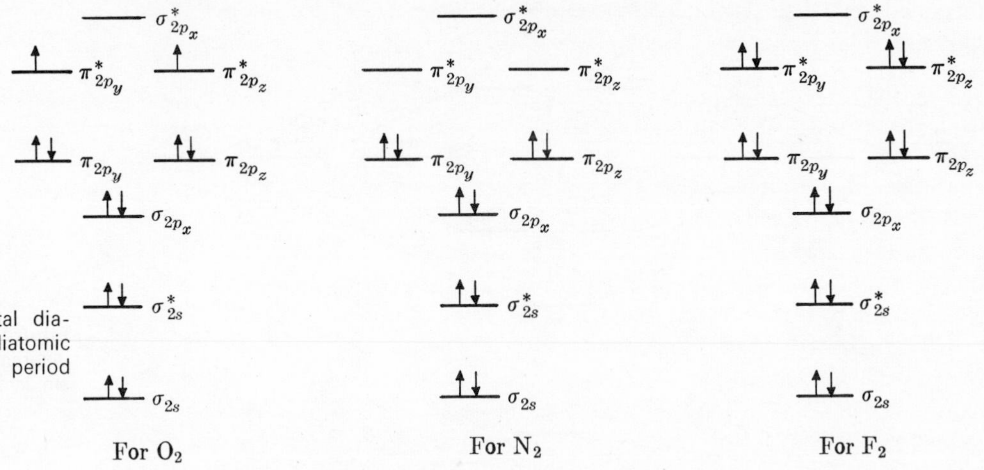

Figure 6.20 Molecular orbital diagrams for homonuclear diatomic molecules containing second period elements.

For O_2 For N_2 For F_2

The diagram of Figure 6.19 with altered energies is used for other diatomic molecules formed from second period elements. For example, in N_2, 10 valence electrons must be added to the diagram of Figure 6.19. For F_2, 14 valence electrons must be added. This is illustrated in Figure 6.20, from which it is apparent that in both N_2 and F_2 there are more electrons in bonding molecular orbitals than in antibonding molecular orbitals.

A convenient measure of the net bonding in molecular orbital theory is the *bond order* defined as one-half the difference between the number of electrons in bonding molecular orbitals and the number of electrons in antibonding molecular orbitals. For several diatomic cases this is:

Bond order

For O_2 $\quad \frac{1}{2}(8 - 4) = 2$

For N_2 $\quad \frac{1}{2}(8 - 2) = 3$

For F_2 $\quad \frac{1}{2}(8 - 6) = 1$

For Ne_2 $\quad \frac{1}{2}(8 - 8) = 0$ (unstable)

Intermolecular Forces of Attraction

One problem that intrigued physical scientists for many years and which still remains only partially solved is: Why do the noble gases form liquids? The atoms of these gases are unreactive; they have virtually no tendency to combine with other atoms, except with fluorine (Chap. 11). Yet they must possess some attractive forces which keep them together in the liquid state.

The same question can be asked of many molecules. Why, for example, is carbon tetrachloride a liquid? Why do carbon tetrachloride molecules, which are composed of atoms all of which have acquired stable electron configurations, not remain separated as a gas refusing to condense into clusters characteristic of the liquid state? The only reasonable answer to this question is that there must exist *forces of attraction between stable molecules*. What then is the nature of these forces and how do they differ from the forces responsible for chemical bonds?

The most widely accepted current theories recognize three types of forces which cause attraction between molecules. These are *van der Waals forces*, *dipolar forces*, and *hydrogen bonding*.

Van der Waals Forces. These are very short-range attractive forces that are believed to be present in all atoms, molecules, and ions. They are very weak forces compared with bonding forces. They are important, for example, in keeping carbon tetrachloride a liquid at room temperature, and in making possible the liquefaction of the noble gases. Unlike valence forces, which seem to become satisfied or "saturated" when an appropriate number of electrons is shared or transferred, *van der Waals forces* in a given species can attract as many molecules as can surround the species.

It is suspected that these forces arise from a mutual polarization or distortion of the outermost electron clouds in the species interacting. For example, if two argon atoms were to come very close to one another, the exterior electron clouds might be distorted because of electrostatic repulsion of the electrons of the two atoms. This distortion would result in electrically lopsided atoms—atoms with the nucleus displaced toward one side leaving a high concentration of negative charge on the opposite side. However, such an arrangement is unstable and would result in an oscillation of the electron cloud. The atoms would thus become oscillating dipoles and attract other atoms which are similarly oscillating. In this way noble atoms and stable molecules may generate forces of attraction great enough to hold molecules together in the liquid and solid states.

Ordinarily, molecules and atoms with easily distorted or polarized electron clouds exhibit stronger van der Waals forces than those with stiff, hard-to-distort structures. For example, the van der Waals forces are stronger in iodine, I_2, than in fluorine, F_2, presumably because the outermost electrons in iodine are much farther from the nucleus than those in fluorine. Hence the nuclei in iodine molecules have less control over the electrons and the molecules are more polarizable than are fluorine molecules.

One would expect the van der Waals forces to be greater, the larger the number of electrons and nuclei there is in each molecule. This, in a general way, is the case, as may be seen in the data in Table 6.3. Here are listed

Table 6.3 Variation of the Boiling Point of the Noble Gases with Number of Electrons

Element	Nuclear Charge	Number of Electrons	Boiling Point (°C)
He	2	2	−269
Ne	10	10	−246
Ar	18	18	−186
Kr	36	36	−153
Xe	54	54	−107
Rn	86	86	−62

the boiling points of the simplest types of "molecules," the atoms of the noble gas elements. Each of these has a single nucleus, but the charge on the nucleus, and hence the number of electrons around the nucleus, differ from one to another. The increase in van der Waals forces between molecules as the number of nuclei and electrons increases is also shown in Table 6.4, which gives the boiling point increases for a group of normal

Table 6.4 Variation of the Boiling Point of Normal Hydrocarbons with Number of Nuclei and Electrons

Compound	Nuclei	Electrons	Boiling Point (°C)
CH_4	5	10	-162
C_2H_6	8	18	-88
C_3H_8	11	26	-42
C_4H_{10}	14	34	0
C_5H_{12}	17	40	$+36$
C_6H_{14}	20	46	$+69$

hydrocarbons (Chap. 10). When the number of nuclei and electrons in a molecule becomes very large, the van der Waals forces also become very large.

Dipolar Forces. In Chap. 5 it was observed that many covalent bonds have a polar character. The presence of dipoles in molecules results in intermolecular attraction. The positive end of the dipole in one molecule is attracted to the negative end of the dipole in an adjacent molecule. The positive end of the second attracts the negative end of another, and so on. These attractions increase as the dipole moment increases but in some cases it is less important than van der Waals attraction. Table 6.5

Table 6.5 Estimated Values for Intermolecular Attractive Energies in Simple Molecular Solids (in kcal/mole)

Molecule	Dipolar Energy	Van der Waals Energy	Total Attractive Energy
Argon	0.00	2.03	2.03
Carbon monoxide, CO	1×10^{-4}	2.09	2.09
Hydrogen iodide, HI	6×10^{-3}	6.18	6.21
Hydrogen bromide, HBr	0.164	5.24	5.52
Hydrogen chloride, HCl	0.79	4.02	5.05
Ammonia, NH_3	3.18	3.52	7.07
Water, H_2O	8.69	2.15	11.30

gives some estimated values for the dipolar attractive energies and for the van der Waals energies in some simple molecules. The total attractive energy includes a minor contribution from interaction between permanent dipoles and dipoles induced on neighboring molecules.

The Hydrogen Bond. Certain molecules that contain hydrogen atoms bonded to other atoms which have high electron-attracting power, such as fluorine, chlorine, oxygen, and nitrogen, exhibit stronger forces of attraction than might be expected on the basis of their van der Waals forces or measured dipole moments. The additional attractive force in these cases is called a "hydrogen bond." It is believed that this bond arises because the hydrogen atom covalently bonded in one molecule is highly polarized and attracted by the electronegative atom in a neighboring molecule. In hydrogen fluoride, for example, the situation might be visualized as

$$H:\ddot{F}:---H:\ddot{F}:$$
Hydrogen bond

Hydrogen bonding is also found in molecules such as H_2O, NH_3, and HCN (Figure 6.21). The boiling points, melting points, and heats of

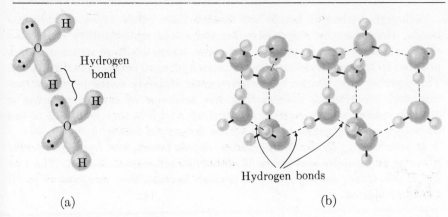

(a)

(b)

Figure 6.21 Hydrogen bonding in water. (a) Note that the unshared electrons in one molecule are interacting with a hydrogen atom in another molecule. (b) Hydrogen bonding gives rise to an "open" structure in ice, thereby accounting for the decrease in the density of the water system on freezing.

vaporization of compounds exhibiting hydrogen bonding are considerably higher than for comparable compounds in which such bonding is unlikely. This is illustrated in Figure 6.22 where the boiling point of the hydrides of the elements of the nitrogen family, the oxygen family, and the halogen family are plotted against the period number. In all three families anomalous boiling points of the substances exhibiting hydrogen bonding are observed when compared to the boiling points of the other members of the series. For example, in the oxygen family the boiling points of hydrogen telluride, H_2Te, hydrogen selenide, H_2Se, hydrogen sulfide, H_2S, are $-1.8°C$, $-41.5°C$, and $-60.8°C$, respectively. If this trend were to continue, the boiling point of water would be about $-75°C$ rather than the observed value of $100°C$.

The fact that water expands on freezing is attributed to the formation of hydrogen bonds. This will be discussed in detail in Chap. 16.

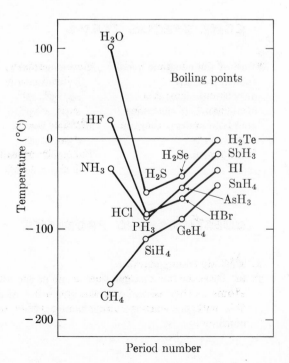

Figure 6.22 Boiling points of the hydrides of families of nonmetals. The period number is the number of the period in the periodic table to which the central atom belongs.

Although hydrogen bonds are weaker than other types of chemical bonds, they may be responsible for the shape and stability of certain chemical structures. In protein molecules, which are huge structures, it is possible to have several thousand or more hydrogen bonds in one molecule. This number of hydrogen bonds gives great stability to the protein structure and biochemists believe that the behavior of certain proteins is directly related to the shape of the protein, which in turn is related to the hydrogen bonding present. This will be developed further in Chap. 33.

In summary, van der Waals forces, dipole forces, and hydrogen bonds give rise to the principal forces of attraction between molecules. The van der Waals forces are especially important because they are present in all chemical species.

SUMMARY

In this chapter some important aspects of molecular structure have been presented. The nature of the covalent bond, its strength and length, the orientation of the bonds in space, the hybridization of atomic orbitals, the make-up of multiple bonds, the concept of resonance, and an introduction to the molecular orbital theory have been developed. In addition, the forces of attraction between stable molecules—van der Waals forces, polar covalent bonds, and hydrogen bonds—have been identified.

Perhaps as a result of this elementary introduction it is clear that chemists have some well-developed ideas about molecules, their shapes, the forces that are responsible for these shapes, and the forces that cause liquids and solids to form.

SOME SPECIAL TERMS

Nature of the covalent bond	**Stereochemistry**	**Intermolecular attractive**
orbital overlap	hybridization	**forces**
directional character	sp, sp^2, sp^3	van der Waals
localization of electrons	dsp^3, d^2sp^3	dipolar
potential energy diagram	**Multiple bonds**	H-bonding
bond energy	resonance	
bond length	**Molecular orbitals**	
	σ and π bonds	

QUESTIONS AND PROBLEMS

1. Why do atoms combine?
2. (a) Describe the changes that occur in the atomic orbitals of two hydrogen atoms as they combine in the formation of a covalent bond. (b) Contrast this with the corresponding changes that occur when two fluorine atoms combine.

3. Draw structural formulas indicating the stereochemistry in each of the following: (a) $BeCl_2$, (b) H_2Se, (c) PCl_3, (d) PCl_5, (e) NH_4^+, (f) $SiCl_4$, (g) PO_4^{-3}, (h) SF_6, (i) H_2NOH, (j) H_2NNH_2.

4. Discuss the nature of the bonding in each of the following. Indicate the number of σ bonds, the stereochemistry, and the type of hybridization expected. (a) F_2O, (b) $HOCl$, (c) SF_6, (d) AsF_5, (e) SO_4^{-2}, (f) NF_3, (g) H_3BO_3, (h) CH_3OH, (i) IF_7.

5. A compound formed between PCl_5 and BCl_3 appears to be ionic, probably composed of PCl_4^+ and BCl_4^-. Are such ions reasonable in terms of the theory of bonding? What is their stereochemistry?

6. A compound formed between PCl_5 and ICl probably is composed of the ions PCl_4^+ and ICl_2^-. What is the expected stereochemistry of ICl_2^- ?

7. Discuss the nature of the bonding in each of the following. Indicate the number of σ and π bonds, the stereochemistry, and type of hybridization expected.

(a) CO_2

(b)
```
Cl
  \
   C=O
  /
Cl
```

(c)
```
      O
     //
H — C
     \
      O—H
```

(d) HNO_3
(e) H_2CO_3
(f) HCN
(g) $HONO$

8. Write electron-dot formulas for and discuss the bonding and stereochemistry in the following: (a) O_2^{-2}, (b) NO_2^+, (c) BH_4^-, (d) S_3^{-2}, (e) OF^+.

9. The compound OF_6 has not been prepared. Discuss the advisability of attempting to synthesize it.

10. Discuss the resonance possibilities in each of the following: (a) NO_3^-, (b) NO_2^-, (c) HCO_2^-, (d) CO, (e) N_3^-.

11. Discuss as many aspects as you can of the structure and bonding in each of the following:

(a) $CaCO_3$

(c) $H_2N—C—NH_2$ with $\parallel$ O below C

(d) $H_2C=C=CH_2$

(b) Na_2C_2 (sodium acetylide)

12. The compound $XeOF_4$ is believed to have a square pyramid structure with the four fluorine atoms surrounding the xenon atom in the base plane; the oxygen atom lies above or below this plane bonded to the xenon atom. This structure is said to contain 5 σ bonds and 1 π bond. Suggest a rationale for this structure in terms of the orbitals available and suggest other possible structures for this substance.

13. It is said that the van der Waals forces between I_2 molecules are stronger than those between Cl_2 molecules, and that the van der Waals forces between N_2 molecules are stronger than those between O_2 molecules. Offer an explanation for each case.

14. Arrange the following in order of increasing boiling point and justify your assignments: CH_3F, CH_3Cl, CH_3Br, CH_3I.

15. Calculate the distance between hydrogen atoms in the water molecule from the knowledge that the O—H bond distance is 0.96 A and the bond angle is 104°.

16. Assuming the order of energies of molecular orbitals is that given in Figure 6.19, compare the binding energies in each of the following groups: (a) Be_2, B_2, C_2, (b) C_2, N_2, O_2, F_2, Ne_2, (c) O_2, O_2^+, O_2^-, (d) N_2^-, F_2^+, O_2, (e) CO, CO^+, N_2, (f) NO, BO, CO, (g) CN, CN^+, CN^-, (h) H_2, H_2^-, He_2^+, He_2.

REFERENCES

BARROW, G. *The Structure of Molecules.* New York: Benjamin, 1963.
COMPANION, A. L. *Chemical Bonding.* New York: McGraw-Hill, 1964.
COULSON, C. A. *Valence.* 2d ed.; New York: Oxford Press, 1961.
DOUGLAS, B. E., and D. H. MCDANIEL. *Concepts and Models of Inorganic Chemistry.* Waltham, Mass.: Blaisdell, 1965.
GILLESPIE, R. J. "The Valence-Shell Electron-Pair Repulsion Theory of Directed Valency," *J. Chem. Educ.,* *40* (1963), p. 295.
GRAY, H. B. *Electrons and Chemical Bonding.* New York: Benjamin, 1964.
SEBERA, D. K. *Electronic Structure and Chemical Bonding.* Waltham, Mass.: Blaisdell, 1965.

PART TWO

STRUCTURE AND
REACTIVITY: SOME
FAMILIES AND ELEMENTS

Some Chemical Principles Illustrated by the Chemistry of Hydrogen

If the views we have ventured to advance be correct, we may almost consider the πρὼἰηῦλη [the first matter] of the ancients to be realized in hydrogen.... If we actually consider this to be the case ... the absolute weights of all bodies ... must be multiples of the absolute weight of the first matter.... William Prout (1785–1850)

Hydrogen is unique among all the elements. It has the lightest and also the simplest atom—one containing only one electron. It has the lowest density of any element or compound. It is the element from which other elements are synthesized at the high temperature of the sun and the stars. It combines with nearly every other active element. Because of its intermediate electronegativity it forms compounds of a variety of properties; for example: (a) compounds with highly electronegative elements, such as fluorine and oxygen in which the hydrogen atoms acquire a positive character; (b) those with elements having low electronegativity, such as calcium and aluminum in which the hydrogen atoms acquire a negative character; and (c) compounds in which the bonds are essentially nonpolar, such as those with carbon.

In this chapter we shall discuss some of the important chemistry of hydrogen and hydrogen compounds, starting first with some properties and uses of hydrogen and following this with a discussion of the stable chemical states, as well as with some reactions of hydrogen atoms, hydrogen nuclei, and hydrogen molecules. We shall then take a closer look at chemical reactions, examining briefly and simply the concept of chemical equilibrium, some acid-base reactions, and some oxidation-reduction reactions. This will be followed by application of some of the principles of oxidation-reduction in the preparation of hydrogen.

Some Facts About Hydrogen

Occurrence. Hydrogen is by far the most abundant element in the universe—about 92 per cent of the atoms of the universe are hydrogen atoms. Any free hydrogen which was originally in the earth's atmosphere

131

Table 7.1 Some Properties of
Hydrogen

Atomic weight	1.008 a.m.u.
Melting point	14.1°K*
Boiling point	20.4°K
Density (S.T.P.)	0.0899 g/liter
Atomic diameter	1 A
Covalent bond length	0.75 A
H—H bond strength	103 kcal/mole

* °K is read "degrees Kelvin" and is defined as 273.15+°C.

when the earth was formed has no doubt escaped to interstellar space
because of the high velocity of the gaseous hydrogen molecules which are
moving at an average velocity of over 4,000 miles per hour at ordinary
temperatures.* On the earth hydrogen occurs in large amounts combined
in substances such as water, petroleum, and plant and animal tissue. In
terms of the number of atoms, it is the third most abundant element in the
materials of the earth's crust,† the oceans, and the atmosphere. Water,
which is combined hydrogen and oxygen, contains 11.2 per cent by weight
hydrogen.

Chemical Composition

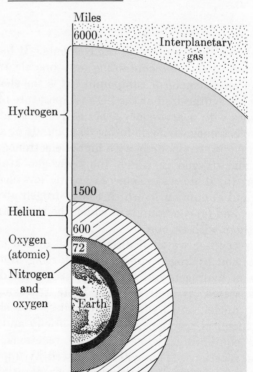

Figure 7.1 Principal components of the atmosphere up to 6,000 miles above the earth.

* This is about one-sixth the escape velocity of a particle from the earth's gravitational
field—25,000 miles per hour.
† The earth's crust may be defined as the surface layer of the earth, which has a thickness
of about 10 miles.

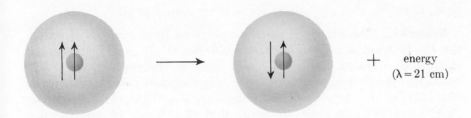

$+$ energy
$(\lambda = 21$ cm$)$

Figure 7.2   Prior to 1965 only two chemical species were identified in interstellar space—hydrogen atoms and hydroxyl radicals. In 1966 deuterium and helium atoms were detected. The hydrogen atoms are identified by the energy emitted when atoms having parallel electron and nuclear spins undergo a transition during which the spins become antiparallel. The hydroxyl radicals are identified by the energy absorbed by the several types of rotational changes this radical is known to undergo. [See *Scientific American* (July 1965), pp. 26–33.]

Hydrogen is a gas at ordinary temperatures. It is odorless, tasteless, and colorless, and it has a very low solubility in water. In some metals it dissolves readily, usually as atoms rather than as diatomic molecules. Since hydrogen atoms are more reactive than hydrogen molecules, these metals serve as catalysts for the reactions of hydrogen with other substances.

Because of their electron configuration, a single electron in the $1s$ shell, hydrogen atoms are much too reactive to exist in the free state under ordinary conditions, especially if there are other atoms or groups of atoms to combine with. Hence we find atomic hydrogen only in interstellar space. Hydrogen molecules, H_2, exist over a wide temperature range; even at 4000°C about 40 per cent of the particles in a volume of hydrogen gas are H_2 molecules.

The hydrogen molecule is nonpolar. This helps explain the low boiling point (20.4°K) and freezing point (14.1°K), since hydrogen molecules are but slightly polarizable and will have only very weak van der Waals forces between them.

Uses. Hydrogen is one of the most important industrial gases. Large amounts are used for synthesis of ammonia, hydrogenation of vegetable oils to produce butter and lard substitutes, hydrogenation of hydrocarbons in the production of gasoline, hydrogenation of carbon monoxide in the production of methyl alcohol, as a reducing atmosphere for metallurgical operations, as a coolant for large generators, and as one of the most powerful rocket fuels. In the future, large amounts may also be used in the hydrogenation of coal and carbon monoxide to produce lubricating oil, gasoline, and other products.

In the past, hydrogen was used (and still is to a limited extent) for inflating balloons. The high flammability of hydrogen makes it unsafe to use for this purpose, so that in the United States it has been replaced by the noncombustible gas, helium.

Hydrogen

Deuterium

Tritium

Figure 7.3 Three kinds of hydrogen atoms. (Legend: + = proton, n = neutron.)

Hydrogen Isotopes. Of the three isotopes of hydrogen, the mass 1 isotope is by far the most abundant—making up about 99.98 per cent of naturally occurring hydrogen. Most of the other 0.02 per cent is deuterium, D or $^2_1$H, with only 10^{-15} per cent tritium, T or $^3_1$H.*

Deuterium. The isotope of mass 2 is obtained by electrolysis of water. the O—H bond is slightly weaker than the O—D bond. Hence, on electrolysis of water, the O—H bonds break in preference to the O—D bonds and the D_2O concentrates in the water mixture being electrolyzed. The D_2O can then be electrolyzed to produce D_2. High-purity deuterium is now available, its chief use being that of a tracer in studying the mechanism of chemical reactions. Deuterium has a boiling point of 23.6°K and a freezing point of 18.6°K.

Water made of deuterium rather than hydrogen has the following properties:

Boiling point	101.4°C
Freezing point	3.8°C
Density at 25°	1.108 g/cc
Temperature of maximum density	11.2°C

In general, the properties of isotopes of a given element are very similar. However, for very light elements, several of the properties which depend on bond strength, mass, and reaction rates show wide variation. These are indicated in the differences in some of the properties of D_2O and H_2O. Several other differences are as follows:

Bond energy	O—H = 110 kcal/mole	O—D = 121 kcal/mole
Bond energy	H—H = 103 kcal/mole	D—D = 105 kcal/mole
Relative rates of reaction	$H_2 + Cl_2$ is 13 times as fast as $D_2 + Cl_2$ under comparable conditions.	

These differences, now called *isotope effects*, are appreciable only where the difference in mass of the isotopes is a significant fraction of the mass of the isotope. Hence, isotope effects are observed mainly with the isotopes of the light elements.

Tritium. This isotope of mass 3 is present in nature as the result of the nuclear reaction† of neutrons (n) in the upper atmosphere with nitrogen nuclei.

$$^1_0n + ^{14}_7N \longrightarrow ^3_1H + ^{12}_6C$$

Tritium is radioactive. Half of an original sample of tritium will decompose in 12 years, forming helium (see Chap. 25). The main use of tritium is that of a radioactive tracer. Tritium shows an even greater isotope effect than deuterium.

---

* The atomic number of an isotope is often indicated by a subscript before the symbol and the atomic mass number by a superscript. For example, $^2_1$H indicates the isotope of mass 2 and atomic number 1. The mass number is the sum of the neutrons and protons in the nucleus and is very nearly equal to the atomic mass in atomic mass units.

† Nuclear equations are written as chemical equations but, in addition, the mass and atomic number of each isotope are indicated with superscripts and subscripts, respectively.

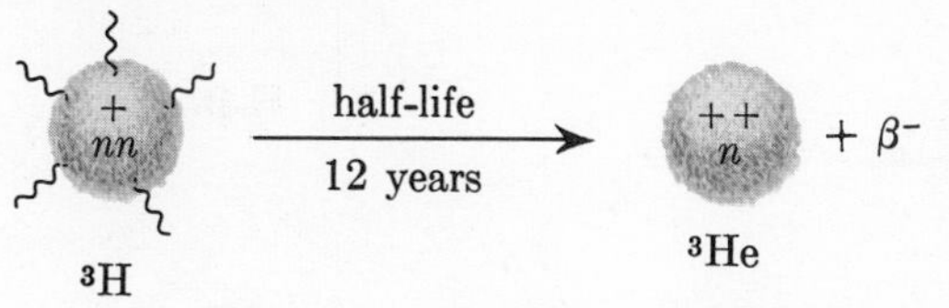

Tritium, T; also ^{3}H

$$^3\text{H} \xrightarrow[\text{12 years}]{\text{half-life}} {}^3\text{He} + \beta^-$$

Figure 7.4 Radioactive decay of tritium.

Stable Chemical States (Oxidation States). Hydrogen exhibits three stable chemical states called $+I$, 0, and $-I$ *oxidation states*. The oxidation state of an ion is the charge on the ion. For example, the oxidation state of Ca^{+2} is $+II$, of Al^{+3} is $+III$, of Cl^- is $-I$. The number indicating the oxidation state of an *atom* in a covalent molecule such as carbon in CCl_4 or in CO_2 is determined by a set of rules listed on page 147.

An example of hydrogen in the $-I$ oxidation state is sodium hydride, NaH. Here the hydrogen atom has accepted an electron from a sodium atom, thereby forming the hydride ion, H^-. An example of hydrogen in the $+I$ oxidation state is hydrogen chloride, HCl. Here a covalent bond exists between hydrogen and chlorine atoms, but, because the chlorine atom has a higher electronegativity than the hydrogen atom, the oxidation state of the hydrogen atom is arbitrarily assigned a value of $+I$, suggesting that the hydrogen atom donates a good portion of its electron to the chlorine atom. The rule for assigning numbers to the oxidation states of hydrogen is: In binary compounds with nonmetals, the oxidation state of hydrogen is assigned a value of $+I$; in binary compounds with metals, the oxidation state of hydrogen is assigned a value of $-I$. The oxidation state of an uncombined or free element is assigned a value of zero. For hydrogen the stable species in the 0 oxidation state is the hydrogen molecule, H_2.

The fact that hydrogen forms three stable oxidation states is related to the structure of the hydrogen atom. This atom may complete its valence shell by adding one electron or it may donate (at least in part) its one valence electron.

Reactions of Hydrogen Atoms. About 103 kcal of energy is necessary to break all the covalent bonds in a mole of hydrogen molecules, thereby forming hydrogen atoms. Hydrogen atoms are also formed from hydrogen molecules on the surfaces of some catalysts, and by passing electricity through gaseous hydrogen. The hydrogen atom is a very vigorous reactant since it has a single unpaired electron which can pair off readily with the single electron of another atom or group of atoms to form a new bond. For example,

$$H\cdot + H\cdot \longrightarrow H\!:\!H + \text{energy (103 kcal/mole)}$$

$$2H\cdot + \cdot \ddot{O}\!: \longrightarrow H\!:\!\underset{\ddot{H}}{\overset{\cdot\cdot}{O}}\!: + \text{energy (220 kcal/mole)}$$

Hydrogen atoms may react with molecules such as those of chlorine to form hydrogen chloride and chlorine atoms as follows:

$$H\cdot + Cl_2 \longrightarrow HCl + \cdot\ddot{\underset{\cdot\cdot}{Cl}}\!:$$

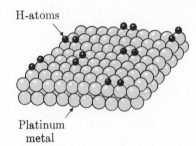

H-atoms

Platinum metal

Figure 7.5 Hydrogen molecules adsorb on surfaces of some metals as atoms due to the catalytic action of the metals which weakens or breaks the bonds between hydrogen atoms.

Figure 7.6 Atomic energy produced by fusion in the sun and also in the hydrogen bomb.

$$4H^+ + 2e^- \xrightarrow{10,000,000° C} He^{+2} + energy \qquad 4H^+ + 2e^- \xrightarrow{10,000,000° C} He^{+2} + energy$$

The heat generated in the atomic hydrogen torch is the result of the recombination of hydrogen atoms to form hydrogen molecules.

Hydrogen atoms, in reactions with a few metals such as sodium and lithium, will take on another $1s$ electron and form the negative ion H^-.

Reactions of Hydrogen Nuclei. The nucleus of hydrogen of mass 1 is a proton which has a very high affinity for an electron and, hence, forms hydrogen atoms readily. About 310 kcal of energy is necessary to pull all the electrons away from all the hydrogen atoms in a mole of hydrogen atoms, thereby leaving hydrogen nuclei.

$$H^{\cdot} \longrightarrow H^+ + e^-$$

A high concentration of hydrogen nuclei is never formed except at the high temperatures of the sun and stars or of the electric arc.

At temperatures of about 10,000,000°C the velocities of protons are so high that the repulsion of the positive charges is overcome and the protons come so close together on collision that the extremely strong but very short-range forces of the atomic nuclei become effective, causing the nuclei to fuse together to form helium nuclei and releasing a tremendous amount of energy. This is one of the main energy-producing reactions of the universe; it is also the first step in the formation of the elements.

$$4_1^1H + 2_{-1}^0e \longrightarrow {}_2^4He + 6.5 \times 10^{11} \text{ cal/mole}$$

This is about 1,000,000 times more energy than is released when hydrogen burns to form water:

$$2H_2 + O_2 \longrightarrow 2H_2O + 1.4 \times 10^5 \text{ cal/2 moles}$$

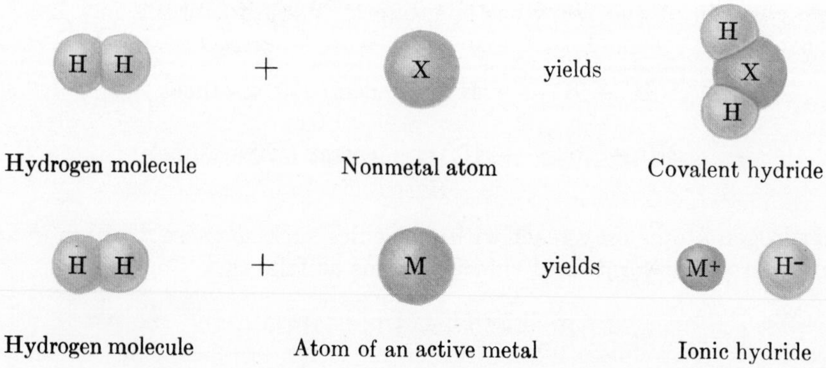

H H $\qquad$ + $\qquad$ X $\qquad$ yields $\qquad$ H X H

Hydrogen molecule $\qquad$ Nonmetal atom $\qquad$ Covalent hydride

Figure 7.7 Hydrogen reacts with nonmetals to form covalent hydrides; with active metals it forms ionic hydrides.

H H $\qquad$ + $\qquad$ M $\qquad$ yields $\qquad$ M$^+$ H$^-$

Hydrogen molecule $\qquad$ Atom of an active metal $\qquad$ Ionic hydride

Reactions of Hydrogen Molecules. Most of the reactions of hydrogen molecules are those in which the covalent bond between hydrogen atoms is broken and another one is formed with another atom. For example:

The combustion of hydrogen	$2H_2 + O_2 \longrightarrow 2H_2O$
The synthesis of ammonia	$3H_2 + N_2 \longrightarrow 2NH_3$
The reaction with halogens	$H_2 + Cl_2 \longrightarrow 2HCl$
The hydrogenation of un-saturated organic compounds	$H_2 + C_2H_4 \longrightarrow C_2H_6$

In reactions of hydrogen with active metals, such as those with lithium, sodium, potassium, and calcium, the covalent bond in the hydrogen molecule is broken, but the new bonds formed are predominantly ionic in character. For example:

$$2Li + H_2 \longrightarrow 2LiH$$
$$Ca + H_2 \longrightarrow CaH_2$$

As was stated earlier, hydrogen forms compounds with nearly all active elements. However, it has not been possible (as yet) to bring about the direct reaction of hydrogen with all active elements. Hydrogen will react directly with all elements of low electronegativity (1.2 or less) and with those of high electronegativity (2.3 or higher). In order to synthesize hydrogen compounds of elements of intermediate electronegativities, it is usually necessary to use reactions of the type illustrated for the preparation of aluminum hydride, AlH_3, and silane, SiH_4.

$$AlCl_3 + 3LiH \longrightarrow AlH_3 + 3LiCl$$
$$Mg_2Si + 4H_2O \longrightarrow 2Mg(OH)_2 + SiH_4$$

Chemical Equilibria Involving Hydrogen Molecules

Chemical Equilibria. Experiment has shown that many reactions never reach completion. In such reactions the starting materials (reactants) never completely disappear to form products, no matter how long the reaction is allowed to continue. At the start of the reaction the reactants are present in relatively large amounts. As time proceeds, the amounts of reactants decrease. Eventually, this decrease ceases and the reaction appears to stop, even though appreciable amounts of reactants may still be present. When this occurs, the reaction is most likely in a state of *chemical equilibrium.*

The Equilibrium in the Reaction $H_2 + I_2 \rightarrow 2HI$. The principle underlying chemical equilibrium is the fact that many chemical reactions are reversible to a measurable extent. The reaction of hydrogen with iodine

$$H_2 + I_2 \rightleftharpoons 2HI$$

illustrates this reversibility and how chemical equilibrium is attained.

Starting with a mixture of hydrogen and iodine, the reaction proceeds so that hydrogen iodide is formed. As the amount of hydrogen iodide increases, the molecules of this substance react with one another to form hydrogen and iodine. Ultimately, a condition is reached in which the

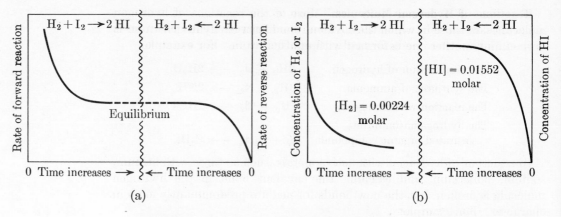

Figure 7.8 The approach to equilibrium in the formation and decomposition of hydrogen iodide : $H_2 + I_2 \rightleftarrows 2HI$. (a) Graph of changes in the rates of the reaction. (b) Graph of changes in concentrations.

speed or rate of formation of HI from H_2 and I_2 is exactly equal to the rate of decomposition of HI to form H_2 and I_2 again. When these rates become equal, the reaction appears to stop and is said to be in a state of chemical equilibrium, or simply in equilibrium. Reversibility is commonly indicated in equations by two arrows, one pointing to the right and the other to the left.

Table 7.2 consists of data taken from an experiment in which 0.01000 mole of hydrogen and 0.01000 mole of iodine vapor were placed in a one-liter flask at 410°C. These data show the changes in concentration and in the rate of the reaction for the reversible formation and decomposition of hydrogen iodide. The various columns in the table show how the rate of the forward reaction decreases and that of the reverse reaction increases as the reaction proceeds, together with the changes in concentration of hydrogen and hydrogen iodide which cause these changes in rate. These data are plotted in Figure 7.8.

Both Figure 7.8 and Table 7.2 show that the rates of the two opposing reactions gradually approach each other and become equal at equilibrium. When equilibrium has been reached, the concentrations of hydrogen and

Table 7.2 Rates of the Reactions Indicated by $H_2 + I_2 \rightleftarrows 2HI$ at 410°C

Time (min)	Concentration of Hydrogen and of Iodine (molar) $\times 10^{+4}$ *	Rate of Forward Reaction (mole HI formed/liter/min) $\times 10^{+6}$ *	Rate of Reverse Reaction (mole HI disappearing/liter/ min) $\times 10^{+6}$ *	Concentration of Hydrogen Iodide (molar) $\times 10^{+4}$ *
0	100	150	0	0
34	80	96	0.5	40
90	60	54	2.0	80
220	40	24	4.5	120
470	30	13.5	6.1	140
960	23	7.9	7.3	154
1,400	22.5	7.6	7.4	155
Very long	22.4	7.5	7.5	155

* All experimental values have been multiplied by 10^x to make for easier reading of the table. The value of x is chosen to eliminate all exponentials from table values. The actual value of the first entry in the second column is 100×10^{-4}.

iodine have been reduced to 0.00224 mole/liter and the concentration of hydrogen iodide is 0.0155 mole/liter. Thus, 22.4 per cent of the original gases remain, when equilibrium has been established.

The theory of chemical equilibria is of great importance in indicating the extent of reaction and will be discussed in considerable detail in Chaps. 21, 22, and 23.

Indication of Extent of Reaction. In this chapter we need to consider only qualitative statements describing the position (or point) of equilibrium of a reaction. For this purpose we define the position of equilibrium as the measure of the relative amounts of reaction products (in the equation as written) and of reactants. If, when equilibrium has been reached, more than half of the reactants have been converted to products, we say that the position of equilibrium lies to the right. On the other hand, if the equilibrium mixture contains more of the reactants than the products, we say that the position lies to the left. Alternatively, we may say that the reaction goes, or proceeds, to a great extent, or to a slight extent, meaning that the concentration of products at equilibrium is high, or low, respectively. For example, in the hydrogen iodide reaction (Table 7.2), since, at 410°C, 77.6 per cent of the reactants have been changed to products when equilibrium is established, we say that the position of equilibrium lies to the right at this temperature.

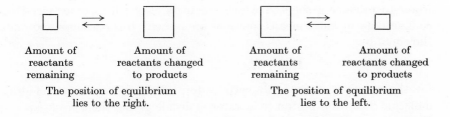

| Amount of reactants remaining | Amount of reactants changed to products | Amount of reactants remaining | Amount of reactants changed to products |

The position of equilibrium lies to the right.   The position of equilibrium lies to the left.

The position of equilibrium is determined by the particular reaction in question, the temperature, and the relative concentrations of two or more starting materials. The laws of equilibrium are so well known that it is possible to give an exact numerical statement about the extent of reaction (the position of equilibrium) if information about these three factors is available.

Equilibria Involving Hydrogen Ions: Acids and Bases

The terms *acid* and *base* have been used by chemists for several centuries; today we make use of several general definitions of these terms. The definitions in current use are interrelated, but each focuses attention on a different aspect of the properties of acids or bases. The choice of definition often depends upon the information sought or the goal desired in its use. For example, one definition is limited to reactions of hydrogen compounds in water solutions (the Arrhenius definition), another to hydrogen compounds in any solvent (the Brønsted definition), and another emphasizes the making and breaking of coordinate covalent bonds in acid-base reactions (the Lewis definition). In this section we shall emphasize definitions of acids and bases that are of use in considering water solutions.

Accordingly, an *acid* may be defined as a hydrogen-containing substance which, when dissolved in water, forms a solution that tastes sour, turns litmus red, reacts with many metals, and conducts electricity well. A *base* may be defined as a substance which, when dissolved in water, forms a solution that tastes brackish or bitter, turns litmus blue, conducts electricity well, and reacts with an acid to destroy the acid properties. These definitions are based on experimental observations, and any substance suspected of being an acid or a base can be so classified if it meets the experimental criteria specified in the definition.

However, it sometimes is more useful to use the definitions which emphasize the chemical makeup of acids and bases so that one can predict whether a given substance will act as an acid or a base when placed in water. Such definitions were advanced in 1923 by J. N. Brønsted and M. Lowry, who defined an acid as *a proton donor*, and a base as *a proton acceptor*. In effect, they said that an acid-base reaction involved the *transfer of a proton* from an acid to a base.

Perhaps the two different definitions can be interrelated if we consider first some acids and then some bases in the light of both viewpoints.

Acids. The gaseous compound, hydrogen chloride, is an acid. This means, among other things, that it is a proton donor and it dissolves in water to produce a solution which conducts electricity. Since electrical conductivity in water means that ions are present, it is reasonable to write the equation

$$HCl + H_2O \rightleftharpoons H_3O^+ + Cl^-$$

for the reaction of the acid with water. Here the hydrogen chloride molecule donates a proton to a water molecule giving the *hydronium ion*, H_3O^+, and a chloride ion. Other acids should donate protons to water in a similar manner. For example, the equations for the reactions of nitric, sulfuric, acetic, and hydrocyanic acids with water may be written:

$$HNO_3 + H_2O \rightleftharpoons H_3O^+ + NO_3^-$$

$$H_2SO_4 + H_2O \rightleftharpoons H_3O^+ + HSO_4^-$$

$$HSO_4^- + H_2O \rightleftharpoons H_3O^+ + SO_4^{-2}$$

$$CH_3CO_2H + H_2O \rightleftharpoons H_3O^+ + CH_3CO_2^-$$

$$HCN + H_2O \rightleftharpoons H_3O^+ + CN^-$$

● ● ●   THEORIES OF ACIDS COMPARED

The Arrhenius Theory. An acid is a compound which produces H_3O^+ ions in solution. Examples: HCl, HNO_3, H_2SO_4. A base is a compound which produces OH^- ions in solution. Examples: $NaOH$, $Ba(OH)_2$, NH_3, Na_2O, BaO.

The Brønsted Theory. An acid is a proton donor. Examples: HCl, HNO_3, H_2SO_4, H_2O, NH_4^+. A base is a proton acceptor. Examples: NH_3, H_2O, $CH_3CO_2^-$, NH_2^-, OH^-, O^{-2}.

The Lewis Theory. An acid is an electron pair acceptor. Examples: H_3O^+, $AlCl_3$, BF_3. A base is an electron pair donor. Examples: H_2O, NH_3, OH^-, NH_2^-, CH_3OH.

Note that in each case the hydronium ion* is a product of the reaction. Evidently, the sour taste, the reaction with litmus, and the reactivity with metals are characteristics of the hydronium ion.

Returning to the definition of an acid, we may note that any compound which reacts with water to give hydronium ions can meet the experimental criteria needed to be designated as an acid, but in order to produce hydronium ions, the compound must have donated protons to water molecules. This, then, is the interrelation between the Arrhenius and the Brønsted-Lowry definitions of an acid.

All reactions of acids with water are examples of acid-base reactions in which water acts as the base or proton acceptor. All such reactions are reversible in that the hydronium ion formed in the reaction may donate a proton to the anion giving the starting acid and water. For example:

Forward reaction $HCN + H_2O \longrightarrow H_3O^+ + CN^-$

Reverse reaction $H_3O^+ + CN^- \longrightarrow H_2O + HCN$

The strength of an acid is measured by the extent of the over-all reaction of the acid with water before the forward and reverse reaction rates become equal and equilibrium is established. For strong acids the over-all reaction goes far to the right; in fact, virtually to completion. For weak acids the over-all reaction goes only slightly to the right before the rates become equal.

Before discussing equilibrium in acid-base reactions, we shall attempt to interrelate the definitions of a base.

Bases. A number of compounds—ammonia, sodium hydroxide, and calcium oxide—produce solutions which have a bitter taste, the ability to destroy acids, and other properties that are characteristic of bases. Examination shows that each of these solutions contains an appreciable concentration of hydroxide ions, OH^-, and leads to the Arrhenius definition of a base as a substance which produces hydroxide ions in solution. Often, as in the case of sodium hydroxide, these hydroxide ions are present in the original base and are simply dissolved in the water. In other cases, the hydroxide ions are formed by reaction with water as shown in the equations

$$NH_3 + H_2O \longrightarrow NH_4^+ + OH^-$$

$$Ca^{+2}O^{-2} + H_2O \longrightarrow Ca^{+2} + 2OH^-$$

In each of these equations there has been a transfer of a proton from the water molecule to another entity, and this leads to the Brønsted definition of a base as a proton acceptor. Thus, ammonia and oxide ion, O^{-2}, (proton acceptors) are bases according to the Brønsted theory. The hydroxide ion itself is a base, since it can accept a proton, as illustrated by the equation

$$H_3O^+ + OH^- \rightleftarrows 2H_2O$$

---

* The actual structure of the positive ion produced when an acid reacts with water may be more complex than H_3O^+; the species $H_9O_4^+$ has been suggested. This structure may be regarded as an hydrated hydronium ion (Chap. 8). For lack of more precise information, we shall use the hydronium ion to represent the acid cation.

where, by accepting a proton, the hydroxide ion becomes a water molecule.

It should be noted that in the Brønsted theory bases may be neutral (NH_3), negative (OH^-), or positive ($Al(H_2O)_5OH^{+2}$),

$$H_2O + Al(H_2O)_5OH^{+2} \longrightarrow Al(H_2O)_6{}^{+3} + OH^-$$

whereas the Arrhenius theory recognizes only neutral bases (NaOH, NH_3, CaO). Both theories include neutral and negative acids (H_2SO_4, $HSO_4{}^-$), but only the Brønsted theory includes positively charged acids ($NH_4{}^+$):

$$NH_4{}^+ + H_2O \rightleftarrows H_3O^+ + NH_3$$

We shall use the Brønsted theory generally in what follows.

Reactions of bases with water to give hydroxide ions are acid-base reactions in which water acts as an acid.

$$H_2O + NH_3 \longrightarrow NH_4{}^+ + OH^-$$

Water also acts as a base in some reactions.

$$HCl + H_2O \longrightarrow H_3O^+ + Cl^-$$

It can use an unshared pair of electrons on the oxygen atoms to form coordinate covalent bonds with a proton.

Equilibrium in Acid-Base Reactions. Let us now examine a typical acid-base reaction, the reaction of acetic acid, CH_3CO_2H, with water:

$$CH_3CO_2H + H_2O \rightleftarrows H_3O^+ + CH_3CO_2{}^-$$

In the forward reaction the acetic acid molecule donates a proton to the water molecule which acts as the base. In accepting the proton, the water molecule becomes an acid (it now has an extra proton), and the acetic acid molecule, having lost a proton, now becomes the acetate ion, $CH_3CO_2{}^-$, a base. Thus, in the forward reaction, one acid and one base are destroyed but a new acid and a new base are formed. The new acid and new base are called the *conjugate acid* and the *conjugate base* of the original base and acid. Thus hydronium ion is the conjugate acid of the base, water, and acetate

Table 7.3 Some Acids and Their Conjugate Bases Arranged in Order of Acid and Base Strength

	Acid	Conjugate Base	
Strong acids	$HClO_4$	$ClO_4{}^-$	Weak bases
	HNO_3	$NO_3{}^-$	
	HCl	Cl^-	
	H_2SO_4	$HSO_4{}^-$	
	H_3O^+	H_2O	
	$HSO_4{}^-$	$SO_4{}^{-2}$	
Increasing acid strength	H_3PO_4	$H_2PO_4{}^-$	Increasing base strength
	CH_3CO_2H	$CH_3CO_2{}^-$	
	$Al(H_2O)_6{}^{+3}$	$Al(H_2O)_5(OH)^{+2}$	
	H_2CO_3	$HCO_3{}^-$	
	H_2S	HS^-	
	$NH_4{}^+$	NH_3	
	HCN	CN^-	
	$HCO_3{}^-$	$CO_3{}^{-2}$	
	HS^-	S^{-2}	
Weak acids	H_2O	OH^-	Strong bases
	NH_3	$NH_2{}^-$	

ion is the conjugate base of acetic acid. Note that the conjugate acid or base has one more or one less proton than the parent base or acid. Some acids and their conjugate bases are given in Table 7.3.

Let us now consider the reverse reaction in the acetic acid-water system. Here the hydronium ion donates a proton to the acetate ion to give one molecule of acetic acid and one of water. As a result of the reverse process, chemical equilibrium will be established and the forward reaction will appear to stop. At equilibrium two acids (CH_3CO_2H and H_3O^+) and two bases (H_2O and $CH_3CO_2^-$) will be present in the reaction mixture. In this particular case, experiment shows that the forward reaction will proceed only slightly to the right before equilibrium is established so that at equilibrium the relative amounts of hydronium ion and acetate ion will be much less than those of acetic acid and water.

Applying the reasoning of the preceding two paragraphs to all acid-base reactions, we can state the principle, *the equilibrium mixture in any acid-base reaction always contains at least two acids and two bases.* This is illustrated by the following equations:

$$
\begin{array}{llll}
\text{Acid} & + \text{ base} \rightleftarrows & \text{conjugate acid} + & \text{conjugate base} \\
HCl & + H_2O \rightleftarrows & H_3O^+ & + & Cl^- \\
HNO_3 & + H_2O \rightleftarrows & H_3O^+ & + & NO_3^- \\
H_2SO_4 & + H_2O \rightleftarrows & H_3O^+ & + & HSO_4^- \\
HSO_4^- & + H_2O \rightleftarrows & H_3O^+ & + & SO_4^{-2} \\
H_3O^+ & + OH^- \rightleftarrows & H_2O & + & H_2O \\
H_2O & + NH_3 \rightleftarrows & NH_4^+ & + & OH^- \\
CH_3CO_2H & + NH_3 \rightleftarrows & NH_4^+ & + & CH_3CO_2^- \\
HCN & + OH^- \rightleftarrows & H_2O & + & CN^-
\end{array}
$$

How Nearly Complete Are Acid-Base Reactions? One of the initial questions in acid-base reactions is: How far will the over-all reaction go as written before equilibrium is established? We define the strength of an acid in terms of the position of equilibrium in its reaction with water. If the position of equilibrium lies far to the right, we say that the acid is a strong acid. If the position of equilibrium lies to the left, we say that the acid is a weak acid. Similarly the strength of a base is measured by the position of equilibrium in its reaction with water. Thus ammonia in the equation third from the botton (above) is classified as a weak base because, at equilibrium, a relatively small fraction of the ammonia originally added is present as ammonium ion.

What now is the behavior on reaction of acids and bases with each other? A *strong* acid and a strong base react almost completely, whereas a *weak* acid and a *weak* base react to only a slight extent before the rate of the reverse reaction becomes equal to the rate of the forward reaction and equilibrium is established. If one knows the relative strengths of the acids or bases involved in the equilibrium, it is possible to make a qualitative prediction of the extent of the reaction. The general principle is: At equilibrium the weaker acid and the weaker base predominate in concentration.

Table 7.3 is a list of some common acids arranged in order of decreasing acid strength. These acid strengths were determined by experiment, using a method to be described in Chap. 21. The acid strength is a measure of the tendency of the acid to lose a proton to a water molecule.

Opposite each acid in Table 7.3 is its conjugate base. The order of base strengths for these bases is exactly opposite that of the corresponding acids. A strong acid has a strong tendency to lose a proton but once the proton is lost the conjugate base that remains has only a slight tendency to accept a proton. Thus, a strong acid produces a weak conjugate base. Conversely, a weak acid which loses its proton reluctantly forms a strong conjugate base—one that has a great affinity for protons.

Method of Indicating the Strength of an Acid. The tendency of an acid to lose a proton to water is a measure of the strength of an acid and can be expressed by a value called the ionization constant of the acid, K_{ion}. This constant is a measure of the extent to which the forward reaction of the acid with water proceeds before equilibrium is established. It is also a measure of the relative amounts of products and reactants in the reaction mixture. The form of the equilibrium constant is known to be (Chap. 21)

$$K_{ion} = \frac{[H_3O^+]_{eq} \times [X^-]_{eq}}{[HX]_{eq}}$$

where the symbols $[H_3O^+]_{eq}$, $[X^-]_{eq}$, and $[HX]_{eq}$ represent the equilibrium concentrations in moles per liter of the hydronium ion, H_3O^+, the anion, X^-, and the acid, HX, respectively.

● ● ● RELATION BETWEEN THE MAGNITUDES OF K_{ion} AND THE STRENGTH OF AN ACID

Assume that three acids, HA, HB, and HC, each of a different acid strength, are dissolved in water and the acid-base reaction is allowed to come to equilibrium. The situation may be described as follows. In the diagrams the boxes represent relative amounts of material present at equilibrium.

Case I. $HA + H_2O \rightleftarrows H_3O^+ + A^-$ where K_{ion} is very small.

Point of equilibrium lies far to the left

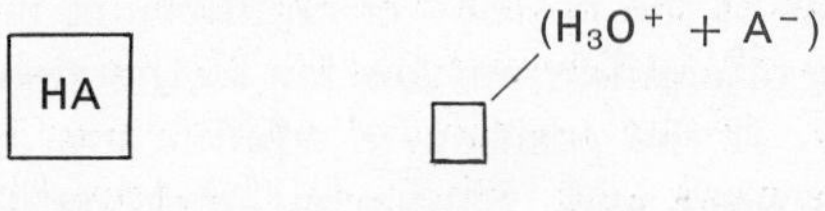

| HA | $(H_3O^+ + A^-)$ □

Case II. $HB + H_2O \rightleftarrows H_3O^+ + B^-$ where $K_{ion} = 1$.

Point of equilibrium such that
$[HB] = [H_3O^+] \times [B^-]$

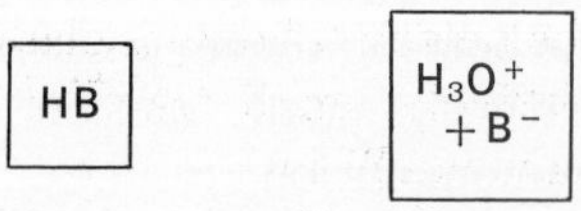

| HB | | H_3O^+ $+ B^-$ |

Case III. $HC + H_2O \rightleftarrows H_3O^+ + C^-$ where K_{ion} is very large.

Point of equilibrium lies far to the right

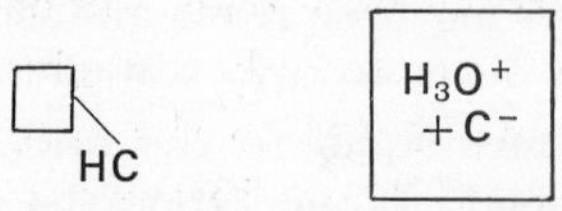

□ HC | H_3O^+ $+ C^-$ |

Acid strength

measured by magnitude of $K_{ion} = \dfrac{[H_3O^+][A^-]}{[HA]}$

Base strength

measured by magnitude of $K_{ion} = \dfrac{[BH^+][OH^-]}{[B]}$

Table 7.4 Ionization Constants of Some Acids in Water

Name	Formula	Ionization Constant (25°C)
Acetic	CH_3CO_2H	1.8×10^{-5}
Aluminum ion	$Al(H_2O_6)^{+3}$	1.1×10^{-5}
Ammonium ion	NH_4^+	5.5×10^{-10}
Arsenic	H_3AsO_4	2.5×10^{-4}
	$H_2AsO_4^-$	5.6×10^{-8}
	$HAsO_4^{-2}$	3.0×10^{-13}
Arsenious	H_3AsO_3	6.0×10^{-10}
Boric	H_3BO_3	6.0×10^{-10}
Carbonic	H_2CO_3	4.2×10^{-7}
Chloroacetic	$ClCH_2CO_2H$	1.4×10^{-3}
Chromic	H_2CrO_4	1.8×10^{-1}
	$HCrO_4^-$	3.2×10^{-7}
Formic	HCO_2H	2.1×10^{-4}
Hydrochloric	HCl	Very large
Hydrocyanic	HCN	4.0×10^{-10}
Hydrofluoric	HF	6.9×10^{-4}
Hydrogen sulfide	H_2S	1.0×10^{-7}
Hypochlorous	$HClO$	3.2×10^{-8}
Hypoiodous	HOI	5×10^{-3}
Iodic	HIO_3	1.6×10^{-1}
Nitric	HNO_3	Very large
Nitrous	HNO_2	4.5×10^{-4}
Oxalic	$H_2C_2O_4$	3.8×10^{-2}
	$HC_2O_4^-$	5.0×10^{-5}
Perchloric	$HClO_4$	Very large
Phosphoric	H_3PO_4	7.5×10^{-3}
	$H_2PO_4^-$	6.2×10^{-8}
	HPO_4^{-2}	1.0×10^{-12}
Sulfuric	H_2SO_4	Very large
	HSO_4^-	1.2×10^{-2}
Sulfurous	H_2SO_3	1.3×10^{-2}
	HSO_3^-	5.6×10^{-8}

High values for K_{ion} mean that the over-all reaction proceeds far to the right before equilibrium is established. This is the case with strong acids like hydrochloric acid, nitric acid, and perchloric acid. In these cases the over-all reactions proceed virtually to completion and K_{ion} becomes infinity because $[HX]_{eq}$ approaches zero.

Low values for K_{ion} mean that the over-all reaction proceeds only slightly to the right before equilibrium is established. This is the case with weak acids such as acetic acid where K_{ion} is 1.8×10^{-5} at 25°C. Table 7.4 gives values for the ionization constants of some weak acids.

● ● ●   SUMMARY OF REACTIONS OF ACIDS AND BASES

In water solutions acids may be defined as proton donors and bases as proton acceptors. An acid-base reaction involves the transfer of a proton from an acid to a base. The products in such reactions, also acids and bases, are called conjugate acids or bases. The equilibrium in an acid-base reaction involves two acids and two bases as represented in the relation

$$HA + B \rightleftharpoons HB^+ + A^-$$

Acid　Base　　Conjugate　Conjugate
　　　　　　　　acid　　　base

The distribution of material at equilibrium always lies in favor of the weaker acid and base. Strong acids have large values of K_{ion}; weak acids have small values.

We shall discuss K_{ion} and other equilibrium constants in detail in Chap. 21. In the following chapters we shall use the value of K_{ion} as an indication of the strength of acids and bases.

Other Theories of Acids and Bases. Thus far we have limited our discussion of acids and bases to a consideration of water solutions. At other points in the text the concept of acids and bases will be expanded to include other solvents and to systems in which proton transfer does not occur. We shall find that the reasoning used in this chapter will serve as the basis for consideration of acids and bases in nonaqueous media.

Reactions of Hydrogen Illustrating Oxidation-Reduction

Competing in importance with acid-base reactions is the large class of chemical changes known as oxidation-reduction reactions. The important characteristic of these reactions is that certain elements involved undergo a change in oxidation state during the reaction. Two simple examples of oxidation-reduction reactions involving hydrogen are:

$$H_2 + Cl_2 \rightleftharpoons 2HCl \tag{1}$$

$$Ca + H_2 \rightleftharpoons CaH_2 \tag{2}$$

Since hydrogen has a I oxidation state in combination with nonmetals and a $-$I in combination with metals (page 147), we note that in the first reaction hydrogen has changed from a zero oxidation state in reactants to a I oxidation state in the products. In the second reaction hydrogen has changed from a zero oxidation state in the reactants to a $-$I oxidation state in the products. The oxidation state of chlorine has changed from 0 to $-$I and the oxidation state of calcium has changed from 0 to II. (See rules for assigning oxidation numbers in the following paragraphs.)

Oxidation and Reduction. Of special importance is the fact that hydrogen has *increased* in oxidation state in the first process and has *decreased* in oxidation state in the second. When an element *increases* in oxidation state in a reaction it is said to have been *oxidized*; when an element *decreases* in oxidation state in a reaction it is said to have been *reduced*. Oxidation and reduction refer to processes in which elements undergo an increase or a decrease in oxidation state. This is illustrated in the diagram below,

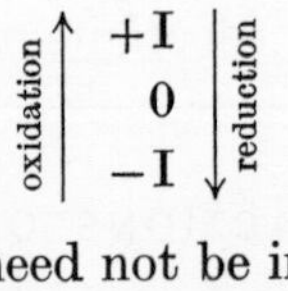

$$\text{oxidation} \uparrow \begin{array}{c} +I \\ 0 \\ -I \end{array} \downarrow \text{reduction}$$

which shows that an element need not be in its zero oxidation state to be oxidized or reduced. For example, hydrogen in the $-$I oxidation state may be oxidized to the I oxidation state as in the reaction

$$LiH + Cl_2 \longrightarrow LiCl + HCl$$

or hydrogen in the I oxidation state may be reduced to the zero oxidation state as in the process

$$Na + H_2O \longrightarrow NaOH + \tfrac{1}{2}H_2$$

A closer examination of reactions (1) and (2) above reveals that while hydrogen is being oxidized in reaction (1), chlorine is being reduced, and while hydrogen is being reduced in reaction (2), calcium is being oxidized. This is invariably true—*oxidation always accompanies reduction* or vice versa. Moreover, it is also true that the *amount of oxidation must be equivalent to the amount of reduction* in any oxidation-reduction reaction. In reaction (2), two hydrogen atoms are each reduced by one oxidation unit while each calcium atom is oxidized by two oxidation units.

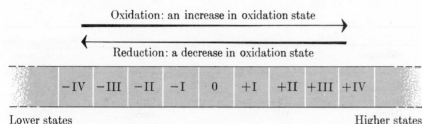

Figure 7.9 Scale of oxidation states indicating the processes of oxidation and reduction.

Oxidizing Agents and Reducing Agents. An oxidizing agent is a reagent or chemical species which can oxidize another species. In oxidizing the other species it is itself reduced. Therefore, in reaction (1), chlorine, Cl_2, is the oxidizing agent (it is reduced to Cl^-), and in reaction (2), hydrogen, H_2, is the oxidizing agent (it is reduced to H^-). Similarly, a reducing agent is a reagent or chemical species which is responsible for reducing another species. In reducing the other species it is itself oxidized. In reaction (1), hydrogen, H_2, is the reducing agent, and in reaction (2), calcium is the reducing agent.

Equilibrium in Oxidation-Reduction Reactions. Oxidation-reduction reactions are reversible. When a strong oxidizing agent and a strong reducing agent are allowed to react, the over-all reaction will approach completion. When a weak oxidizing agent and a weak reducing agent are allowed to react, the over-all reaction will proceed only slightly to the right before the forward and reverse rates become equal and equilibrium is established. In many ways oxidation-reduction equilibria are analogous to acid-base equilibria.

Later it will be shown that a measure of the strength of an oxidizing or reducing agent is a value called the oxidation potential, E° (see Chaps. 8 and 22).

Rules for Assigning Numbers to Oxidation States. The assignment of oxidation states to the elements in a compound may be made by observing certain rules:

1. *The oxidation state of a free element (that is, one not combined with another element) is zero.*

2. *Hydrogen has an oxidation state of* I *and oxygen has an oxidation state of* − II *when they are present in most compounds.* Exceptions to this are that hydrogen has an oxidation state of − I in hydrides of active metals, and oxygen has an oxidation state of − I in peroxides, and of II in its compound with fluorine.

3. *The algebraic sum* (the sum taking account of positive and negative signs) *of the oxidation states of all atoms in a neutral molecule must be zero.* If the substance is an ion rather than a molecule, the algebraic sum of the oxidation states of the atoms in the ion must equal the charge on the ion.

For simple ions the oxidation state is equal to the charge on the ion: the electrovalence. For compounds containing covalent bonds, the oxidation state of an element must be determined by applying rules such as those above.

The common oxidation states of several elements are given in Table 7.5.

Table 7.5 Oxidation States of Some Common Elements

Element	Type of Compound	Example	Oxidation State of Element
Aluminum	All	$AlCl_3$	III
Bromine	Bromides	NaBr	$-$I
Calcium	All	$CaSO_4$	II
Chlorine	Chlorides	NaCl	$-$I
Chlorine	Chlorates	$KClO_3$	V
Chromium	Chromic	$CrCl_3$	III
Chromium	Chromates	K_2CrO_4	VI
Copper	Cupric	$CuSO_4$	II
Iron	Ferrous	$FeSO_4$	II
Iron	Ferric	$FeCl_3$	III
Manganese	Manganous	$MnSO_4$	II
Manganese	Permanganates	$KMnO_4$	VII
Nitrogen	Nitrides	AlN	$-$III
Nitrogen	Nitrates	$NaNO_3$	V
Phosphorus	Phosphates	$Ca_3(PO_4)_2$	V
Potassium	All	KCl	I
Sodium	All	$NaNO_3$	I
Sulfur	Sulfides	CuS	$-$II
Sulfur	Sulfites	Na_2SO_3	IV
Sulfur	Sulfates	$BaSO_4$	VI

Examples of the Calculation of Oxidation State

PROBLEM 1. ■ Calculate the oxidation state of sulfur in sulfur dioxide (SO_2).

SOLUTION
If the oxidation state of oxygen is $-$II, the total oxidation state of two oxygen atoms must be -4.* Hence, the oxidation state of sulfur in sulfur dioxide must be IV in order that Rule 3 may be satisfied.

$$2O = 2 \times (-2) = -4$$
$$S = \underline{+4 \text{ (IV)}}$$
$$0$$

---

* Current rules of nomenclature call for Roman numerals to designate oxidation states. In numerical problems, however, it is often more convenient to use Arabic numbers.

PROBLEM 2. ■ Calculate the oxidation state of sulfur in hydrogen sulfate (H_2SO_4).

SOLUTION

The total oxidation state for 2H is $2H = 2 \times (+1) = +2$
The total oxidation state for 4O is $4O = 4 \times (-2) = -8$
Therefore, the oxidation state of S in H_2SO_4 is $S = \underline{+6}$ (VI)
                                              0

PROBLEM 3. ■ Calculate the oxidation state of chlorine in potassium chlorate ($KClO_3$).

SOLUTION

The electrovalence of potassium is $+1$; hence,
the oxidation state for 1K is $K = +1$
The total oxidation state for 3O is $3O = 3 \times (-2) = -6$
Therefore, the oxidation state of Cl in $KClO_3$ is $Cl = \underline{+5}$ (V)
                                              0

PROBLEM 4. ■ Calculate the oxidation state of manganese in the permanganate ion (MnO_4^-).

SOLUTION

The total oxidation state for 4O is $4O = 4 \times (-2) = -8$
Therefore, the oxidation state of Mn must be $Mn = \underline{+7}$ (VII)
in order that the charge on the ion may be -1 (Rule 3). -1

Preparation of Hydrogen: Application of Oxidation-Reduction Principles. Since molecular hydrogen does not occur freely in nature, it must be prepared from compounds of hydrogen. Nearly all such compounds contain hydrogen in the I oxidation state, so the problem is one of reducing the hydrogen from the I to the zero oxidation state. A reducing agent is needed and it remains only to select reducing agents strong enough for this purpose. Three types of reducing agents are used to reduce the hydrogen in water or in acids: (a) the very active or moderately active metals, (b) heated carbon, and (c) electrons at a cathode.

Hydrogen from Metals and Water or Acids. Metals are reducing agents because they are oxidizable—i.e., they can be converted from zero to positive oxidation states as they lose electrons in chemical reactions. In the process of being oxidized in a reaction, metals make it possible for another element to be reduced. The most active metals are those which are oxidized most readily and are therefore the strongest reducing agents among the metals.

Water and strong acids such as hydrochloric acid and sulfuric acid are common laboratory sources of hydrogen. In water solutions of acids the species which reacts with the metal is the hydronium ion, H_3O^+; in water itself it may be the water molecule that reacts with the metal. The following equations for reactions of metals with water and hydronium ions indicate that the hydronium ion appears to be a stronger oxidizing agent than water. As a result, the very active metals will react with both water and acids to produce hydrogen, moderately active metals will react only with acids, and less active metals will react with neither water nor acids to produce hydrogen.

1. *Active metals* + water

$$2Li + 2H_2O \longrightarrow 2LiOH + H_2$$
$$2Na + 2H_2O \longrightarrow 2NaOH + H_2$$

Reactions of strong reducing agents (active metals) with a moderately weak oxidizing agent (water) proceed readily.

2. *Moderately active metals* + steam

$$Mg + H_2O \longrightarrow MgO + H_2$$
$$Ca + H_2O \longrightarrow CaO + H_2$$

Reactions of moderately strong reducing agents with a moderately weak oxidizing agent proceed at elevated temperatures.

3. *Moderately active metals* + acids
(H_3O^+ from HCl or dilute H_2SO_4)

$$Mg + 2H_3O^+ \longrightarrow Mg^{+2} + H_2 + 2H_2O$$
$$Zn + 2H_3O^+ \longrightarrow Zn^{+2} + H_2 + 2H_2O$$

Reactions of moderately strong reducing agents with a stronger oxidizing agent (H_3O^+) proceed readily.

4. *Less active metals* + acids
(HCl or dilute H_2SO_4)

$$Cu + H_3O^+ \longrightarrow \text{no reaction}$$
$$Ag + H_3O^+ \longrightarrow \text{no reaction}$$

Reactions of weak reducing agents with the oxidizing agent H_3O^+ are unsuccessful.

Hydrogen from Reaction of Water with Hot Carbon. An important industrial process, called the Bosch process, for the production of hydrogen is the reaction of steam with hot carbon. Two reactions may occur:

$$H_2O + C \xrightarrow{\text{hot}} CO + H_2$$

$$CO + H_2O \xrightarrow{\text{hot}} CO_2 + H_2$$

Hydrogen by Electrolysis of Water. Another industrial method for the preparation of hydrogen is the electrolysis of water. The electrolysis is done in an alkaline or acidic solution.

In acid solution

At cathode $2H_3O^+ + 2e^- \longrightarrow H_2 + 2H_2O$

At anode $6H_2O \longrightarrow O_2 + 4H_3O^+ + 4e^-$

In alkaline solution

At cathode $2H_2O + 2e^- \longrightarrow H_2 + 2OH^-$

At anode $4OH^- \longrightarrow O_2 + 2H_2O + 4e^-$

Hydrogen as a Reducing Agent. The chief chemical property of hydrogen is its strength as a reducing agent. This is illustrated by the reactions of hydrogen molecules (page 137).

SUMMARY

The purpose of this chapter is threefold: (a) to summarize the chemistry of hydrogen, the simplest element; (b) to introduce certain principles related to chemical reactions, e.g., chemical equilibria and the fundamentals of both acid-base and oxidation-reduction reactions; and (c) to use these principles to discuss the reactions of hydrogen and some of its compounds.

Many of the ideas associated with chemical reactions presented here will be used constantly throughout the remainder of the text. Concepts and terms such as extent of reaction, position of equilibrium, acid, base, ionization constant, oxidation, reduction, oxidizing agent, reducing agent are essential parts of a basic understanding of the elementary principles of chemical reactions.

SOME SPECIAL TERMS

Acids
    Arrhenius theory of acids
    Brønsted theory of acids
    conjugate acid
    conjugate base
    Lewis theory
    proton acceptor
    proton donor
    strong acid
    weak acid
    hydronium ion
Equilibrium
    chemical equilibrium
    equilibrium constant
    position of equilibrium

Escape velocity
Electronegativity
Reaction
    rate of reaction
    reversible reaction
    electrolysis
Oxidation-Reduction
    oxidation state
    oxidizing agent
    reducing agent
Radioactive tracer
Hydrogen
    tritium
    deuterium
    hydride

QUESTIONS AND PROBLEMS

1. Indicate the location and relative abundance of hydrogen in the free state; in the combined state.
2. Of what importance is hydrogen in the formation of plant and animal tissue? in the formation of the chemical elements?
3. Describe several physical properties of hydrogen, deuterium, and tritium.
4. How does a hydride differ from a hydrate? a hydroxide? a hydronium compound?
5. Give examples of several weak and strong acids; of several weak and strong bases.
6. What quantitative method can be used to indicate the strength of an acid or base?
7. What species and what relative amounts of them are present in a dilute H_2SO_4 solution?
8. Show by chemical equations: (a) preparation of hydrogen from water by electrolysis, (b) preparation of hydrogen from water by active metals, (c) preparation of hydrogen from acids, (d) reduction property of hydrogen in reaction with an oxide, (e) formation of atomic hydrogen from molecular hydrogen, (f) neutralization of an acid with a base.
9. Compare the three theories of acids, illustrating each by chemical equations.
10. Name several commercial uses of hydrogen.
11. Calculate the oxidation state of the underlined element in each of the formulas: (a) $H_2\underline{S}O_4$, (b) $H\underline{N}O_3$, (c) $\underline{N}H_3$, (d) $\underline{C}Cl_4$, (e) $Na\underline{H}_2PO_4$, (f) $H_2\underline{S}O_3$, (g) $K\underline{Cl}O_3$, and (h) $\underline{C}H_2Cl_2$.

12. Calculate the mass loss when four moles of protons combine to form one mole of helium ions with an evolution of 6.5×10^{11} cal. If 1 g of coal gives 7,000 cal when it burns, calculate how many tons of coal must be burned to give the amount of heat that would be evolved when 1 g of matter is converted to energy.

13. If, at equilibrium, the rate of the forward reaction equals the rate of the reverse reaction, does this mean that half of the reactants have reacted? Explain. What determines the position of equilibrium?

14. Write the equations for the reactions of each of the following bases with water and with one other acid.

$$CH_3CO_2^- \qquad CN^-$$
$$NH_3 \qquad Cl^-$$
$$NH_2^- \qquad SO_4^{-2}$$
$$H_2O$$

15. Calculate the number of grams of hydrogen gas formed when 10 g of zinc react with dilute sulfuric acid.

16. How many grams of sodium hydroxide is required to neutralize 50 g of perchloric acid?

17. Does it appear that there is a relation between the electronegativity of an element and its strength as an oxidizing or reducing agent? Justify your answer.

18. How many grams of sulfuric acid in dilute solution is required to oxidize 25 g of iron from Fe° to Fe^{+2}?

19. In the reaction

$$H_2 + I_2 \rightleftharpoons 2HI$$

at a given temperature, equilibrium is established when the following concentrations are present:

$$H_2 = 0.1 \text{ mole/liter}$$
$$I_2 = 0.1 \text{ mole/liter}$$
$$HI = 1.8 \text{ moles/liter}$$

Calculate the value of the equilibrium constant at that temperature.

20. If 1.0 mole of hydrogen and 1.0 mole of iodine are added to a 5.0 liters container at a given temperature and the system is allowed to come to equilibrium, and at this time 0.10 moles of hydrogen iodide has been formed, calculate the value of the equilibrium constant at that temperature.

REFERENCES

ROBERTS, M. S. "Hydrogen in the Galaxies," *Scientific American*, vol. *208*, no. 6 (1963), p. 94.

ROBINSON, B. J. "Hydroxyl Radicals in Space," *Scientific American*, vol. *213*, no. 1 (1965), p. 26.

VAN DER WERF, C. A. *Acids, Bases and the Chemistry of the Covalent Bond.* New York: Reinhold, 1961.

8

The Alkali and Alkaline Earth Elements: Two Families of Representative Metals

I used potash in igneous fusion [and electrolyzed it] ... *small globules having a high metallic lustre, and being precisely similar to quicksilver, appeared, some of which burnt with explosion and bright flame—these globules, numerous experiments soon showed to be the substance I was in search of* [potassium]. ...
Sir Humphry Davy (1778–1829)

The family of metals forming the simplest compounds is the alkali metals —lithium, sodium, potassium, rubidium, cesium, and francium. These six elements constitute Group I of the periodic table. The atoms of these elements have a single valence electron beyond a well-shielded nucleus. Perhaps the next simplest compounds of metals are those of the alkaline earth metals in Group II of the periodic table—beryllium, magnesium, calcium, strontium, barium, and radium. The atoms of these elements have two valence electrons beyond a well-shielded nucleus. See Figure 8.1.

These two families contain the most reactive of the metals. Hence the chemistry of these elements will be presented in a single chapter. In this way the variations in properties of the metals and their compounds can be related to the structure and size of the atoms and their ions.

Comparison of the Two Families

The properties of the Group I and Group II elements are found to be those that would be predicted from a knowledge of their electron configurations, ionization energies, atom or ion size, and crystal structure. The interplay among these factors is complex but gives rise to certain trends in properties within the families. Chemists have found it useful to look for these trends and, having found them, to explain them in terms of atomic and crystal structure. These explanations are helpful correlative tools for organizing and remembering the properties of the elements and predicting possible new uses of these metals.

$_3Li_{6.939}$	$_4Be_{9.0122}$
$_{11}Na_{22.9898}$	$_{12}Mg_{24.312}$
$_{19}K_{39.102}$	$_{20}Ca_{40.08}$
$_{37}Rb_{85.47}$	$_{37}Sr_{87.62}$
$_{55}Cs_{132.905}$	$_{56}Ba_{137.34}$
$_{87}Fr_{(223)}$	$_{88}Ra_{(226)}$

Figure 8.1 Elements of Group I and Group II.

In this section we shall examine and compare the properties of the elements in Group I and Group II, exclusive of francium and radium, under three broad headings:

1. The properties of the atoms, including electron configuration, ionization energy, and size.
2. Some physical properties such as densities, melting and boiling points, heats of fusion and vaporization, thermal conductivity, and electrical resistivity.
3. Some chemical properties such as stable oxidation states, strength as reducing agents, strengths of acids and bases formed, and solubilities of salts.

Properties of Atoms. The electron configurations assigned the atoms of Group I and Group II elements (Table 8.1) imply:

1. That the elements should readily lose their valence electrons, thereby forming positive ions which have stable noble gas configurations.
2. That the ease of formation of these ions should increase as the amount of shielding due to intervening shells of electrons increases (as the atomic weight increases) because the nucleus will exert less attraction on valence electrons.
3. That the atomic and ionic radii should increase within each family as the atomic weight increases because of the greater number of electron shells which accompany an increase in atomic weight.

Each of these implications can be verified by experiment.

Table 8.1 Electron Configurations of the Atoms of the Alkali and Alkaline Earth Elements

Alkali Metals		Alkaline Earth Metals	
Li	$1s^2$ $2s^1$	Be	$2s^2$
Na	$1s^2\,2s^2\,2p^6$ $3s^1$	Mg	$3s^2$
K	$1s^2\,2s^2\,2p^6\,3s^2\,3p^6$ $4s^1$	Ca	$4s^2$
Rb	$1s^2\,2s^2\,2p^6\,3s^2\,3p^6\,3d^{10}\,4s^2\,4p^6$ $5s^1$	Sr	$5s^2$
Cs	$1s^2\,2s^2\,2p^6\,3s^2\,3p^6\,3d^{10}\,4s^2\,4p^6\,4d^{10}\,5s^2\,5p^6$ $6s^1$	Ba	$6s^2$
Fr	$1s^2\,2s^2\,2p^6\,3s^2\,3p^6\,3d^{10}\,4s^2\,4p^6\,4d^{10}\,4f^{14}\,5s^2\,5p^6\,5d^{10}\,6s^2\,6p^6$ $7s^1$	Ra	$7s^2$

Note: Boxed sections indicate filled orbitals; the boxed section in each alkaline earth element contains the same number of orbitals and electrons as the comparable element among the alkali metals.

Verification that each alkali element has only one valence electron comes from an examination of the observed ionization energies for the elements under consideration given in Table 8.2. The energy required to remove the first electron from Group I atoms is only a small fraction of that needed to remove the second electron from these atoms—e.g., for lithium only 124 kcal is needed to remove the first electrons from a mole of the atoms, while 1,743 kcal/mole is needed to remove the second electrons.

Among the Group II elements the first two electrons have much lower ionization energies than the third in every case, thus verifying the prediction that the two valence electrons might be lost more readily than the third electron. The higher ionization energies for the Group II elements as compared with those in Group I indicate that electrons may be removed from Group I atoms more readily than from those in Group II.

Table 8.2 also shows that the ionization energies decrease from the elements of lower to those of higher atomic weight in each family as predicted in implication 2 above.

Table 8.2 Ionization Energies for Alkali and Alkaline Earth Elements (kcal/mole of atoms)

Alkali Element	1st Electron	2nd Electron	Alkaline Earth Element	1st Electron	2nd Electron	3rd Electron
Li	124	1743	Be	215	420	3547
Na	118	1090	Mg	176	346	1847
K	100	733	Ca	141	274	1180
Rb	96	634	Sr	131	254	
Cs	90	548	Ba	120	200	

The values of the radii of the atoms and of the corresponding ions of Group I and Group II elements estimated from crystal structure studies (Chaps. 5 and 15), given in Figure 8.2 verify the prediction that the atomic radius increases as the atomic weight increases within each family. Thus, the atomic radii for the Group I atoms increase steadily from 1.55 A for lithium to 2.67 A for cesium. Similar trends exist for Group II atoms and for the ions of both families.

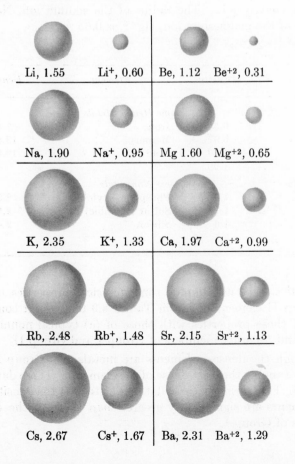

Li, 1.55   Li$^+$, 0.60 | Be, 1.12   Be^{+2}, 0.31

Na, 1.90   Na$^+$, 0.95 | Mg 1.60   Mg^{+2}, 0.65

K, 2.35   K$^+$, 1.33 | Ca, 1.97   Ca^{+2}, 0.99

Rb, 2.48   Rb$^+$, 1.48 | Sr, 2.15   Sr^{+2}, 1.13

Cs, 2.67   Cs$^+$, 1.67 | Ba, 2.31   Ba^{+2}, 1.29

Figure 8.2 Relative sizes of atoms and ions of Group I and Group II elements (in angstroms).

Three additional comparisons pertaining to atomic and ionic radii are important:

1. Taken as a group, the atoms and ions of these elements are the largest atoms and ions among the metals. For example, the lithium atom is larger than the gold atom (1.55 A compared with 1.44 A) even though gold weighs more than 28 times as much as lithium, and the sodium atom is larger than the lead atom (1.90 A compared with 1.75 A).

2. In all cases the ions are smaller than the corresponding atoms as might be anticipated since the valence shell of the atom is vacated when the ion is formed. The actual decrease is quite large. For example, the beryllium atom, Be, shrinks from 1.12 A to 0.31 A in the ion Be^{+2}, and the sodium atom, Na, drops from 1.90 A to 0.95 A in the ion Na^{+}.

3. The ions of the Group II elements are smaller than the corresponding Group I ions even though the electron configurations of the two corresponding *ions* are identical in each case. For example, the lithium ion (Li^{+}) and the beryllium ion (Be^{+2}) have the same electron configuration; also sodium and magnesium ions have the same; potassium and calcium ions, the same, etc. However, the Group II ion is always the smaller of the pair because it has a higher nuclear charge than the Group I ion. This higher charge causes the electron cloud to be drawn closer to the nucleus. In sodium ion, for example, 10 electrons are attracted to a nucleus having a nuclear charge of $+11$; in magnesium ion 10 electrons are attracted to a nucleus of nuclear charge $+12$. The radius of the sodium ion, Na^{+}, is 0.95 A; the radius of the magnesium ion, Mg^{+2}, is 0.65 A.

Table 8.3 Comparison of Densities of Some Common Elements (room temperature, g/cc)

Element	Density	Element	Density
Alkali Metals		*Some Heavy Metals*	
Lithium	0.53	Iron	7.86
Sodium	0.97	Mercury	13.6
Rubidium	1.53	Gold	19.3
Cesium	1.90		
Alkaline Earth Metals		*Some Nonmetals*	
Beryllium	1.8	Phosphorus (violet)	2.35
Magnesium	1.7	Sulfur (rhombic)	2.07
Calcium	1.6	Silicon	2.4
Barium	3.5		

Physical Properties. Let us examine some physical properties of the Group I and Group II elements given in Tables 8.3 to 8.5 and compare the magnitudes of these properties with those of (a) typical nonmetals, (b) other metals, and (c) other members of Group I and Group II.

Density. Although the densest elements are metals, the Group I and Group II metals are among the least dense of the elements. These data are shown in Table 8.3. Furthermore, these data indicate that the densities of the Group II elements are significantly greater than those of the corresponding members of Group I.

The especially low densities of these elements has been explained in terms of (a) the relatively large sizes of their atoms and (b) the packing pattern of their atoms in the metallic crystal. The relatively large size of the Group I and Group II atoms limits the number of atomic nuclei that can be packed in a given volume of the metal, thereby lowering the density. The greater densities of Group II elements compared with those of Group I can be attributed to the significantly smaller sizes of the Group II atoms compared with those of Group I. Also important is the fact that the Group I atoms are arranged or packed in the crystal in a much more open structure or less efficient manner than are those of Group II (see Chap. 15).

The gradual increase in density in moving down each family is a result of the fact that in moving from one member to the member below it in a family the increase in nuclear mass is greater than the increase in atomic radius. Thus, in passing from potassium to rubidium the mass changes from 39 to 85 a.m.u., an increase of about 120 per cent, while the atomic radius changes from 2.35 to 2.48 A, an increase of about 6 per cent (the volume per atom changes by about 20 per cent). This results in a greater mass per unit volume, i.e., in a greater density.

Melting Point. The Group I elements have low melting points which decrease systematically from 180.5°C for lithium to 28.6°C for cesium; the melting points for the Group II elements are much higher (Figure 8.3).

Low melting points are usually associated with weak forces of attraction among the building blocks of the crystal. For these families of elements the metallic bonding is apparently much weaker in the Group I metals than in those of Group II. Could this be because Group I metals contribute one electron per atom to the bonds between atoms while Group II elements contribute two electrons per atom?

Is the systematic decrease in melting point in proceeding down the two families due to a weakening of the metallic bond in the heavier elements brought about because the atomic nuclei have less control of the bonding electrons as the atoms increase in size? These questions are examples of problems encountered by researchers who study the metallic and solid state.

Boiling Point. There is a very wide liquid range between the boiling points of these elements and their melting points; this is common to metals. For example,

	Melting Point	Boiling Point
Lithium	180°C	1326°C
Potassium	63°C	757°C
Calcium	810°C	1492°C

This wide liquid range suggests that the forces holding the atoms in the liquid are quite strong. Consequently it has been suggested that when a metal melts, only a small fraction of the metal bonds are broken and that considerable metallic bonding exists in the liquid state. When the metal boils, all of the metallic bonds must be broken. This occurs at considerably higher temperatures than those required for melting.

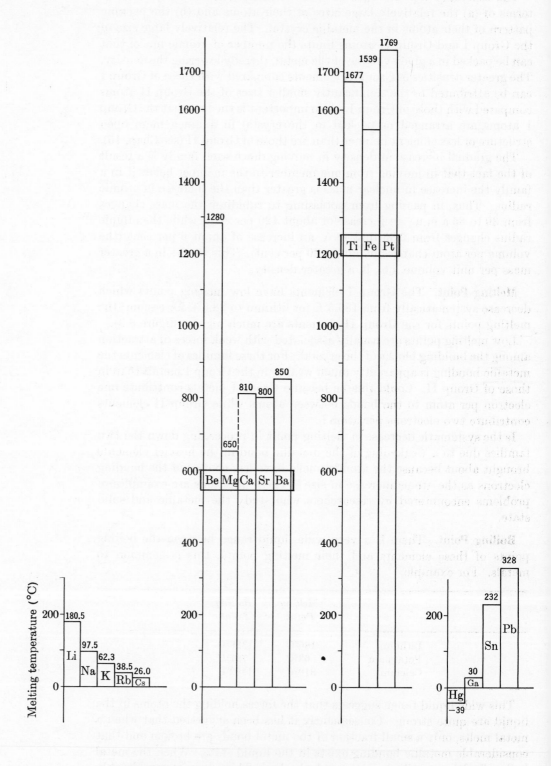

Figure 8.3 Comparison of melting points of Group I and Group II metals. The melting points of several other metals are listed for comparison.

Substance	Heat of Fusion	Heat of Vaporization
Metals		
Alkali		
Lithium	0.72	32.2
Sodium	0.62	21.3
Potassium	0.55	18.5
Rubidium	0.52	16.5
Cesium	0.50	15.6
Alkaline earth		
Beryllium	2.8	70.4
Magnesium	2.14	30.8
Calcium	2.1	35.8
Strontium	2.2	33.2
Barium	1.8	36.1
Other Substances		
Water	1.45	9.7
Iodine	2.97	6.1
Sodium chloride	6.8	40.1

Table 8.4 Comparison of Heat of Fusion and Heat of Vaporization of Several Elements and Compounds (in kcal/mole)

The boiling points of the alkaline earth metals are much higher than those of the alkali metals, again pointing toward stronger metallic bonds among the Group II elements.

Heats of Fusion and Vaporization. The heat of fusion is the energy needed to melt a solid at its melting point; the heat of vaporization is the energy needed to vaporize a liquid at its boiling point. In essence, the heat of fusion is a measure of the energy needed to collapse the crystal; the heat of vaporization is a measure of the energy needed to separate the building blocks of the liquid.

For these two families of elements the heats of fusion are very small, decreasing from top to bottom in each family (Table 8.4). However, the heats of vaporization of the elements in these two families are especially high by comparison with the heat of fusion.

The low values for the heat of fusion of the alkali and alkaline earth metals emphasize again that only a small fraction of the metallic bonds need be broken in order to collapse the crystal. The very high values for the heat of vaporization indicate that much energy is needed to break all metallic bonds and to separate the atoms. It is interesting to note that the energy needed to break a large fraction of the metallic bonds and to separate the atoms of these elements is about the same as that required to vaporize the ions from melted ionic compounds, such as sodium chloride, and considerably higher than that needed to separate water or iodine molecules.

Thermal and Electrical Conductivity. Among the elements, only silver, copper, gold, and aluminum are better conductors of heat and electricity than are the members of these families. Table 8.5 shows that the trends in thermal conductivity parallel those of electrical conductivity in Group I and in copper and silver. This suggests that the factors responsible for electrical conductivity also are responsible for thermal conductivity.

Table 8.5 Electrical and Thermal
Conductivities of Group I Metals

Metal	Electrical Conductivity (microohm-cm^{-1} at 0 to 20°C)	Thermal Conductivity (cal/cm/sec/deg at 25°C)
Li	0.117	0.17
Na	0.238	0.32
K	0.163	0.23
For comparison		
Cu	0.598	0.99
Ag	0.628	1.01

Since, electrically, conductivity is related to the relative electron mobility, it is reasonable to conclude that heat also is conducted in metals by the moving electrons.

Chemical Properties. Group I and Group II elements are the most reactive metals known. They react readily with oxygen of the air, with halogens, and with sulfur. All except beryllium react with water—some react spectacularly. In this section we shall:

1. Summarize the reactivity pattern of these elements, emphasizing some specific reactions and some trends in reactivity within each series, drawing comparisons between the two series.
2. Present a quantitative measure of the reactivity of the metals in water solutions.
3. Attempt to relate energy changes to chemical reactivity for representative members of the families.
4. Discuss two important reactions of the ions of these metals.

Group I
M, M$^+$

Group II
M, M^{+2}

Figure 8.4 Stable oxidation states.

Stable Oxidation States. The alkali elements exhibit only the 0 and I oxidation states in normal reactions, while the alkaline earth elements show only the 0 and II oxidation states. These are precisely those anticipated from families of elements having one or two valence electrons.

These elements are very reactive metals because the valence electrons are not tightly bound to the atom. This is illustrated by an examination of the ionization energies of the elements. In general, the reactivity increases with increasing atomic weight in each series in accord with opposite trends of the ionization energies (Table 8.2), indicating that the large atoms lose electrons more readily than the small ones. In several cases the Group II elements have especially high second ionization energies. In these cases the energy needed to remove the second electron from an atom must be supplied by some additional process if the divalent ion is to form. When the metal reacts with water, this additional reaction is that caused by the attraction of the metal ion for the dipolar water molecules. This reaction is highly exothermic for small divalent ions so that elements like magnesium and calcium form divalent ions in water in spite of the relatively high energies needed to remove their second electrons. When the metal reacts in the absence of a polar solvent, the additional reaction often is the formation of the ionic crystal lattice, which is a highly exothermic process.

Some Typical Reactions. The following equations represent some typical reactions of Group I and Group II metals.

Group I	*Group II*

With halogens (X = any halogen)
$$2M + X_2 \longrightarrow 2MX \text{ (halide)} \qquad\qquad M + X_2 \longrightarrow MX_2 \text{ (halide)}$$

With sulphur
$$16M + S_8 \longrightarrow 8M_2S \text{ (sulfide)} \qquad\qquad 8M + S_8 \longrightarrow 8MS \text{ (sulfide)}$$

With hydrogen
$$2M + H_2 \longrightarrow 2MH \text{ (hydride)} \qquad\qquad M + H_2 \longrightarrow MH_2 \text{ (halide)}$$
$$\text{(except Be and Mg)}$$

With nitrogen
$$6M + N_2 \xrightarrow{\text{spark}} 2M_3N \text{ (nitride)} \qquad\qquad 3M + N_2 \longrightarrow M_3N_2 \text{ (nitride)}$$

In nearly all of these reactions an increase in reactivity with increasing atomic number is observed within each family.

The alkali metals give some unexpected and unusual oxides in reactions with excess oxygen. These reactions are illustrated by the equations:

$$4Li + O_2 \longrightarrow 2Li_2O \text{ (lithium oxide)}$$

$$6Na + 2O_2 \longrightarrow 2Na_2O + Na_2O_2 \text{ (sodium oxide and sodium peroxide)}$$

$$3K + 2O_2 \longrightarrow K_2O_2 + KO_2 \text{ (potassium peroxide and potassium superoxide)}$$

$$Rb + O_2 \longrightarrow RbO_2 \text{ (rubidium superoxide)}$$

$$Cs + O_2 \longrightarrow CsO_2 \text{ (cesium superoxide)}$$

Only lithium gives the expected oxide, while sodium gives both the oxide and the peroxide. Potassium gives both a peroxide and a superoxide, while rubidium and cesium give a superoxide.

The peroxides contain the O_2^{-2} ion and the superoxides contain the O_2^{-1} ion. Both of these species are strong oxidizing agents. When lithium reacts with air the nitride as well as the oxide is formed.

Among the alkaline earth elements, beryllium, magnesium, and calcium yield monoxides on treatment with oxygen; strontium produces both a peroxide and a superoxide; barium gives a peroxide.

All of the alkali metals react with cold water according to the equation

$$2M + 2H_2O \longrightarrow 2M^+ + 2OH^- + H_2$$

giving strongly basic solutions. Lithium is somewhat slower in reacting than the others. This presumably is due to the fact that the heat of reaction is sufficient to melt the lower melting elements but is not sufficient to melt lithium. The liquid metals react considerably more vigorously than the solid metals.

The alkaline earth elements are somewhat more selective in their reaction with water. Beryllium will not react with water even at high temperatures; magnesium reacts readily with boiling water, while calcium, strontium, and barium react vigorously even with cold water in accordance with the equation

$$M + 2H_2O \longrightarrow M^{+2} + 2OH^- + H_2$$

Group I
Very strong
Group II
Strong

Figure 8.5 Strength of Group I and Group II metals as reducing agents.

Metals of both families react with aqueous solutions of acids according to the equations

$$2M + 2H_3O^+ \longrightarrow 2M^+ + H_2 + 2H_2O$$

$$M + 2H_3O^+ \longrightarrow M^{+2} + H_2 + 2H_2O$$

Strength as Reducing Agents. In all of their reactions these metals act as reducing agents; they are oxidized during the process. Since they are the most reactive metallic elements, they are also excellent reducing agents. A quantitative measure of their strength as reducing agents in *water* solutions is given by their own tendency to be oxidized. This tendency is measured by the oxidation potential obtained in experiments with electrochemical cells.

Table 8.6 Standard Oxidation Potentials for Group I and Group II Metals

Group I Elements	$E°$ Volts	Group II Elements	$E°$ Volts
$Li \rightleftarrows Li^+ + 1e^-$	3.045	$Be \rightleftarrows Be^{+2} + 2e^-$	1.85
$Na \rightleftarrows Na^+ + 1e^-$	2.71	$Mg \rightleftarrows Mg^{+2} + 2e^-$	2.37
$K \rightleftarrows K^+ + 1e^-$	2.92	$Ca \rightleftarrows Ca^{+2} + 2e^-$	2.87
$Rb \rightleftarrows Rb^+ + 1e^-$	2.92	$Sr \rightleftarrows Sr^{+2} + 2e^-$	2.89
$Cs \rightleftarrows Cs^+ + 1e^-$	3.08	$Ba \rightleftarrows Ba^{+2} + 2e^-$	2.90

The standard oxidation potential $E°$ indicates in volts the reducing strength of the substance in a $1M$* solution compared with the reducing strength of hydrogen taken as a standard.

Values for the standard oxidation potentials for the Group I and Group II elements are given in Table 8.6. These values show that the Group I elements are stronger reducing agents than Group II elements, as anticipated from a comparison of their ionization potentials.

● ● ●   THE OXIDATION POTENTIAL, $E°$

One of the most useful methods of indicating the strength of an atom, molecule, or ion as an oxidizing or a reducing agent *in solution* is by means of the quantity, $E°$, which indicates the ease of removal of electrons from the molecule, atom, or ion *in aqueous solution*. $E°$ is called the standard oxidation potential. The more positive the $E°$ value, the easier the atom or ion can be oxidized, and hence the better reducing agent it is.

The value of $E°$ for a metal is obtained as follows :

A voltaic cell is constructed containing hydrogen gas adsorbed on platinum (an inert electrode) in contact with a hydrochloric acid solution having a concentration of approximately one molar* as one electrode, and a metal in contact with a solution of one of its salts as the other electrode, and the voltage is measured when no current is flowing.

Consider such a cell in which the metal electrode is a strip of zinc immersed in a solution containing zinc ions. When the cell is connected, it is observed that electrons flow from the zinc to the hydrogen electrode. The cell voltage at 25°C is 0.76 volt when the H_3O^+ and Zn^{+2} concentrations are each very nearly 1 mole/liter*.

Since electrons flow from zinc to hydrogen in this cell, the zinc electrode reaction may be written

$$Zn \longrightarrow Zn^{+2} + 2e^-$$

---

* See Chap. 23 for a more precise statement concerning these concentrations.

Two Common Reactions of Ions. The ions of these elements undergo a number of reactions, two important ones being hydration (or solvation) and reduction.

Hydration Reactions. These involve the reaction of the ion with water. The attractive force here is the interaction of the positive charge on the ion with the negative end of the water dipole. Considerable heat is liberated in this process as shown in Table 8.7. These data show that the

Table 8.7. Hydration Energies of Group I and Group II Ions (in kcal/mole)

Li^+	Na^+	K^+	Rb^+	Cs^+	Be^{+2}	Mg^{+2}	Ca^{+2}	Sr^{+2}	Ba^{+2}
−123	−97	−77	−70	−63	−587	−460	−395	−355	−305

Note: The negative sign indicates energy is evolved.

hydration energies increase as the ions become smaller and as their charge increases. In the attraction of the ion for the water dipole, small, highly charged ions exert very strong attraction for water molecules.

The extraordinarily high oxidation potential for lithium (Table 8.6), near that of cesium, is the result of the additional driving force supplied by a strong exothermic reaction of lithium *ions* with water due to their small size. The effect of the large energy of hydration is such as to make lithium *in water solution* a better reducing agent than cesium in spite of the higher ionization energy of lithium. The other Group I ions also react with water but release less energy (see Table 8.7).

The equation for the hydration of ions may be written

$$M^+ + xH_2O \longrightarrow M(H_2O)_x{}^+$$

The values of x are not precisely known but are believed to be 4 for lithium and beryllium, 8 for barium, and 6 for all other members of the two families.

---

and the reaction at the hydrogen electrode is

$$2e^- + 2H_3O^+ \longrightarrow H_2 + 2H_2O$$

If the cell voltage is regarded as a sum of contributions from the two electrode systems,

$$E_{cell} = E_{H_2\ electrode} + E_{Zn\ electrode}$$

we can obtain relative values for the electrode voltages by assigning a value to one electrode system and relating all other electrode systems to this one.

In practice, the hydrogen electrode (at 25°C, 1 atm H_2 pressure, $1M$ HCl) is assigned a potential, known as the standard oxidation potential, $E°$, of 0. The standard oxidation potential, $E°$, of any electrode system can now be evaluated by measuring the voltage of a cell containing the desired electrode (at 25°C and having ionic concentrations of 1 mole/liter) and the standard hydrogen electrode. The zinc-hydrogen cell described above illustrates this method. Here the cell voltage is 0.76 volt, but since the $E°$ value for the hydrogen electrode is 0, the $E°$ for the zinc electrode becomes 0.76 volt.

Cells containing hydrogen electrodes and electrodes from other metals, and set up in the same way, are used to obtain $E°$ values for these metals.

The value of $E°$ can be used as a measure of the tendency of the oxidation reaction of the metal to go as written. If the data are obtained for a series of elements, we can then list these elements in the order of their relative reducing power in solution. Such a list is called the Electrochemical Series.

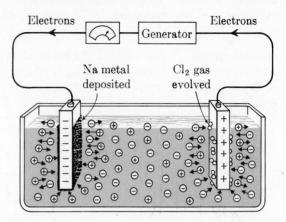

Figure 8.6 Electrolysis of molten sodium chloride. In the molten state, sodium chloride is composed of the ions of Na^+ and Cl^- in thermal motion. Such a liquid is an excellent conductor of an electric current. The positively charged ions will move to the negatively charged electrode and pick up electrons as shown by the half-reaction $Na^+ + e^- \rightarrow Na$ to become electrically neutral atoms; hence, the Na^+ ions are reduced.

At the positive electrode the chloride ions, Cl^-, give up electrons and become chlorine molecules, Cl_2. Hence, the Cl^- ions are oxidized.

Water tightly bonded to the ion often becomes a part of the framework of crystals. This is the case in hydrated salts such as $Na_2SO_4 \cdot 10H_2O$. Usually, hydrates are observed in salts containing small or highly charged cations, e.g., lithium, sodium, beryllium, magnesium, or calcium salts.

In many cases, the bonding forces of the metal ion are so strong that the H—O bond in the water molecule is weakened and the ion undergoes an acid-base reaction in which the ion acts as an acid and the water solvent acts as the base.

The hydrolysis reaction of hydrated beryllium ions is an example:

$$Be(H_2O)_4^{+2} + H_2O \rightleftharpoons Be(H_2O)_3OH^+ + H_3O^+$$

As a result, beryllium salts form solutions which are acidic. Aluminum, copper, zinc, and all small multivalent cations act in a similar manner; in fact, all small multivalent ions undergo hydrolysis reactions.

Reduction Reactions. Reduction of the ions in the alkali and alkaline earths involves converting (reducing) the ion to the metal *atom*. Strong reducing agents are needed for this reaction because the ions do not accept electrons readily; hence, they are extremely weak oxidizing agents. This is anticipated, for if the metal atoms lose electrons very readily, their ions will accept electrons only with some difficulty.

The most widely used process for reducing these ions is reaction at the cathode of an electrolysis cell (Figure 8.6). The method used is to electrolyze the fused salt. Thus the reaction

$$2MX \xrightarrow[\text{fused}]{\text{electrolysis}} 2M + X_2$$

is a general reaction for reduction of the metal ion and for the preparation of the metals.

Sodium is prepared in this way from fused sodium chloride; to this, sodium carbonate or calcium chloride is added to lower the melting temperature of the salt. Most of the magnesium produced today is obtained from sea water from which it is precipitated as the hydroxide. The hydroxide is dissolved in hydrochloric acid solution and magnesium is recovered by electrolysis of this solution. All of the other metals of these families are prepared by electrolysis.

Occasionally, an active metal is used to reduce the ion as in the processes

$$3BaO + 2Al \longrightarrow Al_2O_3 + 3Ba$$

$$KCl + Na \longrightarrow NaCl + K$$

Both of these processes take place at very high temperatures in the absence of oxygen. Their success is due to the relatively low boiling points of barium and potassium which evaporate from the reaction mixtures.

Occurrence. Calcium, sodium, potassium, and magnesium are among the most abundant elements in the earth's surface, ranking fifth, sixth, seventh, and eighth, respectively, in order of abundance (Table 8.8). The

Table 8.8 Distribution of Alkali and Alkaline Earth Elements in Nature

Element	Per Cent of Earth's Crust	Element	Per Cent of Earth's Crust
Lithium	4×10^{-5}	Beryllium	1×10^{-5}
Sodium	2.65	Magnesium	1.94
Potassium	2.40	Calcium	3.39
Rubidium	1×10^{-6}	Strontium	2×10^{-4}
Cesium	1×10^{-7}	Barium	5×10^{-2}
Francium		Radium	1×10^{-12}

remaining members of the two groups are present in relatively small amounts, with francium being almost nonexistent.

Because of their reactivity, all elements in both groups occur in nature in the combined state. Compounds of the alkali metals have high solubilities in water. Consequently the largest sources of these elements are the oceans and salt seas, or salt beds well protected from the contact with ground water. They also occur in a variety of clays which are not soluble in water. In general, compounds of the alkaline earth elements are much less water-soluble than are those of the alkali elements. As a result, some important sources of the Group II elements are insoluble deposits of compounds of alkaline earth metals such as the carbonates, sulfates, phosphates and some silicates. Tables 8.9 and 8.10 summarize the important minerals of the Group I and Group II elements.

Uses of the Metals. Sodium is the only alkali metal having wide commercial use, being used for the manufacture of soap, organic chemicals, dyes, tetraethyl lead, sodium peroxide, sodium cyanide, and a variety of other products. Liquid sodium has been used in nuclear reactors and in the centers of exhaust valves in aircraft engines because it is a rapid and effective heat conductor. This metal is also used as a reducing agent in the preparation of other metals from their chlorides.

Cesium and rubidium are used to a limited extent in photoelectric cells, because these metals emit electrons when visible light falls on them.

Beryllium is used in small quantities in alloys to harden the base metal. Certain alloys of beryllium in copper have a higher tensile strength than

Table 8.9 Mineral Sources of Several Alkali Metals

Metal	Mineral	Formula
Lithium	Amblygonite	$AlPO_4 \cdot LiF$
	Spodumene	$LiAl(SiO_3)_2$
	Lepidolite	$KLi_2Al(Si_4O_{10})(OH, F)_2$
Sodium	Halite	$NaCl$
	(rock salt)	
Potassium	Carnallite	$KCl \cdot MgCl_2 \cdot 6H_2O$
	Sylvite	KCl
Rubidium	Occurs in traces in several minerals	
Cesium	Pollucite	$H_2Cs_4Al(SiO_3)_9$

steel, make excellent springs, and are sometimes used in electric motors to reduce sparking.

Magnesium alloys have lightness and high tensile strength and consequently are used extensively in the construction of airplanes and portable tools. In addition, magnesium is used in incendiaries—signals and flares—because the metal emits an intense white light when it burns. An example of a magnesium compound is the chlorophyll of green plants.

Some Important Compounds of Group I and Group II Elements

Compounds of Sodium. Sodium compounds are some of the most numerous both in nature and in the laboratory. Most of the compounds are prepared from sodium chloride, since it is abundant and inexpensive. However, since all simple sodium compounds are soluble, the sodium compounds to be prepared cannot be obtained directly from the chloride

Table 8.10 Some Common Minerals Containing the Elements of Group II

METAL	MINERAL	
	Name	Formula
Beryllium	Beryl	$3 BeO \cdot Al_2O_3 \cdot 6SiO_2$
Magnesium	Magnesite	$MgCO_3$
	Talc, or soapstone	$H_2Mg_3(SiO_3)_4$
	Asbestos (Tremolite)	$CaMg_5Si_8O_{22}(OH)_2$
	Dolomite	$MgCO_3 \cdot CaCO_3$
	Spinel	$Mg(AlO_2)_2$
	Carnallite	$MgCl_2 \cdot KCl \cdot 6H_2O$
Calcium	Calcite	$CaCO_3$
	Gypsum	$CaSO_4 \cdot 2H_2O$
	Fluorspar	CaF_2
	Fluorapatite	$CaF_2 \cdot 3Ca_3(PO_4)_2$
Strontium	Strontianite	$SrCO_3$
	Celestite	$SrSO_4$
Barium	Barite	$BaSO_4$
	Witherite	$BaCO_3$
Radium	Usually in uranium ores (Chap. 28)	

by precipitation. Except for a few cases, it is found most economical either to change the chloride to the carbonate by a series of reactions known as the Solvay process or to change it to the hydroxide by electrolysis in aqueous solutions. The hydroxide and the carbonate then can be changed readily into other compounds.

The Preparation of Sodium Carbonate. In the United States most of the sodium carbonate is made from sodium chloride by a process devised by the Belgian chemical engineer Ernest Solvay and known as the Solvay process. In this process ammonia and carbon dioxide are passed into a concentrated solution of sodium chloride. This causes the formation of sparingly soluble sodium hydrogen carbonate which precipitates, is removed by filtration, and is changed to sodium carbonate by heating.

$$NH_3 + CO_2 + NaCl + H_2O \longrightarrow NaHCO_3 + NH_4Cl$$

$$2NaHCO_3 \xrightarrow{\text{heat}} Na_2CO_3 + CO_2 + H_2O$$

The ammonia can be recovered from the ammonium chloride by heating the ammonium chloride with calcium hydroxide.

$$2NH_4Cl + Ca(OH)_2 \longrightarrow 2NH_3 + 2H_2O + CaCl_2$$

The Preparation of Sodium Hydroxide. *The Electrolysis of* NaCl *Solution.* If a direct electric current is passed through an aqueous solution of sodium chloride, using platinum electrodes, the products of the reaction are found to be hydrogen, chlorine, and sodium hydroxide. Evidently water molecules decompose at the cathode, giving hydrogen and leaving hydroxide ions in solution. At the other electrode (anode) the chloride ions will give up their electrons readily. Hence chlorine gas is formed at this electrode. Thus, as the chloride ions are gradually converted to chlorine and are removed from solution, and as water molecules decompose, giving hydrogen and hydroxide ions, the two ions that predominate are sodium and hydroxide ions. This is the industrial process for making much of these three substances.

$$2NaCl + 2H_2O \xrightarrow{\text{electrolysis}} 2NaOH + H_2 + Cl_2$$

● ● ●   HISTORICAL

One of the earliest practical applications of electrochemistry was in the production of the alkali metals by Sir Humphry Davy in 1807. He had tried first to decompose saturated solutions of the alkali metals, but he succeeded only in decomposing water. He reported, "The presence of water appearing thus to prevent any decomposition, I used potash in igneous fusion" (October 6, 1807). To his surprise, on electrolysis of fused alkali he noticed a bright light and a flame at the negative electrode. When he reversed the current, he observed this flame again at the negative electrode. After several experiments he identified the metal which was being formed at the electrode and which was igniting in the air to give the flame and bright light as a new element. He named it potassium because he had obtained it from potash. A few days after isolation of potassium he prepared another new element, sodium, by the same electrolytic process. This work soon led to the discovery of the alkaline earth metals by a similar electrochemical method. Beryllium was discovered twenty years later by Wöhler, and radium by Madame Curie in 1898.

[*Note:* It should be stated that, contrary to the results obtained with platinum electrodes, if a mercury cathode (negative electrode) is used in the electrolysis of a sodium chloride solution instead of a platinum electrode, sodium rather than hydrogen is produced. This is due to the formation of a sodium-mercury amalgam.]

Preparation of NaOH *with* Na_2CO_3. This process consists in treating calcium hydroxide suspended in water with a solution of sodium carbonate. The reaction occurs because the calcium carbonate formed is only very slightly soluble.

$$Na_2CO_3 + Ca(OH)_2 \longrightarrow \underline{CaCO_3} + 2NaOH$$

Properties of Sodium Hydroxide. This compound is a white, crystalline, brittle solid. It is often called *caustic soda*. It is a corrosive substance and has a strong disintegrating action upon both animal and vegetable tissues. When exposed to the air it absorbs both moisture and carbon dioxide and is changed into sodium carbonate. It is very soluble in water, and a great deal of heat is liberated in the process of solution due to the hydration of the ions. Its solution has a soapy feel and a strong cleansing action.

Production and Uses of Sodium Hydroxide. About 5,800,000 tons of sodium hydroxide are produced annually in the United States (Table 8.11),

Table 8.11 Approximate Yearly production of Sodium Compounds

Compound	Tons	Compound	Tons
Chloride	19,000,000	Bicarbonate	5,000,000
Carbonate	5,576,000	Phosphate	1,103,000
Hydroxide	5,814,403	Chromate	133,872
Silicate	826,000	Metal	125,566
Sulfate	1,232,634		

more than half of which is prepared by the electrolytic process. The compound is used in many chemical industries. Large quantities are used in the manufacture of soap, rayon, and various chemicals; in the refining of petroleum; and in the preparation of wood pulp, from which paper is made.

In general, the methods of preparation of the compounds of the other alkali metals are similar because of their similar properties. The com-

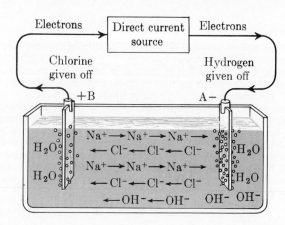

Figure 8.7 Electrolysis of aqueous sodium chloride. In industry more complex cells are used to prevent diffusion of the chlorine and hydrogen. One cell, called the Hooker cell, uses a diaphragm to prevent mixing of products; there are several other types of diaphragm cells. Another cell important in industry uses mercury as an amalgam—no hydrogen is released at this electrode. Two types of mercury cells in use are the Castner cell and the De Nora cell.

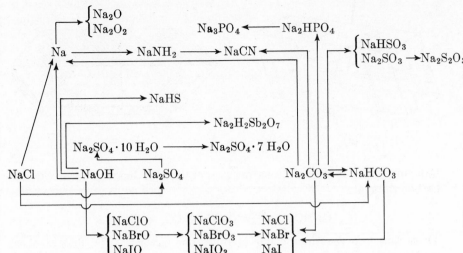

Figure 8.8 Steps in the preparation of important compounds of sodium starting with sodium chloride.

pounds of sodium have considerably wider use because they are more abundant and far less expensive than those of other metals.

Other Compounds of Sodium. Several compounds of sodium and routes for their preparation are indicated in Figure 8.8.

Calcium Compounds. In nature the most abundant calcium compound is calcium carbonate.

Calcium Carbonate. Calcium carbonate occurs in nature in two crystalline forms, calcite and aragonite. Marble is made up of minute, snow-white calcite crystals. In the impure form calcium carbonate occurs as limestone. It is used in agriculture to "sweeten" soil, in the building industry as a structural stone, and in the steel industry as a flux in blast furnaces.

Calcium carbonate reacts with acids to give CO_2:

$$CaCO_3 + 2HCl \longrightarrow CaCl_2 + H_2O + CO_2$$

The net reaction is:

$$CO_3^{-2} + 2H_3O^+ \longrightarrow 3H_2O + CO_2$$

On heating, calcium carbonate is converted to the oxide:

$$CaCO_3 \xrightarrow{heat} CaO + CO_2$$

The oxide reacts with water to form the hydroxide:

$$CaO + H_2O \longrightarrow Ca(OH)_2$$

Exposure of the oxide or hydroxide to the carbon dioxide in the air produces the carbonate:

$$Ca(OH)_2 + CO_2 \longrightarrow CaCO_3 + H_2O$$

Additional carbon dioxide causes the soluble bicarbonate to form

$$CaCO_3 + CO_2 + H_2O \longrightarrow Ca(HCO_3)_2$$

Figure 8.9 Natural crystals of calcite and aragonite, the two crystal forms of pure calcium carbonate: (a) Calcite; note the double refraction (birefrigence) property. (b) Aragonite.

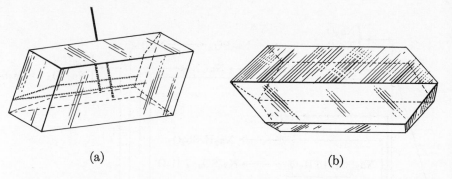

(a)   (b)

Calcium bicarbonate solutions on evaporation or heating form calcium carbonate again:

$$Ca(HCO_3)_2 \xrightarrow{heat} CaCO_3 + CO_2 + H_2O$$

These last two reactions occur in limestone caverns. The first of these explains the solvent action of carbonated water on limestone, thus causing the caverns, and the latter explains the formation of stalactites and stalagmites in the caverns.

Calcium Sulfate, $CaSO_4$. Calcium sulfate occurs in several forms, the most common of which is the hydrated calcium sulfate, $CaSO_4 \cdot 2H_2O$. It is used in making plaster, cement, fertilizers, and plaster of paris.

On being heated, gypsum loses water to form plaster of paris.

$$\underset{\text{Gypsum}}{2CaSO_4 \cdot 2H_2O} \rightleftharpoons \underset{\text{Plaster of paris}}{(CaSO_4)_2H_2O + 3H_2O}$$

The reaction is reversible and the reverse represents the reaction of the "setting" of plaster of paris.

Calcium Phosphate, $Ca_3(PO_4)_2$. Calcium phosphate is an insoluble compound which is converted to a soluble form as $CaHPO_4$ or $Ca(H_2PO_4)_2$ by acid and is used chiefly as a fertilizer.

Calcium Carbide, CaC_2. Calcium carbide is made by heating calcium oxide with coal or coke.

$$CaO + 3C \longrightarrow CaC_2 + CO$$

The importance of the carbide is in making acetylene, a very important compound for the production of many plastics and other organic compounds.

$$CaC_2 + H_2O \longrightarrow Ca(OH)_2 + C_2H_2$$

Magnesium Compounds. In nature magnesium is found chiefly as the carbonate and in salt brine and sea water. The compounds of magnesium are usually prepared from the carbonate, which is readily converted into other compounds by the action of acids.

Magnesium Carbonate, $MgCO_3$. Magnesium carbonate occurs in a number of localities as *magnesite*, which is usually amorphous but which sometimes forms crystals resembling calcite. More frequently magnesium carbonate is found associated with calcium carbonate. The mineral *dolomite* has the composition $CaCO_3 \cdot MgCO_3$. Limestone which contains smaller quantities of magnesium carbonate is known as *dolomitic limestone*. Dolomite is one of the most common rocks, forming whole mountain masses. It is harder and less readily attacked by acids than limestone. It is valuable as a building stone and for foundations, for lining certain types of furnaces, and as ballast for roadbeds.

Magnesium Oxide, MgO; *Magnesium Hydroxide*, $Mg(OH)_2$. Magnesium oxide, a very soft and light white powder, can be prepared by any of the general methods of preparing oxides. Commercially it is obtained by heating the carbonate and is known as *magnesia*. With water it forms the hydroxide, but the combination takes place rather slowly. Because of its highly infusible character (melting point, 2800°C), it is used in the manufacture of firebrick (as a lining for furnaces), for making crucibles, and for other purposes for which a highly refractory substance is needed. It is used also for making flooring, and for stucco and other cement building materials.

Magnesium hydroxide is but slightly soluble in water. When heated it is easily decomposed into the oxide and water. Magnesium salts as a rule are not toxic. Precipitated magnesium hydroxide is a white, insoluble, jellylike compound which acts as a milk alkali. Suspended in water (*milk of magnesia*), it is useful in neutralizing digestive acidity and as an antidote in acid poisoning.

Magnesium Sulfate, $MgSO_4$. Like the chloride, this salt is to be found in many salt beds, and deposits of the nearly pure compound occur in Wyoming and Washington. Commercially, it is prepared from the chloride. A number of hydrates are known. The monohydrate occurs as *kieserite*, but the form most commonly found is the heptahydrate, $MgSO_4 \cdot 7H_2O$, known, from its occurrence in the waters of the famous spring at Epsom, England, as *Epsom salt*.

Magnesium Silicates. Many silicates containing magnesium are known, and some of them are important substances. *Serpentine*, *asbestos*, *talc* (or *soapstone*), and *meerschaum* are examples of such substances.

SUMMARY

In this chapter we have examined the chemistry of the most reactive metals. We have seen that not only their reactivity but also their physical properties can be explained in terms of the electron configurations and ionization energies of their atoms, the sizes of their atoms and ions, and the crystal structure and binding in the metals. In addition we have introduced a quantitative measure of reactivity—the standard oxidation potential.

Once again we have applied the principles of oxidation-reduction, acid-base chemistry, and ion-dipole interactions to explain and to help us predict the behavior of these elements and their compounds. But we also have learned that not all properties are predictable in terms of our simple theory. For example, the reactions of the metals with oxygen give, in many cases, unexpected peroxides and superoxides.

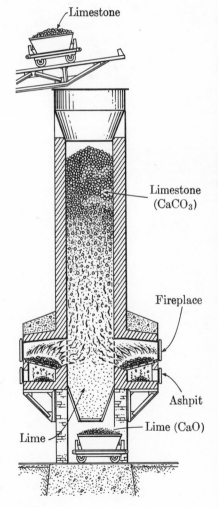

Figure 8.10 A vertical section of a limekiln.

SOME SPECIAL TERMS

Metal
  alkali metals
  alkaline earth metals
  nonmetal
  strength as reducing agent
Electrochemistry
  anode; cathode
  electrical conductivity
  electrolysis
  hydrogen electrode
  ionization energy
  oxidation potential

Energy changes
  heat of fusion
  heat of vaporization
  thermal conductivity
Compounds of metals
  gypsum
  lime (hydrated)
  limestone
  peroxide
  superoxide

QUESTIONS AND PROBLEMS

1. Predict the following properties of francium and radium from the data on the other members of those two families of elements: (a) ion size, (b) electron configuration, (c) ionization energy, (d) density, (e) oxidation state, (f) strength as reducing agent.

2. How do you account for the softness and high reactivity of the alkali metals as compared with the hardness and low reactivity of the alkaline earth metals?

3. Why is the second electron much more difficult to remove from the alkali metal atoms than the first electron?

4. How do you account for the fact that the ionic radii of the alkali and alkaline earth metals increase as the atomic weights increase?

5. What factors are involved in causing the densities of the alkali metals to increase as the masses and atomic radii increase?

6. How do you account for the low melting points of the alkali metals as compared to other metals?

7. The range between the melting point and the boiling point is much greater for metals than for water, ammonia, and other liquids. What does this suggest with reference to metallic bonds? Explain.

8. Describe the nature of the bond between atoms in metals which makes it possible to explain high electrical and thermal conductivity.

9. How many grams of bromine are required to oxidize 10 g of sodium from Na° to Na^+?

10. Calculate the number of grams of NaOH formed when a sufficient amount of sodium reacts with water to form 10 g of hydrogen.

11. How do you account for the fact that a small atom such as lithium has almost the same E° value as a large atom such as cesium?

12. In terms of E° values, which of the following in each pair of elements is the best reducing agent? (a) Li and Cs, (b) K and Mg, (c) Ba and Na, and (d) Li and Ba.

13. Compare the reactions that occur when (a) fused sodium chloride is electrolyzed and (b) a solution of sodium chloride is electrolyzed. Explain why any difference in the two processes occurs.

14. Describe a process, together with any equilibria involved, for the following preparations: (a) Na_2CO_3 from NaCl, (b) NaCl from Na_2CO_3, and (c) NaOH from NaCl.

15. (a) Calculate the per cent of sodium in Na_2CO_3. (b) Calculate the per cent of chlorine in $KCl \cdot MgCl_2 \cdot 6H_2O$.

16. Describe several uses of (a) $NaOH$; (b) $NaHCO_3$; (c) Na_3PO_4; (d) $CaSO_4$; (e) $Ca_3(PO_4)_2$; (f) $CaCO_3$.

17. Give equations for the following reactions: (a) "burning" limestone, (b) hydration of calcium oxide, (c) reaction of carbon dioxide with hydrated lime, (d) setting of plaster of paris, (e) sweetening the soil with lime, (f) formation of stalactites and stalagmites in limestone caverns, and (g) formation of acetylene from calcium carbide.

18. Write the equation for the neutralization of calcium hydroxide with sulfuric acid. Calculate the weight of calcium hydroxide required to neutralize 500 g of sulfuric acid.

REFERENCES

FERN, W. O. "Potassium," *Scientific American*, vol. *181*, no. 2 (1949), p. 16.

GILMAN, H., and J. J. EISCH. "Lithium," *Scientific American*, vol. *208*, no. 1 (1963), p. 88.

HEILBRUNN, L. V. "Calcium and Life," *Scientific American*, vol. *184*, no. 6 (1951), p. 60.

SCHUBERT, J. "Beryllium and Berylliosis," *Scientific American*, vol. *199*, no. 2 (1958), p. 27.

WILLIAMS, L. P. "Humphry Davy," *Scientific American*, vol. *202*, no. 6 (1960), p. 106.

9

The Halogen Family: A Family of Nonmetals

*The mother liquor from seaweed ash contains quite a large quantity
of a very peculiar and curious substance. . . . The substance which
is precipitated in the form of a black, shining powder immediately
after the addition of sulfuric acid, rises, when heated, in vapor of
a superb violet color . . . the vapor condenses in the form of very
brilliant crystalline plates having a luster equal to that of crystalline lead sulfide.*   Nicolas Clement (1779–1841)

In the preceding chapter the chemistry of two families of *metals* was
discussed. In this chapter the chemistry of the halogen family—fluorine,
chlorine, bromine, iodine, and astatine—will be presented. So little is
known about astatine that we shall not discuss its properties here. This
family of elements constitutes Group VII of the periodic table and contains
some of the most reactive *nonmetals*.

It is our plan here to point out those properties characteristic of the
halogens and their compounds; to illustrate the trends in these properties
in proceeding from one halogen to another; and to relate these characteristic properties and their trends to atomic structure, atomic or ionic size,
and electronegativity.

A Broad Overview of the Halogen Family

The halogens differ from the metals of Group I and Group II in three
especially important properties:

1. The atoms of the halogen elements need only one more electron to
give them a stable noble gas configuration. The metals of Group I and
Group II have but one or two valence electrons beyond a noble gas configuration. Table 9.1 gives the electron configurations of the halogen
atoms.

2. The electronegativity of the halogens is the highest of any family of
elements and much higher than that of the Group I and Group II metals.
Compare, for example, the electronegativity of lithium (1.00) and strontium (1.00) with that of fluorine (4.0) and iodine (2.5).

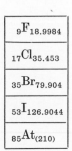

$_9F_{18.9984}$

$_{17}Cl_{35.453}$

$_{35}Br_{79.904}$

$_{53}I_{126.9044}$

$_{85}At_{(210)}$

Figure 9.1 The halogen elements.

174

Element	Electron Configuration
Fluorine	$\boxed{1s^2}\ 2s^2\ 2p^5$
Chlorine	$\boxed{1s^2\ 2s^2\ 2p^6}\ 3s^2\ 3p^5$
Bromine	$\boxed{1s^2\ 2s^2\ 2p^6\ 3s^2\ 3p^6\ 3d^{10}}\ 4s^2\ 4p^5$
Iodine	$\boxed{1s^2\ 2s^2\ 2p^6\ 3s^2\ 3p^6\ 3d^{10}\ 4s^2\ 4p^5\ 4d^{10}}\ 5s^2\ 5p^5$

Table 9.1 Electron Configurations of the Atoms of the Halogen Elements

3. Except for fluorine the halogens exhibit a variety of oxidation states whereas the Group I and Group II elements show only two oxidation states (zero and one other). Chlorine, for example, forms stable species in the $-\text{I}$, 0, I, III, IV, V, and VII oxidation states. Examples of halogen species in the various oxidation states are given in Table 9.2.

Oxidation State	Fluorine	Chlorine	Bromine	Iodine
VII		$HClO_4$		HIO_4, H_5IO_6
V		$HClO_3$	$HBrO_3$	HIO_3
III		$HClO_2$		
I		$HClO$	$HBrO$	HIO
0	F_2	Cl_2	Br_2	I_2
$-$I	F^-	Cl^-	Br^-	I^-

Table 9.2 Some Halogen Species in Various Oxidation States

Bonding. Because of their high electronegativity the halogen elements usually form ionic bonds when combined with elements having low electronegativity (the metals). In such compounds the halogens will exist as negative ions as in sodium chloride or potassium iodide. In combination with hydrogen or other nonmetals—elements with moderate to high electronegativity—the halogens form covalent bonds—e.g., hydrogen chloride, HCl, dichlorine oxide, Cl_2O, and nitrogen trifluoride, NF_3. This change in bond type with its accompanying change in properties is illustrated in Table 9.3, in which the melting points of the fluorides and chlorides of the elements of the third period of the periodic table are recorded. Most compounds of the halogens with the metals have the high melting points characteristic of ionic bonding; compounds of the halogens with nonmetals have the low melting points characteristic of covalent bonding.

In general, the stability of the covalent compounds of the halogens increases as the differences in electronegativity between the halogen and the

● ● ● IMPORTANT PROPERTIES OF THE HALOGEN FAMILY

1. Their atoms have high electronegativity.
2. They exhibit multiple oxidation states ($-$I to VII).
3. Bonding varies from covalent, X_2, to ionic, NaX.
4. Many are strong oxidizing agents.
5. They form a variety of oxyacids, HXO_n.

other nonmetals increases. The most stable halogen species appears to be the halide ion X^-. This species not only possesses a noble gas configuration but in it none of the electrons is shared with other elements.

Table 9.3 Melting Points of Fluorine and Chlorine Compounds of Third-Period Elements

Compound	NaF	MgF$_2$	AlF$_3$	SiF$_4$	PF$_3$	S$_2$F$_2$	ClF
Melting point (°C)	995	1263	1290	−90.3	−151.3	−120.5	−155.6
Compound	NaCl	MgCl$_2$	AlCl$_3$	SiCl$_4$	PCl$_3$	S$_2$Cl$_2$	Cl$_2$
Melting point (°C)	808	714	192	−68	−92	−77	−102.4

Positive Oxidation States. The positive oxidation states exhibited by the halogens may be thought of as arising when the halogen atom uses one or more of its valence electrons to form covalent bonds with elements of higher electronegativity, as in dichlorine oxide, Cl_2O. Here the chlorine has a I oxidation state,

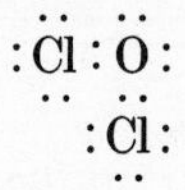

$$:\overset{..}{\underset{..}{Cl}}:\overset{..}{\underset{..}{O}}:$$
$$:\overset{}{\underset{..}{Cl}}:$$

Dichlorine oxide

and the oxygen has a −II oxidation state. Other examples are perchloric acid, $HClO_4$, and bromic acid, $HBrO_3$, as illustrated below. Here the chlorine is using seven valence electrons in bond formation and has an oxidation state of VII; and the bromine atom is using five valence electrons in bond formation and has a V oxidation state.

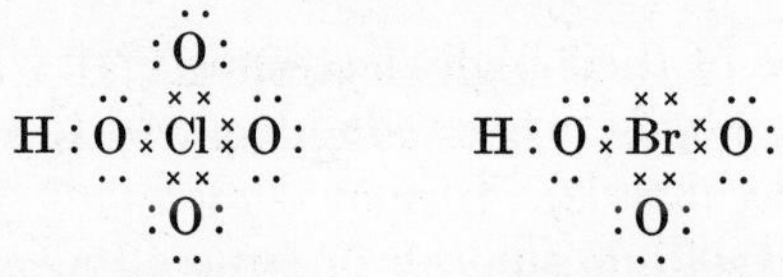

Perchloric acid   Bromic acid

The highest stable oxidation state of the halogens is the VII state, in which all seven valence electrons in the halogen atom are used in bond formation. Perchloric acid is an example of a halogen compound containing chlorine in its highest oxidation state. The V, III, and I states also exist and represent cases in which the halogen has one, two, or three fewer covalent bonds than in perchloric acid.

Oxidizing Agents. The great stability of the halide ion, X^-, accounts for the observation that the halogens and their compounds in all but the −I oxidation state range from good to strong oxidizing agents. Evidently there is a strong tendency for the species of higher oxidation state to revert to the most stable state. For example, potassium chlorate, $KClO_3$, is a strong oxidizing agent. Here chlorine is in the V oxidation state. The resultant chlorine-containing product of most reactions in which potassium *chlorate* acts as an oxidizing agent is potassium *chloride*; in this, chlorine is in its very stable −I state.

Acids. The halogens combine with hydrogen or with hydrogen and oxygen to form numerous acids. All four acids of the general formula HX are known and all but hydrofluoric acid, $(HF)_x$, are strong acids in water. In the positive oxidation states chlorine, bromine, and iodine form a number of oxyacids. These compounds have the formula HXO_n where n may vary from one to four as shown in Table 9.2. The strength of these oxyacids increases with increase in electronegativity of the halogen for a fixed value of n, and it increases as n increases for a given halogen. A detailed examination of the reasons for these changes in acid strength will be presented later.

Occurrence. Because of their high reactivity, the halogen elements are not found in nature in the free state. All four members are found in the form of the very stable halide ions in sea water.

Most of the fluorine is found in the minerals cryolite, Na_3AlF_6, and fluorspar, CaF_2. The principal sources of chlorine and bromine are sea water, brine wells, and mineral deposits. Sodium and chloride ions make up about 2.5 per cent of sea water. The most important source of iodine is the sodium iodate found in the huge nitrate deposits of northern Chile.

It is estimated that fluorine occurs to the extent of 0.1 per cent in the earth's crust, and that chlorine, bromine, and iodine make up 0.2, 0.001, and 0.001 per cent of the earth's crust, respectively.

Uses. Large quantities of fluorine, which is now available commercially, are used in the preparation of fluorine-containing hydrocarbons (called fluorocarbons), such as (a) the Freons, used as refrigerants and as the inert pressurizing ingredient in cans of hair spray, insecticide, etc., and (b) plastics such as Teflon, an excellent insulator and chemically inert material suitable for containers for corrosive chemicals. Hydrogen fluoride is an important intermediate in a number of industrial processes including the manufacture of high-octane gasolines.

Chlorine is one of the most important industrial chemicals. It is used as a bleaching agent, especially for wood pulp and paper and for cotton cloth. Compounds of chlorine such as the hypochlorites are used as bleaching agents and disinfectants.

Strong oxidizing agents such as the chlorates are used in explosives and propellants. Other uses of chlorine include the manufacture of important organic compounds used as drugs and dyes. Because of its painful and destructive physiological effects chlorine was the first war gas used.

The demand for bromine has fluctuated greatly in recent years. Potassium and sodium bromides find use as medicinal agents, and silver bromide is used in photography. Today a chief use of bromine is in the preparation of ethylene dibromide, a constituent of "ethyl gasoline." It is also used in the manufacture of certain dyes and other organic compounds.

The chief use of iodine is in the manufacture of potassium and sodium iodides and of certain organic drugs and dyes. Silver iodide (AgI) is an important compound of iodine used in photography. The ordinary *tincture of iodine*, used largely as an antiseptic, is a solution of iodine and potassium iodide in alcohol; a colloidal dispersion of the element is also used for the same purpose. Iodine is also a valuable reagent in the laboratory.

Properties of the Halogen Elements

The halogen elements occur as the diatomic molecules F_2, Cl_2, Br_2, and I_2. The single covalent bond between the atoms enables each atom to obtain a stable electron configuration, as illustrated below.

These elements are very reactive oxidizing agents; fluorine is the most reactive, followed by chlorine, bromine, and iodine in that order.

Physical Properties. Some physical properties of the halogen elements are given in Table 9.4. The *melting* and *boiling points* and the *heats of*

Table 9.4 Some Physical Properties of the Halogen Elements

Element	Density (g/cc)	Melting Point (°C)	Boiling Point (°C)	Heat of Fusion (kcal/ mole)	Heat of Vaporiza- tion (kcal/mole)	Color of Gas
Fluorine	1.108	−219.62	−187.9	0.061	0.782	Pale yellow
Chlorine	1.57	−102.4	−34.0	0.77	2.439	Yellow- green
Bromine	3.14	−7.2	58.2	1.26	3.59	Brown- red
Iodine	4.942	113.6	184.2	1.87	4.99	Violet

fusion and *vaporization* are very low, suggesting that the forces of attraction among X_2 molecules are not strong. All four of these properties rise systematically in proceeding from fluorine to iodine (Table 9.4), indicating that the attractive forces increase regularly in the order of increasing atomic number from fluorine to iodine (as illustrated in Figure 9.2). This increase has been attributed to an increase in the polarizability of the atoms as the atomic diameter increases. This variation in attractive forces presumably is the reason iodine is a solid and bromine is a liquid, while both fluorine and chlorine are gases at room temperature and pressure.

The *color* of the halogen element is the result of the absorption of certain wavelengths of visible light. The energy absorbed excites valence electrons to higher energy levels. The energy difference between the excited state and the ground state changes in the same order as do the ionization potentials of the atoms F > Cl > Br > I (Table 9.5). This means that short wavelength photons are required to excite fluorine, but progressively longer wavelength photons are required to excite chlorine, bromine, and iodine. As a consequence, fluorine absorbs short wavelength violet radiation and appears yellow while iodine absorbs longer wavelength yellow and green light and appears violet.

Properties of Atoms. Table 9.5 lists the electronegativities, atomic and ionic radii, and X—X bond energies of the halogens. As stated earlier these elements have a very high electronegativity—fluorine has the highest electronegativity of all the elements. In proceeding down the family the

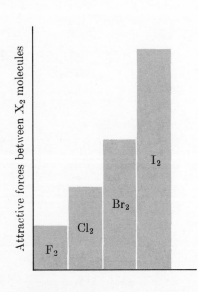

Figure 9.2 Attractive forces between halogen molecules.

Table 9.5 Some Properties of the Halogen Atoms, Molecules, and Ions

Element	Electro-negativity of Atom	Ionization Energy (kcal/mole)	Atomic Radius (A)	Ionic Radius (A)	X—X Bond Energy (kcal/mole)
Fluorine	4.0	402	0.72	1.36	36
Chlorine	3.0	300	0.99	1.81	57
Bromine	2.8	273	1.14	1.95	45
Iodine	2.5	241	1.33	2.16	35

electronegativity decreases. However, even iodine has a relatively high electronegativity, for only oxygen, nitrogen, and the other halogens have higher values.

Both the *atomic* and *ionic* radii of the halogen atoms and the halide ions increase regularly from fluorine to iodine as illustrated in Figure 9.3. The atomic radii are determined from the X—X bond distance in halogen molecules while the ionic radii are determined from X-ray studies of crystals containing halide ions. The halide ion is invariably larger than the corresponding atom. This is due in part to a greater repulsion among the valence electrons in the ion compared with that in the atom, and in part to the fact that atomic radii are one-half the X—X bond distance which actually is shorter than one-half the atomic diameter (Figure 9.3).

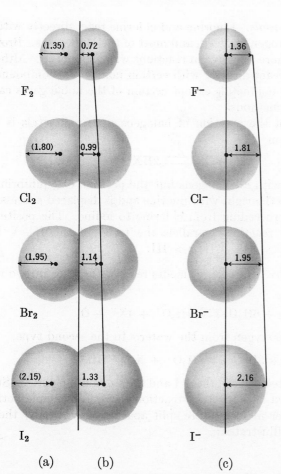

F₂ (1.35) 0.72   F⁻ 1.36

Cl₂ (1.80) 0.99   Cl⁻ 1.81

Br₂ (1.95) 1.14   Br⁻ 1.95

I₂ (2.15) 1.33   I⁻ 2.16

(a)   (b)   (c)

Figure 9.3 Relative sizes of halogen atoms and halide ions. Note the differences among the van der Waals radii (a), the covalent radii (b), and the ionic radii (c) for these elements.

Dissociation Energies. The energy needed to dissociate the halogen molecules into atoms decreases regularly from chlorine to iodine, indicating that the covalent bond in iodine is weaker than that in chlorine, Cl_2, or in bromine, Br_2. This is the order of the decrease in the ability of the various atoms to attract electrons.

Fluorine has a much lower dissociation energy than chlorine, which is somewhat surprising in view of its higher electronegativity. No completely satisfactory explanation for this observation has been reported. However, it has been suggested that the F—F bond is weakened because nonbonding electrons in the small, very stiff and nonpolarizable fluorine atom repel the bonding electrons to the point of weakening the bond considerably.

The X—X bond energies are important factors in the reactions of halogen molecules because energy is required to break these bonds if the reactions are to proceed.

Chemical Properties. In a great many of their reactions the halogens act as oxidizing agents, being reduced to the $-I$ oxidation state in the process. The chemical properties of these elements may be summarized with four types of reactions:

Reaction with Metals. Fluorine and chlorine react directly with all metals to give metal halides; bromine and iodine are somewhat less reactive but react directly with all but the noble metals such as gold and platinum.

Reaction with Nonmetals. Fluorine and chlorine react directly with all nonmetals except nitrogen, oxygen, and most of the inert gases. Bromine and iodine are even more selective in reactions with nonmetals. Although the halogens do not react directly with certain nonmetals, compounds of the halogens with all nonmetals except certain of the noble gases can be prepared by indirect methods.

A good example of the reaction of halogens with nonmetals is their reaction with hydrogen:

$$H_2 + X_2 \rightleftharpoons 2HX$$

This reaction occurs with all halogens but the position of equilibrium at $298°K$ lies farthest to the right with fluorine and is displaced successively more to the left in proceeding from chlorine to iodine. The position of equilibrium in these reactions parallels the trend of the H—X bond energies which is $HF > HCl > HBr > HI$.

Reactions with Water. Halogen elements react with water in two ways. In the first type,

$$2X_2 + 6H_2O \rightleftharpoons 4H_3O^+ + 4X^- + O_2 \tag{1}$$

the halogen displaces oxygen from the water. In the second type,

$$X_2 + 2H_2O \rightleftharpoons H_3O^+ + X^- + HOX \tag{2}$$

the halogen is converted to both the $-I$ and the I oxidation states. Such a reaction may be called an hydrolysis reaction, since in principle both the halogen and the water molecules are split apart giving initially the HX and XOH species as illustrated:

$$\begin{array}{c} \text{X} \quad \text{O—H} \\ | \; + \; | \\ \text{X} \quad \text{H} \end{array} \longrightarrow \begin{bmatrix} \text{X---O—H} \\ \vdots \quad \vdots \\ \text{X---H} \end{bmatrix} \longrightarrow \begin{array}{c} \text{X—OH} \\ \\ \text{X—H} \end{array}$$

The HX species, a strong acid, ionizes almost completely in water giving hydronium ions and X^- ions.

The first reaction—displacement of oxygen—proceeds very rapidly with fluorine and much less rapidly with the other halogens. The second reaction is not observed with fluorine because the first process is so rapid and complete. However, chlorine, bromine, and iodine all hydrolyze to some extent in water.

Interestingly, all halogens react with hydrogen sulfide, H_2S, to displace sulfur in a reaction similar to reaction (1) above.

$$8X_2 + 8H_2S \longrightarrow 16HX + S_8 \qquad (3)$$

This behavior with respect to hydrogen sulfide suggests that the ready occurrence of reaction (1) requires that the electronegativity of the halogen be greater than that of oxygen. All of the halogens are more electronegative than sulfur and all react readily according to Equation (3).

Reactions with Other Reducing Agents. The halogen elements will react with (are reduced by) strong and moderately strong reducing agents such as sulfides, sulfites, arsine, AsH_3, many metal ions such as tin(II) ion, Sn^{+2}, iron(II), Fe^{+2}, and vanadyl ion, VO^{+2}, and a great many organic compounds.

Formation of Polyhalide Anions. Anions such as I_3^-, IBr_2^-, and ICl_2^- are formed in solution and are stable in salts with large cations.

Oxidation Potentials. The values of the standard oxidation potentials, E°, for the halide ions are given in Table 9.6. The values are a measure of the tendency for the reaction

$$X^- \rightleftarrows \tfrac{1}{2}X_2 + e^- \qquad (4)$$

to occur in water at 25°C. The negative values indicate that the reactions proceed only with difficulty and that the reaction involving fluoride is the most difficult—i.e., has the largest negative value. Conversely, the reaction with iodide, though difficult, proceeds more readily than the others. In essence this means that in water solution fluoride ions lose electrons only with great difficulty while iodide ions do so with less difficulty.

Equation (4) represents an oxidation (the halogen changes from the $-I$ to the 0 oxidation state) so the E° values are measures of the relative strengths of X^- ions as reducing agents. Evidently iodide ion can be oxidized most easily of the group and must therefore be the strongest

Table 9.6 Standard Oxidation Potentials for Halide Ions

Conversion	E° (volts)
$F^- \rightarrow \tfrac{1}{2}F_2 + 1e^-$	-2.87
$Cl^- \rightarrow \tfrac{1}{2}Cl_2 + 1e^-$	-1.36
$Br^- \rightarrow \tfrac{1}{2}Br_2 + 1e^-$	-1.07
$I^- \rightarrow \tfrac{1}{2}I_2 + 1e^-$	-0.53

reducing agent of the group. By the same reasoning fluoride ion is the most difficult to oxidize so it must be the weakest reducing agent of this group of poor reducing agents.

The reverse of the reaction represented by Equation (4)—i.e.,

$$e^- + \tfrac{1}{2}X_2 \rightleftarrows X^- \tag{5}$$

is a reduction, and the $E°$ values with their signs reversed are measures of the ease with which these reactions occur. In this case fluorine has the largest and iodine the smallest tendency to be reduced with all reactions being strongly favored. Evidently then, fluorine is the strongest oxidizing agent and iodine is the weakest in this group of strong oxidizing agents. This trend is in accord with electronegativity considerations which indicate that fluorine should attract electrons more strongly than does iodine.

Preparation of the Halogen Elements

In most cases the halogen elements are prepared by oxidizing the halide ions, which are the largest natural source of the halogens. Compounds of iodine in the V or VII oxidation state occur in nature; these compounds must be reduced to produce the free element (the 0 oxidation state species).

Use of Oxidizing Agents. If the naturally occurring halide ions are used to prepare the halogen elements, an oxidizing agent must be used to oxidize the halide ion from its $-I$ to the 0 oxidation state. The general reaction then becomes

$$X^- + \text{oxidizing agent} \rightleftarrows \tfrac{1}{2}X_2 + \text{reduced form of oxidizing agent} \tag{6}$$

Since the X_2 species is itself an oxidizing agent, the oxidizing agent used should be at least as strong as X_2 if the reaction is to proceed very far to the right before equilibrium is established.* A number of oxidizing agents or systems have been used but the following three are used most often.

Electrolysis (Oxidation by an Anode Reaction). The fused halide salts of all the halogens can be electrolyzed to give the halogen element and the metal of the salt used (Figure 8.6). For example, the electrolysis of fused sodium chloride gives chlorine at the anode and sodium at the cathode. The over-all reaction is

$$NaCl \xrightarrow[\text{electrolyzed}]{\text{fused}} Na + \tfrac{1}{2}Cl_2$$

At the anode the reaction is

$$Cl^- \longrightarrow \tfrac{1}{2}Cl_2 + e^-$$

---

* Under certain conditions a weaker oxidizing agent may be used. For example, if one of the products is removed from the reaction mixture as fast as it is formed, the reverse reaction in Equation (6) is prevented from taking place. Meanwhile the forward reaction will proceed at its normal pace. The result will be a continuous production of product which can be removed rapidly. Thus a slightly weaker oxidizing agent may produce amounts of product in a *nonequilibrium* situation which it could not produce under equilibrium conditions.

This method can be used for all the halogens and is the only method suitable for the preparation of fluorine. For fluorine preparation, cells of Monel metal or copper must be used because of the great reactivity of this halogen.

Chlorine, bromine, and iodine can be prepared also by electrolyzing water solutions of their halide salts. However, in fluoride solutions water is decomposed at the anode more easily than fluoride ion is oxidized; hence oxygen is produced rather than fluorine gas. Dilute solutions containing chloride ions give both oxygen and chlorine when electrolyzed, suggesting that the ease with which water is decomposed and the ease of discharge of chloride ion are of the same order of magnitude.

Manganese Dioxide. Acid solutions containing chloride, bromide, or iodide ions give the corresponding halogens upon reaction with a strong oxidizing agent such as manganese dioxide. The reaction may be represented:

$$2X^- + 4H_3O^+ + MnO_2 \rightleftharpoons Mn^{+2} + X_2 + 6H_2O$$

This method is commonly used to prepare small quantities of the halogen elements in the laboratory.

Manganese dioxide, a weaker oxidizing agent than fluorine, is stronger than bromine or iodine and just slightly weaker than chlorine. The oxidation of chloride ion is successful because the gaseous chlorine escapes from the reaction mixture so that equilibrium is never established.

Manganese, in the course of this reaction, is reduced from the IV to the II oxidation state.

A Stronger Oxidizing Halogen. The oxidizing strength of the halogen elements decreases in the order $F_2 > Cl_2 > Br_2 > I_2$, as indicated earlier. Conversely, the reducing strength of halide ions is in the opposite order, increasing regularly from fluoride to iodide ion. This means that while fluorine attracts electrons strongly, iodide ion loses electrons relatively easily.

These facts can be used to select methods of preparing the weaker oxidizing halogens from stronger ones. For example, in the reaction

$$\tfrac{1}{2}Cl_2 + I^- \rightleftharpoons \tfrac{1}{2}I_2 + Cl^-$$

the position of equilibrium lies far to the right because chlorine is a stronger oxidizing agent than iodine and iodide ion is a stronger reducing agent than chloride ion. As indicated in Chap. 7, the equilibrium lies in favor of the weaker oxidizing and reducing agents.

This situation may be generalized as follows: A stronger oxidizing halogen can be used to prepare a weaker oxidizing halogen from its anion. In practice, chlorine water is used to produce bromine and iodine from bromides and iodides, respectively. Such reactions are not limited to halogens but apply equally well to other nonmetals and to their ions.

Use of Reducing Agents. Potassium iodate and potassium periodate, found in Chile saltpeter, can be reduced to iodine. Sodium hydrogen sulfite—an inexpensive reducing agent—can be used. The reaction may be represented:

$$2H_3O^+ + 2IO_3^- + 5HSO_3^- \longrightarrow I_2 + 5HSO_4^- + 3H_2O$$

Much commercially available iodine is prepared in this way.

Some Compounds of the Halogens

Interhalogens. Compounds formed between two different halogens are called interhalogens. The best known of these is iodine monochloride, ICl, which is used as an indicator and in the synthesis of other iodine compounds. Examples of some interhalogen compounds which have been made and characterized are given in Table 9.7.

Table 9.7 Some Interhalogen Compounds

ClF	BrCl	BrF	IF
			ICl
ClF$_3$		BrF$_3$	ICl$_3$
		BrF$_5$	IF$_5$
			IF$_7$

The existence of compounds of the type XY_n where n is three or more is probably due to the fact that larger halogen atoms may use d orbitals as well as s and p orbitals in bonding.

Interhalogens are usually prepared by the reaction of two halogen elements with each other. For example, fluorine reacts with moist chlorine at 25°C to give chlorine fluoride, ClF, according to the reaction

$$F_2 + Cl_2 \xrightarrow{\text{water vapor}} 2ClF$$

The reactions of the interhalogens are not very different from those of the halogen elements. For example, reactions of the type

$$ICl + 2H_2O \longrightarrow HOI + H_3O^+ + Cl^-$$

proceed so that the more electronegative halogen appears in the $-I$ oxidation state and the less electronegative halogen appears in the I oxidation state.

The structures of IF$_5$ and IF$_7$ are interesting because the iodine atoms have 12 and 14 electrons, respectively, in their valence shells. In the former the structure is a square pyramid.

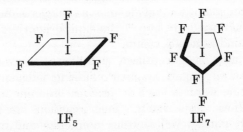

IF$_5$ IF$_7$

In the latter it is believed to be a pentagonal bipyramid. In both cases the iodine atoms appear to be using hybridized orbitals formed from s, p, and d atomic orbitals. In the formulas written above, the geometry or stereochemistry of the structure is being emphasized. Hence the lines between atoms are not to be regarded as bonds, but as guides to help visualize the shape of the structure. In these formulas a covalent bond connects each fluorine atom to the central iodine atom.

The Hydrogen Halides and Halide Ions. Some properties of the hydrogen halides are listed in Table 9.8. From the relative magnitudes of *bond*

Table 9.8 Some Properties of the Hydrogen Halides

Properties	Compound			
	HF	HCl	HBr	HI
Bond length (A)	0.917	1.275	1.410	1.62
Dipole moment (D*)	1.91	1.03	0.80	0.42
Bond energy (kcal/mole)	135	102	87	71
Melting point (°C)	− 83.07	− 114.19	− 86.86	− 50.79
Boiling point (°C)	19.9	− 85.03	− 66.72	− 35.35
Heat of fusion (kcal/mole)	1.094	0.4750	0.5751	0.6863
Heat of vaporization (kcal/mole)	7.24	3.86	4.210	4.724
Approximate ionization constant (K_{Ion} at 25°C)	10^{-4}	10^7	10^9	10^{11}

* One Debye unit (D) is 1×10^{-18} e.s.u.-cm.

length, dipole moment, and *bond energy* it is apparent that in passing from hydrogen fluoride to hydrogen iodide: (a) the H—X bond distance increases regularly as the size of the halogen atom increases; (b) the polarity of the H—X bond decreases regularly as the halogen atom decreases in electronegativity; and (c) the H—X bond energy decreases, indicating that hydrogen iodide can be dissociated into atoms more easily than can hydrogen fluoride. The relative sizes of the four HX molecules are shown in Figure 9.4.

Physical Properties. The relatively low values of the *melting* and *boiling points* and the *heats of fusion* and *vaporization* (Table 9.8) indicate that the forces of attraction between molecules are relatively weak except in hydrogen fluoride, in which hydrogen bonding significantly increases the boiling point, melting point, and the heat of fusion. Hydrogen bonding is also responsible for the excellent solvent properties of *liquid* hydrogen fluoride, which acts like an assembly of very large aggregates of hydrogen fluoride molecules.

Interestingly, the melting and boiling points of the other three HX acids increase in the order HCl < HBr < HI (Figure 6.22). This suggests that the attractive forces between molecules also increase in this order. Since the polarity of the molecules is greatest in HCl and least in HI, evidently van der Waals forces are more important here than are the polar forces.

Chemical Properties. As *reducing agents* the HX compounds and their anions, X^-, are relatively poor, with fluoride ion being the weakest and iodide ion the strongest, as has been previously indicated. An example of the reducing strength of hydrogen iodide is the fact that solutions of this compound will react slowly with oxygen from the air to give iodine, which is indicated by the brown color that gradually forms in the hydrogen iodide solutions.

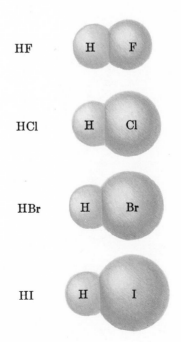

Figure 9.4 Relative sizes of HX molecules.

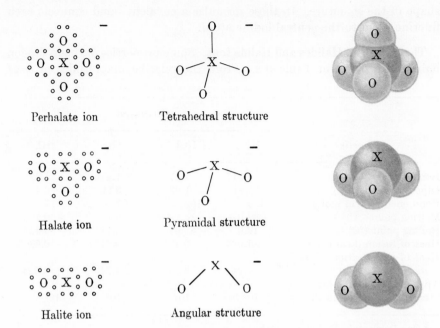

Perhalate ion   Tetrahedral structure

Halate ion   Pyramidal structure

Figure 9.5 Oxyanions of the halogens.

Halite ion   Angular structure

As *acids* the HX compounds ionize in water according to the equation

$$HX + H_2O \rightleftarrows H_3O^+ + X^- \tag{7}$$

Water solutions of HX compounds are called *hydrohalic acids*. This equilibrium lies far to the right; in fact the reaction is essentially complete for all HX compounds except hydrogen fluoride. For this reason hydrochloric, hydrobromic, and hydriodic acids are considered strong acids in water.

Approximate values for the ionization constants of the hydrohalic acids are given in Table 9.8. The order of acid strengths is HF $\ll$ HCl < HBr < HI.

The explanation for this order is complex, but in essence it is related to the concept that the small fluoride ion has a greater attraction for protons than do the increasingly larger chloride, bromide, and iodide ions. In the process of ionization, the proton must be separated from the newly formed halide ion. And this is most difficult in the case of fluoride ion.

Hydrofluoric acid undergoes a unique reaction with the silicates or with silicon dioxide due to the formation of the covalent gaseous compound, SiF_4, as illustrated by the equations

$$Na_2SiO_3 + 6HF \longrightarrow 2NaF + SiF_4 \uparrow + 3H_2O$$

$$CaSiO_3 + 6HF \longrightarrow CaF_2 + SiF_4 \uparrow + 3H_2O$$

$$SiO_2 + 4HF \longrightarrow SiF_4 \uparrow + 2H_2O$$

Since glass is a mixture of sodium and calcium silicates, together with some silicon dioxide, hydrofluoric acid can be used to attack or etch glass objects such as thermometers, flasks, or fine glassware.

Preparation. The hydrogen halides can be prepared by at least three methods:

1. Direct union of the elements.

$$H_2 + X_2 \rightleftarrows 2HX$$

All four halogen elements undergo this reaction. Usually, special care must be exercised to avoid explosions when fluorine and chlorine are involved. In practice, only hydrogen chloride is prepared in this way.

2. Action of sulfuric acid on a salt (limited to HF and HCl preparation).

3. The method usually employed in the preparation of hydrogen bromide and hydrogen iodide consists of the action of water upon phosphorus tribromide or triiodide. The compounds are formed by the union of phosphorus with bromine or iodine. Water acts upon these compounds with the formation of the hydrogen halide and phosphorous acid:

$$PX_3 + 3H_2O \longrightarrow H_3PO_3 + 3HX \uparrow \quad (X = Br\ or\ I)$$

This general method could be used also to prepare HCl, since the compound PCl_3 is easily prepared and hydrolyzes readily. However, the action of sulfuric acid on salt is much more convenient.

Oxyacids. The common oxyacids of the halogens are listed in Table 9.2. The generalized names of the acids and their ions are given in Table 9.9.

Nomenclature. The *nomenclature* pattern of Table 9.9 can be applied to any halogen oxyacid or its salt by substituting the appropriate stem—i.e., *chlor*, *brom*, or *iod* for the more general stem, *hal*, used in the table. Thus the compounds having the formulas $HBrO_3$ and HIO_3 are bromic and iodic acids, respectively, and the compounds represented by $KBrO_3$ and KIO_3 are potassium bromate and potassium iodate, respectively.

The *electronic structures and shapes* of four oxyanions are illustrated in Figure 9.5.

The tetrahedral shape of the perhalate ion arises because the halogen atom uses sp^3 hybrid orbitals in forming four covalent bonds to the oxygen atoms. The angular shape of the halite ion is the result of the halogen atom using two of its p orbitals to form the bonds to oxygen. Like water, this structure also may contain sp^3 hybrid orbitals.

Iodine forms two oxyacids in the VII oxidation state. These are *para*periodic acid, H_5IO_6, and *meta*periodic acid, HIO_4. The structure of the *para*periodic acid is illustrated below:

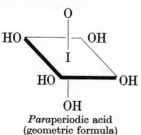

*Para*periodic acid
(geometric formula)

Formula	Name	Formula	Name	
HXO_4	Perhalic acid	XO_4^-	Perhalate ion	**Table 9.9** Names of Halogen Oxyacids and Oxyacid Anions
HXO_3	Halic acid	XO_3^-	Halate ion	
HXO_2	Halous acid	XO_2^-	Halite ion	
HXO	Hypohalous acid	XO^-	Hypohalite ion	

This structure presumably arises because of the large size of the iodine atom, its relatively low electronegativity, and the fact that d orbitals on the iodine atom can be used to form bonds. Salts, such as $Na_2H_3IO_6$, containing this structure can be obtained from water solutions of sodium *meta*periodate.

Chemical Properties. Two important chemical properties of the halogen oxyacids are their abilities to act as oxidizing agents and as acids.

These compounds are good to strong oxidizing agents; they are easily reduced to lower oxidation states—often giving the halogen in the $-I$ state. In general the chloro oxyacids are stronger oxidizing agents than the corresponding bromo and iodo compounds. This is consistent with electronegativity considerations since chlorine, the most electronegative of the three halogens (chlorine, bromine, and iodine), has the most stable $-I$ oxidation state and hence has the strongest tendency to reach that state.

Among the chloro oxyacids, hypochlorous acid is the strongest and perchloric acid is the weakest oxidizing agent, suggesting that one important point here is the fact that perchlorate ion must break four bonds while hypochlorite ion must break only one bond to reach the $-I$ oxidation state.

These oxidizing properties are used in many ways. For example, the hypochlorite ion is used to prepare other oxyanions such as chromate ion (CrO_4^{-2}), selenate ion (SeO_4^{-2}), periodate ion (IO_4^-), and ferrate ion (FeO_4^{-2}) from compounds of the respective elements in their lower oxidation states. Hypochlorites and chlorites are excellent for bleaching cotton or other cellulose-type fibers or cloth. They are also used as disinfectants and antiseptics. Mixtures of chlorates with sulfur, sugar, or other reducing agents are powerful explosives. All three halate ions are used in quantitative analysis procedures in which the halate ion acts as an oxidizing agent. For example, iodate is used to determine the amount of antimony in a sample or to estimate the concentration of chloride in a solution. Salts of perchloric acid are used as the oxidants in solid rocket fuels.

Acid Strengths. The halogen oxyacids vary in *acid strength* from very strong to extremely weak acids, as illustrated by their ionization constants (Table 9.10). While the data are incomplete, two trends in acid strengths

Table 9.10 Acid Strengths of Halogen Oxyacids

Acid	Ionization Constant (at 25°C)	Acid	Ionization Constant (at 25°C)	Acid	Ionization Constant (at 25°C)
$HClO_4$	Very large			H_5IO_6	5×10^{-4}
$HClO_3$	Large	$HBrO_3$	Large	HIO_3	2×10^{-1}
$HClO_2$	1×10^{-2}				
$HClO$	3.8×10^{-8}	$HBrO$	2×10^{-9}	HIO	1×10^{-11}

are apparent: The first is an increase in acid strength as the number of oxygen atoms in the molecule increases, provided the halogen atom remains the same. For example, in the series $HClO$, $HClO_2$, $HClO_3$, $HClO_4$ the acid strength increases regularly from a very low to a very high value. A similar trend is observed among the iodo acids.

The second trend is a decrease in acid strength as the electronegativity of the halogen atom decreases—provided the number of oxygen atoms remains constant. For example, the acid strengths decrease systematically in the series HOCl > HOBr > HOI. A similar trend appears among the halic acids.

Both of these trends may be explained in terms of the electronegativity or the apparent electronegativity of the halogen atoms in the compounds in question.

As the number of oxygen atoms in the molecule of the oxyacid increases, the halogen atom is sharing more and more of its valence electrons. In effect this increases the electronegativity of the halogen atom which then attracts electrons from the hydrogen-oxygen bond thereby increasing the ease of proton removal. These effects also tend to stabilize the anion relative to the acid.

In the hypohalous acids a highly electronegative halogen atom attracts electrons from the oxygen atom to which it is bonded. In effect this increases the electronegativity of that oxygen atom (since its nucleus now has less control of the electrons) so that it attracts electrons from the oxygen-hydrogen bond. This then increases the ease of proton removal. The magnitude of these effects depends upon the electronegativity of the halogen atom. For example, in hypochlorous acid there is probably a net attraction of electrons toward the chlorine and away from the hydrogen-oxygen bond; in hypoiodous acid this attraction is less because the electronegativity of iodine is less than that of chlorine. The proton is removed more easily in the chloro acid because the bonding electrons are pulled away from the proton and toward the oxygen to a greater extent here than in the iodo acid. Again, these electron-withdrawing effects tend to stabilize the anion relative to the acid.

Both of these trends appear to be general for the oxyacids of the non-metals. Thus the acid strengths of the oxyacids of the Group V and Group VI elements increase with the number of oxygen atoms in the molecule and with increasing electronegativity of the central atom, just as for the halogen oxyacids of Group VII.

Preparation. Preparation of the oxyacids is often difficult, but their salts can be prepared by the reaction of the halogen elements with bases or by electrolysis of solutions of halides.

The Reaction of Halogen Elements with a Base. The position of equilibrium in the general reaction

$$X_2 + 2H_2O \rightleftharpoons HOX + H_3O^+ + X^-$$

lies to the left for chlorine, bromine, and iodine, as indicated in Equation (2). However in the presence of *cold* sodium or potassium hydroxide the acids are converted to their salts and the position of equilibrium is displaced sharply to the right. This reaction may be written as two steps or simply as

$$X_2 + 2OH^- \longrightarrow X^- + OX^- + H_2O$$

If *hot* base is used, the hypohalite ion undergoes a disproportionation reaction of the type

$$3XO^- \longrightarrow 2X^- + XO_3^-$$

This is a method for preparing the halate salts. For example, potassium chlorate may be prepared by the action of chlorine on hot aqueous potassium hydroxide. When the resulting solution is evaporated, the potassium chlorate, being much less soluble than potassium chloride, separates first. By repeated crystallization it can be obtained in the pure state.

This method of making halates is not economical because in the over-all reaction of halogen to halate,

$$3X_2 + 6OH^- \longrightarrow 5X^- + XO_3^- + 3H_2O$$

5 moles of halide are produced for every mole of halate formed.

Electrolysis of Halides. More economical methods for preparing halates and hypohalites involve the electrolysis of halides in basic solution. By controlling the temperature and other experimental variables it is possible to oxidize halide ions to any stable higher oxidation state. Thus chlorine, hypochlorites, chlorites, chlorates, and perchlorates can be prepared electrolytically.

Electrolytic methods are not used to prepare iodates, periodates, or hypoiodites since iodides are very readily oxidized by chemical oxidizing agents. An example is the oxidation of iodide ion to iodate by hypochlorites.

$$I^- + 3HOCl + 3H_2O \rightarrow IO_3^- + 3Cl^- + 3H_3O^+$$

SUMMARY

In this chapter we have discussed some of the important chemistry of the halogen elements, a series of nonmetals having high electronegativity and forming both ionic and covalent compounds in a variety of oxidation states. This family is outstanding for its numerous strong oxidizing agents and its many acids of varying strength.

The structure, properties, and reactivity of the elements and compounds belonging to this family have been related to the principles of atomic and molecular structure established earlier in the text. In addition the ideas of acid-base equilibria and oxidation-reduction presented earlier have been applied and extended in introducing the important reactions of the family.

SOME SPECIAL TERMS

Halogens
  covalent and ionic radii
  electronegativity
  hydrohalic acid
  interhalogen
  oxyhalogen
  oxyacids
  multiple oxidation states

Halogen structures
  sp^3 hybridization
  square pyramid
  pentagonal bipyramid
Dipole moment
Dissociation energy
Ionization constant

QUESTIONS AND PROBLEMS

1. What physical and chemical properties of the halogens characterize them as nonmetals?
2. Cite evidence to support the statement that fluorine is the most active nonmetal.
3. How do you account for the following: (a) a chloride ion (Cl^-) has a greater radius than a chlorine atom; (b) the ionic radii of the halide ions increase with the atomic weight; and (c) hydrogen chloride is a covalently bonded compound, but in water solution it forms a strong acid?
4. List the oxidation states of chlorine. In which ones will chlorine be an oxidizing agent? In which a reducing agent? Under what circumstances will this be true?
5. List some commercial uses of fluorine. What property of fluorine makes it more desirable than chlorine for this purpose?
6. How can you account for the relatively low values of the boiling point, freezing point, heat of fusion, and heat of vaporization of the halogens?
7. What is the distinction between covalent radius, ionic radius, and van der Waals radius of halogen atoms?
8. Calculate the weights of the five halogens required to oxidize 10 g of hydrogen from the 0 to the I oxidation state.
9. Calculate the weight of calcium that can be oxidized with 10 g of fluorine.
10. Write the value of the oxidation state of chlorine in HCl, Cl_2, $HClO$, ICl_3, $HClO_3$, $HClO_4$, and CCl_4.
11. Give equations for three methods of preparation of chlorine, bromine, and iodine. What methods of preparation of these elements cannot be used for the preparation of fluorine? Why not?
12. How do you account for the facts that: (a) hydrofluoric acid is a weak acid but hydrochloric acid is a strong acid; (b) the polarity of hydrogen halides decreases as the electronegativity of the halogen decreases; and (c) hydrogen fluoride reacts with silicates but hydrogen chloride does not?
13. Describe a method of preparation of an acid of chlorine in the $-I$, I, III, and V oxidation states.
14. Show by equations and oxidation numbers how oxygen can be oxidized by fluorine.
15. Account for the fact that both BrF_3 and IF_3 are T-shaped molecules.

REFERENCES

DOUGLAS, B. E., and D. H. McDANIEL. *Concepts and Models of Inorganic Chemistry*. Waltham, Mass.: Blaisdell, 1965.

JOHNSON, R. C. *Introductory Descriptive Chemistry*. New York.: Benjamin, 1966.

PHILLIPS, C. S. G., and R. J. P. WILLIAMS. *Inorganic Chemistry*. Vol. *1, Principles and Non-metals*. New York: Oxford, 1965.

REMY, H. *Treatise on Inorganic Chemistry* (translated by J. S. Anderson). Vols. *1* and *2*. New York: Elsevier, 1956.

SNYDER, A. E. "Desalting Water by Freezing," *Scientific American*, vol. *207*, no. 6 (1962), p. 41.

WELLS, A. F. *Structural Inorganic Chemistry*. 3d ed.; New York: Oxford, 1962.

WILLIAMS, L. P. "Humphry Davy," *Scientific American*, vol. *202*, no. 6 (1960), p. 106.

10

The Uniqueness of Carbon

... I fell into a reverie. ... The atoms were gamboling before my eyes ... I saw how two small ones united to form a pair; how the larger ones seized two of the smaller ones; how still larger ones kept hold of three or four smaller ones. ... I saw how the larger ones formed a chain. ... This was the origin of the Structure Theory.   C. F. Kekulé von Stradonitz (1829–1896)

We have discussed the chemistry of some important classes of elements including (a) the simplest element, hydrogen (Chap. 7), (b) a group of reactive metals (Chap. 8), and (c) a group of reactive nonmetals (Chap. 9). To extend our overview of several classes of elements, we shall now discuss the chemistry of the element carbon—an element which forms many times more compounds than all the other elements except hydrogen. In this chapter we shall show how the many and varied kinds of structures of carbon-containing molecules arise, and we shall attempt to relate these to the structure and properties of the carbon atom itself.

The element carbon (in Group IV of the periodic table) has an electronegativity of 2.4. This value is intermediate between the high and low values of the other elements and reflects the tendency of carbon to form covalent bonds with other elements. In particular it forms covalent bonds with all the nonmetallic elements below and to the right of its position in the periodic table. Its electronegativity is nearly the same as that of hydrogen, and it forms very stable covalent bonds with hydrogen atoms.

The electron configuration of the ground state of the carbon atom is $1s^2\, 2s^2\, 2p^2$. As discussed in Chap. 5, however, promotion of an electron to the $1s^2\, 2s^1\, 2p^3$ state permits the atom to form compounds containing the stable sp^3, sp^2, or sp hybridized orbitals characteristic of most carbon compounds (Figure 10.1). None of the combined carbon atoms has more than eight electrons in the valence shell.

Carbon Compounds with Single Bonds: sp³ Hybridized Carbon Atoms

Carbon-to-Carbon Bonds. One of the characteristics of carbon atoms is that they can form strong bonds with other carbon atoms. If the strengths of the covalent bonds between two atoms of the same element are compared for different elements, it is found that the strength of the single bond from carbon atom to carbon atom is greater than the strength of any other like-atom *single* bonds except those between hydrogen atoms (Table 10.1).

H—H	103	N—N	38
F—F	36	C—C	82
Cl—Cl	57	S—S	54
Br—Br	45	Si—Si	53
I—I	35	Li—Li	25
O—O	34	Na—Na	17
		K—K	12

Table 10.1 Single Bond Energies (kcal/mole)

A further distinctive characteristic of carbon is that a carbon atom attached to another carbon atom by a single shared pair of electrons has used only one of its four available valence electrons in forming that bond. Three other electrons then remain to form bonds with additional carbon atoms or with atoms of other elements. This ability of a carbon atom to form strong bonds with other carbon atoms while yet combining with atoms of other elements is one of the major factors that make possible the great variety and number of the compounds of carbon. More than two million compounds of carbon have been described and characterized; this number is ten times greater than the number of known compounds of all the other elements except hydrogen. Since, in earlier days, much of the interest of chemists was in those carbon compounds which are important in the metabolism of living organisms, the study of carbon compounds was given the name *organic chemistry*, and this term is still used today.

● ● ●   CONVENTIONS FOR FORMULA WRITING

In the *structural formulas* for organic compounds a line is used to represent a pair of shared electrons in a covalent bond :

An atom, of carbon or other elements, is presumed to be attached to each of the lines extending out from the carbon symbol, as in Figure 10.3. Each carbon atom has four dashes, corresponding to the use of four orbitals per carbon atom for bonding purposes.

Very often the hydrogen atoms attached to a carbon atom are not written separately but are represented by a single symbol with a subscript indicating the number of hydrogen atoms bonded to the carbon atom. Examples of this are CH_4, methane, and CH_3—CH_3, ethane, where there are four and three hydrogen atoms bonded to the respective carbon atoms in these compounds. Such formulas are called *condensed formulas* (Table 10.2).

Occasionally we write *skeleton* formulas, which show just the carbon atoms and not the attached atoms (Figure 10.2).

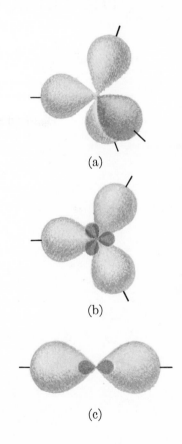

Figure 10.1 Carbon uses sp^3, sp^2, or sp hybrid orbitals. (a) Four sp^3 hybrid orbitals. (b) Three sp^2 hybrid atomic orbitals with a common origin. (c) Two sp hybrid atomic orbitals with a common origin.

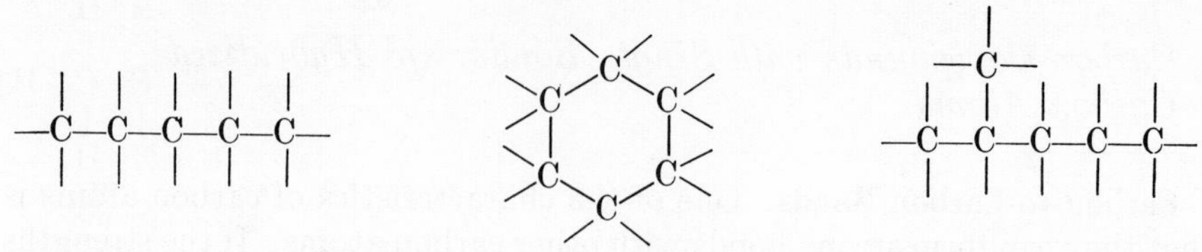

Figure 10.2 Chain, ring, and branched-chain structures.

Chains and Rings. Another factor* that makes possible the diversity of carbon compounds is that carbon atoms are able to combine with each other either to form long chains, or to form rings, as illustrated in the skeleton formulas in Figure 10.2. Examples of a few of these compounds are given in Table 10.2.

Hydrocarbons. If all the valence electrons not used in binding carbon atoms together are used to bind hydrogen to carbon, the resulting compound, containing carbon and hydrogen only, is called a hydrocarbon. Table 10.2 gives some examples. The five- and six-carbon atom hydrocarbons corresponding to the two end skeletons shown in Figure 10.2 would have the formulas in Figure 10.3.

Figure 10.3

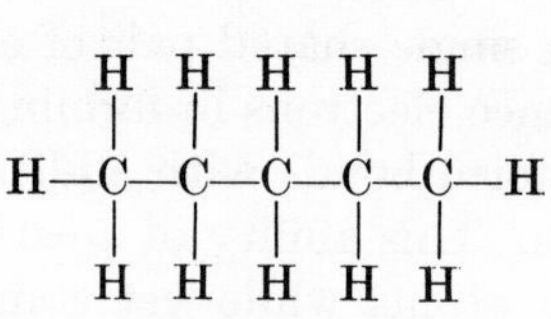

Pentane, C_5H_{12}

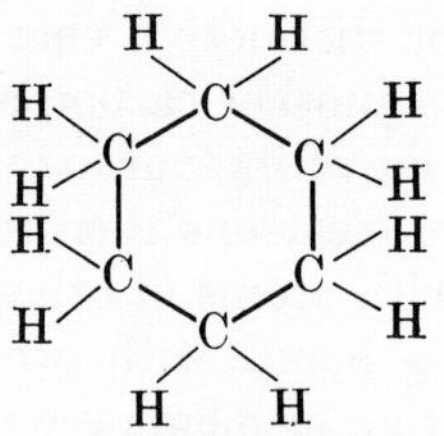

Cyclohexane, C_6H_{12}

The carbon-to-hydrogen bond is also a strong one, and has a bond energy of 98 kcal/mole. The ability of carbon to form strong bonds with hydrogen is in fact so great and hydrogen atoms are so abundant that only a minute fraction of the known organic compounds is found to contain no hydrogen.

Petroleum is the main source of hydrocarbons in nature.

Derivatives of Hydrocarbons. Organic compounds can conveniently be classified as hydrocarbons and derivatives of hydrocarbons, as if they were formed by replacing a hydrogen atom attached to carbon with another atom or group. Examples of derivatives are chloromethane, CH_3Cl, and hydroxymethane, CH_3OH (methyl alcohol). Note that these compounds may be named from their relation to the hydrocarbon from which they are derived. Similarly, the compound whose formula has a chlorine atom attached to the *second carbon atom* in the chain of five carbon atoms in Figure 10.3 is named from its relation to the hydrocarbon having the same number of carbon atoms, and is called 2-chloropentane (Figure 10.4). The other compounds in Figure 10.4 are similarly named as hydrocarbon derivatives.†

---

* Two other factors are the possibilities for isomerism and for substitution.

† The method of naming organic compounds is described in Chap. 29.

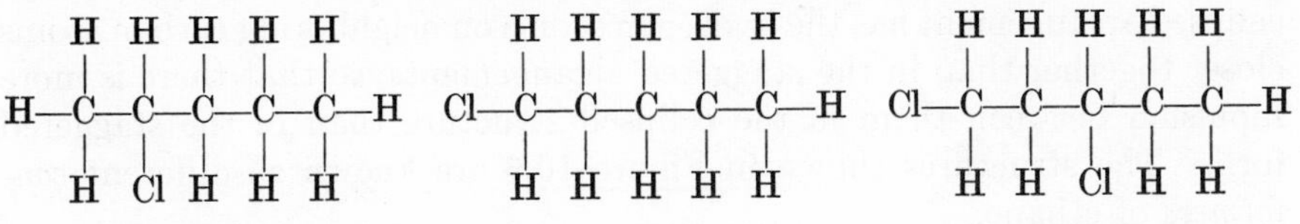

2-Chloropentane   1-Chloropentane   1,3-Dichloropentane

Figure 10.4

Molecular Models. In all the examples shown in Figures 10.2, 10.3, and 10.4 the carbon atoms have the sp^3 hybridized structure. As discussed earlier (Chap. 6), this structure is characterized by the angle 109° 28' between each pair of bonds, so that lines drawn from the carbon nucleus toward the positions of maximum density of bonding electrons will be directed toward the corners of a tetrahedron. Hence molecules containing carbon cannot be correctly represented as two-dimensional (planar) figures on paper. Figure 10.5 shows a photograph of a "ball-and-stick" model of cyclohexane. In this type of model the balls represent carbon and hydrogen nuclei, and the sticks the connecting valence bonds. Such models give the proper angular arrangements, but differences in atom sizes and bond lengths are completely disregarded. The sizes and lengths can be simulated in scale models, in which the atoms are conceived of as small spheres attached to each other with distances between centers proportional to measured bond lengths (distances between atomic nuclei) in the actual molecules. A photograph of a scale model of cyclohexane is also shown in Figure 10.5.

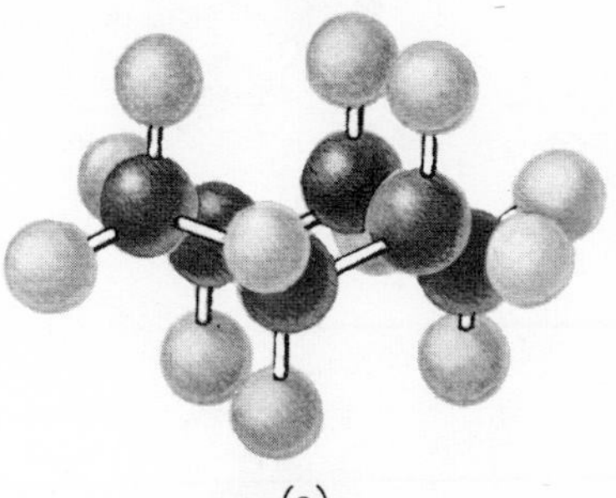

Rotation Within Molecules. Of considerable importance is the prediction, based on examination of the models, that chain-like molecules should have considerable flexibility, this being made possible by rotation of the atoms about the single bonds in the structure. Experimental evidence shows that such rotation occurs freely in most simple chain compounds, with the result that ethane, for example, is a homogeneous mixture of molecules in the two forms shown in Figure 10.6. It is nevertheless true that the stable states are those in which the hydrogen atoms on adjacent carbon atoms are in the "staggered" arrangements, rather than in the "eclipsed" arrangement shown in Figure 10.6. The reason is that the

(a)

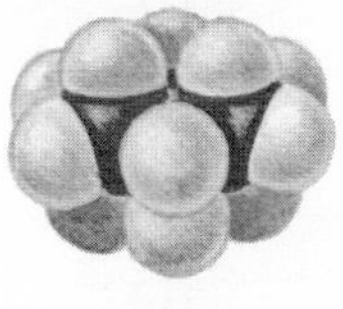

(b)

Figure 10.5 Models of carbon containing structures. (a) Ball and stick model. (b) Scale model.

Table 10.2 Some Chain and Ring Compounds of Carbon and Hydrogen

Some Straight-Chain Compounds	Some Branched-Chain Compounds	Some Cyclic Compounds

Methane, CH_4
 Ethane, CH_3—CH_3
 Propane, CH_3—CH_2—CH_3
 Butane, CH_3—CH_2—CH_2—CH_3
 Pentane,* CH_3—CH_2—CH_2—CH_2—CH_3
 Hexane,
 CH_3—CH_2—CH_2—CH_2—CH_2—CH_3
 Heptane, CH_3(—CH_2—)$_5CH_3$
 Octane, CH_3(—CH_2—)$_6CH_3$
	Isobutane, CH_3—CH—CH_3
	                       |
	                      CH_3
	
	 Isopentane,* CH_3—CH—CH_2—CH_3
	                          |
	                         CH_3
	
	                        CH_3
	                        |
	 Neopentane,* CH_3—C—CH_3
	                         |
	                        CH_3
		
		 Cyclopentane
		
		 Decalin

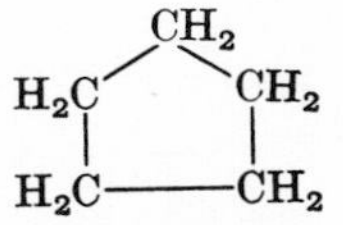

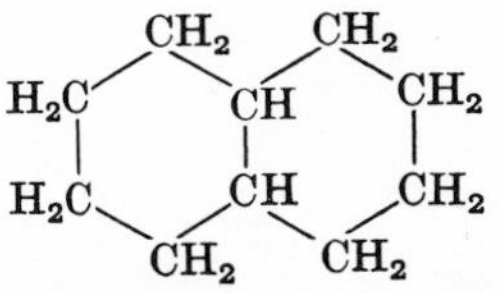

* See Figure 10.8 for a systematic method of naming the pentanes.

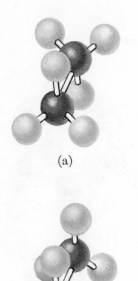

(a)

(b)

Figure 10.6 Forms of the ethane molecules arising from internal rotation. (a) Staggered form. (b) Eclipsed form.

eclipsed arrangement has the hydrogen atoms on neighboring carbon atoms closer together than in the staggered arrangements, so that there is more repulsion between them in the eclipsed structure than in the staggered form. The structures shown in Figure 10.6 are known as different *conformers* of ethane.

Strained Structures. A further consequence of the tetrahedral angle requirements of the sp^3 hybrids is that rings containing three or four carbon atoms are very reactive, since the bond angles suffer a marked distortion from the normal value of 109° 28′ when such rings are formed. For example, in a ring of four carbon atoms,

$$
\begin{array}{ccc}
C & \!\!-\!\! & C \\
| & & | \\
C & \!\!-\!\! & C
\end{array}
$$

the bond angles between the atoms in the ring are 90°. As a result such substances tend to undergo reactions which relieve the strain by "opening" the ring. A slight puckering out of a plane will permit a five-membered ring to form, and seven-membered and larger rings can form easily without angular distortion. With rings of between 8 and 14 carbon atoms, however, hydrogen atoms are of necessity brought close together, and these are less stable than five-, six-, or seven-membered rings, or rings with 15 or more carbon atoms. Examples of strained structures are given in Figure 10.7.

Reaction Centers in Molecules. In a hydrocarbon molecule such as ethane,

$$
\begin{array}{ccc}
 & H & H \\
 & | & | \\
H\!-\!\!&\!\!C\!-\!\!C\!\!&\!\!-\!H \\
 & | & | \\
 & H & H
\end{array}
$$

all the hydrogen atoms have the same reactivity. However, in a hydrocarbon like propane,

$$
\begin{array}{cccc}
 & H & H & H \\
 & | & | & | \\
H\!-\!\!&\!\!C\!-\!C\!-\!C\!\!&\!\!-\!H \\
 & | & | & | \\
 & H & H & H
\end{array}
$$

or butane,

$$
\begin{array}{ccccc}
 & H & H & H & H \\
 & | & | & | & | \\
H\!-\!\!&\!\!C\!-\!C\!-\!C\!-\!C\!\!&\!\!-\!H \\
 & | & | & | & | \\
 & H & H & H & H
\end{array}
$$

the hydrogen atoms on the end carbon atoms are usually less reactive than those attached to the internal carbon atoms. This difference in reactivity is measurable but quite small, and in general all C—H bonds are relatively unreactive at room temperature. By contrast the presence of a chlorine atom in the hydrocarbon chain imparts to the molecule a new reaction site. Since the C—H bond is stronger than the C—Cl bond, most of the reactions of a chlorine-containing molecule, such as chloropentane or chlorohexane, will be associated with the C—Cl bond, and in general *these reactions will be the same, no matter how long the carbon chain in the molecule containing the C—Cl bond*. This makes for a considerable simplification in the study of organic chemistry, since one needs to study mainly the properties of certain bonded groups or reaction centers which occur in the multitude of compounds rather than to attempt to remember the properties of each organic substance.

Functional Groups. An atom or group of atoms which imparts characteristic chemical properties to organic molecules containing it is known as a *functional group*. Examples other than the chlorine group include the hydroxyl group, —OH, the amino group, —NH$_2$, the carbonyl group,

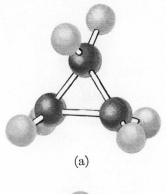

(a)

$$\begin{array}{c} \diagdown \\ \diagup \end{array} C{=}O$$

the acid group,

$$-\overset{\displaystyle O}{\underset{\displaystyle OH}{\overset{\|}{C}}}$$

the amido group,

$$-\overset{\displaystyle O}{\underset{\displaystyle NH_2}{\overset{\|}{C}}}$$

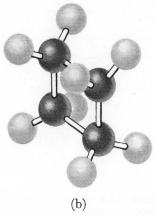

(b)

Figure 10.7 Examples of strained structures. (a) Cyclopropane. (b) Cyclobutane.

and many others. Formulas of simple compounds containing these functional groups are given in Table 10.3. It should be remembered, however, that there are literally thousands of known compounds containing each of these functional groups. The principal difference among the compounds containing a given functional group is the number and arrangement of carbon and hydrogen atoms present. As an example of the unique reaction of a functional group and to emphasize that the reaction is probable wherever that functional group occurs, regardless of the number of carbon atoms present, let us consider the reaction of a chlorohydrocarbon with sodium hydroxide to form an alcohol:

$$CH_3{-}CH_2Cl + OH^- \longrightarrow CH_3{-}CH_2OH + Cl^-$$
Chloroethane   Ethanol, an alcohol

$$CH_3{-}CH_2{-}CH_2Cl + OH^- \longrightarrow CH_3{-}CH_2{-}CH_2OH + Cl^-$$
1-Chloropropane   1-Propanol, an alcohol

$$CH_3{-}CHCl{-}CH_3 + OH^- \longrightarrow CH_3{-}CHOH{-}CH_3 + Cl^-$$
2-Chloropropane   2-Propanol, an alcohol

$$CH_2Cl{-}CH_2{-}CHCl{-}CH_2{-}CH_3 + 2OH^- \longrightarrow$$
1,3-Dichloropentane

$$CH_2OH{-}CH_2{-}CHOH{-}CH_2{-}CH_3 + 2Cl^-$$
1,3-Pentanediol, a dihydroxy alcohol

In each case the hydroxide ion replaces the chlorine atom to form an alcohol. If R represents the hydrocarbon portion of the molecule, the *general* equation for the reaction of the functional group —Cl with the hydroxyl ion OH$^-$ may be written

$$R—Cl + OH^- \longrightarrow ROH + Cl^-$$

This equation is seen to fit each of the special cases above. However, the amount of main product formed often is reduced due to the formation of other products. These result from secondary reactions often called *side reactions*. Aromatic hydrocarbons containing chlorine do not normally undergo this reaction.

Isomers. Examination of the molecular formulas of 2-chloropentane and 1-chloropentane (Figure 10.4) shows that they have the same molecular formula, namely, $C_5H_{11}Cl$, but different structural formulas. Similarly the molecular formulas of 1-chloropropane and 2-chloropropane are the same: C_3H_7Cl. In each of the pairs the compounds of the same formula differ from each other only in the *position* of attachment of the chlorine atom on the hydrocarbon chain; in one it is attached to the end carbon atom and in the other to the carbon atom second from the end. *Compounds*, such as the two chloropentanes and the two chloropropanes, *which have the same molecular formula but different structural formulas are known as isomers.* In the particular cases of the chlorohydrocarbons under discussion, which differ in the point of attachment of the functional group to the carbon chain, the isomers are known as *position isomers*.

Figure 10.8 shows condensed structural formulas for some five-carbon hydrocarbons of formula C_5H_{12}.

Table 10.3 Some Functional Groups

Group	Representative Compound	Formula	Class of Compounds Which Contain the Group
—Cl	Ethyl chloride	$CH_3—CH_2Cl$	Chlorinated hydrocarbons
—OH	Ethanol	$CH_3—CH_2OH$	Alcohols
$\diagdown$C$=$O$\diagup$	Acetone	$CH_3—\overset{\|\|}{\underset{O}{C}}—CH_3$	Ketones
—C$\overset{O}{\diagdown}$OH	Acetic acid	$CH_3—C\overset{O}{\diagdown}OH$	Carboxylic acids
—NH$_2$	Ethyl amine	$CH_3—CH_2NH_2$	Amines
—C$\overset{O}{\diagdown}$NH$_2$	Acetamide	$CH_3—C\overset{O}{\diagdown}NH_2$	Amides

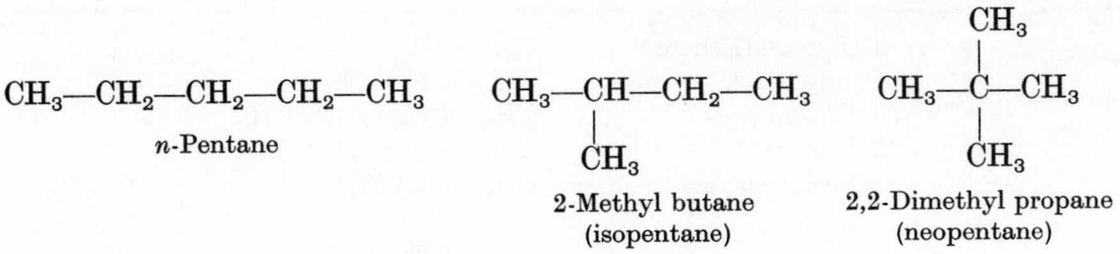

$$CH_3—CH_2—CH_2—CH_2—CH_3$$

n-Pentane

$$CH_3—\underset{\underset{CH_3}{|}}{CH}—CH_2—CH_3$$

2-Methyl butane
(isopentane)

$$CH_3—\underset{\underset{CH_3}{|}}{\overset{\overset{CH_3}{|}}{C}}—CH_3$$

2,2-Dimethyl propane
(neopentane)

Figure 10.8 Isomers having the formula C_5H_{12}.

These are the only structural formulas for C_5H_{12} hydrocarbons that can be written, if the carbon atom is to be tetravalent. Experimentally, three, and only three, compounds with the formula C_5H_{12} have been found; this fact may be taken as support for the theory which predicts that only three position isomers should exist. Similarly, the chemist predicts from theory and he finds by experiment that there should be one, and only one, CH_4, one C_2H_6 and one C_3H_8; but two compounds of formula C_4H_{10}, five of formula C_6H_{14}, nine C_7H_{16}, eighteen C_8H_{18}, and so on. This exact agreement between theory and experiment is one of the best proofs we could have of the chemist's theory of position isomerism in organic compounds.

There are other kinds of isomers in addition to position isomers. The chemist finds three compounds of molecular formula C_3H_8O. The structural formulas of two of them are

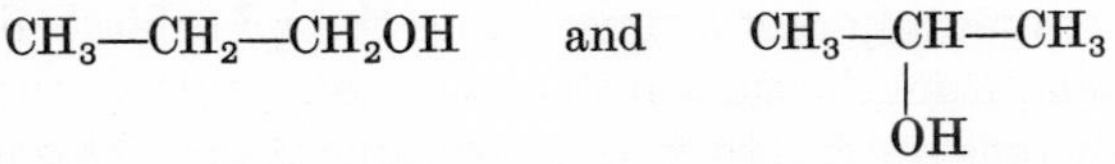

$$CH_3—CH_2—CH_2OH \quad \text{and} \quad CH_3—\underset{\underset{OH}{|}}{CH}—CH_3$$

In each of these each carbon is tetravalent, each hydrogen monovalent, and the oxygen bivalent, as required by their electron configurations. These two are position isomers, as discussed above. Another structural formula which maintains the valency requirements can be written; it is

$$CH_3—O—CH_2—CH_3$$

This last compound contains the functional group —O—, which is characteristic of the class of compounds known as ethers, and is a *functional group isomer* of the three-carbon alcohols. Since the chemical properties of organic compounds are those characteristic of their functional groups, there is usually no difficulty in identifying the existence of functional group isomers.

Later we shall find two other types of isomers, namely, geometrical isomers (page 201) and optical isomers.

Compounds with Double Bonds; sp^2 Hybridized Carbon Atoms

The compounds of carbon discussed thus far contain only single bonds. A wide variety of compounds containing carbon atoms *doubly* bonded to other atoms are known. The formulas for a few of the simpler hydrocarbons containing carbon-carbon double bonds are given in Table 10.4. These substances are known collectively as *alkenes* and the names of the

Table 10.4 A Few of the Many Hydrocarbons Which Contain Double Bonds

Ethylene (Ethene)	$H_2C{=}CH_2$
Propylene (Propene)	$CH_3{-}CH{=}CH_2$
1-Butene	$CH_3{-}CH_2{-}CH{=}CH_2$
2-Butene	$CH_3{-}CH{=}CH{-}CH_3$
2-Methylpropene	$CH_3{-}C{=}CH_2$
	$\quad\quad\quad\;\; \mid$
	$\quad\quad\quad CH_3$

individual compounds end in *ene*. In addition to compounds containing carbon-to-carbon double bonds there are substances such as carbon dioxide, $O{=}C{=}O$, formaldehyde, $H_2C{=}O$, acetone,

$$CH_3{-}\overset{\textstyle \|}{\underset{\textstyle O}{C}}{-}CH_3$$

and thousands of others in which a carbon atom is doubly bonded to an oxygen atom.

As stated in Chap. 6, a double bond consists of one σ and one π bond. The π bond is formed by the sideways overlap of unhybridized p orbitals, one from each of the two atoms forming the bond. The σ bonds in most organic compounds containing double bonds are formed by end-to-end overlap of the sp^2 hybrid orbitals on the carbon atoms with appropriate orbitals on the three adjacent atoms. Since the sp^2 orbitals lie in the same plane and extend from the carbon atom at angles of 120°, the carbon atom and the three atoms bonded to it lie in the same plane. This is the explanation for the planar structure of the formaldehyde molecule,

$$\begin{array}{c} H \\ \diagdown \\ \quad\quad C{=}O \\ \diagup \\ H \end{array}$$

In ethylene,

$$\begin{array}{cc} H \quad\quad H \\ \diagdown \quad\quad \diagup \\ C{=}C \\ \diagup \quad\quad \diagdown \\ H \quad\quad H \end{array}$$

all atoms lie in the same plane, but this is a consequence of both the sp^2 hybridization and the π bonds between the atoms. The π bond prevents rotation of the carbon and hydrogen atoms around the bond axis connecting the carbon atoms. Figure 10.9 is an orbital model of ethylene which illustrates the nature of the bonding and the shape of molecule. The bonding and shape of the propylene molecule

$$\begin{array}{c} H \\ | \\ H{-}C{-}C{=}C{-}H \\ |\quad |\quad | \\ H\;\; H\;\; H \end{array}$$

is discussed on page 116.

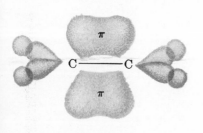

Figure 10.9 Orbital model of ethylene.

Geometrical Isomerism. In addition to the *position* isomers represented by the formulas illustrating 1-butene, 2-butene, and 2-methylpropene (Table 10.4), the existence of the double bond permits another type of isomerism known as *geometrical* isomerism. An important feature of the double bond is that it does not permit rotation of the group at one end of the bond with respect to the group at the other, in contrast to the behavior of groups connected by a single bond (Figure 10.6). This means that a compound such as 2-butene can exist in two distinguishable forms, which we can represent as

$$
\begin{array}{cc}
\overset{\displaystyle H \qquad\qquad H}{\underset{\displaystyle CH_3 \qquad\quad CH_3}{C=C}} & \overset{\displaystyle H \qquad\qquad CH_3}{\underset{\displaystyle CH_3 \qquad\quad H}{C=C}} \\
\textit{cis}\text{-2-Butene} & \textit{trans}\text{-2-Butene}
\end{array}
$$

Molecules related to each other as *cis*-2-butene* is related to *trans*-2-butene* are known as geometrical isomers. Two geometrical isomers will commonly have different physical properties and *are readily identified as two different compounds*. Chemical reactivity often will show which is the cis and which the trans isomer, but certain physical techniques such as spectroscopy or X-ray diffraction (Chap. 15) are sometimes more convenient.

Reaction at the Double Bond. Double bonds may be changed to single bonds by *addition* reactions, in which a reagent such as bromine, hydrogen bromide, or hydrogen reacts at the double bond to form a *saturated* compound containing only single bonds, as shown in the following equations for ethylene:

$$
\overset{\displaystyle H \qquad\qquad H}{\underset{\displaystyle H \qquad\qquad H}{C=C}} + Br_2 \longrightarrow
\overset{\displaystyle H \qquad\quad Br}{\underset{\displaystyle Br \qquad\quad H}{H-C-C-H}} \qquad (1)
$$

$$CH_2{=}CH_2 + HBr \longrightarrow CH_3{-}CH_2Br \qquad (2)$$

$$CH_2{=}CH_2 + H_2 \xrightarrow{\text{catalyst}} CH_3{-}CH_3 \qquad (3)$$

The first reaction serves as a simple qualitative test for the presence of carbon-to-carbon double bonds, since the color of a carbon tetrachloride solution of bromine disappears if a compound containing a carbon-to-carbon double bond is added. The last reaction has important synthetic uses, and, if carried out quantitatively, can be used to determine the number of double bonds present in an unknown compound.

---

* The cis- and trans- nomenclature refers to the fact that a plane, perpendicular to the paper, passing through the double bond divides the molecules into two parts. In the cis isomer each part contains two of the same kinds of atoms or groups—in the 2-butenes, these are two hydrogen atoms or two CH_3 groups. In the trans isomer each part contains one of each kind of atom or group—e.g., in *trans*-2-butene one hydrogen atom and one CH_3 group.

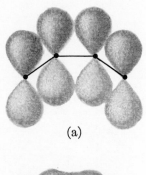

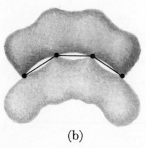

Figure 10.10 Illustrating delocalization in butadiene. (a) Localized *p* orbitals. (b) Delocalized *p* orbitals.

Conjugated Double Bonds and Resonance. In accord with the principle of independent reactivity of functional groups, it would be predicted that in molecules containing several carbon-to-carbon double bonds each of the double bonds in a molecule should react with bromine or hydrogen in the same way, to form single bonds as above. This is found to be the case in all polyenes (compounds having two or more double bonds) except those in which the double bonds occur on alternate carbon atoms as in butadiene, $CH_2{=}CH{-}CH{=}CH_2$. Double bonds thus arranged are known as *conjugated* double bonds. Note that the double bonds must occur on alternate carbon atoms; the double bonds in 1,4-hexadiene ($CH_2{=}CH{-}CH_2{-}CH{=}CH{-}CH_3$) are not conjugated double bonds.

The importance of conjugation is that when π-bonding electrons are on alternate carbon atoms (numbers 2 and 3 in butadiene), they interact not only with those on atoms 1 and 4, but also with each other. The result is that these electrons are *delocalized*, or smeared out over all four carbon atoms, instead of being localized about atoms 1 and 2 or 3 and 4 separately. This is supported experimentally in a lengthening of the bond distance between atoms 1 and 2 and between 3 and 4, as compared to the distance for normal double bonds, and a corresponding shortening of the usual single-bond distance between atoms 2 and 3. Since the bond distance for normal double bonds is less than that for normal single bonds, the lengthening means that the conjugated double bonds have become a little bit like single bonds, and the shortening suggests that the single bond has become a little bit like a double bond, as the result of the delocalization of the π-bonding electrons.

The mathematics of wave mechanics applied to the theory of bonding describes the effect of delocalization (Figure 10.10) in terms of structures which place the bonding electrons in specified positions. These structures are known as resonance hybrids (Chap. 6).

Aromatic Compounds. It is important to realize that molecules possessing possibilities for resonance are considerably more stable than can be accounted for on the basis of normal σ and π bonding. This is particularly noticeable in compounds having six-membered ring structures in which single and double bonds alternate in a threefold conjugation. These compounds are known as aromatic compounds. The most common is benzene, C_6H_6, for which two main contributing resonance structures, three of less importance, and a single generalized formula are shown.

The benzene molecule is planar and the C—C—C angles are 120°, as required for sp^2 hybrid bonds. All the C—C bond distances are found to be alike, and equal to 1.39 A, in contrast to 1.54 A for normal single bonds and 1.30 A for normal double bonds; hence the bonds are neither double bonds nor single bonds, but something intermediate between them.

A measure of the increased stabilization due to resonance can be obtained by examining heats of hydrogenation. While the heat of hydrogenation of the one double bond in cyclohexene

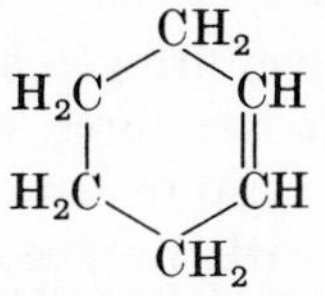

$$\begin{array}{ccc} & CH_2 & \\ H_2C & & CH \\ & & \| \\ H_2C & & CH \\ & CH_2 & \end{array}$$

is 28.6 kcal/mole and that of the two conjugated double bonds in 1,3-cyclohexadiene

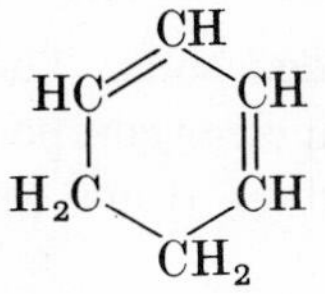

$$\begin{array}{ccc} & CH & \\ HC & & CH \\ \| & & \| \\ H_2C & & CH \\ & CH_2 & \end{array}$$

is twice this (about 55.4 kcal/mole), the heat of hydrogenation of the three double bonds in benzene is only 49.8 kcal/mole. The difference between the expected value, 3×28.6 kcal/mole, and the measured value, 49.8 kcal/mole, namely, 36.0 kcal/mole, represents the *resonance energy* of benzene. This very large value shows how much more stable benzene is than even its similar compound with conjugated double bonds, 1,3-cyclohexadiene, since by subtraction of the second equation below from the first,

$$C_6H_6 + 3H_2 \longrightarrow C_6H_{12} \quad \text{(heat evolved is 49 kcal)}$$

$$C_6H_8 + 2H_2 \longrightarrow C_6H_{12} \quad \text{(heat evolved is 55 kcal)}$$

with their accompanying heat effects, it is evident that the reaction

$$C_6H_6 + H_2 \longrightarrow C_6H_8 \quad \text{(heat absorbed is 6 kcal)}$$

requires the *addition* of 6 kcal/mole instead of the *evolution* of about 30 kcal/mole expected for hydrogenation of a double bond. Most of the resonance energy thus disappears with the loss of the third double bond, which is present in benzene but not in cyclohexadiene.

Heterocyclic Aromatic Compounds. There are a number of other ring compounds in which one of the atoms in the ring is not a carbon atom (that is, *heterocyclic* compounds) and which show a stability similar to that of benzene. Pyridine, C_5H_5N, for example, has three conjugated double bonds and has a resonance energy of 43 kcal/mole—higher even than benzene. This unusual stabilization is signalized by the larger number of resonance structures which can be written for pyridine as compared to benzene:

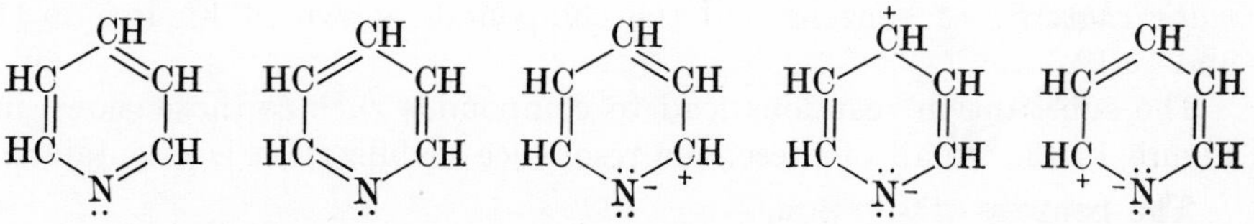

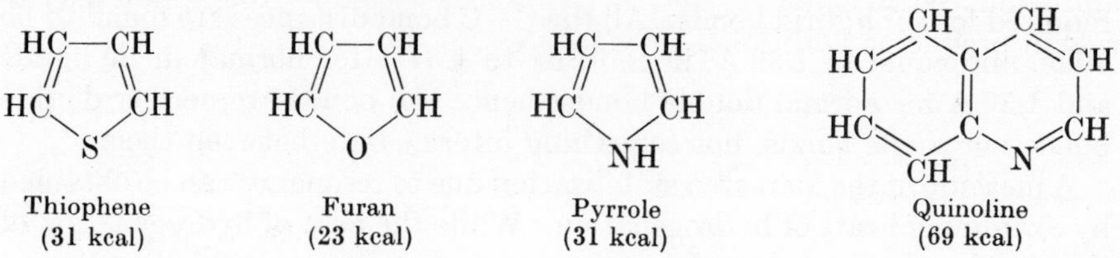

Figure 10.11 Some aromatic heterocyclic compounds and their resonance energies (in kcal/mole).

Thiophene (31 kcal)   Furan (23 kcal)   Pyrrole (31 kcal)   Quinoline (69 kcal)

The more highly electronegative nitrogen atom attracts the electron pair strongly enough to permit the last three structures to form without the great increase in energy otherwise to be expected for the change in the number of shared electrons with its accompanying charge separation. Structures of some other heterocyclic compounds are given in Figure 10.11; the resonance stabilization energies of these compounds are also given, in kcal/mole.

Polynuclear Aromatic Hydrocarbons. The last formula shown in Figure 10.11 is an example of a polynuclear compound. Such compounds are also found in series with only carbon atoms present in the ring (homocyclic series) (Figure 10.12).

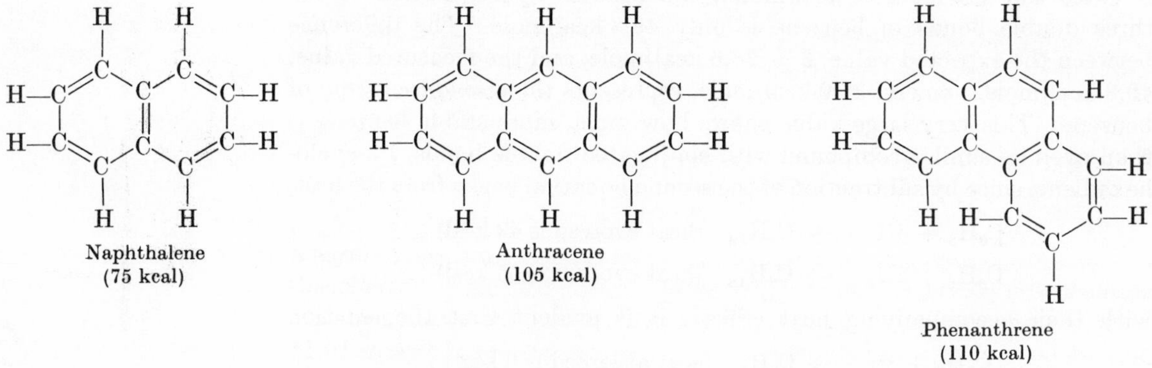

Naphthalene (75 kcal)   Anthracene (105 kcal)   Phenanthrene (110 kcal)

Figure 10.12 Some polynuclear aromatic hydrocarbons and their resonance energies (in kcal/mole).

Aromatic Character. The large resonance stabilization of benzene and similar compounds gives to benzene resistance to the characteristic reactions of addition to double bonds which would result in the reduction of the stable character of the molecule by loss of resonance energy (compare benzene and cyclohexadiene, p. 203). Hence the reactions of benzene are not usually those of *addition*, as for other compounds containing double bonds (unsaturated compounds) but rather reactions of *substitution*, in which another atom or group is substituted for one of the hydrogen atoms, while the six-membered ring remains intact. This reluctance to undergo the expected addition of reagents is said to be characteristic of the *aromatic character* of benzene and the compounds shown in Figures 10.11 and 10.12.

The substitution reactions lead to compounds such as those shown in Figure 10.13. In all of these, the resonance stabilization is maintained, and enhanced in some, as electron pairs of the substituting group play a role in producing additional resonance structures.

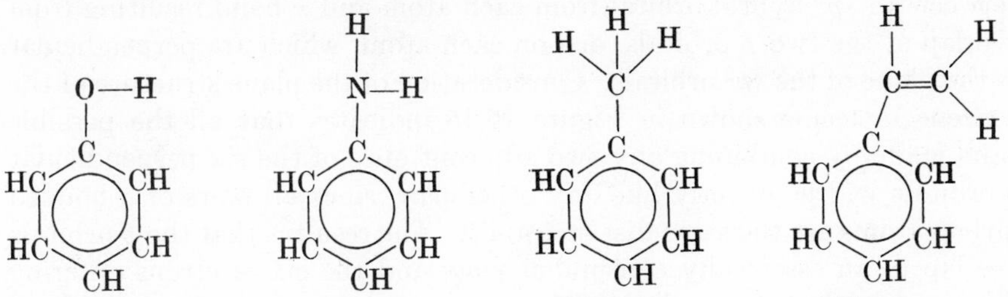

Phenol
(46 kcal)

Aniline
(45 kcal)

Toluene
(39 kcal)

Styrene
(46 kcal)

Figure 10.13 Some substituted benzenes and their resonance energies (in kcal/mole).

The reactions of these substituted benzenes are mainly those of the substituted functional group, such as —OH or —NH_2, because of the unusual stability of the aromatic structure.

The usual convention for showing formulas of benzene derivatives is to write the benzene ring as a simple hexagon,

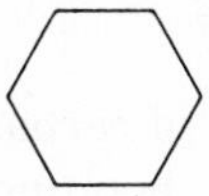

or to show a hexagon with a dashed or solid circle inside representing the bonds in the resonance structure

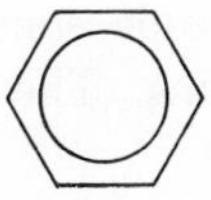

and to show only the attached groups, which have replaced the hydrogen atoms of the parent molecule. Since six hydrogen atoms can be replaced, many isomers can be formed, depending upon whether the substituents are present on adjacent carbon atoms or on more distant ones. Figure 10.14 shows the di- and tri- substituted bromobenzenes.

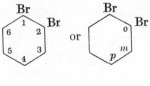

or

1,2-Dibromobenzene or ortho
(o) dibromobenzene

1,3-Dibromobenzene,
or meta (m) dibromo-
benzene;

1,4-Dibromobenzene,
or para (p) dibromo-
benzene;

1,2,3-Tribromobenzene;

1,2,4-Tribromobenzene

1,3,5-Tribromobenzene,
or s tribromobenzene

Figure 10.14 The di- and tri-
bromobenzenes

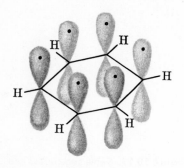

Figure 10.15 The *p* orbitals of benzene before overlap.

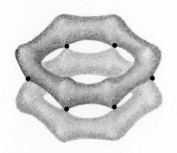

Figure 10.16 The delocalized *p* orbitals of benzene after overlap.

Orbital Explanation of Aromatic Character. It will be recalled that a double bond between carbon atoms can be described in terms of a σ bond between an sp^2 hybrid orbital from each atom and π bond resulting from overlap of the two p orbitals, one on each atom, which are perpendicular to the plane of the sp^2 orbitals. Consideration of the plane structure of the benzene molecule shown in Figure 10.15 indicates that all the possible pairs made by combining any two adjacent ones of the six perpendicular p orbitals will be exactly like any other pair, since all pairs of σ-bonded carbon atoms are the same distance apart. The result is that the p orbitals overlap in an essentially continuous ring, and the six electrons entering this ring are shared equally by all six carbon atoms in cyclic delocalized orbitals as shown in Figures 6.16 and 10.16. The situation is somewhat analogous to the community sharing of electrons in metals (Chap. 5), except that in this case the "community" contains only the six carbon nuclei.

Compounds with Triple Bonds: sp Hybridization on Carbon Atoms

Only a relatively few compounds of carbon are known in which the carbon atom uses sp hybrid orbitals for bonding. These compounds include (a) the *alkynes* or acetylenes, compounds containing triple bonds between adjacent carbon atoms; (b) the cyanides or nitriles, compounds containing triple bonds between adjacent carbon and nitrogen atoms; (c) carbon dioxide and the allenes, compounds containing carbon atoms linked by double bonds to *two* adjacent atoms. The formulas for some compounds in this class are given in Table 10.5.

Carbon atoms using sp hybrid orbitals to form σ bonds have two unhybridized p orbitals perpendicular to one another and to the axis of the sp hybrid orbitals. These p orbitals may interact with two similar orbitals on one or both adjacent atoms to form π bonds. In the alkynes both p orbitals may be thought of as interacting with similar orbitals on the adjacent carbon atoms to form the C≡C bonds characteristic of these compounds. In carbon dioxide one of the p orbitals from the carbon atom forms a π bond with one of the oxygen atoms, and the second p orbital forms a π bond with the other oxygen atom.

Because sp hybrid orbitals are oriented at 180° from one another, the molecular geometry in the vicinity of carbon atoms using this hybridization is *linear*, as illustrated in Table 10.5.

Triple bonds may be changed to double bonds or, more often, to single bonds by addition reactions. These reactions are analogous to the addition reactions occurring at double bonds discussed earlier. Some examples of addition to triple bonds may be illustrated with acetylene.

$$H—C≡C—H + H_2 \longrightarrow \underset{\overset{|}{H}\ \overset{|}{H}}{H—C=C—H} \xrightarrow{H_2} \underset{\overset{|}{H}\ \overset{|}{H}}{\overset{\overset{H}{|}\ \overset{H}{|}}{H—C—C—H}}$$

$$H-C\equiv C-H + Br_2 \longrightarrow H-\underset{\underset{Br}{|}}{\overset{\overset{Br}{|}}{C}}=\underset{\underset{Br}{|}}{\overset{\overset{Br}{|}}{C}}-H \xrightarrow{Br_2} H-\underset{\underset{Br}{|}}{\overset{\overset{Br}{|}}{C}}-\underset{\underset{Br}{|}}{\overset{\overset{Br}{|}}{C}}-H$$

$$H-C\equiv C-H + HBr \longrightarrow H-\underset{\underset{H}{|}}{\overset{}{C}}=\underset{\underset{Br}{|}}{\overset{}{C}}-H \xrightarrow{HBr} H-\underset{\underset{H}{|}}{\overset{\overset{H}{|}}{C}}-\underset{\underset{Br}{|}}{\overset{\overset{Br}{|}}{C}}-H$$

Evidence for the Structure of Carbon Compounds

In the preceding sections of this chapter the wide variety of structural possibilities associated with carbon compounds was described. In most instances our current knowledge was summarized without discussion of the tremendous body of research that was needed to develop this knowledge. In this section we shall attempt to bring together a few examples of the approaches to problems, the types of experimental techniques, and the thinking that have enabled chemists to learn what they now know about the way in which atoms are linked together in carbon compounds. Many of these activities will be described in greater detail in Chaps. 29, 30, 31, and 32, but they are included here to emphasize again the nature of the knowledge-obtaining process of the scientist.

Proof of Structure. Intense work with carbon compounds began about 1825, and during the next 25 years chemists learned how to (a) make a number of organic compounds, (b) isolate the various products from the complex reaction mixtures, and (c) analyze these products and determine their formulas. From this it was discovered that a single carbon atom had the ability to combine with four hydrogen atoms or four chlorine atoms or more generally with four univalent atoms of nonmetals. The ability of carbon atoms to combine with other carbon atoms was recognized early, and this fact, coupled with the observation that carbon is tetravalent, made it possible to write structural formulas for organic compounds and to predict the existence of isomers. Time and time again the predicted number of isomers was found. However, the major problem then as now is to

Compound	Structural Formula	Compound	Structural Formula
Ethyne or acetylene	$H-C\equiv C-H$	Acetonitrile	$CH_3-C\equiv N$
		Carbon dioxide	$O=C=O$
Propyne	$CH_3-C\equiv C-H$		
1-Butyne	$CH_3-CH_2-C\equiv C-H$		
2-Butyne	$CH_3-C\equiv C-CH_3$	Allene	$\underset{H}{\overset{H}{\diagdown}}C=C=C\underset{H}{\overset{H}{\diagup}}$
Hydrogen cyanide	$H-C\equiv N$		

Table 10.5 Formulas for Some Compounds in Which Carbon Atoms Exhibit *sp* Hybridization

ascertain just which one of the various isomeric structures is to be assigned to a particular compound. The solution to this problem, known as the *proof of structure*, has been the organic chemist's stock in trade in developing the structural chemistry of carbon.

There is no single pattern or method for structure proof. Each substance presents a different challenge and the chemist must use every available device—both experimental and intellectual—to develop evidence that will enable him to assign a certain structure to the substance under consideration.

In the early days of the science, physical instruments were not available and only a meager knowledge of organic compounds existed. Hence structure proofs were based on the results of chemical reactions—i.e., on the number, yield, and analysis of the reaction products. While chemists became proficient at proving structures by this technique, it was recognized that it might be both more satisfying and simpler if procedures could be developed for determining more directly the molecular size and shape. In recent years physical techniques such as molecular spectroscopy, mass spectrometry, X-ray, and electron diffraction have made this possible, and much structure proof is now done in this way. However chemical reactions are still used in a great many cases.

The following examples illustrate how one might attack the problem of assigning a structure to a compound.

CASE I. ■ Two compounds having the molecular formula C_2H_6O have been isolated. Their melting and boiling points are:

	Compound A	Compound B
Melting point (°C)	−130	−114
Boiling point (°C)	−24.9	78.3

Since carbon is tetravalent, oxygen is divalent, and hydrogen is monovalent, the structural formulas can be written for compounds having the molecular formula C_2H_6O. Only two structures are possible:

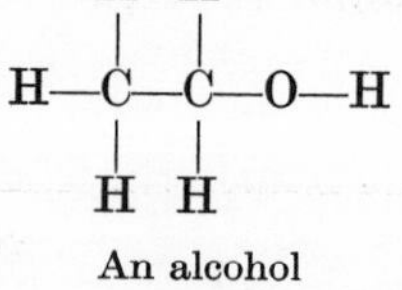

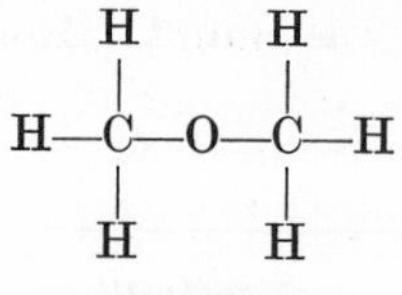

The problem is to assign one of these structures to compound A and the second to compound B. We shall try to make an assignment based on (a) an examination of the melting and boiling points, (b) some reactions which structure I can undergo but structure II cannot undergo, and (c) the synthesis of compounds having structures I and II and a comparison of the properties of those compounds with those of compounds A and B.

Deductions from physical properties. It is not difficult to guess that the *liquid* (compound B) is an alcohol and that the *gas* (compound A) is an ether, because the alcohol, containing an hydroxyl (OH) group, should have a higher boiling point due to hydrogen bonding between the molecules. On this basis then, structure I might be assigned to compound B and structure II assigned to compound A. To most chemists, however, this would not be enough evidence to consider the case settled. Perhaps an examination of some reactions of compounds A and B will supply more compelling evidence.

Evidence from chemical reactions. We might raise the question: What chemical reactions will structure I undergo that structure II cannot undergo? If we recall the reaction of sodium with water,

$$2Na + 2HOH \longrightarrow 2HO^-Na^+ + H_2$$

we might predict that structure I, having an OH group, might react similarly to liberate hydrogen.

$$2Na + 2CH_3CH_2OH \longrightarrow 2CH_3CH_2O^-Na^+ + H_2$$

The ether (structure II), having no OH group, would not be expected to undergo this reaction. Experiment shows that the introduction of a piece of sodium into compound B produces hydrogen, while the sodium is recovered unchanged when put into compound A. Further, the sodium-containing product from the reaction of compound B has the expected formula C_2H_5ONa. These results confirm the assignment based on physical properties—i.e., that compound B has structure I and compound A has structure II. There now seems little doubt as to the correctness of the assignment. However the uncontestable piece of evidence would be to prepare compounds having structures I and II by chemical reactions that can be expected to give the desired structures. The compounds thus prepared can be compared with compounds A and B.

Synthesis of structures I and II. It should be possible to synthesize structure I by adding water to the double bond of ethylene according to the equation

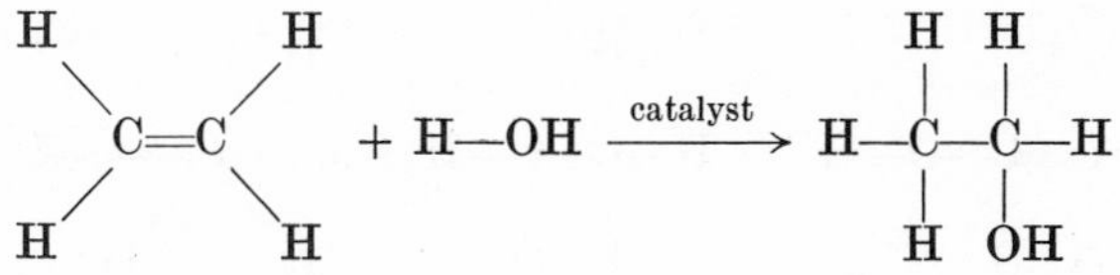

The compound prepared by this reaction has the same properties as compound B.

Structure II can be synthesized by causing methanol to react with methyl iodide.

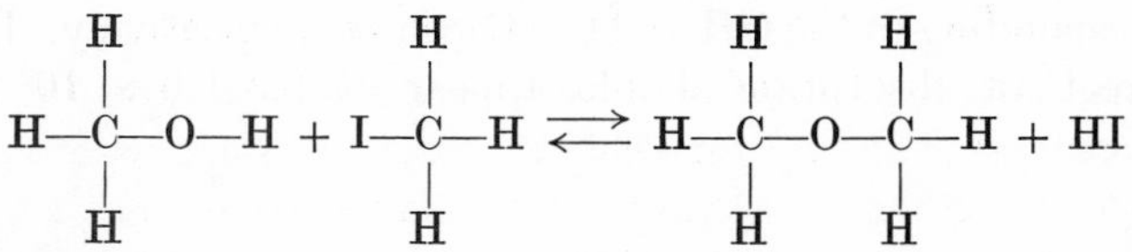

The organic product from this reaction has the same properties as compound A.

On the basis of these pieces of evidence the structure assignments for compounds A and B may be considered settled for all time.

Table 10.6 Wavelengths of Infrared Absorption Bands Characteristic of Functional Groups (angstroms × 10⁴ or microns)

Functional group	—OH	$\diagup$C=O$\diagup$	C=C	—C—H
Wavelength absorbed	2.8–3.2	5.3–6.0	6.0–6.2	3.0–3.6

Physical methods of structure determination. The principles of structure determination used above are the primary ones on which the structures of organic compounds were originally based. At the present day, however, this assignment could be made by measurement of the absorption spectra of compounds A and B. This is possible because functional groups (which have been identified on the basis of chemical properties) absorb certain characteristic wavelengths of infrared radiation. For example, alcohols, which have been chemically identified as such (by their reaction with sodium, for example), have an infrared absorption spectrum characteristic of the presence of the —OH group, while ethers, chemically identified by their inertness toward reaction with sodium, show a different spectrum, characteristic of molecules with the grouping

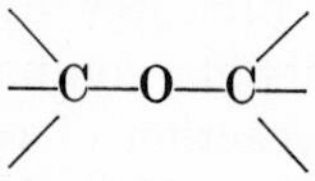

$$\diagdown\text{C—O—C}\diagup$$

It is thus no longer necessary, in many cases, to examine the chemical evidence in a "proof of structure"; one might seek to examine the absorption spectrum. Table 10.6 shows the wavelengths that are absorbed by the various functional groups in organic compounds. We can illustrate the use of infrared absorption spectra (Figure 10.17) to assign structures with the following example. However, see pages 251–255.

CASE II. ■ A certain compound has the formula C_2H_4O and we wish to assign a structure to this substance; how can we approach this problem? First we can write the possible structures corresponding to C_2H_4O. These include:

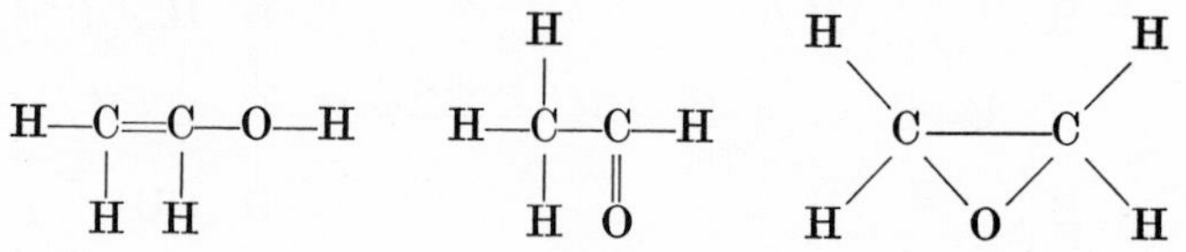

$$\begin{array}{ccc}
\text{H—C=C—O—H} & \text{H—C—C—H} & \text{C——C} \\
\text{I} & \text{II} & \text{III}
\end{array}$$

The infrared absorption spectrum of the compound should immediately tell us which of these structures is the correct one. If structure I is correct absorptions should appear in the range 2.8–3.2 × 10⁴ A and 6.0–6.2 × 10⁴ A corresponding to the OH and C=C groups, respectively. If structure II is correct an absorption should appear at 5.3–6.0 × 10⁴ A, due to the

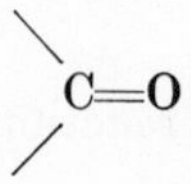

$$\diagdown\text{C=O}\diagup$$

group. If structure III is correct there will be no absorptions corresponding to OH, C=C, or C=O groups.

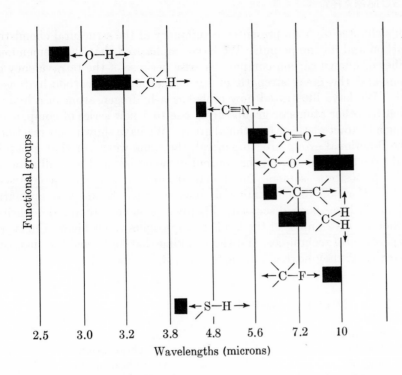

Figure 10.17 Wavelengths (in microns) of infrared radiation absorbed by various functional groups.

CASE III. ■ A chemist has prepared and isolated the compounds represented by the formulas

$$
\begin{array}{ccc}
\text{H} \qquad \text{H} & & \text{H} \qquad \text{Cl} \\
\diagdown \quad \diagup & & \diagdown \quad \diagup \\
\text{C}=\text{C} & \text{and} & \text{C}=\text{C} \\
\diagup \quad \diagdown & & \diagup \quad \diagdown \\
\text{Cl} \qquad \text{Cl} & & \text{Cl} \qquad \text{H}
\end{array}
$$

the *cis-* and *trans-*1,2-dichloroethenes, but he does not know which compound is the cis and which is the trans isomer. One of these compounds boils at 59°C, the other at 48°C. The slight difference in boiling point suggests the possibility that the attractive forces are stronger in the one compound than in its isomer. Could this mean that one of these compounds has a higher dipole moment (Chap. 5) than the other? Examination of the structures reveals that the trans isomer should have no dipole moment because the two C—Cl dipoles are so directed that they cancel one another. On the other hand the cis isomer should have a dipole moment because the two C—Cl dipoles are oriented so as to reinforce each other to some extent. When the dipole moments of these compounds are measured, it is found that the higher boiling isomer has a dipole moment of 1.8 debye while the lower boiling compound has no dipole moment. This evidence serves as the basis for the assignment of the cis structure to the liquid which boils at 59°C and the trans structure to the liquid which boils at 48°C.

It is customary to obtain evidence from several sources before making a final structure assignment.

SUMMARY

In this chapter we have presented a summary of the structural chemistry of carbon and its compounds. We have emphasized that the tremendous number of known carbon compounds arise because of the tetravalency of carbon and the great strength of carbon-carbon and carbon-hydrogen bonds. We have illustrated how replacing a hydrogen atom in a hydrocarbon by other atoms or groups gives rise to a new series of compounds having a characteristic or functional group. We have shown that reactions of the functional group are, in general, the same wherever that group is found. We have introduced the concept of isomerism and have illustrated this with position isomers, functional group isomers, and geometrical isomers. Compounds containing double or triple bonds and aromatic compounds have been discussed. Finally, we have attempted to bring together a few examples of the kinds of approaches to problems, the types of experimental techniques, and the thinking that have enabled chemists to learn what they have about carbon and its compounds.

SOME SPECIAL TERMS

Hydrocarbon
  alkenes
  alkynes
  aromatic compound
  heterocyclic aromatic compound
  polynuclear aromatic compound
  saturated compound
Organic chemistry
Isomer
  cis isomer
  functional group isomer
  geometrical isomerism
  position isomer
  trans isomer
Formula
  condensed formula
  empirical formula
  skeleton formula
  structural formula
Functional group
Resonance energy

Bonds
  sp hybridization
  sp^2 hybridization
  sp^3 hybridization
  single-bond energy
  σ bonds
  π bonds
  delocalized electrons
Structures of molecules
  conformers
  conjugated double bonds
  eclipsed forms
  scale model
  staggered forms
  strained structures
Reactions
  general
  substitution
  addition
  reaction centers

QUESTIONS AND PROBLEMS

1. Describe several of the unique characteristics of carbon atoms.
2. How do you account for the large number of compounds formed by carbon? Give examples.
3. Write the structural formula for each of the following: (a) ethane, (b) hexane, (c) isobutane, (d) cyclopentane, (e) benzene, (f) toluene, (g) acetylene, and (h) ethylene.

4. Draw a structural formula for methane and show what is meant by the tetrahedral carbon atom.

5. Cite evidence to support the conclusion that rotation around single bonds occurs within molecules.

6. Show how a number of organic compounds can be classified by functional groups.

7. Show by a chemical equation how an organic chloride can be converted to an alcohol.

8. Write the structural formulas for the isomers of hexane.

9. Calculate the percentage of hydrogen in (a) C_2H_6, (b) C_2H_4, and (c) C_2H_2. What other data, in addition to (or rather than) the percentage composition, are used to identify a compound?

10. Show by diagrams the difference between a σ bond and a π bond.

11. Contrast the chemical properties of substances containing a single bond with those of substances containing double bonds.

12. Give examples of each of the following: (a) an addition reaction, (b) a substitution reaction, (c) an unsaturated hydrocarbon, (d) a ring compound, (e) a saturated compound, (f) conjugated double bonds, (g) polynuclear aromatic compounds, (h) the three dichloro isomers of benzene, and (i) the production of acetylene.

13. Account for the aromatic character of benzene in terms of π bonding.

14. Show what orbitals are involved in common reactions of alkynes.

15. Why would you expect an alcohol (OH functional group) to have a higher boiling point than an ether with the same molecular weight?

16. What is the relation between the type of functional group and the infrared absorption spectrum of a compound?

17. What would you predict might be the relationship between freezing point and the symmetry of a molecule? (Examples: C_6H_6 and $C_6H_5CH_3$ or cis and trans isomers.) Give reasons for your prediction; then check your conclusion with appropriate data.

18. In the formation of CH_4 molecules, one s orbital and three p orbitals are used; however, the bonds are said to be equivalent. How could you show by experiment that they are equivalent?

19. What contributions did Kekulé, Wöhler, and Liebig make to organic chemistry?

REFERENCES

HART, H, and R. A. SCHUETZ. *Organic Chemistry*. 3d ed.; Boston: Houghton Mifflin, 1966.

HERZ, W. *The Shape of Carbon Compounds*. New York: Benjamin, 1963.

MORRISON, R. T., and R. N. BOYD. *Organic Chemistry*. 2d ed.; Boston: Allyn and Bacon, 1966.

ROBERTS, D., and M. C. CASERIO. *Basic Principles of Organic Chemistry*. New York: Benjamin, 1964.

11

The Periodic Table; the Noble Gases

Первая проба, сделанная в этом отношении, была
следющая{:} я отобрал тела с наименьшим атомым весом и
расположил их по порядку величины их атомного веса. При
этом оказалось, что существует [как бы] период свойств
простых тел, и даже по атомности элементы следуют друг
за другом в порядке арифметической последовательности
величины их пая.*   (Dmitri Mendeleev, 1834–1907)

The periodic table was originally devised by Mendeleev as an aid to the
memory; it still is an important memory aid used by chemists. An
extraordinary amount of information is available in this simple chart,
once the chemist has learned to interpret it. In this chapter we shall
examine how some of this information can be obtained from the periodic
table.

From an organizational viewpoint the periodic table is an arrangement
of the elements in families designated as Groups IA, IB, etc. The A groups
consist of representative elements; the B groups and Group VIII contain
transition metals; Group 0 includes the noble gases.

The modern periodic table is devised from electronic structure data. In
Chap. 4 it was shown that the electron arrangement in atoms, as indicated
from spectroscopy, is also consistent with information about the original
classification of elements in the periodic table as determined by their
properties. We showed how the families of the elements in the first two rows
and potassium and calcium in the third row follow a consistent pattern

---

* "The first attempt which was made in this direction was the following: I chose substances
of the smallest atomic weight and arranged them in the order of the value of their atomic
weights. From this it appeared that there seemed to be a periodicity in the properties of the
individual substances, and indeed that, if one considered the valences, one element followed
the other in the arithmetical sequence of their atomic weights." (The quotation is from
Journal of the Russian Chemical Society, 1, 1869.)

of electrons filling *s* and *p* orbitals. However, following calcium we find the 3*d* orbitals begin to fill before the 4*p* orbitals; hence, we find an explanation for the transition elements that were troublesome for Mendeleev to place in the table. A comparison of the rows of transition elements (see Table 11.2) with the electron configurations (see Table 4.6) leads to the discovery that the properties of these series can be explained in terms of inner *d* and *f* orbitals filling. The properties resulting from this peculiarity of electron structure will be discussed in Chaps. 26, 27, and 28.

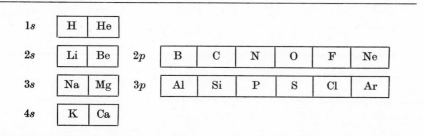

Table 11.1 *s* and *p* Valence Electron Groupings of the First Twenty Elements

But the modern periodic table gives much more information than just the electron configurations of the atoms. To learn how to extract some of this information let us first recall that we have been able to correlate many of the properties of the elements—both metals and nonmetals—discussed in Chaps. 7, 8, and 9 with the properties of their atoms—electron configuration, ionization energy, and size. If we can find a simple way to relate ionization energy and atomic size to the position of the element in the periodic table, we should have a mechanism for predicting properties of the elements or trends in these properties in moving vertically or horizontally in the table. For example, we know that as we proceed from lithium to the heavier elements in Group I the valence electron configuration of the atoms remains the same. We would predict identical behavior of these elements if we did not also know that the ionization energy decreases and the atomic size increases as we proceed down the family. The changes in ionization energy and atomic size account for the increase in reactivity, and for the increase in density of the metals as well as for variations in a number of other properties of these elements. In a similar way, if we can focus quickly on electron configuration, ionization energy, and atomic size in considering an element or a group of elements in comparison with other atoms or groups, we should be able to make predictions or correlations of many properties.

Table 11.2 The Transition Elements

Element Atomic Numbers				Element Symbols									
21–29	Sc	Ti	V	Cr	Mn	Fe	Co	Ni	Cu				
39–47	Y	Zr	Nb	Mo	Tc	Ru	Rh	Pd	Ag				
57, 72–79	La	Hf	Ta	W	Re	Os	Ir	Pt	Au				
Lanthanides													
57–71	La	Ce	Pr	Nd	Pm	Sm	Eu	Gd	Tb	Dy	Ho	Er	Tm	Yb	Lu
Actinides 89–103	Ac	Th	Pa	U	Np	Pu	Am	Cm	Bk	Cf	Es	Fm	Md	No	Lw

PERIODIC TABLE OF THE ELEMENTS Figure 11.1

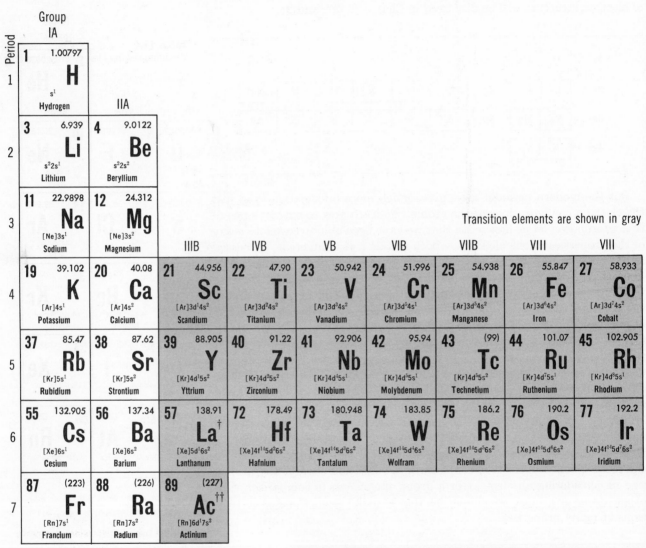

Transition elements are shown in gray

Group IA	IIA		IIIB	IVB	VB	VIB	VIIB	VIII	VIII
1 1.00797 **H** s¹ Hydrogen									
3 6.939 **Li** s²2s¹ Lithium	**4** 9.0122 **Be** s²2s² Beryllium								
11 22.9898 **Na** [Ne]3s¹ Sodium	**12** 24.312 **Mg** [Ne]3s² Magnesium								
19 39.102 **K** [Ar]4s¹ Potassium	**20** 40.08 **Ca** [Ar]4s² Calcium		**21** 44.956 **Sc** [Ar]3d¹4s² Scandium	**22** 47.90 **Ti** [Ar]3d²4s² Titanium	**23** 50.942 **V** [Ar]3d³4s² Vanadium	**24** 51.996 **Cr** [Ar]3d⁵4s¹ Chromium	**25** 54.938 **Mn** [Ar]3d⁵4s² Manganese	**26** 55.847 **Fe** [Ar]3d⁶4s² Iron	**27** 58.933 **Co** [Ar]3d⁷4s² Cobalt
37 85.47 **Rb** [Kr]5s¹ Rubidium	**38** 87.62 **Sr** [Kr]5s² Strontium		**39** 88.905 **Y** [Kr]4d¹5s² Yttrium	**40** 91.22 **Zr** [Kr]4d²5s² Zirconium	**41** 92.906 **Nb** [Kr]4d⁴5s¹ Niobium	**42** 95.94 **Mo** [Kr]4d⁵5s¹ Molybdenum	**43** (99) **Tc** [Kr]4d⁵5s² Technetium	**44** 101.07 **Ru** [Kr]4d⁷5s¹ Ruthenium	**45** 102.905 **Rh** [Kr]4d⁸5s¹ Rhodium
55 132.905 **Cs** [Xe]6s¹ Cesium	**56** 137.34 **Ba** [Xe]6s² Barium		**57** 138.91 **La**† [Xe]5d¹6s² Lanthanum	**72** 178.49 **Hf** [Xe]4f¹⁴5d²6s² Hafnium	**73** 180.948 **Ta** [Xe]4f¹⁴5d³6s² Tantalum	**74** 183.85 **W** [Xe]4f¹⁴5d⁴6s² Wolfram	**75** 186.2 **Re** [Xe]4f¹⁴5d⁵6s² Rhenium	**76** 190.2 **Os** [Xe]4f¹⁴5d⁶6s² Osmium	**77** 192.2 **Ir** [Xe]4f¹⁴5d⁷6s² Iridium
87 (223) **Fr** [Rn]7s¹ Francium	**88** (226) **Ra** [Rn]7s² Radium		**89** (227) **Ac**†† [Rn]6d¹7s² Actinium						

KEY

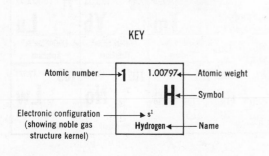

Atomic number → **1** 1.00797 ← Atomic weight
H ← Symbol
Electronic configuration → s¹ ← Name
(showing noble gas structure kernel) Hydrogen

†
6

58 140.12 **Ce** [Xe]4f²5d⁰6s² Cerium	**59** 140.907 **Pr** [Xe]4f³5d⁰6s² Praseodymium	**60** 144.24 **Nd** [Xe]4f⁴5d⁰6s² Neodymium	**61** (147) **Pm** [Xe]4f⁵5d⁰6s² Promethium	**62** 150.35 **Sm** [Xe]4f⁶5d⁰6s² Samarium
90 232.038 **Th** [Rn]6d²7s² Thorium	**91** (231) **Pa** [Rn]5f²6d¹7s² Protactinium	**92** 238.04 **U** [Rn]5f³6d¹7s² Uranium	**93** (237) **Np** [Rn]5f⁵6d⁰7s² Neptunium	**94** (242) **Pu** [Rn]5f⁶6d⁰7s² Plutonium

††
7

Noble gases

					2 4.0026 **He** s^2 Helium

IIIA	IVA	VA	VIA	VIIA	
5 10.811 **B** $s^2 2s^2 2p^1$ Boron	6 12.0111 **C** $s^2 2s^2 2p^2$ Carbon	7 14.0067 **N** $s^2 2s^2 2p^3$ Nitrogen	8 15.9994 **O** $s^2 2s^2 2p^1$ Oxygen	9 18.9984 **F** $s^2 2s^2 2p^5$ Fluorine	10 20.183 **Ne** $s^2 2s^2 2p^6$ Neon
13 26.9815 **Al** $[\text{Ne}]3s^2 3p^1$ Aluminum	14 28.086 **Si** $[\text{Ne}]3s^2 3p^2$ Silicon	15 30.9738 **P** $[\text{Ne}]3s^2 3p^3$ Phosphorus	16 32.064 **S** $[\text{Ne}]3s^2 3p^1$ Sulfur	17 35.453 **Cl** $[\text{Ne}]3s^2 3p^5$ Chlorine	18 39.948 **Ar** $[\text{Ne}]3s^2 3p^6$ Argon

VIII	IB	IIB						
28 58.71 **Ni** $[\text{Ar}]3d^8 4s^2$ Nickel	29 63.54 **Cu** $[\text{Ar}]3d^{10} 4s^1$ Copper	30 65.37 **Zn** $[\text{Ar}]3d^{10} 4s^2$ Zinc	31 69.72 **Ga** $[\text{Ar}]3d^{10} 4s^2 4p^1$ Gallium	32 72.59 **Ge** $[\text{Ar}]3d^{10} 4s^2 4p^2$ Germanium	33 74.992 **As** $[\text{Ar}]3d^{10} 4s^2 4p^3$ Arsenic	34 78.96 **Se** $[\text{Ar}]3d^{10} 4s^2 4p^4$ Selenium	35 79.909 **Br** $[\text{Ar}]3d^{10} 4s^2 4p^5$ Bromine	36 83.80 **Kr** $[\text{Ar}]3d^{10} 4s^2 4p^6$ Krypton
46 106.4 **Pd** $[\text{Kr}]4d^{10} 5s^0$ Palladium	47 107.870 **Ag** $[\text{Kr}]4d^{10} 5s^1$ Silver	48 112.40 **Cd** $[\text{Kr}]4d^{10} 5s^2$ Cadmium	49 114.82 **In** $[\text{Kr}]4d^{10} 5s^2 5p^1$ Indium	50 118.69 **Sn** $[\text{Kr}]4d^{10} 5s^2 5p^2$ Tin	51 121.75 **Sb** $[\text{Kr}]4d^{10} 5s^2 5p^3$ Antimony	52 127.60 **Te** $[\text{Kr}]4d^{10} 5s^2 5p^4$ Tellurium	53 126.904 **I** $[\text{Kr}]4d^{10} 5s^2 5p^5$ Iodine	54 131.30 **Xe** $[\text{Kr}]4d^{10} 5s^2 5p^6$ Xenon
78 195.09 **Pt** $[\text{Xe}]4f^{14} 5d^{10} 6s^0$ Platinum	79 196.967 **Au** $[\text{Xe}]4f^{14} 5d^{10} 6s^1$ Gold	80 200.59 **Hg** $[\text{Xe}]4f^{14} 5d^{10} 6s^2$ Mercury	81 204.37 **Tl** $[\text{Xe}]4f^{14} 5d^{10} 6s^2 6p^1$ Thallium	82 207.19 **Pb** $[\text{Xe}]4f^{14} 5d^{10} 6s^2 6p^2$ Lead	83 208.980 **Bi** $[\text{Xe}]4f^{14} 5d^{10} 6s^2 6p^3$ Bismuth	84 (210) **Po** $[\text{Xe}]4f^{14} 5d^{10} 6s^2 6p^4$ Polonium	85 (210) **At** $[\text{Xe}]4f^{14} 5d^{10} 6s^2 6p^5$ Astatine	86 (222) **Rn** $[\text{Xe}]4f^{14} 5d^{10} 6s^2 6p^6$ Radon

63 151.96 **Eu** $[\text{Xe}]4f^7 5d^0 6s^2$ Europium	64 157.25 **Gd** $[\text{Xe}]4f^7 5d^1 6s^2$ Gadolinium	65 158.924 **Tb** $[\text{Xe}]4f^9 5d^0 6s^2$ Terbium	66 162.50 **Dy** $[\text{Xe}]4f^{10} 5d^0 s^2$ Dysprosium	67 164.930 **Ho** $[\text{Xe}]4f^{11} 5d^0 6s^2$ Holmium	68 167.26 **Er** $[\text{Xe}]4f^{12} 5d^0 6s^2$ Erbium	69 168.934 **Tm** $[\text{Xe}]4f^{13} 5d^0 6s^2$ Thulium	70 173.04 **Yb** $[\text{Xe}]4f^{14} 5d^0 6s^2$ Ytterbium	71 174.97 **Lu** $[\text{Xe}]4f^{14} 5d^1 6s^2$ Lutetium
95 (243) **Am** $[\text{Rn}]5f^7 6d^0 7s^2$ Americium	96 (247) **Cm** $[\text{Rn}]5f^7 6d^1 7s^2$ Curium	97 (247) **Bk** $[\text{Rn}]5f^7 6d^2 7s^2$ Berkelium	98 (251) **Cf** $[\text{Rn}]5f^9 6d^1 7s^2$ Californium	99 (254) **Es** Einsteinium	100 (253) **Fm** Fermium	101 (256) **Md** Mendelevium	102 (254) **No** Nobelium	103 (257) **Lw** Lawrencium

Properties of Atoms and Positions of Elements in the Periodic Table

Correlation of Ionization Energies with Families of Elements. Figure 11.2 is a graph of ionization energy against atomic number. The stepped or zig-zag curve which results clearly shows a periodicity in ionization energy values. This periodicity correlates well with the periodic table arrangement of elements into families. For example, each of the major peaks of the curve in Figure 11.2 corresponds to the ionization energy of one member of the noble gas family of elements. The lowest points in each trough correspond to the ionization energy of the Group I elements, and so on.

It may be noted in Table 11.3, which gives values for the ionization energies of the elements, that these energies generally increase* in proceeding from left to right across a period (horizontal row) of the table and decrease in proceeding from top to bottom in a given family as discussed in Chap. 4.

Periodicity Indicated by Atomic Volumes. One of the earliest experimental observations of periodicity in the chemical elements was made in 1869 by Lothar Meyer, who examined the relationship between the volume occupied by one mole of each solid element ("atomic volume") and the atomic weight of the element. The volume occupied by one mole is easily calculated by dividing the atomic weight by the density; for tin, for example, it is:

$$\frac{18.7 \text{ g}/1 \text{ mole}}{7.31 \text{ g}/1 \text{ cc}} = \frac{118.7 \text{ g}}{1 \text{ mole}} \times \frac{1 \text{ cc}}{7.31 \text{ g}} = 16.3 \text{ cc/mole}$$

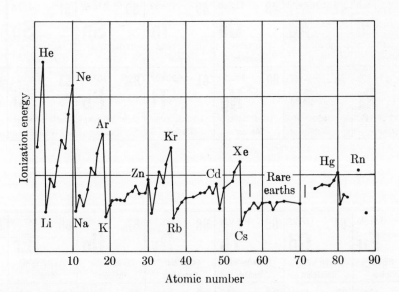

Figure 11.2 Variation of ionization energies of the elements with atomic number.

---

* While the ionization energy generally increases in proceeding from left to right across the table, there are certain anomalies. For example, the ionization energy of oxygen is less than that of nitrogen. Such anomalies, as explained in Chap. 4, are related to the subshell occupied by the electron being removed.

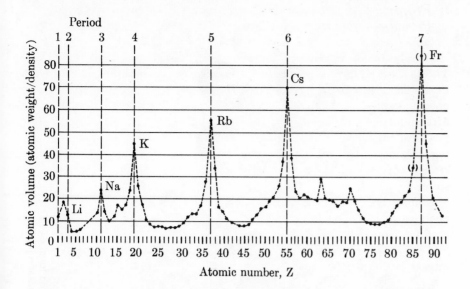

Figure 11.3 Variation of the atomic volumes of the elements with atomic number.

A graph similar to that of Meyer, using modern values of the densities and plotting the atomic volumes against the atomic number instead of the atomic weight, is given in Figure 11.3. The general similarity between this graph and that for the ionization energies in Figure 11.2 is evident, and shows that the atomic volume is also a periodic property.

A more useful measure of atomic properties would be the size of an atom itself, rather than the volume occupied by a mole of them. Atom sizes can be obtained by dividing the atomic volume by the Avagadro number, but such values are not nearly so reliable or accurate as those obtained from spectroscopic data or X-ray data of crystals.

Chemists have been able to prepare a table of atom sizes. These values are in reasonable agreement with each other regardless of the method of measurement used, and they permit a comparison of sizes of different atoms. Such a table is reproduced in Figure 11.4, where the atoms have been assumed to be spherical, and the circles have the relative radii of these spheres. We see then that in general the atomic size decreases from left to right in a period and increases from top to bottom in a group. An exception to this is the noble gases, all of which are larger than the nearest neighbor of lower atomic number.

Table 11.3 Ionization Energies of the Elements Related to Position in the Periodic Table

| X ← | — Symbol |
| 00 ← | — Ionization Energy (kcal/mole) |

H_{313}																	He_{567}
Li_{124}	Be_{215}											B_{191}	C_{260}	N_{336}	O_{314}	F_{402}	Ne_{497}
Na_{118}	Mg_{176}											Al_{138}	Si_{188}	P_{254}	S_{239}	Cl_{300}	Ar_{363}
K_{100}	Ca_{141}	Sc_{151}	Ti_{158}	V_{156}	Cr_{156}	Mn_{171}	Fe_{182}	Co_{181}	Ni_{176}	Cu_{178}	Zn_{216}	Ga_{138}	Ge_{187}	As_{231}	Se_{225}	Br_{273}	Kr_{323}
Rb_{96}	Sr_{131}	Y_{152}	Zr_{160}	Nb_{156}	Mo_{166}	Tc_{167}	Ru_{173}	Rh_{176}	Pd_{192}	Ag_{175}	Cd_{207}	In_{133}	Sn_{169}	Sb_{199}	Te_{208}	I_{241}	Xe_{280}
Cs_{90}	Ba_{120}	La_{129}	Hf_{127}	Ta_{138}	W_{184}	Re_{182}	Os_{201}	Ir_{212}	Pt_{207}	Au_{213}	Hg_{241}	Tl_{141}	Pb_{171}	Bi_{185}			Rn_{248}

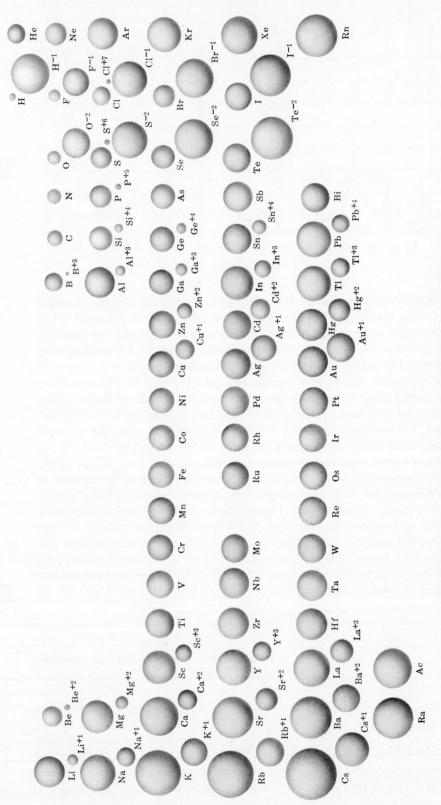

Figure 11.4 Periodic table showing relative sizes of atoms and ions. Scale : 0.2 cm = 1 A. (Adapted from Campbell, *Journal of Chemical Education.*)

Effect of Atomic Size on Ionization Energy. Comparison of Figure 11.4 with Table 11.3 and Figure 11.2 shows that the general trend is for the ionization energy to increase as the atomic size *decreases*. This is true both for changes along a row in the periodic table, and from bottom to top of a family (group). It is understandable, since the smaller the atom, the closer the electrons in the valence shell must be to the nucleus, and the more tightly they are held. These relationships are shown in Figure 11.5.

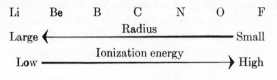

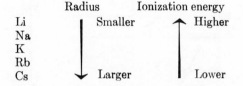

Figure 11.5 Relation of atom radius to ionization energy.

Two Effects: Increased Charge on Nucleus Versus Increased Number of Electrons. A question now arises: How is it that the sizes of the atoms increase from top to bottom in most columns in the periodic table, in spite of the increased nuclear charge, which would be expected to exert a more constricting effect on the electrons in its neighborhood? The answer must lie in the effectiveness of electrons near the nucleus in screening the nuclear charge from exerting its full effect on the more distant electrons. This is understandable on the basis of the Bohr theory, from which we can easily imagine that the electrons in the inner orbits also act to shield the electrons in the outer orbits from the full effect of the positive charge on the nucleus. The calculations on the basis of wave mechanics lead to a similar conclusion. For each model the addition of electrons in the next higher principal quantum number level causes a notable expansion in the size of the atom, as shown in the increases from fluorine (atomic number 9) to sodium (atomic number 11), from chlorine (atomic number 17) to potassium (atomic number 19).

When there is no change in the principal quantum number of the added electrons, the expected decrease in atomic size with increasing nuclear charge is observed, as in the first two rows of the periodic table. In the third row, however, there are exceptions to this prediction; note, for example, the increase in atom size in the Ni–Cu–Zn series.

Lanthanide Contraction and Its Consequences. Returning now to considerations of the trends in atomic radii in the periodic table, we note that there is no significant increase in atomic size in passing from the elements in the *second* transition series ($_{39}$Y–$_{47}$Ag) to the corresponding members of the *third* transition series ($_{57}$La–$_{79}$Au). The third transition series atoms might be expected to be the larger of the two series since they have electrons in energy levels with higher principal quantum numbers. In fact, however, we find almost the same size for corresponding atoms in the families of these two series; for example, niobium, $_{46}$Nb, and tantalum, $_{73}$Ta, in their metallic crystals, have atomic radii of 1.456 and 1.457 A, respectively. Similarly molybdenum, $_{42}$Mo, and tungsten, $_{74}$W, atoms are nearly identical in size, having radii of 1.383 and 1.395 A, respectively. This correspondence in size coupled with matching outer electron configurations for the respective members of the *second* and *third* transition series accounts for the unusual similarity in properties among members of these series. These similarities will be discussed in Chap. 28.

The explanation for the similarity in size is that the lanthanide elements are filling the 4*f* orbitals. The increase in nuclear charge without an increase in the number of electron shells under the 5*s* level results in a contraction of the atoms, which persists in the atoms following the lanthanides. This contraction is known as the lanthanide contraction (Figure 11.6).

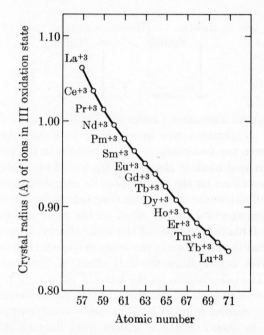

Figure 11.6   Crystal radii of lanthanide(III) ions.

Overview. Having learned the trends in ionization energies and atomic size in the periodic table we are now in a position to extend our thinking to correlations of chemical and physical properties of the elements. We have seen in general that the oxidation states of the elements are related to the valence electron configurations of their atoms (transition elements also often make use of *d* electrons and/or *d* orbitals); reactivity is related to the ease of loss or gain of electrons, with metals tending to lose and nonmetals tending to gain electrons; the larger atoms in a period or family tend to lose electrons more readily than the smaller atoms (exception: noble gases); atoms tending to lose and those tending to gain electrons usually form predominantly ionic bonds when they combine; two atoms having a tendency to gain electrons usually form predominantly covalent bonds on combination; a group of atoms all of which tend to lose electrons form metallic bonds when they interact. While these are all sweeping generalizations and must be tempered by closer examination of the properties of the atoms and the chemical or physical environment in individual cases, they are a point of departure for extracting information from the periodic table, as is discussed on the following pages.

Brief Survey of Information Stored in the Periodic Table

Group (Family) Number and Chemical Similarities. The elements in each vertical column or family in the periodic table have similar valence electron configurations. In the case of the transition elements this similarity sometimes extends to the outermost and next inner shell of electrons.

This similarity of electron configurations gives to each group chemical properties which set it apart from the other groups. All the atoms of Group IA, for example, form monovalent positive ions (e.g., Na^+), by loss of the single outer electrons; those of Group IIA form divalent ions (Ca^{+2}) by loss of the two outer electrons; those of Group VIIA form monovalent negative ions (Cl^-) by gaining a single electron to add to the seven already present in the outer shell. For the A groups, therefore, the periodic table records the number of valence electrons in the atom. This is related to combining capacity as shown in Chap. 5.

Oxidation State. The oxidation state of an element in a compound is defined as the charge which an atom of that element would have if it existed as an ion in the substance in question (Chap. 6.).

The group (family) number records the maximum positive oxidation state, and, for those elements which show a negative oxidation state, its value is eight minus the group number. For example, sulfur, a Group VI element, has a maximum oxidation state of VI and a minimum oxidation state of $-II$. There are a few exceptions, especially among transition elements, but even among the representative elements oxygen shows a maximum oxidation state of II (not VI), fluorine has no positive oxidation states, and hydrogen does not fit the pattern as a member of either Group IA or Group VIIA.

In addition to the maximum oxidation states recorded in the group numbers, many elements form compounds in which the oxidation state is less than the maximum. Chlorine, as we have seen, forms compounds in the I, III, IV, and V states as well as in the expected $-I$ and VII states (Figure 11.7).

These considerations, with some reservations, apply to transition elements. For example, manganese, a member of Group VIIB, forms compounds in all positive oxidation states from I to VII; however it also forms

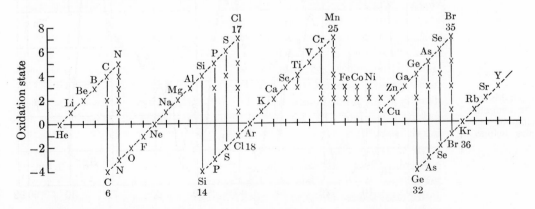

Figure 11.7 Periodicity in some common oxidation states of the lighter elements.

compounds in the −I and −III states. These compounds would not have been predicted on the basis of the generalizations of this section. Similarly the members of Groups IIIB, IVB, and VB all form compounds in the highest oxidation state predicted from their group number, but they exhibit unusual negative oxidation states. Among Group VIII elements only osmium shows an oxidation state of VIII and most of these elements show negative oxidation states. Among the Group IB elements, copper and silver form compounds in the II state and gold shows the III state in many of its compounds.

Metals and Nonmetals. As we have already seen, metals are those elements whose atoms have only a few valence electrons, which become delocalized, conduction electrons in the pure solid element; they are also elements with relatively low electronegativity. Nonmetals include those elements whose atoms have many valence electrons and form covalent compounds or electrovalent compounds in which the nonmetal is found in the negative ion; they are elements with relatively high electronegativity. The stair-step line in Figure 11.1 separates these two groups; it is evident that there are many more metallic elements than nonmetallic elements.

It must not be supposed, however, that there is an abrupt change from metallic to nonmetallic in crossing this line. As we have seen, the ionization potential generally increases across a row in the periodic table, and decreases down a column. The first of these effects means that the metals at the left-hand end of a row of the table *gradually* change toward the nonmetals of Group VII, and the second means that within a column there is in general a *gradual* change toward more metallic characteristics as one examines the elements from top to bottom. In some of the groups the

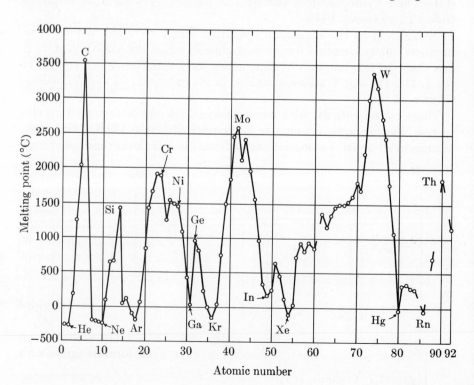

Figure 11.8 In 1869 Lothar Meyer published evidence for the periodic relationships by demonstrating the periodicity of atomic volumes, melting points, and volatility.

change from nonmetals to metals is complete; nitrogen, a nonmetal, is at the top of Group V, for example, and bismuth, a metal, is at the bottom. As one might expect, the properties of the intermediate elements tend to be intermediate between the properties of metals and nonmetals; thus, arsenic and antimony show, although weakly, some properties both of metals and nonmetals.

Trends in Electronegativity. Examination of the electronegativity values in Table 5.4 shows that the trends in electronegativity are those to be expected from a consideration of the nuclear charge, electron configuration, and size of the atoms. Small atoms will attract electrons more strongly than large atoms, and there is a general trend toward smaller electronegativity from top to bottom of each column in the A-group elements. For atoms of about the same size, the attraction for electrons should increase with increasing nuclear charge. Thus there is a general trend toward larger electronegativity from left to right in the rows of the periodic table.

Electronegativity differences between atoms provide a useful but not always accurate prediction of bond type. In Chap. 5 we saw that in general electronegativity differences of 1.7 or more resulted in the formation of predominantly ionic bonds while smaller differences usually resulted in covalent bond formation. Exceptions to this are more likely among very small atoms, very large atoms, or those in higher oxidation states. For example, in both beryllium fluoride, BeF_2 (electronegativity difference 2.0), and silicon tetrafluoride, SiF_4 (electronegativity difference 2.2), the bonding is known to be at least partially covalent. Silicon tetrafluoride has a melting point of $-90°C$. In both cases the covalent bonding is a result of several factors including the fact that both cations, should they form, would be very small and would have extremely high charge densities (in Be^{+2} a charge of $+2$ would be distributed over an ion having a radius of 0.38 A; in Si^{+4} a charge of $+4$ would be distributed over an ion having a radius of 0.41 A). Such high charge densities would result in strong attraction for and polarization of the electron clouds of the fluoride ions, thereby giving the bonds their covalent character.

Example of Trends Across a Row in the Periodic Table: Hydrogen Compounds of the Elements from Lithium to Fluorine. Since hydrogen forms compounds with each of the elements in the first row of the periodic table, these compounds (LiH, $(BeH_2)_x$, B_2H_6, CH_4, NH_3, H_2O, HF) make a convenient group for examination to illustrate trends across the table. The group is also of interest in that the electronegativity of hydrogen is intermediate between the values for the elements at the left and right ends of the first row, so that there is a change in the direction of the polarity of the bonds as we pass along from left to right. Further, as the number of electrons in the valence orbitals of the atoms changes, the configuration of the hydride molecules changes.

Let us consider as an example the melting points of the hydrides (Figure 11.9).

The very high value of the melting point of LiH hints that it is an electrovalent compound whose formula is Li^+H^-; this formula agrees with the observed crystal structure of the compound.

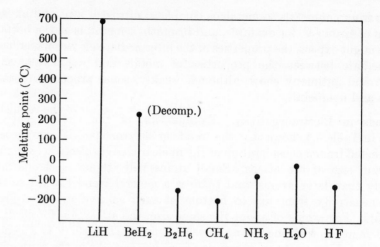

Figure 11.9 Melting points of the hydrides of second period elements.

Beryllium hydride, which has *sp* hybridization, is a linear molecule but appears to form the network structure

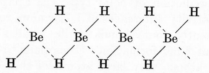

which therefore has a higher melting point than single molecules of BeH_2 would be expected to have.

The hydride of boron, also, is not formed as a single molecule but rather forms the dimer, B_2H_6, which has a higher melting point than we would expect BH_3 to have.

The molecule B_2H_6 shows an unusual type of bonding known as a *three-center bond*. Note that the predicted formula, BH_3, would give to the boron atom only six electrons; it is said to be electron deficient, meaning that there are more orbitals than there are electrons to fill them. The substance finds itself a more stable arrangement in which two hydrogen atoms form a bridge between two boron atoms, to produce the structure

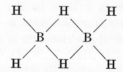

The four B—H bonds at the left and right of the structural formula are covalent, electron-pair bonds of the ordinary type, and in the diagrams as drawn they lie in a plane through the boron atoms perpendicular to the plane of the paper. The two bridge hydrogen atoms and the two boron atoms lie in the plane of the paper.

Methane, CH_4, has the highly symmetrical tetrahedral arrangement characteristic of sp^3 hybridization, and the C—H bonds are essentially nonpolar. It has the least intermolecular attraction and the lowest melting point.

The melting points of ammonia, water, and hydrogen fluoride are in some measure determined by hydrogen bonding between molecules of the compounds. The difference in electronegativity of hydrogen and oxygen makes an H—O bond polar; the angular structure produces a net dipole moment and a polar molecule; hydrogen bonding occurs; hence water has a much higher melting point than we would otherwise expect it to have.

Much the same situation exists with the NH_3 molecule as with water; it is polar covalent but is polar to a lesser extent than water. The molecule has the sp^3 bonding and has an umbrella shape as a result of the repulsion of the extra electron pair for the bonding pairs.

$$\ddot{N} \diagup\!\!\!\diagup \diagdown$$
$$H \quad H \qquad H$$

Hence the molecule has a net dipole moment resulting in an extra attraction between the molecules (Chap. 6) and a higher melting point. The attraction between molecules is increased as a result of hydrogen bonding. The extra electron pair makes the molecule a base, vulnerable to attack of other reagents, as indicated by the formation of a coordinate covalent bond in the ammonium ion, $NH_4{}^+$.

In hydrogen fluoride the hydrogen is the most positive in all the bonds we have considered. This gives the molecule the most acidic character of those considered, and it can release a proton to a water molecule when dissolved, forming H_3O^+ and F^-. The high dipole moment produces a large intermolecular attraction, but with only a single hydrogen, the molecules cannot form the extensive network of hydrogen bonds possible in the case of water, so that the melting and boiling points of hydrogen fluoride are lower than those of water.

The Noble Gases: Group 0 Elements

The periodic table was devised in 1869, but it was not until 1892 that argon, the first of the noble gases, was discovered. Of interest here is the fact that the periodic table was built to fit the then *known* elements, but with the discovery of the noble gases about a quarter of a century after the table was described we find a whole *family* of elements that fitted into the table without any necessity of revising the table. Missing elements in families had been discovered after 1869 and found to fit in place. In fact, the properties of many of them were predicted; but in the case of the noble gases we find there is a place for an entire family, Group 0.

Properties of the Noble Gases. The atoms of these elements have completed outer electron shells. Hence, their tendency to form chemical bonds is the lowest of any of the elements. For many years it was believed that these gases were totally inert.

Recently, compounds of xenon, krypton, and radon have been prepared. Examples of these compounds are given in Table 11.4. Xenon fluorides are made by allowing a mixture of xenon and fluorine to flow through a nickel tube heated to temperatures around 300°C:

$$Xe + 2F_2 \xrightarrow[\text{Ni tube}]{300°C} XeF_4$$

Table 11.4 Some Compounds of the Noble Gases

Name	Formula	Properties
Xenon hexafluoroplatinate(V)	$XePtF_6$	Orange-red solid
Xenon(VI) fluoride	XeF_6	Colorless solid, decomposes at 42°C
Xenon(IV) fluoride	XeF_4	Colorless solid, m.p., 100°C
Xenon(II) fluoride	XeF_2	Transparent solid, m.p., 120°C
Xenon(VI) oxide	XeO_3	Colorless solid, explosive
Xenic acid	$Xe(OH)_6$	Forms salts $Na_4XeO_6 \cdot 8H_2O$
Krypton(II) fluoride	KrF_2	Explosive
Radon(IV) fluoride	RnF_4	

Krypton(II) fluoride is made by irradiating a mixture of krypton and fluorine at $-150°C$ with electrons. The first noble-gas compound, xenon hexafluorplatinate(V), was made by oxidizing xenon with platinum(VI) fluoride, a stronger oxidizing agent than fluorine.

$$Xe + PtF_6 \longrightarrow Xe^+PtF_6^-$$

Slow hydrolysis of xenon(VI) fluoride with air-free water at 0°C gives xenic acid:

$$XeF_6 + 6H_2O \longrightarrow Xe(OH)_6 + 6HF$$

Salts of the acid are prepared by addition of base to an aqueous solution of the acid as in

$$Xe(OH)_6 + 4Na^+ + 6OH^- + 2H_2O \longrightarrow Na_4XeO_6 \cdot 8H_2O$$

Xenon difluoride is linear, the tetrafluoride is square-planar, and the hexafluoride is octahedral. The xenon-fluorine bond distance in xenon(IV) fluoride is 0.95 A; the xenon-oxygen bond distance is estimated to be 1.76 A in xenon(VI) oxide. The bond energy of the Xe—F bond in xenon(IV) fluoride is 32 kcal/mole; that of the Xe—O bond in xenon(VI) oxide is about 20 kcal/mole. For comparison, the bond energy of iodine molecules, I_2, is 35 kcal/mole.

Historical. *Argon.* The first clue to the existence of additional elementary gases in the atmosphere (besides oxygen and nitrogen) was obtained by Henry Cavendish. In 1785, in the course of his experiments on air, he passed electric sparks through an enclosed column of air (nitrogen and

• • •   BONDING IN NOBLE-GAS COMPOUNDS

The nature of the bonding in such compounds as XeF_2, XeF_4, and XeF_6 is still under discussion by chemists. From the fact that compounds of xenon form most readily with the highly electronegative elements, fluorine and oxygen, and that there is difficulty in forming compounds with krypton and argon, which have higher ionization energies than xenon, there seems to be little doubt that the Xe—F bond has a polar character. An assumption of completely ionic bonding, however, is incompatible with the crystal structures and volatility of the compounds, as well as with the excessively high energies which would be required to form even a doubly charged xenon atom to make Xe^{+2}, $(F^-)_2$, and a polar covalent bond is indicated. The major contribution to the bonding appears to come from the *p*-orbitals of xenon, and there is some evidence that only 5*p*-orbitals are involved in the formation of the linear molecule F—Xe—F. For the other compounds, however, contributions from hybridized 5*s* and 5*d* orbitals appear to be important in explaining the properties and structure.

oxygen), introducing more oxygen from time to time, so as to make certain that the quantity of oxygen present should be sufficient to combine with all the nitrogen. After repeated sparking, the oxides of nitrogen formed by the union of the gases, together with the excess of oxygen, were removed by absorbing them in appropriate liquids. In this experiment Cavendish observed that even after repeated trials there always remained a small residue of gas, in volume about $\frac{1}{120}$ of the air taken, which would not combine with oxygen and therefore presumably was not nitrogen.

No attention was paid to this observation until 1892, when Lord John Rayleigh observed that one liter of nitrogen prepared from its compounds was lighter by about five parts in 1000 than the same volume prepared from air. He repeated his experiments many times, always with the same results. He was inclined to explain that this discrepancy was due to a ozonelike (O_3) modification of nitrogen (N_3). Sir William Ramsay called his attention to the observation of Cavendish, and Rayleigh began to think that the difference in densities could be due to a new element. Finally, Rayleigh and Ramsay showed by means of the spectroscope that there was indeed a residue of extremely inert gas in nitrogen from air. This gas was named argon ("lazy one") because of its inert character.

Helium. In 1889 the American chemist W. F. Hillebrand found that certain minerals containing the element uranium evolve a gas when heated. After a brief investigation he concluded that the gas so evolved was nitrogen. In 1895, shortly after the discovery of argon, the attention of Ramsay

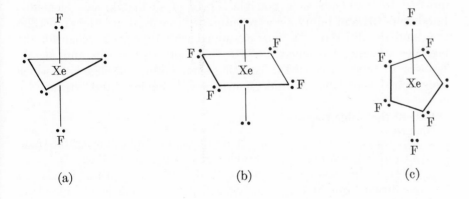

(a)   (b)   (c)

Figure 11.10 (a) XeF_2. Five pairs of electrons distributed in a trigonal bipyramid to give a linear molecule as observed; sp^3d hybridization. (b) XeF_4. Six pairs of electrons distributed in an octahedral arrangement to give a square-planar molecule as observed; sp^3d^2 hybridization. (c) XeF_6. Seven pairs of electrons distributed in a pentagonal bipyramid with fluorine atoms at the vertices, to give a distorted octahedral molecule as observed; sp^3d^3 hybridization.

One simple qualitative picture which gives the right answers suggests that all eight of the valence electrons of the xenon atom and one electron from each attached fluorine atom take part in the bonding. The structures of the molecules then arise from grouping these electrons in pairs around the xenon atom in such a way that their repulsive energies will be at a minimum, allowing for the fact that lone-pair lone-pair repulsions are usually greater than lone-pair bond-pair repulsions. These results would predict the structures in Figure 11.10.

While this qualitative picture is in agreement with the observed structures, its predictions are quantitatively incorrect, since the observed distortion from a regular octahedron for xenon hexafluoride is much smaller than would be expected if the lone-pair repulsion were really operating. Further, straightforward application of the model would predict distorted octahedra for the iso-electronic species $TeCl_6^{-2}$, $TeBr_6^{-2}$, $SbBr_6^{-3}$; actually, regular octahedra are observed.

was called to this experiment, with the suggestion that argon might be present in the gas that Hillebrand had obtained. Ramsay repeated the experiment, obtained the gas, and studied its spectrum. Some of the lines of this spectrum corresponded to no known element on the earth. Strangely enough, they did correspond to some lines found by the French astronomer Pierre Janssen in 1868 in the spectrum of the corona of the sun and attributed by Sir Joseph Lockyer to an unknown element, helium, in the atmosphere of the sun. Shortly after the identification of helium in the gases evolved on heating uranium minerals, Ramsay was able to obtain the gas in fairly pure state and study its properties. Since that time helium has been found to be a constituent of our own atmosphere, of the gases from certain springs, and of natural gas in certain regions of Texas and elsewhere.

At very low temperatures liquid helium exhibits two very unusual properties known as superfluidity and superconductivity. The superfluid liquid behaves as if it has almost no viscosity; placed in a beaker, the liquid will creep over the walls and out of the container. Superconductivity is almost infinite electrical conductivity; once a current is started in a superconductor, it may continue to flow without stimulation, sometimes even for years.

Neon, Krypton, and Xenon. Following the discovery of argon and helium an exhaustive examination of various gases was made, especially of those obtained from minerals, in the hope that still other elements might be discovered. These investigations proved fruitless until they were finally directed to liquid air as a possible source of such unknown elements. Large quantities of liquid air were subjected to careful fractional distillation, and the different fractions examined with the spectroscope for the presence of unknown elements. By this method Ramsay and M. W. Travers, in 1898, succeeded in isolating three additional elements, which were named neon, krypton, and xenon ("new," "hidden," and "stranger").

Uses of the Noble Gases.

1. The use of helium in the inflation of balloons and other lighter-than-air aircraft is especially desirable because it will not burn.
2. Workers in caissons and diving bells suffer from the "bends," a condition brought on by nitrogen which dissolves in the blood (in the lungs) at high pressure. No harm is done if the affected person

Table 11.5 Some Properties of the Noble Gases

	Boiling Point (°C)	Melting Point (°C)	Heat of Vaporization (kcal/mole)	Ionization Energy (kcal/mole)	Atmosphere Content (per cent by volume)	Stable Compounds Formed
Helium	−268.9	−272.2	0.022	567	5.24×10^{-4}	
Neon	−246.3	−248.7	0.44	497	1.82×10^{-3}	
Argon	−185.8	−189.2	1.50	363	0.764	
Krypton	−152.9	−169.0	2.31	323	1.14×10^{-3}	Yes
Xenon	−107.1	−140.0	3.27	280	8.7×10^{-6}	Yes
Radon*	−64.99		4.3	248	6×10^{-18}	Yes

* Radioactive: decays by alpha emission to polonium.

passes through a "decompression chamber"; but the nitrogen escapes as bubbles in the blood, which block circulation, if the transition from high to normal pressure is made too rapidly. An artificial atmosphere of oxygen and helium greatly lessens the danger because of the extremely low solubility of helium.

3. By evaporating liquid helium under reduced pressure, a temperature of $-272.3°C$ has been reached. Still lower temperatures have been attained (to within about 0.001° of the absolute zero) by other physical methods which also involve the use of liquid helium.

4. Neon signs consist of glass tubes of the desired forms, containing neon gas, at reduced pressure, through which an electric discharge passes. Sometimes a certain percentage of argon or helium (or both) is added to give a different color; and sometimes mercury is also introduced.

5. Argon is now extensively used in gas-filled electric-filament lamps.

SOME SPECIAL TERMS

Atomic number	Periodic law
Ionization energy	Transition element
Lanthanide contraction	Xenic acid
Noble gas	Three-center bond
Periodic function	Distorted octahedron

QUESTIONS AND PROBLEMS

1. Is the periodic law considered a qualitative or a quantitative law? Explain your answer with examples.
2. What are the transition elements? How do they fit into the periodic table?
3. If element 104 is prepared, where will it fit in the table? Explain your answer. Predict several important properties of this element.
4. Assume elements 104 to 134 are prepared in the next decade. Where would they fit in the periodic table? Explain your answer.
5. For many years the noble gases were considered to be inert. Why?
6. What are some compounds now known of the noble gases? How were they made?
7. How can you account for the fact that fluorine compounds of the high-atomic-weight noble gases are more stable than those of the low-atomic-weight gases?
8. Name several uses for the noble gases.
9. Would you expect helium to occur to a greater extent in the sun or the stars than in the earth's atmosphere? Explain your answer.
10. What is the source of radon?
11. How does the variation in the ionization energies of the elements change (a) with the increase in atom size in families of elements; (b) with the change from metallic to nonmetallic properties in rows of elements? How do you account for these variations?
12. How do you account for the anomaly that the ionization energy of beryllium is higher than that of boron?
13. What is the relationship between the atomic volume of an element and its position in the periodic table?

14. If a phenomenon called the lanthanide contraction occurs in the rare earth series, would you predict such a phenomenon also in the actinide series? Why?

15. Using the hydrides as examples, show the effect of the trend from metals to nonmetals or from low electronegativity to high electronegativity in rows across the periodic table. Explain the observed differences.

16. Make a table showing the periodic relationship observed in oxidation states and the atomic number.

17. Show how the periodic table illustrates the "simplification by classification" procedure often used by scientists.

18. How do you explain the fact that helium has 92 per cent the lifting power of hydrogen but its atomic weight is about four times the atomic weight of hydrogen?

REFERENCES

FOWLER, W. A. "Theory of the Origin of the Elements," *Scientific American*, vol. *195*, no. 3 (1956), pp. 82–91. *Chemical and Engineering News, 42* (1964), pp. 90–104.

POLLACK, G. "Solid Noble Gases," *Scientific American*, vol. *215*, no. 4 (1966), pp. 64–74.

SELIG, H., *et al.* "The Chemistry of the Noble Gases," *Scientific American*, vol. *210*, no. 5 (1964), p. 66.

SISLER, H. H. *Electronic Structure, Properties and the Periodic Law.* New York: Reinhold, 1965.

PART THREE

ENERGY AND THE
STATES OF MATTER

12

Energy and Molecules of Gases

Common air, when reduced to half its wonted extent, obtained near
about twice as forcible a spring as it had before; so this thus
comprest air being further thrust into half this narrow room, ob-
tained thereby a spring about as strong as that it last had, and
consequently four times as strong as that of the common air.
Robert Boyle (1627–1691)

The search for an understanding of the nature of the gaseous state of matter began early in the history of science, and still continues. The early work is a classic example of the deductive method of reasoning that led from the laws or habits of gases to a theory of the gaseous state—the kinetic-molecular theory. In its original form, the kinetic-molecular theory explained the behavior of gases in terms of the kinetic energy of motion of minute spheres without internal structure. The preceding chapters of this book have shown, however, that molecules are made up of atoms held together by bonding electrons, and have structures characteristic of the nature and arrangement of these atoms. Hence this chapter will later discuss the kind of mental models the scientist has made in order to interpret the nature of the internal make-up of molecules which makes it possible for them to hold energy.

The Gas Laws

The springiness of gases, their compressibility and diffusibility, aroused the curiosity of the scientists of the seventeenth century. They sought to know the nature of this thing or substance that man could not see but which had such curious properties. The scientists' studies on gases led to general laws or statements of the habits of all types of gases, and to a theory of the nature of the gaseous state. The gas laws are known by the names of their discoverers: Boyle, Charles, Gay-Lussac, Dalton, and Graham.

Boyle's Law. While studying the effect of pressure on the springiness and compressibility of air, Robert Boyle, in 1662, obtained data somewhat like that in Table 12.1 when he measured the change in volume with the

Table 12.1 Change in Volume with Change in Pressure for a Given Amount of Gas at a Constant Temperature

Pressure (mm Hg)	Volume (liters)	P × V
200	3.00	600
500	1.20	600
1000	0.600	600
1500	0.400	600

change in pressure while keeping the amount of air and the temperature constant. The data of Table 12.1 are plotted in Figure 12.1. Comparison of the data in columns 1 and 2 shows that the volume decreases as the pressure increases.

Data similar to those of Table 12.1 can be obtained for any kind of gas, they show that the qualitative effect of a decrease in volume when the pressure is increased is common to all gases.

A further study of the data in column 3 of Table 12.1 reveals that the product of the pressure times volume is a constant value:

$$PV = \text{constant value} = K \quad \text{[amount and temperature constant]} \quad (1)$$

or, for a given quantity of gas at two different pressures, P_1 and P_2:

$$P_1V_1 = P_2V_2, \quad \text{or} \quad \frac{V_1}{V_2} = \frac{P_2}{P_1} \quad (2)$$

The results above may be summarized in the *quantitative* statement known as Boyle's law: *The volume which a gaseous substance occupies is inversely proportional to the pressure under which it is measured, provided that the temperature and the amount of gas are held constant.* The significance of the phrase "inversely proportional" may be better understood

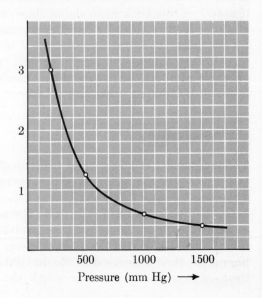

Figure 12.1 Graphic representation of the data in Table 12.1. The effect on the volume of change in the external pressure of the gas at a constant temperature.

by dividing both sides of the experimental Equation (1) by P to obtain the equation in the following form:

$$V = K \times \frac{1}{P} \qquad \text{[amount and temperature constant]} \qquad (3)$$

This shows in symbols that the volume is proportional to the reciprocal of the pressure, that is, *inversely* proportional to the pressure, and that K is the proportionality constant. The value of K, however, depends upon the amount and kind of gas, upon the temperature, and, of course, upon the units used for P and V.

Methods of Measuring Gas Pressures: the Mercury Barometer. In the experiments recorded in Table 12.1, the pressure is given in millimeters of mercury. This unit of measurement implies that the pressure-measuring instrument was adapted from a mercury barometer. Such an instrument may be constructed by filling a glass tube (about 80 cm long and closed at one end) with mercury, and then inverting it and thrusting the open end into a well of mercury. The mercury column falls until the weight of the mercury in the tube is exactly equal to the weight of a column of air of a cross section equal to that of the mercury column and extending from the surface of the mercury in the well to the top of the atmosphere. As the weight of the air changes, owing to changes in the atmospheric pressure, the level of the mercury in the tube moves up or down. The height of the mercury column, read off on a meter stick placed alongside, thus serves as a measure of the atmospheric pressure (see Figure 12.2).

Above the mercury in the tube is a vacuum called the Torricellian vacuum in honor of the Italian, Evangelista Torricelli, who, while a young student assistant of Galileo, made the first barometer in very much this way about 1643.

Units of Pressure. From the measurement of the height of the mercury column which the gas can support with its pressure, we obtain the term *millimeters of mercury*, or *torr* (after Torricelli), as the pressure unit. Other units are also used frequently. The average barometer reading at sea level is 760 mm Hg (760 torr), and the pressure may be expressed in multiples or fractions of an *atmosphere* (abbreviated *atm*). A pressure, it may be remembered, is a force per unit area, and this is expressed as *dynes per square centimeter*, or in the common English units of pressure: *pounds per square inch* (abbreviated *psi*).

Charles' Law. Experiments show that all gases expand when the temperature is raised (if the pressure is kept constant). To make this *qualitative* statement *quantitative*, experiments must be performed to show *how much* the volume of a given quantity of gas changes for a *measured* change in temperature at constant pressure. The results of four such experiments are given in Table 12.2.

By trying various mathematical operations with these data, we find that a graph of the volume against the temperature gives, for each case, a straight line, as shown in Figure 12.3. The slopes and intercepts of these lines differ according to the amount of gas used (A compared to C), the (constant) pressure under which the measurements are carried out

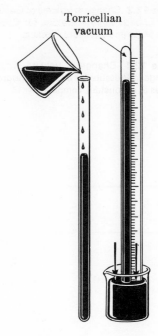

Torricellian vacuum

Figure 12.2 A simple barometer made by filling a glass tube with mercury and inverting it in a well of mercury.

Table 12.2 Change in Volume of Gases with Change in Temperature, for Constant Mass and Constant Pressure

Temperature (°C)	A Volume (liters) of 1 g O_2 at 1,500 torr	B Volume (liters) of 1 g O_2 at 2,500 torr	C Volume (liters) of 0.5 g O_2 at 1,500 torr	D Volume (liters) of 0.5 g SO_2 at 1,500 torr
−33	0.312	0.187	0.156	
+7	0.364	0.218	0.182	
+47	0.416	0.250	0.208	0.104
+87	0.468	0.281	0.234	0.117
+127	0.520	0.312	0.260	0.130

(compare A with B), and the kind of gas used (C and D). The curious fact emerges, however, that if the curves are extended (extrapolated) to lower and lower temperatures, *all four meet at the same point*, which lies on the temperature axis at −273°C (more precisely, −273.15°C). This means that if we could lower the temperature of a gas to −273°C, the gas would occupy zero volume, regardless of the *kind of gas*, the *weight* of it present, or the *pressure* under which it was measured. Of course, such a contraction to zero volume could never occur, because before such a low temperature was reached the gas would have changed to a liquid or a solid.

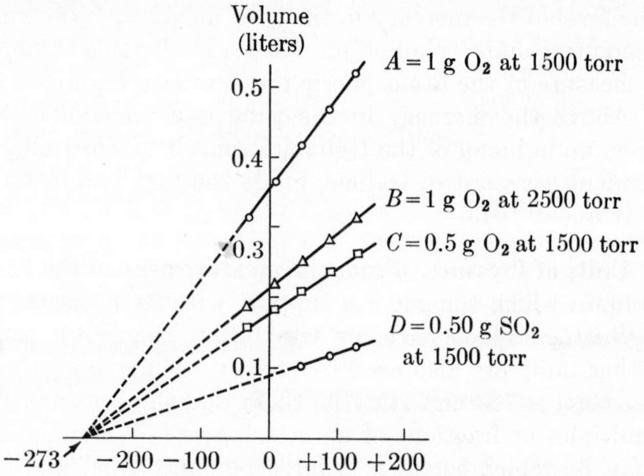

Figure 12.3 Graphic representation of the data in Table 12.2—the effect on the volume of varying the temperature of a gas at constant pressure. The curves, when extrapolated, all cross the temperature axis at the same point.

Absolute Temperature. Nevertheless, we should take advantage of such a uniformity of behavior of all gases at temperatures where they are still gases, and we do this by changing the zero of the temperature scale to −273°C. On this new *absolute temperature scale*, zero of temperature corresponds to zero of volume, and the *volume* becomes *directly proportional to the absolute temperature, provided that the quantity of gas and its pressure remains constant*. This italicized sentence is a statement of Charles' law; expressed in symbols it is

$$V = K'T \qquad \text{[amount and pressure constant]} \qquad (4)$$

where T is an absolute temperature and K' a proportionality constant. This is an equation for a straight line of zero intercept, as shown in Figure

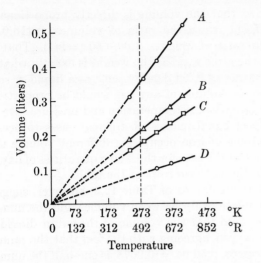

Figure 12.4 The gas volumes of Table 12.2 plotted as a function of absolute temperature.

12.4 for the data of Table 12.2. The value of the proportionality constant K' again depends upon other conditions, which are specified in the concluding phrase in the statement of the law: "provided that the quantity of gas and its pressure remains constant."

Two absolute temperature scales are in use. The more common one, known as the *Kelvin* scale, maintains the size of the degree the same as the size of the Centigrade degree, but changes the zero point by 273, so that $0°K = -273°C; 273°K = 0°C; 373°K = 100°C;$ etc. These values are given in the upper row of figures on the horizontal axis of Figure 12.4. The other scale is known as the *Rankine* scale, built on the Fahrenheit scale by shifting the zero point by 460 (precisely, 459.67). Thus $0°R = -460°F, 460°R = 0°F, 492°R = 32°F = 0°C,$ and, of course, $0°R = 0°K.$ The lower row of figures in Figure 12.4 gives the Rankine temperatures. The Rankine scale is frequently used by engineers.

A useful form of Equation (4) for the same quantity of gas at two different temperatures is

$$\frac{V_1}{V_2} = \frac{T_1}{T_2} \tag{5}$$

Dependence of Volume upon the Amount of Gas. Boyle's law and Charles' law describe the dependence of volume upon the pressure and temperature for constant quantity of gas. What, now, is the dependence of volume upon the quantity, for fixed pressure and temperature?

The data necessary are already available in Table 12.2. If we choose the temperature 47°C and the pressure 1,500 torr, we find the three sets of values in the first and third columns of Table 12.3. Comparison of the first

Table 12.3 Volume as a Function of Quantity of Gas at 47°C and 1,500 torr

Quantity	Molecular Weight	Volume (liters)	Moles
1.00 g O_2	32	0.416	0.0312
0.50 g O_2	32	0.208	0.0156
0.50 g SO_2	64	0.104	0.0078

two rows of the table shows that the volume is directly proportional to the weight of oxygen present, since the ratio of volumes, 0.416/0.208 (= 2/1), is the same as the ratio of weights, 1.00/0.50 (= 2/1). That the volume should increase in the same ratio as the weight is exactly what we should expect for any substance of fixed density, such as a liquid or solid, and we would predict that the volume of any gas would be proportional to the weight of it present, at constant temperature and pressure. On the other hand, we might expect equal masses of *different* gases to occupy *different* volumes, just as 100 g of iron occupies a different volume than 100 g of silver, and this is in fact the case for the 0.50 g quantities of oxygen and sulfur dioxide listed in the last two rows of the table.

Examination of the last two columns of Table 12.3, however, suggests that there exists a definite relationship between volumes and the number of moles of gas, when it is noted that the volume of the sulfur dioxide is one-half the volume of the oxygen, agreeing with the fact that the number of *moles* of sulfur dioxide present, 0.50/64 = 0.0078, is one-half the number of moles of oxygen, 0.50/32 = 0.0156. Since a mole represents a definite number of molecules, the implication is that the volume is determined by the number of molecules present, as if each molecule of a gas required a certain amount of space, no matter what its weight or chemical nature. This was in fact suggested in 1811 by Amedeo Avogadro in his statement, often known as Avogadro's law, that *equal volumes of all gases, measured at the same temperature and pressure, contain the same number of molecules*.

The relationship suggested by the data for oxygen and sulfur dioxide is found to be general, and we write it in symbols:

$$V = K''n \qquad \text{[constant temperature and pressure]} \qquad (6)$$

where n is the number of moles present. Equation (6), like the two preceding equations, Equations (3) and (4), holds for all gases, with the value of K'' depending upon the values of the chosen temperature and pressure.

The General Gas Law. The three variables considered above, namely, pressure, temperature, and number of moles, are independent of each other. The experimenter can change the volume and any one of the three, without affecting the values of the other two. Equations (3), (4), and (6) show that the volume is proportional to $1/P$, to T, and to n. It is an axiom of algebra that a quantity which is proportional to each of several independent variables is proportional to their product, and we write

$$V = R \times n \times T \times \frac{1}{P} \qquad (7)$$

using the conventional symbol, R, for the over-all proportionality constant. Rearrangement gives

$$PV = nRT \qquad (8)$$

We say that a *perfect* or *ideal* gas is one that obeys this equation.

Equation (8) connects all the experimental variables affecting the expansion or compression of a perfect gas. By rearrangement to the form

$$\frac{PV}{nT} = R \qquad (9)$$

the product of pressure times volume divided by the product of moles times absolute temperature has a constant value, R, for a perfect gas.

Actually, under ordinary laboratory conditions, most *real* gases obey Equation (8) closely enough so that it can be used for all purposes in which high accuracy is not required. However Equation (8) cannot be used for accurate calculations of gas volumes at *high pressure* and *low temperature* for reasons that will be discussed later. But for all gases the value PV/nT approaches the constant value of R at *low* pressures and *high* temperatures.

Derivation of the Gas Laws from the General Equation $PV = nRT$. Since the general equation or law was obtained from Equations (3), (4), and (6), we must be able to derive or retrieve those equations from it.

Boyle's Law. If we keep n and T constant then the equation $PV = nRT$ becomes $PV = K$ or $V = K \times 1/P$, which is Equation (3). This can be converted to the form

$$\frac{V_1}{V_2} = \frac{P_2}{P_1}$$

which is Equation (2).

PROBLEM ■ Calculate the volume occupied by a certain sample of gas at 760 torr if at 700 torr and at the same temperature its volume is 1,000 ml.

SOLUTION
Since n and T are fixed ("a certain sample"; "at the same temperature"), the conditions of Equation (2) are satisfied. Tabulation gives

$$P_1 = 700 \text{ torr} \qquad P_2 = 760 \text{ torr}$$
$$V_1 = 1000 \text{ ml} \qquad V_2 \text{ is to be found}$$

Substituting and rearranging,

$$V_2 = \frac{700 \text{ torr} \times 1000 \text{ ml}}{760 \text{ torr}} = 923 \text{ ml}$$

Charles' Law. If we keep n and P constant then equation $PV = nRT$ reduces to $V = K'T$, which is Equation (4) and which can be converted to the form

$$\frac{V_1}{V_2} = \frac{T_1}{T_2}$$

which is Equation (5).

PROBLEM. ■ Calculate the volume occupied by a certain sample of gas at 25°C if at the same pressure and at 0°C its volume is 1.14 liters.

SOLUTION
Since n and T are fixed ("a certain sample"; "at the same pressure") Equation (5) applies. Tabulation gives

$$V_1 = 1.14 \text{ liters} \qquad V_2 \text{ to be found}$$
$$T_1 = 0 + 273 = 273°\text{K} \qquad T_2 = 25 + 273 = 298°\text{K}$$
$$\frac{V_1 \times T_2}{T_1} = \frac{1.14 \times 298}{273} = V_2 = 1.24 \text{ liters}$$

Gay-Lussac's Law. If we keep n and V constant then equation $PV = nRT$ reduces to $P = K''T$ which is a law derived by Gay-Lussac.

Volume as a Function of Both Pressure and Temperature at Constant Number of Moles. In the laboratory we often wish, for comparison with the data of other investigators, to convert the volume of a gas measured at our laboratory conditions of pressure P_1 and temperature T_1 to the volume it would occupy at some other pressure P_2 and temperature T_2. Here the number of moles n is in constant and equation (7) becomes

$$PV = K'''T \quad \text{or} \quad \frac{PV}{T} = K'''$$

Hence for values of V_1 and V_2 at P_1 and P_2 as well as T_1 and T_2,

$$\frac{P_1 V_1}{T_1} = \frac{P_2 V_2}{T_2} \tag{10}$$

Standard Conditions. In order conveniently to compare gas volumes, a set of pressure and temperature conditions have been chosen as 760 torr pressure and 0°C. Any convenient set could have been chosen but these are agreed upon and called *standard* conditions.

PROBLEM. ■ Calculate the volume at standard conditions which will be occupied by a gas which measured 635 ml at 721 torr and 27°C.

SOLUTION

Equation (10) applies, since no change in the number of moles is indicated. We have

$$P_1 = 721 \text{ torr} \qquad P_2 = 760 \text{ torr}$$
$$T_1 = 27 + 273 = 300°\text{K} \qquad T_2 = 0 + 273 = 273°\text{K}$$
$$V_1 = 635 \text{ ml} \qquad V_2 \text{ is to be found}$$

Solving Equation (10) for V_2 and substituting,

$$V_2 = \frac{P_1 V_1 T_2}{P_2 T_1} = \frac{721 \times 635 \times 273}{760 \times 300} = 549 \text{ ml}$$

Answers to problems such as this should be checked to see that they are at least qualitatively correct. In this case both the pressure increase and the temperature decrease require a diminution of volume, by Boyle's law and Charles' law. Since 549 is less than 635, the answer is of the correct magnitude.

Numerical Values of R. In all the solved problems above, the conditions were such that the constant R canceled. To use the general equation (7) the numerical value of R must be known. To obtain this, we measure the volume V occupied by a known number of moles at a measured low pressure (P) and high temperature (T), where the gas behaves more nearly as a perfect gas, and substitute these values in Equation (9), $PV/nT = R$.

For $n = 1.00$ mole, $P = 1.00$ atm, $T = 273°\text{K}$, we find V = 22.4 liters and

$$\frac{PV}{nT} = R = \frac{1 \text{ atm} \times 22.4 \text{ liters}}{1 \text{ mole} \times 273°\text{K}} = 0.0821 \text{ liter-atm/deg/mole}$$

The value of R and its units will depend upon the units used for P, V, n, and T (Table 12.4). In this chapter

$$R = 0.0821 \text{ liter-atm/°K/mole}$$

will be used most often. Later we shall find that

$$R = 1.987 \text{ cal/°K/mole}$$

will be used often.*

Calculations from the Perfect Gas Equation When R Is Known. The perfect gas law may be used to calculate a value for any one of the four variables if the other three are known.

PROBLEM. ■ Calculate the pressure that will be exerted by 0.200 mole of a perfect gas in a 50.0-liter flask at 25°C.

SOLUTION
Solving the perfect gas law for pressure, we obtain

$$P = \frac{nRT}{V} = \frac{(0.200 \text{ mole}) \times \left(0.0821 \dfrac{\text{atm} \times \text{liters}}{\text{moles} \times \text{°K}}\right) \times (298°\text{K})}{(50.0 \text{ liters})}$$
$$= 0.0979 \text{ atm}$$

The perfect gas law may also be used to calculate the gram-molecular weight of a gas. The perfect gas law equation must be revised as follows to calculate this value.

The number of moles is equal to the mass of gas, g, divided by the gram-molecular weight of the gas, M, or $n = g/M$, hence we may substitute g/M for n in the perfect gas law and obtain the expression

$$PV = \frac{g}{M}RT \qquad \text{or} \qquad M = \frac{gRT}{PV} \tag{11}$$

Table 12.4 Values and Units of R

Pressure	Volume	Temperature	Quantity	Value of R
Atmospheres	Liters	Degrees Kelvin	Gram-mole	0.0821 liter atm/deg/mole
Torr	ml	Degrees Kelvin	Gram-mole	62,400 torr ml/deg/mole
Dynes per sq cm	Cubic cm	Degrees Kelvin	Gram-mole	8.31×10^7 ergs/deg/mole
Dynes per sq cm	Cubic cm	Degrees Kelvin	Gram-mole	1.987 cal/deg/mole
Pounds per sq in.	Cubic ft	Degrees Rankine	Pound-mole*	10.71 psi ft^3/deg R/lb-mole

* *R in English Units.* Although a mole has been defined as an Avogadro number of particles (molecules), it is also shown that the weight of a mole of molecules is equal to its molecular weight in grams. This has prompted engineers to define a mole (usually called a pound-mole) as equal to the molecular weight in pounds. Such a pound-mole contains 2.73×10^{26} molecules, and, of course, a pound-mole of a gas at a given temperature and pressure occupies a larger volume than a gram-mole. If the other variables in Equation (8) are also expressed in English units—pounds per square inch, cubic feet, degrees Rankine—the value of R is found to be 10.71 psi cubic feet per degree Rankine per pound mole.

This equation says that if we know the pressure, temperature, volume, and mass of a perfect gas we can calculate its gram-molecular weight.

PROBLEM. ■ 0.533 g of a perfect gas occupies a volume of 250 ml at 740 torr pressure and 25.0°C. Calculate its gram-molecular weight.

SOLUTION

$$M = \frac{gRT}{PV} = \frac{(0.533 \text{ g}) \times \left(0.0821 \frac{\text{atm} \times \text{liters}}{\text{moles} \times {}^\circ\text{K}}\right) \times (298{}^\circ\text{K})}{\left(\frac{740}{760} \text{ atm}\right) \times (0.250 \text{ liters})} = 33.2 \text{ g/mole}$$

The perfect gas law may also be used to calculate the gas density at a specified temperature and pressure. Can you show how this calculation can be made?

Dalton's Law and Graham's Law. In addition to the generalization obtained from experiments on the pressure-volume-temperature-amount relationship of gases, the results of two other sets of experiments, formalized as Dalton's law and Graham's law, throw light on the properties of gases.

Dalton's Law. As a result of a large number of experiments which he conducted with mixtures of gases, John Dalton found that, *in a mixture of gases, the total pressure is equal to the sum of the pressures each gas would exert if it alone were present in the volume occupied by the mixture.* Thus if p_1 and p_2 are the partial pressures gases 1 and 2 would exert if they were alone, the total pressure is

$$P = p_1 + p_2 \tag{12}$$

A frequent use of Dalton's law is to calculate the pressure p_2 of a gas when P and p_1 are known as in the example below.

PROBLEM. ■ If oxygen is collected over water at 25°C and a total pressure of 740 torr, what is the pressure due to the oxygen (i.e., its partial pressure) (Figure 12.5)?

SOLUTION

$P = 740$ torr (if the water levels inside and outside the test tube are equal)

$p_{\text{water}} = 24$ torr (This is the pressure of water vapor over liquid water at 25°C. See Table 3, Appendix B.)

$p_{\text{oxygen}} = P - p_{\text{water}} = 740 - 24 = 716$ torr

The partial pressure of each individual gas is determined by the number of moles of it present; if n_1 and n_2 moles of each one is present, then

$$P = \frac{n_1 RT}{V} + \frac{n_2 RT}{V} \tag{13}$$

where V is the total volume of the mixture.

Graham's Law. The Scot, Thomas Graham, carried out a series of studies on the rate at which gases would pass through the fine holes in unglazed pottery. He found that the volumes of different gases, measured at the same pressure and temperature, which passed through in a given time

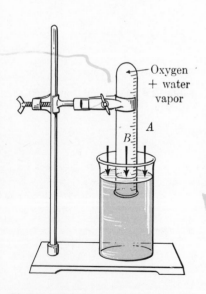

Oxygen + water vapor

A

B

Figure 12.5 Measuring the volume of a gas collected over a liquid. When the liquid levels are the same inside and outside the container, the pressure of the atmosphere (at A) is exactly balanced by the pressure inside the vessel (at B).

depended inversely upon the square root of the densities of the gases. If the volume passing through in unit time is defined as the rate of diffusion, we may express this result as

$$\frac{\text{Rate gas}_1}{\text{Rate gas}_2} = \sqrt{\frac{\text{density gas}_2}{\text{density gas}_1}}$$

Graham's Law

The general gas law shows that the density is directly proportional to the molecular weight at constant pressure and constant temperature [density $= g/V = P/RT \times M$, from Equation (11)], so that Graham's law may also be written

$$\frac{\text{Rate gas}_1}{\text{Rate gas}_2} = \sqrt{\frac{\frac{P}{RT} M_2}{\frac{P}{RT} M_1}} = \sqrt{\frac{M_2}{M_1}} \qquad (14)$$

where M_1 and M_2 are the molecular weights of gases 1 and 2 respectively. Note that the lighter gas diffuses more rapidly than the heavier.

PROBLEM. ■ Calculate how much more rapidly hydrogen will diffuse than oxygen.

SOLUTION
Substituting molecular weights in Equation (14),

$$\frac{\text{Rate H}_2}{\text{Rate O}_2} = \sqrt{\frac{32}{2}} = \frac{4}{1}$$

Hydrogen diffuses four times more rapidly than oxygen.

The Meaning of Laws in Science. The five laws just considered are merely general statements in regard to the conduct of gases *as determined by experiment.* Like all other scientific laws, they offer no explanation of the facts which they state, nor do they place any restriction upon nature which compels obedience, as the laws of a country bind society. They are simply concise statements of what might be called the *habits of nature* as observed in experiment.

The Kinetic-Molecular Theory

Forming a Theory. Now that we have found it possible to describe in concise form (laws) the conduct of gases under varying conditions of temperature and pressure, many questions arise in our minds. Why do all gases expand and contract in the same way, regardless of their other widely differing properties? Why does heating a gas cause it to expand? How does a gas exert pressure?

To answer these questions we begin by a process of imagining. We imagine that the similar conduct of all gases is probably due to some simple mechanical structure which they all share, and we try to form a mental picture of this structure. *The process of constructing a mental picture of this kind is called forming a theory;* the structure which we imagine is often called a *model.* After constructing a theory and a model which answers all our questions, we then try to make the theory and the

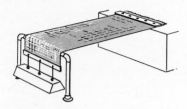

A continuous fabric resists stretching.

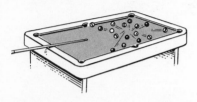

Individual particles may be separated easily.

A stream of bullets directed at a suspended target pushes the target back.

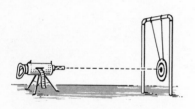

A stream of molecules directed at a piston tends to push the piston back. An opposing force on the piston required to keep the piston from moving, when divided by the area of the piston, measures the pressure of the gas.

model serve as the basis for the prediction of new effects and try to find new facts and laws which will subject the theory and model to severe and critical test. One of the most penetrating and far-reaching of all our theories, and one of the most fertile in prediction and forecast, is the famous *kinetic-molecular theory of gases*. So much evidence has now been collected in support of this theory that scientists no longer doubt that it is a truthful picture of things as they really are. To illustrate how a theory might evolve, let us take several important properties which all gases have in common and imagine, if we can, the kind of internal structure a gas must have in order to display these properties. For convenience, we can prepare three columns: one for the observation, another to summarize the thinking in connection with it, and a third for a summarizing statement or postulate of the evolving theory.

Observation	Thinking	Postulate
Gases are infinitely *expansible*.	For this to be possible the internal structure of a gas must be discontinuous—composed of small pieces. If it were continuous, the fabric could be stretched so far and no farther, and there would be a limit to the expansibility.	1. All gases are made up of minute particles. Let us call them molecules; in a few cases these particles are atoms.
Gases move from place to place in *diffusion*.	If the particles are in motion, they can move from place to place. Since gases move in all directions, the motion of the particles must be in all directions.	2. The molecules are in chaotic motion.
Gases are highly *compressible*.	There must be a tremendous amount of empty space available for compressing the gas.	3. The molecules are very small compared to the distances between them.
The gas exerts a *pressure*, that is, a force, on the walls of the container, or on a piston in a cylinder containing the gas.	This would be easy to explain if the gas were continuous, since the gas, like a compressed spring, would push back on the piston.	
	It could be explained on the basis of moving particles if the particles bombard the piston exerting a force somewhat like that produced by a stream of machine-gun bullets striking a target.	4. Pressure results from the bombardment of the walls of the container by the moving molecules.
The pressure remains *constant over long periods of time*, if the temperature, volume, and amount of gas remain constant.	The average speed and average kinetic energy of the particles must remain constant under these conditions, even though collisions between particles must be occurring constantly.	5. No energy is lost by the molecules as a result of collisions; that is, all collisions between molecules and molecules and between molecules and the walls are elastic.

Observation	Thinking	Postulate
At constant volume and constant amount of gas, the pressure is directly proportional to the absolute temperature (a quantitative statement).	For the pressure to increase, either the frequency of collisions with the wall must increase, or else the force of each collision must increase, or both. Since it is unreasonable to think that the mass of the molecule changes with change in temperature, we guess that the speed of motion changes. However if the speed were proportional to the temperature, both the frequency of collision and the force of each collision would change and the pressure would increase as the square of the temperature. To make the pressure proportional to the first power of the temperature, the speed must be proportional to the square root of the temperature.	6. The kinetic energy, $\frac{1}{2}mv^2$, is proportional to the absolute temperature.

The postulates given above constitute a formal statement of the kinetic-molecular theory. Although these postulates were developed much more extensively and convincingly than we have done here, nevertheless the treatment given above is illustrative of a scientist's approach to model building or theory making.

Molecular Motion. The implications of the kinetic-molecular theory are many and exciting. Not only does it postulate the existence of tiny particles, each of which must have a definite mass, but it also postulates that the particles are in constant motion, having velocities that increase as the temperature increases.

The ceaseless random motion, or thermal agitation, of the molecules is really *heat* itself, or, rather, the *kinetic energy* of this random motion of the molecules is heat. A great many effects of various sorts find their explanation in terms of this heat motion. For instance, the tendency of a gas to spread, or *diffuse*, is attributed to the moving molecules darting here and there. The molecules travel at high velocity, like bullets, in straight lines except when they strike the walls of the containing vessel or bump into one another and bounce off like billiard balls. The pressure of a gas against the containing walls is the result of a continuous bombardment of the walls by the moving molecules, just as the flying fists of a fighter in the prize ring push his opponent back against the ropes. The magnitude of the pressure depends upon the rapidity of the bombardment—the number of collisions with the walls occurring in unit time—and the force with which the molecules strike. This concept of the pressure of a gas as the result of a bombardment of the walls by the moving molecules makes it possible to explain the observed pressure-volume-temperature relationships of gases as recorded in the gas laws.

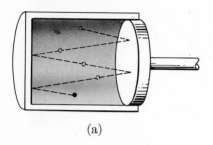

(a)

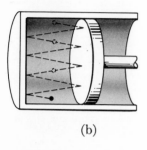

(b)

Figure 12.6 Illustrating the motion of gas molecules in a container.

Boyle's Law. Consider an idealized case in which there is only a single gas molecule in a container; let it be moving in a horizontal direction, so that it bounces back and forth from one wall to the other [Figure 12.6 (a)]. It will be moving at a certain speed, so that it will take a definite time to get back and forth. Suppose that the size of the container and the speed are such that it makes four thousand collisions with the right-hand wall in a certain time interval, say, one second, and in so doing produces a certain pressure. Now suppose that the volume of the vessel is decreased to one half by moving the wall on the right closer to the wall on the left [Figure 12.6(b)]. In the same time interval as before, the molecule will make *eight* thousand round trips instead of four thousand, since it has only half as far to go. Hence it will make twice as many collisions with the right-hand wall as before, and the pressure, which depends upon the number of collisions in a given time, will be twice as great. This is Boyle's law, that halving the volume has doubled the pressure, or *the volume is inversely proportional to the pressure.*

Gay-Lussac's Law and Charles' Law. According to the sixth postulate of the kinetic-molecular theory, the kinetic energy is proportional to the absolute temperature. The kinetic energy of any moving particle is given by the expression $\frac{1}{2}mv^2$, where m is the mass and v the speed. Since experiment shows that mass is not altered by a change in temperature, any change in the kinetic energy of a molecule that is produced by a change in temperature must come about by a change in the speed with which the molecule is moving. Hence, if we return to the situation pictured in Figure 12.6(a), and raise the temperature of the gas, the molecule at the higher temperature will make the transit from wall to wall in a shorter time than before. Furthermore, since the molecule is moving faster, it will hit harder. As a result of these two effects (an increased frequency of impact and a greater impact), the pressure on the walls is increased at the higher temperature. This is Gay-Lussac's law, that *the pressure of a gas is proportional to the absolute temperature, at constant volume.* If the pressure is to be kept constant, then in order to compensate for the increased speed of the molecules, the walls must be drawn farther apart, so that they will not be hit as often. This is Charles' law, that *if the pressure is kept constant, the volume is proportional to the absolute temperature.*

Dalton's Law. Since a gas volume is made up largely of free space, it follows that in a mixture of gases the molecules of each type of gas are acting independently of the molecules of any other type. Hence *the partial pressure exerted by a single gas is that which it would exert if it alone occupied the total volume.*

● ● ●   THE KINETIC-MOLECULAR THEORY AND PROPERTIES OF MOLECULES

The kinetic-molecular theory states or implies that molecules have the following properties:

$$
\begin{aligned}
\text{mass} &\;—\; m \\
\text{speed} &\;—\; v \\
\text{momentum} &\;—\; mv \\
\text{kinetic energy} &\;—\; \tfrac{1}{2}mv^2
\end{aligned}
$$

Graham's Law. While the molecules of a given gas do not all have the same speed (some travel faster than others), and so do not all have the same kinetic energy, there is an average speed and an average kinetic energy. It is this average kinetic energy to which the postulate of the kinetic-molecular theory refers. James Clerk Maxwell proved from the postulates of the theory that at any one temperature the average kinetic energy of the molecules of all gases is the same; specifically, for any two gases at the same temperature the average kinetic energy of the molecules of one gas is equal to the average kinetic energy of the molecules of the other. This is true regardless of how large or small the masses of the two different molecules may be:

$$\tfrac{1}{2}m_1v_1{}^2 = \tfrac{1}{2}m_2v_2{}^2$$

If m_1 is small, v_1 must be relatively large; if m_2 is large, v_2 is relatively small. Solving for v_1 and v_2, we obtain

$$\frac{v_1{}^2}{v_2{}^2} = \frac{m_2}{m_1} \qquad \text{or} \qquad \frac{v_1}{v_2} = \frac{\sqrt{m_2}}{\sqrt{m_1}}$$

Since the molecules continually collide with one another, they do not travel far between collisions, nevertheless, it is reasonable to suppose that the rate at which the molecules work forward in a particular direction depends upon the molecular speeds. Accepting this, the rate of diffusion should be proportional to the speeds, and we obtain Graham's law: *The rate of diffusion is inversely proportional to the square root of the masses of the molecules, or the molecular weights.*

Distribution of Molecular Speeds. The kinetic-molecular theory postulates that all molecules are in motion and that molecular speeds increase as temperature increases. Having accepted this, an important question immediately arises: Do all the molecules in a sample of a certain gas have the same speed at a given temperature? Surely not, for collisions among molecules will result in some molecules increasing in speed while others decrease in speed. As a consequence the molecules of a gas sample will have a variety of different speeds centered around some average value. This is called a *distribution of molecular speeds* and it is possible to measure the speeds (and kinetic energies) of gas molecules and to estimate the number of molecules having a given speed. Figure 12.7 is a sketch of the apparatus for determining molecular speeds. The results of such measurements are summarized in the graph of Figure 12.8 in which the number of molecules having a given speed is plotted against speed. This figure shows that most molecules have speeds near the average value but a few have considerably higher than average and a few have considerably lower than average speeds.

Figure 12.8 also shows the distribution of speeds for the gas at a higher temperature. Increasing the temperature causes a general shift of the distribution toward one with more molecules having high speeds. Moreover, at the higher temperature the distribution is more random—i.e., there are fewer molecules having speeds near the average value and a more uniform distribution of speeds among the molecules.

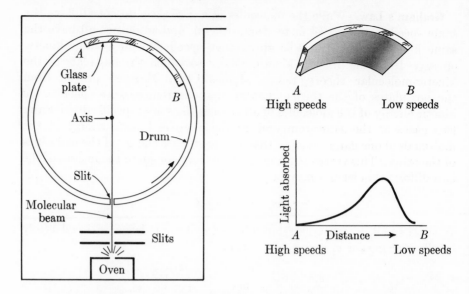

Figure 12.7 Determining the distribution of molecular speeds. Atoms of a metal escape from an oven into a vacuum. Those not going in the right direction are blocked off by a series of slits, and the molecular beam enters the slit of a rotating drum each time the opening of the drum passes the beam. The atoms impinge upon a glass plate *AB* opposite the opening. If a slowly moving atom enters the drum, the drum will have turned a long way before the atom meets the glass, and it will land near *B* on the plate. A fast-moving atom will travel across the drum very quickly and will land near *A* before the drum has turned much. After an experiment the plate is examined in a bright light, and the light absorbed at different positions on the plate measures the relative numbers of metal atoms deposited at these positions. A plot of light absorbed against distance from *A* to *B* is obtained which is the reverse of that given in Figure 12.8.

The Scientific Method. What we have been saying in the last few pages is a fine illustration of the application of the scientific method. During the past two or three hundred years, measurements of various sorts were made in connection with gases; thus, *facts* were gathered, and this knowledge was organized and formulated in *laws*. Then a theory, the kinetic-molecular theory, was invented to explain the laws, and to give a plausible reason for the various ways in which gases behave. The theory was successful from the beginning, and was fortunate in having such masters as Rumford, Joule, Clausius, Maxwell, Kelvin, Boltzmann, Jeans, and

Figure 12.8 Distribution of speeds in a gas. At the higher temperature, T_2, the maximum is lower and the curve is broader than at T_1.

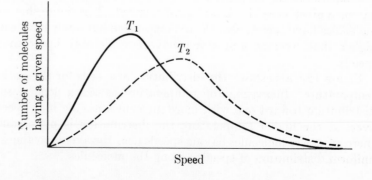

Langmuir to nurse it along and develop it. The theory suggested further pioneering experimental work, and was itself gradually improved and strengthened until now it gives us a convincing and deeply satisfying insight into the nature of material-particle behavior.

Internal Energy of Molecules

The kinetic-molecular theory has assumed that gases are made up of molecules which have no internal structure. But molecules are made up of atoms, which in turn have nuclei and electrons. The presence of positive nuclei and negative electrons produces deviations from the general gas law because they generate attractive forces between the molecules; this feature of real gases has been discussed in Chap. 5 and will appear again in Chap. 13. The internal structure also permits molecules to absorb and hold energy internally, in addition to the kinetic energy of motion (translational energy) of molecules as a whole which is the essence of the kinetic-molecular theory. A close study indicates that important aspects of the energy of a molecule can be described in terms of four components or modes of motion: a component due to the translational motion of the molecule, a component due to the vibrations of the atoms in the molecule with respect to each other, a component due to the rotation of the molecule around its center of gravity, and a component related to the electron arrangement in the molecule. Moreover, molecules absorb only discrete quantities of energy in increasing their vibrational, rotational, and electronic energies.

Absorption Spectrum. If the internal energy of the molecules is changed by absorption of light, then the light quantum absorbed must raise the energy by an amount corresponding to the separations of the electronic, vibrational, or rotational levels. Since there are many energy levels, quanta of several different magnitudes may be absorbed, producing an absorption *spectrum*. Examination of the spectra of molecules reveals that the spacing between the energy levels in molecules is greatest between electronic levels and least between rotational levels.

For example, for the carbon monoxide molecule, CO, we find the approximate energy level separations given in Table 12.5.

The data in Table 12.6 give the energy required and the wavelength of photons needed for various electronic energy transitions, for vibrational energy transitions, and for rotational energy transitions. The relative separations between the levels are illustrated in Figure 12.9.

The data in Table 12.6 tell us that many molecules may be raised to higher rotational energy levels by absorbing photons in the far infrared

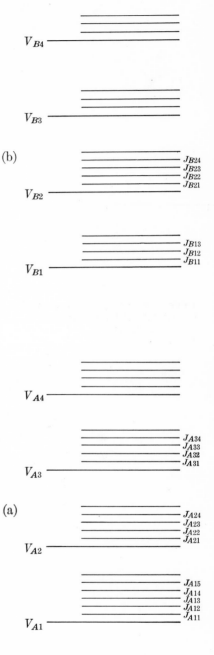

Figure 12.9 Schematic diagram of energy levels in a molecule. (a) and (b) represent different levels of electronic energies. V_{A1}, V_{A2} . . . , V_{B1}, V_{B2} . . . , etc., represent different levels of vibrational energy in the two electronic states. J_{A11}, J_{A12}, J_{A21}, J_{A22} . . . , etc., represent rotational levels. Transitions from one of the levels of (b) to one of the levels in (a) will produce a spectral line in the ultraviolet ; transition from a level in V_{A2}, V_{A3} . . . , etc., to a level in V_{A1} will produce a line in the infrared.

Table 12.5 Separation Between Energy Levels in Carbon Monoxide

Electronic	10^{-12} erg
Vibrational	10^{-13} erg
Rotational	10^{-16} erg

or microwave portion of the spectrum (because microwave photons have energies of about 10^{-16} erg corresponding to the energy difference between rotational levels). If infrared photons (energy $\sim 10^{-13}$ erg) are absorbed, many molecules may be raised to higher vibrational energy levels; but in being elevated to a higher vibrational level the molecule also may change its rotational energy level. This would mean that the molecule would change simultaneously in its vibrational amplitude and its rotational velocity.

When molecules absorb visible or ultraviolet light, electrons within them are raised to higher energy levels. Since this visible or ultraviolet light has high enough energy to cause electronic transitions, it can also change the vibrational frequency of the atoms and the rotational velocity of the molecule.

Types of Rotational and Vibrational Motion. It is of interest to picture the motions of the molecule as it absorbs energy. In the simple diatomic

Table 12.6 Energy Required and Wavelengths of Photons Needed for Electronic, Vibrational, and Rotational Transitions

Type of Transition	Energy Required (kcal/mole)	Wavelength of Photon Needed (A)
Electronic Excitation		
In general	10–300	1,000–8,000
		Ultraviolet—visible
Electrons in several types of bonds:		
C—C		Below 1,600
C=C		1,625
C≡C		1,775
C=O		1,875
Vibrational Excitation		
In general	3–8	10,000–500,000
		Visible—near infrared
Atoms in several types of molecules:		
O—H		28,000–32,000
C=C		60,000–62,000
C=O		54,000–61,000
Rotational Excitation		
In general	1	$5,000,000 - 3 \times 10^9$
		Near infrared—microwave
Example: 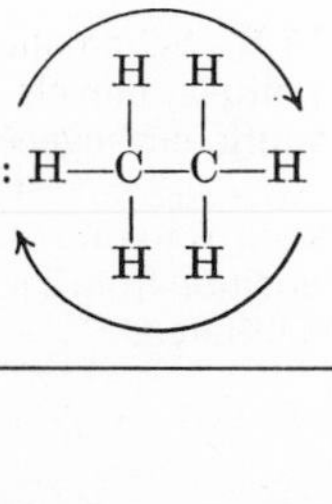 H—C—C—H	3	

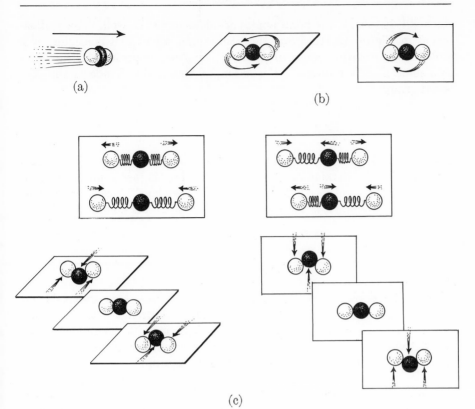

(a)

(b)

(c)

Figure 12.10 Rotational and vibrational motions of carbon dioxide. (a) Translation of center of gravity. (b) Rotation about two axes. (c) Vibration in four normal modes.

molecule CO, the rotational motion is about axes through the center of gravity of the molecule perpendicular to the line joining the carbon and oxygen atoms. There are two such axes—in the plane of the paper and perpendicular to the plane of the paper. The vibrational motion is a stretching and compression of the bond between the two atoms.

For more complicated molecules, both bending and stretching vibrations are possible. Certain of these are known as the fundamental modes of vibration, and all actual vibrations may be described as mixtures of these fundamental modes. The fundamental modes for the linear triatomic molecule, carbon dioxide, are shown in Figure 12.10.

Nonlinear molecules, such as H_2O or NH_3, have similar bending and stretching vibrations and three mutually perpendicular axes about which rotation can occur.

Spectra and Molecular Structure. By observing the spectrum of a molecule scientists learn much about molecular structure. For example, from the microwave spectra of simple molecules it is possible to learn not only the allowed rotational energies but often the molecular geometry,

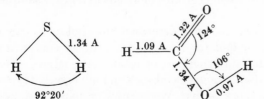

Figure 12.11 Bond angles and bond distances determined from microwave spectra.

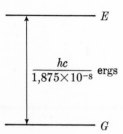

Figure 12.12 Ground state, G, and first excited electronic state of π bond in

C=O

the bond distances, the bond angles are determined as well. This is illustrated in Figure 12.11. From the visible and ultraviolet spectrum of a molecule information concerning the types of bonds present in the molecule sometimes is obtained. For example, the double bonds of the carbonyl group

C=O

absorb ultraviolet light at wavelengths close to 1,875 A. The energy corresponding to this wavelength, $hc/1875 \times 10^{-8}$ erg, is just sufficient to promote an electron in the π bond to a higher energy level. Absorption at this wavelength, therefore, is a "trademark" of compounds containing the

C=O

structure.

Infrared spectra of molecules give data on vibrational energy levels and equally important information on the kinds and strengths of the bonds present. In fact, infrared spectra provide chemists with one of their most useful tools for studying the structure of molecules and for identifying substances, as illustrated in the following paragraph.

Infrared Spectrophotometry. Infrared spectrophotometers are instruments in which a beam of infrared radiation of known wavelength and intensity is allowed to fall on a cell containing the sample being studied, and the intensity of the radiation after passing through the cell is measured. The difference between the incident and the transmitted intensity represents the light absorbed, and this magnitude is displayed upon a recorder. The wavelength of the incident beam is now slowly varied, so that the per cent of light absorbed is automatically traced out by the recorder as a function of wavelength. Such a recorder graph is shown in Figure 12.13. The valleys correspond to wavelengths at which the molecule shows absorption. The wavelength of the valleys (transposed to represent $h\nu$) gives the energy level difference between the vibrational-rotational levels in the molecules. Each valley is associated with the presence in the molecule of a certain structure or bond. Molecules which contain the O—H bond absorb photons having wavelengths in the 28,000–32,000 A range; those containing the C=C structure absorb in the 60,000–62,000 A wavelength range, and those containing the C=O group absorb in the 54,000–61,000 A region. The chemist soon learns to know in general what absorption position in the infrared region to expect from a certain group of atoms in a given environment and can then use the infrared spectrum to determine the presence or absence of various groups of atoms in a given sample.

Bond-Breaking Energies. We have described how molecules can absorb energy and move faster or undergo transitions to higher energy states of electronic energies, vibrational energies, or rotational energies. The next question to be asked is: Can a molecule absorb enough energy to break the bonds or to ionize one or more atoms? We are now prepared to answer this

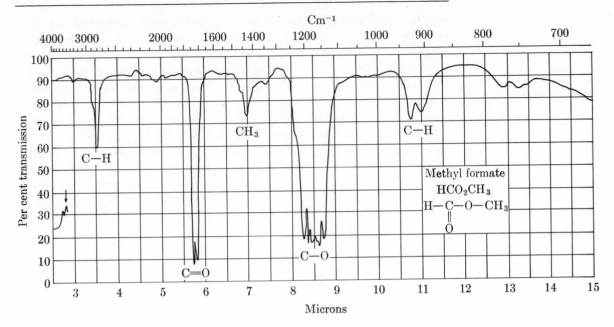

Figure 12.13   The infrared absorption spectrum of methyl formate, HCO_2CH_3.

question from data given in Table 6.1 on bond strengths, and information given in Chap. 4 on the calculations of radiant energy for various wavelengths, $E = h\nu$ and $\lambda = c/\nu$ where c is 3×10^{10} cm/sec, and ν and λ are the frequency and wavelength of radiation. Using these data we find these values for the energy associated with visible light:

	λ *Wavelength*	*Energy* (cal/mole)
Violet light	~ 4000 A	71,500
Red light	~ 7000 A	40,900

Hence, if a molecule has energy levels that can and do absorb radiation having greater energy than the bond strength, we expect the bond to break. Iodine molecules, for example, have bond strengths of 36,000 cal/mole and are broken by radiation of $\lambda = 7,000$ A. But a molecule must *absorb* energy before it can be used to break bonds and a sufficient amount of that energy must be concentrated in the vibration frequency of the particular bond to cause the bond to break.

What do X-rays and γ-rays do to molecules? The answer is that their wavelengths are so short, and hence their energies so high, that both ionization and bond breaking occurs when they are absorbed. This is the main cause of radiation damage of biological tissue by X-rays and γ-rays.

Heat Capacities. The change of energy in a molecule from one quantum state to another by absorption of radiation is specific; each quantum absorbed, $h\nu$, changes the energy of a single molecule from a lower to a higher energy state. The energy of a collection of molecules can also be changed by adding heat to the collection. For monatomic gases the heat added goes only into increasing the kinetic energy of the molecules, but for more complex molecules the energy distributes itself among translational, rotational, and vibrational energies. (Electronic excitation may also occur, but, in view of the large quantum jumps, this is not significant except for high temperatures.) Since the rotational and vibrational energies represent additional ways in which complex molecules can hold energy, as compared to the translational way (only) for a monatomic gas, it takes more heat to raise the temperature of a given number of complex molecules by a fixed amount than it does for the same number of monatomic molecules. In other words, the complex molecules have a greater *capacity* for energy (heat). To be quantitative, we speak of the molar heat capacity, defined as the amount of heat necessary to raise the temperature of 1 mole of substance by 1°C. For a monatomic gas the molar heat capacity at constant volume is $\frac{3}{2}R$; for diatomic gases it is approximately $\frac{5}{2}R$ at low temperatures and increases toward $\frac{7}{2}R$ at high temperatures as a result of the increased energy of molecular vibration.

Plasma

At several thousand degrees gas molecules are traveling with such high energies that on collision they drive off electrons. This process may continue to strip off each of the electrons of an atom until at very high temperatures all of the electrons may be removed. This process produces a high concentration of high-energy charged particles that have become known as *plasma*. This is believed to be the condition of much of the gaseous material in the sun, stars, and interstellar space. Electrons may also be driven off in other processes involving the absorption of a great deal of energy. Today the term plasma is used for a high concentration of these high-energy particles that have lost one or more electrons.

At very high temperatures, 10,000,000°C and higher, the plasma particles have gained so much translational energy that on collision their nuclei approach within 10^{-12} cm of each other where the powerful nuclear attractive forces take effect and cause nuclear fusion processes to occur. These are some of the main reactions that produce the energy and the light elements in the sun and stars. The fusion process will be discussed in Chap. 26.

The study of plasma is one of the new and very important fields of research today.

SUMMARY

A study of the gases reveals that all gases obey certain laws of nature that have become known as gas laws.

A theory, known as the kinetic-molecular theory, has been devised to explain the gas laws and to give a concept of the gaseous state of matter.

A general equation can be derived to make calculations of the pressure, volume, and temperature changes for n moles of a gas:

$$PV = nRT$$

The kinetic energy of a gas, $\frac{1}{2}mv^2$, is proportional to the absolute temperature.

In addition to translational energy, gas molecules can have rotational, vibrational, and electronic energy.

Rotational, vibrational, and electronic energies are not continuous but are quantized. The separations of the energy levels are indicated by the frequencies of lines in the band spectra (molecular spectra).

Interpretation of molecular spectra gives useful information about the identity and structure of molecules.

A collection of high-energy charged particles is called plasma. At very high temperature (and therefore at high translational energies) fusion reactions of the light elements occur.

SOME SPECIAL TERMS

Gas laws and theory
  Boyle's law
  Charles' law
  general gas law
  Gay-Lussac's law
  Dalton's law
  Graham's law
  kinetic-molecular theory

Spectra
  infrared spectra
  band spectrum
  excitation spectrum
  spectrophotometer

Energy
  kinetic energy
  electronic energy
  vibrational energy
  rotational energy
  heat capacity

Properties of gases
  volume
  pressure
  partial pressure
  expansible
  compressible
  diffusion
  ideal gas or perfect gas
  elastic collision
  barometer
  atmosphere pressure
  standard conditions
  R (gas constant)
  pound-mole
  distribution of molecular speeds
  plasma

QUESTIONS AND PROBLEMS

1. How does the kinetic-molecular theory account for the experimental observations that gases (a) are infinitely expansible, (b) are highly compressible, (c) diffuse readily, (d) exert a pressure, (e) exert a pressure which is constant at constant temperature, constant volume, and constant quantity, and (f) exert a pressure which is proportional to the absolute temperature at constant volume and constant quantity?

2. What experimental facts lead to the choice of $-273.15°C$ as the zero of temperature on the Kelvin scale?

3. Prove that Avogadro's law follows logically from the general gas law.

4. How does the kinetic-molecular theory account for the quantitative information (a) that the volume of a given mass of gas is proportional to the absolute temperature at constant pressure, (b) that the pressure of a given mass of gas is inversely proportional to the volume at constant temperature, (c) that the partial pressure of a gas does not depend upon the pressure of other gases in the same container, (d) that the ratio of the rates of diffusion of two gases is inversely proportional to the ratio of the square roots of their molecular weights, (e) that the pressure of a gas, at constant volume and constant temperature, is proportional to the mass of gas present?

5. On a single set of axes, draw curves showing the distribution of molecular speeds for three temperatures, T_1, T_2, and T_3 such that $T_3 > T_2 > T_1$. Label the axes.

6. What is the greatest speed that a molecule can have at temperature T_3? at T_2? Is the number of molecules having the average speed greater at T_3 than at T_1? What evidence can you cite to justify your answer?

7. Calculate the average velocity of molecules of each of the following gases at 25°C: O_2, H_2, SO_2, knowing that the average kinetic energy per mole is given by $KE = \frac{3}{2}RT$.

8. What kinds of energy are possible in a monatomic gas? A diatomic gas?

9. What are the relative magnitudes of the quantum jumps in the several kinds of energy which a polyatomic gas molecule may have? How do the relative wavelengths of the light absorbed vary for the different kinds of energy?

10. In what wavelength region would you expect the compound acrolein

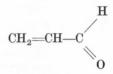

to absorb light?

11. Predict the molar heat capacity for the following gases: argon, krypton, iodine, carbon dioxide, carbon tetrachloride.

12. Why are not all gases perfect gases?

13. Calculate the volume at 1,000 torr and 28°C of a quantity of gas which occupied 250 cc at 700 torr and 28°C.

14. Calculate the volume occupied at 87°C and 950 torr by a quantity of gas which occupied 20 liters at 27°C and 570 torr.

15. Sixteen grams of sulfur dioxide, SO_2, was measured at 20°C and 740 torr pressure. What was the volume found?

16. Calculate the molecular weight of the gas for which 12 lb occupied 35 cu ft at 40°F and 12 lb/sq in. pressure.

17. A flask which can withstand an internal pressure of 2,500 torr, but no more, is filled with a gas at 21°C and 758 torr, and heated. At what temperature will it burst?

18. A flask of volume 1.2 liters is filled with carbon dioxide at room temperature to a pressure of 650 torr. A second flask, of volume 900 cc, is filled, at room temperature, with nitrogen to a pressure of 800 torr. A stopcock connecting the two volumes is then opened and the gases allowed to mix, at room temperature. What is the partial pressure of each gas in the final mixture, and what is the total pressure of the mixture?

19. Calculate the number of molecules present in a quantity of gas which occupies 26,880 cc at 546°C and 380 torr.

20. Calculate the atomic weight of the hypothetical element "statine" from the following data on the volumes of its gaseous compounds and their analyses.

Compound	Volume (liters) of 5 g	Temperature °C	Pressure (torr)	Per cent "statine"
With hydrogen	5.2	117	741	93.7
With oxygen	2.4	27	361	55.2
With oxygen	3.4	47	380	38.1
With carbon	11.1	247	95	76.7

REFERENCES

BARROW, G. M. *The Structure of Molecules; An Introduction to Molecular Spectroscopy.* New York: Benjamin, 1963.

FITZGEREL, R. K., and F. H. VERHOEK. "The Law of Dulong and Petit," *J. Chem. Educ.*, 37 (1960), p. 545.

HILDEBRAND, J. H. *An Introduction to Molecular Kinetic Theory.* New York: Reinhold, 1963.

13

Attractive Forces; Three States of Aggregation

*Tot hiertoe hebben we de molekulen steeds als stoffelijke punten
beschouwd, en dus een eenvoudigheid in de beschouwing ingevoerd,
die ten eenenmale in strijd is met de werkelijk bestaaende ver-
schijnselen. . . . Zelfs een molekuul in de eenvoudigste gedaante,
dus als het slechts uit een atoom bestaat, zal een zekere uitgebreid-
heid innemen; de verschillende krachten, die door de andere
molekulen daarop worden uitgeofend, zullen dus niet kunnen
aangemerkt worden, in één punt aan te grijpen.**

J. D. van der Waals (1837–1923)

The gas laws hold true for gases at low pressures and at ordinary and high
temperatures. Thus under these conditions gases behave as ideal gases.
But at high pressures deviations from the gas laws appear. Why do these
deviations occur at high pressures rather than at low pressures? If gases
behave ideally when the molecules are far apart (large volume), why should
they deviate from ideal behavior when the molecules are close to each
other? What is wrong with the model postulated in the kinetic-molecular
theory? Could it be that tiny but significant attractive forces exist
between gas particles? Could these eventually cause a gas to liquefy?

Deviations from Perfect-Gas Behavior. To correct the model, let us first
examine how the behavior of a real gas differs from that predicted by the
general gas law, $PV = nRT$. Let us measure corresponding values of
P, V, and T for 1 mole of nitrogen, multiply $P \times V$ and divide by $R \times T$
to form the function PV/RT, known as the compressibility factor, and
plot it against the pressure, as in Figure 13.1.

Since we chose 1 mole, PV/RT would always be 1 for an ideal gas, as
indicated by the horizontal dotted line in the figure. The actual behavior

---

* "Thus far we have always considered molecules to be material points, and thus have
introduced a simplification in the model which is at once in contradiction with the actual
phenomena. Even a molecule in the simplest form, consisting of a single atom, must have a
certain extension; the various forces exerted upon it by the other molecules can thus not be
considered to act upon a single point." (The quotation is from van der Waals' doctoral
dissertation "Over de Continuiteit van den Gas- en Vloeistof-Toestand," presented at
Leiden, Holland, June 14, 1873.)

does not give a horizontal straight line; at high pressures and lower temperatures the curves deviate considerably from the ideal.

If we consider the curve for $-50°C$, it is seen that the nature of the deviation from the perfect-gas law is of two kinds: (a) There is a pressure region in which the compressibility factor of the gas falls below the perfect-gas curve; in this region the gas is more compressible than the perfect gas. (b) At higher pressures the compressibility factor changes and gradually rises above the perfect-gas curve; in this region the gas is less compressible than the perfect gas. These deviations become less pronounced at higher temperatures, as shown by the curves for $0°C$ and $100°C$, which are coming closer to the horizontal line for the ideal gas. If we can find an explanation for the two kinds of deviations, then we may have a deeper understanding of gas behavior than that provided by the kinetic-molecular theory.

Causes of the Deviations: Attractive Forces and Volume of Molecules. If the gas is more compressible than a perfect gas, one imagines that something in addition to the applied pressure is causing the volume to decrease. Could this be the result of attractive forces between molecules? If they are present, such forces would have the effect of slightly decreasing the volume. The presence of such forces would also cause the pressure of the real gas to be less than that of an ideal gas having no intermolecular attractive forces under the same conditions. As an hypothesis we might suppose that intermolecular attractive forces are responsible for the observation that real gases are sometimes more compressible than perfect gases.

But what causes a gas to be less compressible than a perfect gas? This occurs at very high pressures and small volumes. Is it possible that under these conditions the "compressible space" in the gas has decreased to the point that a further increase in pressure cannot bring about a corresponding decrease in volume? This would happen if there were insufficient empty or free space between molecules. Another way to look at this is to

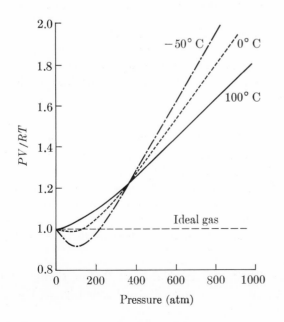

Figure 13.1 Compressibility factor of nitrogen as a function of pressure at three temperatures.

imagine that at high pressures the gas molecules themselves are occupying an appreciable fraction of the total volume of the gas whereas at low pressures the gas molecules are occupying only a very small fraction of the total volume. At low pressures there is ample compressible space; at high pressures compressible space is limited and the gas becomes less compressible.

Modification of the $PV = nRT$ Equation. If we assume that deviations from perfect-gas behavior arise (a) from intermolecular attractive forces and (b) from a decrease in compressible space brought about by the volume occupied by the molecules themselves, then perhaps we can modify the perfect gas law equation to account for these deviations. The modified equation should be more reliable than the perfect-gas law for predicting compressibility behavior of real gases. Several such equations have been devised; one such equation was developed by the Dutch chemist Johannes van der Waals and bears his name. The form of van der Waals equation is based upon the following new considerations about real gases:

1. The pressure of the real gas will be less than that of a perfect gas due to the intermolecular attractive forces. These require a pressure correction term an^2/V^2 to be added to the real-gas pressure, where a is a constant, n the number of moles, and V the volume. Hence the pressure term to be substituted in the perfect-gas equation is

$$\left(P + \frac{an^2}{V^2}\right)$$

2. The volume of the real gas is made up of the free space and the volume the molecules appear to occupy (sometimes called the effective volume). If b is the effective volume occupied by one mole of molecules, the compressible volume of n moles of a real gas is

$$(V - nb)$$

The corrected equation then is

$$\left(P + \frac{an^2}{V^2}\right)(V - nb) = nRT$$

This is the van der Waals equation. The constants a and b can be obtained for each gas from experiments similar to those summarized in Figure 13.1. *Values of a are regarded as reliable measures of intermolecular attractive forces.*

When Does a Real Gas Fit the $PV = nRT$ Equation? Using the van der Waals equation as a guide we may say that whenever the correction term an^2/V^2 and nb become small, compared to P and V respectively, the gas will behave like a perfect gas. Both of these terms will become unimportant if the volume becomes very large while the number of moles of gas remains small. Of course the volume becomes large at very low pressures and at high temperatures so it is under these conditions that real gases most closely approach perfect-gas behavior.

The Van der Waals Constant a and Values of Boiling Points. We have already used the concept of intermolecular attraction to explain the fact that gases condense to liquids, and we have used boiling point as a measure of the strength of the attractive forces (Chap. 5). We now see that van der Waals *a* is also a measure of the strength of these forces; the two should change in a parallel manner. Table 13.1 shows that they do; the higher the boiling point, the larger the value of *a*.

Further Evidence of Attractive Forces: Surface Tension. The molecules in the interior of a liquid are surrounded by other molecules, but those in the surface have no liquid molecules on top of them. The attractive forces on a surface molecule are thus different from those on an interior molecule, and give rise to a pull of the molecules toward the interior of the liquid which tends to make the surface as small as possible for a given amount of liquid. The attractive force is called *surface tension*. (See Figure 13.2.)

Figure 13.2 Surface tension, making the surface as small as possible for a given volume, pulls liquids into spherical drops.

Factors Involved in Liquefaction of Gases. We can couple the information from the kinetic-molecular theory with the evidence for attractive forces between particles and predict the conditions required to liquefy a gas. The kinetic theory indicates that the molecules are moving at high velocities. One requirement to liquefy a gas is to cool the gas (reduce the velocity of the particles) to a sufficiently low temperature so the attractive forces can hold them to each other. The temperature above which it is not possible to liquefy a gas is called the *critical temperature*. A second requirement to liquefy a gas is to increase the pressure sufficiently to push the molecules close enough together so the attractive forces can hold the particles to each other. The pressure required to liquefy a gas at the critical temperature is called the *critical pressure*. Values of the critical temperature and critical pressure of several gases are given in Table 13.2.

All gases can be liquefied. Helium has the lowest boiling point and freezing point of any gas. Hydrogen gas is the next most difficult to liquefy.

Why Do Most Gases Cool When They Expand? All gases but hydrogen and helium cool when, at room temperature, they are allowed to expand through a valve into a space at lower pressures. This cooling effect is called the *Joule-Thomson effect*. The loss in energy, which results in the cooling, is due to the energy used to overcome the attractive forces in separating the molecules from each other.

This cooling effect is made use of in liquefaction of gases. If the expanded and cooled gas is allowed to flow back over the container of compressed gas, it becomes so cold that, after the still further cooling produced by additional expansion, it will liquefy (Figure 13.3).

Table 13.1 Boiling Points and Van der Waals Constants

Gas	Boiling Point (°C)	a $\left(\dfrac{\text{liters}^2\ \text{atm}}{\text{mole}^2}\right)$	b $\left(\dfrac{\text{liters}}{\text{mole}}\right)$	Gas	Boiling Point (°C)	a $\left(\dfrac{\text{liters}^2\ \text{atm}}{\text{mole}^2}\right)$	b $\left(\dfrac{\text{liters}}{\text{mole}}\right)$
He	−269	0.0341	0.0237	CH_4	−162	2.253	0.0428
Ne	−246	0.2107	0.0171	C_2H_6	−88	5.489	0.0683
Ar	−186	1.345	0.0322	C_3H_8	−42	8.664	0.0845
Kr	−153	2.318	0.0398	C_4H_{10}	0	14.47	0.1226
Xe	−107	4.194	0.0511	C_5H_{12}	+36	19.01	0.1460

Table 13.2 Critical Temperature and Pressure of Several Gases

Gas	Critical Temperature (°C)	Critical Pressure (atm)
He	−268	2.3
H_2	−240	12.8
O_2	−119	49.7
N_2	−147	33.5
H_2O	−374	218
CO_2	31	73

Liquids and Gases. Liquids differ from gases in that they do not distribute themselves uniformly throughout the whole volume of a containing vessel, but retain their own volumes. Because of their mobility, however, liquids do take the shape of the portion of the containing vessel which they occupy. Further, liquids contract only slightly even upon application of great pressure—a result which finds an interpretation in terms of our picture of the molecules of a liquid as being already crowded together with little free space between molecules.

Evaporation. When a liquid such as water is placed in an open vessel, it gradually passes into the air in the form of gas or vapor, and the process is called *evaporation*. In a confined space, as in a closed bottle (Figure 13.4), evaporation proceeds until the air above the liquid contains a definite percentage of gaseous water, and then apparently ceases; the air is said to be *saturated* with water vapor. But the evaporation process does *not* cease—it simply establishes an equilibrium with the condensation process. We can understand this if we consider the question from a kinetic point of view. The molecules of a liquid are in random heat motion, just as they are in a gas; some of them have speeds greater than the average and others have speeds less than the average (Figure 12.8). From the surface of the liquid the more rapidly moving molecules will escape, breaking free from the attraction of their neighbor molecules. They will then move about in the air space above as gas molecules, and as more and more of them

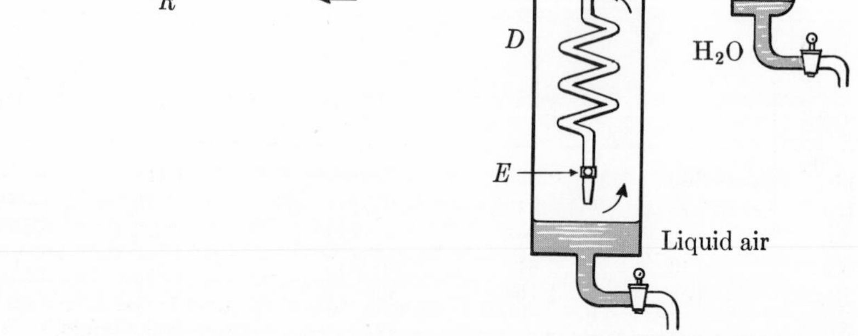

Figure 13.3 Liquefaction of air. Entering (*I*) and recirculated (*R*) air is compressed in *A* and passes through the cooling coil *B* to remove the heat produced in the compression. Water vapor present condenses and is removed at *C*. The dry gas then passes through a coil in *D* so arranged that the gas, cooled by expansion through the throttling valve *E*, circulates back over the coil and cools the incoming compressed gas. On expansion through *E*, part of the gas liquifies and the remainder is recirculated (*R*).

accumulate there, many will strike the surface of the liquid and will return to the liquid, as represented in Figure 13.4. Eventually enough molecules of water vapor will accumulate in the air space so that the number returning to the liquid in one second will be equal to the number escaping from the liquid into the vapor in the same time, and a state of equilibrium (Chap. 6) will be reached. Although molecules continue to escape, there is no further *net* loss of molecules from the surface. The equilibrium between the tendencies to escape into the gas space (evaporation) and to return to the liquid (condensation) may be represented in the following manner:

$$\text{Liquid} \rightleftharpoons \text{vapor}$$

Vapor Pressure. The pressure of the saturated vapor in equilibrium with the liquid is the *vapor pressure* of the liquid. It is commonly *expressed in millimeters of mercury* or *torr*, and it is a measure of the tendency of the liquid to evaporate. Experimentally the value of the vapor pressure of a liquid at any temperature may be measured in many different ways. A simple procedure is illustrated in Figure 13.5. Liquids differ greatly among themselves in the magnitude of their vapor pressures at a given temperature. Those with high vapor pressure at room temperature are said to be *volatile.* Such liquids include ether, alcohol, and benzene.

Effect of Temperature upon Vapor Pressure. Measurements show that the vapor pressure increases with rising temperature; and in Figure 13.7 the experimental values of the vapor pressures of four liquids are plotted against temperature. How can this effect be explained?

Suppose we have a liquid in equilibrium with its vapor in an enclosed space. If the temperature is raised, the average kinetic energy of the molecules in both the vapor and the liquid is increased. But the small fraction of the liquid molecules that have a kinetic energy far above the average, the "hot" molecules that are able to escape through the surface into the vapor, is markedly increased. Consequently, the rate of evaporation becomes greater than the rate of condensation, and the concentration of molecules in the vapor phase increases. As this increase takes place, however, the rate of condensation will begin to increase and will shortly overtake the rate of evaporation and establish a new equilibrium:

$$\text{Liquid} \rightleftharpoons \text{vapor}$$

The concentration of vapor molecules and the vapor pressure will be higher than at the lower temperature (compare Figures 13.4 and 13.6).

Boiling Point. During the heating of a liquid at ordinary temperatures, a portion of the energy given to it goes to raise its temperature, and a portion to change it into a vapor at its surface. When the pressure of the vapor arising from the liquid just exceeds the opposing atmospheric

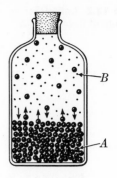

Figure 13.4 Diagram of a liquid (large black dots, *A*) evaporating into air (small dots, *B*) in a closed bottle.

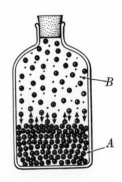

Figure 13.6 Diagram of the same liquid as in Figure 13.4 at a higher temperature.

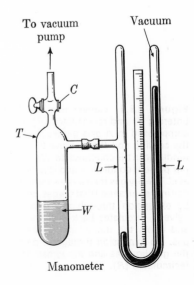

Figure 13.5 Measurement of vapor pressure with a manometer. A liquid, such as water, *W*, is placed in the tube, *T*, and the stopcock *C*, is opened to a vacuum pump. If air and water vapor are pumped out of the system on the left-hand side of the U-tube, the mercury will be at the same level (*L, L*) in both arms of the manometer. Then if the stopcock is closed, the water evaporates and establishes an equilibrium vapor pressure at the temperature of the tube *T*. The difference in the level of the mercury columns indicates the vapor pressure of the liquid.

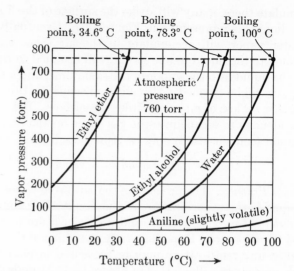

Figure 13.7 Vapor-pressure curves showing boiling points of several liquids.

pressure, all the heat energy goes to change the liquid into vapor (in freeing the molecules from the attraction of their neighbors) and into mechanical work in pushing back the atmosphere. The temperature then remains constant, notwithstanding the fact that heat is being applied to the liquid. This temperature is called the boiling point under the pressure of the experiment. *The boiling point may be defined as the temperature at which the vapor pressure of the liquid just exceeds the opposing pressure of the atmosphere.* The boiling point at standard atmospheric pressure is often called the *normal* boiling point. By suitably altering the pressure on a liquid, it may be caused to boil at temperatures higher or lower than its normal boiling point. Thus, at high altitudes the boiling point of water is less than 100°C (Figure 13.8).

Heat of Vaporization and Condensation. Since only the fastest-moving ("hottest") molecules in a liquid are able to escape through its surface, the liquid becomes colder when it loses these molecules. Heat must be supplied to maintain the evaporation. The quantity of heat absorbed in changing 1 g of a liquid into 1 g of vapor at constant temperature is called the *heat of vaporization*. Conversely, the condensation of a gas or vapor to a liquid liberates a quantity of heat exactly equal to the heat of vaporization. The heat of vaporization of water at its boiling point is exceptionally large, amounting to 539 cal/g. A quantity more useful in chemistry is the molar heat of vaporization, representing the heat needed to change 1 mole of substance from liquid to vapor at constant temperature. The molar heat of vaporization of water at 100°C is

$$\frac{539 \text{ cal}}{1 \text{ g}} \times \frac{18 \text{ g}}{1 \text{ mole}} = 9700 \text{ cal/mole}$$

Values for other liquids are given in Table 13.3.

Changing a Liquid to a Solid. As a liquid is cooled, the translational motion of the molecules becomes less and less. At a certain temperature the translational motion is reduced to a point where the attractive forces between the particles of the liquid overcome the kinetic energies of the

	cal/mole		cal/mole
Ammonia	556	Mercury	14,166
Argon	150	Methane	2320
Ethane	3810	Methyl alcohol	8410
Ethyl alcohol	7344	Sulfur dioxide	607
Helium	24	Water	9700

Table 13.3 Molar Heats of Vaporization at the Boiling Point

particles and the particles take positions in a pattern or latticework of particles which we call a solid. The temperature at which this change occurs for a pure liquid is called the *freezing point* or the *melting point*; the temperature remains constant until all of the liquid has crystallized. Solids formed in this way are always crystalline. In order to explain the sublimation of some solids and the specific heat values of all solids we must assume that there is vibrational motion of the particles in the solid.

Liquids which are composed of large molecules become so viscous near the freezing point that the big molecules cannot orient themselves in a regular crystal pattern. Such substances are called *amorphous* solids. Glasses, glazes, tar, glue, and gum are examples of such materials.

Freezing Point and Melting Point. Sometimes when a crystallizable liquid is cooled, it does not begin to crystallize at its freezing point. Indeed, liquid water has been cooled far below 0°C without freezing. A liquid below its freezing point is said to be *undercooled*. If a crystal of the substance once forms, or if a "seed crystal" is dropped into the undercooled liquid, solidification at once begins, heat is given out in the process, and the temperature rises to the true freezing point and remains there as long as both liquid and solid are present. The freezing point is defined as

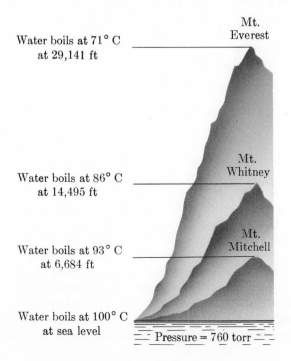

Water boils at 71° C at 29,141 ft

Mt. Everest

Water boils at 86° C at 14,495 ft

Mt. Whitney

Water boils at 93° C at 6,684 ft

Mt. Mitchell

Water boils at 100° C at sea level

Pressure = 760 torr

Figure 13.8 Boiling point of water at various elevations.

the temperature at which both solid and liquid will remain in contact with each other without change of temperature. The more viscous a liquid is at its freezing point, the more readily undercooling takes place; and with very viscous liquids, crystallization may never occur, as in the glasses.

Conversely, when a crystalline solid is slowly heated, its temperature steadily rises to a certain definite point (unless the solid should undergo decomposition). Further application of heat does not raise the temperature, but the solid begins to melt. If the substance is pure, the temperature remains constant until the melting is complete, and then rises again. While the solid and liquid are in contact with each other, in equilibrium, the addition of heat energy will cause the solid to change to liquid (at the melting point), and the removal of heat will result in the conversion of the liquid to solid (at the freezing point):

$$\text{Solid} \rightleftharpoons \text{liquid}$$

The temperature of the melting point is the same as that of the freezing point.

Heat of Fusion and of Solidification. The heat energy supplied to a substance during the process of melting has no effect on the temperature, but is used up in altering the physical state of the substance. The heat absorbed in converting 1 g of a solid at its melting point into a liquid at the same temperature is called the *heat of fusion* of the substance. For ice this amounts to about 80 cal/g or 1440 cal/mole. The heat given out when a liquid solidifies is the same in quantity as the heat of fusion and represents the difference in energy between the orderly, rigid arrangement of molecules in a solid and the relative disorder and mobility of molecules in a liquid.

Vapor Pressure of Solids; Sublimation. Many solids give off appreciable vapor at ordinary temperatures, due to the motions of the particles of the solid. This is evident from the odor in a room where pieces of such solids as camphor and naphthalene (moth balls) are present. Here, again, an equilibrium exists, between the solid and the vapor:

$$\text{Solid} \rightleftharpoons \text{vapor}$$

As the temperature is raised, the pressure of the vapor increases. If, before the melting point is reached, the vapor pressure of the solid increases to the point where it just exceeds the pressure of the atmosphere, the solid cannot be heated to a higher temperature in an open vessel, just as a liquid cannot be heated (at the pressure of the atmosphere) above its boiling point. To melt such a solid it is necessary to heat it in a closed vessel. This behavior is illustrated by solid carbon dioxide, whose vapor pressure reaches 760 torr at $-78.5°C$, but which does not melt until $-56.6°C$. At this latter point its vapor pressure is more than 5 atm. When the vapors from such solids are cooled, they pass directly back into the solid form. The process of converting a solid into a vapor and condensing the vapor to a solid again without going through the liquid state is called *sublimation*, and the solid is said to *sublime* on heating. The corresponding process with liquids is called *distillation*. Solids which have a sufficient vapor pressure are often separated from nonvolatile impurities by sublimation.

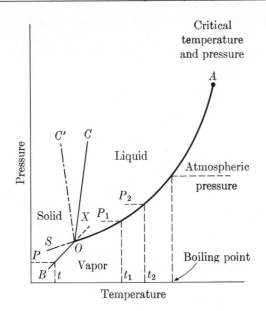

Pressure

Critical
temperature
and pressure

A

C' C

Liquid

Atmospheric
pressure

Solid X P_1

P_2

S

P O

B | t

Vapor

t_1 | t_2

Boiling point

Temperature

Figure 13.9 Diagram illustrating the equilibria among solid, liquid, and gaseous states.

Diagram Illustrating Equilibria Among Solid, Liquid, and Vapor. In the preceding pages we have seen that a number of different types of equilibrium exist in a system containing a substance in different physical states. Thus, with water we have an equilibrium between the vapor and the liquid, between the vapor and the solid, and between the liquid and the solid. We can show the general character of these three equilibria in a very compact form in a diagram (Figure 13.9) in which we represent temperature along the horizontal axis and pressure along the vertical axis. The curve OA is a plot of the experimentally measured vapor pressures of the liquid over a range of temperatures—for example, the vapor pressure is P_1 at temperature t_1, and P_2 at t_2. This curve ends at a point, A, which is the critical temperature, above which the substance can no longer exist in the liquid state. OB is the vapor-pressure curve of the solid, usually called the sublimation curve. The point O, where these two curves intersect, is the freezing point of the liquid under its own vapor pressure; and at that point the vapor pressures of solid and liquid are equal. Since the two curves intersect at this point, the solid, liquid, and vapor can coexist at this temperature and pressure; but they can do so at no other point, so long as no air or dissolved matter is present. If no solid makes its appearance at the freezing point, the vapor pressure of the liquid will be represented by the extension of the curve AO toward S. It will be seen that the vapor pressure of such an undercooled liquid is greater than that of the solid at the same temperature, as at t. This indicates that the undercooled liquid is in a more unstable condition. Very few (if any) solids can be heated above the melting point without melting; so the curve BO can rarely be prolonged beyond the melting point, as at X.

If, when the solid and liquid and vapor are all in equilibrium, at the point O (often called the *triple point*), one applies a steady outside pressure, as with a piston, greater than the pressure of the vapor [Figure 13.10(a)], the vapor will all condense, and only solid and liquid will remain [Figure 13.10(b)]. Then, if the applied pressure is increased more and more, the

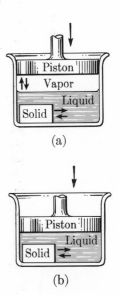

Figure 13.10 Illustrating the principle of Le Châtelier in equilibria among states.

result is that the freezing point, or melting point, is raised for all known substances (with several exceptions). This effect is indicated by the line *OC* (Figure 13.9), which represents the equilibrium between melting solid and freezing liquid.

SUMMARY

The deviations of real gases from ideal behavior can be accounted for in terms of attractive forces between molecules and the volume occupied by the molecules themselves. As the temperature of a gas is lowered, the average kinetic energy of the molecules decreases but the attractive forces remain approximately constant. At some temperature for each gas the attractive forces should overcome the molecular momentum and the molecules should cluster together forming the liquid state.

Continuing to use this model, we predict that liquids should exhibit properties reflecting an interplay between the attractive forces and the kinetic energy of the molecules. The equilibrium between a liquid and its vapor is a dramatic corroboration of this prediction. Other properties of liquids—boiling point, surface tension, viscosity, and heat of vaporization—are all generally explicable in terms of this interplay.

Even the equilibrium between a liquid and a solid may be viewed as a process in which some molecules acquire sufficient energy to overcome the attractive forces in the solid and pass to the liquid, while an equal number of liquid molecules lose enough kinetic energy so that they are captured and held in the solid.

Temperature is of special importance in nearly all physical properties of gases, liquids, or solids because a change in temperature brings about a corresponding change in kinetic energy. Diagrams showing the equilibrium among the solid, liquid, and gaseous states of a single substance over a wide range of temperature and pressure are useful in obtaining a view of the regions of stability of the various phases.

SOME SPECIAL TERMS

Gas
   compressibility factor
   van der Waals equation
   critical temperature
   critical pressure
   Joule-Thomson effect
   manometer

Liquids
   surface tension
   evaporation
   vapor pressure
   volatility
   boiling point
   heat of vaporization
   freezing point
   distillation

Solids
   heat of fusion
   amorphous
   sublimation
Equilibrium
   triple point

QUESTIONS AND PROBLEMS

1. How does a real gas differ from an ideal gas?
2. Sketch curves showing the compressibility factor as a function of pressure at constant temperature for a typical gas for two temperatures, $T_1 > T_2$.

How do you explain the fact that the curve for the higher temperature T_1 is closer to the curve for an ideal gas than the curve for the lower temperature?

3. Show, by algebraic operation, that the van der Waals equation for 1 mole gives for the compressibility factor

$$\frac{PV}{RT} = \frac{1}{1 - \dfrac{b}{V}} - \frac{a}{RTV}$$

Using this equation, show that the compressibility factor becomes unity when the volume becomes very large.

4. Calculate the compressibility factor and the pressure exerted by 1 mole of butane when it is confined at 300°C in the volumes (a) 20, (b) 2.0, (c) 0.40, (d) 0.30, and (e) 0.20 liters, using the van der Waals equation. Plot the compressibility factor against the pressure for butane at 300°C. How would this curve be altered if the temperature was 300°K? If butane was an ideal gas at 300°C, what would be the pressure of 1 mole confined in 2 liters?

5. What two features of real gases are taken into consideration in introducing the van der Waals constants a and b into the equation for real gas?

6. Why do most gases cool when they expand at room temperature?

7. Why are liquids much less compressible than gases?

8. Does the vapor pressure of a liquid depend upon the amount of liquid surface exposed to the vapor? On the basis of the equilibrium picture, explain why or why not.

9. Calculate the weight of water vapor in the air of a room 20 × 12 × 8 ft if the humidity is 65 per cent at 70°F.

10. It is claimed that the vapor pressure of a liquid increases because the rate of *evaporation* increases as the temperature is raised. How does an increase in temperature affect the rate of condensation? Suppose a system could be devised to prevent evaporation and allow condensation only, and the system were arranged to feed in additional vapor molecules as fast as they condensed, thus keeping the number of vapor molecules constant. Would the rate of condensation change if the temperature increased? In the light of your answer, discuss the vapor pressure equilibrium.

11. A pure solid substance is heated at a constant rate. At first the temperature rises regularly, then it stays constant for a measurable time, and then rises again. Why?

12. The curve OC' (Figure 13.9) has a slope corresponding to the ice $\rightleftarrows$ water equilibrium at not too high pressures. It is claimed that ice-skating is possible because liquid water acts as a lubricant under the blades of the skates. Discuss the relationship between these two facts.

REFERENCES

BERNAL, J. D. "The Structure of Liquids," *Scientific American*, vol. *203*, no. 2, (1960), p. 124.

DREISBACH, D. *Liquids and Solutions*. Boston, Mass.: Houghton Mifflin, 1966.

FRENKEL, J. *Kinetic Theory of Liquids*. New York: Dover, 1955.

HILDEBRAND, J. H. *An Introduction to Molecular Kinetic Theory*. New York: Reinhold, 1963.

ROWLINSON, J. S. *Liquids and Liquid Mixtures*. London: Butterworth, 1959.

14

Solutions—Homogeneous Mixtures

*Almost all the chemical processes which occur in nature, whether in
animal or vegetable organisms, or in the non-living surface of
the earth, . . . take place between substances in solution.*
                                        Wilhelm Ostwald (1853–1932)

Why—
Do sugar and salt dissolve in water, but not in benzene?
Does sand not dissolve in water?
Does alcohol dissolve in water, but gasoline does not?
Do large volumes of ammonia dissolve in water, but only tiny volumes
    of oxygen?
Does sodium chloride dissolve in water but barium sulfate does not?
Do water solutions of sodium chloride and hydrogen chloride conduct an
    electric current?

The Process of Dissolving

In the search for an answer to these questions let us use the information we
have gathered about attractive forces between particles of solids, liquids,
and gases. Let us compare the process of the passage of a substance into
solution with the process of evaporation (Figure 14.1). In each case the
faster-moving particles escape from the surface. But the dissolution
process differs from evaporation in one respect. In evaporation the vapor
space does not attract the particles of the evaporating substance, whereas
the particles of dissolving substance, the solute, *are* attracted by the
molecules of a solvent. These attractive forces may be van der Waals
forces of various strengths, such as those that cause deviations from the
gas laws (Chaps. 6, 13), or they may be the very strong forces which
produce chemical combination. If the attractive forces of the solvent for
the solute are strong enough to overcome the attractive forces that hold
the particles of the solute to each other, the substance will dissolve.

As a rule, substances with a very high melting point, whose particles are
bound very rigidly together, do not dissolve appreciably in a solvent.

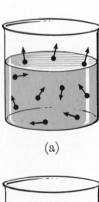

(a)

(b)

Figure 14.1 Both evaporation and
dissolution involve the escape of
particles at the surface. (a) Evaporation. (b) Dissolution.

272

Examples are silica, the heavy-metal silicates, barium sulfate, calcium carbonate, and the heavy-metal sulfides. The ions of some compounds, even though they are bound very tightly together, have such a strong attraction for water molecules that they become jacketed, or *solvated*, by water molecules; hence they dissolve. Examples of such compounds are sodium chloride, calcium chloride, potassium nitrate, and copper sulfate.

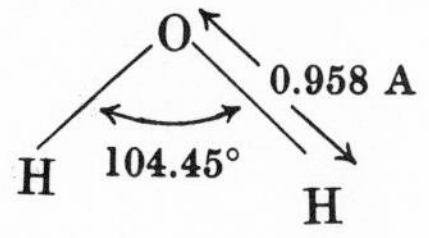

Oil and water proverbially do not mix, or dissolve in each other. Water does not dissolve in oil because water molecules attract one another so strongly that they will not respond to the much feebler attraction of the oil molecules for them; nor will the water molecules, because of this strong attraction, separate from one another far enough to allow the oil molecules to penetrate among them.

Water as a Solvent. Probably the most abundant compound on the earth is water. Water is a good solvent for many substances; it also forms hydrates with many atoms, molecules, and ions. The reason for the good solvent properties of water can be understood when we recall that water is a triangular, polar covalent molecule; as a result it is a dipole (Figure 14.2). Hence we find ion-dipole attractive forces causing ions to be surrounded by water molecules (Figure 14.3); this process is called hydration or solvation. Neutral atoms and molecules which are polar, such as sucrose, for example, may also become hydrated by dipole-dipole forces. The forces that cause hydration or solvation seem to be the main cause of solution of soluble compounds.

Figure 14.2   The water molecule.

Figure 14.3   Hydration of ions.

Bonding between a water molecule and an ion can become essentially covalent if the ion has empty orbitals to which the water molecule can donate an unshared pair of electrons. Examples of hydrated ions in which bonding of this type occurs are $Co(H_2O)_6^{+3}$, $Zn(H_2O)_6^{+2}$, $Cu(H_2O)_6^{+2}$.

When a solvent sheath is formed around an ion the next step usually is the dissolving of the ion. The solvent sheath keeps the + and − ions separated and insulates them from each other. Water has a high dielectric constant—i.e., it has good insulating properties. If, however, the hydration tendency of the ions is low, as it is with silver ions, Ag^+, and sulfate ions, SO_4^{-2}, or if the electrostatic attraction between a pair of ions is high, as it is with aluminum ions, Al^{+3}, and phosphate ions, PO_4^{-3}, the solvent sheath will be squeezed out, and the ions will come together and precipitate from solution.

Polar Solvents. Water is one of the most highly polar solvents known, hence it is one of the best solvents for ions. Methyl alcohol has polar properties somewhat similar to water, as do ethyl alcohol and other alcohols and many other molecules such as acetone, CH_3COCH_3, acetic acid, CH_3CO_2H, ammonia, NH_3, hydrogen chloride, HCl, etc.

Acid-Base Solvents. Closely associated with polar properties are the acid-base properties of many solutes and solvents as these are defined in terms of Lewis acids—i.e., electron-pair donors and acceptors. For example, water, alcohol, ether, and ammonia have electron pairs that can be donated. These electron pairs become important factors in increasing the solubility of substances by coordinate covalent bond formation. For example, ammonia dissolves in water in large amounts probably due to the reaction

$$NH_3 + H_2O \rightleftharpoons NH_4^+ + OH^- \tag{1}$$

Hydrogen chloride is very soluble in water due largely to the reaction

$$HCl + H_2O \rightleftharpoons H_3O^+ + Cl^- \tag{2}$$

Energy of Hydration. A measure of the strength of the bonds formed when ions hydrate is obtained from calculations of the heat energy released on hydrate formation. Table 14.1 gives the hydration energies for some

Table 14.1 Hydration Energies of Some Common Ions

Ion	Hydration Energy (kcal/mole)	Ion	Hydration Energy (kcal/mole)
Li^+	121.3	Zn^{+2}	485
Na^+	95.2	Al^{+3}	1,110
K^+	75.0	Fe^{+3}	1,042
Ag^+	111.9	OH^-	87
Mg^{+2}	456	F^-	122
Ca^{+2}	377	Cl^-	89.8

common ions. One of the highest energies of hydration is observed when sulfuric acid dissolves in water. This is largely due to the very high hydration energy of the proton (259 kcal/mole). So much energy is released in the dilution of concentrated sulfuric acid that it is dangerous to add water to concentrated sulfuric acid because the first small amount of water may be suddenly turned to steam.

Heat of Solution. The heat of solution is the sum of the energy changes that occur when a substance dissolves. Energy is *released* when the solute particles become solvated or form new bonds; energy is *absorbed* in demolishing the structure of solids, in separating molecules in the crystal from each other, or in ionizing molecules such as acetic acid. Whether the over-all solution process results in heating or cooling depends upon the relative amounts of heat absorbed and evolved in each step. Dissolving sulfuric acid gives off a large quantity of heat; sodium chloride shows only a very small temperature change, but ammonium nitrate cools on dissolving.

Constituents and Varieties of Solutions. One constituent of a solution (usually the more abundant one) we think of as the medium in which the other (less abundant) constituent is dissolved; the medium we call the *solvent*, the dissolved constituent the *solute*.

Solutions of Solids in Liquids

A solid dissolved in a liquid is by far the most familiar type of solution; an example is a solution of sodium chloride in water. It is sometimes said that zinc "dissolves" in hydrochloric acid. In this case, however, the solution is preceded by a chemical reaction whereby the zinc is converted into zinc chloride, and it is this compound which is obtained when the solution is evaporated. Solutions of solids in liquids, such as we are now considering, are those in which evaporation will leave the solute in its original chemical condition.

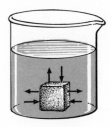

Figure 14.4 Illustrating the equilibrium in a saturated solution.

Equilibrium in Saturated Solutions. When a lump of sugar is placed in a small beaker and covered with water (Figure 14.4), it gradually passes into solution; that is, particles leave it due to attraction to the solvent molecules and wander through the solvent. If there is enough sugar, and if a long enough time elapses, the concentration of the sugar in the solution reaches *a definite limiting value*; and we say that the solution is *saturated*. The solution action, however, does not cease when the saturation point is reached. Molecules of the sugar continue to leave the lump and pass into the solution, while other molecules of sugar, previously dissolved, return to the lump from the solution. The rate of these two processes is exactly equal at saturation, so that the number of molecules of solute leaving the solid and entering the solution in unit time is equal to the number of solute molecules leaving the solution and crystallizing out on the solid in the same unit of time. This is, then, another example of an equilibrium process (Chap. 6); and a saturated solution may be defined as one in which the dissolved solute is in *equilibrium with the undissolved solute*.

$$\text{Undissolved solute + solvent} \rightleftarrows \text{dissolved solute}$$

The amount of solute present in a given quantity of solvent, when the solution is saturated, is called its *solubility*.

We can demonstrate that the molecules or ions of a solute are still dissolving and crystallizing after saturation is reached by making a saturated solution, using "tagged" atoms of a radioactive substance, and then dropping in a crystal of the same material which does not contain any radioactive atoms. We soon find that the nonradioactive crystal has acquired some radioactive atoms from the solution, having traded some of its ordinary molecules for some dissolved molecules containing radioactive atoms.

Factors That Affect the Rate of Solution and the Solubility. The size of the solid solute particles, the rate of stirring, and the temperature affect the rate of solution of a given solute in a given solvent. But the particle

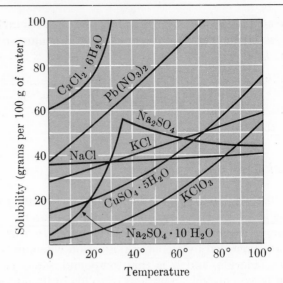

Figure 14.5 Change of solubility with change in temperature.

size and stirring rate do not affect the solubility; they simply control the rate at which the solubility equilibrium is attained. A change in temperature does change the solubility of a substance (Figure 14.5). Most solid solutes are more soluble as the temperature is increased, but a few, including calcium hydroxide, $Ca(OH)_2$, decrease in solubility as the temperature increases.

Supersaturated Solutions, a Nonequilibrium Condition. Since the solution of most solids increases with increasing temperature, we can readily obtain a saturated solution by approximately saturating a solution at a high temperature and then reducing the temperature to the desired point, *taking care to have some of the solid present all the time.* The excess of solute will crystallize out as the temperature is lowered, and almost at once the solution will come to *saturation* equilibrium at the lower temperature.

If we neglect to have some of the solid present while a concentrated solution cools, it may happen that the excess of solute will fail to crystallize. The solution will then contain *more than the normal saturation quantity of the solute*, and is said to be *supersaturated.* Supersaturation occurs especially in the case of very soluble solids, with salts containing much water of hydration—for example, with sodium sulfate ($Na_2SO_4 \cdot 10H_2O$), and sodium thiosulfate ($Na_2S_2O_3 \cdot 5H_2O$). The introduction of even the smallest fragment of the solid solute into a supersaturated solution will bring about the crystallization of the excess of solute, and thus restore the equilibrium condition appropriate to the lowered temperature.

Concentration. The term *concentration* denotes *the quantity of solute dissolved in a given quantity of solvent or of solution.* The concentration of a solution may be expressed in a number of ways. Sometimes it is stated on a percentage basis. More often it is desirable to state the number of *moles* which a given volume of the solution contains. If, for example, a given solution contains one mole of solute for each liter of solution, we say this is a 1-molar ($1M$) solution; similarly, a $0.5M$ solution contains one-half mole of solute for each liter of solution and a $6M$ solution contains six moles of solute per liter of solution (Figure 14.6). Other examples using weights of solutes are: a $1M$ solution of sodium hydroxide contains 40.00 g NaOH

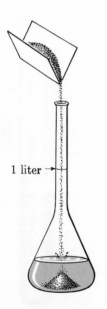

1 liter →

Figure 14.6 Preparation of a 1-molar solution. One mole of solute is added to water. After the solute has dissolved, more water is added, stirring to keep the composition uniform, in order to bring the final volume to the 1-liter mark.

per liter of solution; 63.02 g (one mole) of nitric acid dissolved in 2 liters of solution is a $0.5M$ solution. By dipping up or pouring out the proper number of milliliters of a solution of known molar concentration, one can measure out a known fraction of a mole of the solute substance.

Because molar solutions depend on the volume of solution (and this is temperature dependent), it is often convenient to use a concentration unit known as *molality*. Molality is defined as the number of moles of solute in each kilogram (1,000 g) of solvent. Thus, for example, a 2-molal (2m.) solution contains two moles of solute for each kilogram of solvent, and a 0.1m. aqueous sucrose solution contains 0.1 mole (34.3 g) of sucrose in 1,000 g of water.

A third concentration unit is known as the mole fraction and is defined as the number of moles of solute divided by the number of moles of solvent plus the number of moles of solute—i.e., by the total number of moles. Thus, for example, a solution having a mole fraction of 0.1 contains one mole of solute for every nine moles of solvent, or

$$\frac{1 \text{ mole solute}}{9 \text{ moles solvent} + 1 \text{ mole solute}} = 0.1$$

Properties of a Solvent Modified by a Solute. The properties which a solvent (such as water) possesses when pure are often greatly modified when a solid is dissolved in it. Among these properties are *vapor pressure*, *boiling point*, and *freezing point*. These effects are not only interesting and important in themselves, but on them are based methods for finding the molecular weights of solutes. In the present treatment we shall deal only with covalent solutes, which *do not furnish ions*; later, solutions containing ions will be considered.

Lowering of the Vapor Pressure. A solution of a solid in a liquid has a lower vapor pressure than that of the liquid itself. This can be easily shown, with a manometer, for solutions of sugar in water (Figure 14.7). No completely satisfying explanation for the lowering is known. Perhaps the sugar molecules act as a "screen" and interfere with the escape of solvent molecules, and so lower the vapor pressure.

After many years of careful experimental work, the French scientist François Raoult found (a) *that the lowering of vapor pressure at a given temperature is directly proportional to the molal concentration of the solution,* and (b) *that the percentage decrease in vapor pressure is the same for all solutes, regardless of their chemical nature, provided that they do not have an appreciable vapor pressure of their own and do not dissociate into ions.* In other words, at a given temperature the lowering of the vapor pressure of a given solvent depends on the *number* and not the *kind* of solute molecules in a given quantity of the solvent. Raoult's law holds true only for dilute solutions. Raoult's law may be written

$$\Delta vp = k_p m.$$

where Δvp is the lowering of the vapor pressure, k_p is a proportionality constant, and m. is the molality.

Elevation of the Boiling Point. Since the boiling point of a liquid is the temperature at which its vapor pressure just exceeds the opposing pressure of the atmosphere, it is evident that any condition which *lowers the vapor*

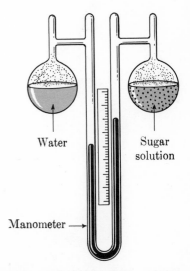

Figure 14.7 Vapor-pressure lowering. The air is pumped out of the apparatus. Then the difference in levels of the mercury columns gives the difference in pressure between the water and the solution.

pressure will raise the boiling point, since the liquid will have to be heated to a higher temperature to regain its original vapor pressure. This is shown schematically in Figure 14.8, where the curve showing the change of vapor pressure as a function of temperature for a pure liquid, as in Figure 13.9, is compared with the corresponding curve for a solution of a definite concentration. In the course of his experiments, Raoult found that the *elevation of the boiling point*, like the lowering of the vapor pressure, *is proportional to the molal concentration of the solution*, or in mathematical terms, $\Delta T_b = k_b$m., where ΔT_b is the rise and the boiling point, m. is the molality, and k_b is a proportionality constant.

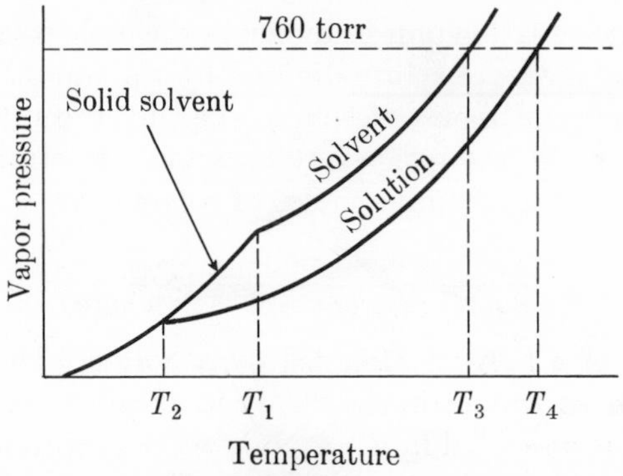

Figure 14.8 Comparison of the change of vapor pressure with temperature for solution and solvent. Comparison of T_4 with T_3, and of T_2 with T_1 shows that the boiling point of the solution is raised, and the freezing point of the solution lowered, compared to the corresponding values for the pure solvent.

It follows that molar quantities of any substances not electrovalent and not having a vapor pressure of their own, when dissolved in a definite weight of a solvent, produce the same rise in the boiling point of the solution. The boiling-point elevation produced by 1 mole of solute added to 1,000 g of water (a molal solution) is 0.52°C. Since the boiling-point elevation is proportional to the concentration, the boiling point of a 0.50-molal solution will be $0.50 \times 0.52 = 0.26$°C higher than that of water. The rise in boiling point is different for different solvents.

Lowering of the Freezing Point of the Solvent. When an unsaturated solution is cooled sufficiently, it does not freeze as a solution, but crystals of the pure solvent are formed. Since at the freezing point the vapor pressure of the solid solvent is equal to that of the liquid, and since the vapor pressure of the solution is less than that of the pure solvent, it is evident, as shown in Figure 14.8, that the freezing point of the solution is below that of the pure solvent. It is to lower the freezing point of water that we add various compounds (usually alcohol, or ethylene glycol) to the water in an automobile radiator in cold weather.

Raoult found that the *freezing-point depression is proportional to the molal concentration of the solution*, and is the same for covalent solutes in the same solvent, as shown for water in Table 14.2. Thus a mole of solute dissolved in 1,000 g of water lowers the freezing point approximately 1.86°C (called the freezing-point constant, k_f, for water).

Every solvent has its own characteristic freezing-point constant; thus for acetic acid it is 3.9°C, for benzene 5.1°C, for naphthalene 6.8°C. The equation relating the freezing-point depression to the molality is

$$\Delta T_f = k_f \text{m.}$$

Solute	Formula	Lowering Produced in 1,000 g of Water by 1 Mole of Solute (°C)
Methyl alcohol (methanol)	CH_3OH	1.86
Ethyl alcohol	C_2H_5OH	1.83
Dextrose	$C_6H_{12}O_6$	1.90
Glycerin	$C_3H_5(OH)_3$	1.92
Urea	$CO(NH_2)_2$	1.86

Table 14.2 Lowering of the Freezing Point of Water

where ΔT_f is the freezing-point depression, m. is the molality, and k_f is the freezing-point constant.

If the concentration of the solution is such that the solution is saturated at the freezing point, then a lowering of the temperature will cause both solid solute and solid solvent to crystallize. The mixture of solids formed is called the *eutectic*, and the temperature at which the eutectic forms is called the *eutectic temperature*: it is the lowest freezing point of the solution (Table 14.3).

Salt	Eutectic Temp. (°C)	Eutectic Composition (moles salt/moles water)
Potassium nitrate	− 2.8	0.022
Potassium chloride	−10.7	0.059
Ammonium chloride	−15.4	0.082
Ammonium nitrate	−16.7	0.168
Sodium nitrate	−18.1	0.130
Sodium chloride	−21.3	0.092
Calcium chloride	−49.8	0.070
Hydrogen chloride	−86.0	0.163

Table 14.3 Eutectic Temperature and Composition of Ice with Various Salts

Molecular Weight Determination. Since the vapor-pressure lowering, boiling-point elevation, and freezing-point depression are each proportional to the molal concentration of a solution, that is, to the number of solute molecules in a solution, it is possible to determine the molecular weight of a dissolved compound from measurements on one of the above-mentioned properties—for example, the freezing-point depression.

PROBLEM. ■ On a sensitive thermometer the freezing point of water was found to be exactly 0°C, while a solution of 0.775 g of ethylene glycol, dissolved in 25.0 g of water, froze at −0.93°C. Calculate the molecular weight of ethylene glycol.

SOLUTION
Since the freezing-point depression is proportional to the molal concentration, the molal concentration is evidently

$$m. = \frac{\Delta T_f}{k_f} = \frac{0.93}{1.86} = 0.5 \text{ molal}$$

Thus the number of moles of solute present in the 25.0 g of water taken is

Number of moles = molality × kg water = 0.5 × 0.0250 = 0.0125

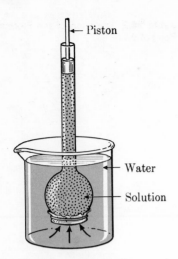

← Piston

← Water

← Solution

Figure 14.9 Illustrating the meaning of osmotic pressure.

This tells us that the 0.775 g of ethylene glycol solute contains 0.0125 moles so the molecular weight (the number of grams per mole) is

$$\text{Molecular weight} = \frac{\text{grams}}{\text{mole}} = \frac{0.775 \text{ g}}{0.0125 \text{ moles}} = 62.0$$

Osmosis. Closely related to the lowering of the vapor pressure, to the elevation of the boiling point, and to the depression of the freezing point is the phenomenon of *osmosis*. This is the passage of a solvent from a dilute solution (or from a pure solvent) through a membrane into a more concentrated solution. This is an important process in plant and animal life.

The membrane must be semipermeable—that is, such that it will allow molecules of solvent to pass through readily, but will not allow molecules of solute to pass. A piece of parchment paper or nonwaterproof cellophane is semipermeable in this sense, and may be used to demonstrate osmosis. The membrane is fastened tightly over the bell of a thistle tube (Figure 14.9). A sugar solution is placed in the vessel so constructed, which is then immersed in pure water. Osmosis starts, and the volume of the sugar solution slowly increases as the water enters through the membrane.

Osmotic Pressure. If we could fit the tube in Figure 14.9 with a piston, as shown, and with it apply a sufficiently large pressure on the solution, osmosis would stop. In fact, by pushing hard enough on the piston, water could be squeezed out of the solution, through the membrane, and back into the outer vessel.

The pressure which, when applied to a solution, will just prevent the entrance of solvent into it through a semipermeable membrane is the osmotic pressure of the solution. The pressure need not be applied with a piston. The hydrostatic pressure of a long vertical column of the solution may serve the same purpose.

If the solution on each side of the membrane were of the same concentration, no pressure would develop. Solutions having the same osmotic pressure are called *isotonic solutions*.

The osmotic pressure of a solution is approximately equal to the gas pressure which the solute would exert if it were a gas occupying the same volume as the solvent, at the same temperature. For instance, 1 mole of a gas, in 22.4 liters at 0°C, exerts a pressure of 1 atm. At 20°C the pressure is $293/273 \times 1$ atm $= 1.07$ atm. Similarly 1 mole of sugar dissolved in 22.4 liters of water, at 20°C, has an osmotic pressure of about 1.07 atm.

Other Types of Solutions

Other types of solutions very often encountered are solutions of liquids in liquids; solutions of gases in gases, liquids, and solids; and solutions of solids in solids.

Solutions of Liquids in Liquids. Two liquids may conduct themselves toward each other in either of two ways: they may each reach a definite limit of saturation with the other, or they may be freely soluble (or miscible in all proportions. Several properties of liquid solutions are of importance

1. *Vapor pressure.* Before mixing, each liquid has its own characteristic vapor pressure at the temperature in question. After mixing, it is found

that each liquid has diminished the vapor pressure of the other, depending upon the relative amounts of the two liquids. The vapor pressure of the solution is never as great as the sum of the two original pressures; it may be greater or less than that of either liquid taken separately, or it may have an intermediate value.

2. *Boiling point.* On heating a solution of one liquid in another the total vapor pressure increases; and when it just exceeds the opposing pressure of the atmosphere, the solution boils. From what has been said in regard to the vapor pressure of solutions, it will be seen that the boiling point of a solution may be lower or higher than that of either constituent. Usually it has an intermediate value [Figure 14.10 (a)].

3. *Fractional distillation.* When distilling a solution the component having the greater vapor pressure will in general pass away from the solution more rapidly than the one of lower vapor pressure (higher boiling point). If the vapors are condensed and the resulting liquid is collected in successive portions by changing the receiver at intervals, the first portions will be richer in the more volatile constituent, and the higher-boiling liquid will be largely obtained in the later portions. By repeating the process with each portion obtained in the first operation the two liquids may in time be separated from each other. Such a process is called *fractional distillation.*

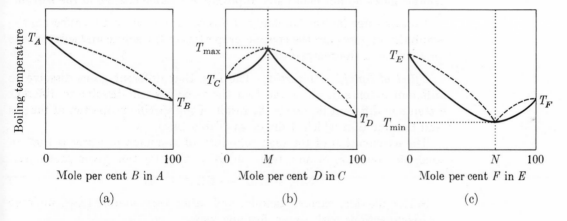

(a)   (b)   (c)

Figure 14.10 Boiling point as a function of composition for three types of liquid pairs boiling under constant pressure. In graph (a), fractional distillation will separate the liquids into the two components. Graphs (b) and (c) show maximum and minimum boiling points for liquid pairs C, D, and E, F. Both graphs may be separated into two parts (vertical dotted lines) each of which looks like (a). Fractional distillation will separate only into the extremes of the two parts, for example, into C and M [Graph (b)] or M and D, but not into C and D. At each temperature the composition of the vapor (dashed curves) is richer in the lower boiling material except for the constant-boiling mixtures where liquid and vapor have the same composition. Hence these constant boiling mixtures boil unchanged, and no separation of the two components occurs.

At a different pressure the position of the curves will be different just as, for example, T_A or T_B differ at different pressures.

4. *Constant-boiling solutions.* It occasionally happens that there is one particular concentration of a solution which has a lower vapor pressure (higher boiling point) than any other concentration or than that of either constituent taken separately [Figure 14.10(b)]. When such a solution is distilled, one or the other constituent vaporizes more readily, and the

concentration tends toward that of lowest vapor pressure. When this concentration is reached, the solution boils with a constant boiling point like a pure substance, and the distillate has the same composition as the solution remaining in the still. Such a constant-boiling solution cannot be altered in composition by repeated distillation (under a given pressure). A common example of a constant-boiling solution is a solution of approximately 95 per cent ethyl alcohol and 5 per cent water by volume. Mixtures of minimum boiling point are also known [Figure 14.10 (c)].

Solutions of Gases in Gases. Dalton's law of partial pressures applies to such systems.

Solutions of Gases in Liquids. The solubility of a gas in a liquid depends upon the temperature and pressure and may be expressed in a variety of ways; the most prevalent usage is to state the number of volumes of gas dissolved in 100 volumes of the solvent.

In respect to solubility, gases fall roughly into two classes: those of rather small solubility, such as oxygen, nitrogen, and hydrogen; and those of much larger solubility, such as ammonia, hydrogen chloride, and sulfur dioxide. In the case of the latter group there is always a change in the volume of the solvent when a large volume of gas is absorbed; the volume may increase markedly, as for solutions of ammonia in water. The slightly soluble gases do not cause any appreciable volume change in the solvent.

Factors Affecting the Solubility of Gases. The main factors affecting the solubility of gases are the specific properties of the solute and solvent, the pressure, and the temperature.

Effect of Specific Properties. The fact that different gases dissolve to different extents in water and that the same gas will dissolve to different extents in different liquids is the result of the specific properties of the gas and the liquid in which it dissolves (Table 14.4).

The explanation of the high solubility of ammonia in water is that an acid-base reaction occurs, represented by the equation given previously.

$$NH_3 + H_2O \longrightarrow NH_4^+ + OH^- \tag{1}$$

Sulfur dioxide, carbon dioxide, and other very soluble gases undergo similar reactions with water, forming ions.

Effect of Pressure. Gases become more soluble in liquids, as the pressure is increased.

Table 14.4 Solubility of Gases in 100 ml of Water

Gas	Amount Dissolved at 0°C and under 760 torr Pressure	
	(g)	(ml)
Hydrogen	0.000191	2.14
Nitrogen	0.0029	2.33
Oxygen	0.0070	4.96
Carbon dioxide	0.339	171.3
Hydrogen sulfide	0.67	437
Sulfur dioxide	23.35	7,979
Hydrogen chloride	82.97	50,600
Ammonia	100.12	129,890

The change in solubility with change in pressure follows no standard rules for the more soluble gases. For the slightly soluble gases, however, such as oxygen or hydrogen, *the weight of gas dissolved by a definite quantity of a given solvent is directly proportional to the pressure, provided the temperature remains constant* (Figure 14.11). This statement is known as Henry's law, after the English chemist William Henry (1774–1836).

When a mixture of two or more gases of low solubility is maintained over a liquid, *each dissolves independently of the others and in accordance with its own partial pressure.* This is a necessary consequence of Dalton's law.

Effect of Temperature. With a rise in temperature, gases become less soluble, and, except in special cases in which constant-boiling solutions (page 281) are formed, all of a dissolved gas can be driven out by boiling the solution. Gases do not dissolve in ice.

Solutions of Gases in Solids. Although not commonly recognized, solutions of gases in some solids appear to exist. The helium gas found in some uranium ores is probably very nearly in atomic dispersion since it is formed one atom at a time. Other cases that appear to be solution of gases in solids may be due to adsorption over a large active surface, and some cases may be due to occlusion in imperfections or voids in the crystal lattice. Some metals, notably palladium, dissolve large quantities of hydrogen; this metal also adsorbs hydrogen. Some large complex organic molecules form cages that occlude atoms and small molecules; such substances are called clathrate compounds.

Solutions of Solids in Solids. These are discussed in Chap. 16.

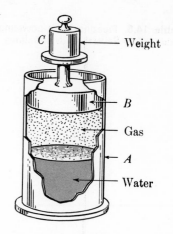

Figure 14.11 A gas standing over water in the cylinder, *A*, dissolves under the pressure of a weight, *C*, which is placed on the piston, *B*.

Ionization | start |

Irregularities in the Effects Produced by Solutes in Liquid Solvents. Experiments show that compounds can be divided into two classes on the basis of the effects they produce on the properties of the solvent liquid: (a) those which give the normal molecular effects on freezing point, vapor pressure, boiling point, and osmotic pressure discussed earlier in this chapter, and (b) those which produce excessive effects on these properties. This distinction may be seen by considering the lowering of the freezing point (Table 14.5).

The substances in the second and third groups are said to have *abnormal* freezing-point depressions. Experiments show that solutions of these compounds also show abnormal boiling-point elevations and abnormal osmotic pressures.

The Theory of Ionization. In his experiments on electricity, Michael Faraday (1791–1867) had observed that while pure water was a very poor conductor of electricity, solutions of certain substances, which he called *electrolytes*, made it a good conductor. Svante Arrhenius (1859–1927) noted in 1883 that Faraday's electrolytes included all the compounds whose solutions showed abnormal effects in freezing-point depression and boiling-point elevation. Arrhenius knew from Raoult's law that the freezing-point lowering was proportional to the number and not the kind of dissolved

Table 14.5 Freezing-Point Lowering Produced by Several Kinds of Solutes

Substance	Formula	Lowering of Freezing Point (°C) Produced by Dissolving 1 Mole in 1,000 g of Water
Dextrose	$C_6H_{12}O_6$	1.90
Alcohol	C_2H_5OH	1.83
Urea	$CO(NH_2)_2$	1.86
Acetic acid	CH_3CO_2H	1.93
Ammonia	NH_3	1.93
Sodium hydroxide	$NaOH$	3.44
Sodium chloride	$NaCl$	3.37
Sodium nitrate	$NaNO_3$	3.02
Hydrogen sulfate	H_2SO_4	4.04
Calcium nitrate	$Ca(NO_3)_2$	4.59
Magnesium sulfate	$MgSO_4$	2.02

molecules; if each solute molecule separated, on dissolving, into two or more particles, each of which had the same effect on the freezing-point depression as that of the whole molecule, then the observed abnormal effect would appear. If, in turn, these fragments of molecules were electrically charged, and by motion through the solution would transport charge from one electrode to the other, their presence would also account for the conductive properties of the solution.

The assumption that substances dissociate into charged particles rather than neutral atoms was also necessary to explain chemical behavior. For example, a compound such as sodium chloride could not separate into sodium and chlorine *atoms* in water solution, since sodium reacts with water to produce hydrogen, and no hydrogen is evolved when sodium chloride dissolves in water. If it separated into the charged *ions* Na^+ and Cl^-, however, these would not be expected to show the properties of the uncharged atoms.

Ions from Some Covalent Molecules. Solutions containing ions are sometimes formed when covalent molecules are dissolved in water. It has been mentioned earlier that when ammonia dissolves, reaction takes place with the formation of ions:

$$NH_3 + H_2O \rightleftharpoons NH_4^+ + OH^- \tag{1}$$

Further, when the covalent gas hydrogen chloride dissolves in water, hydronium and chloride ions are formed as a result of reaction with the water. In the case of hydrogen chloride this reaction is nearly complete, so that the solution contains practically no hydrogen chloride molecules; with ammonia or acetic acid the reaction is incomplete [cf., double arrows in Equation (1)], and most of the solute remains as molecules rather than as ions.

Interionic Attraction. The data in Table 14.5 show that the freezing-point depression produced by the electrolytes is not as great as that to be expected for complete separation of the ions. For sodium chloride, for example, the freezing-point depression for the molal solution is not quite twice that for a molal solution of a nonelectrolyte, as would be expected if two ions were formed for each molecule. Similarly the freezing-point depression for calcium nitrate is not that to be expected for three ions from each molecule, and for magnesium sulfate the effect is only slightly greater than for a nonelectrolyte. The reason for this was interpreted by G. N. Lewis and by Peter Debye. They showed that the electrostatic forces between the ions are not obliterated completely in the solution, but are still sufficiently powerful to pull the ions toward one another. As a result of this interionic attraction, the ions are not completely freed from one another, and the partial effects recorded in the table are observed experimentally. Similar partial effects are observed for vapor-pressure lowering, boiling-point elevation, and osmotic pressure.

1. *Effect of charge.* As one would suppose, the electrostatic forces are greater, the higher the charge on the ions. This explains the difference between sodium chloride, for example, and magnesium sulfate (Table 14.5). The doubly charged magnesium (Mg^{+2}) and sulfate (SO_4^{-2}) ions have a greater attraction for each other than Na^+ and Cl^-, and consequently a smaller effect on the depression of the freezing point.

2. *Effect of solvent.* The magnitude of the attractive forces between ions depends upon the solvent in which they are dissolved, and is determined by the insulating properties of the solvent as expressed by the dielectric constant. In water, with a high dielectric constant, the electrostatic forces are small, so that the ions are relatively free. Most other solvents have smaller dielectric constants than water, so that the electrostatic forces are greater, with consequent greater interionic attraction.

3. *Effect of dilution.* Besides the dependence of the electrostatic forces on the charge of the ions and on the solvent, they also depend upon the distance between the ions, being smaller the farther apart the ions are.

Strong and Weak Electrolytes. In the data of Table 14.5 it is seen that the freezing-point depression for the second and third groups of compounds is greater than the average value of 1.86 for the covalent compounds dextrose, alcohol, and urea. But the freezing-point depression for acetic acid and ammonia is much less than for sodium hydroxide and the other compounds of the third group. The difference in freezing-point depression of these two groups must be due to the difference in the number of ions present in the 1-molal solutions examined. For ammonia and acetic acid, ions are formed from covalent molecules in reversible reactions, illustrated by Equations (1) and (3).

$$CH_3CO_2H + H_2O \rightleftharpoons H_3O^+ + CH_3CO_2^- \qquad (3)$$

At ordinary concentrations the ionization is not very great, but it increases with dilution, owing to the lessened chance that the ions have of recombining, the farther apart they are.

Electrolytes which are similar to sodium hydroxide and sodium chloride in their freezing-point depressions are called *strong electrolytes*; this class includes most salts and strong acids and bases such as hydrochloric acid and sodium hydroxide. Those of the acetic acid type are called *weak electrolytes*; ammonium hydroxide (ammonia) belongs to this class. The difference between the two classes is that strong electrolytes have only ions present in solution, held together to a greater or less extent by interionic attractive forces determined by the charge, the solvent, and the dilution. Weak electrolytes, on the other hand, exist in solution predominantly as covalent molecules, only a few of which are ionized at any one time. The difference between strong and weak electrolytes is experimentally more evident from a consideration of the conductivity of solutions containing electrolytes.

Electrolytic Conduction. If two oppositely charged electrodes are placed in a solution containing ions, the positive ions will be drawn toward the negative electrode, and the negative ions will be drawn toward the positive electrode. This movement of charged particles through the solution results in a transfer of electric charge; we recognize this as an electric current, and say that the solution conducts the electric current. This type of conduction, which results from the motion of ions through the solution, is called *ionic* or *electrolytic conduction* in order to distinguish it from *electronic* or *metallic conduction*, which occurs when a current of electrons flows through a wire.

The amount of charge transferred across the solution in unit time will depend upon the number of ions present in the solution and the speed with which they move. In the case of strong electrolytes, the dissolved substance is all in the form of ions, and the conductivity is high; in the case of weak electrolytes, mostly covalent molecules are present in the solution, with comparatively few ions, and the conductivity is low.

Electrolytic conduction can also occur if an ionic crystal is melted. The ions are released from the rigid-patterned arrangement of the crystal (Figure 5.8) and are free to move; hence if electrodes are placed in the melt, the ions will move toward the electrode of opposite charge, and the melt will conduct a current.

Figure 14.12 Apparatus for testing the conductivity of a solution. Equal volumes (to cover the electrodes to the same height) of solutions of different substances of equal concentrations are placed in the bottle, and the intensity of the glow from the lamp is observed. In precise determinations of conductivity the electrical resistance of the solution is measured by special Wheatstone-bridge circuits using low-intensity alternating current.

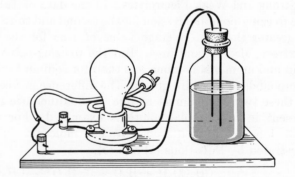

Speed of Ionic Reactions. Reactions involving only electrolytes in solution are usually much more rapid than most of those involving nonelectrolytes. For example, if solutions of sodium chloride and silver nitrate (both electrolytes) are mixed at room temperature, a precipitate of silver chloride forms immediately. On the other hand, if silver nitrate solution is added to a nonelectrolyte containing chlorine, such as carbon tetrachloride, a precipitate forms only after heating for a long period of time. The reason for the behavior of the two electrolytes is that the formation of silver chloride consists solely in the combination of the silver ions and chloride ions *already present in the solutions* of silver nitrate and sodium chloride before mixing, so that the reaction is

$$Ag^+, NO_3^- + Na^+, Cl^- \longrightarrow AgCl(s) + Na^+, NO_3^- \qquad (4)$$

or simply,

$$Ag^+ + Cl^- \longrightarrow AgCl(s) \qquad (5)$$

No chloride ions are present in the solution of the nonelectrolyte carbon tetrachloride, and no reaction with silver ions occurs, until hydrochloric acid has been formed by the slow chemical reaction of carbon tetrachloride with the water present.

Properties of Ionic Solutions Are Those of the Ions. It is evident also that all solutions containing the chloride ion will behave similarly toward the silver ions, since it makes no difference whether the chloride ion was originally paired with the sodium ion or potassium ion or hydrogen ion or any other. The essential reaction is still the simple combination of silver and chloride ions represented by Equation (5).

Just as all solutions containing chloride ions will show the property characteristic of that ion—forming a precipitate with the silver ion—so the properties characteristic of other ions will be shown by all solutions containing those ions. The copper ion, for example, has a characteristic blue color, and this blue color of the copper ion is shown by all solutions of copper salts, unless the negative ion is also colored.

SUMMARY

The process of dissolving is seen as one in which the attractive forces of the solvent for the solute are strong enough to overcome the attractive forces that hold solute particles together. For polar solvents, such as water, the solvent molecules are dipoles which are attracted to ionic or polar solutes. Usually the solvent molecules surround the solute particle and tend to insulate it from other solute particles.

Convenient expressions of the concentrations of solutions are the molarity, M, defined as the number of moles of solute present in each liter of solution, and the molality, m., defined as the number of moles of solute dissolved in each kilogram of solvent.

The presence of a solute has a marked effect on the vapor pressure, boiling point, and freezing point of the solvent. The lowering of the vapor pressure and of the freezing point and the rise in the boiling point of the solvent caused by the presence of a nonvolatile, nonelectrolyte solute are proportional to the molality of the solution. Use is made of this fact to determine molecular weights of such solutes and to achieve temperatures below the freezing point of the solvent.

Solutions of certain solutes have unusually low vapor pressures and freezing points. The same solutions are good conductors of electricity. These observations are explained if the solutes are ionized in solution. Careful studies of solutions of electrolytes show that ions of opposite sign in solution still are attracted to one another. The effects of this interionic attraction are seen in the vapor-pressure lowering, the boiling-point elevation, the freezing-point depression, and in the conductivity of the solution.

If the solute is completely ionized, it is known as a strong electrolyte. Weak electrolytes are partially ionized in solution; the ions exist in equilibrium with un-ionized species. Weak acids and bases are weak electrolytes in water solutions.

SOME SPECIAL TERMS

Concentration of solution	**Dipole-dipole forces**
saturated solution	**Dielectric constant**
supersaturated solution	**Osmosis**
molar solution	**Osmotic pressure**
molality	**Fractional distillation**
mole fractions	**Constant boiling solution**
Solubility	**Electrolysis**
solute	abnormal freezing-point depression
solvent	interionic attraction
heat of solution	strong electrolyte
solvation	weak electrolyte
hydrate	electrolytic conduction
energy of hydration	
Henry's law	
eutectic	
Raoult's laws	

QUESTIONS AND PROBLEMS

1. Compare evaporation and solution; melting and solution.
2. Consider the hydration energies of the monovalent cations in Table 14.1. Can you suggest reasons why the order is $Li^+ > Ag^+ > Na^+ > K^+$? Will these same reasons explain the order $Mg^{+2} > Ca^{+2}$? $F^- > Cl^-$?
3. The process of dissolving sodium chloride in a large amount of water may be considered to take place in three hypothetical steps: (a) dissociation of the ions in the crystal, (b) dissolving first one ion and then (c) the other to make the final solution. If the heat of the complete process is 3.5 kcal/mole of sodium chloride, what is the energy associated with step (a)?
4. Sodium thiosulfate dissolves with the absorption of heat. If a supersaturated solution of the salt is prepared and a small crystalline fragment of sodium thiosulfate is dropped into the solution, will you expect to observe a rise or fall in temperature as a result of the process initiated by the fragment? Explain the basis for your answer.
5. Discuss what will happen in the following cases: (a) A solution of such a concentration that it is not saturated at 20°C is prepared at 40°C and cooled to 20°C. (b) A solution of such a concentration that it is saturated at 20°C is prepared at 40°C and cooled to 10°C. (c) A water solution of such a concentration that it is not saturated at 0°C is prepared at 25°C and cooled to 0°C. (d) A 1-molal solution of urea in water is prepared at 25°C and cooled to −5°C. (e) A 1-molal solution of potassium nitrate is prepared at room temperature and cooled to −3°C. (f) A saturated solution of ammonium chloride is prepared at room temperature and cooled to −20°C.

6. Why does putting salt on an icy sidewalk in the winter time cause the ice to melt? Does the sidewalk get warmer?

7. A mixture of two liquids is said to form an ideal solution if the partial pressure P_A and P_B of the liquids in the vapor above the mixture are given by the equations $P_A = P_A{}^0 N_A$ and $P_B = P_B{}^0 N_B$, where $P_A{}^0$ and $P_B{}^0$ are vapor pressures of the pure liquids A and B at the temperature of the mixture, and N_A and N_B are their mole fractions in the mixture. (a) Calculate the pressures above ideal liquid mixtures containing (i) 1 mole of A to 3 moles of B, and (ii) 3 moles of A to 1 mole of B, at a temperature at which $P_A{}^0 = 80$ torr and $P_B{}^0 = 120$ torr. (b) Plot a graph showing the change of vapor pressure with composition for the whole range from $N_A = 1$ to $N_A = 0$. (c) Using this graph, discuss what will happen if the pressure above a mixture of 10 moles of A and 10 moles of B is reduced to 90 torr. (d) If the pressure is maintained at 90 torr until action ceases, what will be the mole fraction of A in the final solution?

8. It is suspected that a compound of empirical formula AB_2 is really an ionic substance of formula $AB^+AB_3{}^-$. One formula weight of AB_2 is dissolved in 1,000 g of water and the freezing point of the resulting solution is measured. Will the results of this measurement distinguish between the two formulas, AB_2 and $AB^+AB_3{}^-$?

9. What values of the ratios of the molal freezing-point depressions of salt solutions compared to those of sugar solutions would you expect to be approached at infinite dilution by the following salts: $NaCl$, $MgSO_4$, $AlCl_3$, $K_4Fe(CN)_6$, $MgCl_2$, Li_2SO_4? If you were to plot a graph of this ratio against the concentration for each salt, how would you predict the curves to look in comparison to each other? Sketch six such curves on a graph.

10. The following pairs of solutions are mixed together. Which pairs would you expect to show an appreciable heat effect? Explain why or why not. (a) 1-molar sodium chloride and 1-molar potassium nitrate. (b) 1-molar sodium chloride and 1-molar silver nitrate. (c) 1-molar magnesium chloride and 1-molar sodium nitrate. (d) 1-molar sodium hydroxide and 1-molar hydrochloric acid. (e) 1-molar sodium sulfate and 10-molar sulfuric acid.

11. List the following in the order of decreasing freezing point: (a) water, (b) 1-molal urea solution, (c) 0.5-molal sugar solution, (d) 1-molal calcium chloride solution, (e) 0.5-molal sodium chloride solution, (f) 2-molal potassium chloride solution.

12. Calculate the molar concentrations of the solutions prepared by dissolving the quantities of substances listed in the left-hand column and adding water until the final volume, given in the right-hand column, is reached.

Substance	Final Volume
60 g of urea, $CO(NH_2)_2$	500 cc
202 g of potassium nitrate, KNO_3	1600 cc
55.5 g of calcium chloride, $CaCl_2$	2.0 liters
21.9 g of calcium chloride, $CaCl_2 \cdot 6H_2O$	100 cc

13. Calculate the concentrations of potassium chloride, calcium chloride, potassion ion, calcium ion, and chloride ion in a solution prepared by dissolving 7.46 g of KCl and 5.55 g $CaCl_2$ in sufficient water to make 500 cc of final solution.

14. What weight of ammonium chloride is present in 600 g of a 2.0 molal solution of that salt?

15. Which of the following solutions will have the lower freezing point? (a) A solution of 100 g of urea in 600 g of water; (b) a solution of 100 g of alcohol (CH_3CH_2OH) in 460 g of water.

16. Calculate the freezing-point depression of a solution of 3.2 g of methyl alcohol (CH_3OH) dissolved in 50 g of water.

17. A solution of 3.5 g of a covalent substance X dissolved in 80 g of water was found to raise the boiling point 0.302°C. What is the molecular weight of X?

18. Calculate the osmotic pressure developed by a solution of 4.4 g of dioxane ($C_4H_8O_2$) dissolved in 350 cc of water at 25°C.

19. At 0°C 100 cc of water dissolves 4.96 cc of oxygen when the oxygen is at atmospheric pressure; for nitrogen the corresponding figure is 2.33 cc. Using the approximation that air is $\frac{1}{5}$ oxygen and $\frac{4}{5}$ nitrogen, calculate the number of cubic centimeters of each of the pure gases, measured at standard conditions, which is present in 100 cc of water saturated with air at atmospheric pressure at 0°C. Compare the concentration of oxygen in normal air with its concentration in water under these conditions, expressing each in moles per liter. Compare the ratio of oxygen to nitrogen in dissolved air with that in normal air.

20. Using data presented in Figure 14.5, calculate the number of moles of lead nitrate which would crystallize out if 500 g of a solution of lead nitrate ($Pb(NO_3)_2$), saturated at 70°C, was cooled to 0°C.

21. Carbon dioxide and sulfur dioxide are more soluble in water than are oxygen and nitrogen. Can you suggest a reason why this should be so?

REFERENCES

DREISBACH, D. *Liquids and Solutions*. Boston: Houghton-Mifflin, 1966.

HOLDEN, A., and P. SINGER. *Crystals and Crystal Growing*. New York: Doubleday, 1960.

15

The Solid State

*Si maintenant l'on admet qu'une cause quelconque intervienne pour disposer l'Assemblage qui se constitue, au moment de la cristallisation, à une structure symétrique plutôt qu'à une structure non symétrique, il est clair que l'Assemblage définitivement formé appartiendra à l'une de nos sept classes ... (Première classe: le cube, le cube centré, le cube à faces centres; deuxieme classe: ...). L'observation des corps crystallisés, naturels ou artificiels, prouve à posteriori qu'il en est ainsi; aussi la division géométrique des Assemblages correspond-elle fidèlement à celle qu'une étude patiente et attentive a porté à établir entre les différents systèmes cristallins.**
Auguste Bravais (1811–1863)

One of the major frontiers of research in modern physical science is the solid state. Such useful devices as the transistor, the laser or optical maser, and the solar battery have been developed as a result of scientific enquiries into the nature of solids. Although scientists have been interested in this topic for over a hundred years, modern crystal chemistry began during the early years of this century—about the time that Bohr and Rutherford were conducting their famous researches into the structure of atoms.

X-Rays and Crystal Structure

The development of the tool, the X-ray, which led to a clear understanding of the internal structure of crystals, emerged from: (a) the idea, held by many nineteenth-century crystallographers, that the external symmetry of crystals was the result of a symmetrical arrangement of the atoms or other building blocks within the crystal; (b) the prediction by the German

---

* "If one agrees that some force or other acts, at the moment of crystallization, to cause the grouping being formed to favor a symmetric rather than an unsymmetric structure, it is clear that the grouping finally formed will belong to one of our seven classes ... (Class 1: the cube, the body-centered cube, the face-centered cube; class 2: ...). Examination of crystalline substances, natural or man-made, shows *a posteriori* that this is the case; further the geometrical classification of the groupings corresponds exactly to that which a patient and careful study has established for the different crystal systems." (The quotation is from *Journal de l'Ecole polytechnique, 33* (1850), p. 127.)

scientist Max von Laue (1879–1960), dramatically confirmed by experiment, that a beam of X-rays would be scattered or diffracted from crystals giving a scattering or diffraction pattern that indicated the arrangement of the building blocks in the crystal; and (c) development of an equation by the British scientists, Sir William Henry Bragg and his son, Sir William Lawrence Bragg, which made it possible to calculate from the diffraction pattern the distances between the planes of building blocks in a crystal.

Subsequent investigations of the internal structure of crystals with beams of X-rays have led to the following generalizations:

1. The fundamental building blocks of crystals may be atoms, molecules, or ions arranged in systematic three-dimensional patterns in space.

2. The three-dimensional pattern is described in terms of arrays of identical points in space called space lattices. A crystal structure is described in terms of the space lattices by replacing the lattice points by identical atoms, molecules, or ions for each of the space lattices involved in the description. There are many different kinds of crystal structures. For example, in the diamond structure each carbon atom has four near neighbors; in sodium chloride each ion has six near neighbors; in metallic zinc each atom has twelve neighbors.

3. The macro crystal presumably consists of stacks of repeating units or repeating groups of building blocks. Each repeating unit is called the *unit cell*.

4. The arrangement of atoms, molecules, or ions in a crystal is related precisely to the external symmetry of the crystal. For example, there are cubic space lattices (three) which result in cubic crystals, tetragonal space lattices (two) which give tetragonal crystals, orthorhombic (four), rhombohedral (one), monoclinic (two), triclinic (one), and hexagonal (one) lattices which give crystals of the seven recognized crystal systems illustrated in Figure 15.1.

As an analogy one might compare a crystal with a truckload of cases of canned goods. The space lattice can be imagined to be related to the way the cans are packed in the cases: the unit cell to be analogous to the case itself and the external crystal symmetry to be related to the shape of the stack of cases. The shape of the stack is, of course, related to the shape of each case, and the shape of the case is related to the packing pattern of cans in the case.

In this chapter some examples of various types of crystals and their structures will be examined with a view toward explaining the properties of solids. Perhaps before doing this, it will be useful to present an elementary picture of the principles underlying the interaction of X-rays with crystals.

Diffraction of X-Rays. When X-rays pass through a crystal, they interact with the electrons of the atoms or ions in the crystal in such a way that the atoms or ions act as if they were new sources of X-radiation, and we say that the incident X-ray beam is scattered by the structural units in the crystal. The scattered beams move out from the structural units in all directions, as a wave on the surface of water moves out in circles from a dropped stone. The structural units are in a regular pattern, however, so that the waves from one unit overlap the waves from another, sometimes

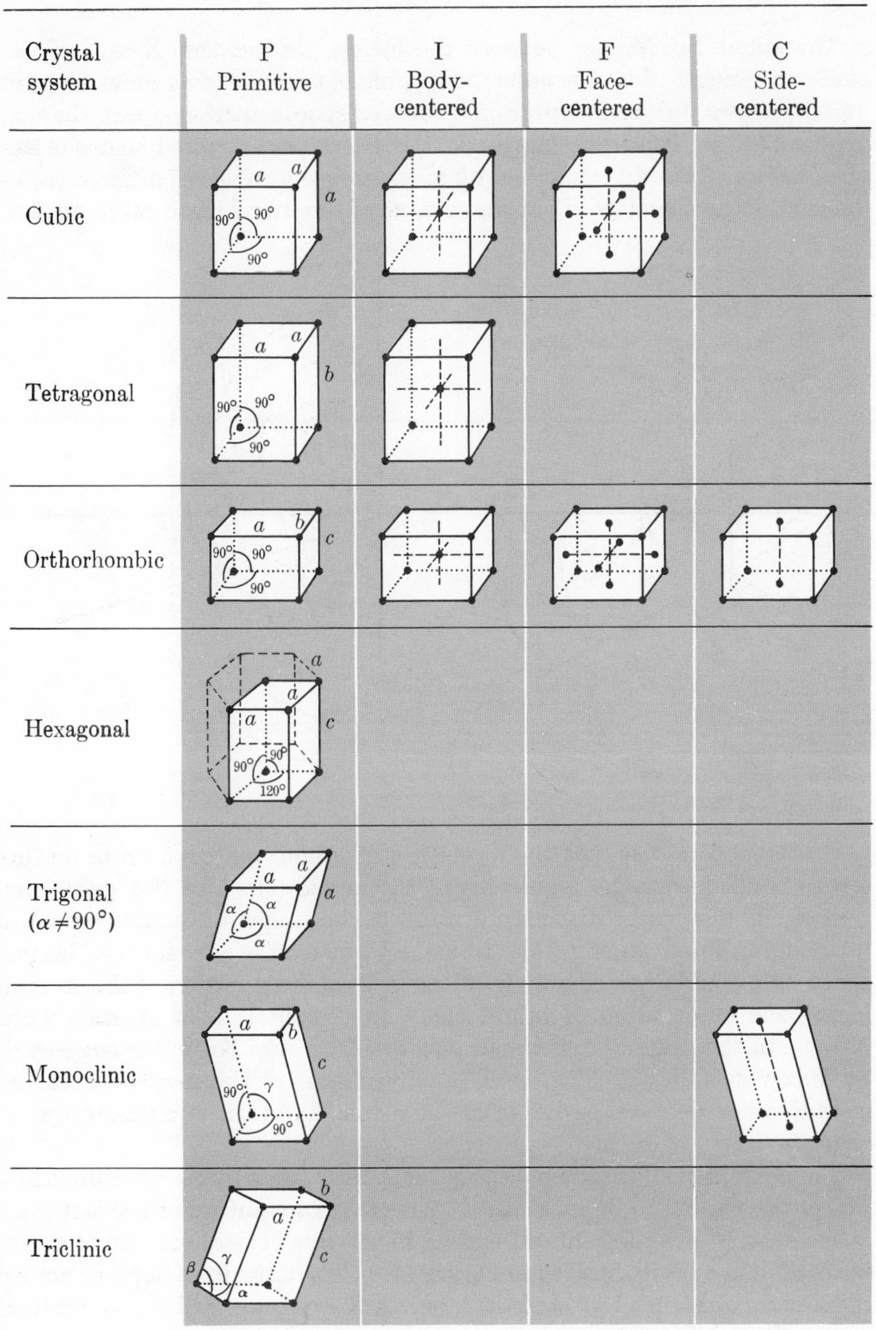

Crystal system	P Primitive	I Body-centered	F Face-centered	C Side-centered
Cubic				
Tetragonal				
Orthorhombic				
Hexagonal				
Trigonal ($\alpha \neq 90°$)				
Monoclinic				
Triclinic				

Figure 15.1 The seven crystal systems.

reinforcing, and sometimes destroying, the other. Reinforcement occurs when the crest of one wave coincides with the crest of another. This is shown in Figure 15.2 (a) in which the semicircles represent advancing wave fronts from the sources aa, and two reinforced beams are shown as the tangents to the advancing fronts. One of these proceeds in the straight-ahead direction, another at an angle. If these beams now fall upon a screen, one will observe light spots where the beams strike, and dark spots between. This phenomenon is known as diffraction.

The angular difference between the beams, for incident X-rays of the same wavelength, depends upon the spacing of the scattering units. Figure 15.2(b) shows diffraction from two sources spaced farther apart than in Figure 15.2(a). Evidently the angle θ_b between the scattered beams is less than before. It is thus possible, by measuring the angles of diffraction, to determine the spacings (d) in the crystal, if the wavelength (λ) is known.

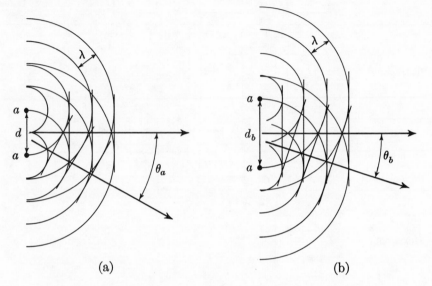

Figure 15.2 (a) Scattering from two point sources. (b) Scattering from two sources farther apart than in (a).

(a)   (b)

It should be noted that the formation of bright and dark areas on the screen results from the regularity of the arrangement of the scattering centers. If these were dispersed at random, no single line could be drawn tangent to the advancing wave fronts, and instead of a pattern of bright spots, one would observe only a diffuse general illumination of the screen. Hence the observation of bright spots on illumination of crystals with X-rays, in the original experiments of Friedrich and Knipping suggested by Max von Laue (1913), is itself a confirmation of the regularity of the crystal lattice deduced earlier from the regularity of the external shape of crystals.

The possibility of distance measurement in crystals by X-ray diffraction was put to use in the Bragg method. This takes advantage of the fact that in the orderly arrangement of building blocks in a crystal one can identify series of planes, as illustrated in Figure 15.3. The units in each plane act as the sources of Figure 15.2, and the incident X-ray beam will act as if it had been reflected from these evenly spaced planes. This too will give rise to reinforcement of the beam at certain angles, and destruction at others, so that the spacings between planes can be determined. The condition for reinforcement is that the wavelength of the X-ray, λ, and the distance, d, between planes are related to the angle of incidence (and "reflection") by

$$n\lambda = 2d \sin \theta$$

where n is an integer. Consequently, if one knows λ for the X-ray and by experiment can determine the angle θ at which the intensity of the reflected beam is at a maximum, then one can calculate d, the only un-

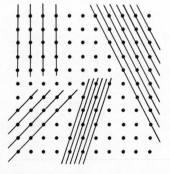

Figure 15.3 Planes in a regular arrangement of lattice points.

Figure 15.4 "Reflection" of an X-ray beam.

known quantity in the equation; d is the distance between the regularly spaced reflecting layers (Figure 15.4).

Electron Density Maps. It is relatively easy, by means of X-ray diffraction studies, to determine the spacing between planes, and hence the pattern of the crystal lattice, in simple crystals. A much more complex problem is that of identifying the scattering units in complex crystals. To do this one measures the intensity of the scattered radiation as a function of the scattering angle θ. For each scattering unit, the intensity depends upon the number of electrons in the unit, and the observed intensity is a sum of factors from all the scattering centers. By complicated and mathematically tedious processes, recently made easier by the employment of electronic computers, it is possible from the X-ray measurements to identify regions of high and low electron density within the crystal. These regions may be outlined on a contour map in which the regions of high and low density are represented as hills and valleys. Since the regions of high electron density represent the locations of atoms or groups of atoms, it is often possible to visualize, with the aid of the electron density map, how the molecules are packed in the solid, or, as has been done in a few cases, to determine the particular arrangement of atoms within the molecules of the crystal. Figures 15.5 and 15.6 illustrate these two points. In Figure 15.5 the electron density map for naphthalene crystals is given along with the structural formula for naphthalene molecules. The arrangement of these molecules in the crystal stands out clearly. In Figure 15.6 the electron density map of the potassium benzyl penicillin crystal is given. Before this map was made, chemists did not know how the atoms were arranged in the penicillin molecule. The figure also shows the molecular structure assigned penicillin by crystallographers and since confirmed by several other methods.

While elucidation of such complex structures is currently occupying the interest of many X-ray crystallographers, their results will mean little to us unless we can understand more about the structure of simpler crystal systems. Accordingly we shall now direct our attention to results of X-ray studies of metallic crystals.

Metallic Crystals

Packing of Similar Spheres. In attempting to understand the structure of solids it will be helpful to begin the study with metallic crystals, which are some of the simplest crystal systems. The building blocks of metallic crystals are atoms. If the sample is a pure metal, all atoms will be of the same size and electron configuration. X-ray studies have shown that most metallic crystals can be regarded as a pile of similar spheres packed together so that as many spheres touch as possible. There are two "closest-packed" patterns for similar spheres, known as the *hexagonal close-packed* and the *cubic close-packed* structures. These are illustrated in Figure 15.7.

If a group of spheres (marbles, oranges, or baseballs) is placed on a level surface so that they are in contact, an arrangement similar to that in Figure 15.8(a) is obtained. The second layer may be added by placing spheres in the depressions created by the groups of three spheres in the first layer. Only alternate depressions can be used since the spheres are too large to put into every depression. Imagine then that the second layer is formed by placing spheres in the depressions marked z in Figure 15.8(a).

When spheres are added to form the third layer, it is discovered that two types of depressions are available. One type of depression ($x,x, \ldots$) is *directly above a sphere* in the first layer; the second type of depression ($y,y, \ldots$) is *directly above a hole* in the first layer; see Figure 15.8(b). The two kinds of depressions alternate so that in forming the third layer *all the*

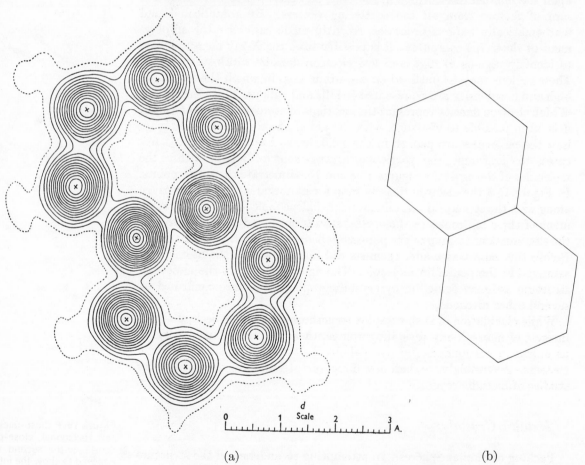

(a)   (b)

Figure 15.5 Naphthalene. (a) Electron density contours at intervals of 0.5 electrons per cubic angstrom. (b) Conventional structural formula. [Part (a) from J. M. Robertson, *Acta Crystallographica*, vol. *2* (1949), p. 241.]

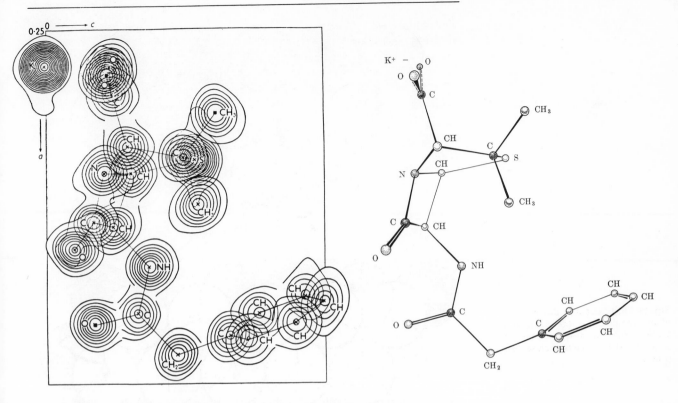

Figure 15.6 Potassium benzyl penicillin. (a) Projection on a single one of the planes of the electron density contours taken for each atom on planes parallel to each other but passing through each atomic nucleus at different levels in the crystal. (b) A diagram showing the structural arrangement of the atoms in the benzyl penicillin anion. [Part (a) from G. J. Pitt, *Acta Crystallographica*, vol. *5* (1952), p. 772.]

spheres in that layer must be placed in only one kind of depression—i.e., all must be placed above spheres or all must be placed above holes. Herein lies the difference between hexagonal and cubic close-packing. If in the third layer (and in each successive third layer) spheres are placed over spheres in the first layer, hexagonal close-packing obtains; if spheres are placed over holes in the first layer, cubic close-packing obtains.

Another way to look at the differences between hexagonal and cubic close-packing is to note that in the hexagonal pattern the layers appear to

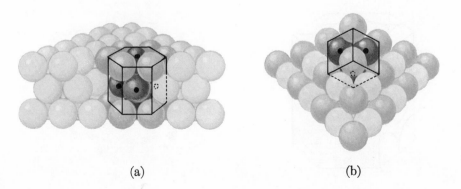

(a)   (b)

Figure 15.7 Close-packed structures: (a) Hexagonal close-packing. One sphere in the second row has been removed to show the interior structure. (b) Cubic close-packing.

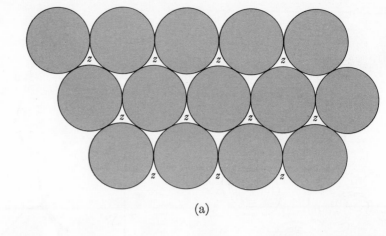

(a)

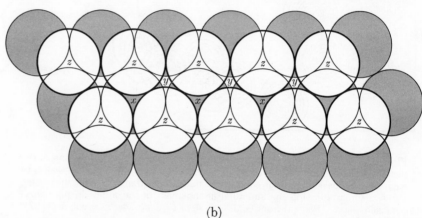

(b)

Figure 15.8 Looking down on layers of spheres placed in contact on a level surface: (a) One layer of close-packed spheres. (b) Two layers of close-packed spheres.

be in groups of two, whereas in the cubic pattern each layer appears to be related in the same way to the layers above and below.

The unit cells for both patterns are outlined in black on the stacks of spheres in Figure 15.7 and are represented more clearly in Figure 15.9. In the latter figure, the right angles between faces in the unit cell of the cubic form and the 120° and 60° angles between faces in the hexagonal cell are apparent. This figure also focuses attention on the number of atoms in the unit cell. Note that there are atoms (or fractions of atoms) at all corners

Figure 15.9 Unit cells of close-packed structures: (a) A hexagonal close-packed unit cell. (b) A cubic close-packed unit cell (face-centered cubic). (From *Chemical Systems*, by the Chemical Bond Approach Project. Copyright © 1964, Earlham College Press, Inc., published by Webster Division, McGraw-Hill.)

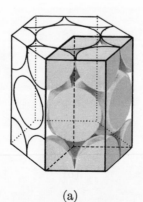

(a)

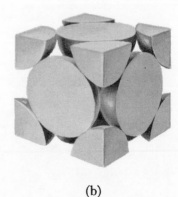

(b)

and in the center of every face of the cubic cell. For this reason this close-packed structure is sometimes called face-centered cubic.

Another interesting aspect of the close-packed lattices is the fact that each point is surrounded by twelve close neighbors—three above, three below, and six around its equator. Each sphere in these structures is said to have a *coordination number* of twelve. The coordination number is a useful concept for describing the packing in crystals. It will be used frequently in this chapter.

X-ray diffraction studies have shown that about fifty metallic elements crystallize in one or the other of these two close-packed structures. What causes a given metal to choose one or the other form is not known. Table 15.1 lists the packing patterns of the metallic elements. Some metals such as iron, cobalt, thallium, and lanthanum crystallize in more than one pattern; the different structures are stable under different temperature and pressure conditions.

About a dozen metals including those in Group I of the periodic table crystallize at room temperature in what is known as a body-centered lattice illustrated in Figure 15.10. This is not a close-packed structure since the spheres at the corners do not touch each other. At lower temperatures most of these metals revert to a close-packed structure. The coordination number in body-centered lattices is eight. The "open" packing results in a lower density for metals using the body-centered pattern.

Crystal Structure and Properties of Metals. Properties characteristic of metals include: metallic luster, high density, high melting point, malleability, ductility, high tensile strength, good heat and electrical conductivity, hardening, and thermionic emission. Not all metals possess all of these properties. For example, the melting points of mercury and the Group I metals are very low: the densities of the Group I metals are also low; the thermal conductivity of bismuth is only about 2 per cent of that of silver; many of the transition metals are hard and brittle. Nevertheless, the metals as a class do exhibit these properties. Presumably the properties are a result of the bonding and packing of the atoms in the crystal. Explanations for some of the properties of metals in terms of the crystal structure and bonding follow.

Metal Luster. Metallic luster arises because the "free" electrons in the metal (Chap. 5) are able to absorb and quickly re-emit light photons of all frequencies. This makes for excellent reflecting surfaces.

Electrical Conductivity and Thermionic Emission. These properties are also due to the "free" electrons in the metal. Electrical conductivity in solids is said to be a flow of electrons. Conductivity usually decreases with temperature because the vibrations of the atomic kernels in the crystal

Figure 15.10 A body-centered unit cell. (From *Chemical Systems*, by the Chemical Bond Approach Project. Copyright © 1964, Earlham College Press, Inc., published by Webster Division, McGraw-Hill.)

Table 15.1 Crystal Structures of Metals

(Abbreviations: h, hexagonal; c, cubic close-packed; b, body-centered cubic; d, diamond; o, other)

Li,b	Be,h												Al,c	
Na,b	Mg,h												Ga,o	Ge,d
K,b	Ca,c	Sc,o	Ti,h	V,c	Cr,c	Mn,o	Fe,b,c	Co,h,c	Ni,c	Cu,c	Zn,h		In,o	Sn,d
Rb,b	Sr,c		Zr,h			Tc,o	Ru,h	Rh,c	Pd,c	Ag,c	Cd,h			
Cs,b	Ba,b	La,h	Hf,h	Ta,b	W,b	Re,o	Os,h	Ir,c	Pt,c	Au,c	Hg,o	Tl,h		Pb,c

increase with temperature, thus providing an increased resistance to the flow of electrons. Thermionic emission is the emission of electrons from surfaces of heated metal cathodes placed in a vacuum. This phenomenon, which amounts to "boiling off" electrons from the hot metal surface, is the basis of an important part of the science of electronics.

Heat Conductivity. Heat conductivity is believed to result from electronic motion in metal crystals.

Malleability and Ductility. Malleability and ductility are related to deformation of the crystal lattice by an imposed stress. The stress is usually relieved by the slippage of adjacent crystal planes past one another as illustrated in Figure 15.11. No fundamental change in the crystal structure occurs when this happens because the attractive forces holding the crystal together are unaltered. Slippage occurs most easily along close-packed planes, and is more likely to occur the greater the symmetry of the crystal. As a result, metals with cubic close-packed lattices are usually more malleable and ductile than those with body-centered cubic structures.

Work Hardening. In work hardening the metal is made hard and brittle by bending or hammering. The hardening is believed to be caused in part by distortions of the crystal lattice which prevent adjacent planes from slipping past one another when the metal is put under stress.

Crystal Structure and Alloys. Most of the metals of commerce are alloys —mixtures of metal elements "tailor-made" for a given purpose. An enormous number of alloys is possible because a given alloy may contain more than two elements—perhaps up to five or more. Some common alloys and their properties are listed in Table 15.2.

The relation between the structure and properties of alloys has not been fully established. However, as a class, alloys are considerably harder than the pure metals. Presumably this hardness is due to the destruction of the

Table 15.2 Common Alloys and Some of Their Properties

Trade Name	Composition by Weight	Melting Point (°C)	Density (g/cc)	Use
Sterling silver	92.5% Ag, 7.5% Cu	920		Tableware
Monel	60% Ni, 33% Cu, 7% Fe	1360	8.9	Table tops
Plumber's solder	67% Pb, 33% Sn	275	9.4	
Type metal	82% Pb, 15% Sb, 3% Sn			Typesetting
Soft solder	50% Pb, 50% Sn	200–250	8.9	
Yellow brass	67% Cu, 33% Zn	940	8.4	
Babbitt metal	90% Sn, 7% Sb, 3% Cu	235		Bearings
Duralumin	95.5% Al, 4% Cu, 0.5% Mg			Structural purposes
Stainless steel	80.6% Fe, 0.4% C, 18% Cr, 1% Ni			Food processing and surgical utensils
Duriron	84.3% Fe, 0.85% C, 14.5% Si, 0.35% Mn	1265	7.0	Laboratory plumbing
Vanadium steel	98.9% Fe, 1% C, 0.1% V			Truck, auto, and train parts
Spring steel	98.6% Fe, 1% Cr, 0.4% C			Springs and saw blades

slippage planes brought about by dispersing slightly larger or slightly smaller atoms throughout the crystal.

Several structurally distinct classes of alloys are known, and in certain cases it is possible to recognize a relation between properties and structure. Examples of some of these classes follow.

Solid Solutions. These are homogeneous solids whose composition can be varied over a wide range without loss of homogeneity. The particles of the dissolved metals (the solute particles) are distributed at random among the particles of the solvent metal. Two important types of solid solutions are *substitutional solutions* and *interstitial solutions*.

Substitutional solutions arise when solute metal atoms are present at random in positions in the crystal lattice of the solvent metal normally occupied by atoms of the solvent metals (Figure 15.12). The existence of such solid solutions is dependent upon the relative sizes of the atoms of the two metals involved. Examination of a number of solid solutions reveals that in all cases the size differences between atoms is 14 per cent or less. While solid solutions do not necessarily form if the atom sizes are within this limit, a size difference greater than 14 per cent is sufficient to prevent the formation of solid solutions.

Metal pairs which are within the 14 per cent range and form solid solutions often form alloys of more than one crystal structure. For example, pure copper has a face-centered cubic structure. Zinc dissolves in it without change in the crystal symmetry up to a ratio of about 40 atoms of zinc to 60 atoms of copper. Solutions containing a higher proportion of zinc take on a body-centered cubic structure, which persists until the atom ratio is about 60 atoms of zinc to 40 atoms of copper. Further addition of zinc produces other crystalline structures known as the γ and ϵ phases. Exactly similar changes in structure are noted for solutions of other metals in copper, though the atom ratios, at which the structure changes, depend upon the solute metal; similar behavior is also observed for solvent metals other than copper.

William Hume-Rothery was the first to note that these changes occur at a characteristic ratio of the number of valence electrons to atoms in the crystal. The change from the face-centered to the body-centered phase (frequently called the β phase) occurs at an electron-to-atom ratio of about 1.4 to 1, or

40 Zn	=	80 valence electrons
60 Cu	=	60 valence electrons
100 atoms	=	140 valence electrons, a ratio of 1.4 to 1

The body-centered (β) phase continues through the range 1.5 to 1 (21/14), which is often given as its characteristic ratio, and changes to the γ phase at a ratio of about 21 to 13, or

60 Zn	=	120 valence electrons
40 Cu	=	40 valence electrons
100 atoms	=	160 valence electrons, a ratio close to 21/13 = 1.61

Similarly, the γ phase changes to the ϵ phase at the ratio 21/12. Solid solutions conforming to these "Hume-Rothery rules" are often assigned "formulas," such as those given in Table 15.3.

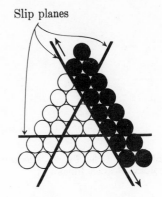

Figure 15.11 Slip planes in a metal crystal.

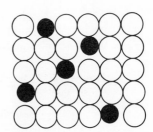

Figure 15.12 Substitutional solid solution (a two-dimensional view).

The interpretation of these results appears to be that there are, for each structure, a certain number of energy levels per atom to be filled by electrons, and that electrons from any kind of metal atom can fill these levels. Once filled, no additional electrons can be accommodated except by changing to a new structure with additional energy levels.

Interstitial solutions arise when very small atoms such as those of carbon, boron, or nitrogen are dissolved in the transition metals. The atomic radii of the former elements are so small that they are accommodated in the

Table 15.3 Solid Phases Illustrating the Hume-Rothery Rules

Alloy	Electrons	Atoms	Ratio
β Phases			
CuZn	1 + 2	2	21:14
AgCd	1 + 2	2	21:14
Cu_3Ga	3 + 3	4	21:14
Cu_5Sn	5 + 4	6	21:14
γ Phases			
Cu_5Zn_8	5 + 16	13	21:13
Cu_9Ga_4	9 + 12	13	21:13
$Cu_{31}Sn_8$	31 + 32	39	21:13
ε Phases			
$CuZn_3$	1 + 6	4	21:12
Cu_3Ge	3 + 4	4	21:12
Cu_3Sn	3 + 4	4	21:12

holes within the close-packed crystal structure of the metal (Figure 15.13). Since there are so many holes in the structure, the solubility of these small atoms varies over wide limits. However, even very small amounts of interstitially substituted atoms may cause profound changes in the properties of the metal. In the case of carbon-iron alloys, as little as 0.5 per cent carbon causes sufficient distortion of the close-packed structure to destroy most of the slippage planes, thereby creating the hard, high tensile structure characteristic of steel.

Extending the interstitial-solution concept, one would predict that boron, nitrogen, silicon, or beryllium could be substituted for carbon in steel. This has been done and, although carbon steels are by far the most versatile and readily made alloys of this class, boron steels are becoming more and more important, and some of the other steels show promise.

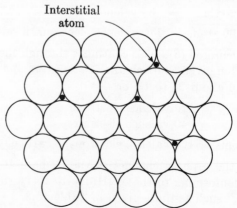

Interstitial atom

Figure 15.13 Interstitial solid solution (a two-dimensional view).

Intermetallic Compounds. At least two types of intermetallic compounds are recognized. These may be called *superlattice compounds* and *saltlike compounds*. Like other compounds these substances have a definite composition and a definite melting point or decomposition temperature. Some alloys containing compounds consist of a single compound; others are mixtures of compounds, and still others may be heterogeneous solids consisting of small crystals of a compound distributed throughout the metal much like feldspar is distributed throughout granite.

An example of a superlattice compound is the gold-copper alloy containing 25 atom per cent gold. X-ray studies show that this alloy crystallizes in a face-centered cubic structure in which the gold atoms occupy the corners of the cubes and the copper atoms occupy the centers of each face of the cube (Figure 15.14). The formula for this compound is Cu_3Au.

Examples of saltlike compounds of metals are $MgCu_2$, Mg_2Pb, Li_3Bi, and Mg_3Sb_2. In this class of compounds the two metals involved have widely different electronegativities. The stabilities and melting points of these compounds generally decrease as the electronegativity difference between atoms decreases.

One example of the use of metal compounds to harden a metal element is the addition of about 4 per cent copper to aluminum. The product, known as *duralumin*, is used in the construction of large buildings. The hardness of this alloy is apparently produced by formation of the compound $CuAl_2$ which precipitates from the aluminum crystal. The small crystals of the compound are dispersed throughout the aluminum, thus distorting the crystal structure of the aluminum and providing a hard, high tensile structure. The tensile strength of duralumin is five times that of pure aluminum.

Addition of about 0.5 per cent magnesium to the copper-aluminum alloy makes it possible to work annealed duralumin at room temperature. After a few days, precipitation of $CuAl_2$ occurs and the crystal becomes hard. This alloy has an advantage over steel because steel must be worked at high temperatures.

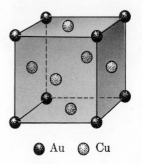

@ Au   @ Cu

Figure 15.14 The Cu_3Au superlattice.

Ionic Crystals

It was pointed out in Chap. 5 that ionic compounds are solids at room temperature because of the strong attractive forces between oppositely charged ions in the crystal. X-ray studies have shown that the positive and negative ions in such crystals are arranged in alternating three-dimensional arrays, such as that shown in Figure 15.15. One might imagine that crystals grow large because the attractive forces between spherical ions extend uniformly in all directions so that once a minute crystal starts to form, more and more ions will be attracted to it. Evidently then all ions in the interior of the crystal are surrounded by ions of opposite charge.

Packing of Dissimilar Spheres. The building blocks in ionic crystals differ from those in metals in two ways:

1. Two kinds of ions are present in ionic crystals.
2. The positive and negative ions in a given crystal nearly always differ in size whereas in pure metals the atoms are identical in size.

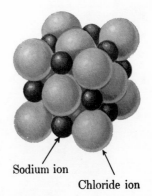

Sodium ion

Chloride ion

Figure 15.15 Crystal structure of sodium chloride.

In ionic crystals, the first factor manifests itself in the alternating array of oppositely charged ions in the lattice; the second factor is responsible for the lattice symmetry since the coordination number of the ions will depend upon the relative sizes of the two kinds of ions. For example, in a crystal such as that of lithium iodide, composed of small lithium ions and large iodide ions, each kind of ion has a coordination number of six; in cesium iodide where the ions are closer to the same size, each kind of ion has a coordination number of eight. Since the coordination number determines the packing pattern of the ions, the crystal structure of lithium iodide is different from that of cesium iodide. Undoubtedly there is a factor related to the relative sizes of the two kinds of ions that determines the coordination number of ions in any given case.

Let us now proceed to a discussion of how the crystallographers sought this factor and, having found it, used it to predict the crystal structure of various ionic compounds. The important facets in the discovery of this factor may be summarized as follows.

1. Diffraction studies showed that most binary salts (compounds such as NaCl containing equal numbers of positive and negative ions) occur in one of four structures. The coordination numbers of the ions in these structures are four (two forms), six, or eight as illustrated in Figure 15.16.

Figure 15.16 Coordination numbers in ionic crystals: (a) Tetrahedron, 4. (b) Octahedron, 6. (c) Body-centered cube, 8.

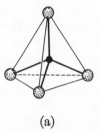 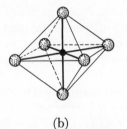 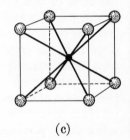

(a) (b) (c)

2. Ionic radii for common ions were estimated from X-ray data. This can be done by determining the interionic distance by X-ray diffraction. Then, using the nuclear charge and an electronic screening factor for each ion, fractions of the interionic distance are calculated as the radii of the two ions.

3. A radius ratio r_+/r_-, defined as the ratio of the cation (positive ion) radius to that of the anion, was calculated for a large number of compounds. The reason for this calculation will become obvious.

4. Some simple relations between radius ratio and coordination number were immediately apparent. For example, it was observed that when the radius ratio was greater than 0.732, a coordination number of eight was usually observed; when the radius ratio was greater than 0.414 but less than 0.732, a coordination number of six was usually observed; when the radius ratio was greater than 0.225 but less than 0.414, a coordination number of four was often observed. Some examples of these relationships are given in Table 15.4.

To explain this relation between radius ratio and coordination number, we remember that attractive forces between ions of unlike charges are greatest when the oppositely charged ions are close together, and the

Coordination Number (Observed)	Salt	Radius Ratio	Salt	Radius Ratio
8	CsCl	0.93	TlCl	0.85
	CsBr	0.87	TlBr	0.78
	CsI	0.78		
6	LiF	0.44	NaBr	0.49
	NaF	0.70	KBr	0.68
	NaCl	0.52	NH_4Br	0.71
	KCl	0.73	NH_4I	0.65
4	ZnS	0.23	CuBr	0.26
	ZnO	0.31	HgS	0.33
	CuCl	0.28		

repulsive forces between ions of like charges are greatest when the like charged ions are close together. Stable arrangements will therefore be those in which ions of unlike charges are as close together as possible, while ions of like charges are as far apart as possible.

To understand the changes from one structure to another as the radius ratio changes, let us imagine anions of a particular size and consider the packing patterns which will appear, under the conditions of the preceding paragraph, as the size of the cation, around which the anions are grouped, decreases.

When the cation is about as big as the anion (radius ratio close to 1.0), we can easily arrange the anions at the corners of a cube with the cation at the center, without having the anions touch. This arrangement is known as the cesium chloride structure (coordination number 8). Three ions of such a structure are shown in Figure 15.17(a) which depicts the situation when the cation and anion have the same radius. If now the cation is smaller, so that the radius ratio is 0.732, we have the situation of Figure 15.17(b) in which, with the cesium chloride structure, all nine ions of the unit cell are in contact. If the cation grows still smaller, the anions at the cube corners can no longer touch the cation at the center, and the attractive force between cation and anion can be increased by changing to a different structure in which they are closer together. Note that if ions the size of those in Figure 15.17(b) are arranged in the sodium chloride structure (coordination number 6) of Figure 15.15, the cation will be at the center of an octahedron, as shown in Figure 15.16(b). The face of the cube then corresponds to the horizontal plane as shown in Figure 15.17(c). In this structure contact between cation and anion leaves the anions still separated, and the structure is more stable than the cesium chloride structure would be for the same radius ratio.

The sodium chloride structure reaches its limiting form when the radius ratio is 0.414. At this ratio, as shown in Figure 15.17(d), all seven ions are again in contact. Further decrease in cation size must again separate the anions from the cation, reducing the attractive force and making the structure unstable. Increased stability can be obtained if the pattern shifts to one of the two zinc sulfide structures (coordination number 4), in which the anions are arranged at the corners of a tetrahedron about the cation.

Contact of anions with the cation, for the tetrahedral structure with radius ratio 0.414, leaves the anions separated from each other, reducing the repulsive force between them and stabilizing the new structure. The limiting radius ratio for the tetrahedral structure is 0.225; at this value all five ions would be in contact.

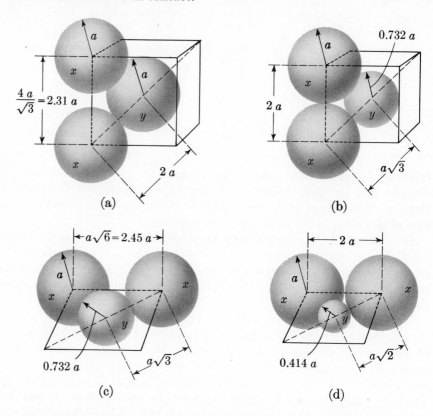

Figure 15.17 Cation-anion and anion-anion distances for several radius ratios. In each figure, spheres x, x represent two of the eight anions at the corners of a cube ; y is a cation. In (a) and (b) the center of y is at the mid-point of the cube diagonal (body-centering) ; in (c) and (d) the center of y is at the mid-point of the diagonal of the front face of the cube (face-centering).

(a) Coordination number 8
$r_+ = a$
$r_- = a$
$\dfrac{r_+}{r_-} = 1.0$
(Note anions do not touch)

(b) Coordination number 8
$r_+ = a(\sqrt{3} - 1) = 0.732a$
$r_- = a$
$\dfrac{r_+}{r_-} = \sqrt{3} - 1 = 0.732$
(Note anions just in contact)

(c) Coordination number 6
$r_+ = a(\sqrt{3} - 1) = 0.732a$
$r_- = a$
$\dfrac{r_+}{r_-} = 0.732$
(Note anions do not touch)

(d) Coordination number 6
$r_+ = a(\sqrt{2} - 1) = 0.414a$
$r_- = a$
$\dfrac{r_+}{r_-} = \sqrt{2} - 1 = 0.414$
(Note anions just in contact)

An alternative way of looking at the sodium chloride structure and at the two zinc sulfide structures is to imagine that in sodium chloride the chloride ions pack in a cubic close-packed pattern with the sodium ions occupying the holes surrounded by six chloride ions. In zinc sulfide the sulfide ions pack in the cubic close-packed pattern in one structure (zinc blende) and in the hexagonal close-packed pattern in the second structure (wurtzite); in both structures the zinc ions occupy alternate tetrahedral holes in the close-packed pattern—holes that are formed between groups of four sulfide ions.

Not all simple ionic structures can be predicted from the radius ratio of the ions but it is usually true that for a given radius ratio the coordination number may be less than predicted but rarely greater than predicted.

Finally, it can be shown that in binary compounds, the coordination number of both kinds of ions is the same so prediction or determination of this number for the smaller ion fixes it for the larger ion as well.

Structure of AB₂ Salts. In salts having the formula AB_2, such as calcium fluoride, CaF_2, the problem is one of efficiently packing two ions of one charge for each ion of the opposite charge while still maintaining the alternating arrangement of positive and negative ions. This can be accomplished if the coordination number of the ion in short supply is twice that of the second ion. Diffraction studies on calcium fluoride show that the coordination number of calcium ion is eight while that of fluoride ion is four. In magnesium fluoride the coordination number of magnesium ion is six; that of fluoride ion is three. Here again the coordination number is related to the radius ratio. In calcium fluoride this is 0.73; in magnesium fluoride it is 0.48. As in the case of binary compounds the smaller radius ratio results in a lower coordination number.

The particular arrangement of ions to give different coordination numbers to the anion and cation is of interest. In calcium fluoride this arrangement is illustrated in Figure 15.18. It might be described as a simple cube of fluoride ions placed just inside a face-centered cube of calcium ions. Each fluoride ion is then surrounded by three calcium ions from the faces and one calcium ion from a corner of the cube of calcium ions in a tetrahedral ralationship. A calcium ion in the face of a unit cell is surrounded by four fluoride ions inside each of two adjacent unit cells, for a total of eight.

Structure of Complex Ionic Crystals. The structural ideas developed in this section are not limited to crystals with simple spherical ions but apply to all ionic crystals. However, the packing pattern becomes much more complex when ions such as nitrate, sulfate, carbonate, or phosphate occupy positions in the crystal lattice. For example, calcite, $CaCO_3$, which contains both calcium and carbonate ions, crystallizes in hexagonal units composed of the triangular-shaped carbonate ion surrounded by six calcium ions as shown in Figure 15.19.

Hydrates such as blue vitriol, $CuSO_4 \cdot 5H_2O$, are still more complex in that here the cation is surrounded by water molecules so that both ions are non-spherical thus making efficient packing more difficult.

Perhaps the most complex ionic crystals are those such as mica and asbestos which contain fiberlike and layerlike anions held together by small cations placed at various positions between the fibers or layers.

Molecular Crystals

When molecules crystallize they usually pack in the most efficient manner possible consistent with their shape and with the most favorable orientation of their attractive forces. As a result there are almost as many

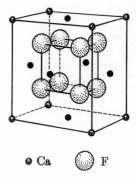

○ Ca   ◯ F

Figure 15.18 The calcium fluoride structure.

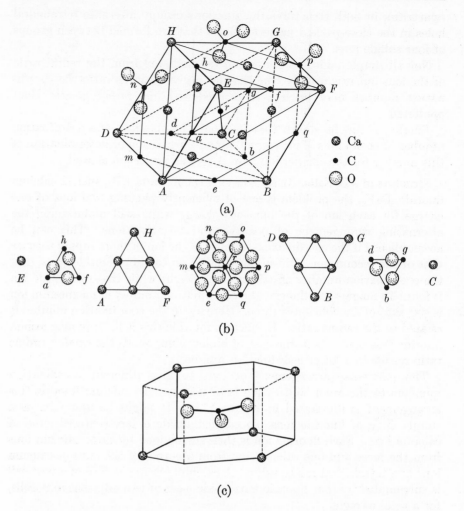

Figure 15.19 (a) The unit cell of calcite, CaCO$_3$. To avoid cluttering the figure, oxygen atoms are shown for only three of the carbonate ions at *n, o, p*. (b) The arrangements in consecutive planes perpendicular to the axis *EC* in the unit cell of (a). (c) A portion of the calcite structure showing the orientation of the CO$_3^-$ with respect to Ca^{+2}. [Parts (a) and (b) adapted from Bragg, *Introduction to Crystal Analysis,* G. Bell and Sons (1928), p. 78.]

packing patterns for molecular crystals as there are varieties of molecules. Figure 15.20 shows four packing patterns with the three substances, nitrogen, carbon dioxide, and water, as examples.

Nitrogen. The nitrogen molecule crystallizes in two allotropic forms—a hexagonal close-packed structure [Figure 15.20(a)] stable between 35°K and the melting point, and a face-centered cubic structure [Figure 15.20(b)] stable below 35°K. At each lattice point there is one dumbbell-shaped molecule. In the high temperature form the distance between molecule centers is 4.07 A, and it appears that the molecules precess about these centers, presenting a nearly spherical shape to their neighbors. In the face-centered cubic structure, the distance between molecule centers is 3.99 A, but the molecules themselves appear to be fixed in the staggered arrangement shown, perhaps with some vibration about these positions. This is what might be expected. At the low temperatures where kinetic energies of vibration are small, the van der Waals forces between atoms on adjacent molecules are sufficient to hold the molecules in a preferred orientation. As the temperature rises, the vibrations become greater and greater and change to rotations, as the atoms lose their grip on the atoms of the neighboring molecules. The rotating molecule requires a little more space and the packing pattern changes. Still higher temperatures, of course, are needed to overcome the van der Waals forces holding the molecules together in the solid, and melting does not occur until 63.2°K. In both allotropes, the distance between atoms is slightly greater than 1 A, as in gaseous nitrogen, emphasizing that the distance between molecules is considerably greater than the distance between atoms in the same molecule.

Carbon Dioxide. These linear molecules pack so that the oxygen atoms are oriented toward carbon atoms in adjacent molecules. The reason for this is that the oxygen atom is the negative end of a polar bond; the carbon atom is the positive end. Thus the packing is controlled by the most favorable orientation of the polar attracting forces in the molecule.

Water. Hydrogen bonding is the important attractive and orienting force in ice. Here, each oxygen atom is surrounded by four hydrogen atoms. Two are covalently bonded to it. The other two, one from each of two neighboring molecules, are held by hydrogen bonds whose length is over twice as great as that between the O—H in the water molecule. Each water molecule is now bonded to four other water molecules giving a very strong structure with a very large number of hydrogen bonds.

The strong orientation of hydrogen atoms toward oxygen atoms in adjacent molecules makes for inefficient packing in the crystal. This "open" structure is the reason ice floats on water—its density is less than that of liquid water near the freezing point.

Macromolecular Crystals. In macromolecular (often called network-type) crystals the entire structure is tied together by covalent bonds. Examples include diamond, carborundum (silicon carbide), quartz (silicon dioxide), boron nitride, and a few other substances. In all of these crystals the coordination number of the atoms is four. The resulting structures are characterized by great strength, high melting points, and extreme hardness.

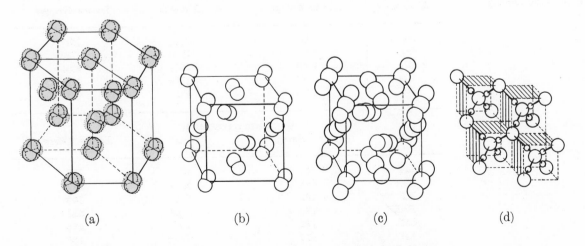

(a)   (b)   (c)   (d)

Figure 15.20 (a) The hexagonal close-packed (high temperature) allotropic form of solid nitrogen. (b) The face-centered cubic (low temperature) form of solid nitrogen. (c) The structure of solid carbon dioxide. (d) The structure of solid water (ice). Four oxygen atoms are arranged tetrahedrally around a fifth and held together by hydrogen bonds.

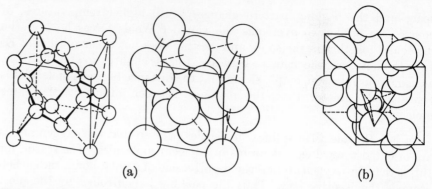

Figure 15.21 (a) The diamond structure showing the tetrahedral bonding. In the right-hand drawing, the top front corner atom of the cube has been omitted for greater clarity. (b) The structure of the room-temperature form of quartz.

Figure 15.21 shows the tetrahedral network in diamond and the spiral arrangement in quartz.

Carbon and boron nitride may also crystallize in a pattern with a coordination number of three. This results in the layer or sheetlike crystals illustrated for graphite in Figure 15.22. Only van der Waals forces hold the sheets together, so when the crystal is placed under stress, these sheets will easily slip past one another. Three electrons per atom are used in the sp^2 hybrid bonds forming the hexagons, and the fourth is mobile, contributing an electrical conductivity in the direction parallel to the layers.

Lattice Energy and Crystal Stability

Stability of Crystals. The stability of a crystal can be expressed in terms of its *lattice energy*. The lattice energy may be defined as the energy needed to disrupt the crystal and to convert the building blocks into gaseous particles (atoms, ions, molecules) at an infinite distance from each other. Methods of obtaining lattice energies are discussed in Chap. 20.

Table 15.5 Lattice Energies of Molecular and Ionic Crystals (kcal/mole)

	MOLECULAR CRYSTALS *		
Molecule	*Lattice Energy*	*Molecule*	*Lattice Energy*
N_2	1.64	NH_3	7.07
O_2	2.06	H_2O	11.30
Cl_2	7.43	HCl	5.05
CO	2.09	HBr	5.52
CH_4	2.70	HI	6.21
	IONIC CRYSTALS †		
Salt	*Lattice Energy*	*Salt*	*Lattice Energy*
LiF	244	KI	152
NaF	215	RbI	147
KF	192	CsI	140
RbF	185	AgF	218
CsF	173	TlCl	170
LiI	177	TlBr	165
NaI	164	TlI	161

* Solid separated into molecules infinitely distant from each other.
† Solid separated into cations and anions infinitely distant from each other.

Table 15.5 gives lattice energies for some metallic, ionic, and molecular crystals. The high stability of ionic crystals compared with crystals composed of simple molecules is immediately obvious. This stability difference merely reflects the difference in the strength of the ionic bonding forces compared with intermolecular forces such as van der Waals forces.

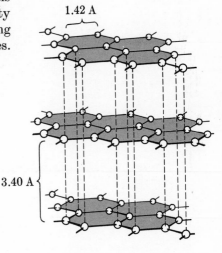

SOME SPECIAL TERMS

Crystal structure
    space lattice
    Bravais lattice
    Bragg equation
    electron density map
    hexagonal close-packed structure
    cubic close-packed structure
    unit cell
    coordination number
    octahedral structure
    tetrahedral structure
    molecular crystal
    lattice energy
    radius ratio

Metals
    metallic luster
    malleability
    ductility
    thermal conductivity
    thermionic emission
    work hardening

Alloys
    substitutional solid solution
    interstitial solid solution
    Hume-Rothery rules
    intermetallic compounds
    superlattice compounds

X-rays
    diffraction
    interference

Figure 15.22 The structure of graphite.

QUESTIONS AND PROBLEMS

1. Consider the following figures, representing the visible faces of cubic forms.

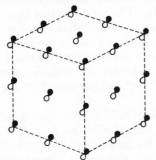
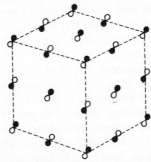

Do these have the same space lattice? The same "crystal structure"? Outline the unit cell in each figure. Make a sketch of the unit cell for each figure, showing the positions and orientations of the structural units on the visible faces.

2. The accompanying figure shows a face-centered cubic structure. Using the Pythagorean theorem where necessary, calculate the distance between planes through atomic centers (a) parallel to a plane through $ABCD$; (b) parallel to a plane through $CDEF$; (c) parallel to a plane through FBH.

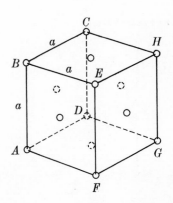

3. Compare and contrast the basic structural units in a crystal of sodium, sodium chloride, nitrogen, and carbon, and describe for each what phenomena would be observed as the substance is gradually heated to reach eventually 3000°C. Estimate the temperature range at which each of these phenomena would be observed.

4. How would you distinguish experimentally between a solid solution of two metals and a superlattice compound between the two metals?

5. Alloys, in general, are harder, lower melting, and poorer conductors of electricity than the pure metals of which they are composed. Why?

6. What is the coordination number of Ca^{+2} in CaF_2? of F^-? (Figure 15.18.) How many moles of calcium fluoride are there in a unit cell of calcium fluoride? If the density of calcium fluoride is 3.18 g/cc, what is the length of the cube edge?

7. From the ionic radii given in the following table, suggest the most probable structures for the following salts: KBr, RbBr, CsBr, MgO, MgS, MgSe, MgTe, BaS, SrS, and ZnS.

Ionic Radii (A)

K^+	1.33	Ba^{+2}	1.35	Br^-	1.95
Rb^+	1.48	Sr^{+2}	1.13	O^{-2}	1.40
Cs^+	1.69	Zn^{+2}	0.74	S^{-2}	1.84
		Mg^{+2}	0.65	Se^{-2}	1.98
				Te^{-2}	2.21

8. The combination of 1 mole of gaseous sodium atoms with 1 mole of gaseous chlorine atoms to form solid sodium chloride evolves 153 kcal of heat.

$$Na(g) + Cl(g) \longrightarrow NaCl(s) \qquad \text{(heat evolved is 153 kcal)}$$

To ionize 1 mole of gaseous sodium atoms requires the addition of 118 kcal; ionization of 1 mole of chlorine atoms evolves 88 kcal. Calculate the lattice energy of sodium chloride.

9. An X-ray from a copper target of wavelength 1.754 A is reflected from two parallel planes 2.82 A apart. What is the angle of reflection for $n = 1$?

10. The energy required to separate the molecules of solid oxygen or nitrogen and produce gaseous molecules at an infinite distance from each other is 2.06 and 1.64 kcal/mole, respectively. For solid chlorine the value is 7.43 kcal/mole. What difference in the nature of the chlorine molecules or atoms as compared to oxygen and nitrogen could account for the higher strength of binding in solid chlorine? In a similar vein, account for the differences in the energies required to separate molecules of methane, ammonia, and water from their positions in the solids (2.70 kcal/mole, 7.07 kcal/mole, and 11.30 kcal/mole, respectively).

11. The energy required to place the ions of solid lithium fluoride at an infinite distance from each other is 244 kcal/mole; for cesium fluoride it is 173 kcal/mole. A similar difference appears for lithium iodide (177 kcal/mole) and cesium iodide (140 kcal/mole). What differences between lithium and cesium ions might account for this? Why are the values for these four compounds so much larger than the values reported in Question 10, above?

REFERENCES

ADDISON, W. E. *Structural Principles in Inorganic Compounds*. New York: Wiley, 1961.

BRAGG, L. "X-ray Crystallography," *Scientific American*, vol. *219*, no. 1 (1968), p. 58.

ETZEL, H. W. "Ionic Crystals," *J. Chem. Educ.*, *38* (1961), p. 225.

HOLDEN, A. *The Nature of Solids*. New York: Columbia University Press, 1965.

HUME-ROTHERY, W. *Electrons, Atoms, Metals and Alloys*. New York: Dover, 1963.

MOORE, W. J. *Seven Solid States*. New York: Benjamin, 1967.

PART FOUR

FAMILIES OF ELEMENTS

16

The Oxygen Family

What surprised me more than I can well express, was that a candle burned in this air with a remarkably brilliant flame.
Joseph Priestley (1733–1804)

The elements oxygen, sulfur, selenium, tellurium, and polonium constitute Group VI of the periodic table. The atoms of these elements all have the valence electron configuration s^2p^4. As a group they are considered non-metals although the heavier elements show some properties characteristic of metals. These elements have lower electronegativities than the corresponding halogens but on the whole their electronegativities have the relatively high values characteristic of nonmetals and decrease with increasing atomic number.

Oxygen is undoubtedly the most important member of the family. On a weight basis, oxygen atoms make up about one-half the earth's crust, about nine-tenths of the oceans, about one-fifth of the air, and about three-fourths of the human body. In terms of the number of atoms, oxygen is the third most abundant element in the universe. In addition, oxygen forms binary compounds with more other elements than any except the halogens. About 180 oxides of the elements are known.

The valence electron configurations and some other important properties of the atoms of the elements in Group VI are given in Table 16.1.

Table 16.1 Some Properties of Oxygen Family Atoms and Ions

Element	Atomic Weight (a.m.u.)	Valence Electron Configuration	Atomic Radius (van der Waals radius) (A)	Ionic Radius of X^{-2} (A)	First Ionization Energy (kcal/mole)	Electronegativity
Oxygen	15.9994	$2s^2\,2p^4$	0.74	1.40	314	3.50
Sulfur	32.064	$3s^2\,3p^4$	1.04	1.84	239	2.60
Selenium	78.96	$4s^2\,4p^4$	1.17	1.98	225	2.55
Tellurium	127.60	$5s^2\,5p^4$	1.37	2.21	208	2.30
Polonium	210	$6s^2\,6p^4$	1.64			2.1

An Overview of Oxygen Family Chemistry

Some important characteristics of the oxygen family elements are summarized in the following statements:

1. Due to their high electronegativity the atoms of these elements, like those of the halogens, show a tendency to react with metallic elements by taking up electrons. To acquire a noble gas configuration two electrons are needed by each atom and the resulting species is the doubly charged negative ion X^{-2}. The numerous metal oxides, sulfides, selenides, and tellurides are formed in this manner although many of these compounds contain bonds with some covalent character.

2. The members of this family exhibit oxidation states varying from $-II$ to VI. For example, sulfur, selenium, and tellurium all form compounds having formulas XO_3, XO_2, and H_2X where the oxygen family element X is present in the VI, IV, and $-II$ oxidation states respectively. Some of the most familiar of these are SO_3, SO_2, and H_2S. This pattern of oxidation states is predictable from the structure of the oxygen family atoms. Because of its high electronegativity (second only to fluorine) oxygen shows an oxidation state of $-II$ in all oxides except in F_2O where it has a positive oxidation state of II, and in peroxides (for example, in H_2O_2) where it has an oxidation state of $-I$.

3. Among its compounds in the $-II$ oxidation state the family contains some strong reducing agents, such as hydrogen sulfide, hydrogen selenide, and hydrogen telluride. Some moderate to strong oxidizing agents, such as sulfuric acid and selenium and tellurium trioxides, are found among the compounds of the elements in their higher oxidation states.

4. A variety of oxyacids and the five binary acids (H_2X) containing members of this family are known. The formulas for some of these acids are given in Table 16.2.

Table 16.2 Some Acids Containing Oxygen Family Elements

Oxidation State	Oxygen	Sulfur	Selenium	Tellurium
VI		H_2SO_4	H_2SeO_4	H_6TeO_6
IV		H_2SO_3	H_2SeO_3	$HO(TeO_2)_xH$
II		H_2SO_2		
$-II$	H_2O	H_2S	H_2Se	H_2Te

5. The elements of this family form a number of compounds in which two or more atoms of the Group VI element are bonded to one another, forming short chains. Examples of such compounds are the peroxides, the peroxyacids, and the thionous and thionic acids.

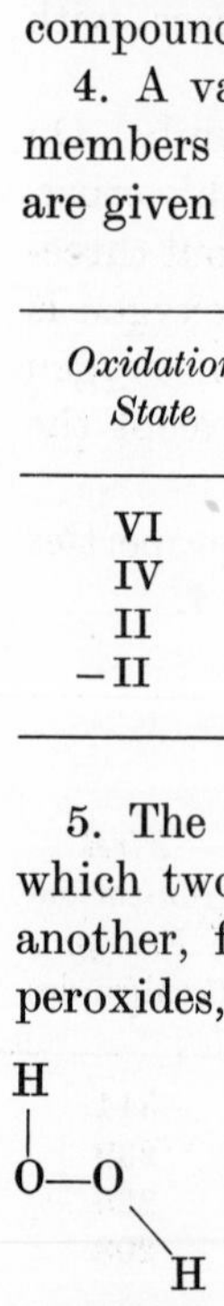

Hydrogen peroxide 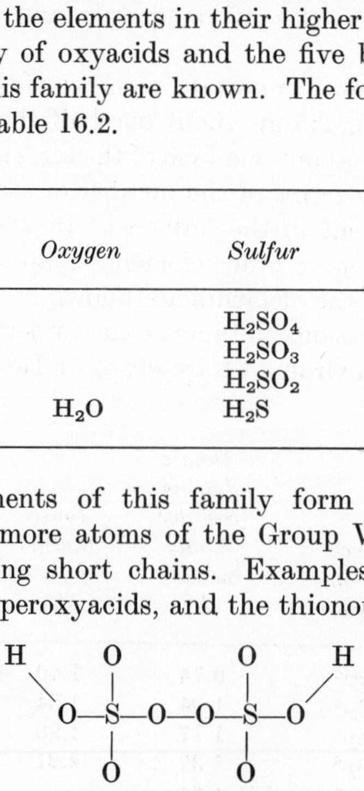   Peroxydisulfuric acid 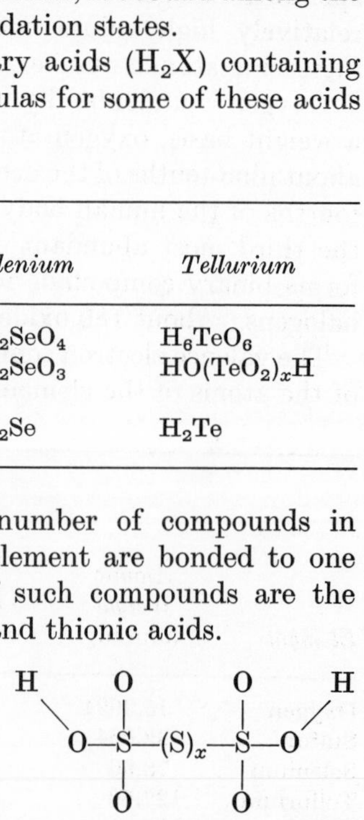   A thionic acid

This tendency toward catenation also appears in the free elements; for example, they form ozone, O_3,

and elemental sulfur, S_8,

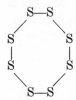

6. Sulfur, selenium, and tellurium form a number of polymeric compounds which have a simple repeating unit containing the oxygen family element. Examples are solid sulfur trioxide, selenium dioxide, and polytellurous acid.

$$-O-\underset{\underset{O}{|}}{\overset{\overset{O}{|}}{S}}-O-\underset{\underset{O}{|}}{\overset{\overset{O}{|}}{S}}-O-\underset{\underset{O}{|}}{\overset{\overset{O}{|}}{S}}-O-\underset{\underset{O}{|}}{\overset{\overset{O}{|}}{S}}- \qquad -\overset{\overset{O}{|}}{Se}-O-\overset{\overset{O}{|}}{Se}-O-\overset{\overset{O}{|}}{Se}-O-\overset{\overset{O}{|}}{Se}-$$

(poly)Sulfur trioxide (poly)Selenium dioxide

Bonding. Bonding in species containing oxygen family elements varies from ionic to covalent. In the H_2X compounds the bonding is predominantly covalent. However in the MX type of compounds, where M represents a metal, the bonds are often ionic. The melting points of the H_2X and the Na_2X compounds of this family given in Table 16.3 reflect

Compound	Melting Point (°C)	Compound	Melting Point (°C)	Compound	Melting Point (°C)
H_2O	0.00	Na_2O	1193	MgO	3075
H_2S	−85.5	Na_2S	1000	MgS	>2000
H_2Se	−65.73	Na_2Se	>875		
H_2Te	−51	Na_2Te			

Table 16.3 Comparison of Melting Points of H_2X and MX Compounds

these differences in bonding. As in the halogens, the oxygen family elements show a trend from typically ionic to typically covalent compounds when combined successively with the elements in a horizontal row or period in the periodic table. This is illustrated in Table 16.4 where the

Oxide	Na_2O	MgO	Al_2O_3	SiO_2	P_4O_{10}	SO_2	Cl_2O
Melting point (°C)	1193	3075	2300	1710	422	−72.5	−116
Sulfide	Na_2S	MgS	Al_2S_3	SiS_2	P_4S_{10}	S_8	S_2Cl_2
Melting point (°C)	1000	>2000	1100	1090	268	116	−76.5

Table 16.4 Melting Points of Oxides and Sulfides of Third Period Elements

melting points of oxides and sulfides of the elements in the third period are recorded. Because of its high electronegativity, oxygen forms ionic bonds with more metals than do the other members of the family.

Bonding in the Oxygen Molecule. A simple electronic formula for the oxygen molecule is sometimes written—e.g., $: \overset{..}{O} :: \overset{..}{O} :$, in which each oxygen atom has acquired an octet of electrons and a double covalent bond connects the atoms. However, the high reactivity of oxygen gas and its paramagnetism cannot be explained by such a structure. Only the molecular orbital theory (Chap. 6) can satisfactorily explain the paramagnetism of the O_2 molecule. According to this theory the electrons of greatest energy are in antibonding $\pi^*_{2p_y}$ and $\pi^*_{2p_z}$ molecular orbitals, thereby giving rise to both paramagnetism and enhanced reactivity.

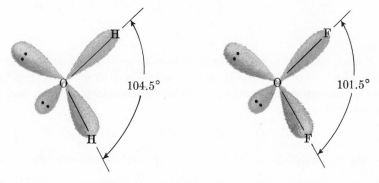

Figure 16.1 Water and fluorine oxide. In these molecules the four pairs of electrons are believed to exist in sp^3 hybrid orbitals with only two pairs being used to form σ bonds in each molecule. The bond angles are less than the tetrahedral angle of 109°28' because the lone pair–lone pair repulsion of the electrons in the nonbonding orbitals distorts the regularity of the expected sp^3 tetrahedral orientation.

Stereochemistry in Oxygen Compounds. The spatial arrangements of the atoms in covalent molecules containing oxygen family elements have been determined by various techniques including X-ray diffraction, electron diffraction, and microwave spectroscopy. These arrangements are explicable in terms of the various types of hybridization possible in the atoms of this family.

In most of the simple inorganic covalent oxides, the oxygen atom apparently utilizes sp^3 hybrid orbitals in forming bonds; the "lone pairs" affect the geometry of the molecules. Examples are water and fluorine oxide where the bond angles are 104.5° and 101.5° respectively (Figure 16.1).

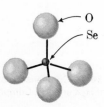

Figure 16.2 Selenate ion showing the tetrahedral arrangement of oxygen atoms around the selenium atom.

Compounds of sulfur, selenium, and tellurium having formulas of the type XB_2, such as SCl_2 and H_2Se, have bond angles close to 90°. This can be interpreted as a further distortion of the tetrahedral sp^3 hybrid, or as p^2 bonding involving perpendicular p orbitals. Grouping of four similar atoms around the oxygen family atom, as in the ions SO_4^{-2} (Figure 16.2) and SeO_4^{-2}, leads to the tetrahedral sp^3 structure.

Figure 16.3 A gaseous sulfur trioxide molecule showing the planar-triangular arrangement of the oxygen and sulfur atoms. Here the three pairs of electrons forming the σ bonds exist in sp^2 hybrid orbitals on sulfur. The π bond accounts for the fourth pair of electrons. This bond is delocalized so that it includes all three oxygen atoms. This is conventionally indicated by drawing three resonance structures, and by the single orbital diagram at the right.

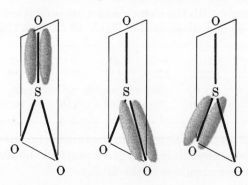

Since SO_3 is a planar, triangular-shaped molecule, it is reasonable to postulate that in this case the sulfur atom uses sp^2 hybrid orbitals in forming the three σ bonds to the oxygen atoms. The fourth pair of electrons around the sulfur atom forms a delocalized π bond with the oxygen atoms (Figure 16.3).

Table 16.5 gives the shapes of some common covalent species containing oxygen family elements. It also includes the type of hybridization used by the central atom and the number of σ and π bonds present in the structure.

Example	Shape	Probable Hybridization on the Central Atom	σ Bonds in Structure	π Bonds in Structure
H_2O, F_2O	V-shaped	sp^3	2	0
H_2S, Cl_2S	V-shaped	sp^3 (or p^2)	2	0
H_2Se, H_2Te	V-shaped	sp^3 (or p^2)	2	0
SO_2	V-shaped	sp^2	2	1
SO_3	Planar-triangular	sp^2	3	1
SO_4^{-2}, SeO_4^{-2}	Tetrahedral	sp^3	4	2
SF_6, SeF_6	Octahedral	sp^3d^2	6	0
$Te(OH)_6$	Octahedral	sp^3d^2	6	0

Table 16.5 Stereochemistry of Oxygen Family Structures

Acids. The acids of this family vary in strength from very strong, such as sulfuric acid, to extremely weak, such as water. The ionization constants for a number of oxygen family acids are given in Table 16.6. All binary acids of this family are weak; water is the weakest of the group.

Compound	Ionization Constant at 25°C K_I	K_{II}	Compound	Ionization Constant at 25°C K_I	K_{II}
H_2O	1.3×10^{-16}	$\sim 10^{-24}$	H_2SO_4	large	1.2×10^{-2}
H_2S	8.7×10^{-8}	1×10^{-14}	H_2SO_3	1.0×10^{-2}	1.0×10^{-7}
H_2Se	1.9×10^{-4}	1×10^{-11}	H_2SeO_4	large	1.0×10^{-2}
H_2Te	2.3×10^{-3}	1×10^{-11}	H_6TeO_6	1.6×10^{-9}	

Table 16.6 Acid Strengths of Oxygen Family Elements

Note: K_I is for first ionization, K_{II} for second ionization: (1) $H_2X + H_2O \leftrightarrows H_3O^+ + HX^-$; (2) $HX^- + H_2O \leftrightarrows H_3O^+ + X^{-2}$.

As in all diprotic acids (those having two ionizable protons) the second ionization constant, K_{II}, is invariably much less than the first ionization constant due to the fact that the negative charge on the ion HX^- makes removal of the second proton difficult.

The strengths of the oxyacids can be explained in terms of the electronegativity of the central atom and the number of oxygen atoms as was done for the halogen oxyacids. Thus H_2SO_4 is weaker than $HClO_4$ because chlorine has a higher electronegativity than sulfur; but H_2SO_4 is stronger than H_2SO_3 because of the additional oxygen atom on the former. Telluric acid does not appear to follow the pattern set by the oxyacids of simpler structure.

Oxidizing and Reducing Agents. Because of oxygen's small atomic radius and its high electronegativity, the $-$II oxidation state is the most stable state for this element. For sulfur, selenium, and tellurium the IV state appears to be the most stable although this state is only slightly more stable than certain others. As a result, the VI oxidation-state compounds of sulfur, selenium, and tellurium are all moderate to strong oxidizing agents while the $-$II and 0 oxidation-state species are good to strong reducing agents. Thus when sulfur burns in air the reaction may be represented by the equation

$$S_8 + 8O_2 \longrightarrow 8SO_2$$

wherein sulfur acts as the reducing agent, being oxidized to the IV state, and the oxygen acts as the oxidizing agent, being reduced to its stable $-$II state. Similarly, the reactions between sulfuric acid and hydrogen sulfide might be expected to give as products sulfur dioxide and sulfur or only sulfur dioxide along with water.

$$3H_2SO_4 + H_2S \longrightarrow 4SO_2 + 4H_2O$$

In this case sulfuric acid acts as the oxidizing agent (sulfur in oxidation state VI is reduced to the IV state), and hydrogen sulfide acts as the reducing agent (sulfur in oxidation state $-$II is oxidized to the IV state).

The relative strength of the H_2X compounds as reducing agents is $H_2Te > H_2Se > H_2S > H_2O$ as expected from electronegativity considerations. Among the free elements of the family, oxygen is by far the strongest oxidizing agent; sulfur is considerably weaker; and the other elements are extremely weak oxidizing agents. This is consistent with the great stability of the $-$II oxidation state of oxygen and the decreasing stability of the $-$II state of the other members. Interestingly, the oxidizing strengths of the VI oxidation-state species appear to follow the order $SO_3 < TeO_3 < SeO_3$. Presumably this order is related to an interplay among several factors including an electronegativity factor and an atomic size factor.

The strengths of various species as oxidizing agents in water solution are recorded in the values of the standard oxidation potentials listed in Table 16.7.

Occurrence. It has been pointed out that oxygen, in large quantities, is all around us and is a vital part of us. Sulfur is much less abundant but it was one of the few elements known to the ancients. It is the *brimstone* of the Bible.

Table 16.7 Standard Oxidation Potentials for Some Species Containing Oxygen Family Elements

Reaction				Volts at 25°C
H_2Po		$\leftrightarrows 2H^+_{(aq)} + Po$	$+ 2e^-$	1.0
H_2Te		$\leftrightarrows 2H^+_{(aq)} + Te$	$+ 2e^-$	0.72
H_2Se		$\leftrightarrows 2H^+_{(aq)} + Se$	$+ 2e^-$	0.40
H_2S		$\leftrightarrows 2H^+_{(aq)} + S$	$+ 2e^-$	-0.14
SO_2	$+ 2H_2O$	$\leftrightarrows 4H^+_{(aq)} + SO_4^{-2}$	$+ 2e^-$	$-0.17 \ (-0.20)$
TeO_2	$+ 4H_2O$	$\leftrightarrows 2H^+_{(aq)} + H_6TeO_6$	$+ 2e^-$	-1.02
SeO_2	$+ 2H_2O$	$\leftrightarrows 4H^+_{(aq)} + SeO_4^{-2}$	$+ 2e^-$	-1.15
$2H_2O$		$\leftrightarrows 4H^+_{(aq)} + O_2$	$+ 4e^-$	-1.23

Free sulfur occurs in many parts of the world, including Sicily, Japan, Spain, Iceland, and Mexico, as well as in different localities in the United States, especially in Texas and Louisiana. Some of the most important sulfur compounds in nature are the sulfides galena (PbS), sphalerite (ZnS), chalcopyrite ($CuFeS_2$), and pyrite (FeS_2), and the sulfates gypsum ($CaSO_4 \cdot 2H_2O$), barite ($BaSO_4$), celestite ($SrSO_4$), and Epsom salt ($MgSO_4 \cdot 7H_2O$). The origin of the great deposits of free sulfur is not well understood. A tentative but very probable explanation is that it was formed in the photosynthesis process in the early period of the history of the earth when there was a much higher concentration of H_2S in the atmosphere. Much of the oxygen in the earth's atmosphere is formed by photosynthesis:

$$CO_2 + H_2O \xrightarrow[\text{chlorophyll}]{\text{sunlight}} \text{sugar} + O_2$$

$$CO_2 + H_2S \xrightarrow[\text{chlorophyll}]{\text{sunlight}} \text{sugar} + S_8$$

Sulfur is one of the most important raw materials of the chemical industry. About three-fourths of the total sulfur, from all sources, is burned and converted into sulfuric acid. Other important uses include those in the vulcanization of rubber, the preparation of wood pulp for paper, and the preparation of medicinals and insecticides.

Tellurium was discovered by Franz Müller (Baron von Reichenstein) and Martin Klaproth toward the end of the eighteenth century, and Jakob Berzelius isolated selenium in 1817.

Selenium is frequently found in small quantities in natural sulfur. Combined with metals, it occurs also along with some of the sulfides, especially pyrites (FeS_2). Occasionally compounds of selenium occur in the soil and are absorbed by certain varieties of plants. Thousands of cattle and sheep who have fed on these plants have died from poisoning.

Tellurium is found free and combined with metals, especially gold, silver, lead, and bismuth, forming compounds known as tellurides. No important use has been found for tellurium.

Properties of the Elements

Under ordinary temperature and pressure oxygen is a gas consisting of diatomic molecules; sulfur is a yellow solid composed of molecules present as puckered rings of eight atoms (Figure 16.4), selenium is a grey solid containing zigzag chains of atoms, tellurium is a grey metallic solid, and polonium is a metallic substance with the atoms packed in a cubic lattice.

Table 16.8 gives some physical properties of these elements. Among the solid elements, the density, melting point, boiling point, and heats of fusion and vaporization increase systematically from sulfur to tellurium. Polonium has a higher density than tellurium, but both its melting and boiling temperatures are lower.

The systematic increase in density can be accounted for in terms of (a) the increasing density of the atoms in proceeding from sulfur to polonium, and (b) the changes in molecular and crystal structure. The relatively high and steadily increasing values for melting and boiling points and for the heats of fusion and vaporization reflect increasingly stronger forces of attraction among the atoms of these elements.

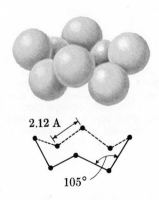

Figure 16.4 The puckered ring of eight sulfur atoms in solid sulfur.

Table 16.8 Some Physical Properties of Oxygen Family Elements

Element	Density of Solid (g/cc at 25°C)	Melting Point (°C)	Boiling Point (°C)	Heat of Fusion (kcal/mole)	Heat of Vaporization (kcal/mole)
Oxygen		−218.9	−182.96	0.053	0.81
Sulfur	2.06	119.0	440.60	0.34	2.3
Selenium	4.82	220.2	688	1.25	6.29
Tellurium	6.25	450	1390	4.28	12.1
Polonium	9.51	254	962		

Properties of Atoms. Table 16.1 lists the electronegativities, ionization energies, and the atomic and ionic radii of the atoms of these elements. In electronegativity oxygen is second only to fluorine.

In spite of the regularities in many properties of the atoms of this family there are significant differences between the behavior of atoms of oxygen and those of the other members of this family. Three major differences in behavior and their apparent causes are:

1. Oxygen atoms form double bonds which are of greater stability than those formed by the other members of this family. Hence oxygen forms O_2 molecules rather than chains or rings of atoms as does sulfur. The tendency to form multiple bonds is related to the fact that underlying the valence shell in oxygen is a filled shell of two electrons while shells of eight or more lie under the valence shells of the other elements. The increased shielding of the nuclei in the larger atoms presumably inhibits π-bond formation which can occur readily with oxygen atoms.

2. Oxygen atoms only rarely form combinations in which they are in positive oxidation states whereas the other atoms in the family do so readily. The high electronegativity of the oxygen atom and its small size prevents the formation of the positive state in most cases. Conversely the larger, more polarizable, less electronegative atoms of the other elements of the family readily form positive oxidation states.

3. The other members of the family sometimes form compounds by expanding their valence shell or by using d orbitals, but oxygen apparently is unable to do this. Thus, compounds such as SF_6, $Te(OH)_6$, and SeF_6 are stable, presumably because of the ability of the central atom to expand its octet (Figure 16.5).

Figure 16.5 The SF_6 molecule showing (a) the S–F bonds and (b) the octahedral configuration. The sulfur atom uses s, p, and d orbitals in the octahedral sp^3d^2 hybridization.

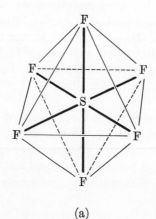

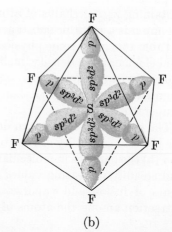

(a)   (b)

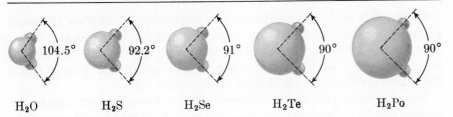

$$H_2O \qquad H_2S \qquad H_2Se \qquad H_2Te \qquad H_2Po$$

Figure 16.6 The H_2X molecules of the oxygen family.

Chemical Properties. Oxygen acts almost exclusively as an oxidizing agent, being a reducing agent only in its reactions with fluorine. All other elements in this family may act as both oxidizing and reducing agents.

Reactions with Metals. These elements act as oxidizing agents in their reactions with the metals. In nearly all cases these reactions give salts with the oxygen family element as an anion in its $-$ II oxidation state.

$$M + X \longrightarrow MX$$

Exceptions to this general reaction are the formation of peroxides and superoxides with alkali metals and the synthesis of polysulfides of the type M_2S_4 and M_2S_6 with active metals.

Reactions with Nonmetals. Most nonmetals form binary covalent compounds in reactions with sulfur family elements. The latter elements may exhibit positive or negative oxidation states depending upon whether the other element is more or less electronegative. In their binary compounds with hydrogen, oxygen family elements have $-$ II oxidation states. However, positive states are exhibited by the heavier elements of the family in combination with oxygen.

Table 16.9 Some Properties of Binary Hydrogen Compounds of Oxygen Family Elements

Compound	Melting Point (°C)	Boiling Point (°C)	Heat of Fusion (kcal/mole)	Heat of Vaporization (kcal/mole)	H—X—H Bond angle (deg)	Dipole Moment (Debye units)
H_2O	0	100	1.44	9.72	104.45	1.84
H_2S	-85.6	-60.8	0.57	4.46	92.2	0.92
H_2Se	-60.4	-41.5	0.60	4.75	91.0	
H_2Te	-51	-1.8		5.70	89.5	

Important Compounds of Oxygen Family Elements
1. Negative Oxidation States (Chiefly $-$ II Oxidation States)

Binary Hydrogen Compounds. All members of the family form covalent binary compounds with hydrogen (Table 16.9). The molecules all have V-shaped structures as illustrated in Figure 16.6. In spite of this similarity in structure, water is markedly different from the others. For example, at room temperature water is a liquid while hydrogen sulfide, hydrogen selenide, and hydrogen telluride are gases. Water has unusually high values for melting and boiling points, and for heats of fusion and vaporization, as a result of the greater polarity of the water molecule and of the importance of hydrogen bonding among water molecules. Even in liquid water, large clusters of molecules appear to be bound together by hydrogen bonds.

Presumably hydrogen bonding is also responsible for another abnormal property of water—the fact that water expands (or decreases in density) as it is cooled from 3.98°C through its freezing point. This results in a lower density for ice (near its freezing point) than for liquid water and is the reason ice floats on the surface of rivers and lakes.

The explanation for the expansion of water at lower temperatures is that cooling results in formation of more and more hydrogen bonds among the molecules. As the number of these bonds approaches a maximum, the water molecules become oriented in a tetrahedral pattern with considerable empty space between neighboring molecules. The rigid bonding prevents other water molecules from entering this space. Therefore the more "open" or expanded structure of lower density results as illustrated in Figure 15.20.

Chemical Properties of Water. In addition to its powerful solvent properties, water undergoes a variety of chemical reactions. Four types of these are:

1. *Acid-Base Properties.* Water can act as either an acid (proton donor) or a base (proton acceptor) in reactions such as

$$H_2O + CN^- \text{ (from NaCN)} \rightleftharpoons HCN + OH^-$$

and

$$HCl + H_2O \rightleftharpoons H_3O^+ + Cl^-$$

The first ionization constant of water (K_1) is 1.3×10^{-16}, and the second (K_2) is about 10^{-24} at 25°C.

2. *Oxidation-Reduction Reactions.* Water can act as either a weak oxidizing or a weak reducing agent. In reactions with active metals—e.g.,

$$2Na + 2H_2O \longrightarrow 2Na^+OH^- + H_2 \uparrow$$

it acts as an oxidizing agent with hydrogen being reduced. When acting as a reducing agent, the oxygen is oxidized as in

$$2F_2 + 2H_2O \longrightarrow 4HF + O_2$$

3. *Hydrolytic Reactions.* Reactions such as

$$PBr_3 + 3H_2O \longrightarrow H_3PO_3 + 3HBr$$

and

$$SO_2Cl_2 + 2H_2O \longrightarrow H_2SO_4 + 2HCl$$

are known as hydrolytic reactions, and the compounds are said to undergo hydrolysis. In such reactions a water molecule may be imagined to split into a hydrogen ion, H^+, and a hydroxide ion, OH^-, as each of these ions becomes attached to a different portion of the molecule to be hydrolyzed.

4. *Hydration Reactions.* Small cations with large charges, especially transition element ions, form aquo complexes with water. The reaction might be represented by the equation

$$M^{+n} + xH_2O \longrightarrow M(H_2O)_x^{+n}$$

For most ions x is 6 although for some small ions such as lithium and copper ions x is 4, and for larger ions like barium ion, x is 8.

The water molecules may be bonded to the metal ion by ion-dipole or covalent bonds (as discussed in Chap. 27).

These bonds are so strong in some cases that when the metallic salts are crystallized from water solution, water is carried into the crystals containing the ion. Examples of such hydrates are $Cd(NO_3)_2 \cdot 4H_2O$, $MgCl_2 \cdot 6H_2O$, $CuSO_4 \cdot 5H_2O$.

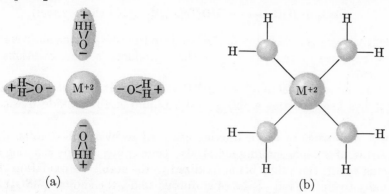

(a)   (b)

Figure 16.7 Hydration of positive ions: (a) Ion-dipole bond. (b) Covalent bond.

Hydrogen Sulfide, Hydrogen Selenide, and Hydrogen Telluride. These compounds are weak acids although all of them are stronger acids than water, as shown by the values listed in Table 16.6. Their reducing strengths increase regularly from H_2S to H_2Te and their thermal stability decreases in the same order.

Hydrogen sulfide and metal sulfides react with oxygen as follows:

$$2H_2S + 3O_2 \longrightarrow 2H_2O + 2SO_2$$

$$2MS + 3O_2 \longrightarrow 2MO + 2SO_2$$

Polysulfides, Polyselenides, and Polytellurides. When sulfur is added to solutions of sulfide ions or when selenium or tellurium are added to solutions of selenide or tellurium ions respectively, the corresponding *poly*-sulfides, *poly*selenides, or *poly*tellurides are formed. These reactions may be illustrated by the general equation, where X represents S, Se, or Te atoms,

$$X^{-2} + nX \longrightarrow X_{n+1}^{-2}$$

and where n varies from 1 to 4. The structures of these are

$$: \overset{..}{\underset{..}{X}} : \overset{..}{\underset{..}{X}} :^{-2} \qquad \left(\begin{array}{c} X \\ X \end{array} \diagdown \begin{array}{c} X \\ X \end{array} \right)^{-2}$$

Acidification of solutions containing polysulfides reverses the reaction resulting in the formation of sulfur and of sulfide ion.

2. The IV Oxidation States of Sulfur, Selenium, and Tellurium

Burning sulfur, selenium, or tellurium in air gives sulfur dioxide, selenium dioxide, or tellurium dioxide. Sulfur dioxide is a colorless gas with a sharp irritating odor. It is composed of V-shaped molecules. Selenium dioxide exists as colorless crystals which sublime at 315°C and melt to an orange liquid. It is composed of long chains as shown on page 317. Tellurium dioxide appears to be an ionic solid.

All three dioxides react with water according to the equations

$$SO_2 + H_2O \longrightarrow H_2SO_3 \quad \text{(sulfurous acid)}$$

$$SeO_2 + H_2O \longrightarrow H_2SeO_3 \quad \text{(selenous acid)}$$

$$nTeO_2 + H_2O \xrightarrow[\text{slowly}]{} HO(TeO_2)_nH \quad \text{(polytellurous acid)}$$

Evidently water is able to break the bonds in the SeO_2 chains more readily than it ruptures those in TeO_2. All three products in these reactions are weak acids

Sulfur dioxide liquefies at $-10.02°C$ at 1 atm. It is liquefied so easily that it has been used as a refrigerant. Liquid sulfur dioxide freezes at $-75.5°C$.

Large quantities of sulfur dioxide are used to bleach foodstuffs, wool, silk, straw, and paper-making materials. Here sulfur dioxide is acting as a reducing agent, the sulfur being oxidized to the stable VI oxidation state —usually to sulfate ion. Salts of sulfurous acid—the sulfites (MSO_3) and the bisulfites [$M(HSO_3)_2$]—are also excellent reducing agents. These compounds are used as food preservatives and bleaching agents.

3. The VI Oxidation States of Sulfur, Selenium, and Tellurium

Sulfur trioxide, made by catalytic oxidation of sulfur dioxide with air, is a colorless volatile solid. Solid sulfur trioxide exists in three forms, two having long chains of SO_3 units as shown on page 317, and the third composed of cyclic trimer molecules. The structure of gaseous sulfur trioxide molecules is given in Chap. 6.

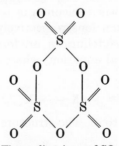

The cyclic trimer of SO_3

Selenium trioxide, formed by passing an electric discharge through selenium vapor mixed with oxygen, is a colorless solid. Tellurium trioxide, an orange solid, is made by heating telluric acid.

All three trioxides vary from good to strong oxidizing agents with selenium trioxide being the strongest, strong enough to oxidize chloride ion to chlorine.

$$SeO_3 + 2Cl^- \rightleftarrows SeO_3^{-2} + Cl_2$$

Sulfuric Acid, H_2SO_4. Known since the time of alchemy, sulfuric acid is not only one of the most important laboratory reagents but also one of the most important industrial chemicals. It is prepared commercially by the catalytic oxidation of sulfur dioxide either on a catalyst surface (called a *heterogeneous catalyst*), such as platinum or vanadium pentoxide, in the contact process, or with nitric oxide, NO, in a *homogenous catalytic process* in the lead chamber process. The sulfur trioxide formed in either process is converted to sulfuric acid by water.

The chemical conduct of the acid may be described as follows:

1. *Acid Properties.* In concentrated aqueous solutions hydrogen sulfate forms the ions H_3O^+ and HSO_4^-, and the latter, a weak acid, ionizes to some extent into hydronium ions, H_3O^+, and sulfate ions, SO_4^{-2}. In a 1-molar solution of hydrogen sulfate, only 51 per cent of its hydrogen is present as free ions.

2. *Action as an Oxidizing Agent.* Sulfuric acid is a very good oxidizing agent because the sulfur of concentrated sulfuric acid is easily reduced from the VI oxidation state to the IV state, giving SO_2. With copper the equation representing the reaction is

$$Cu + 2H_2SO_4 \longrightarrow CuSO_4 + SO_2 + 2H_2O$$

or in ionic form,

$$Cu + 3H^+(aq) + HSO_4^- \longrightarrow Cu^{+2} + SO_2 + 2H_2O$$

3. *Action on Metals.* A *dilute* solution of sulfuric acid acts upon the metals above hydrogen in the electrochemical series to form sulfates of the metals and liberate hydrogen. Such a solution has no action upon the metals below hydrogen in the series, except when the oxygen of the air first oxidizes the metal.

4. *Action on Salts.* When a salt of a low-boiling acid is heated with an acid having a high boiling point, we might predict that the low-boiling acid would be liberated and escape as a gas or vapor. Since sulfuric acid has a higher boiling point than that of any other of the common acids, and since it is an inexpensive compound, it is admirably adapted to the preparation of other acids from their salts.

$$H_2SO_4 + NaCl \rightarrow NaHSO_4 + HCl$$

$$(H_3O^+ + HSO_4^- + Na^+ + Cl^- \rightarrow HCl\uparrow + Na^+ + HSO_4^- + H_2O)$$

$$NaHSO_4 + NaCl \rightarrow Na_2SO_4 + HCl$$

$$(Na^+ + HSO_4^- + Na^+ + Cl^- \rightarrow HCl\uparrow + SO_4^{-2} + 2Na^+)$$

5. *Action on Water.* When the concentrated acid is mixed with water a marked contraction in volume takes place. Moreover, the process is attended by the evolution of a large amount of heat, which may even be sufficient to cause the liquid to boil. Care must therefore be taken, in mixing the acid with water, to *pour the acid into the water*, not the reverse, and to keep the solution thoroughly stirred during the process.

When hydrogen sulfate and water are mixed in molecular proportions— namely, 98 parts by weight of the sulfate to 18 of water—and the resulting solution is cooled, the two unite to form the hydrate $H_2SO_4 \cdot H_2O$. This is a white crystalline substance melting at 8.62°C.

6. *Action on Organic Substances.* Not only can sulfuric acid combine with water, but it will often withdraw the elements hydrogen and oxygen from a compound containing them, thus decomposing the compound and forming H_2O molecules. For this reason most organic substances, such as sugar, wood, cotton, and woolen fiber, and even animal tissues, all of which contain such oxygen and hydrogen in addition to carbon, are decomposed by the concentrated acid, leaving the black carbon as a residue.

Selenic and Telluric Acids. Selenic acid, H_2SeO_4, is a solid, a strong acid and oxidizing agent, and like sulfuric acid forms two series of salts, the selenates and the biselenates, $M(HSeO_4)_2$.

Telluric acid, H_6TeO_6, is a white solid made by reacting tellurium with aqua regia and a chlorate. It is a very weak acid having an octahedral structure:

$$
\begin{array}{c}
\text{OH} \\
| \\
\text{HO} \diagdown \quad \diagup \text{OH} \\
\text{Te} \\
\text{HO} \diagup \quad \diagdown \text{OH} \\
| \\
\text{OH}
\end{array}
$$

Thiosulfates. Sulfur reacts with sulfite ion in alkaline solution to form thiosulfate:

$$SO_3^{-2} + S \longrightarrow S_2O_3^{-2} \quad \text{(thiosulfate ion)}$$

The name thiosulfate indicates that the structure is similar to sulfate except that one oxygen atom has been replaced by a sulfur atom. Accordingly the ion has the tetrahedral structure represented by the formula

$$
\begin{array}{c}
O^{-2} \\
| \\
S \\
\diagup \ | \ \diagdown \\
O \quad S \quad O
\end{array}
$$

Thiosulfates are numerous, moderately stable, and usually very soluble in water. They yield a precipitate of sulfur on acidification:

$$S_2O_3^{-2} + H_3O^+ \longrightarrow HSO_3^- + H_2O + S$$

● ● ●   THE PRODUCTION AND USES OF SULFURIC ACID

The annual production of sulfuric acid in the United States fluctuates widely but is more than 25,000,000 tons calculated as 100 per cent H_2SO_4; about two-thirds of this is produced by the contact process. The fertilizer industry consumes approximately one-third of the output. Its minor uses are innumerable.

The Relative Amounts of Sulfuric Acid in the United States
(tons of 100 per cent H_2SO_4 on a yearly basis)

Fertilizers	10,430,000	Coal products	570,000
Chemicals	2,815,000	Paints and pigments	1,900,000
Petroleum	700,000	Rayon	570,000
Iron and steel	1,170,000	Miscellaneous	1,300,000

Thiosulfates are good reducing agents, being oxidized by iodine, for example, to tetrathionates as illustrated in the equation

$$2 \; \underset{\underset{S}{\overset{O}{|}}}{\overset{O^{-2}}{\underset{|}{S}}}\!\!\diagup\!O \;\; + \; \overset{I}{\underset{I}{|}} \; \longrightarrow \; \underset{O}{\overset{O}{O}}\!\!S\!-\!S\!-\!S\!\underset{O}{\overset{O^{-2}}{O}} \; + \; 2I^-$$

They are used in the fixing of photographic films, plates, and prints because of the tendency of the thiosulfate ion to form complex ions with Ag^+ ions:

$$Ag^+ + 2S_2O_3^{-2} \longrightarrow Ag(S_2O_3)_2^{-3}$$

SUMMARY

Oxygen family elements, because of their relatively high electronegativities, act predominantly as nonmetals although the heavier members have some metallic properties. Because of their s^2p^4 valence-shell configuration, oxidation states between $-II$ and VI are common. However, oxygen, with its especially high electronegativity, exhibits positive oxidation states only in combination with fluorine, and polonium compounds in the VI state are unknown.

These elements form both ionic and covalent bonds. In reactions with metals the bonds are predominantly ionic with the oxygen family element forming X^{-2} anions. In reactions with hydrogen or with nonmetals the bonds usually are predominantly covalent. The stereochemistry of the covalent species varies from angular to trigonal planar and from tetrahedral to octahedral. Complex ions such as sulfate and selenate, SeO_4^{-2}, are common, as are oxyacids such as H_2SO_3, H_2SeO_4, and H_6TeO_6. Acid strengths vary from very weak (H_2O) to very strong (H_2SO_4).

Strong reducing agents such as the H_2X compounds (except H_2O) and strong oxidizing agents such as SeO_3, TeO_3, and SO_3 are found in this family.

Catenation, or the forming of chains or rings of similar atoms, is observed in the oxygen family, particularly with sulfur. Polymerization also is prevalent, as in solid sulfur trioxide or polyselenium dioxide.

SOME SPECIAL TERMS

Bonding
   hydrogen bonding
   ion-dipole bond
   catenation
Reactions
   photosynthesis
   hydrolytic
   hydrolysis

Acid
   diprotic acid
   acid strength
   oxyacid
polarizable atom
heterogeneous catalyst
bleaching agent
stereochemistry
peroxide
superoxide
polysulfide

QUESTIONS AND PROBLEMS

1. Give the electronic configurations of the simple negative ions of the elements of the oxygen family. Write electron-dot structures for the hydrides of these elements.

2. How many electrons take part in bonding in SO_2? in SO_3? in SO_4^{-2}? in $S_2O_3^{-2}$? Draw electron-dot structures for each of these molecules, labeling the σ and the π bonds.

3. Sulfur dioxide is a V-shaped molecule; carbon dioxide is a linear molecule. Draw the electron-dot structures of the two, and suggest why the structural difference should occur.

4. Draw the electron-dot structure of S_2Cl_2, and predict the molecular shape.

5. Write equations to show reactions you might expect to occur (a) if hydrogen telluride was added to 1-molar sulfuric acid solution; (b) if hydrogen selenide was added to 1-molar selenic acid solution.

6. Suppose you wish to prepare sulfuric acid. As a raw material source of sulfur would you choose free sulfur, sphalerite, or Epsom salt? Write equations for all reactions which would occur for the raw material of your choice. Could either of the other two serve as the sulfur source if your choice was not available? If so, write equations to show how you could prepare sulfuric acid from them.

7. Table 16.8 shows that the melting point, boiling point, heat of fusion, and heat of vaporization increase in the order of increasing atomic weight, for elements of the oxygen family. Is this what would be expected from consideration of the changes in the properties listed in Table 16.1? Discuss.

8. Write equations for the following reactions: (a) zinc with sulfur, (b) hydrogen with selenium, (c) water with calcium, (d) phosphorus tri-iodide with water, (e) hydrogen sulfide with excess oxygen, (f) water with selenium dioxide, (g) 1 mole of sulfuric acid with 1 mole of sodium hydroxide both in water solution, (h) concentrated sulfuric acid with bismuth, (i) dilute sulfuric acid on zinc, (j) concentrated sulfuric acid on sodium chloride, (k) dilute sulfuric acid on sodium thiosulfate, and (l) the reaction that would take place if sodium thiosulfate solution was added to silver bromide.

9. Consider the trend in the heats of vaporization of the oxygen family hydrides, as shown in Table 16.9. How do you account for the fact that water does not follow the trend set by the other compounds? Discuss.

10. Write equations to show that water can act either as an acid or a base, and to show that pure water is ionized.

11. Discuss and explain the facts that the ionization constants, and the strengths as reducing agents, of the Group VI hydrides increase in the order $H_2Te > H_2Se > H_2S > H_2O$.

REFERENCES

Brasted, R. C., M. C. Sneed, and J. L. Maynard. *Comprehensive Inorganic Chemistry*, vol. 7: *Sulfur, Selenium, Tellurium, Polonium and Oxygen.* Princeton, N. J.: Van Nostrand, 1961.

Jolly, W. L. *The Chemistry of the Nonmetals.* Englewood Cliffs, N. J.: Prentice-Hall, 1965.

Phillips, C. S. G., and R. J. P. Williams. *Inorganic Chemistry*, vol. *1*, New York: Oxford, 1965.

17

The Nitrogen Family

*Die Hochdrucksynthese des Ammoniaks aus seinen Elementen
fortan unter die Prozesse gerechnet werden darf, auf welche die
Landwirtschaft ihre Hoffnungen setzt, wenn sie angesichts der
abnehmenden Ergiebigkeit der chilenischen Salpeterlager und der
beschränkten Ausdehnungsfähigkeit der Ammoniakgewinnung aus
dem gebundenen Stickstoff der Kohle nach neuen Quellen für
ihren wichtigsten Bedarfstoff umsieht.* Fritz Haber (1868–1934)*

The chemistry of the Group V elements—nitrogen, phosphorus, arsenic,
antimony, and bismuth—is more diverse than that of the groups of
elements previously discussed. It illustrates the variations in structure and
reactivity resulting from atoms of moderate electronegativity, needing
three electrons to complete the valence shell octet. Table 17.1 gives some

Table 17.1 Some Properties of Nitrogen Family Atoms

Element	Valence Electron Configuration	Atomic Radius (A)	Electronegativity	First Ionization Energy (kcal/mole)
Nitrogen	$2s^2\, 2p^3$	0.74	3.05	336
Phosphorus	$3s^2\, 3p^3$	1.10	2.15	254
Arsenic	$4s^2\, 4p^3$	1.21	2.10	231
Antimony	$5s^2\, 5p^3$	1.41	2.05	199
Bismuth	$6s^2\, 6p^3$	1.52	2.00	185

important properties of the atoms of these elements. All have valence
electron configurations of the s^2p^3 type; all are larger and less electronegative than the atoms of the corresponding halogen or oxygen family

---

* "The high-pressure synthesis of ammonia from its elements may henceforth be considered
among those processes upon which agriculture sets its hopes, when, in view of the decreasing
productivity of the nitrate deposits in Chile and the limited possibility for expanding the
production of ammonia from the combined nitrogen of coal, it looks about for new sources
of the material it needs most." (The quotation is from *Chemische Zeitung*, April 5, 1910,
p. 345.)

elements, and all show a distinct tendency to form covalent rather than ionic bonds. As with the halogen and oxygen families, the lighter elements are nonmetals while the heavier elements show characteristics of metals.

An Overview of Nitrogen Family Chemistry

Some important characteristics of the nitrogen family include:

1. Although it might be predicted from a knowledge of halogen and oxygen family chemistry that nitrogen family elements would readily take on three electrons per atom to form an ion of charge -3 according to the relation

$$\cdot \ddot{X} \cdot + 3e^- \longrightarrow :\ddot{\underset{..}{X}}:^{-3}$$

this type of ion is rare. It is found in a few compounds of nitrogen with active metals and probably in an even smaller number of phosphorus compounds. Both the lower electronegativity of nitrogen family atoms and the high polarizability of the relatively large X^{-3} ions are responsible for the failure of these atoms to form stable simple anions.

2. All members of the family exhibit multiple oxidation states between $-III$ and V as expected from the electron configurations of their atoms. Perhaps the most important of these for the entire family are the $-III$, 0, III, V states. Nitrogen itself shows all integral oxidation states between $-III$ and V. The oxidation state pattern and some examples of each state are given in Table 17.2.

Table 17.2 Some Nitrogen Family Species in Various Oxidation States

Oxidation State	Nitrogen	Phosphorus	Arsenic	Antimony	Bismuth
V	N_2O_5	P_4O_{10}	As_2O_5	Sb_2O_5	Bi_2O_5
IV	NO_2	P_4O_8		Sb_2O_4	
III	N_2O_3	P_4O_6	As_4O_6	Sb_4O_6	Bi_2O_3
II	NO				
I	N_2O				
0	N_2	P_4	As	Sb	Bi
$-I$	NH_2OH				
$-II$	NH_2NH_2	PH_2PH_2			
$-III$	NH_3, NH_4^+	PH_3	AsH_3	SbH_3	BiH_3

3. Except for nitrogen, all atoms of this family show a capacity for coordinating five or six other atoms around them. Examples are: PCl_5, AsF_5, $Sb(OH)_6^-$, and BiF_5. In these compounds the nitrogen family atoms have expanded their octets and are using d orbitals as well as s and p orbitals in forming bonds.

4. The family contains both strong oxyacids such as HNO_3, nitric acid, and $H_4P_2O_7$, pyrophosphoric acid, and weak oxyacids such as HNO_2, nitrous acid, H_3PO_3, phosphorous acid, and H_3AsO_4, arsenic acid. It includes one binary acid, the explosive hydrazoic acid HN_3.

5. The XH_3 compounds are all bases because of the high electronegativity and the unshared pair of electrons on X. Thus the reaction

$$:XH_3 + HY \rightleftharpoons XH_4^+ + Y^-$$

is common, and of the XH_4^+ species, ammonium ion, NH_4^+, and phosphonium ion, PH_4^+, are well known.

6. The III oxidation state compounds which might be represented by the formula HOXO or $(HO)_3X$ are (a) *acidic* if X is nitrogen or phosphorus, (b) *amphoteric* (acting as both an acid and a base) if X is arsenic or antimony, and (c) basic if X is bismuth. This can be explained by comparing the strength of the X—OH bond with that of the H—O bond. If the X—OH bond is much stronger than the H—O bond, then the latter will rupture preferentially as in the equation

$$H—OXO + H_2O \longrightarrow H_3O^+ + XO_2^-$$

This reaction occurs when X is an element of relatively high electronegativity such as nitrogen or phosphorus. Conversely if the H—O bond is the stronger, then the X—OH bond will rupture preferentially, giving

$$HO—XO \longrightarrow HO^- + XO^+$$

This occurs when X is an element of low electronegativity such as bismuth. The amphoteric compounds are those in which the two bonds are of comparable strengths so that both reactions might occur as in

$$HOXO$$
$$\overset{H_2O}{\underset{}{\rightleftarrows}} \qquad \rightleftarrows$$
$$H_3O^+ + OXO^- \qquad\qquad HO^- + XO^+$$

In the presence of excess acid the position of equilibrium shifts toward the right, and more XO^+ is formed, and we say HOXO acts as a base; in excess base the position of equilibrium shifts toward the left, more XO_2^- forms, and we say HOXO acts as an acid. This behavior is characteristic of antimony and bismuth and accounts for species often represented as SbO^+ and BiO^+ in compounds such as $SbOCl$, $(BiO)_2SO_4$, $BiOCl$.

7. The V oxidation state species are strong oxidizing agents with the exception of the phosphorus compounds. Thus HNO_3, Bi_2O_5, As_2O_5, and Sb_2O_5 are readily reduced even by weak reducing agents forming, in most cases, the corresponding III state. In acid solution the order of oxidizing strength of the V state species is Bi > N > Sb > As >> P.

8. Compounds of these elements in negative oxidation states are all good reducing agents; they are oxidized to the 0 or the III state in most cases. The order of reducing strength among —III state compounds is BiH_3 > AsH_3 > SbH_3 > PH_3 >> NH_3 with the more metallic hydrides being the better reducing agents.

9. Like the oxygen family, these elements, particularly phosphorus, form polymers and polyacids containing —X—O—X— bonds and —X—X—X— bonds.

The polyphosphoric acids are formed by removing the components of water from adjacent molecules:

$$H—O—\overset{\overset{O}{\|}}{\underset{\underset{OH}{|}}{P}}—OH + H—O—\overset{\overset{O}{\|}}{\underset{\underset{OH}{|}}{P}}—OH \longrightarrow H—O—\overset{\overset{O}{\|}}{\underset{\underset{OH}{|}}{P}}—O—\overset{\overset{O}{\|}}{\underset{\underset{OH}{|}}{P}}—OH + H_2O$$

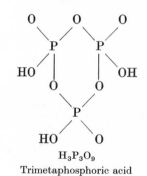

Pyrophosphoric acid

$H_3P_3O_9$
Trimetaphosphoric acid

Portion of Sb_2O_3 chain in the mineral valentinite

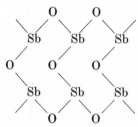

Polymetaphosphoric acid

Figure 17.1 Some polymeric oxygen compounds of phosphorus and antimony.

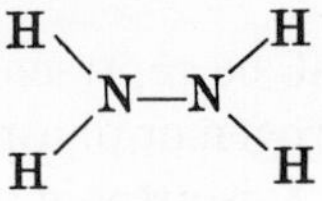

Hydrazine 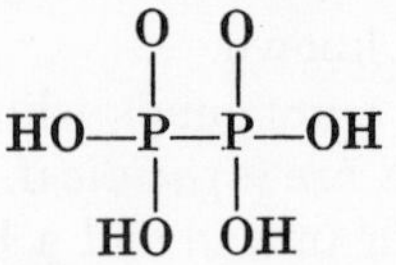   Hypophosphoric acid 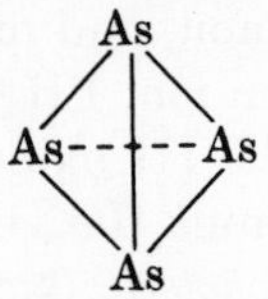   A molecule of
                                                yellow arsenic

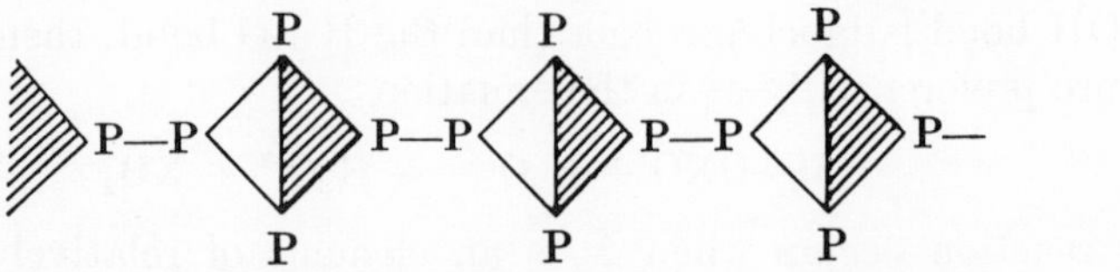

Figure 17.2 Structures containing —X—X—X— bonds.

Suggested arrangement of phosphorus atoms in red phosphorus

Bonding. The elements of the nitrogen family form covalent bonds in nearly all cases. The nitride ion, N^{-3}, is found in the nitrides of active metals, such as Li_3N, and hydrated bismuth ions, Bi^{+3}, appear in salts with sulfates and nitrates and some other stable anions. Other common ionic forms include amide ion, NH_2^-, nitrate and nitrite ions, NO_3^- and NO_2^-, phosphate ion, PO_4^{-3}, ammonium ion, NH_4^+, antimonyl ion, SbO^+, and bismuthyl ion, BiO^+, all of which contain covalent bonds. It is important to realize the extremes in bonding in this family, for the lightest element nitrogen has sufficiently high electronegativity to form a simple anion, while the heavier elements antimony and bismuth have such low electronegativities that they form simple cations. Intermediate between these extremes are the vast majority of structures containing these elements in covalently bonded arrays of atoms.

These arrays of covalently bonded atoms may be small molecules (Figure 17.3), or they may be *macromolecules*—solids in which the entire crystal is one huge molecule and in which the atoms in forming the bonds create a massive three-dimensional network such as in aluminum nitride, AlN (m.p. 2000°C), or boron nitride, BN (m.p. > 3000°C) (Figure 17.4). Small molecules are usually formed when nitrogen family atoms combine

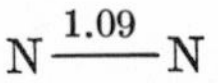

N_2, Nitrogen 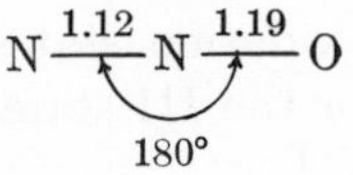 N_2O, Nitrous oxide 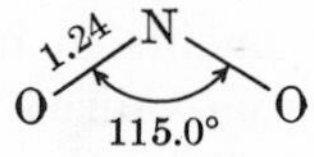 NO_2^-, Nitrite ion 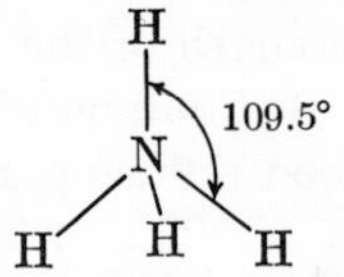 NH_4^+, Ammonium ion

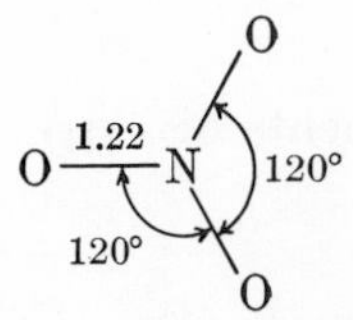

NO_3^-, Nitrate ion 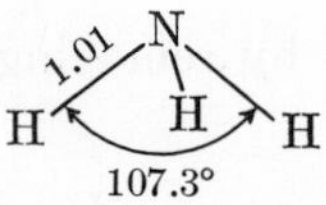 NH_3, Ammonia 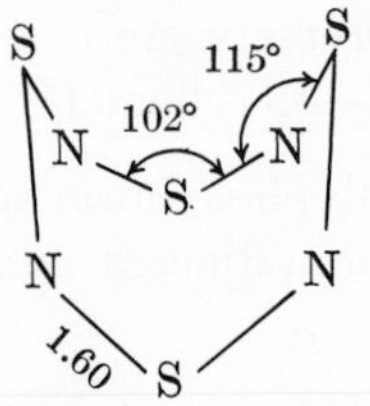 S_4N_4, Tetranitrogentetrasulfide

Figure 17.3 Structure of some small molecules and ions.

with halogen or oxygen family atoms—those capable of forming only one or two bonds. Macromolecules are formed when nitrogen family atoms combine with other trivalent atoms such as aluminum or boron. In this case the three-dimensional network is possible.

Bonding in the free elements nitrogen and phosphorus emphasizes the differences in bonding tendencies between an atom having a shell of only two electrons below the valence shell (N) and one having a shell of eight electrons below the valence shell (P). The nitrogen atom forms π bonds readily; π bonding in phosphorus is less common. As a result molecular nitrogen is diatomic. Its molecule, the most stable diatomic molecule known, has one σ and two π bonds between atoms. By contrast molecular phosphorus consists of tetrahedral molecules where only σ bonds exist between atoms.

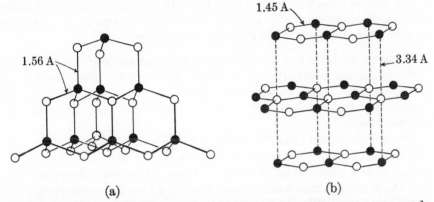

1.45 A

1.56 A

3.34 A

(a)   (b)

Figure 17.4 The structure of BN illustrating its macromolecular nature and similarity to diamond and graphite. (a) The arrangement of boron and nitrogen atoms in the diamond form of BN. (b) The arrangement of boron and nitrogen atoms in the graphite form of BN.

Stereochemistry. The shapes of molecules of some nitrogen compounds are shown in Figure 17.3. In N_2O the shape is presumably due to sp hybridization of the central nitrogen atom; in NO_3^- the nitrogen atom is using sp^2 hybrid orbitals while sp^3 hybridization characterizes the bonding orbitals in ammonium ion. Table 17.3 summarizes the stereochemistry of representative structures of the family.

Table 17.3 Stereochemistry of Some Nitrogen Family Structures

Molecule or Ion	Shape	Hybridization of Central Atom	Kinds of Covalent Bonds
N_2O	Linear	sp	$2\sigma, 1\pi$
NO_3^-	Angular-planar	sp^2	$3\sigma, 1\pi$
NH_4^+, PH_4^+, PCl_4^+	Tetrahedral	sp^3	4σ
NH_3, PH_3, AsH_3, SbH_3	Pyramidal	sp^3	3σ
PO_4^{-3}, AsO_4^{-3}	Tetrahedral	sp^3	$4\sigma, 1\pi$
PF_5, AsF_5	Trigonal-bipyramidal	sp^3d	5σ
$Sb(OH)_6^-$, PCl_6^-	Octahedral	sp^2d^2	6σ

The stereochemistry of phosphorus and arsenic structures is most often tetrahedral as in PO_4^{-3}, PH_4^+, AsO_4^{-3}, PH_3. Trigonal bipyramid structures also occur as in PF_5 and AsF_5. In the tetrahedral structures phosphorus and arsenic atoms use sp^3 hybrid orbitals to form bonds; in trigonal bipyramid structures these atoms use sp^3d hybridization. Antimony atoms often exhibit octahedral stereochemistry with accompanying sp^3d^2 hybridization as in $SbCl_6^-$ or $Sb(OH)_6^-$

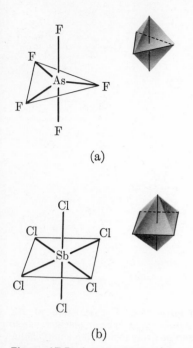

Figure 17.5 Some halides of arsenic and antimony. (a) AsF_5 molecule showing trigonal bipyramid structure. The valence bonds are shown with heavy lines; the trigonal base is outlined with light lines. (b) $SbCl_6{}^-$ ion showing octahedral structure. The valence bonds are shown with heavy lines; the square base is shown with light lines.

It is interesting to contrast the stereochemistry of the V-state oxyanions in the family. These substances, nitrate ion, $NO_3{}^-$, phosphate ion, $PO_4{}^{-3}$, arsenate ion, $AsO_4{}^{-3}$, and hexahydroxoantimonate ion, $Sb(OH)_6{}^-$, contain respectively three, four, and six oxygen atoms around the central atom. The inability of the nitrogen atom to expand its octet, coupled with its tendency to form strong π bonds permits only three oxygen atoms around the nitrogen atom in nitrate ion. The four available orbitals on the nitrogen atom are used in the formation of three σ bonds and one π bond. Phosphorus and arsenic atoms, on the other hand, do not form π bonds readily. Therefore each of the four bonding orbitals on these atoms forms a σ bond with one oxygen atom giving rise to the $XO_4{}^{-3}$ structures. The octahedral symmetry of the V-state antimony ions reflects the ease with which this atom expands its octet. The nearly equivalent $5s$, $5p$, and $5d$ energy levels in this atom readily interact to give six bonding orbitals designated as sp^3d^2 hybrids. Each orbital forms a σ bond with an oxygen atom to produce the $Sb(OH)_6{}^{-1}$ structure.

Strengths of Acids and Bases. Some important acids of this family and their ionization constants are given in Table 17.4. Nitric acid is the strongest acid in the family while pyrophosphoric acid, $H_4P_2O_7$, and hypophosphorous acid, $H(H_2PO_2)$, are moderately strong. The remainder are weak acids.

The trends in acid strength within the family can be explained in terms of the electronegativity of the central atom and the number of oxygen atoms in the molecule as described earlier. Thus orthophosphoric acid, H_3PO_4, is weaker than sulfuric acid, H_2SO_4, which in turn is weaker than perchloric acid, $HClO_4$, because the electronegativity increases in the order $P < S < Cl$. Also, nitric acid is stronger than nitrous acid, HNO_2, because the latter compound has fewer oxygen atoms. As an extrapolation of this principle, one would predict that pyrophosphoric acid,

$$\underset{\substack{|\\OH}}{\overset{\substack{O\\||}}{HO-P-O}}-\underset{\substack{|\\OH}}{\overset{\substack{O\\||}}{P-OH}}$$

will be stronger than orthophosphoric acid,

$$HO-\underset{\substack{|\\OH}}{\overset{\substack{O\\||}}{P}}-OH$$

because the former contains the unit

$$-O-\underset{\substack{|\\OH}}{\overset{\substack{O\\||}}{P}}-OH$$

at the position where the latter contains only an OH. The dihydrogenphosphate unit, being more electronegative than an hydroxyl group, should increase the acid strength of pyrophosphoric acid over that of orthophosphoric acid. This prediction is verified by the measured dissociation constants which show that the pyro acid is about 19 times stronger than the ortho acid.

Although all the binary compounds of nitrogen family elements with hydrogen are weak bases, ammonia is the strongest and most important base in the series. In water solution ammonia accepts a proton from water to form ammonium ion as in

$$:NH_3 + H_2O \rightleftharpoons NH_4{}^+ + OH^-$$

The ionization constant for this reaction is 1.4×10^{-5} at 25°C. While phosphine, PH_3, undergoes the same reaction, it is a much weaker base than ammonia. Hydrazine, H_2NNH_2, is also a weaker base than ammonia. It is a diprotic base—one capable of accepting two protons—and forms two acids $H_2NNH_3{}^+$ and $^+H_3NNH_3{}^+$. Another important base in the family is bismuthyl hydroxide, $BiO(OH)$, which produces OH^- on ionization, showing the metallic nature of the heavier members.

Table 17.4 Some Nitrogen Family Acids and Their Ionization Constants at 25°C

Oxidation State	Nitrogen	Phosphorus	Arsenic	Antimony
V	Nitric acid, HNO_3 $K = \infty$	Orthophosphoric acid, H_3PO_4 $K_I = 7.5 \times 10^{-3}$ $K_{II} = 6.2 \times 10^{-8}$ $K_{III} = 1.2 \times 10^{-12}$ Pyrophosphoric acid, $H_4P_2O_7$ $K_I = 1.4 \times 10^{-1}$	Orthoarsenic acid, H_3AsO_4 $K_I = 2.5 \times 10^{-4}$ $K_{II} = 5.0 \times 10^{-8}$ $K_{III} = 3.0 \times 10^{-13}$	Antimonic acid, $HSb(OH)_6$
III	Nitrous acid, HNO_2 $K = 4.5 \times 10^{-4}$	Orthophosphorous acid, $H_2(HPO_3)$ $K_I = 1.6 \times 10^{-2}$ $K_{II} = 7 \times 10^{-7}$	Arsenious acid, H_3AsO_3 $K_I = 6 \times 10^{-10}$	
I	Hyponitrous acid, $H_2N_2O_2$	Hypophosphorous acid, $H(H_2PO_2)$ $K = 1 \times 10^{-2}$		
$-\frac{1}{3}$	Hydrazoic acid, HN_3 $K = 1.8 \times 10^{-5}$			

Occurrence, Preparation and Uses. Table 17.5 gives a few brief statements about the occurrence, preparation, and uses of the elements.

The occurrence of nitrogen as a constituent of the proteins of living tissues is of interest because humans and animals are not able to synthesize these substances from the free nitrogen of the atmosphere. Animal life is therefore dependent upon a source of compounds of nitrogen, obtained by eating plant foods containing proteins (especially beans and peas), or other animal flesh or secretions. Plants, especially those belonging to the legume family, act as hosts to certain "nitrogen-fixing" bacteria, which enter the root cells from the soil. The bacteria are parasitic and obtain their food from the plant, assimilating a part of it into their own tissues and oxidizing a part of it. They utilize the energy thus made available in building up

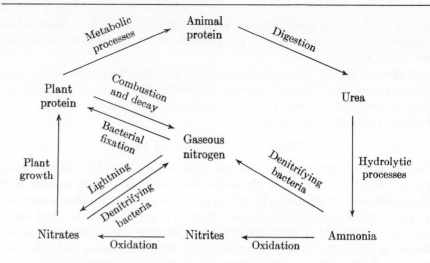

Figure 17.6 The nitrogen cycle : transformations of nitrogen in nature.

nitrates from the free nitrogen absorbed by the soil from the atmosphere. The nitrates formed, as well as other nitrates present in the soil, are converted by the plant into plant protein. Earlier, it was thought that only a few microorganisms were able to fix the nitrogen of the atmosphere in the forms essential to higher plant and animal life, but it is now known that many have this capability, including the algae of the sea.

When an animal eats plant protein, this protein is changed by digestion into nitrogen compounds called amino acids, which are rebuilt into animal protein tissues. These in turn are eventually converted by body processes into such animal waste products as urea and ammonia (Figure 17.6).

Table 17.5 Occurrence, Preparation, and Uses of the Elements of the Nitrogen Family

Element	Occurrence	Preparation	Uses
Nitrogen	Free in air (78%). Nitrates ($NaNO_3$, KNO_3). Proteins in living tissue.	From air by liquefaction.	Source of nitrogen compounds in fertilizers, explosives.
Phosphorus	Phosphates (apatite, $CaCl_2 \cdot 3Ca(PO_4)_2$; phosphorite, $Ca(OH)_2 \cdot 3Ca(PO_4)_2$). Bones, teeth, living tissue.	From phosphates by reduction with coke and sand: $$2Ca_3(PO_4)_2 + 6SiO_2 + 10C \longrightarrow 6CaSiO_3 + 10CO + P_4$$	As alloying element in phosphor bronzes; phosphorus compounds are used in fertilizers, matches.
Arsenic	Sulfides (realgar, As_2S_2, orpiment, As_2S_3). Occasionally free.	From the oxide obtained as by-product in metallurgical processes involving ores of various metals. $$As_4O_6 + 6C \longrightarrow As_4 + 6CO$$	In alloys; arsenic compounds in insecticides and medicinals.
Antimony	Sulfides (stibnite, Sb_2S_3). Occasionally free.	From the oxide by reduction with carbon, or from the sulfide: $$Sb_2S_3 + 3Fe \longrightarrow 3FeS + 2Sb$$	In alloys, particularly with lead in lead storage batteries and in type metal.
Bismuth	Often free, also as oxide and sulfide. Not an abundant element.	When free, separated from the ore by heating until bismuth melts (271°C) and runs off; from oxide by-product by reducing with carbon.	In low-melting alloys, in sprinkler systems and electrical fuses; compounds in pharmaceutical preparations.

The Elements

Physical Properties. Nitrogen is the only element of Group V which is a gas at ordinary conditions. All the others are solids and most exist in several crystalline modifications. These are so numerous that the physical properties of the elements are difficult to compare directly. Table 17.6 lists some physical properties of these elements.

Table 17.6 Some Physical Properties of Nitrogen Family Elements

Element	Density (g/cc at 25°C)	Melting Point (°C)	Boiling Point (°C)	Heat of Fusion (kcal/mole)	Heat of Vaporization (kcal/mole)
Nitrogen	—	−209.9	−195.8	0.086	0.67
Phosphorus (white)	1.82	44.1	280	0.15	2.97
Arsenic (gray)	5.727	817 (36 atm)	613(s)	6.62	34.5
Antimony	6.684	630.5	1325	4.74	16.23
Bismuth	9.80	271	1559	2.6	36.2

Allotropes. Elementary phosphorus exists in at least three allotropic forms known as white phosphorus, violet or red phosphorus, and black phosphorus. The white form consists of P_4 molecules arranged in a cubic lattice and held in the crystal structure by van der Waals forces. This allotrope is very reactive, low-melting (44.1°C), soluble in a number of solvents, and has a relatively low density (1.82) at room temperature. Violet or red phosphorus is less reactive, less soluble, much higher-melting, and has a higher density (2.2). It is believed to consist of chains of P_4 molecules arranged as shown in Figure 17.7. Black phosphorus is similar to graphite in appearance, and, like graphite, it conducts electricity. Its crystals are composed of phosphorus atoms in double layers widely separated from one another. It is stable at room temperature although it is formed by heating white phosphorus to temperatures above 300°C.

Arsenic and antimony exist in a number of allotropic modifications. A metallic or gray form and a yellow form are common to both. The stable forms at room temperature are the metallic forms; they are soft, brittle, and gray or silver-white in appearance. They are composed of puckered sheets of covalently bonded atoms; each atom in the sheet is bonded to three other atoms, and the different sheets are held together by metallic bonding. The yellow forms of arsenic and antimony resemble white phosphorus in general behavior; however, they are even more reactive. The units in the crystal are As_4 or Sb_4 tetrahedra. Yellow arsenic and antimony are more stable at lower temperatures than are the metallic allotropes of the elements. This suggests that the metallic bonding may change to covalent bonding at lower temperatures.

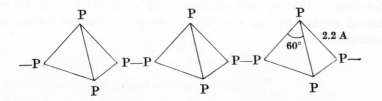

Figure 17.7 Portion of a chain in red phosphorus.

Bismuth occurs only in a metallic form which is soft, reddish-white, and brittle. The crystal is composed of puckered sheets of covalently bonded atoms; the different sheets are held together by metallic bonds. Bismuth differs from normal metals in having a lower electrical conductivity in the solid than in the liquid.

Chemical Properties. *Reactions in Solution.* In the usual aqueous environment these elements tend to remain in the uncombined state. This is understandable from the values of the standard oxidation potentials in Table 17.7, which show that compounds in negative oxidation states

Table 17.7 Standard Oxidation Potentials for Reactions of the Elements of the Nitrogen Family (in acid solution at 25°C)

Reaction	$E°$ volts
$BiH_3 \longrightarrow Bi + 3H^+_{(aq)} + 3e^-$	~ 0.80
$AsH_3 \longrightarrow As + 3H^+_{(aq)} + 3e^-$	0.60
$SbH_3 \longrightarrow Sb + 3H^+_{(aq)} + 3e^-$	0.51
$P + 3H_2O \longrightarrow H_3PO_3 + 3H^+_{(aq)} + 3e^-$	0.50
$PH_3 \longrightarrow P + 3H^+_{(aq)} + 3e^-$	-0.06
$Sb + H_2O \longrightarrow SbO^+ + 2H^+_{(aq)} + 3e^-$	-0.21
$As + 2H_2O \longrightarrow HAsO_2 + 3H^+_{(aq)} + 3e^-$	-0.25
$2NH_4^+ \longrightarrow N_2 + 8H^+_{(aq)} + 6e^-$	-0.28
$Bi + H_2O \longrightarrow BiO^+ + 2H^+_{(aq)} + 3e^-$	-0.32
$N_2 + 4H_2O \longrightarrow 2HNO_2 + 6H^+_{(aq)} + 6e^-$	-1.45

readily oxidize to the free element, and that these in turn have no great tendencies to oxidize to positive oxidation states. The order of the free elements with respect to oxidizing strength ($N_2 > P_4 > As_4 \sim Sb_4 > Bi$) is the same as the order of decreasing metallic character [increasing ionization energy (Table 17.1)] indicating the correlation between oxidizing strength and actual ionization of the atoms. Considering the elements as reducing agents, only phosphorus has a positive value of the oxidation potential, and nitrogen has a high negative value. As observed, therefore, we might expect nitrogen to occur in the free state in nature, but not phosphorus.

All of the elements are oxidized by hot concentrated sulfuric acid; nitrogen and arsenic form oxides, phosphorus gives phosphoric acid, and antimony and bismuth form sulfates.

Reactions under Anhydrous Conditions. Though not highly reactive, nitrogen family elements combine with nonmetals such as halogens, oxygen, and sulfur at elevated temperatures, according to the equations

$$2X + 3Cl_2 \longrightarrow 2XCl_3$$

$$2X + 3S \longrightarrow X_2S_3$$

$$4X + 3O_2 \longrightarrow X_4O_6 \ (2X_2O_3)$$

Nitrides of lithium and alkaline earth elements (Group II) can be obtained readily by the reaction of nitrogen with the metals at high temperatures.

$$6Li + N_2 \longrightarrow 2Li_3N$$

$$3Ca + N_2 \longrightarrow Ca_3N_2$$

Similar reactions occur at very high temperatures with boron and aluminum.

Sodium will react with white phosphorus at elevated temperatures to give a mixture of sodium phosphides such as NaP_3 and Na_2P_5. No effective reactions of the other elements in this family with metals have been reported.

Compounds in the − III Oxidation State

The Binary Hydrides; Ammonia. The simple hydrides of formula XH_3, ammonia (NH_3), phosphine (PH_3), arsine (AsH_3), stibine (SbH_3), and bismuthine (BiH_3) are all colorless gases composed of pyramidal-shaped molecules as illustrated in Figure 17.8.

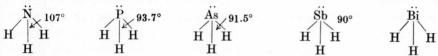

Figure 17.8 Structure of hydrides of the nitrogen family.

In this group, only ammonia is an important and widely used compound. The others are highly toxic, thermally unstable, spontaneously flammable in air, and used only rarely as reducing agents. There is no close similarity between ammonia and the other hydrides because:

1. Ammonia has a much more polar molecule than the others and forms strong hydrogen bonds between molecules.
2. Nitrogen is more electronegative than hydrogen, but the other elements in the family are less electronegative than hydrogen. This means that nitrogen is at the negative end of the ammonia dipole while hydrogen is the negative portion in the other hydrides.

These factors are reflected in the physical properties of the compounds which are given in Table 17.8. Thus ammonia has a higher melting point, and higher heats of fusion and vaporization than the others—facts which are consistent with the greater polarity of the ammonia molecule and with the existence of hydrogen bonds between molecules.

Preparation of XH_3 Compounds. Because of their low reactivity, direct reaction of hydrogen with nitrogen family elements gives very low yields of the XH_3 compounds. In spite of this, much commercially available

Table 17.8 Some Physical Properties of Nitrogen Family Hydrides

Compound	Melting Point (°C)	Boiling Point (°C)	Heat of Vaporization (kcal/mole)	Heat of Fusion (kcal/mole)	Dipole Moment of Gas (debyes)
NH_3	− 77.74	− 33.40	5.58	1.35	1.47
PH_3	− 133.75	− 87.22	3.49	0.27	0.55
AsH_3	− 116.3	− 62.5	4.18	0.56	0.16
SbH_3	− 88	− 17			0.11
BiH_3		22			
NH_2NH_2	1.8	113.5			1.35
PH_2PH_2	− 99	51.7			

ammonia is prepared by the direct combination of nitrogen and hydrogen. The process, called the Haber process, uses a catalyst at temperatures between 400°C and 600°C and under high pressures (up to 1,000 atm). The equation for the reaction is

$$2N_2 + 3H_2 \rightleftharpoons 2NH_3$$

Phosphine may be prepared by the reaction of water with calcium phosphide—i.e., by hydrolysis.

$$Ca_3P_2 + 6H_2O \longrightarrow 2PH_3 + 3Ca(OH)_2$$

Chemical Properties of Ammonia. Ammonia is a weak base and a moderately strong reducing agent. The products from the reactions in which it acts as a base are, in most cases, salts of the ammonium ion, NH_4^+, such as ammonium chloride, NH_4Cl, ammonium sulfate, $(NH_4)_2SO_4$, etc. These salts are similar in behavior to the corresponding sodium or potassium salts having the same anion, principally because the ammonium ion has approximately the same radius as the potassium ion (1.45 compared with 1.33 A). In acting as a reducing agent, ammonia is usually oxidized to stable molecular nitrogen as in

$$2NH_3 + 3Cl_2 \longrightarrow N_2 + 6HCl$$

Ammonia undergoes two other kinds of reactions:

1. It reacts with active metals to give hydrogen and the amide salt of the metal, MNH_2, as illustrated by the equation

$$2Na + 2NH_3 \longrightarrow 2NaNH_2 + H_2$$

The metal amides are ionic compounds containing the very strong base amide ion, NH_2^-.

2. It reacts with metal ions, especially transition metal ions to give species of the type $M(NH_3)_x^{+n}$ which are called ammine complex ions. This is illustrated by the equation

$$Co^{+3} + 6NH_3 \longrightarrow Co(NH_3)_6^{+3}$$

The ammonia molecule may be bonded to the metal by ion-dipole bonds or by covalent bonds involving the unshared pair of electrons on the ammonia molecule. Such reactions are discussed in detail in Chap. 26.

Ammonia as a Solvent. Liquid ammonia (b.p. −33.4°C), because of the polar nature of its molecules, is a good solvent for a variety of ionic and polar substances. That it is a more basic solvent than water is illustrated by the fact that acetic acid, which is only slightly ionized in water, is almost completely present in the salt form, $CH_3CO_2^- + NH_4^+$, in liquid ammonia. Like water, liquid ammonia undergoes self-ionization according to the equation

$$NH_3 + NH_3 \rightleftharpoons NH_4^+ + NH_2^-$$

Acids placed in liquid ammonia react to give ammonium ions:

$$CH_3CO_2H + NH_3 \rightleftharpoons NH_4^+ + CH_3CO_2^-$$

Bases (B) placed in liquid ammonia may form amide ions:

$$B + NH_3 \rightleftharpoons BH^+ + NH_2{}^-$$

As shown by the self-ionization equation above, $NH_4{}^+$ and $NH_2{}^-$ play the same role in liquid ammonia as H_3O^+ and OH^- do in water. Hence compounds containing ammonium ions behave as acids in liquid ammonia while those containing amide ion behave as bases in this solvent. Many reactions which cannot be carried out in less basic solvents can be effected in liquid ammonia.

Compounds in Positive Oxidation States

Oxides. The important oxides of the family are listed in Table 17.2. All of the oxides of nitrogen, except dinitrogen pentoxide, N_2O_5, are gases while those of the other elements are solids. Some physical properties and the molecular structures of some representative oxides are given in Table 17.9.

The oxides of nitrogen and phosphorus are acid anhydrides, i.e., they give acids on reaction with water as in

$$N_2O_5 + 3H_2O \longrightarrow 2H_3O^+ + 2NO_3{}^-$$

$$P_4O_{10} + 6H_2O \longrightarrow 4H_3PO_4$$

Table 17.9 Properties and Structure of Some Oxides of Nitrogen Family Elements

Compound	Formula	Melting Point (°C)	Boiling Point (°C)	Appearance	Molecular Structure
Nitrous oxide	N_2O	−90.8	−88.5	Colorless gas	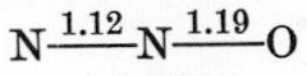 N—1.12—N—1.19—O
Nitric oxide	NO	−163.6	−151.7	Colorless gas	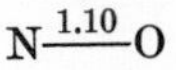 N—1.10—O
Dinitrogen trioxide	N_2O_3	−103	3.5	Brown gas, Blue liquid	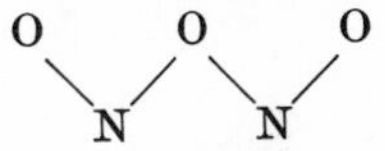
Nitrogen dioxide	NO_2	−11.2	21.2	Brown gas	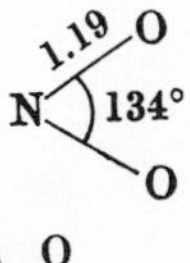
Dinitrogen pentoxide	N_2O_5	32.4 (sublimes)		White solid	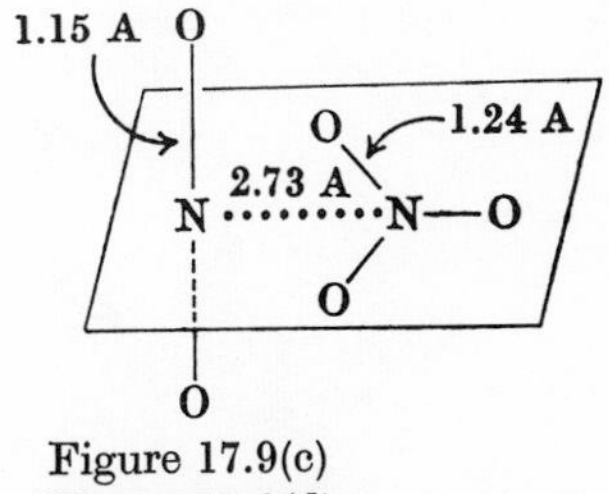
Phosphorus(V) oxide	P_4O_{10}	422		White solid	Figure 17.9(c)
Phosphorus(III) oxide	P_4O_6	23.8	173	White solid	Figure 17.9(d)
Arsenic(V) oxide	As_4O_{10}	(d 400)		White solid	Similar to P_4O_{10}
Arsenic(III) oxide	As_4O_6	315		White solid	Similar to P_4O_6
Antimony(III) oxide	Sb_4O_6	655			Similar to P_4O_6
Bismuth(III) oxide	Bi_2O_3	817		Yellow solid	Ionic with eight oxygen atoms surrounding each bismuth atom

Antimony oxides and, to a lesser extent, arsenic oxides, are amphoteric, acting as an acid in the presence of base and as a base in the presence of an acid, as in

$$Sb_2O_3 + 6OH^- + 3H_2O \longrightarrow 2Sb(OH)_6{}^{-1}$$

$$Sb_2O_3 + 2H_3O^+ \qquad \longrightarrow 2SbO^+ + 3H_2O$$

Bismuth oxides are basic:

$$Bi_2O_3 + H_2O \longrightarrow 2BiO(OH) \xrightarrow{3H_2O} (H_2O)_2Bi(OH)_2{}^+ + OH^-$$

The ion

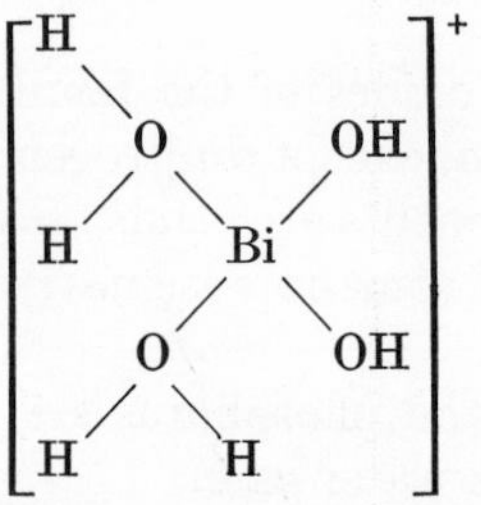

$$\left[\begin{array}{c} \text{H} \\ \text{O} \quad \text{OH} \\ \text{H} \quad \text{Bi} \\ \text{O} \quad \text{OH} \\ \text{H} \quad \text{H} \end{array} \right]^+$$

is the hydrated form of BiO^+. Undoubtedly BiO^+ ions exist as the hydrated form in water solution.

Nitric Oxide and Nitrogen Dioxide. These compounds are of interest for many reasons but primarily because they are paramagnetic, each containing one unpaired or odd electron in its molecule. They are the products of many reactions in which nitric acid acts as an oxidizing agent.

The presence of an unpaired electron in nitric oxide is readily understood from the molecular energy level diagram calculated by molecular orbital theory (Chap. 6). The order of increasing energy for homonuclear diatomic molecules was given on page 121 as $\sigma_{2s} < \sigma^*_{2s} < \sigma_{2p} < \pi_{2p} < \pi^*_{2p} < \sigma^*_{2p}$. The order for the heteronuclear molecule NO is the same. Hence the eleven $2s$ and $2p$ electrons of the nitrogen and oxygen atoms will fit into these levels, filling lowest levels first, to give the configuration $(\sigma_{2s})^2 (\sigma^*_{2s})^2 (\sigma_{2p})^2 (\pi_{2p})^4 (\pi^*_{2p})$. The single electron in the antibonding π^*_{2p} orbital, with its unpaired spin, confers paramagnetism on the molecule. Similar calculations suggest that NO_2 should have an unpaired electron, as observed.

While both compounds are well-characterized, stable substances, the odd electron makes them reactive. Colorless nitric oxide readily reacts with oxygen to give brown nitrogen dioxide

$$2NO + O_2 \rightleftarrows 2NO_2$$

Very often when nitric oxide is formed in a reaction, it is oxidized so rapidly to nitrogen dioxide that students conclude that the latter compound is the reaction product. Nitrogen dioxide exists in equilibrium with N_2O_4.

$$2NO_2 \rightleftarrows \quad \begin{array}{c} \text{O} \qquad \text{O} \\ \diagdown \qquad \diagdown \\ \text{N---N} \\ \diagup \qquad \diagup \\ \text{O} \qquad \text{O} \end{array}$$

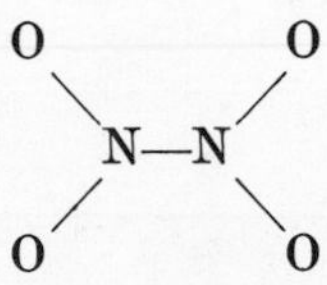

This compound is colorless and has no unpaired electrons. Lowering the temperature causes the color of the equilibrium mixture to fade indicating that more N_2O_4 is being formed. The NO_2/N_2O_4 mixture is a strong oxidizing agent—about as strong as bromine.

The Oxides of Phosphorus, Arsenic, and Antimony. The simple oxides P_4O_{10}, P_4O_6, As_4O_{10}, As_4O_6, and Sb_4O_6 are all related structurally to the tetrahedral X_4 molecules such as P_4 and As_4. If it is imagined that each P—P bond in the P_4 tetrahedron is converted to a P—O—P bridge, a molecule of P_4O_6 results. While the low-temperature Sb_4O_6 structure is similar to that of P_4O_6, at temperatures above 570°C this is converted to the macromolecular structure shown on page 333.

Some Nitrogen Family Acids

The strengths of the common acids of the family and the structure and bonding in some of them were discussed earlier. In this section we shall examine several specific acids in detail.

Nitric Acid. Widely utilized in the industrial world in the manufacture of explosives, fertilizers, dyes, and many other products, nitric acid is probably the most widely used acid of the family. It is made commercially from ammonia by the series of reactions

$$4NH_3 + 5O_2 \xrightarrow{\text{Pt}} 4NO + 6H_2O$$

$$2NO + O_2 \longrightarrow N_2O_4$$

$$3N_2O_4 + 2H_2O \longrightarrow 4HNO_3 + 2NO$$

In the laboratory it can be prepared by the action of sulfuric acid on sodium nitrate—a method first reported by Geber in the ninth century. The reaction may be represented

$$Na^+\,NO_3^- + H_2SO_4 \rightleftarrows HNO_3 + Na^+\,HSO_4^-$$

The reaction is a reversible one, but if a gentle heat is applied the volatile nitric acid is removed from the reaction mixture while the higher boiling sulfuric acid remains in the mixture.

Pure nitric acid or hydrogen nitrate is a faintly yellow liquid (containing small amounts of nitrate ion, NO_3^-, and nitronium ion, NO_2^+) which boils at 83°C, freezes at −41°C, and has a density at 0°C of 1.54 g/cc. An aqueous solution containing 68 per cent hydrogen nitrate has a constant boiling point of 121.9°C and distills with unchanging concentration. This solution is the *concentrated nitric acid* of commerce.

The molecule is planar as is nitrate ion. Presumably the nitrogen atom uses sp^2 hybrid orbitals to form the three σ bonds to the oxygen atoms. The bond angles and bond distances are 120° and 1.218 A, respectively.

All the metals, with the exception of gold, platinum, and a few of the rare metals, are acted upon more or less readily by nitric acid. In discussing the action of nitric acid upon these metals it is convenient to divide them into two classes: those above hydrogen in the electrochemical series, and those below.

At first thought it might be expected that hydrogen would be evolved

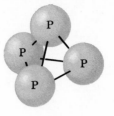

(a)

(b)

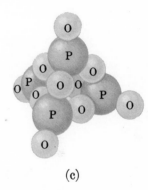

(c)

Figure 17.9 Structures of molecules of phosphorus and its oxides: (a) P_4. (b) P_4O_6. (c) P_4O_{10}.

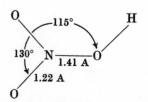

Figure 17.10 Configuration of a molecule of hydrogen nitrate, HNO_3.

when a dilute solution of nitric acid is acted upon by any of the metals occurring above hydrogen in the electrochemical series. It is evolved to a certain extent with a few of the metals, such as magnesium and zinc, especially at high dilution.

When one recalls, however, that nitric acid is a strong oxidizing agent, while hydrogen has strong reducing properties, it would be expected that hydrogen, if formed, would immediately be oxidized by less dilute nitric acid, yielding reduction products. Whether or not hydrogen is formed first is not clear, but the formation of reduction products of nitric acid is clearly shown by experiment. The particular products formed in any case depend upon the metal, the concentration of the acid, the temperature, and other conditions under which the reaction takes place. The following compounds represent successive steps in the reduction of nitric acid, with the corresponding changes in the oxidation state of nitrogen:

$$
\overset{V}{HNO_3} \longrightarrow \overset{IV}{NO_2} \longrightarrow \overset{III}{HNO_2} \longrightarrow \overset{II}{NO} \longrightarrow
$$

$$
\overset{I}{N_2O} \longrightarrow \overset{0}{N_2} \longrightarrow \overset{-I}{NH_2OH} \longrightarrow \overset{-III}{NH_3}
$$

With $2M$ to $3M$ nitric acid at $25°C$, powdered zinc gives ammonia:

$$4Zn + 10H_3O^+ + NO_3^- \longrightarrow 4Zn^{+2} + NH_4^+ + 13H_2O$$

However, with nitric acid stronger than $4M$, nitric oxide, NO, is the principal compound formed. The equation for the reaction is

$$3Zn + 8HNO_3 \longrightarrow 3Zn(NO_3)_2 + 2NO\uparrow + 4H_2O$$

$$(3Zn + 8H_3O^+ + 2NO_3^- \longrightarrow 3Zn^{+2} + 2NO + 12H_2O)$$

Those metals that occur below hydrogen in the electrochemical series, when acted upon by dilute nitric acid, usually yield nitric oxide. The general equation representing the reaction with copper, for example, is the following:

$$3Cu + 8HNO_3 \longrightarrow 3Cu(NO_3)_2 + 2NO\uparrow + 4H_2O$$

The equation may be written as two electronic partial equations:

Oxidation $\quad 3 \times (Cu \longrightarrow Cu^{+2} + 2e^-)$

Reduction $\quad 2 \times (4H_3O^+ + NO_3^- + 3e^- \longrightarrow NO\uparrow + 6H_2O)$

Since two electrons are lost in the first equation and three gained in the second, it is necessary to multiply the first by 3 and the second by 2 before adding to obtain the ionic equation

$$3Cu + 8H_3O^+ + 2NO_3^- \longrightarrow 3Cu^{+2} + 2NO\uparrow + 12H_2O$$

If concentrated acid is used instead of dilute, nitrogen dioxide is liberated rather than nitric oxide, as shown in the following equation:

$$Cu + 4HNO_3 \longrightarrow Cu(NO_3)_2 + 2NO_2\uparrow + 2H_2O$$

$$(Cu + 4H_3O^+ + 2NO_3^- \longrightarrow Cu^{+2} + 2NO_2 + 6H_2O)$$

Nitrates. The salts of nitric acid are called nitrates. They can be obtained by the general method used for preparing salts, such as the action of nitric acid upon the metals themselves or upon their oxides or hydroxides. Some of these salts, especially sodium nitrate and potassium nitrate, are found in nature. The nitrates of most of the metals are white, crystalline solids; the exceptions are copper (blue), nickel (green), and cobalt (cherry-red). All the normal nitrates are soluble in water and furnish the metallic ions and nitrate ions.

When heated, the nitrates undergo decomposition. As a rule the metal is left in the form of its oxide, while oxygen and oxides of nitrogen are evolved.

$$2Cu(NO_3)_2 \longrightarrow 2CuO + 4NO_2 \uparrow + O_2 \uparrow$$

In the case of a few nitrates, however, oxygen alone is evolved. Thus, sodium nitrate, when heated, forms sodium nitrite ($NaNO_2$) and oxygen:

$$2NaNO_3 \longrightarrow 2NaNO_2 + O_2 \uparrow$$

Nitrous Acid. This acid, known only in solution, can be made by dissolving a mixture of nitric oxide and nitrogen dioxide in ice water. The reaction is

$$NO + NO_2 + H_2O \longrightarrow 2HNO_2$$

The acid itself is unstable but its salts, such as sodium nitrite, $NaNO_2$, are stable. It is easily reduced to nitric oxide or lower oxidation states, and it is oxidized to nitric acid. Typical reactions are:

$$2HNO_2 + 2I^- + 2H_3O^+ \longrightarrow 2NO + I_2 + 4H_2O$$

$$HNO_2 + Cl_2 + 4H_2O \longrightarrow NO_3^- + 2Cl^- + 3H_3O^+$$

Orthophosphoric Acid. This acid is the form into which all other acids of phosphorus tend to pass when in solution, either by hydration or by oxidation.

$$
\begin{array}{c}
H \\
\overset{..}{\underset{..}{O}} \\
H\!:\!\overset{..}{\underset{..}{O}}\!:\!\overset{..}{\underset{..}{P}}\!:\!\overset{..}{\underset{..}{O}}\!:\!H \\
\overset{..}{\underset{..}{O}} \\
H
\end{array}
$$

The acid is prepared by burning in air the vapor of phosphorus liberated in the preparation of the element and combining the resulting oxide with water or by treating calcium phosphate with concentrated sulfuric acid and filtering off the nearly insoluble calcium sulfate:

$$Ca_3(PO_4)_2 + 3H_2SO_4 \longrightarrow 2H_3PO_4 + 3CaSO_4 \downarrow$$

In solution, hydrogen phosphate acts as a tribasic acid. It is therefore capable of forming three series of salts, according to whether one, two, or three hydrogen atoms are replaced by metals. The formulas and the method of naming such salts are illustrated in Table 17.10. The heavy metals,

Table 17.10 Sodium Salts of Orthophosphoric Acid

Formula	Name
Na_3PO_4	Trisodium phosphate; normal, or tertiary, sodium phosphate
Na_2HPO_4	Disodium phosphate; secondary sodium phosphate
NaH_2PO_4	Monosodium phosphate; primary sodium phosphate

such as silver or mercury, form only the normal, or tertiary phosphates. Salts are also known in which there is more than one kind of cation. The most familiar ones are microcosmic salt ($NaNH_4HPO_4 \cdot 4H_2O$) and magnesium ammonium phosphate ($MgNH_4PO_4$).

The normal phosphates of the alkali metals sodium and potassium are very strongly hydrolyzed in solution:

$$3Na^+, PO_4^{-3} + H_2O \rightleftharpoons 2Na^+, HPO_4^{-2} + Na^+, OH^-$$

Because of the alkaline character of solutions of trisodium phosphate, this salt has a wide use for cleansing purposes and for softening hard water. The normal calcium phosphate ($Ca_3(PO_4)_2$) is only very slightly soluble. When treated with sulfuric acid it is changed into the more soluble primary salt, thus:

$$Ca_3(PO_4)_2 + 2H_2SO_4 \longrightarrow Ca(H_2PO_4)_2 + 2CaSO_4$$

Advantage is taken of this reaction in the manufacture of fertilizers, so as to obtain the phosphorus in a more soluble or available form. Nearly one-third of the total production of sulfuric acid is used for this purpose. The mixture of soluble acid phosphate and calcium sulfate formed when rock phosphate is treated in this way is called superphosphate.

Phosphorous Acid. The common oxyacid of phosphorus in the III state is (ortho) phosphorous acid, H_2HPO_3. The molecule of this acid has the structure indicated in Figure 17.11.

Note that this is a *dibasic* acid because the third hydrogen atom is bonded to the phosphorus atom—a manifestation of the tendency of phosphorus atoms to form tetrahedral structures.

Phosphorous acid is prepared by the reaction of phosphorus(III) oxide, P_4O_6, and water,

$$P_4O_6 + 6H_2O \longrightarrow 4H_2(HPO_3)$$

or by the hydrolysis of phosphorus trichloride,

$$PCl_3 + 6H_2O \longrightarrow H_2(HPO_3) + 3H_3O^+ + 3Cl^-$$

A moderately strong acid and a strong reducing agent, this acid forms two families of salts, the *phosphites* containing HPO_3^{-2} ions and the *hydrogen phosphites* containing $H(HPO_3)^{-1}$ ions.

Halides. All members of this family form halides with the four halogens. All except nitrogen form fluorides of the types XF_3 and XF_5. Nitrogen forms only NF_3. The XF_3 compounds are pyramidal; the XF_5 structures are trigonal bipyramidal. Both PCl_5 and PBr_5, which are trigonal bipyramid structures as gases, form ionic solids with PCl_4^+ and PCl_6^- or the corresponding bromophosphorus ions occupying the sites in the crystal lattice.

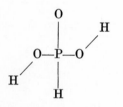

Figure 17.11 The phosphorous acid structure.

SUMMARY

Nitrogen family chemistry is very diverse. Because the atoms are somewhat larger than their corresponding members among the halogen and oxygen families and because they have only moderate electronegativities, their properties vary from typically nonmetallic (nitrogen and phosphorus) through amphoteric (antimony) to distinctly metallic (bismuth). The s^2p^3 valence electron configuration gives rise to multiple oxidation states between $-$III and V. All elements show a distinct tendency to form covalent bonds. The stereochemistry varies from pyramidal for the MH_3 compounds to trigonal planar for nitrate ion, tetrahedral for phosphate ion and arsenate ion, trigonal bipyramid for XF_5 structures, and octahedral for hexahydroxoantimonate(V) ion, $Sb(OH)_6^-$.

Compounds in the $-$III state may act either as bases or as reducing agents. Compounds in the V state, except for those of phosphorus, are good to strong oxidizing agents. In their positive oxidation states nitrogen, phosphorus, and arsenic form oxyacids. However, the corresponding antimony compounds are amphoteric, and the bismuth compounds are bases.

As in the oxygen family, both catenation and polymerization are observed in the nitrogen family. The polyphosphoric acids and the oxides of arsenic and antimony are examples of polymers.

All elements exist in several crystalline modifications in the zero oxidation state. In white phosphorus, yellow arsenic, and yellow antimony the lattice sites of the crystal are occupied by molecules consisting of four atoms covalently bonded and tetrahedrally arranged. In violet and black phosphorus these phosphorus tetrahedra are linked by covalent bonds making chains or sheets of tetrahedra. This polymerization accounts for the low reactivity of violet and black phosphorus.

Ammonia has many uses including that as a solvent more basic than water. Nitric acid, the nitrates, the phosphates, and polyphosphates have importance in chemistry and in commerce.

SOME SPECIAL TERMS

Nitrogen fixation
  protein
  legume
  Haber process

Amphoteric substance
Acid anhydride
Normal salt
Paramagnetic substance

Polymeric compound
  macromolecule

QUESTIONS AND PROBLEMS

1. Explain why ions of the type X^{-3} are not commonly found in nature. List the formulas of some compounds of nitrogen in oxidation state $-$III, and discuss the bonding in these compounds.
2. What experimental differences in properties would you expect to find between the gray and yellow forms of arsenic and antimony? How would you interpret these differences in terms of the structures of the two forms?
3. In terms of the electronic structure, why would you expect ammonia, phosphine and hydrazine to be basic in character? Are there reactions other than their reactions with water or protons which show their basic character? If so, write equations for the reactions.
4. Write formulas for some compounds of the nitrogen family elements in the V and III oxidation states other than those given in Table 17.2.
5. Write equations to show the acid and/or basic and/or amphoteric properties of the hydroxyl-containing compounds of the nitrogen family elements in the III oxidation state.

6. How do you explain the trend in the nitrogen family from a typical anion-forming element (nitrogen) to a typical cation-forming element (bismuth) with increasing atomic weight?

7. Contrast the bonding in N_2 and P_4.

8. Draw sketches showing the spatial arrangement of atoms in the compounds or ions PO_4^{-3}, NH_4^+, NO_3^-, PF_5, and $Sb(OH)_6^-$, and discuss the reasons why these are different.

9. The first ionization constants of the following acids decrease in the order given: $HClO_4 > HNO_3 > H_2SO_4 > H_4P_2O_7 > H_3PO_4 > H_2(HPO_3) > HNO_2$. What explanations can you offer for this sequence?

10. Note in Table 17.6 that the heat of vaporization of gray arsenic is nearly ten times greater than that of white phosphorus. Compare this with the corresponding change in Table 16.8 between sulfur and selenium. What explanations can you offer?

11. Interpret, on the basis of their properties, the fact that nitrogen occurs in the free state in nature, but phosphorus does not.

12. Write equations to show the following reactions: (a) bismuth with chlorine at high temperature, (b) hot nitrogen with metallic lithium, (c) hot concentrated sulfuric acid with (i) phosphorus, (ii) bismuth, (d) calcium nitride with water, (e) ammonia with sodium, (f) ammonia with oxygen on a platinum catalyst, (g) phosphoric acid with ammonia, (h) water with the acid anhydride of phosphoric acid, (i) bismuth(III) oxide with water.

13. Write equations to show: (a) the dimerization of nitrogen dioxide, (b) the reactions of nitric acid with (i) zinc, (ii) copper, (iii) bismuth, (iv) antimony, (c) the difference in reactions of copper nitrate and sodium nitrate on heating, (d) that nitrous acid may be oxidized, and that it may be reduced, (e) the formation of calcium dihydrogen phosphate from phosphate rock (calcium phosphate) and sulfuric acid, (f) the reactions of sodium hydroxide with phosphorous acid.

14. What experimental data, other than bond angles, are recorded in this chapter which show that the hydrides of the nitrogen family elements are almost surely not planar molecules?

15. How do we know that ammonia forms hydrogen bonds in the liquid state?

16. What arguments can you propose to prove that the bonding in ammonia is covalent?

17. Write an equation or equations to show how the ion NO_2^+ could be formed in pure hydrogen nitrate. Write the electron-dot structure for this compound. Would you expect it to (a) have a dipole moment? (b) be paramagnetic?

18. Compare the electron-dot structures of nitric acid and nitrate ion. How do you explain the facts that the nitric acid molecule has two N—O bond distances and two

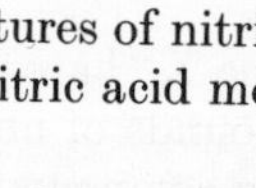

bond angles, but the nitrate ion has only one of each?

REFERENCES

JOLLY, W. L. *The Inorganic Chemistry of Nitrogen.* New York: Benjamin, 1964.

JOLLY, W. L. *The Chemistry of Nonmetals.* Englewood Cliffs, N.J.: Prentice Hall (1966), p. 539.

18

The Carbon Family

. . . With a point of diamond it is engraved on the tablet of their heart. Jeremiah 17: 1 (ca. 600 B.C.)

The atoms of the five carbon family elements all have the valence electron configuration s^2p^2. The first two members, carbon and silicon, are non-metals, and the remaining elements, germanium, tin, and lead, are metals, but all five elements form predominantly covalent compounds; and all except lead seem to prefer tetrahedral stereochemistry. The electronegativities of the atoms below carbon in the family vary from 2.0 to 1.6—values too high to form cations and too low to form anions readily.

The elements carbon and silicon play a large role in nature. The "organic" world, the world of living and growing things, is largely formed of compounds which have carbon as their central element. The "inorganic" world, the world of the rocks and the inanimate substances of the earth's crust, is in large part composed of compounds of silicon with oxygen, and of these two with other elements. The importance of the compounds of carbon and silicon lies in the fact that these compounds often have very large molecules which are chainlike or exist in a network pattern. It is these structural features of carbon and silicon compounds which account for the particular qualities of some rocks, the toughness of wood, the strength of silk, and the elasticity of rubber.

In studying the chemistry of these compounds, therefore, we are attempting to gain an insight into the structural features of the world about us.

A Broad Overview of the Carbon Family

Some important features relating to the chemistry of the carbon family are:

1. The atoms of these elements are larger and their electronegativities are lower than those of the corresponding members of the nitrogen, oxygen, or halogen families. As a result they are less nonmetallic than the corresponding elements in these families; and the trend within the carbon family

from nonmetals to metals is more pronounced than in the other families of nonmetals. Table 18.1 gives some important properties of carbon family atoms.

Table 18.1 Some Properties of Carbon Family Atoms

Element	Valence Electron Configuration	Atomic Radius (A)	First Ionization Energy (kcal/mole)	Electronegativity	X—X Single Bond Energy (kcal/mole)
Carbon	$2s^2\, 2p^2$	0.771	260	2.5	82
Silicon	$3s^2\, 3p^2$	1.173	188	1.8	53
Germanium	$4s^2\, 4p^2$	1.223	182	2.0	65
Tin	$5s^2\, 5p^2$	1.412	169	1.8	42
Lead	$6s^2\, 6p^2$	1.538	171	1.6	< 23

2. A most important characteristic of the family as a whole is the tendency of all atoms to form four covalent bonds utilizing sp^3 hybrid orbitals thereby producing tetrahedral structures as in

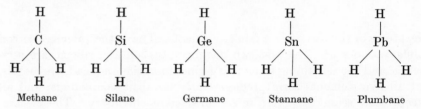

Methane   Silane   Germane   Stannane   Plumbane

In order to form the four covalent bonds, the atom must promote an s electron and hybridize the s and p orbitals. Lead has the least tendency to do this.

3. The ability of carbon atoms to combine with each other to form chain or ring structures has already been mentioned (Chap. 10). Chains are also formed with other members of the family, except lead, but the compounds are much more reactive than are those of carbon. Some compounds in this family illustrating catenation (see Chap. 16) are:

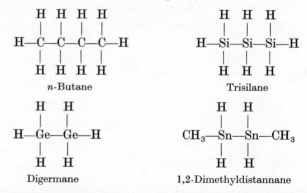

n-Butane   Trisilane

Digermane   1,2-Dimethyldistannane

The carbon family atoms maintain tetrahedral stereochemistry in these compounds. Of the family, only carbon forms compounds in which the atoms are held together by double or triple bonds as in ethylene and acetylene (Chap. 10). Both diamond and graphite are examples of catenation, for these are networks of a great number of covalently bonded carbon atoms. (See Figure 18.3.)

4. Polymeric or macromolecular structures such as those found in polysilicic acid, asbestos, silicones, tin(II) sulfide (SnS) and a host of similar compounds are common in this family. The stability of these polymers testifies to the strong covalent bonds formed between oxygen or sulfur and the carbon family elements. The structural formulas for the substances named above are given below.

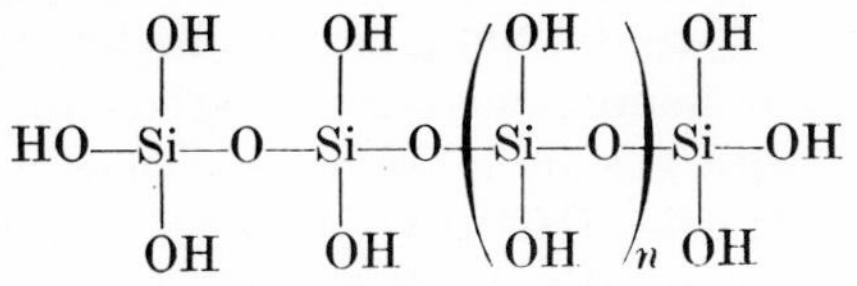

$$\text{HO—Si—O—Si—O} \left(\text{Si—O} \right)_n \text{Si—OH}$$

Polysilicic acid (page 354)

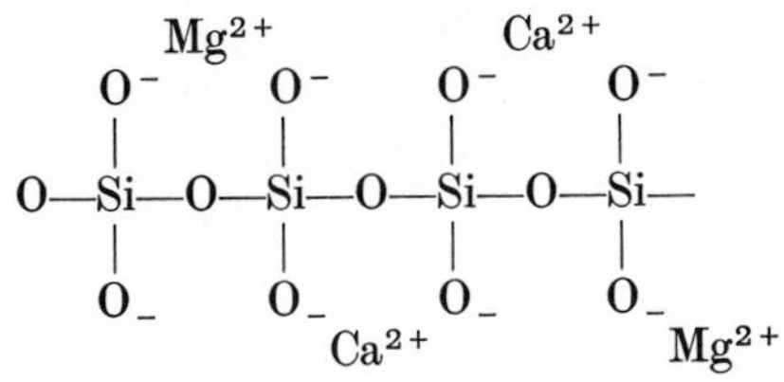

Portion of an asbestos structure (see also Figure 18.10)

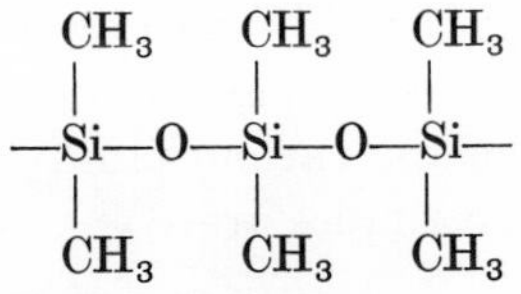

Portion of a silicone molecule

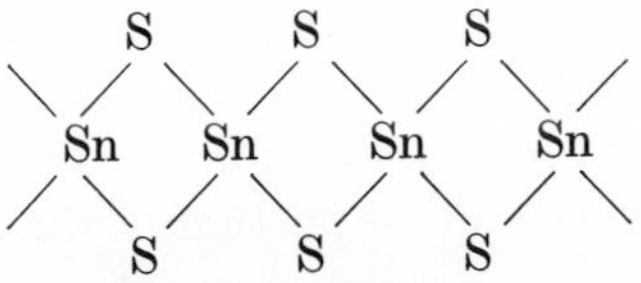

Portion of tin(II) sulfide structure

5. Because of the many structural variations arising as a result of catenation and polymerization, the concept of oxidation state is not as important in this family as it is in many others. A strict application of the rules for determining oxidation state shows that the carbon family elements appear in the $-IV$, 0, II, and IV states. With the heavier elements only the 0 and positive states are stable. Table 18.2 gives the oxidation state pattern for the family.

Oxidation State	Carbon	Silicon	Germanium	Tin	Lead
IV	CO_2	SiO_2	GeO_2	SnO_2	PbO_2
II	CO	(SiO)	GeO	SnO	PbO
0	C	Si	Ge	Sn	Pb
$-IV$	CH_4	SiH_4	GeH_4	SnH_4	PbH_4

Table 18.2 Oxidation State Pattern for Carbon Family Elements

6. The family contains some strong reducing agents and at least one strong oxidizing agent. The reducing agents include the $-IV$ oxidation state compounds whose reactivity in the gas phase decreases in the order $PbH_4 > SnH_4 > SiH_4 > GeH_4 > CH_4$. In acid solution methane is a stronger reducing agent than ammonia. The elements act as reducing agents in the 0 oxidation state, and, except for lead, in the II states. Since

the IV states of all but lead are quite stable, all lower states tend to act as reducing agents, being oxidized in most cases to the stable IV state.

The IV state of lead is very reactive compared with the II state. Consequently PbO_2, for example, is a potent oxidizing agent, being readily reduced to the II state. The stability of the II state has been ascribed to the tightness with which the high charge on the lead nucleus holds the s electrons, making them less available for use in bonding.

7. The hydroxides of these elements are acidic for carbon and silicon, and amphoteric for the remaining members. Carbon apparently forms the very unstable $C(OH)_4$ which easily loses one molecule of water to give the weak, unstable carbonic acid, $(HO)_2CO$, or H_2CO_3. Silicon forms silicic acid, H_4SiO_4, and a variety of polysilicic acids formed by removing the components of water from adjacent molecules, as in trisilicic acid, $H_8Si_3O_{10}$.

$$\begin{array}{c} OH \\ | \\ H{-}O{-}Si{-}OH \\ | \\ OH \end{array} + \begin{array}{c} OH \\ | \\ H{-}O{-}Si{-}OH \\ | \\ OH \end{array} + \begin{array}{c} OH \\ | \\ H{-}O{-}Si{-}OH \\ | \\ OH \end{array} \longrightarrow \begin{array}{c} OH \quad OH \quad OH \\ | \qquad | \qquad | \\ HO{-}Si{-}O{-}Si{-}O{-}Si{-}OH \\ | \qquad | \qquad | \\ OH \quad OH \quad OH \end{array} + 2\,H_2O$$

Trisilicic acid, $H_8Si_3O_{10}$

The hydroxides of tin and lead in both the II and IV state are amphoteric, forming salts of both acids and bases. For example, in the presence of bases these hydroxides form salts in which the carbon family element is present in the anion portion of the salt. Examples are:

$$Sn(OH)_2 + OH^- \longrightarrow Sn(OH)_3^- \quad \text{or} \quad (HSnO_2^- + H_2O)$$
$$Pb(OH)_2 + OH^- \longrightarrow Pb(OH)_3^- \quad \text{or} \quad (HPbO_2^- + H_2O)$$

In the presence of acids the hydroxides of tin and lead form salts in which the atoms of these metals are present in the cation.

$$Pb(OH)_2 + 2H_3O^+ \longrightarrow Pb^{+2} + 4H_2O$$

Bonding. Like nitrogen family elements, the atoms of this family form covalent bonds in nearly all cases. The only stable simple ionic forms of these atoms are:

1. The C^{-4} ion appears to exist in compounds like Be_2C and Al_4C_3.

2. The Si^{+4} ion has been reported to exist in glass in those cases where the silicon atoms are found in a random pattern throughout the structure. For the most part silicon in glass is in a covalent network of groups of this sort:

$$\begin{array}{c} | \\ O \\ | \\ {-}O{-}Si{-}O{-} \\ | \\ O \\ | \end{array}$$

3. Lead(II) ions, Pb^{+2}, are recognizable in lead fluoride, PbF_2, and lead sulfide, PbS. Compounds like tin(II) chloride, $SnCl_2$, germanium(II) oxide, GeO, and the tetrachlorides of all the elements are predominantly covalent. However there is an obvious trend toward the formation of

ionic bonds, or toward covalent bonds with increasing amounts of ionic character, as the electronegativity decreases or as the metallic nature of the elements increases.

The structures resulting from the covalent bonding involving these elements may be relatively small molecules like most of the hydrocarbons and their derivatives which comprise organic chemistry, or they may be macromolecules such as the dioxides of silicon, germanium, and tin, or the silicates found in rocks and minerals, or in diamond, graphite, free silicon, germanium, and tin. Simple molecules are usually formed when the carbon family element combines with a monovalent element such as hydrogen or chlorine. Macromolecules result when the combination is with a polyvalent atom. A structural formula for the quartz form of silicon dioxide is given in Figure 15.21(b).

The capacity of carbon for catenation and the ability of silicon to form network Si—O—Si structures has been attributed to the unusually high bond energies of the C—C, C—H, and Si—O bonds which are 82, 98, and 185 kcal/mole respectively.

Undoubtedly silicon forms Si—O—Si bonds in preference to Si—Si bonds because the bond energy of the Si—O bond is 185 kcal/mole compared with 53 kcal/mole for the Si—Si bond. Conversely the bond strengths for both the C—C and the C—O bonds are very high and nearly the same, 82 compared with 84 kcal/mole respectively. This confers great stability on compounds with both C—C and C—O bonds.

There is a marked difference in properties between the anhydrous halides of the heavier members and the hydrated forms of these compounds. For example, anhydrous tin(IV) chloride, $SnCl_4$, is a liquid while the hydrate $SnCl_4 \cdot 4H_2O$ is an ionic solid. The former consists of $SnCl_4$ molecules while the latter presumably is made up of hydrated tin(IV) ions, $Sn(H_2O)_4{}^{+4}$, and chloride ions. Evidently the more basic water molecule displaces the less basic chloride ion in the covalent bond to tin as illustrated below:

$$H \quad \diagdown \diagup \qquad\qquad H \quad \diagdown \diagup \qquad +$$
$$O: + Sn - Cl \longrightarrow \qquad O: Sn \qquad + Cl^-$$
$$H \quad \diagup \qquad | \qquad\qquad H \quad \diagup \qquad |$$

Reactions of this type occur generally in compounds in which halogens are covalently bonded to metals as in Al_2Cl_6, $BiCl_3$, $GeCl_2$, $SnCl_2$.

Table 18.3 gives the melting points of some oxides, sulfides, and hydrides of carbon family elements and illustrates the variation in bonding which is

OXIDES		HYDRIDES		SULFIDES	
Compound	Melting Point (°C)	Compound	Melting Point (°C)	Compound	Melting Point (°C)
CO_2	−56.5	CH_4	−185.2	CS_2	−111.8
SiO_2	1710	SiH_4	−184.7	SiS_2	1090
GeO_2	1116	GeH_4	−165.9	GeS_2	800
SnO_2	1927	SnH_4	−150	SnS_2	800
PbO_2	752(d)			PbS	1114

Table 18.3 Melting Points of Some Oxides, Sulfides, and Hydrides of the Carbon Family

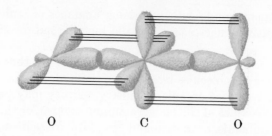

Figure 18.1 Bonding in CO_2 showing *sp* hybrid orbitals on carbon which give rise to the linear structure and showing the π bonds between carbon and oxygen.

possible in the family. All the hydrides, and the carbon oxides and sulfides, are small molecules, as indicated by the low melting points. The remaining oxides and sulfides, except for lead sulfide, are macromolecules having melting points 1000°C to 2000°C above those of the small molecules. Lead sulfide is an ionic solid.

Stereochemistry. As indicated earlier, the atoms of the family form tetrahedral structures using sp^3 hybrid orbitals more than any other type of stereochemistry. However the carbon atom, perhaps because of its capacity to form π bonds, is also able to form the following:

1. *sp* hybrid orbitals which result in linear molecules such as carbon dioxide and acetylene, H—C≡C—H (Figure 18.1).
2. sp^2 hybrid orbitals which result in triangular planar structures as in formaldehyde, H_2CO (Figure 18.2), and ethylene, C_2H_4.

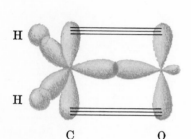

Figure 18.2 Bonding in formaldehyde, H_2C=O, showing sp^2 hybrid orbitals which give rise to triangular planar structures.

Silicon atoms, with their decreased tendency to form π bonds, produce structures with other than tetrahedral symmetry only rarely. The ability of these atoms to expand the octet accounts for the octahedral hexafluorosilicate ion, SiF_6^{-2}, and its salts.

Germanium, tin, and lead show tetrahedral symmetry in the −IV and IV states as in GeH_4 and $SnCl_4$. Their dihalides, e.g., $SnCl_2$, are angular molecules in the gas phase and in the solid state they appear to consist of chains of molecules arranged as illustrated below:

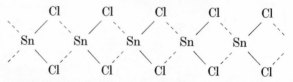

The heavier elements in the family also form stable octahedral complex ions such as hexachlorostannate ion, $SnCl_6^{-2}$,

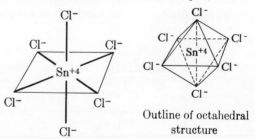

Outline of octahedral structure

$SnCl_6^{-2}$ complex ion

and hexafluorogermanate ion, GeF_6^{-2}. A salt, ammonium hexachloroplumbate, $(NH_4)_2PbCl_6$, has been prepared.

Table 18.4 Occurrence and Uses of Carbon Family Elements and Compounds

Element	Occurrence	Use
Carbon	Free in diamond, graphite, and the complex mixtures of coal. As gas or liquid in carbon dioxide, natural gas, petroleum. As solid in carbonate rocks and products of living organisms: carbohydrates, fats, proteins.	Important to life in photosynthesis and metabolism; in fuels, foods, drugs, plastics, etc.
Silicon	In the siliceous minerals comprising the overwhelmingly predominant compounds of the earth's crust: granite, sandstone, feldspar, shale, clay, etc.	In the ceramic industries, in metal refining, and as constituent of alloys.
Germanium	In the mixture of coal, and as the complex ore germanite which contains the germanium mostly as the ion, GeS_6^{-8}.	A semiconductor, germanium doped with tiny amounts of elements of the boron or nitrogen families is used in transistors.
Tin	As cassiterite, SnO_2. Not found in the U.S.	As corrosion-resistant covering for steel in tin plate; as alloying element in bronzes (with copper), solder (with lead), bearing metals.
Lead	As galena, PbS; cerussite, $PbCO_3$; anglesite, $PbSO_4$. Plentiful in the U.S.	In storage-battery plates; as alloying element in solder, pewter, type metal, shot; compounds as paint pigments.

Table 18.4 summarizes data on the occurrence and uses of the carbon family elements.

The Elements

Physical Properties. Table 18.5 gives some physical properties of the members of this family. All of these elements are solids at room temperature and well above. The first three members are high melting (3570°C, carbon; 1420°C, silicon; 937°C, germanium) while tin and lead melt at considerably lower temperatures (231.8°C and 327.4°C respectively). The high melting points of the first three are indicative of the macromolecular structure (network of covalently bonded atoms) of carbon, silicon, and germanium, and the lower melting points of tin and lead reflect the less rigid metallic binding in their crystals. The heats of fusion of silicon and germanium are seven or more times higher than those of tin and lead,

Table 18.5 Some Physical Properties of Carbon Family Elements

Element	Density (25°C) (g/cc)	Melting Point (°C)	Boiling Point (°C)	Heat of Fusion (kcal/mole)
Carbon	D3.51; G2.0 *	3570	4200	
Silicon	2.33	1420	2680	11.1
Germanium	5.35	937.2	2830	7.6
Tin	7.28	231.8	2687	1.72
Lead	11.34	327.4	1751	1.14

* D, Diamond; G, Graphite.

Figure 18.3 The crystal structure of two forms of pure carbon—diamond and graphite. (a) Diamond: the carbon atoms are equidistant and each is bonded to four others. (b) The unit cell of diamond: note the grouping of one carbon atom surrounded by four others. (c) Graphite: the carbon atoms are bonded to three other carbon atoms with strong covalent bonds, but the layers are bonded only weakly to each other. In any one hexagon, such as the heavily outlined one in the center, three of the atoms lie directly over others in adjacent layers, and the other three lie over the centers of hexagons in neighboring planes. Atoms of hexagons in alternate planes lie directly over one another, as shown at the right.

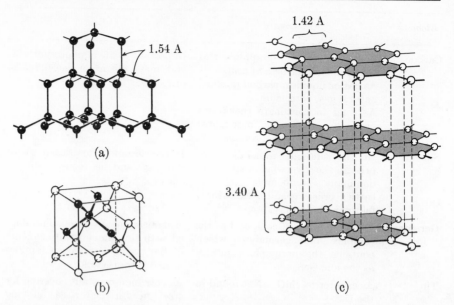

(a)

(b)

(c)

1.54 A

1.42 A

3.40 A

demonstrating also this difference in bonding. Tin and lead have a very wide liquid range, typical of metals, as discussed in Chap. 8. The densities of the solids are relatively high and generally increase from carbon to lead. The higher values reflect the efficient packing in the crystals and the trend from carbon to lead parallels the increasing density of the individual atoms —the lead atom is much more dense than the carbon atom.

Tin, lead, and the graphite form of carbon are moderate electrical conductors.

Allotropes. Carbon exists in two crystalline forms, diamond and graphite. These forms have markedly different properties. For example, diamond is the hardest substance known while graphite is used as a lubricant. The structures of the two forms are shown in Figure 18.3. In the diamond network the covalently bonded atoms are arranged tetrahedrally and are equidistant. This structure is very hard and high melting for it cannot be disrupted without breaking a large number of covalent bonds.

Graphite consists of layers of carbon atoms in which each atom uses *three* of its electrons in sp^2 hybrid orbitals to form covalent bonds with three other atoms. This produces a network of hexagons as shown in Figure 18.3. The layers presumably are held to each other by metallic binding made possible by the *fourth* electron in the unhybridized p orbital on each atom. The distance between layers is 3.40 A and the distance between bonded atoms within a layer is 1.42 A. The conductivity of graphite is due to this metallic binding. Graphite is thermodynamically more stable than diamond at room temperature, and its density is less than that of diamond.

Silicon, a deep-gray solid, crystallizes in the diamond structure and is very hard and brittle. Since Si—Si bonds are weaker than C—C bonds, it is not as hard nor as high melting as diamond. Germanium also crystallizes in the diamond structure but it is not as hard or as high melting as silicon or carbon.

Tin exists in three solid forms which pass into one another at definite transition temperatures:

$$\text{Gray }(\alpha)\text{ tin} \xrightleftharpoons{13.2°} \text{white }(\beta)\text{ tin} \xrightleftharpoons{161°} \text{rhombic }(\gamma)\text{ tin} \xrightleftharpoons{231.8°} \text{liquid}$$

(diamond structure)   (metallic)

The white or metallic form is stable at room temperature but at temperatures below 13.2°C the metal loses its luster and often crumbles to a powder which is the nonmetallic gray form. This transition illustrates the tendency of the electrons in the metallic bonds to become localized at lower temperatures.

Lead crystallizes in the cubic close-packed lattice. The forces holding the large, heavy atoms to particular positions in the crystal are not great, and the crystal is soft and relatively low melting.

Chemical Properties. Some important chemical properties of the carbon family elements are illustrated by the following general equations where M represents the element of this group.

1. $M + O_2 \rightarrow MO_2$. Diamond burns above 800°C; graphite burns at 690°C; silicon burns at 400°C; germanium and tin burn upon heating; lead forms PbO or Pb_3O_4.
2. $M + 2X_2(\text{halogen}) \rightarrow MX_4$. This reaction occurs with varying degrees of difficulty depending upon both the halogen and the carbon family element. Lead forms PbX_2 in most cases.
3. $M + 2S \rightarrow MS_2$. High temperatures are required; diamond requires 1000°C.; lead forms PbS.
4. $M + \text{Acids} \rightarrow M^{+2} + H_2$. Tin and lead form compounds in the II state. Carbon, silicon, and germanium do not react.
5. $3M + 4HNO_3 \rightarrow 3MO_2 + 4NO + 2H_2O$. Oxidizing acids raise the element to the IV state, except for lead, which goes to the II state.

The strengths of the elements as oxidizing and reducing agents in acids can be seen in Table 18.6. These values show that carbon is a weak oxidizing agent but it is the strongest of this group. As with all groups of nonmetals the oxidizing strength parallels the nonmetallic character of the element.

Silicon is the most powerful reducing agent in the group, being stronger than metallic zinc and stronger than all the hydrides in the nitrogen family except for bismuthine, BiH_3. All the elements in the family, except carbon, are stronger reducing agents than hydrogen.

Table 18.6 Standard Oxidation Potentials for Carbon Family Elements (in acid solution at 25°C)

Reaction	$E°$ (volts)
$Si + 2H_2O \longrightarrow SiO_2 + 4H^+_{(aq)} + 4e^-$	0.86
$GeH_4 \longrightarrow Ge + 4H^+_{(aq)} + 4e^-$	0.70
$Sn \longrightarrow Sn^{+2} + 2e^-$	0.14
$Pb \longrightarrow Pb^{+2} + 2e^-$	0.13
$Ge + 2H_2O \longrightarrow GeO_2 + 4H^+_{(aq)} + 4e^-$	0.1
$SiH_4 \longrightarrow Si + 4H^+_{(aq)} + 4e^-$	-0.10
$CH_4 \longrightarrow C + 4H^+_{(aq)} + 4e^-$	-0.13
$C + 2H_2O \longrightarrow CO_2 + 4H^+_{(aq)} + 4e^-$	-0.20

Preparation of the Elements. *Carbon.* Graphite is prepared commercially from coke (the solid residue from heating coal or other organic materials in the absence of air). Massive graphite for crucibles, electrodes, or blocks for atomic reactors is made by first mixing powdered coke with pitch. This mixture is molded, pressed, or extruded to give the desired shape, heated to about 1100°C to drive off volatile impurities, and finally converted to graphite by further heating to about 2500°C.

A number of amorphous forms of carbon are commercially available. These include charcoal, bone black, and carbon black. Charcoal and bone black are prepared by heating wood and bones, respectively, in absence of air. Carbon black, a fluffy, very finely divided powder, is made by burning natural gas and directing the flame against moving metal surfaces. The unburned carbon deposits as a black soot on the metal. It is used in the manufacture of rubber goods (especially tires), to which it adds strength and resiliency, and printer's inks, paints, and black polishes.

Finely divided and porous carbon is remarkable for its property of adsorbing various gases and liquids. Charcoal made from coconut shells, and activated while very hot by a mild oxidation with steam, has a very great adsorptive power for gases; for example, one volume of a certain coconut charcoal at a pressure of 760 torr adsorbs 149 volumes of ammonia at 20°C. Activated charcoal is used in some filters in ventilation systems, in cigarettes, and in gas masks.

Bone black and activated charcoal adsorb many organic substances from their solutions in water. Many dyes are adsorbed in this way, and in the manufacture of sugar the solutions are decolorized before crystallization by filtration through filters of charcoal or of bone black.

Small diamonds for industrial use are made from graphite at temperatures of about 2800°C under a pressure of approximately 1.5 million lb/sq in.

Silicon. Silicon is prepared commercially by thermally reducing sand with carbon or calcium carbide, CaC_2, in an electric furnace:

$$SiO_2 + 2C \longrightarrow 2CO + Si$$

This reaction proceeds more readily in the presence of iron, forming the alloy ferrosilicon used in metallurgy.

Germanium. Silvery-white germanium is prepared commercially by reducing the dioxide GeO_2 with hydrogen or carbon. Very pure germanium for transistors is made by the method of zone refining, wherein a long rod of the solid is moved very slowly through a heated zone, causing the material to melt on entering the zone, and solidify on leaving. Impurities, being either more soluble or less soluble in the melt than in the solid, will tend to concentrate in a short section at one end of the bar. (See Figure 18.4.)

Tin. Tin is obtained from the ore cassiterite in which it is present as the dioxide SnO_2 along with sulfur and arsenic. The latter elements are removed by roasting (heating in air) as the volatile sulfur dioxide and arsenic(III) oxide. The tin(IV) oxide which remains is reduced by carbon in a furnace similar to a blast furnace.

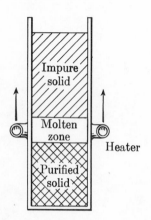

Figure 18.4 Zone refining. A heater encircling the container moves slowly upward. Impurities more soluble in the liquid move toward the top, and purified material crystallizes out below the moving melt. Alternatively, the container may move in the opposite direction past a fixed heater.

Lead. The ores of lead are chiefly sulfides, usually associated with more or less silver sulfide and often a little gold; silver ores are often purposely added to silver-bearing lead ores and the two metals smelted together. When no silver is present, the ores are roasted in air in an open oven until they are partially oxidized to form a mixture of sulfide, sulfate, and oxide of lead. Access to air is then shut off and the temperature raised to bring about the following reactions:

$$PbS + 2PbO \longrightarrow 3Pb + SO_2$$

$$PbS + PbSO_4 \longrightarrow 2Pb + 2SO_2$$

Silver-bearing ores are worked at a higher temperature in a blast furnace charged with the roasted ore and with coke and a flux consisting of limestone and iron ore. The chief reactions that produce lead (and silver) are these:

$$PbS + FeO + C \longrightarrow Pb + FeS + CO$$

$$PbSO_4 + FeO + 5C \longrightarrow Pb + FeS + 5CO$$

The liquid lead, carrying the silver and gold in solution together with varying percentages of copper, antimony, bismuth, and arsenic, collects in the crucible and is tapped off for refining.

Some Inorganic Compounds of the Carbon Family

Oxides. Table 18.7 lists the known oxides of the family and gives some of their physical properties and their structures.

Carbon Oxides. Carbon dioxide is the most stable oxide of carbon at temperatures below 1000°C. Above this temperature the reaction

$$C + CO_2 \longrightarrow 2CO$$

occurs readily.

Table 18.7   Some   Properties   of Carbon Family Oxides

Compound	Formula	Melting Point (°C)	Boiling Point (°C)	Appearance	Molecular Structure
Carbon monoxide	CO	−205.1	−190	Colorless gas	
Carbon dioxide	CO_2	−56.5*	−78.5†	Colorless gas	O=C=O
Carbon suboxide	C_3O_2	−107	−6.8	Gas	O=C=C=C=O
Silicon monoxide	SiO			Gas	
Silicon dioxide	SiO_2	1710	2590	White solid	Si—O—Si network
Germanium monoxide	GeO		710†	Black solid	Ge—O—Ge network
Germanium dioxide	GeO_2	1116	1200	White solid	Ge—O—Ge network
Tin monoxide	SnO	Decomp.		Black solid	Sn—O—Sn network
Tin dioxide	SnO_2	1927	1900†	White solid	Sn—O—Sn network
Lead monoxide	PbO			Yellow solid	Pb—O—Pb network
Lead dioxide	PbO_2	Decomp.		Brown solid	
Red lead	Pb_3O_4	830		Orange-red	Pb_2PbO_4

* Under 5.11 atm.
† Sublimes.

Solid carbon dioxide sublimes at $-78.51°C$, well below its melting point. Hence no liquid phase exists at atmospheric pressure. At 5.11 atm solid carbon dioxide melts at $-56.40°C$ to give the colorless liquid. Carbon monoxide is more normal in its behavior; however, both its boiling and melting temperatures are considerably lower than those of carbon dioxide.

Preparations of carbon dioxide are based on the fact that it is extremely stable; any organic compound, burned in a sufficient supply of oxygen, will produce carbon dioxide.

$$2C_8H_{18} + 25O_2 \longrightarrow 16CO_2 + 18H_2O$$
Octane

It may also be prepared by heating carbonates:

$$MCO_3 \xrightarrow{\text{heat}} MO + CO_2$$

or by treating carbonates or bicarbonates with acids:

$$CO_3^{-2} + 2H_3O^+ \longrightarrow H_2CO_3 + 2H_2O$$
$$\phantom{CO_3^{-2} + 2H_3O^+ \longrightarrow }\llcorner\!\!\rightarrow H_2O + CO_2$$

Carbon monoxide is prepared by the dehydration of formic acid:

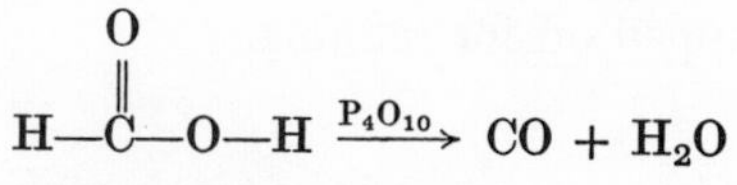

$$\underset{\text{Formic acid}}{H-\overset{\overset{\textstyle O}{\|}}{C}-O-H} \xrightarrow{P_4O_{10}} CO + H_2O$$

and by the high temperature reduction of carbon dioxide by carbon, described above.

The dioxide is so stable that it undergoes only a few reactions. Important among these is its reaction with water to give carbonic acid:

$$CO_2 + H_2O \longrightarrow H_2CO_3$$

Here it might be imagined that one of the π bonds in the carbon dioxide molecule interacts with a water molecule so that in effect the OH portion of the water molecule forms a covalent bond to the carbon atom and the H portion of the water molecule bonds to the oxygen atom as in the diagram.

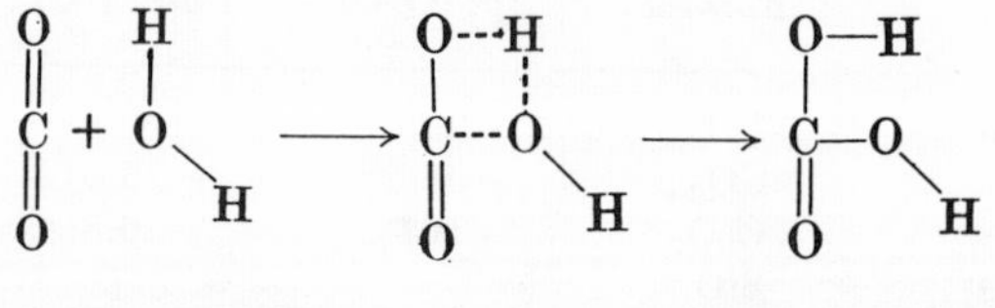

In contrast to the stability of carbon dioxide, carbon monoxide is very reactive when heated. It is a good reducing agent and acts thus to reduce iron oxide in the smelting of iron in the blast furnace.

$$FeO + CO \longrightarrow Fe + CO_2$$

Carbon monoxide also acts as an electron-pair donor in reactions with a number of transition elements, forming compounds known as metal carbonyls:

$$Ni + 4CO \longrightarrow Ni(CO)_4$$

Other metal carbonyls have the formulas $Mn_2(CO)_{10}$, $Cr(CO)_6$, and $Co_2(CO)_8$.

Uses of Carbon Dioxide. Commercially, carbon dioxide is used chiefly in the manufacture of soda water and similar beverages, as a fire extinguisher, and in solid form (Dry Ice) as a refrigerant. Large amounts are used also in the manufacture of sodium carbonate. Ordinary soda water consists of various flavoring extracts, to which is added water charged with carbon dioxide under pressure. When the pressure is removed, some of the gas escapes, producing effervescence.

Figure 18.5 Some crystals of quartz found in nature.

Silicon Dioxide, SiO_2. Although silicon monoxide (SiO) has been prepared in the electric furnace, the dioxide $(SiO_2)_n$, called silica, is far better known. Practically all the silicon of nature occurs either as the dioxide itself or as its hydrated derivatives, so that it is a most important substance. The most common crystalline form is that known as quartz, which forms beautiful crystals belonging to the hexagonal system (Figure 18.5).

Quartz crystals, when pure, are colorless. Often small percentages of impurities are present which color the crystals. Thus amethyst is quartz colored violet by a trace of an oxide of manganese, whereas milky quartz owes its characteristic appearance to the minute air bubbles present. Other varieties of silicon dioxide, some of which also contain combined water, are chalcedony, onyx, jasper, opal, agate, and flint. Sand and sandstone are largely silicon dioxide. It is present also in granite and gneiss.

Quartz has a density of 2.65 and is hard enough to make it useful for grinding and polishing purposes. Silica melts at the temperature of the oxygen-hydrogen flame (above 1700°C) to a viscous liquid which can be drawn into threads or fashioned into laboratory utensils. Silica has a very small coefficient of expansion with temperature, hence quartz vessels can be heated to redness and plunged into water without danger of cracking.

Silicosis. A dust of silica particles, if inhaled into the throat and lungs, can cause the serious disease called silicosis.

Oxides of Tin and Lead. Stannous oxide (SnO) can be obtained as a black powder by heating stannous oxalate (SnC_2O_4). Lead oxide (PbO), called litharge, is made by heating lead in a current of air or by heating the carbonate. In color it ranges from yellow or light brown to orange, depending on the way in which it is made. Its chief use is in making paints, glass, glazes, and other compounds of lead. Mixed with glycerin it forms a cement useful for joining glass and stone.

Tin dioxide (SnO_2) is the chief mineral ore of tin. It may be prepared as a white powder by burning tin in air or by treating it with nitric acid and heating the resulting hydrated oxide. It is used in making opaque glass and enamels. Plumbic oxide (PbO_2), usually called lead dioxide, is dark-brown in color. It is obtained by the action of bleaching powder on sodium plumbite (Na_2PbO_2):

$$Na_2PbO_2 + Ca(OCl)Cl + H_2O \longrightarrow 2NaOH + CaCl_2 + PbO_2$$

PbO_2 is the brown coating on the anodes of storage batteries (Chap. 23, Question 20). It is a good oxidizing agent. For example, with hydrochloric acid it acts much like manganese dioxide, and chlorine is produced:

$$PbO_2 + 4HCl \longrightarrow PbCl_2 + 2H_2O + Cl_2 \uparrow$$

Salts of Carbonic and Silicic Acids—Carbonates and Silicates. The salts of carbonic acid are invariably salts of metacarbonic acid, H_2CO_3, usually called simply carbonic acid. They are readily prepared by neutralizing a solution of the acid by a suitable base or by absorbing carbon dioxide, the acid anhydride, in a solution of the base. Since carbonic acid is dibasic, both normal salts and acid salts are known:

$$CO_2 + OH^- \longrightarrow HCO_3^-$$
Bicarbonate ion

$$HCO_3^- + OH^- \longrightarrow CO_3^{-2} + H_2O$$
Carbonate ion

The normal carbonates are found in large quantities in nature, and are often used in chemical processes. Ordinary limestone is a more or less impure form of calcium carbonate ($CaCO_3$); marble is also largely calcium carbonate; normal sodium carbonate (Na_2CO_3) is the well-known soda ash, largely used in the manufacture of soap and glass.

The most familiar of the acid carbonates is sodium hydrogen carbonate ($NaHCO_3$), or ordinary baking soda. Most acid carbonates readily decompose when heated, forming the normal carbonate, carbon dioxide, and water. The preparation and properties of the acid carbonates may be illustrated by the following example.

If carbon dioxide is passed into a solution of calcium hydroxide (limewater), calcium carbonate at first precipitates:

$$CO_2 + OH^- \longrightarrow HCO_3^-$$

$$HCO_3^- + OH^- \longrightarrow CO_3^{-2}$$

$$Ca^{+2} + CO_3^{-2} \longrightarrow CaCO_3 \downarrow$$

If the current of carbon dioxide is continued, however, the precipitated calcium carbonate soon dissolves. This is due to the formation of calcium hydrogen carbonate which, being soluble, dissolves in the water present. If now the solution is heated, the acid carbonate decomposes, and calcium carbonate once more precipitates:

$$Ca(HCO_3)_2 \longrightarrow CaCO_3 \downarrow\ + H_2O + CO_2$$

The salts of silicic acid are sometimes quite complex, since silicic acid is found in the form of various condensed acids. The natural silicates, which play such an important role in the inorganic world, are found in a variety of structures: fibrous, as in asbestos; platelike, as in mica; and massive as in meerschaum.

The Structure of the Natural Silicates. In the mineral silicates the SiO_4^{-4} grouping of silicon and oxygen atoms plays a dominant role in the crystal lattice. The oxygen atoms are the largest atoms, usually much the largest atoms, present in the lattices. They pack together around the silicon atoms as SiO_4^{-4} tetrahedra, and the metallic ions fit between the tetrahedra, where they can. X-ray analysis of a large number of silicates shows that there are at least five general types of structures.

1. *Separate SiO_4^{-4} Ions.* These separate ions, SiO_4^{-4} (Figure 18.6), and the metallic ions, arrange themselves in various kinds of three-dimensional checkerboard patterns of general resemblance to the Na^+, Cl^- lattice. Garnet [$Ca_3Al_2(SiO_4)_3$, or $3CaO \cdot Al_2O_3 \cdot 3SiO_2$] crystallizes in a lattice of this type.

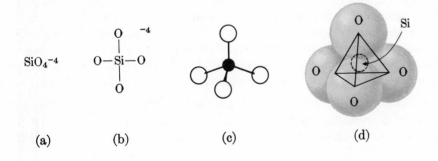

SiO_4^{-4}

(a)   (b)   (c)   (d)

Figure 18.6 Several methods of representing the silicate ion, SiO_4^{-4}: (a) Ionic formula. (b) Conventional structural formula. (c) Structural model. (d) Scale model, showing the tetrahedron produced by connecting the centers of the oxygen atoms.

2. *Separate, More Complex Silicon-Oxygen Ions.* The ion $Si_2O_7^{-6}$ is formed when two silicon atoms share the same oxygen atom between them (see Figure 18.7):

$$(O-\underset{\underset{O}{|}}{\overset{\overset{O}{|}}{Si}}-O-\underset{\underset{O}{|}}{\overset{\overset{O}{|}}{Si}}-O)^{-6}$$

A ring-shaped ion, $Si_6O_{18}^{-12}$, is also known (Figure 18.8). Such complex negative ions as these, together with metallic ions, make up the crystal

Figure 18.7 The $Si_2O_7^{-6}$ ion. Two tetrahedra, joined at a corner. In some cases the Si—O—Si bond is linear (c) ; in others the bases of the two tetrahedra lie in the same plane, and the Si—O—Si linkage is bent (e).

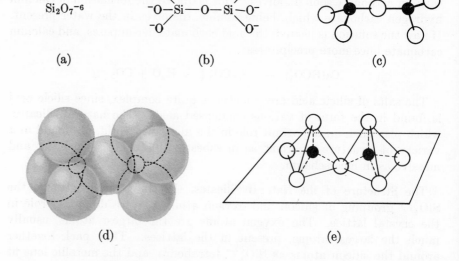

$Si_2O_7^{-6}$

(a)　　　　(b)　　　　(c)

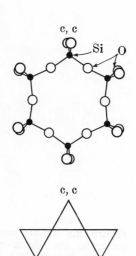

(d)　　　　(e)

Figure 18.8 The ion $Si_6O_{18}^{-12}$. The six silicon atoms and six oxygen atoms shared between tetrahedra lie in the same plane, with the other two oxygen atoms, denoted by c,c, of each tetrahedron above and below that plane. (a) A structural formula. (b) Diagrammatic formula.

Figure 18.9 The structure of beryl. The ring $Si_6O_{18}^{-12}$ ions of Figure 18.8 are piled in columns one above the other, and the viewer is looking straight down on the columns. At each "point" of the "star" are two oxygen atoms (a,a ; b,b) corresponding to those marked c,c in Figure 18.8. The individual $Si_6O_{18}^{-12}$ ions and the columns are held together by Al^{+3} ions (coordination number 6) and Be^{+2} ions (coordination number 4).

lattice. The ring ion is present in the lattice of beryl ($Be_3Al_2Si_6O_{18}$, or $3Be^{+2}$, $2Al^{+3}$, $Si_6O_{18}^{-12}$) (Figure 18.9).

3. *Silicon-Oxygen Strings*. Silicon-oxygen strings are common, occurring in all the fibrous silicates. The strings are extremely long and may run from one end of the crystal fiber to the other. The string may be like those in Figure 18.10, with each SiO_4 tetrahedron attached to its neighbors by two corners, or like those in Figure 18.11, in which alternate tetrahedra are attached by two and by three corners. In both cases the end-on view of the chain [Figure 18.10(d) and Figure 18.11(b)] has a trapezoidal shape and the trapezoids are held together by metallic cations. This is shown in the diagram of the diopside structure [$CaMg(SiO_3)_2$] shown in Figure 18.10, where the magnesium ions have a coordination number of 6 and the calcium ions, which are larger, a coordination number of 8. The string of Figure 18.11 is present in tremolite, $Ca_2Mg_2(Si_4O_{11})_2(OH)_2$, and the presence of the OH group in the structure is indicated in the figure.

4. *Silicon-Oxygen Sheets* (*two-dimensional*). The silicon and oxygen atoms also crystallize in sheets (Figure 18.12), which are held together by positive ions located between the sheets. Each tetrahedron shares three

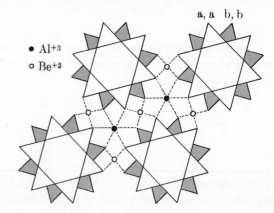

● Al^{+3}
○ Be^{+2}

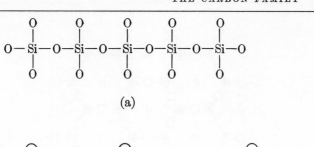

(a)

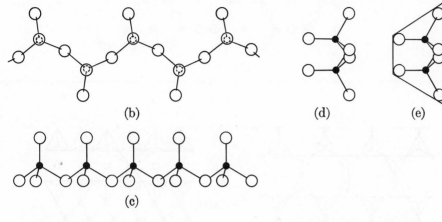

(b)   (d)   (e)

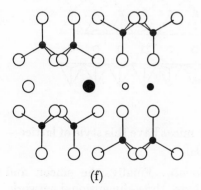

(c)

(f)   (g)

Figure 18.10 Strings of SiO_4^{-4} tetrahedra : (a) Conventional structural formula. (b) Top view of tetrahedra. The silicon atoms (small, solid circles) are under the oxygen atoms at the apices. (c) Side view of a chain. (d) View of a chain looking end-on, along the chain. (e) End view as in (d) with the trapezoid sketched in. (f, g) End-on view of four chains in a crystal of diopside, $CaMg(SiO_3)_2$, showing the alternation of the orientation of the chains in the crystal. The large circles between the chains represent calcium ions, and the smaller, magnesium ions, which serve to bind the chains together. In (g) the tetrahedra at upper left and lower right each present an edge toward the viewer ; at upper right and lower left, the viewer sees in each case a face, with the concealed edge represented by a dotted line.

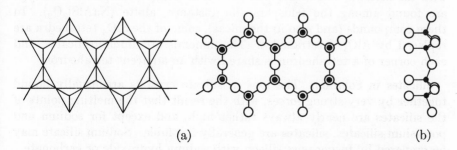

(a)   (b)

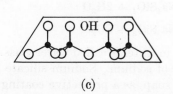

OH

(c)

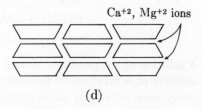

Ca+2, Mg+2 ions

(d)

Figure 18.11 Double silicon-oxygen strings : (a) Top views, looking down on the SiO_4 tetrahedra. (b) End view of the double chain. (c) End view showing the trapezoidal appearance. (d) Packing pattern of the chains in end view.

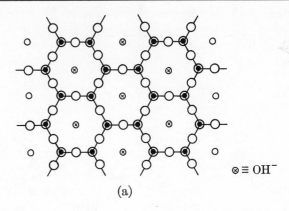

$$\otimes \equiv OH^-$$

(a)

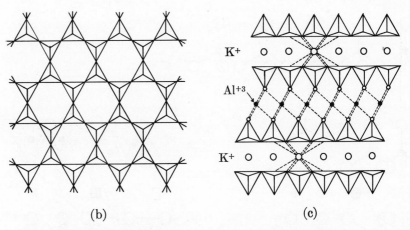

Figure 18.12 Sheets of SiO$_4$ tetrahedra as found in mica [muscovite, KAl$_3$Si$_3$O$_{10}$(OH)$_2$]. (a) Structural representation showing positions of the OH groups. (b) Diagrammatic representation. (c) Sketch looking end-on at the sheets, to show the packing pattern.

(b)   (c)

corners with adjacent tetrahedra. All the micas have this style of lattice—for example, muscovite [KAl$_3$Si$_3$O$_{10}$(OH)$_2$].

5. *Silicon-Oxygen Nets* (*three-dimensional*). Finally, the silicon and oxygen atoms often crystallize in a continuous three-dimensional network, with the metallic ions fitting into the holes. Many examples of this type are found among the feldspars—for instance, albite (NaAlSi$_3$O$_8$). In these compounds (and also in the micas), some of the SiO$_4$ tetrahedra are replaced by AlO$_4^{-5}$ tetrahedra. The minerals are aluminosilicates, and each corner of a tetrahedron is shared with an adjacent tetrahedron.

Silicates in Solution. The ions in silicate crystals are usually bound together by very strong forces, with the result that the melting points of the silicates are nearly always rather high, and except for sodium and potassium silicates, silicates are generally insoluble. Sodium silicate may be prepared by fusing pure silicon with sodium hydroxide or carbonate:

$$4NaOH + SiO_2 \longrightarrow Na_4SiO_4 + 2H_2O$$

$$Na_2CO_3 + SiO_2 \longrightarrow Na_2SiO_3 + CO_2$$

A solution of the products of such fusions in water is called water glass. It consists of a mixture of various silicates of sodium. Sodium silicate has many uses, especially as an ingredient of soap, as a protective coating for porous surfaces (such as those of wood, plaster, or cement), and as a cement or glue, chiefly for pasteboard boxes and cartons.

When salts of the various metals are added to a solution of a sodium silicate, such as Na_2SiO_3, insoluble silicates are precipitated:

$$Na_2SiO_3 + CaCl_2 \longrightarrow CaSiO_3 \downarrow + 2NaCl$$

Most natural silicates, when fused with sodium carbonate, are decomposed, and sodium silicate is formed:

$$CaSiO_3 + Na_2CO_3 \longrightarrow CaCO_3 \downarrow + Na_2SiO_3$$

The melted sodium carbonate forms a liquid in which the silicates are soluble but the carbonates are not. The insoluble carbonate is therefore precipitated. When the melt is cooled and digested with water, the sodium silicate dissolves, while the carbonate and oxides of the other metals are left undissolved.

Fusion of the Silicates. If several different silicates are melted together with an excess of silica, they mix freely to a homogeneous liquid. Crystals may separate from the melt when it is cooled slowly, but usually the liquid solution simply becomes more and more viscous until it is as rigid as a true solid. Such products are called *glasses*, and they are sometimes regarded as very viscous solutions of one silicate in another or in silica. Actually they are randomly oriented solids. The high viscosity makes it difficult for the extended structures of the silicates to arrange themselves in the exact positions needed for crystallization, and incomplete or random networks are present (Figure 18.13). The cations appear among the SiO_4 tetrahedra in no particular order but in random positions.

The Ceramic Industries. A number of most important industries are based upon the silicates and the chemical transformations which they undergo. The oldest of these are the various ceramic industries, including the making of bricks, tile, terra cotta, dishes, porcelain, and glass.

Silicones. Most silicates have a certain amount of linkage in all four directions from the silicon atom. It is this cross-linking, resulting from the fact that silicic acid is tetrafunctional (with four reactive hydroxyl groups), which leads to the great rigidity of the silicates. If one could block off two of the reactive positions so that the silicic acid became bifunctional, dehydration could only lead to chains (or, possibly, rings). The cross-linking between chains would be absent. Such molecules, while they may be large, are threadlike, and can still move past each other. Materials made up of such molecules are less brittle because they can yield somewhat to a strain, but are still tough.

This blocking is accomplished in the case of silicic acid by preparing the compound dimethyl silicon dihydroxide by replacing two chlorine atoms in $SiCl_4$ with methyl groups and hydrolyzing the remaining chlorine atoms:

$$
\underset{\underset{\displaystyle Cl}{|}}{\overset{\overset{\displaystyle Cl}{|}}{Cl-Si-Cl}}
\longrightarrow
\underset{\underset{\displaystyle CH_3}{|}}{\overset{\overset{\displaystyle CH_3}{|}}{Cl-Si-Cl}}
\longrightarrow
\underset{\underset{\displaystyle CH_3}{|}}{\overset{\overset{\displaystyle CH_3}{|}}{HO-Si-OH}}
$$

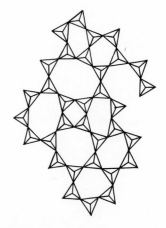

Figure 18.13 Diagram representing the random structure of a glass. Compare this with the regularity of the crystalline material shown in Figure 18.12(b).

Dimethyl silicon dihydroxide dehydrates normally to form a chain. Such a compound is called a silicone; and the particular one formed from dimethyl silicondichloride is a methyl silicone. Other groups, like the ethyl group, C_2H_5, may be substituted for the methyl group; and the molecule chain can be made in various lengths. By including small amounts of the monofunctional $(CH_3)_3SiCl$ along with the bifunctional $(CH_3)_2SiCl_2$, a short methyl silicone molecule may be made. It is represented by the following graphic formula, which shows the bonds of the silicon and oxygen atoms:

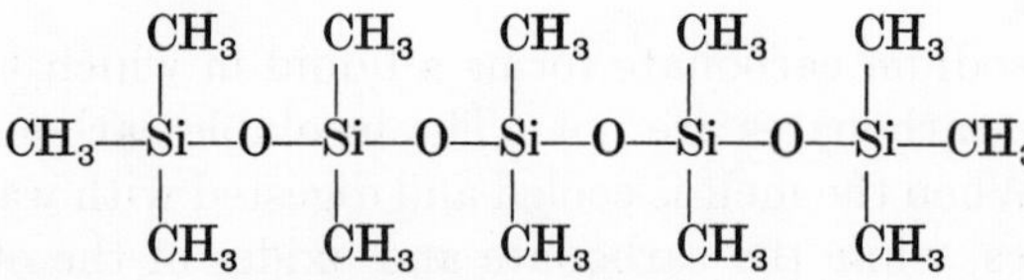

$$CH_3\underset{\underset{CH_3}{|}}{\overset{\overset{CH_3}{|}}{Si}}-O-\underset{\underset{CH_3}{|}}{\overset{\overset{CH_3}{|}}{Si}}-O-\underset{\underset{CH_3}{|}}{\overset{\overset{CH_3}{|}}{Si}}-O-\underset{\underset{CH_3}{|}}{\overset{\overset{CH_3}{|}}{Si}}-O-\underset{\underset{CH_3}{|}}{\overset{\overset{CH_3}{|}}{Si}}-CH_3$$

Properties and Uses of the Silicones. Some of the methyl silicones are oily liquids, and they become more viscous as the chain length increases. They are used as lubricants, either incorporated in greases or as oils, in bearings, gears, etc., and they are used in hydraulic brakes and other hydraulic systems. The outstanding physical attribute of silicone oil is its very small change in viscosity with change in temperature, compared with the behavior of other oils of like viscosity. In the presence of air or oxygen at temperatures as high as 300°F, silicone oils remain free from discoloration, acid formation, sludging, oxidation, and similar phenomena, which frequently limit the usefulness of petroleum products and synthetic organic liquids. In the absence of air or oxygen—for example, in a sealed or evacuated system—silicone oils are stable at temperatures well over 400°F.

Methyl silicones of high molecular weight resemble rubber, and are made into rubberlike tubing and sheets. By introducing trifunctional molecules such as CH_3SiCl_3, bridges, or cross-linkages, can be formed which bind one long molecule to another at several points along the chain. Then the body has resinous properties, and has an extensive use in electrical insulation.

Another interesting and important application of silicones is their use in the treatment of various surfaces to make them water-repellent.

The Halogen Compounds of Tin and Lead. Stannous chloride is made by dissolving tin in hydrochloric acid, and crystallizes from solution as the hydrate $SnCl_2 \cdot 2H_2O$, often called tin salt. It is used as a mordant in the dye industry and also as a reducing agent. The stannous ion of all simple stannous compounds tends to pass into the tetravalent stannic ion, as illustrated in these equations:

$$SnCl_2 + 2HgCl_2 \longrightarrow SnCl_4 + Hg_2Cl_2$$

$$SnCl_2 + 2FeCl_3 \longrightarrow SnCl_4 + 2FeCl_2$$

Anhydrous stannic chloride ($SnCl_4$) is prepared industrially by treating tin scrap (or even used tin cans) with chlorine gas. It is a heavy colorless liquid which boils at 114°C and freezes at −30°C. In moist air it reacts vigorously with the water vapor and forms hydrogen chloride and dense clouds of stannic oxide.

From solutions of this salt in hydrochloric acid a compound called chlorostannic acid (H_2SnCl_6) can be isolated; the corresponding fluostannic acid (H_2SnF_6) is also well known. These compounds yield long series of salts, of which ammonium chlorostannate, $(NH_4)_2SnCl_6$, called pink salt, is the most important. This salt, as well as stannic chloride, is used in weighting silk and cotton cloth and as a mordant.

Lead chloride ($PbCl_2$) is a well-crystallized colorless salt, moderately soluble in hot water and nearly insoluble in cold water. It is precipitated from acid solution when hydrochloric acid is added to a solution of a lead salt:

$$Pb(NO_3)_2 + 2HCl \longrightarrow 2HNO_3 + PbCl_2 \downarrow$$

Lead tetrachloride ($PbCl_4$) is a very unstable heavy liquid that spontaneously loses chlorine, to form ordinary lead chloride.

Other Compounds of Lead. *Tetraethyl Lead*, $Pb(C_2H_5)_4$. This is a covalent compound of tetravalent lead that has come into wide use as an "antiknock" in motor gasoline. A small amount of it greatly improves the quality of a motor fuel for high-compression gasoline engines; but since it is a poisonous compound, gasoline containing it (ethyl gas) should not be used for household purposes. It is made by first making an alloy of sodium in lead of about the composition NaPb, and then treating this alloy with ethyl bromide (C_2H_5Br) or ethyl chloride:

$$4C_2H_5Br + 4NaPb \longrightarrow Pb(C_2H_5)_4 + 4NaBr + 3Pb$$

Lead Carbonates. Normal lead carbonate ($PbCO_3$) can be prepared as a white crystalline precipitate by treating a solution of a lead salt with sodium bicarbonate. A basic carbonate, $(PbCO_3)_2 \cdot Pb(OH)_2$, known as white lead, is of much more industrial importance than the normal salt because of its wide use in the manufacture of paints.

Lead Nitrate, $Pb(NO_3)_2$. This salt is readily obtained by dissolving metallic lead or litharge in nitric acid. It crystallizes in octahedra and is easily soluble in water.

Lead Acetate, $Pb(CH_3CO_2)_2$. The acetate is obtained by dissolving litharge in concentrated acetic acid, from which it crystallizes in snow-white monoclinic crystals of the composition $Pb(CH_3CO_2)_2 \cdot 3H_2O$. The alchemists called it sugar of lead because of its sweetish taste.

Lead Sulfate, $PbSO_4$. Lead sulfate is a white, crystalline solid, insoluble in water and dilute acids. It is therefore formed as a precipitate whenever the ions Pb^{+2} and SO_4^{-2} are brought together in solution. Sublimed White Lead is a trade name given a white pigment made by heating galena (PbS) in a current of air to a suitable temperature. Its composition may be represented as a mixture of lead sulfate, lead oxide, and a little zinc oxide.

Lead Chromate, $PbCrO_4$. This bright-yellow salt, called chrome yellow, results as a precipitate when solutions of a lead salt and a chromate are brought together:

$$Pb(CH_3CO_2)_2 + K_2CrO_4 \longrightarrow PbCrO \downarrow + 2KCH_3CO_2$$

By boiling the normal chromate with a solution of an alkali, a brick-red basic salt is obtained, called chrome red, which has the formula $PbCrO_4 \cdot PbO$. Both the chrome yellow and the chrome red are used as pigments.

Lead Arsenate, $Pb_3(AsO_4)_2$. This compound is a white insoluble powder difficultly soluble in water, prepared by treating lead acetate with sodium arsenate. It is employed as an insecticide.

SUMMARY

The atoms of carbon family elements are larger and less electronegative than those of the corresponding members of the nitrogen, oxygen, or halogen families. Hence carbon family elements are more metallic than their counterparts in the other series of nonmetals. Carbon and silicon are nonmetals; germanium, tin, and lead are metals. However, all five elements form predominantly covalent compounds and all except lead exhibit tetrahedral stereochemistry. The IV oxidation state is stable for all members except lead, and as a consequence, this family has a number of good reducing agents such as carbon, carbon monoxide, and silicon, all of which are oxidized readily to the IV state.

Carbon and silicon form a wide variety of polymeric or macromolecular structures. Many carbon-containing structures are the basic components of plant and animal matter while polymers containing silicon and oxygen form the base structures of the mineral world.

The chemistry of the elements and of their low and high molecular weight compounds is summarized in this chapter.

SOME SPECIAL TERMS

Organic chemistry	**Elasticity**	**Amorphous**
Adsorption	**Zone refining**	**Roasting (of ores)**
Flux	**Dehydration**	
Silicone	**Glass**	
Crosslinking		

QUESTIONS AND PROBLEMS

1. What differences in properties are observed between the carbon family elements on the one hand, and the oxygen family elements on the other, as a result of the smaller electronegativity and larger size of the carbon family elements?

2. Draw electron-dot formulas for *n*-butane and digermane, and indicate the bond angles in these compounds.

3. Write formulas for some carbon compounds in the IV, II, and −IV oxidation states which are not given in Table 18.2.

4. Write equations to show that tin(II) hydroxide is amphoteric.

5. What difference in the two cases accounts for the fact that C—C bonds are common but Si—Si bonds are unusual?

6. Account for the difference in the melting points of silicon dioxide and carbon dioxide, of germanium disulfide and carbon disulfide, of lead sulfide and carbon disulfide.

7. The melting points of tin and lead are much lower than those of silicon and germanium, yet the boiling point of all four are equally high. Why?

8. What differences account for the fact that the graphite form of carbon is less dense than the diamond form? That the diamond (gray) form of tin (5.8 g/cc) is less dense than the white form? That the density of germanium is greater than the density of silicon but the density of silicon is less than the density of the diamond form of carbon?

9. Write equations to show the following: (a) The reaction of germanium at high temperatures with (i) oxygen, (ii) sulfur, (iii) chlorine, (iv) nitric acid. (b) The reaction of sand with coke. (c) The reactions that take place when the ore cassiterite is roasted in air. (d) The reaction of lead sulfide with lead sulfate at high temperatures. (e) The combustion of pentane, C_5H_{12}, in excess oxygen. (f) The effect of heating limestone. (g) The reaction of carbon dioxide with sodium hydroxide solution. (h) The action of carbon monoxide on iron(III) oxide. (i) The preparation of chlorine from hydrochloric acid and lead dioxide. (j) The reaction of carbon dioxide with calcium hydroxide solution. (k) The formation of the molecule shown on p. 370 from dimethyl silicon dichloride and trimethyl silicon chloride. (l) The reduction of iron(III) chloride by tin(II) chloride in water solution. (m) The action of nitric acid on lead carbonate. (n) The reaction of fused sodium carbonate with iron(II) silicate.

10. Draw the electron-dot structures for carbon monoxide, carbon dioxide, and carbon suboxide; indicate whether these are linear or angular molecules; and label the types of bonds (σ or π) and the hybridization of the carbon atom orbitals.

11. Draw sketches of the various ways in which SiO_4 tetrahedra can combine with one another to produce silicate ions having different formulas.

12. Why do silicone coatings make glass water-repellent?

13. Discuss structure and binding in the ion $SnCl_6^{-2}$.

14. Why are lead nitrate and lead acetate soluble in water, while lead chloride, lead sulfate, and lead chromate are not?

REFERENCES

McCONNELL, D., and F. H. VERHOEK. "Crystals, Minerals and Chemistry," *J. Chem. Educ.*, *40*, (1963), p. 572.

19

The Boron Family

*I claim herein as my invention . . . 2. As an improvement in the
art of manufacturing aluminium, the herein-described process,
which consists in dissolving alumina in a fused bath composed of
the fluorides of aluminium and sodium, and then passing an
electric current, by means of a carbonaceous anode, through the
fused mass, substantially as set forth.** Charles Martin Hall (1863–1914)

The elements boron, aluminum, gallium, indium, and thallium constitute
Group III of the periodic table. Their atoms all have the valence electron
configuration $s^2 p^1$. Boron is a nonmetal but the other elements are metals.
Because of its position between families of active metals and families of
nonmetals in the periodic table, this family might be expected to exhibit
bonding and structure characteristics intermediate between those of its
neighbors—characteristics which bring out some of the more subtle factors
which affect bonding and structure. Many of the similarities and trends in
properties found among carbon family elements and compounds appear
again in this family and for the same reasons. Examples are the tendency
to form covalent bonds, the formation of macromolecules, and the reluctance of heavier atoms to use valence s electrons in bonding. In comparison
with the neighboring groups to the left, all members except boron form
stable positive ions similar except in valence to the alkaline earth ions of
Group II.

There are, however, several structural features which are more or less
unique to this family. These include electron-deficient molecules such as
boron trifluoride and *bridge* bonds such as those in aluminum chloride,
Al_2Cl_6, and diborane, B_2H_6:

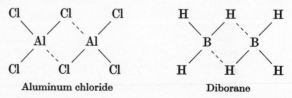

Aluminum chloride   Diborane

---

* U.S. Patent 400766, April 2, 1889.

A Broad Overview of the Boron Family

Important aspects of boron family chemistry are:

1. The atoms of these elements are larger and, except for thallium, less electronegative than those of the corresponding members of the carbon family. In addition they are smaller and more electronegative than those of the corresponding members of Group II. In all cases however, their atomic radii and electronegativities are close to those of the Group IV atoms which accounts in part for the fact that the family as a whole acts like a closer relative to the carbon family than to Group II. Table 19.1 gives some properties of boron family atoms, including the ionization energies for removal of first(I), second(II), and third(III) electrons.

Table 19.1 Some Properties of Boron Family Atoms

Element	Valence Electron Configuration	Atomic Radius (A)	Ionic Radius (A)	Ionization Energies (kcal/mole) I	II	III	Electronegativity
Boron	$2s^2\, 2p^1$	0.80	0.20	191	580	875	2.0
Aluminum	$3s^2\, 3p^1$	1.25	0.50	138	434	656	1.5
Gallium	$4s^2\, 4p^1$	1.25	0.62	138	473	708	1.6
Indium	$5s^2\, 5p^1$	1.50	0.81	133	435	647	1.5
Thallium	$6s^2\, 6p^1$	1.55	0.95(III), 1.44(I)	141	471	688	1.9

The ionization energies for the first three electrons in aluminum are 138, 434, and 656 kcal/mole respectively, compared with 176 and 346 kcal/mole for the ionization energies for the first two electrons in magnesium and 118 kcal/mole for the ionization energy for sodium. As a result of this high-energy barrier for the formation of the $+3$ ion, most of the compounds of these elements in the III oxidation state contain predominantly covalent rather than ionic bonds. The M^{+3} ions when present are very small and their $+3$ charge gives them such a large charge density (ratio of charge to radius) that they attract negative ions and other bases very strongly.

2. The stable oxidation states for the family are all zero or positive because of the relatively low electronegativities of these atoms and the fact that they need five electrons to form an anion having an inert gas configuration. The s^2p^1 valence-shell configurations give rise to the I and III oxidation states. Boron and aluminum form stable III states but much less stable I states while thallium forms a I state that is considerably more stable than the III state. Gallium and indium show a III state and less well-characterized lower oxidation states. The stability of the I state of thallium arises because of the unusual stability of the $6s^2$ energy level as with lead(II).

3. Bonding in the family is predominantly covalent but there are numerous examples of ionic compounds. An interesting comparison between some predominantly ionic and some predominantly covalent compounds of this family is given in Table 19.2. The fluorides of all members except boron have high melting points and are ionic while only indium and thallium chlorides and bromides are ionic. As was mentioned

in connection with tin halides, many covalent halides form ionic compounds when hydrated. This is especially true of the hydrated halides of this family as exemplified by hydrated aluminum chloride, $Al(H_2O)_6Cl_3$, which is ionic, being composed of hexaquoaluminum(III) ions, $Al(H_2O)_6{}^{+3}$, and chloride ions.

Table 19.2 Melting Points of Some Boron Family Halides (predominantly ionic compounds are below the line)

FLUORIDES		CHLORIDES		BROMIDES	
Compound	Melting point (°C)	Compound	Melting Point (°C)	Compound	Melting Point (°C)
BF_3	−128.7	BCl_3	−107	BBr_3	−46
AlF_3	1290	Al_2Cl_6	192	Al_2Br_6	97.5
GaF_3	950	$GaCl_3$	77.5	$GaBr_3$	121.5
InF_3	1170	$InCl_3$	586	$InBr_3$	436
TlF_3	550	$TlCl$	429	$TlBr$	456

4. These elements, particularly boron, form a number of macromolecular compounds. Examples are the oxides, X_2O_3, the sulfides, X_2S_3, and the nitrides, XN, of all but thallium. Typical of macromolecular structures is that of boron nitride (Figure 17.4).

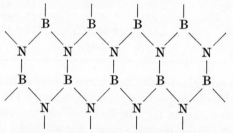

A portion of the boron nitride structure

Since nitrogen atoms supply five and boron atoms supply three valence electrons, this structure is electronically similar to carbon crystals where each atom supplies four valence electrons. Boron nitride, an unreactive, insoluble, refractory material, has a graphite-like structure consisting of layers of alternating boron and nitrogen atoms arranged as shown above. The bonding within each layer involves sp^2 hybrid orbitals on both kinds of atoms with the remaining electrons being used to form π bonds between nitrogen and boron atoms. The layers are arranged so that a boron atom lies directly below a nitrogen atom in the layer above. Van der Waals forces are the primary binding forces between layers. At pressures near 70,000 atmospheres and temperatures about 3000°C, this graphite-like structure can be converted to a structure analogous to diamond. This substance, known as borazon, is one of the hardest substances known.

5. Certain of the covalent compounds of these elements in their III oxidation states are electron-deficient molecules—molecules containing atoms with less than a noble gas valence-shell configuration. Examples are boron trifluoride, BF_3, and gallium triiodide, GaI_3, shown below.

$$
\begin{array}{cc}
\text{F} & \text{I} \\
\ddot{\text{B}}\!:\!\text{F} \quad & \ddot{\text{Ga}}\!:\!\text{I} \\
\text{F} & \text{I}
\end{array}
$$

Note the electron-deficient nature of the central atoms. These molecules, especially the chlorides and fluorides, are able to act as Lewis acids by accepting pairs of electrons from various bases as in the reaction

$$:\overset{..}{\underset{..}{F}}: \ + \ \overset{\overset{..}{F}:}{\underset{\underset{..}{F}:}{B:\overset{..}{F}:}} \ \longrightarrow \ \overset{\overset{..}{F}:}{\underset{\underset{..}{F}:}{:\overset{..}{F}:B:\overset{..}{F}:}}\ ^{-}$$

The fluoroborate ion, BF_4^-, is found in numerous salts such as sodium fluoroborate, $NaBF_4$. The bromoaluminate ion, $AlBr_4^-$, and the chlorogallate ion, $GaCl_4^-$, are also known. The ability of aluminum and gallium ions to expand their octets is illustrated by the AlF_6^{-3} and $GaCl_6^{-3}$ ions.

6. Some of the electron-deficient compounds form *three-center bonds* in which an electron pair interacts with three nuclei. One of the three nuclei then acts as a "bridge" between the other two. This is shown in Figure 19.1 for diborane, B_2H_6, in which two bridge hydrogen atoms are present. In each of these bonds, the hydrogen $1s$ orbital may be imagined to overlap with the sp^3 hybrid orbitals of both boron atoms giving rise to a single molecular orbital capable of holding two electrons.

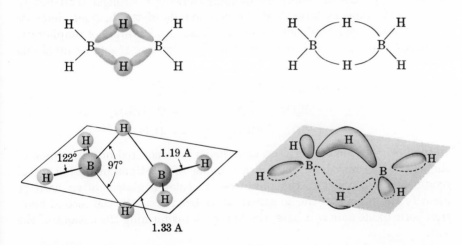

Figure 19.1 Several methods of representing the structure of diborane : The drawings emphasize the overlap of two sp^3 orbitals from boron atoms with the $1s$ orbital of hydrogen to give the bridge-bond, a two-electron bond involving three nuclei. There are two B—H—B bridges in diborane.

Bridge bonds presumed to involve p orbitals occur in aluminum chloride,

and the compound

has been reported.

In addition to three-center BHB bonds, the higher boron hydrides show three-center BBB bonds and *multicenter* bonds, as in the five-center bond

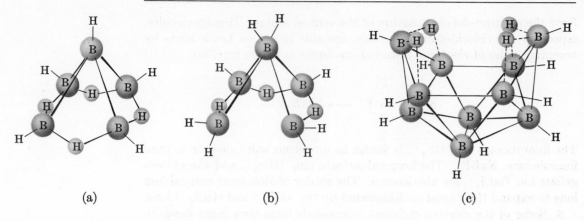

(a)   (b)   (c)

Figure 19.2 Structures of some boron hydrides: (a) Pentaborane-9, B_5H_9. (b) Pentaborane-11, B_5H_{11}. (c) Decaborane, $B_{10}H_{14}$.

binding the apical boron atom in B_5H_9 to the other four boron atoms (Figure 19.2). Here six electrons are used to bind five atoms together.

7. Amphoterism is the outstanding property of the oxides and hydroxides of the family with the boron compounds showing a stronger tendency to act as acids than as bases and the compounds of the heavier elements showing a stronger tendency to act as bases. An example of amphoteric character among the oxides is given in the following reactions involving boric oxide:

$$\text{Acidic oxide} + \text{basic oxide} \longrightarrow \text{salt}$$

$$B_2O_3 + CuO \longrightarrow Cu(BO_2)_2$$

$$P_4O_{10} + 2B_2O_3 \longrightarrow 4BPO_4$$

In the first reaction it acts as an acid, being incorporated into the anion of the salt. This reaction is one of a number of reactions involving metal oxides and boric oxide; the products are colored glasses often used to identify the metals in the so-called borax-bead test. In the second reaction boric oxide acts as a base, the boron atoms forming the cations of the salt.

Aluminum hydroxide exemplifies the amphoteric hydroxides of the family in the following reactions:

$$Al(OH)_3(s) + OH^- \longrightarrow Al(OH)_4^-, \quad \text{or} \quad (AlO_2^- + 2H_2O)$$

$$Al(OH)_3(s) + 3H_3O^+ \longrightarrow Al(H_2O)_6^{+3}$$

These reactions illustrate that either acids or bases will dissolve insoluble aluminum hydroxide. Bases produce the aluminate ion, AlO_2^-, which is probably present in solution as the hydrated species $Al(OH)_4^-$ or $Al(H_2O)_2(OH)_4^-$. Acids neutralize the hydroxide giving the hexaquo-aluminum(III) ion, $Al(H_2O)_6^{+3}$.

Two important acids in the family are (a) boric acid, H_3BO_3, which is so weak that in water it acts essentially as a monobasic acid having a K_I of 6×10^{-10} at 25°C and (b) hexaquoaluminum(III) ion, $Al(H_2O)_6^{+3}$, which undergoes the reaction

$$Al(H_2O)_6^{+3} + H_2O \rightleftarrows Al(H_2O)_5OH^{+2} + H_3O^+$$

for which K_I is 1.1×10^{-5} at 25°C. This equilibrium accounts for the fact that solutions of most aluminum salts are acidic.

The strongest base in the family is thallium(I) hydroxide, TlOH, which is similar in many ways to potassium hydroxide.

8. The metals of the family are slightly stronger reducing agents than the corresponding members of the carbon family and considerably weaker than the Group II metals. The standard oxidation potentials are given in Table 19.3. All of these metals are stronger reducing agents than would be anticipated from an examination of their high ionization potentials. However the very high hydration energy of the small M^{+3} ions lowers the overall energy requirements for the reaction in solution, thereby increasing the reducing strength in aqueous media.

The III oxidation state species of this family are all moderate to weak oxidizing agents with the thallium compounds being the strongest and the boron compounds the weakest in the series.

Occurrence. Boron occurs in nature in boric acid and in salts of various condensed boric acids, such as borax, $Na_2B_4O_7 \cdot 10H_2O$. It constitutes only about 1×10^{-3} per cent of the earth's crust.

Next to oxygen and silicon, aluminum is the most abundant of all the elements. The free element is not found in nature, but its compounds, especially the silicates, are abundant and widely distributed, being essential constituents of all important soils and rocks except limestone and sandstone. The feldspars, which are the most abundant of all the minerals in the earth's crust, are silicates of aluminum and either sodium, potassium, or calcium. Since the soil has been formed largely by the disintegration of these rocks, it is rich in the silicates of aluminum, chiefly in the form of clay. Some of the other forms in which aluminum occurs in nature are the following: corundum (Al_2O_3); bauxite, a mixture of iron oxide and hydrated aluminum oxides ($Al_2O_3 \cdot xH_2O$, formula uncertain) from which aluminum is prepared commercially; emery (Al_2O_3, colored black with oxide of iron).

The other members of the family are elements of rare occurrence in nature and were discovered by spectroscopic analysis of various minerals. Although they are widely distributed in certain classes of minerals, with the exception of a few rare ores of thallium, they have never been found to an extent of more than about 0.1 per cent of any mineral.

Uses. Only boron and aluminum among the elements of this family have much commercial significance. Aluminum and its alloys are among the most widely used of the metals; and boron is used in control rods of atomic reactors and in the manufacture of impact resistant steel. Compounds of boron have many uses.

Table 19.3 Standard Oxidation Potentials for Boron Family Elements

Conversion	$E°$ (volts/electron)
$Al + 6H_2O \longrightarrow Al(H_2O)_6^{+3} + 3e^-$	1.66
$Ga + 6H_2O \longrightarrow Ga(H_2O)_6^{+3} + 3e^-$	0.53
$In + 6H_2O \longrightarrow In(H_2O)_6^{+3} + 3e^-$	0.34
$Tl + 3H_2O \longrightarrow Tl(H_2O)_3^{+} + e^-$	0.34
$Tl + 6H_2O \longrightarrow Tl(H_2O)_6^{+3} + 3e^-$	-0.72

The Elements

Physical Properties. Table 19.4 gives some physical properties of the elements. The densities increase systematically from boron to thallium with boron and aluminum having low values. The melting point and heat of fusion are much higher for boron than for any of the others, suggesting that the boron crystal is a macromolecular structure in which the boron atoms are covalently bonded. Also, solid boron is a poor electrical conductor while the others are much better conductors, suggesting that the latter form metallic crystals. In support of this are the physical appearance, the extremely wide liquid range, the low heat of fusion, and the malleability and ductility, of aluminum, gallium, indium, and thallium. All of these are characteristics of metallic crystals.

Boron crystals are dark brown and very hard; aluminum, a silvery white when first cut, acquires a dull luster due to the formation of a thin oxide film on the metal surface; gallium is silvery white, hard, and brittle; indium is soft, malleable, and ductile with a silver metal luster; thallium is a soft gray metal which is malleable but with poor tensile strength.

Chemical Properties. Some important chemical properties of boron family elements are illustrated by the following general equations where M represents the boron family element:

1. $4M + 3O_2 \rightarrow 2M_2O_3$. High temperature required; gallium is more resistant than others; thallium also gives Tl_2O.
2. $2M + 3X_2 \rightarrow 2MX_3$. Occurs with all halogens; usually requires higher temperatures; thallium also forms TlX.
3. $2M + N_2 \rightarrow 2MN$. Occurs with boron and aluminum only.
4. $2M + 3S \rightarrow M_2S_3$. Occurs at high temperature; boron requires 1200°C; thallium gives Tl_2S.
5. $2M + 6H_3O^+ \rightarrow 2M^{+3} + 2H_2 + 6H_2O$. Occurs with all members except boron; thallium forms Tl^+.
6. $2M + 2OH^- + 2H_2O \rightarrow 2MO_2^- + 3H_2$. Boron forms metal borates on fusion; indium and thallium do not react.

Preparation of the Elements. Boron is best prepared by heating the oxide, B_2O_3, with a large excess of magnesium or aluminum, which metals act not only as reducing agents but as solvents for the reduced boron:

$$B_2O_3 + 3Mg \longrightarrow 2B + 3MgO$$

By dissolving the excess metal with acids, the crystallized boron is obtained. Prepared in this way the product is never entirely pure. Pure

Table 19.4 Some Physical Properties of Boron Family Elements

Element	Density of Solid at 25°C, g/cc	Melting Point (°C)	Boiling Point (°C)	Heat of Fusion (kcal/mole)	Crystal Structure
Boron	2.4	2300	2500	5.3	Hexagonal
Aluminum	2.7	660	2500	2.6	Face-centered cubic
Gallium	5.93	29.8	2070	1.3	Rhombic
Indium	7.29	156	2100	0.78	Cubic close-packed (distorted)
Thallium	11.85	449	1390	1.0	Cubic close-packed

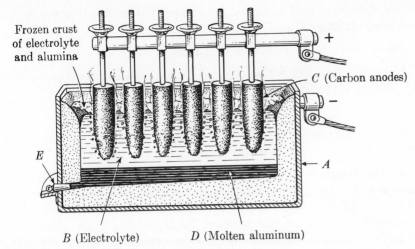

Frozen crust
of electrolyte
and alumina

C (Carbon anodes)

+

−

E

A

B (Electrolyte)   *D* (Molten aluminum)

Figure 19.3 The electrolytic production of aluminum. The process is carried out in a carbon-lined iron box which serves as the cathode, into which project carbon anodes, *C*. The box is partially filled with cryolite, Na_3AlF_6, or an artificial mixture of fluorides, and the current is turned on, generating sufficient heat to melt the cryolite. Purified aluminum oxide is then added ; it dissolves in the liquid cryolite *as an electrolyte*. Upon electrolysis it yields aluminum and oxygen. The temperature is maintained above the melting point of aluminum, and the liquid metal sinks to the bottom of the vessel, from which it is tapped off from time to time through the tap-hole, *E*. Part of the oxygen escapes as gas, and part of it combines with the carbon of the anodes, which are gradually consumed. As the oxide is electrolyzed, more is added, so that the process is continuous.

crystals have been obtained by leading hydrogen and vapor of boron tribromide over a hot (1300°C) wire of tungsten or tantalum.

All the aluminum prepared in the United States is obtained by the electrolysis of aluminum oxide (Al_2O_3) dissolved in melted cryolite, as shown in Figure 19.3.

Gallium, indium, and thallium may all be prepared by electrolysis of aqueous (usually basic) solutions of their salts. Obtaining the crude metals from their ores is sometimes difficult.

Some Important Compounds of the Boron Family

Boric Acid, H_3BO_3. This compound, known also as boracic acid, is obtained from the waters of certain hot springs, chiefly in Italy, but more commonly by treating a hot solution of sodium tetraborate ($Na_2B_4O_7$) with sulfuric acid. Boric acid, being but sparingly soluble in cold water, crystallizes on cooling:

$$Na_2B_4O_7 + 5H_2O + H_2SO_4 \longrightarrow Na_2SO_4 + 4H_3BO_3 \downarrow$$

Boric acid crystallizes in pearly flakes which are slippery to the touch. It is a mild antiseptic and is sometimes used in medicine. Its acid properties are extremely weak. When heated to fusion, it is converted into boric oxide (B_2O_3).

Metaboric Acid and Tetraboric Acid. When boric acid is gently heated, it is converted into metaboric acid, $(HBO_2)_3$:

$$H_3BO_3 \longrightarrow HBO_2 + H_2O \uparrow$$

When metaboric acid is heated to a somewhat higher temperature, the condensed tetraboric acid $H_2B_4O_7$ is formed:

$$4HBO_2 \longrightarrow H_2B_4O_7 + H_2O \uparrow$$

Peroxyborates. The action of peroxides on borates gives peroxyborates (also called perborates), one of the most important of which is

$$NaBO_3 \cdot 4H_2O$$

This is used as an antiseptic in some tooth powders and as a mild bleaching agent.

Sodium Tetraborate, $Na_2B_4O_7$, and Borax, $Na_2B_4O_7 \cdot 10H_2O$. If we add sodium hydroxide to boric acid, we get a salt of tetraboric acid having the formula $Na_2B_4O_7$. If this salt is crystallized from hot water (above 60°C), octahedral crystals of the hydrate $Na_2B_4O_7 \cdot 5H_2O$ are obtained. If crystallized from water at ordinary temperatures, prismatic crystals are obtained, which have the formula $Na_2B_4O_7 \cdot 10H_2O$ and are called *borax*.

Borax is found native in some arid regions, as in parts of California and Tibet. It is extensively used as a constituent of glass of certain kinds, and of enamels and glazes for both metal ware and pottery. It is often used in our homes to soften hard water, as a mild alkali (like washing soda, $Na_2CO_3 \cdot 10H_2O$), and as an antiseptic.

When borax is heated, it swells up in a sort of froth, owing to the escape of steam, and this soon melts to a clear glass. The glass has an excess of the acid anhydride B_2O_3 and easily dissolves many metallic oxides. It is used as a flux in joining metals together, since it dissolves the surface oxides, leaving the surfaces clear.

Structure of Borates. X-ray studies of borates reveal that many are similar to silicates with the planar BO_3 or the tetrahedral BO_4 structure unit replacing the tetrahedral SiO_4 group. For example, a typical divalent metal borate, such as calcium metaborate, $Ca(BO_2)_2$, has the chain structure shown below.

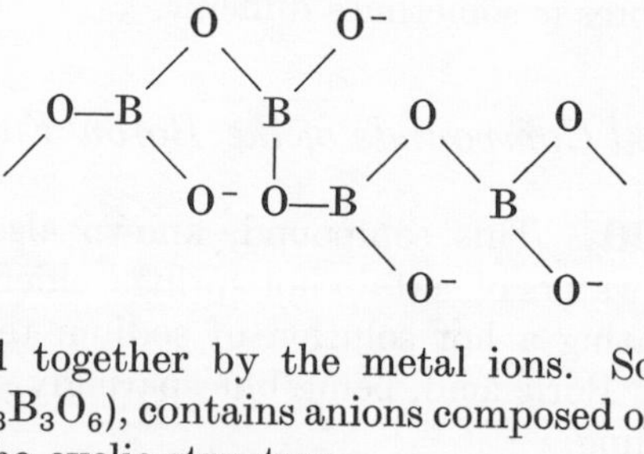

The chains are held together by the metal ions. Sodium metaborate, $NaBO_2$ (actually $Na_3B_3O_6$), contains anions composed of boron and oxygen atoms arranged in the cyclic structure

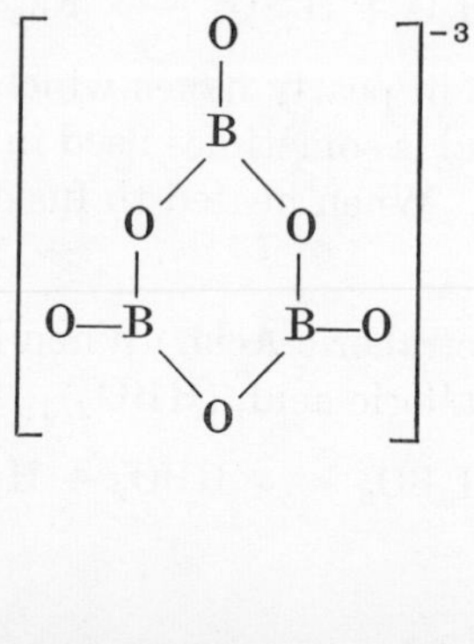

Salts containing the borate ion, BO_3^{-3}, are found only rarely as in magnesium borate, $Mg_3(BO_3)_2$.

Boric oxide, B_2O_3, is composed of imperfectly oriented layers having the structure

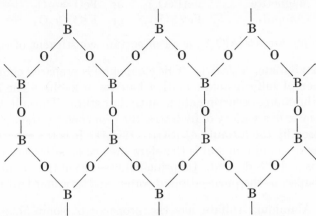

Aluminum Oxide, Al_2O_3. This compound is found in nature as the relatively pure, colorless mineral corundum and as emery when colored brown or black with iron oxide. In transparent crystals, tinted with oxides of various metals, such as chromium, titanium, cobalt, iron, and manganese, it is a precious gem stone, and includes ruby (red), sapphire (blue), Oriental topaz (yellow), and Oriental amethyst (violet). All these substances are almost as hard as diamond, and the cheaper ones, corundum and emery, are used as abrasives. The pure oxide is obtained as a white powder by heating the hydroxide:

$$2Al(OH)_3 \longrightarrow Al_2O_3 + 3H_2O$$

Less strong heating produces a porous oxide containing varying amounts of the elements of water, which, alone or mixed with silica, is used as a catalyst for dehydration reactions and in the manufacture of gasoline.

Aluminum Hydroxide, $Al(OH)_3$. This hydroxide, in a partially dehydrated form, constitutes the mineral bauxite and is the chief ore of aluminum. It is a very weak base and is therefore amphoteric, and its salts are extensively hydrolyzed in solution. It forms a colloidal jelly, which has high adsorptive properties; for this reason the colloidal hydroxide in solutions of various kinds is important in water purification and in dyeing.

Aluminum hydroxide is soluble in strong alkalies, forming metaluminates, such as $NaAlO_2$. The name spinels is given to the naturally occurring

● ● ●   ARTIFICIAL GEMS

Aluminum oxide can be melted in oxyhydrogen furnaces and obtained in crystalline form. The pure, colorless gem so produced is called white sapphire; by adding the requisite metallic oxide almost any desired color can be given the gem stone. The rubies and sapphires so produced are identical in almost every respect with the natural stones and are artificial gems, not imitation ones.

metaluminates of bivalent metals and to similar compounds, such as

Spinel	$Mg(AlO_2)_2$,	or	$MgO \cdot Al_2O_3$
Franklinite	$Zn(FeO_2)_2$,	or	$ZnO \cdot Fe_2O_3$
Magnetite	$Fe(FeO_2)_2$,	or	$FeO \cdot Fe_2O_3$
Chromite	$Fe(CrO_2)_2$,	or	$FeO \cdot Cr_2O_3$

Calcium aluminate, $Ca(AlO_2)_2$, is an important constituent of cement.

Aluminum Sulfate, $Al_2(SO_4)_3$. This compound is prepared commercially by the action of sulfuric acid on either bauxite or kaolin. The latter is a silicate of aluminum occurring abundantly in nature. The sulfate crystallizes from water in a variety of hydrates, the usual one having the composition expressed by the formula $Al_2(SO_4)_3 \cdot 18H_2O$. It is the cheapest of the soluble salts of aluminum and is therefore the one most largely used when a salt of this metal is desired. Its principal uses are in the manufacture of alum and paper, in the purification of water, and as a mordant in dyeing.

Alums. Aluminum sulfate has the property of combining with the sulfates of the alkali metals to form compounds called alums. Thus, with potassium sulfate the reaction is expressed by the equation

$$K_2SO_4 + Al_2(SO_4)_3 + 24H_2O \longrightarrow 2KAl(SO_4)_2 \cdot 12H_2O$$

The sulfates of some other trivalent metals form similar compounds with the alkali sulfates, and these compounds are also called alums, though they contain no aluminum. They all crystallize in octahedra and contain twelve molecules of water of hydration. The alums most frequently prepared are the following:

Potassium alum	$KAl(SO_4)_2 \cdot 12H_2O$
Ammonium alum	$NH_4Al(SO_4)_2 \cdot 12H_2O$
Ammonium iron alum	$NH_4Fe(SO_4)_2 \cdot 12H_2O$
Potassium chrome alum	$KCr(SO_4)_2 \cdot 12H_2O$

Gallium and indium form alums such as $KGa(SO_4)_2 \cdot 12H_2O$, but thallium does not.

Aluminum Silicates. The silicates of aluminum are widely and abundantly distributed. Sometime in the history of the earth's formation its surface must have been composed of a solid igneous rock formed by the cooling of the molten mass. The various silicates of aluminum constitute by far the largest percentage of these igneous rocks. Most important of these are the feldspars, known as orthoclase ($KAlSi_3O_8$), albite ($NaAlSi_3O_8$), and microcline, which has the same chemical composition as orthoclase but is different in crystalline structure. The gradual disintegration, or weathering, of these rocks through various agencies, such as the action of air and water, has resulted in the formation of the mineral constituents of the soil. The changes taking place in the process are often very complex and are not well understood. Thus, in the weathering of orthoclase the potassium is removed, together with a portion of the silica, while at the same time water enters into chemical combination with the residue. In this way there is formed the soft, plastic mineral kaolin or kaolinite ($Al_2Si_2O_7 \cdot 2H_2O$; this is often written $Al_2O_3 \cdot 2SiO_2 \cdot 2H_2O$). Large quantities of this mineral are sometimes found deposited in beds in fairly pure form. More often it has been carried away by running water and mixed with various other products resulting from the crushing and weathering of rocks, especially silica (sand) and compounds of iron, calcium, and magnesium, in this way forming the product known as clay. It is evident, therefore, that clay is extremely variable in composition, though the essential constituent appears to be kaolin. Fuller's earth is a name given to certain clays that possess the property of decolorizing and otherwise purifying fats and oils. Bentonite is a special type of clay mined in South Dakota; it has varied uses.

SUMMARY

The boron family, located between families of active metals and families of nonmetals, shows the properties of both. In physical properties boron is a nonmetal, and aluminum, gallium, indium, and thallium are metals. The tendency to form covalent bonds is strongest with boron and aluminum; the tendency to form ionic bonds is strongest with gallium and thallium. The oxides of all members are amphoteric.

Common oxidation states of these elements are 0, I, and III, with the III state being the most stable for all except thallium. Many of the simple covalent compounds of these elements are electron-deficient since they have only six valence electrons. Some of these electron-deficient compounds act as Lewis acids, accepting pairs of electrons from bases as in the formation of BF_4^-. Certain electron-deficient compounds stabilize their structures by forming bridge structures with multicenter bonds.

Members of this family, especially boron, form a number of macromolecular structures. Among these are boron nitride, boric oxide, the solid borates and metaborates, and aluminum oxide.

SOME SPECIAL TERMS

| Bridge bonds | Electron-deficient | Three-center bonds |
| Alum | molecules | Spinel |

QUESTIONS AND PROBLEMS

1. Account for the fact that thallium forms a stable I oxidation state, while the I states of the other elements of the boron family are unstable.
2. Explain why indium bromide is predominantly ionic, but gallium bromide is covalent.
3. In what respects are the following compounds similar to BN: graphite, AlN, SiC?
4. Draw electron-dot structures for BF_3 and BF^{-4} and suggest likely molecular shapes for these species.
5. Write equations to show: (a) The ionization of aluminum hydroxide in water solution. (b) The reaction of sodium hydroxide with aluminum hydroxide. (c) The reaction of hydrochloric acid with aluminum hydroxide. (d) The reaction of aluminum chloride with water. (e) The reaction of thallium hydroxide with sulfuric acid. (f) The reaction of aluminum with oxygen. (g) The reaction of aluminum with chlorine in the absence of water. (h) The

reaction of aluminum with hydrochloric acid solution. (i) The reactions of aluminum with sodium hydroxide solution. (j) The electrolysis of bauxite in melted cryolite. (k) The reaction of aluminum sulfate with calcium hydroxide solution.

6. Draw a graph of the energy required to remove three electrons from each of the elements Al, Ga, In, Tl against the standard oxidation potentials of these elements in water solution, and discuss any deviations you observe from a straight line or a smooth curve.

7. Describe the differences in the properties of boron as compared with those of the other elements of the family which lead to a classification of boron as a nonmetal and the others as metals. How do you account for these differences in terms of such factors as ionization potential, atomic size, crystal structure, etc.?

8. Distinguish among borax, boric acid, and metaboric acid. Draw a possible structure for the tetraborate ion.

9. Describe the Hall story of the discovery of aluminum (see A. B. Garrett's *The Flash of Genius*).

REFERENCES

LIPSCOMB, W. M. *Boron Hydrides*. New York: Benjamin, 1964.
GARRETT, A. B. *The Flash of Genius*. Princeton, N.J.: Van Nostrand, 1962.

PART FIVE

ENERGY AND
CHEMICAL CHANGE

20

Energy

*En poursuivant mes recherches, j'établis entre autres que, quelle que soit la voie par laquelle une combinaison s'accomplisse, la quantité de chaleur dégagée par sa formation était toujours constante, soit que la combinaison ait lieu directement, soit qu'elle ait lieu indirectement et à différentes reprises.**

Germain Henri Hess (1802–1850)

The chemist is concerned with both of the major entities of the universe—*matter* and *energy*. Having learned something about the particle nature of matter, the structure, combining property, and modes of motion of these particles, chemists then ask such questions as the following about energy:

1. How much energy is involved in chemical change?
2. How is this energy associated with the bonding and motion of chemical species?
3. How can this energy be measured?
4. How can information about energy in chemical change be helpful in predicting whether systems are stable?

The purpose of this chapter is to find the answers to some of these questions and to learn to use energy data to increase our understanding of chemical change. The answers are found in consideration of the following topics:

1. The heat of reaction and its correlation with bond energies.
2. The ways that energy is associated with molecules.
3. Calculation of energies in crystals.
4. The heat capacity of substances.
5. Some applications of thermochemical data.

---

* "In the course of my investigations I ascertained that by whatever steps a compound may come to be formed, *the quantity of heat developed in the formation is always constant*; it makes no difference whether the compound be formed in a direct or indirect way, all at once, or at different times." (The quotation is from *Bulletin de la classe physico-mathématique publié par l'Académie Impériale des Sciences de St. Pétersbourg*, vol. I (1842), p. 150.)

Heats of Reaction

Initial and Final States. In the simple reaction between hydrogen and oxygen to form water,

$$2H_2 + O_2 \longrightarrow 2H_2O \tag{1}$$

there is a change in which the bonds connecting hydrogen atoms to hydrogen atoms and oxygen atoms to oxygen atoms become bonds connecting hydrogen atoms to oxygen atoms. The *initial state*, which has hydrogen atoms connected to hydrogen atoms and oxygen atoms connected to oxygen atoms, changes to the *final state*, which has hydrogen connected to oxygen. The *heat of reaction* represents the energy difference between the initial and final states. We measure the heat of reaction by arranging for the reaction to take place in a calorimeter.

Factors to be Specified in Going from the Initial to the Final State. In order for the energy measurements to be meaningful, we must describe the initial and final states exactly. We must know (a) the physical state of the substance: the energy change in the reaction represented by Equation (1) would evidently depend upon whether liquid water or gaseous water was formed. We must know also (b) the average temperature at which the reaction takes place, since the energy change is different at different temperatures (see Figure 20.7). Further, the temperature rise in the calorimeter must be kept small; otherwise the measurements will be imprecise because they refer to a temperature range rather than to a specific temperature. We must know (c) whether the reaction takes place at constant pressure or at constant volume, especially for gaseous substances. We must of course know (d) how much material reacts. Since in chemistry we may interpret equations in terms of numbers of moles of substances reacting and formed, the measurements are always converted to the reaction of the number of moles specified in the equation. Specifying the necessary quantities for reaction (1),

$$2H_2(g) + O_2(g) \longrightarrow 2H_2O(l); \qquad 25°C; \qquad V \text{ constant} \tag{2}$$

we state that 2 moles of gaseous hydrogen reacts with 1 mole of gaseous

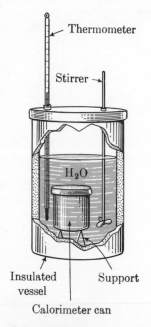

Thermometer

Stirrer

H_2O

Insulated vessel

Support

Calorimeter can

Figure 20.1 A calorimeter.

● ● ● APPARATUS TO MEASURE THE HEAT OF REACTION

A calorimeter consists, typically, of a metal can or thick-walled vessel immersed in a known amount of water in an insulated vessel. Energy liberated in a reaction taking place inside the can will be transferred to the can and water as heat, and raise the temperature. If we measure the temperature rise, and know the masses and specific heats of the can and water, we can calculate how many calories have been absorbed by the can and water, and, hence, how much energy was liberated in the reaction.

Experiment : A reaction took place in a calorimeter consisting of a steel bomb weighing 4,050 g immersed in 1,900 g of water and the temperature rise measured 2.80°C. The specific heat of steel is 0.107 and that of water is 1.00. Calculate the energy in calories liberated by the reaction.

To raise the bomb temperature requires 2.80 × 4050 × 0.107 = 1213 cal.
To raise the water temperature requires 2.80 × 1900 × 1.00 = 5320 cal.
Total heat liberated = 1213 + 5320 = 6533 cal.

oxygen to form 2 moles of liquid water, all at 25°C in a constant-volume calorimeter.

Internal Energy. Our measurements give us only the difference in energy between the initial and final states, but tell us nothing about the actual energies of the two states. Scientists assign to molecules an internal energy, denoted by E, which will include all the unmeasurable and difficultly measurable energies of formation of the particles in the nucleus, of the nucleus itself, of the internal electron shells, and the like, as well as some energies which can be measured, such as the energies of bonding, kinetic energies of motion, etc. If one agrees to this assignment, then the measured energy is the difference in the value of E for the final molecules and E of the initial molecules, which we can write

$$\Delta E = \text{(final state energy)} - \text{(initial state energy)} \qquad (3)$$

Note that the Δ symbol always represents the difference *final* minus *initial* (Figure 20.2). Since the energy for each kind of molecule depends upon the number of molecules present, it is convenient to let the symbol E represent the internal energy per mole of substance. We then have for the change in internal energy in reaction (2):

$$\Delta E = 2E_{H_2O(l)} - (2E_{H_2(g)} + E_{O_2(g)}) \qquad (4)$$

Since energy is evolved in the reaction written, the internal energy $2E_{H_2O(l)}$ is less than the internal energy $2E_{H_2O(g)} + E_{O_2(g)}$, and ΔE is a negative quantity. We write

$$2H_2(g) + O_2(g) \longrightarrow 2H_2O(l); \qquad 25°C; \qquad \Delta E = -134.86 \text{ kcal} \qquad (5)$$

It is no longer necessary to specify that the volume is constant, since the change ΔE is a property of the reactants and products; the quantity which we measure in the calorimeter, however, is equal to ΔE only when the measurement is made at constant volume.

Enthalpy. The value of ΔE is obtained in a closed container such as that used in the calorimeter; the experiment is done at *constant volume*. However, most reactions in the laboratory are carried out in a container open to the atmosphere and are therefore done at constant pressure rather than at constant volume. The heat of reaction at constant pressure will be different from that at constant volume.

To illustrate the significance of the last sentence, let us consider what the energy release would be if we were to burn hydrogen in oxygen in an open container (or at least in a cylinder with a weightless piston). We must imagine the atmosphere pressing down on the system and tending to compress it. If compression occurs, then work is being done on the system, and the system will acquire energy because of the work done on it. If, however, the system expands, it will be doing work on the atmosphere, and pushing it back; hence this system will have less energy by the amount used up in doing work on the atmosphere.

When 2 moles of hydrogen burns in 1 mole of oxygen to form liquid water at 25°C in an open calorimeter,

$$2H_2(g) + O_2(g) \longrightarrow 2H_2O(l); \qquad 25°C; \qquad P \text{ constant} \qquad (2')$$

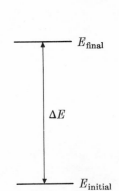

Figure 20.2 Energy difference $\Delta E = E_F - E_I$ between final and initial states.

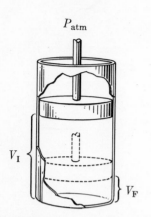

Figure 20.3 Pressure-volume work at constant pressure, $P\Delta V = P(V_F - V_I)$.

there will be a volume decrease. The volume shrinks as 2 moles of hydrogen, occupying about 48,000 ml at 25°C, and 1 mole of oxygen, occupying 24,000 ml, react to form 36 ml of liquid water. The prevailing atmosphere therefore does work on the system, pushing it down into the smaller volume. As a result of doing work, the work energy is added to the system and appears as heat in the calorimeter. The amount of work done is measured by the product of the pressure by the change in volume, $P\Delta V$. (Figure 20.3.)

For our reaction this becomes

$$P\Delta V = 1 \text{ atm} \times (36 \text{ ml} - 72{,}000 \text{ ml}) \tag{6}$$

which, on conversion to calorie units, is equal to -1780 cal, and the amount of heat evolved is increased by this amount. Since most chemical reactions are carried out in open beakers at constant pressure, pressure-volume work of this sort is almost always obligatory. The amount of $P\Delta V$ work done when only solids and liquids are the reactants and products is small, since they do not show much change in volume on reaction, and for these systems the pressure-volume work may be neglected. Whenever gases are involved, however, and there is a change in the number of moles of gas in passing from the initial to the final state, the pressure-volume work becomes important.

It is convenient to have a name and symbol for the energy which includes the pressure-volume work. It is called the *enthalpy* (en'thal py) and is given the symbol H. The enthalpy change and the change in internal energy are related by the equation

$$\Delta H = \Delta E + P\Delta V \tag{7}$$

For the reaction of hydrogen and oxygen at 25°C, ΔH is then $(-134.86 \text{ kcal}) + (-1.78 \text{ kcal})$, and we write

$$2H_2(g) + O_2(g) \longrightarrow 2H_2O(l) \qquad \Delta H_{298} = -136.64 \text{ kcal} \tag{8}$$

Here the subscript on ΔH indicates that the value is for the reaction at 25°C (298°K). Equation (8) implies that each substance has an enthalpy value just as it has a value for the internal energy, and for the reaction written

$$\Delta H = 2H_{H_2O(l)} - [2H_{H_2(g)} + H_{O_2(g)}] = -136.64 \text{ kcal} \tag{9}$$

Since the enthalpy change represents the difference *final* minus *initial*, it is evident that the enthalpy change for the reverse reaction is the nega-

• • •   HEAT AND WORK

The terms *energy, pressure, work,* and *heat* may be defined as follows:

Energy is the capacity to do work.

Pressure is force per unit area, or force/area.

Work is a means of transferring energy which results in a displacement against opposition: Displacement × opposition = distance × force = distance × area × force/area = volume × pressure.

Heat is a means of transferring energy. It may result in a temperature rise, in which case it is measured by the product (heat capacity) × (temperature rise); or it may result in a change of phase such as melting, in which case it is measured by (heat of fusion) × (mass of material).

tive of the enthalpy change of the forward reaction. Thus for the reaction

$$2H_2O(l) \longrightarrow 2H_2(g) + O_2(g) \qquad (10)$$

$$\Delta H = 2H_{H_2(g)} + H_{O_2(g)} - 2H_{H_2O(l)} = +136.64 \text{ kcal} \qquad (11)$$

Enthalpy of Formation. The enthalpy change which occurs when a compound is formed from its elements is a convenient reference quantity.

In order to make it easy to compare in a meaningful way the ΔH values for different reactions, chemists have agreed to a set of *standard states*. The standard states chosen are the physical forms of the elements and compounds stable at 1 atm pressure and a specified temperature, commonly 25°C. The enthalpy change when one mole of a compound in its standard state is formed from its elements in their standard states is known as the *heat of formation* or *enthalpy of formation*, symbolized by $\Delta H_f°$. Since the stable physical forms of hydrogen and oxygen are the gaseous forms at 1 atm and 25°C, the heat of formation of $H_2O(l)$ at 25°C is evidently one-half (for 1 mole) of -136.64, or -68.32 kcal. Heats of formation of other substances are given in Table 20.1.

Addition of Enthalpy Values. A table of heats of formation gives the data for calculating the enthalpy changes of many reactions. These calculations are based upon the law of conservation of energy, as expressed

Table 20.1 Enthalpy of Formation ($\Delta H_{f298}°$ in kcal/mole)

$H_2O(g)$	-57.79	$CO(g)$	-26.41
$H_2O(l)$	-68.32	$CO_2(g)$	-94.05
$HCl(g)$	-22.06	$NaCl(s)$	-98.23
$HBr(g)$	-8.66	$KCl(s)$	-104.18
$HI(g)$	$+6.20$	$CaCl_2(s)$	-190.0
$SO_2(g)$	-70.96	$CaCO_3(s)$ calcite	-288.45
$H_2S(g)$	-4.81	$AlCl_3(s)$	-166.3
$N_2O(g)$	$+19.49$	$CuO(s)$	-37.6
$NO(g)$	$+21.60$	$Cu_2O(s)$	-40.4
$NH_3(g)$	-11.04	$CuSO_4(s)$	-184.00
$Br_2(g)$	$+7.34$	$CuSO_4 \cdot 5H_2O(s)$	-544.45
$Br_2(l)$	0	$PbCl_2(s)$	-85.85
$CH_4(g)$	-17.89	$C_2H_4(g)$	$+12.50$
$CH_3Cl(g)$	-19.6	$C_2H_2(g)$	$+54.19$
$CH_3OH(l)$	-57.02	$C_3H_8(g)$	-24.82
$CHCl_3(l)$	-31.5	$n\text{-}C_4H_{10}(g)$	-29.81
$CCl_4(l)$	-33.3	$n\text{-}C_5H_{12}(g)$	-35.00
$C_2H_6(g)$	-20.24	$iso\text{-}C_5H_{12}(g)$	-36.92
$C_2H_5OH(l)$	-66.35	$neo\text{-}C_5H_{12}(g)$	-39.67
$CH_3CO_2H(l)$	-116.4	$C_6H_6(l)$	$+11.72$
$H^+(aq)$	0	$OH^-(aq)$	-54.96
$Na^+(aq)$	-57.28	$Cl^-(aq)$	-40.02
$K^+(aq)$	-60.04	$Br^-(aq)$	-28.90
$Ag^+(aq)$	$+25.31$	$I^-(aq)$	-13.37
$Ca^{+2}(aq)$	-129.77	$S^{-2}(aq)$	$+10.0$
$Cu^{+2}(aq)$	$+15.39$	$CO_3^{-2}(aq)$	-161.63
$Zn^{+2}(aq)$	-36.43	$SO_4^{-2}(aq)$	-216.90
$H(g)$	$+52.1$	$C(g)$	$+171.7$
$O(g)$	$+59.1$	$N(g)$	$+112.5$

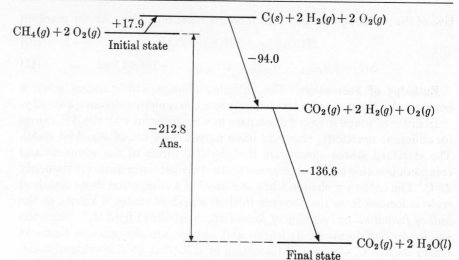

Figure 20.4 Enthalpy changes in the reaction $CH_4(g) + 2O_2(g) \rightarrow CO_2(g) + 2H_2O(l)$.

by Hess' law of constant heat summation (1840) which states that the total change in reaction heat is *independent* of the number and kind of steps by which the reaction is carried out. The enthalpy change for a reaction is simply the *sum of the enthalpy changes for each of the steps that* may be visualized in a reaction. Hence if one wishes to know the enthalpy change in the reaction

$$CH_4(g) + 2O_2(g) \longrightarrow CO_2(g) + 2H_2O(l); \qquad 25°C \qquad (12)$$

one may imagine that the reaction occurred as a result of the following steps (Figure 20.4):

$$CH_4(g) \longrightarrow C(s) + 2H_2(g) \qquad (13)$$

$$C(s) + O_2(g) \longrightarrow CO_2(g) \qquad (14)$$

$$2H_2(g) + O_2(g) \longrightarrow 2H_2O(l) \qquad (15)$$

The enthalpy change in each of these reactions is known, since the first reaction is the reverse of the reaction of formation of methane from its elements, the second represents the formation of carbon dioxide, and the enthalpy change for the third is twice the enthalpy of formation for 1 mole of water, found in the table. Writing the values, one obtains

$$CH_4(g) \longrightarrow C(s) + 2H_2(g) \qquad \Delta H = -\Delta H_f° = +17.9 \text{ kcal} \qquad (13)$$

$$C(s) + O_2(g) \longrightarrow CO_2(g) \qquad \Delta H = \Delta H_f° = -94.0 \text{ kcal} \qquad (14)$$

$$2H_2(g) + O_2(g) \longrightarrow 2H_2O(l) \qquad \Delta H = 2\Delta H_f° = -136.6 \text{ kcal} \qquad (15)$$

Addition of the equations, striking out the quantities appearing on both sides of the arrow, and adding the ΔH values, gives

$$CH_4(g) + C(s) + O_2(g) + 2H_2(g) + O_2(g) \longrightarrow$$

$$C(s) + 2H_2(g) + CO_2(g) + 2H_2O(l) \qquad (16)$$

$$CH_4(g) + 2O_2(g) \longrightarrow CO_2(g) + 2H_2O(l)$$

$$\Delta H_{298} = 17.9 - 94.0 - 136.6 = -212.8 \text{ kcal} \qquad (12)$$

Similar calculations can be made for any reaction in which the enthalpies of formation are known for the compounds appearing in the equation. The step equations to be added are chosen in such a way that addition of these step equations leaves only the over-all equation for the desired reaction, as illustrated above.

Enthalpy Changes in Physical Processes Such as Vaporization. The difference between the enthalpy change in the reaction forming liquid water and that forming gaseous water can be determined by measuring the enthalpy change in a nonchemical process, that of vaporization. The chemist's shorthand for this process is written

$$H_2O(l) \longrightarrow H_2O(g) \tag{17}$$

This again gives the quantity concerned (1 mole) and specifies the physical state. The heat change in this process, at constant temperature and constant pressure, measures the change in enthalpy. At 100°C, the boiling point of water, the measured value is 9713 cal and we write

$$H_2O(l) \longrightarrow H_2O(g) \qquad \Delta H_{373} = 9713 \text{ cal} \tag{18}$$

The positive sign indicates that the enthalpy of the final state, $H_{H_2O(g)}$, is larger than that of the initial state, $H_{H_2O(l)}$, and that heat is absorbed in the vaporization process. If, instead of just *one* mole, a moles are vaporized, the equation is written

$$aH_2O(l) \longrightarrow aH_2O(g) \tag{19}$$

and the enthalpy change would be a times as great as that for one mole: $\Delta H = 9713 \times a$ cal.

If we wish to know the value of the enthalpy at 25°C we may calculate it from the value at 100°C by the method given later in this chapter. (See Figure 20.7.)

The heat of solution (Table 20.3) is another useful thermochemical value for a physical process.

Calculation of Bond Energies

Bond Energies. One of the important uses of a knowledge of enthalpy changes in reactions is for the calculation of bond energies. By the bond energy, we mean the average energy necessary to break all the bonds of a particular type in a mole of gaseous molecules to form gaseous atoms. Thus the bond energy E_{H-H} of the H—H bond is the enthalpy change in the reaction

$$H_2(g) \longrightarrow 2H(g) \qquad \Delta H = 103 \text{ kcal} \tag{20}$$
$$E_{H-H} = 103 \text{ kcal}$$

The bond energy for the O—H bond in water is one-half the enthalpy change for the reaction

$$H_2O(g) \longrightarrow 2H(g) + O(g) \qquad \Delta H = 221 \text{ kcal} \tag{21}$$
$$E_{O-H} = 110.5 \text{ kcal}$$

The bond energy of the C—H bond in methane is one-fourth of the enthalpy change for

$$CH_4(g) \longrightarrow C(g) + 4H(g) \qquad \Delta H = 398 \text{ kcal} \tag{22}$$
$$E_{C-H} = 99.5 \text{ kcal}$$

Bond energy values would be of little use if it were found that their magnitudes were different in different molecules. Fortunately it is an experimental fact that the bond energies remain nearly constant, no matter what other bonds may be present in the molecule. The C—H bond, for example, in all hydrocarbon derivatives has nearly the same value as that in methane, so that one can strike an average value for all the compounds which have been investigated, and rely upon the fact that this value will be a good approximation to the bond energy in any particular molecule. There are a few exceptions, especially in very simple molecules; thus the C=O bond energy in carbon dioxide, CO_2, is 191 kcal, but the average value for double-bonded C=O bonds in other organic molecules is 173 kcal. Table 20.2 gives average bond energies for a number of common atom combinations.

Table 20.2   Average Bond Energies

Bond	Energy (kcal/mole)	Bond	Energy (kcal/mole)
H—H	103	C—N	72
C—H	98	C—O	84
N—H	93	C—Cl	80
O—H	110	Cl—Cl	57
Cl—H	102	Br—Br	45
Br—H	87	I—I	35
I—H	71	C=C	145
C—C	82	C=O	175
N—N	38	C≡C	198
O—O	34	N≡N	225

From the table of bond energies we can estimate the values of enthalpy changes in reactions. Suppose, for example, we wish to determine the enthalpy change in the reaction for the combustion of ethanol:

$$CH_3CH_2OH(l) + 3O_2(g) \longrightarrow 2CO_2(g) + 3H_2O(l) \tag{23}$$

Writing out the structural formula for ethanol, we see that it contains five C—H bonds, one C—C bond, one C—O bond, and one O—H bond.

Hence the enthalpy change is calculated for the steps

$$CH_3CH_2OH(g) \longrightarrow 2C(g) + 6H(g) + O(g)$$
$$\Delta H \simeq 5 \times 98 + 1 \times 82 + 1 \times 84 + 1 \times 110 \tag{24}$$

$$3O_2(g) \longrightarrow 6O(g) \qquad \Delta H \simeq 3 \times 117 \tag{25}$$

$$2C(g) + 4O(g) \longrightarrow 2CO_2(g) \qquad \Delta H \simeq -4 \times 191 \tag{26}$$

$$6H(g) + 3O(g) \longrightarrow 3H_2O(g) \qquad \Delta H \simeq -6 \times 110 \tag{27}$$

Summing of the equations gives for the gas phase reaction

$$CH_3CH_2OH(g) + 3O_2(g) \longrightarrow 2CO_2(g) + 3H_2O(g)$$
$$\Delta H \simeq -307 \text{ kcal} \tag{28}$$

This may now be combined with the vaporization equations

$$CH_3CH_2OH(g) + 3O_2(g) \longrightarrow 2CO_2(g) + 3H_2O(g)$$
$$\Delta H \simeq -307 \text{ kcal} \quad (28)$$

$$CH_3CH_2OH(l) \longrightarrow CH_3CH_2OH(g) \qquad \Delta H_{298} \simeq 9.4 \quad (29)$$

$$3H_2O(g) \longrightarrow 3H_2O(l) \qquad \Delta H_{298} \simeq -3 \times 10.5 \quad (30)$$

and the three equations added:

$$CH_3CH_2OH(l) + 3O_2(g) \longrightarrow 2CO_2(g) + 3H_2O(l)$$
$$\Delta H \simeq -329 \text{ kcal} \quad (23)$$

The experimental value is -326.7 kcal, for 25°C.

The Ways Molecules Hold Energy. The values for the bond energies in Table 20.2 are calculated from ΔH values converted to 0°K. In view of their approximate character, and of the approximate constancy of ΔH values with changes of temperature (page 404), this is of little consequence to us, and we may use the tabulated values for any reasonable temperature. It is of interest, however, to examine the reason for the choice of 0°K for the tabulation.

The energy of an isolated molecule at ordinary temperatures may be thought of as being made up of several kinds of energy. (a) There will be the energy of the ultimate particles (neutrons, protons, and electrons) and of the formation of the nuclei (Chap. 25) and of the ingathering of electrons around the nuclei. We may put all these forms together and call them the *atomic energies*. Since chemical reactions do not concern themselves with the breaking apart of atoms themselves (nuclear reactions do), we are not in this chapter interested in these atomic energies, though we may wish to reserve some part of the energies of the electrons in the valence shell for consideration. (b) The atoms combine into molecules, and a second part of the energy we may call the *energy of bonding*. (c) The bonded atoms (new molecules) will normally be in their ground states (Chap. 4), but may on occasion have electrons in levels of higher energy than their ground states. This energy of *electronic excitation* constitutes another kind of energy in the molecule; it is relatively unimportant in ordinary chemical reactions, and usually needs to be considered only at very high temperatures or in photochemical processes. (d) The atoms in the molecule may vibrate with respect to each other, and the concept of *vibrational energy* is a useful one. (e) The molecule as a whole may rotate around as many as three mutually perpendicular axes through its center of gravity; the energy of this motion is a *rotational energy*. (f) There will be an energy—*translational energy*—associated with the kinetic energy of motion of the molecule in accord with the kinetic theory of gases.

Since we deal with molar quantities, it will be convenient to speak of the energy of a mole of isolated molecules. We write for the energy of a mole of isolated molecules:

$$E_M = \sum_{}^{n} \epsilon_{A_i} + \epsilon_{\text{bonding}} + \epsilon_{\substack{\text{electronic} \\ \text{excitation}}} + \epsilon_{\text{vibration}} + \epsilon_{\text{rotation}} + \epsilon_{\text{translation}} \quad (31)$$

Here the symbol $\sum_{}^{n} \epsilon_{A_i}$ represents the *sum* of the atomic energies, for all the n atoms which are present in the compound. The energy of formation of the mole of isolated molecules therefore is

$$E_M - E_A = \sum_{}^{n} \epsilon_{A_i} + \epsilon_{\text{bonding}} + \epsilon_{\substack{\text{electronic} \\ \text{excitation}}} + \epsilon_{\text{vibration}} + \epsilon_{\text{rotation}}$$

$$+ \ \epsilon_{\text{translation}} - \sum_{}^{n} \epsilon_{A_i} \qquad (32)$$

Any energy of electronic excitation which the atoms had before they became molecules is still included in $\epsilon_{\substack{\text{electronic} \\ \text{excitation}}}$, and the energy of translation of the atoms is shared between the three molecule terms $\epsilon_{\text{vibration}}$, $\epsilon_{\text{rotation}}$, and $\epsilon_{\text{translation}}$, all of which are molecular descriptions of the motion of atoms. The energy of bonding $\epsilon_{\text{bonding}}$ represents the additional energy in the molecule resulting from the distortion or overlapping of the electron clouds of the atoms when the molecule is formed. If to the term $\Delta E = (E_M - E_A)$ we add the obligatory work $P\Delta V$ representing the volume-change work in the formation of the molecules from atoms we have

$$\Delta H = \epsilon_{\text{bonding}} + \epsilon_{\substack{\text{electronic} \\ \text{excitation}}} + \epsilon_{\text{vibration}} + \epsilon_{\text{rotation}} + \epsilon_{\text{translation}} + P\Delta V \quad (33)$$

If the molecules remain in the ground state, we are not concerned with electron excitation. The last four terms are dependent upon the temperature, and become effectively zero at $0°K$; hence at $0°K$, the enthalpy change given, ΔH, closely represents $\epsilon_{\text{bonding}}$. It is for this reason that the ΔH values used in calculating bond energies are those for $0°K$.

$$\Delta H_{0°K} = \epsilon_{\text{bonding}} \qquad (34)$$

Before leaving Equation (33), we note that, if we are dealing not with isolated molecules but with matter in bulk where the molecules are close together, it may be convenient to introduce another energy term corre-

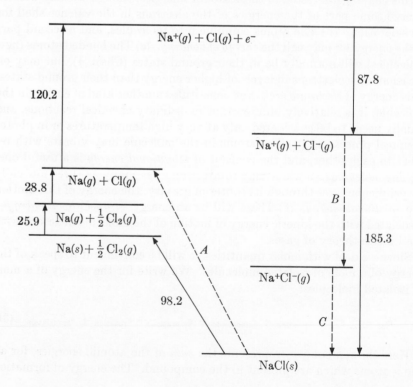

Figure 20.5 Energies in the Born-Haber cycle for sodium chloride, showing graphically the relative values of the energies.

sponding to the energy of interaction between molecules, so that the sum of the pertinent energies of a mole of molecules becomes

$$\epsilon_{\text{bonding}} + \epsilon_{\substack{\text{bonds between} \\ \text{molecules}}} + \epsilon_{\substack{\text{electronic} \\ \text{excitation}}} + \epsilon_{\text{vibration}} + \epsilon_{\text{rotation}} + \epsilon_{\text{translation}} \qquad (35)$$

To this we add the $P\Delta V$ term if we wish to consider the enthalpy. The term of largest value in this expression is, by far, the first one, $\epsilon_{\text{bonding}}$.

Omit ↑

Applications of Thermochemical Measurements

Lattice Energy of a Crystal. The lattice energy of a crystal is the energy which is liberated when sufficient gaseous ions at an infinite distance from each other come together to form a mole of crystalline ionic solid. For sodium chloride, for example, it would represent the energy change in the reaction

$$\text{Na}^+(g) + \text{Cl}^-(g) \longrightarrow \text{NaCl}(s) \qquad (36)$$

It is convenient to consider the reverse of this process, assumed to take place by the following steps (see Figure 20.5):

$\text{Na}(s) \longrightarrow \text{Na}(g)$	(energy of sublimation	$+25.9$ kcal)
$\tfrac{1}{2}\text{Cl}_2(g) \longrightarrow \text{Cl}(g)$	($\tfrac{1}{2}$ [bond energy of Cl_2]	$+28.5$ kcal)
$\text{Na}(g) \longrightarrow \text{Na}^+(g) + e^-$	(energy of ionization	$+120.2$ kcal)
$\text{Cl}(g) + e^- \longrightarrow \text{Cl}^-(g)$	(energy of ionization	-87.8 kcal)
$\text{NaCl}(s) \longrightarrow \text{Na}(s) + \tfrac{1}{2}\text{Cl}_2(g)$	($-$[energy of formation]	$-[-98.2]$ kcal)

The first equation represents the sublimation of a mole of sodium. The second equation represents the formation of a mole of chlorine atoms from $\tfrac{1}{2}$ mole of molecules. The third equation represents ionization of a mole of sodium atoms to form isolated sodium ions; the energy required is the ionization energy. The fourth equation represents ionization of chlorine atoms to form chloride ions by absorption of electrons; in this reaction the energy of the final state is less than the energy of the initial state, and the energy difference between the two is negative. The last equation is the reverse of the equation for the formation of sodium chloride from its elements, the energy of which is recorded in Table 20.1. Adding the several equations, we obtain

$$\text{NaCl}(s) \longrightarrow \text{Na}^+(g) + \text{Cl}^-(g) \qquad \text{(lattice energy} \qquad +185 \text{ kcal/mole)} \qquad (37)$$

This may be compared with the experimental value, determined by subliming $\text{NaCl}(s)$ and observing the equilibrium $\text{NaCl}(g) \rightleftarrows \text{Na}^+(g) + \text{Cl}^-(g)$, equal to 181.3 kcal/mole; the calculated value, 185 kcal/mole, is close to this.

It is instructive to show these values graphically, as in Figure 20.5. The solid arrows in the figure represent the values used in the calculation above; note that they form a closed circuit which may be considered to begin and end with $\text{NaCl}(s)$. In deference to this closed cyclic appearance, the procedure used for calculating the lattice energy is known as the Born-Haber cycle (1919). The steps involved in the experimental determination of lattice energy are represented by the dashed lines B and C, traversed in the reverse direction from the arrows. Here the symbol $Na^+Cl^-(g)$ represents a gaseous ion pair in the 1 to 1 ratio; note that its energy level is below that of $Na(s) + \frac{1}{2}Cl_2(g)$, indicating that this species is stable with respect to the free elements. Note, too, by comparing the vertical height of the arrow A with B plus C, that less energy is needed to dissociate solid sodium chloride into gaseous sodium and chlorine atoms than into gaseous ions. Hence we may expect that heating sodium chloride will produce atoms of the element; this is found experimentally to be the case, as evidenced by the yellow light from electronically excited sodium atoms produced when sodium salts are heated in a Bunsen burner flame.

Stability of Ionic Solids. Diagrams like that of Figure 20.5 are helpful in discussing the stability of ionic solids of different formulas. Chemists frequently give an explanation in terms of the stable eight-in-the-outer-shell arrangement to show that the formula of calcium chloride is $CaCl_2$ and not $CaCl$ or $CaCl_3$. Is this explanation supported by energy considerations? Figure 20.6 is a schematic diagram indicating the energy values for the formation of the three compounds.

The formation of the possible compound $CaCl(s)$ follows a path similar to that for forming $NaCl(s)$ in Figure 20.5. This path is represented in Figure 20.6 by sublimation of $Ca(s)$ (arrow $A \rightarrow B$), dissociation of $\frac{1}{2}Cl_2$ (arrow $B \rightarrow C$), ionization to Ca^+ (arrow $C \rightarrow D$), ionization of Cl^- (arrow $D \rightarrow E$), and lattice formation (arrow $E \rightarrow F$). Values of all these quantities are known except for the lattice energy of $CaCl(s)$; if this were comparable to that of $NaCl(s)$, which seems reasonable, $CaCl(s)$ would be at a lower energy level than $Ca(s) + \frac{1}{2}Cl_2(g)$. Hence the reaction

$$Ca(s) + \tfrac{1}{2}Cl_2(g) \longrightarrow CaCl(s) \tag{38}$$

should have a negative enthalpy of formation, and be a stable compound compared to the free elements.

The path for forming $CaCl_2(s)$ is similar to that of $CaCl$: sublimation of $Ca(s)$ (arrow $A \rightarrow B$), dissociation of 1 mole of Cl_2 (arrow $B \rightarrow G$), requiring twice as much energy as the dissociation of $\frac{1}{2}$ mole along arrow $B \rightarrow C$ in the previous case, removal of two electrons from $Ca(g)$ (arrow $G \rightarrow H$), requiring more than twice as much energy as the removal of a single electron along $C \rightarrow D$ (see Table 8.2), formation of two chloride ions (arrow $H \rightarrow I$, twice as long as arrow $D \rightarrow E$), and formation of the lattice along $I \rightarrow J$. The higher charge on Ca^{+2}, as compared to Ca^+, makes the lattice energy for $CaCl_2(s)$ appreciably greater than that for $CaCl(s)$ and overbalances the added energy for the second ionization $Ca^+ \rightarrow Ca^{+2} + e^-$, so that the final level of $CaCl_2(s)$ is not only below the level of $Ca(s) + Cl_2(g)$ but also below the level of $CaCl(s)$. It is then reasonable to suppose that if $CaCl(s)$ were formed, it would be only a stage on the way to the more stable state $CaCl_2(s)$, especially if more chlorine is present than the 1 to 1 atom ratio in $CaCl$. If the difference AJ is sufficiently large compared to AF, $CaCl_2(s)$ would be formed even in the absence of excess chlorine, and the reaction

$$2CaCl(s) \longrightarrow Ca(s) + CaCl_2(s) \tag{39}$$

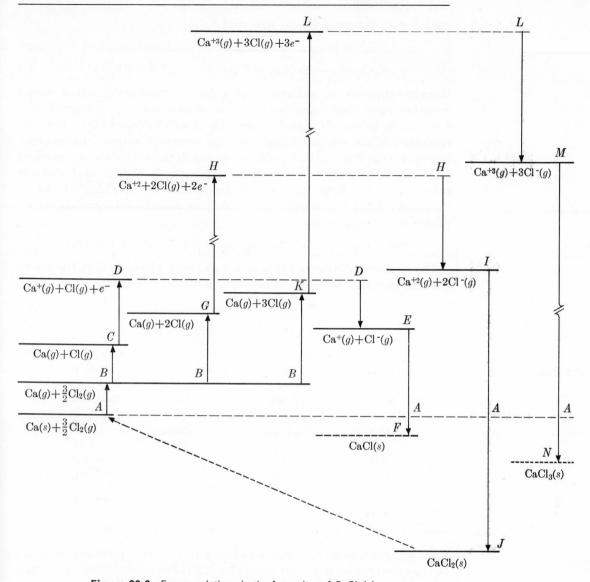

Figure 20.6 Energy relations in the formation of $CaCl_2(s)$.

would take place, forming $CaCl_2$ with the chlorine available and leaving unchanged calcium behind.

The formation of $CaCl_3(s)$ can be discussed in a similar manner. In addition to the increase of $B \to K$ and $L \to M$ to three times the values of $B \to C$ and $D \to E$, there will be a very large increase of $K \to L$ over $G \to H$ because the removal of the third electron from calcium requires that the complete Ar shell $3s^2\, 3p^6$ be broken into, and against the double positive charge already on the ion Ca^{+2}. The increase in lattice energy $M \to N$ over $I \to J$ is not great enough to overcome the high ionization energy, and $CaCl_2(s)$ remains a more stable state than $CaCl_3(s)$.

Formation of Ions in Solution. The enthalpy change for the formation of a salt solution is a quantity which can be measured if heats of solution are known. For example, we may add

$$Na(s) + \tfrac{1}{2}Cl_2(g) \longrightarrow NaCl(s) \qquad \Delta H = -98.2 \text{ kcal} \qquad (40)$$

$$NaCl(s) \longrightarrow NaCl(aq, \text{ std. state}) \qquad \Delta H = +0.9 \text{ kcal} \qquad (41)$$

Here the symbols (aq, std. state—aqueous, standard state) in the second equation have been introduced as a reminder that the properties of a solution, including the enthalpy per mole of solute, depend upon the concentration of the solution (Chap. 14). The numerical value of the enthalpy change for the formation of a solution in which the solute is in its standard state can be measured by measuring the heat of solution of 1 mole of solute in such a large quantity of water that the resulting solution is "infinitely dilute." For sodium chloride this value is $+0.9$ kcal, as shown (Table 20.3). Summation of the two equations gives

$$Na(s) + \tfrac{1}{2}Cl_2(g) \longrightarrow NaCl(aq, \text{ std. state}) \qquad \Delta H = -97.3 \text{ kcal} \qquad (42)$$

The sodium chloride solution is completely ionized, so that the above reaction may be considered to be the sum of two reactions:

$$Na(s) \longrightarrow Na^+(aq) + e^-(aq) \qquad (43)$$

$$\tfrac{1}{2}Cl_2(g) + e^-(aq) \longrightarrow Cl^-(aq) \qquad (44)$$

Table 20.3 Heats of Solution

| | [Substance (1 mole, std. state) + water $\longrightarrow$ solution (inf. dil.)] | | |
Substance	ΔH (kcal/mole)	Substance	ΔH (kcal/mole)
HCl	-17.96	KBr	$+4.79$
NaCl	$+0.93$	NaBr	-0.15
NH_4Cl	$+3.80$	H_2SO_4	-22.99
LiCl	-8.88	$CuSO_4$	-17.51
KCl	$+4.12$	$CaCl_2$	-19.82
$KClO_4$	$+12.1$	$ZnCl_2$	-17.48
KNO_3	$+8.35$	HI	-19.57

Since sodium ions and chloride ions occur also in other reactions, it would be convenient if we knew ΔH values for each of these reactions separately. The hydrated electron, however, is not a stable species; consequently the enthalpy change of these reactions has not been measured. The advantage of having a separate value for each reaction of ion formation is so great, however, that chemists have agreed upon a convention which permits them to assign such values. The convention adopted is to assign the value zero for the enthalpy of the reaction

$$\tfrac{1}{2}H_2(g) \longrightarrow H^+(aq) + e^-(aq) \qquad \Delta H = 0 \qquad (45)$$

On this basis, the enthalpy of the reaction

$$\tfrac{1}{2}H_2(g) + \tfrac{1}{2}Cl_2(g) \longrightarrow H^+(aq) + Cl^-(aq, \text{ std. state}) \qquad \Delta H = -40.0 \text{ kcal} \qquad (46)$$

is all to be assigned to the reaction of chloride ion formation. Subtracting Equation (45) from Equation (46) gives

$$\tfrac{1}{2}Cl_2(g) + e^-(aq) \longrightarrow Cl^-(aq, \text{ std. state}) \qquad \Delta H = -40.0 \text{ kcal} \qquad (47)$$

Subtraction of this equation from Equation (42) gives

$$Na(s) \longrightarrow Na^+(aq, \text{std. state}) + e^-(aq) \qquad \Delta H = -57.3 \text{ kcal} \qquad (48)$$

The values of enthalpies of formation of ions listed in Table 20.1 are based on this convention.

Change in Enthalpy with Change in Temperature

Effect of Temperature Changes on the Heat of Reaction. It is sometimes important to know the value of the enthalpy of reaction at a temperature different from that at which it was measured. This can be calculated by application of the law of conservation of energy. Suppose we know the value ΔH_1 for the reaction at temperature T_1 and wish to find the value ΔH_2 at temperature T_2. We can imagine two different routes for getting from reactants at T_1 to products at T_2 as shown in Figure 20.7. Starting with reactants at T_1, we may allow them to react to products at that temperature, producing the enthalpy change ΔH_1. We may then heat the products to temperature T_2. The energy required in this second process may be calculated if we know the molar heat capacity and the number of moles of each of the product substances present and, of course, the temperature change.

The value of the heat capacity of a substance will be different depending upon whether the substance is heated at constant pressure or at constant volume; in the former process, work is done against the opposing pressure as a result of the thermal expansion on heating, and more energy is required than would be needed if the volume were maintained constant. Since the enthalpy changes are determined by measuring heat changes at constant pressure, it is the molar heat capacity at constant pressure, C_p, which is to be used in the calculation of this paragraph.

Returning now to Figure 20.7, we see that the energy needed to go from reaction products at T_1 to reaction products at T_2 will be given by a sum of terms involving C_p for each reaction product times the number of moles of that product times the change in temperature $T_2 - T_1$. Specifically, for the reaction of Equation (12) the energy needed to get from reactants at T_1 to products at T_2 by the horizontal-then-vertical path, is

$$\Delta H_1 + C_{p_{CO_2}}(T_2 - T_1) + 2C_{p_{H_2O(l)}}(T_2 - T_1)$$

Alternatively we may choose the vertical-then-horizontal path, and heat the reactants to T_2 and allow them to react to form products at that temperature. The energy needed is then

$$C_{p_{CH_4}}(T_2 - T_1) + 2C_{p_{O_2}}(T_2 - T_1) + \Delta H_2$$

Since both paths start at the same place—reactants at T_1—and end at the same place—products at T_2—the energy changes in the two paths must be the same, or

$$C_{p_{CH_4}}\Delta T + 2C_{p_{O_2}}\Delta T + \Delta H_2 = \Delta H_1 + C_{p_{CO_2}}\Delta T + 2C_{p_{H_2O(l)}}\Delta T \qquad (49)$$

where the symbol ΔT represents the difference $T_2 - T_1$ between the final and initial temperatures. Rearrangement then gives

$$\Delta H_2 = \Delta H_1 + [(C_{p_{CO_2}} + 2C_{p_{H_2O(l)}}) - (C_{p_{CH_4}} + 2C_{p_{O_2}})]\Delta T \qquad (50)$$

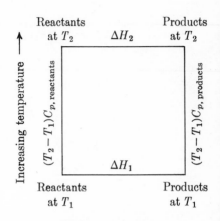

Figure 20.7 Change of heat of reaction with change in temperature.

It is important to note, in this equation, that ΔH_2 differs from ΔH_1 only by the product of a difference in heat capacities and ΔT. Since the molar heat capacities of different substances do not differ greatly from each other, and are small in any case, the term in the brackets, representing the difference between small, nearly equal quantities, cannot be large. Unless, therefore, the temperature difference ΔT is several hundred degrees, or there is a marked change in the total number of moles as shown by the chemical equation, ΔH_2 and ΔH_1 will not be materially different, and as an approximation we may say that the enthalpy changes in reactions are nearly the same at all temperatures. The only caution needed in making this affirmation is that the physical state of the substances must not change; evidently a noticeable difference would be observed if at some higher temperature, gaseous water rather than liquid water were formed in Equation (12).

Applications.

1. *Calculation of the Enthalpy of Formation of Gaseous Water at 25°C from the Value for Liquid Water.* The enthalpy of formation of liquid water at 25°C is known [Equation (8)].

$$H_2(g) + \tfrac{1}{2}O_2(g) \longrightarrow H_2O(l) \qquad \Delta H^\circ_{f298} = -68.3 \text{ kcal} \qquad (51)$$

If the heat of vaporization of water at 25°C was known,

$$H_2O(l) \longrightarrow H_2O(g) \qquad \Delta H_{298} = ? \qquad (52)$$

we could obtain the desired quantity by adding the two equations. We can calculate the heat of vaporization at 25°C from the value $+9713$ cal [Equation (18)] measured at 100°C, using the procedure of Figure 20.7, and known values for the molar heat capacities of liquid water and of steam. We have

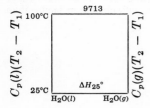

$$\Delta H_{25°C} = 9713 + C_p(l)(100 - 25) - C_p(g)(100 - 25)$$
$$= 9713 + 18 \times 75 - 7.1 \times 75$$
$$= 10.53 \text{ kcal}$$

Using this value above, the enthalpy of formation of gaseous water at 25°C becomes

$$H_2(g) + \tfrac{1}{2}O_2(g) \longrightarrow H_2O(g) \qquad \Delta H = -57.8 \text{ kcal} \qquad (53)$$

2. *Decomposition at High Temperatures.* A problem: Why are substances unstable at high temperatures? Consider, for example, the formation of quicklime by heating limestone (calcium carbonate) in a limekiln:

$$CaCO_3(s) \longrightarrow CaO(s) + CO_2(g) \qquad \Delta H^\circ_{298} = +42.7 \text{ kcal} \qquad (54)$$

According to the equation, 42.7 kcal of heat is necessary at 25°C to decompose 1 mole of solid calcium carbonate. One might guess that the reaction does not take place at this temperature because of the high energy requirement. According to the discussion above, however, the enthalpy change at the high temperature should be about the same as that at the low temperature, and calculation shows that this is the case. In other words, as much energy is needed for decomposition at the high temperature as would be required at the low temperature, yet the reaction proceeds at the high temperature but not at the low. It is evident that the high energy required in the decomposition cannot be the reason—or at least not the only reason—for the stability at 25°C; if it were the reason, limestone should be equally stable at high temperatures. The answer to this difficulty will be discussed in the next chapter.

SUMMARY

In this chapter the energy associated with changes in matter has been considered. Energy released or absorbed in such processes is viewed as a difference between the energy contained in the products and in the reactants. This is expressed in terms of changes in internal energy,

$$\Delta E = (E_{\text{products}} - E_{\text{reactants}})$$

or as changes in enthalpy,

$$\Delta H = (H_{\text{products}} - H_{\text{reactants}})$$

Positive values of ΔE or of ΔH for a process mean that the products need more energy than the reactants supply; negative values of these quantities mean reactants supply more energy than products need. For chemical reactions, a major portion of ΔH or ΔE often is associated with bond-making and bond-breaking. Hence bond energies are considered in some detail.

It is shown that ΔH and ΔE for any process may be regarded as a sum of the ΔH or ΔE values for a series of changes which, added together, give the over-all process. Thermochemical cycles set up in this way are useful in explaining why certain processes are energetically more or less feasible than other processes. These cycles also form the basis for estimating the ΔH or ΔE values for processes which are difficult to measure directly.

SOME SPECIAL TERMS

Heat
  heat of reaction
  heat of vaporization
Total energy
  atomic energy
  chemical energy
  bond energy
  lattice energy
  internal energy
Enthalpy
  enthalpy of formation
Work

Molecular energy
  energy of electronic excitation
  energy of rotation
  energy of vibration
  energy of translation
Calorimeter
Born-Haber cycle
Initial state
  final state
  standard state
Heat capacity
  molar heat capacity

QUESTIONS AND PROBLEMS

1. The internal energy, ΔE, includes what various energies of a molecule?
2. If we can identify the various energies within a molecule, why do we use

the value of the *difference* in energy of the initial and final states rather than the *total* energy of the system?

3. What is the factor that must be added to the value of the internal energy, measured at constant pressure, to give the value of ΔH? Show how the mathematical relationship between ΔE and ΔH can be derived.

4. Calculate the work done against the atmosphere $(P\Delta V)$ in calories when 1.0 g of zinc dissolves at 25°C in HCl to give H_2.

5. Five (5.00) g of carbon was burned to CO_2 in a calorimeter made of copper (sp. heat 0.093) whose mass was 2,000 g and which contained 2,500 g of water. The initial temperature of the water was 20.0°C and the final temperature, 34.5°C. Calculate the heat of combustion of carbon in calories per gram.

6. Calculate the heat of formation of C_2H_2 gas from the following data:

$$C_2H_2(g) + 2\tfrac{1}{2}O_2(g) \longrightarrow 2CO_2(g) + H_2O(l) \qquad \Delta H = -311 \text{ kcal}$$

$$C + O_2 \longrightarrow CO_2(g) \qquad \Delta H = -94.1 \text{ kcal/mole}$$

$$H_2 + \tfrac{1}{2}O_2 \longrightarrow H_2O(l) \qquad \Delta H = -68.1 \text{ kcal/mole}$$

7. Calculate the molar heat of hydrogenation of ethylene according to the equation

$$C_2H_4 + H_2 \longrightarrow C_2H_6$$

Obtain the necessary data from the data table or a handbook.

8. Explain why we can assume that the bond energy for the O—H bond is one-half the value of ΔH for the reaction $H_2O \longrightarrow 2H(g) + O(g)$.

9. From the bond energy values given on page 396, calculate $\Delta H°$ for the reaction

$$CH_4 + 2O_2 \longrightarrow CO_2 + 2H_2O$$

10. Show the reasoning that leads to the conclusion that $\Delta H°$ at 0°K is a measure of the energy of bonding.

11. Obtain the necessary energy values and calculate the lattice energy of KBr by means of the Born-Haber cycle.

12. The lattice energy of NaCl, 181 kcal, is a very high value of energy holding the Na^+ and Cl^- ions in the crystal lattice. Nevertheless, NaCl is readily soluble in water in which process the Na^+ and Cl^- ions of the crystal are pulled away from each other into solution. What new bonds must be formed in this process and what must be the order of magnitude of these bonds if the enthalpy of solution of NaCl(s) is only 0.9 kcal?

13. Of what value to the chemist is the knowledge of the energy values identified in the Born-Haber cycle? Use as an example the possibility of forming MgCl, $MgCl_2$, and $MgCl_3$.

14. Show what data are needed to calculate the value of ΔH at a higher temperature if the value of ΔH is known at a lower temperature. Use as an example the reaction $CH_4 + O_2 \longrightarrow CO_2 + H_2O$.

15. Calculate the value of $\Delta H°$ for the reaction $CaCO_3(s) \rightarrow CaO(s) + CO_2(g)$ from the following data: The heats of formation of $CaCO_3$, CaO, and CO_2 are 288.6, 151.9, and 94.1 kcal/mole, respectively.

16. Why do some oxides (CO_2) have a high temperature of vaporization and others (SiO_2) have a low?

17. Trace what kind of energy and the effect of that kind of energy on a molecule of water as you raise the temperature from solid H_2O at 0°K to a very high temperature such as 1,000,000°C. What may happen at 50,000,000°C?

18. On the basis of what you now know about the different forms of energy that make up the internal energy of a molecule, devise an explanation of why the specific heat of sodium at 25°C is .01 but the specific heat of sugar at 25°C is much higher (0.3).

19. Which gas in each of the following pairs would you expect to conduct heat faster from a hot body? Why? (a) H_2 or N_2, (b) Ar or CO_2, (c) H_2O vapor or dry air (at same temperature and pressure).

20. Why is the temperature usually lower on a hot day near or in a forest or an area of vegetation, than in a city of paved streets?

21. Why are the growing seasons usually longer in land areas surrounding a large body of water, such as Lake Erie, than in land 100 miles from the lake?

REFERENCES

CAMPBELL, J. A. *Why Do Chemical Reactions Occur?* Englewood Cliffs, N.J.: Prentice-Hall, 1965.

MAHAN, B. *Elementary Chemical Thermodynamics.* New York: Benjamin, 1963.

NASH, L. *Elements of Thermodynamics.* Reading, Mass.: Addison-Wesley, 1962.

$$CH_4 + 2O_2 \rightarrow C + 4H + 4O$$

$$C + 2O \rightarrow CO_2 \qquad \Delta H$$

$$4H + 2O \rightarrow 2H_2O \qquad \Delta H$$

21

Chemical Equilibria—Measurement of Extent of Reactions

Tout système en équilibre chimique éprouve, du fait de la variation d'un seul des facteurs de l'équilibre, une transformation dans un sens tel que, si elle se produisait seule, elle amènerait une variation de signe contraire du facteur considéré.*

Henri-Louis Le Châtelier (1850–1936)

Soon after the early chemists adopted a set of atomic weights and learned to use them in chemical calculations involving amounts of products formed from a given amount of reactant, they discovered that some reactions do not proceed to completion. Further investigation showed that many reactions are reversible. This led to the conclusion that reactions are incomplete not because reaction stops, but because an equilibrium is established in which the rate of the forward reaction is equal to the rate of the reverse reaction (Chap. 7). Research on mathematical treatment of equilibria has been done in a number of ways on data from a wide variety of sources. This research has been based on:

1. Empirical treatment of measurements on the concentration of reactants and products at equilibrium (described in this chapter).
2. Data on reaction rates (see Chap. 24).
3. Data on the energy changes during reaction (see Chaps. 20 and 22).
4. Data on the voltage of cells for oxidation-reduction reactions in solution (see Chap. 23).

---

* "Every system in chemical equilibrium undergoes, as a result of a change in one of the factors of the equilibrium, a transformation in such a direction that, if that transformation alone occurred, it would lead to a change of opposite sign in the factor considered." (The quotation is from *Annales de Mines* [8], vol. 13 (1888) p. 157.)

The Equilibrium Constant

Relations Between Concentrations of Reactants and Products at Equilibrium. One of the most useful methods in the study of science is to search for empirical mathematical relationships that may appear among the data. This kind of approach has been illustrated in developing the gas laws in Chap. 12. Another example of such a search makes use of the data in Table 21.1. Here the equilibrium concentrations, in moles per liter, of hydrogen, iodine, and hydrogen iodide in the reaction

$$H_2(g) + I_2(g) \rightleftarrows 2HI(g) \tag{1}$$

are recorded for eight different experiments at the same temperature, starting with different amounts of reactants and products and allowing the reactions to proceed to equilibrium. In the first five experiments various concentrations of hydrogen and iodine were mixed and allowed to come to equilibrium; in the remaining three experiments various amounts of hydrogen iodide were allowed to react and come to equilibrium with the hydrogen and iodine formed. The concentration of each component (H_2, I_2, and HI) was determined at equilibrium. Let us examine the data in an effort to find a useful empirical relationship between the molar concentrations of reactants and products at equilibrium.

Two types of mathematical relationships often are sought in the treatment of data: (a) a functional relationship among the observed quantities which remains constant under changing conditions, and (b) a linear-graphic relationship over a wide range of experiments. In this example we shall search for a treatment of the data which will give a constant value.

The Equilibrium Constant. The procedure that might be used in trying to discover the form of the functional relation may be summarized as follows:

One convenient way to compare two quantities (equilibrium concentrations of products and reactants, in this case) is to set up a ratio such as:

$$\frac{[\text{Products}]_{eq}}{[\text{Reactants}]_{eq}}$$

Table 21.1 Molar Concentrations of H_2, and I_2, and HI at Equilibrium and Ratios of Equilibrium Concentrations at 425.5°C

Trial	$[H_2]_{eq}$	$[I_2]_{eq}$	$[HI]_{eq}$	$\dfrac{[HI]_{eq}}{[H_2]_{eq}[I_2]_{eq}}$	$\dfrac{[HI]^2_{eq}}{[H_2]_{eq}[I_2]_{eq}}$
Starting with H_2 *and* I_2					
1.	4.5647×10^{-3}	0.7378×10^{-3}	13.544×10^{-3}	4.022×10^3	54.47
2.	3.5600×10^{-3}	1.2500×10^{-3}	15.588×10^{-3}	3.531×10^3	55.04
3.	2.9070×10^{-3}	1.7069×10^{-3}	16.482×10^{-3}	3.322×10^3	54.75
4.	2.2423×10^{-3}	2.3360×10^{-3}	16.850×10^{-3}	3.217×10^3	54.20
5.	1.8313×10^{-3}	3.1292×10^{-3}	17.671×10^{-3}	3.084×10^3	54.49
Starting with HI					
6.	1.1409×10^{-3}	1.1409×10^{-3}	8.410×10^{-3}	6.461×10^3	54.34
7.	0.4953×10^{-3}	0.4953×10^{-3}	3.655×10^{-3}	14.90×10^3	54.45
8.	0.4789×10^{-3}	0.4789×10^{-3}	3.531×10^{-3}	15.40×10^3	54.36

Since there are two reactants, hydrogen and iodine, the denominator might be written as a sum, as a difference, as a product, or as a quotient of the equilibrium concentrations of these. Let us try the product—i.e., $[H_2]_{eq} \times [I_2]_{eq}$, since this is proportional to the number of collisions in unit time between the two kinds of molecules (Chap. 24).

Let us use the ratio

$$\frac{[HI]_{eq}}{[H_2]_{eq} \times [I_2]_{eq}}$$

and see if the data of Table 21.1, when substituted into this equation, reveal a simple relationship between the equilibrium concentrations of products and reactants. Column 5 of Table 21.1 shows the results of this calculation—this quotient is *not* constant but varies from 3×10^3 to 15×10^3. Perhaps a different arrangement of terms will prove more successful. Let us try another type of treatment.

If the product $[H_2]_{eq} \times [I_2]_{eq}$ is a measure of the rate of molecular collisions between H_2 and I_2 in the forward reaction, then the product $[HI]_{eq} \times [HI]_{eq}$ should be a measure of the rate of collision between hydrogen iodide molecules in the reverse reaction. Let us try the ratio

$$\frac{[HI]^2_{eq}}{[H_2]_{eq} \times [I_2]_{eq}}$$

Column 6 of Table 21.1 shows that the quotient is a *constant* (within experimental error) for all eight experiments given in the table. Note that the same constant is obtained in approaching the equilibrium from either side—i.e., the ratio is the same whether one starts with hydrogen and iodine or with hydrogen iodide. This constant may be called an *equilibrium constant*.

It is evident then that a relationship exists between the equilibrium concentrations of products and reactants. The form of this relationship for the reaction

$$H_2 + I_2 \rightleftarrows 2HI \tag{1}$$

is

$$\frac{[HI]^2_{eq}}{[H_2]_{eq} \times [I_2]_{eq}} = \text{constant} = K \text{ (the equilibrium constant)} \tag{2}$$

It now remains to be seen if such a relation exists in other equilibria.

All Equilibria Can Be Described with an Equilibrium Constant. Extensive experiments with this and many other chemical equilibria reveal that a constant relation between equilibrium concentrations of products and reactants exists for each equilibrium, at constant temperature. To obtain this constant, the equilibrium concentrations of products and reactants must be substituted into a ratio-type equation of the proper form. The form needed to give a constant is related to the balanced chemical equation and is illustrated below for a generalized equation.

Consider the chemical equation

$$aA + bB \rightleftarrows cC + dD \tag{3}$$

The form of the equation shows that the reaction occurs in the ratio a moles of A to b moles of B to give c moles of C and d moles of D.

The mathematical form needed to obtain a constant relation between equilibrium concentrations of products and reactants is

$$K = \frac{[\text{C}]_{\text{eq}}^{c} \times [\text{D}]_{\text{eq}}^{d}}{[\text{A}]_{\text{eq}}^{a} \times [\text{B}]_{\text{eq}}^{b}} \tag{4}$$

Note that in this form the equilibrium concentrations are raised to the power of the coefficient of the component in the balanced chemical equation. The constant K is known as the equilibrium constant. It is constant for any reaction at a given temperature. The form of the equilibrium-constant equation for several reactions is given in Table 21.2.

Table 21.2 Form of Equilibrium-Constant Equations for Various Chemical Equilibria

Chemical Equation	Form of Equilibrium-Constant Equation
$2\text{H}_2 + \text{O}_2 \rightleftarrows 2\text{H}_2\text{O}$	$K = \dfrac{[\text{H}_2\text{O}]_{\text{eq}}^{2}}{[\text{H}_2]_{\text{eq}}^{2} \times [\text{O}_2]_{\text{eq}}}$
$\text{N}_2\text{O}_4 \rightleftarrows 2\text{NO}_2$	$K = \dfrac{[\text{NO}_2]_{\text{eq}}^{2}}{[\text{N}_2\text{O}_4]_{\text{eq}}}$
$\text{N}_2 + 3\text{H}_2 \rightleftarrows 2\text{NH}_3$	$K = \dfrac{[\text{NH}_3]_{\text{eq}}^{2}}{[\text{N}_2]_{\text{eq}} \times [\text{H}_2]_{\text{eq}}^{3}}$
$4\text{HCl} + \text{O}_2 \rightleftarrows 2\text{H}_2\text{O} + 2\text{Cl}_2$	$K = \dfrac{[\text{H}_2\text{O}]_{\text{eq}}^{2} \times [\text{Cl}_2]_{\text{eq}}^{2}}{[\text{HCl}]_{\text{eq}}^{4} \times [\text{O}_2]_{\text{eq}}}$

We shall find that the equilibrium constant is a very useful tool in the mathematical treatment of all types of equilibria.

Calculation of Values of K_{eq}. The simplest calculation of an equilibrium constant can be made if all the molar concentrations of reactants and products are known, as they are in Table 21.1. It is also possible to obtain equilibrium concentrations of all components if the *inital* concentration of the starting materials and the *equilibrium* concentration of one component are known; this is based on the fact that the chemical equation relates the amounts of reactants consumed to the amounts of products formed.

This is illustrated by the following problem.

PROBLEM 1. ■ Calculate the value of the equilibrium constant, K_{eq}, for the reaction

$$2\text{NO} + \text{O}_2 \; \underset{\longleftarrow}{\overset{\longrightarrow}{}} \; 2\text{NO}_2 \tag{5}$$

if, after mixing 1 mole of NO and 1 mole of O_2 in a 2-liter flask at 1 atm and 10°C, it is found that the equilibrium concentration of NO is 0.3 mole/liter.

SOLUTION
The formula for the equilibrium constant is

$$K_{\text{eq}} = \frac{[\text{NO}_2]_{\text{eq}}^{2}}{[\text{NO}]_{\text{eq}}^{2} [\text{O}_2]_{\text{eq}}} \tag{6}$$

(a) *Calculation of equilibrium concentration of NO, O$_2$, and NO$_2$.* Values for each of these concentrations are obtained from the above data and from information in the balanced equation as follows:

$$2NO + O_2 \rightleftharpoons 2NO_2 \qquad (5)$$

Concentrations of	NO	O$_2$	NO$_2$
At start of experiment	$\dfrac{1\ mole}{2\ liters} = 0.5\ \dfrac{mole}{liter}$	$\dfrac{1\ mole}{2\ liters} = 0.5\ \dfrac{mole}{liter}$	0 moles
At equilibrium	$0.3\ \dfrac{mole}{liter}$ (given in problem)	$0.4\ \dfrac{mole}{liter}$ (calculated)	$0.2\ \dfrac{mole}{liter}$ (calculated)

The calculated values for [O$_2$] and [NO$_2$] are obtained by using information given by the chemical equation. We started with 0.5 mole/liter of NO and ended with 0.3 mole/liter; hence 0.2 mole/liter reacted. According to the chemical equation, 2 moles of NO will use 1 mole of O$_2$ in reacting; hence 0.2 mole/liter of NO will use 0.1 mole/liter of O$_2$, leaving (0.5 − 0.1) = 0.4 mole/liter. Similarly the chemical equation tells us that 2 moles of NO will form 2 moles of NO$_2$; hence 0.2 mole/liter of NO will form 0.2 mole/liter of NO$_2$.

(b) *Calculation of the value of K_{eq}.* Substituting these values of the equilibrium concentrations of NO, O$_2$, and NO$_2$ into the formula for the equilibrium constant,

$$K_{eq} = \frac{[NO_2]_{eq}^2}{[NO]_{eq}^2[O_2]_{eq}} = \frac{(0.2)^2}{(0.3)^2(0.4)} = 1.1\ at\ 10°C \qquad (7)$$

Variety of Equilibrium Processes. Of the great variety of physical and chemical equilibria, those in which we shall be primarily interested in this chapter are:

1. Equilibria in gaseous systems.
   Example: H$_2$(g) + I$_2$(g) $\rightleftharpoons$ 2HI(g)
2. Equilibria in ionization of water.
   Example: H$_2$O + H$_2$O $\rightleftharpoons$ H$_3$O$^+$ + OH$^-$
3. Equilibria in ionization of weak electrolytes.
   Example: CH$_3$CO$_2$H + H$_2$O $\rightleftharpoons$ H$_3$O$^+$ + CH$_3$CO$_2^-$
4. Equilibria in slightly soluble solids.
   Example: AgCl(s) $\rightleftharpoons$ Ag$^+$(aq) + Cl$^-$(aq)
5. Equilibria involving hydrolysis.
   Example: H$_2$O + CH$_3$CO$_2^-$ $\rightleftharpoons$ CH$_3$CO$_2$H + OH$^-$

Uses of K_{eq}. The equilibrium constant is an exact measure of the extent of an over-all reaction. The voltage of cells and the standard free energy changes of reactions are also exact measures of the extent of reaction;

●●●   EXAMPLES OF SEVERAL EQUILIBRIUM PROCESSES

1. Melting $\rightleftharpoons$ freezing
2. Dissolving $\rightleftharpoons$ crystallizing
3. N$_2$ + 3H$_2$ $\rightleftharpoons$ 2NH$_3$

4. AgCl(s) $\rightleftharpoons$ Ag$^+$(aq) + Cl$^-$(aq)
5. H$_2$O + H$_2$O $\rightleftharpoons$ H$_3$O$^+$ + OH$^-$

they will be discussed in Chaps. 22 and 23. A low value of the equilibrium constant indicates that the over-all reaction proceeds only slightly to the right as the equation is written; a large value of K_{eq} indicates that the over-all reaction proceeds far to the right.

An example of a system in which the position of equilibrium is far to the right is

$$H_2(g) + Cl_2(g) \rightleftharpoons 2HCl(g) \tag{8}$$

$$K_{eq} = \frac{[HCl]^2_{eq}}{[H_2]_{eq}[Cl_2]_{eq}} = 2.18 \times 10^{33} \text{ at } 25°C \tag{9}$$

An example of a system in which the position of equilibrium is far to the left is

$$N_2(g) + O_2(g) \rightleftharpoons 2NO(g) \tag{10}$$

$$K_{eq} = \frac{[NO]^2_{eq}}{[N_2]_{eq}[O_2]_{eq}} = 4.26 \times 10^{-31} \text{ at } 25°C \tag{11}$$

A second use of the equilibrium constant is that it makes possible the calculation of the equilibrium concentration of reactants and products at a given temperature.

PROBLEM 2. ■ The value of K_{eq} for the reaction $N_2 + 3H_2 \rightleftharpoons 2NH_3$ is 9.5×10^{-4} at 500°C. Calculate the equilibrium concentration of each of the components if the starting amounts are 1.000 mole of nitrogen and 1.000 mole of hydrogen in a 2.000 liter flask at 500°C.

SOLUTION. (a) *Calculation of concentrations if x moles of NH_3 is formed per liter.*

$$N_2 + 3H_2 \rightleftharpoons 2NH_3 \tag{12}$$

Concentrations of	N_2	H_2	NH_3
At start of experiment	$\dfrac{1.000 \text{ mole}}{2.000 \text{ liters}} =$ 0.500 mole/liter	$\dfrac{1.000 \text{ mole}}{2.000 \text{ liters}} =$ 0.500 mole/liter	0 moles
At equilibrium	$\left(0.500 - \dfrac{x}{2}\right)\dfrac{\text{mole}}{\text{liter}}$ since by the chemical equation $\frac{1}{2}$ mole of N_2 is used to form 1 mole of NH_3	$\left(0.500 - \dfrac{3}{2}x\right)\dfrac{\text{mole}}{\text{liter}}$ since by the chemical equation $\frac{3}{2}$ mole of H_2 is used to form 1 mole of NH_3	$x\dfrac{\text{mole}}{\text{liter}}$

(b) *Calculation of equilibrium concentrations of H_2, N_2, and NH_3.* Substituting the values from (a) in the formula for the equilibrium constant gives

$$K_{eq} = \frac{[NH_3]^2_{eq}}{[N_2]_{eq}[H_2]^3_{eq}} = \frac{x^2}{\left(0.500 - \dfrac{x}{2}\right)\left(0.500 - \dfrac{3}{2}x\right)^3} = 9.5 \times 10^{-4} \tag{13}$$

Algebraic solution for x gives

$$x = 7.4 \times 10^{-3} \text{ mole/liter} = NH_3 \text{ concentration}$$

Therefore,

$$[N_2] = 0.500 - \frac{x}{2} = 0.500 - 0.004 = 0.496 \text{ mole/liter}$$

$$[H_2] = 0.500 - \frac{3}{2}x = 0.500 - 0.011 = 0.489 \text{ mole/liter}$$

A third use of K_{eq} is to calculate the effect of a change in the concentration of one of the reactants on the position of equilibrium. This effect is called the mass-action effect and will be described later in the chapter.

Shifting the Position of Equilibrium

We have indicated that the condition for equilibrium is: speed of forward reaction equals speed of reverse reaction. We now ask what effect such variables as concentration, catalysts, temperature, or pressure will have on the rates of these reactions and, as a result, on the position of equilibrium. Will any of these change the value of K_{eq} or shift the position of equilibrium? Experimentally we shall find the following:

1. *A catalyst* increases the speeds of both the forward and the reverse reactions, making it possible for the reaction to come to equilibrium more quickly, but does not change K_{eq} or the position of equilibrium (Figure 21.1).

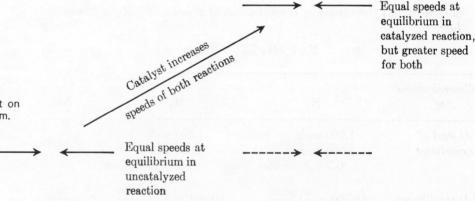

Figure 21.1 Effect of a catalyst on the speeds of reaction at equilibrium.

● ● ●   EXACT VALUES OF EQUILIBRIUM CONSTANTS

While we have said that the equilibrium constant is, for constant temperature, a *constant*, it must be recognized that the quotient involving concentrations of reactants and products is not exactly constant but shows a dependence upon the total amount of dissolved substance or, for gases, upon the total pressure. True constancy would be obtained only if the gaseous reactants and products formed ideal mixtures, or if the solutions similarly were ideal, showing negligible attractive forces between solutes and between solutes and solvent.

For simplicity we shall discuss the principles of chemical equilibria in terms of concentrations and assume for discussion purposes that we are dealing with ideal gas mixtures and ideal solutions. Experimental results indicate that the use of actual concentrations and pressures of real gases gives values that are sufficiently good approximations for many purposes, but this use will be less reliable at high pressures and for concentrated solutions, where deviations from ideality are greatest. For these systems especially, but for precise values in any case, a corrected concentration called the *activity* must be used (Chap. 22).

2. *A change of pressure* will affect the position of equilibrium (but not the value of K_{eq}) only for those reactions in which the volume of the products is not the same as the volume of the reactants. For example, the position of equilibrium and the value of K_{eq} for

$$H_2 + I_2 \rightleftarrows 2HI \qquad (1)$$

are unaffected by pressure changes. However, the position of equilibrium in the reaction

$$N_2 + 3H_2 \rightleftarrows 2NH_3 \qquad (12)$$

$$\underset{\text{reactants} = 4}{\text{Total volume of}} \qquad \underset{\text{products} = 2}{\text{Total volume of}}$$

will be shifted by a change in pressure. An increase in pressure will shift the position of equilibrium in the direction of the smaller volume, in this case towards the formation of more ammonia. This is in accord with a sweeping generalization about equilibria first stated by Henri-Louis Le Châtelier in 1887.

For example, for every four moles of reactants that disappear (3 moles of H_2 and 1 mole of N_2), two moles of products (2 moles of NH_3) appear. In a given vessel, two moles will exert less pressure than four moles. If, therefore, the pressure on this equilibrium mixture is increased, at constant temperature, the system can attempt to relieve this stress by shifting the position of equilibrium to the smaller number of moles—in this case toward the right. If the pressure is decreased, the position of equilibrium will be shifted toward the larger number of moles—in this case toward the left. These predictions are verified experimentally as shown in each horizontal row of Table 21.3. Each row lists the per cent of ammonia

Temperature (°C)	1 atm	50 atm	100 atm	200 atm	600 atm	1,000 atm
200	15.3	74.4	81.5	85.8	95.4	98.3
400	0.48	15.3	25.1	36.3	65.2	79.8
500	0.13	5.6	10.6	17.6	42.2	57.5
600	0.05	2.25	4.5	8.2	3.1	31.4
800	0.022	0.57	1.19	2.2	—	—
1,000	0.004	0.21	0.45	0.9	—	—

Table 21.3 Percentage of Ammonia Present at Equilibrium in an Original Mixture of 1 Mole of Nitrogen and 3 Moles of Hydrogen at Various Pressures and Temperatures

present in equilibrium mixtures at various pressures at a fixed temperature. In each case the initial molar ratio of nitrogen to hydrogen is 1 to 3.

In general, the position of equilibrium is shifted toward smaller volumes at higher pressures and toward larger volumes at lower pressures. If the number of moles on each side of the equation for a reaction is the same, as

● ● ●   THE PRINCIPLE OF LE CHÂTELIER

The effect of forces that tend to disturb a system in equilibrium was studied by Le Châtelier. He made the observation that "if a stress is applied to a system in equilibrium, a new equilibrium will be established in which the position of equilibrium has been shifted in such a direction as to relieve the applied stress."

in $H_2 + I_2 \rightleftarrows 2HI$, a change in pressure at constant temperature will not bring about a change in the position of equilibrium since the system is unable to change in such a way as to relieve the stress.

3. *A change in concentration* will affect the position of equilibrium but not the value of K_{eq}. The effect of a change in concentration on an equilibrium can also be used to illustrate the application of Le Châtelier's principle. Let us consider as an example what would happen to the equilibrium systems of Table 7.2,

$$H_2 + I_2 \rightleftarrows 2HI$$

if, with $[H_2]$ and $[I_2]$ each equal to 0.00224 and $[HI] = 0.01552$, we were to add additional I_2 molecules in amount equivalent to increasing the concentration of iodine by 0.01000 mole/liter. In terms of Le Châtelier's principle this addition of iodine would constitute a *stress*. The new equilibrium to be established must relieve the stress; that is, it must decrease the concentration of iodine. The only way it can do this is for iodine to react with hydrogen to form more hydrogen iodide. Hence, in the reestablished equilibrium there will be more hydrogen iodide and less hydrogen than in the original equilibrium.

Since the quotient

$$\frac{[HI]^2_{eq}}{[H_2]_{eq}[I_2]_{eq}}$$

must remain constant for this reaction at this temperature we may use the equilibrium constant to calculate the concentrations of hydrogen and hydrogen iodide in the new equilibrium. In doing this we find:

$$[H_2]_{eq} = 6.75 \times 10^{-4}M \text{ (down from } 2.24 \times 10^{-3}M)$$

and

$$[HI]_{eq} = 1.865 \times 10^{-2}M \text{ (up from } 1.552 \times 10^{-2}M)$$

Succinctly stated, the application of stress to the equilibrium, in the form of added iodine, has caused the position of equilibrium to shift toward the right, so as to relieve the applied stress (Figure 21.2).

Conversely, if the concentration of any component is decreased, the position of equilibrium will be shifted so that more of that component will be produced. If, for example, some hydrogen iodide were removed from the equilibrium mixture, the new equilibrium would contain less hydrogen and iodine as a result of a shift of the equilibrium position toward hydrogen iodide. In this way the imposed stress—the removal of some or one of the components—is partially relieved.

4. *A change in temperature* will change the value of the equilibrium constant, and hence the position of equilibrium, in a manner which can be predicted by application of Le Châtelier's principle. Therefore, the temperature must be specified for each equilibrium. One needs only to think of an increase in temperature as resulting from the addition of heat, and of a decrease in temperature as the removal of heat. If heat is absorbed in a chemical reaction, we may consider heat to be a reactant. The attempt to raise the temperature is an attempt to add heat—the *stress*—and the position of equilibrium shifts in such a way as to relieve the stress, namely

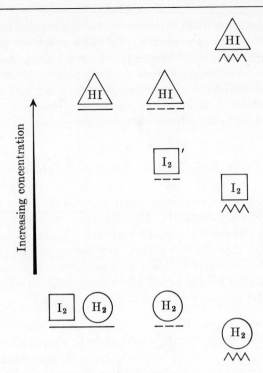

Figure 21.2 Change of position of equilibrium in $H_2 + I_2 \rightleftarrows 2HI$ by adding additional iodine. Equilibrium is originally established at the concentration levels indicated at the left (equilibrium 1). Addition of 0.1 mole/liter of iodine momentarily raises the concentration to $[I_2]'$, disturbing the equilibrium. To relieve the added stress, I_2 and H_2 react, lowering their concentrations to the values at the right (equilibrium 2), and forming HI, which raises its concentration to the new position of equilibrium.

—————   Initial equilibrium 1
– – –   Momentary intermediate state
∧∧∧   Final equilibrium 2

by using heat (the reactant) to produce more of the reaction product. If heat is evolved in a reaction, the attempt to relieve the stress of applied heat (temperature rise) causes the position of equilibrium to shift toward the reactants. The formation of ammonia is an example of the second case:

$$N_2(g) + 3H_2(g) \longrightarrow 2NH_3(g) \qquad \Delta H^\circ_{f_{298}} = -22.08 \text{ kcal} \qquad (14)$$

and increase in temperature shifts the position of equilibrium to the left, as shown in the figures in any one of the vertical columns in Table. 21.3.

The application of Le Châtelier's principle may perhaps be more readily obvious if we include the heat of reaction in the chemical equation

$$N_2 + 3H_2 \rightleftarrows 2NH_3 + \text{Heat} \qquad (15)$$

Addition of heat now pushes the position of equilibrium to the left, since displacement in that direction tends to use up heat in the attempt of the system to relieve the applied stress. The formation of hydrogen iodide, however, is favored by an increase in temperature, since ΔH° is positive,

$$H_2(g) + I_2(g) \longrightarrow 2HI(g) \qquad \Delta H^\circ_{f_{298}} = +12.4 \text{ kcal} \qquad (16)$$

$$\text{Heat} + H_2 + I_2 \rightleftarrows 2HI \qquad (17)$$

and addition of heat causes the position of equilibrium to shift to the right.

Le Châtelier's principle may be used to predict whether the equilibrium constant for a given reaction increases or decreases when the temperature is changed. In endothermic reactions the forward reaction is favored by an increase in temperature and the reverse reaction is favored by a temperature decrease. Hence the change in K_{eq} for these reactions parallels the temperature change, increasing when temperature is increased and decreasing when the temperature is decreased. In exothermic reactions the forward reaction is favored by a temperature decrease and the reverse reaction is favored by a temperature increase. Hence, in exothermic reactions, K_{eq} changes in the opposite sense to the change in temperature.

Equilibria in Ionic Reactions in Aqueous Solution

Reactions involving ionic reactants often proceed at rates too fast to measure by any ordinary methods. Nevertheless, such reactions are frequently reversible, and reach the equilibrium state almost instantaneously because of their high rates. The positions of these equilibria can be measured, and the concentrations existing at equilibrium can be fitted into appropriate expressions for the equilibrium constants. In this section we consider some of the common ionic equilibria.

Ionization of Weak Acids. We have already seen (Chap. 7) that acids react with water to form hydronium ions and the anions of the acid. If the acid is a strong acid, such as hydrochloric acid, this reaction goes so far toward completion that, in the usual dilute solutions of the laboratory, no measurable concentration of hydrogen chloride molecules remains in the solution when equilibrium is established:

$$HCl + H_2O \longrightarrow H_3O^+ + Cl^- \tag{18}$$

With weak acids, however, an equilibrium is established in which undissociated acid molecules remain. For the reaction of acetic acid, for example,

$$CH_3CO_2H + H_2O \rightleftharpoons H_3O^+ + CH_3CO_2^- \tag{19}$$

we write the equilibrium constant

$$K_{eq} = \frac{[H_3O^+]_{eq} \times [CH_3CO_2^-]_{eq}}{[H_2O]_{eq} \times [CH_3CO_2H]_{eq}} \tag{20}$$

However, dilute solutions are virtually all water—the number of moles of solute is negligible when compared with the number of moles of water. Under these conditions the equilibrium concentration of water is both large and constant while the concentrations of the other components in the equilibrium may vary over a relatively wide range. Because it is both inconvenient and unnecessary to include this large constant value of $[H_2O]_{eq}$ in calculations involving K_{eq}, a modified equilibrium-constant expression, noted here as the ionization constant, K_{ion}, is defined. In K_{ion} the equilibrium concentration of water is excluded from the right-hand side of the equation as in

$$K_{ion} = \frac{[H_3O^+]_{eq}[CH_3CO_2^-]}{[CH_3CO_2H]_{eq}} \tag{21}$$

Such modified equilibrium-constant expressions, from which the concentration of solvent water has been excluded, are used for all ionic equilibria in dilute aqueous solutions.*

The value of the ionization constant may be determined by measuring the concentration of ions in the solution of the weak acid.

PROBLEM 3. ■ In a solution made by dissolving 0.10000 mole of acetic acid in enough water to make one liter of solution, the hydronium-ion concentration was found to be 0.00134 molar. Calculate the ionization constant of acetic acid.

SOLUTION

By Equation (19), one acetate ion is formed for each hydronium ion when acetic acid ionizes. Consequently, the acetate-ion concentration is equal to the hydronium-ion concentration:

$$[H_3O^+] = [CH_3CO_2^-] = 0.00134 \text{ molar}$$

Similarly one acetic acid molecule disappears for each hydronium (or acetate) ion formed, and the concentration of acetic acid is equal to the difference between the amount originally present and the amount which ionizes:

$$[CH_3CO_2H] = 0.10000 - 0.00134 = 0.09866 \text{ molar}$$

These values are substituted into the expression for the ionization constant [Equation (21)]:

$$K_{ion} = \frac{(0.00134)(0.00134)}{0.09866} = 1.82 \times 10^{-5} \tag{22}$$

Ionization constants for a number of acids are given in Table 21.4.

Common-Ion Effect. Since the ionization of a weak acid involves an equilibrium, any change in the concentration of one of the substances present must change the position of equilibrium, in the direction predicted by Le Châtelier's principle. If, for example, we add acetate ions to a solution of acetic acid, the position of the equilibrium in reaction (19) must shift toward the left, to relieve the stress of the increased acetate-ion concentration. A shift to the left can occur only by the reaction of acetate ions with hydronium ions already present in the solution; this reaction reduces the concentration of hydronium ions. The observed result is thus a decrease in the acidity of the solution, due to the shift in the position of equilibrium when acetate ions are added to an acetic acid solution. (Of course we cannot add a solution containing acetate ions alone; some positive ions must also be present. Sodium acetate solution, for example, will contain sodium ions and acetate ions, since sodium acetate, being a salt and a strong electrolyte, is completely ionized.) Such a displacement of the position of an ionic equilibrium, due to the addition of an ion involved in the equilibrium, is called the *mass action effect* or *common-ion effect*.

---

* The practice of excluding the water concentration from the ionization-constant expression also covers up our ignorance as to the exact formula for the hydronium ion (Chap. 7). If this were $H_9O_4^+$, the water concentration might have to appear in the denominator as $[H_2O]^4$. Actually the symbol $[H_3O^+]$ in the numerator is an approximation for the activity of hydrogen ion (p. 414) and stands for the concentration of hydrogen ion in all its forms, whether H^+, H_3O^+, $H_9O_4^+$, or whatever. Similarly, the term for water in the denominator should represent its activity; since the solutions are dilute, the activity of water is nearly that of the standard state (pure water), namely, 1 (Chap. 23), and the term for water is equal to 1 and disappears.

Table 21.4 Ionization Constants for Acids at Room Temperature

Acid	K_{ion}	Acid	K_{ion}
$HClO_4$	$\sim 10^{+9}$	CH_3CO_2H	1.82×10^{-5}
HI	$\sim 10^{+7}$	$CH_3CH_2CO_2H$	1.34×10^{-5}
HBr	$\sim 10^{+6}$	$CH_3CH_2CH_2CO_2H$	1.38×10^{-5}
HCl	$\sim 10^{+5}$	$Al(H_2O)_6^{+3}$	1.1×10^{-5}
H_2SO_4	$\sim 10^{+3}$	$C_5H_5NH^+$	6.0×10^{-6}
HNO_3	$\sim 10^{+2}$	HSO_3^-	5.0×10^{-6}
CCl_3CO_2H	2.2×10^{-1}	H_2CO_3	4×10^{-7}
$CHCl_2CO_2H$	5.7×10^{-2}	H_2S	1×10^{-7}
HO_2CCO_2H	2.1×10^{-2}	$H_3NCH_2CH_2NH_3^{+2}$	1×10^{-7}
H_2SO_3	1.3×10^{-2}	$H_2PO_4^-$	7×10^{-8}
HSO_4^-	1.0×10^{-2}	$HOCl$	1.1×10^{-8}
H_3PO_4	8×10^{-3}	$o\text{-}ClC_6H_4OH$	3.3×10^{-9}
$o\text{-}ClC_6H_4NH_3^+$	2.3×10^{-3}	HCN	2.0×10^{-9}
CH_2ClCO_2H	1.4×10^{-3}	$m\text{-}ClC_6H_4OH$	9.6×10^{-10}
$o\text{-}ClC_6H_4CO_2H$	1.1×10^{-3}	NH_4^+	5.7×10^{-10}
HF	6.7×10^{-4}	$p\text{-}ClC_6H_4OH$	4.2×10^{-10}
$m\text{-}ClC_6H_4NH_3^+$	5.8×10^{-4}	$(CH_3)_3NH^+$	1.6×10^{-10}
HCO_2H	1.77×10^{-4}	$H_2NCH_2CH_2NH_3^+$	8.2×10^{-11}
$m\text{-}ClC_6H_4CO_2H$	1.5×10^{-4}	HCO_3^-	4×10^{-11}
$p\text{-}ClC_6H_4NH_3^+$	1.1×10^{-4}	$CH_3NH_3^+$	2.4×10^{-11}
$p\text{-}ClC_6H_4CO_2H$	1.1×10^{-4}	$CH_3CH_2NH_3^+$	2.4×10^{-11}
$C_6H_5CO_2H$	6.68×10^{-5}	$(CH_3)_2NH_2^+$	1.7×10^{-11}
$HO_2CCO_2^-$	5.42×10^{-5}	HPO_4^-	1.3×10^{-12}
$C_6H_5NH_3^+$	2.6×10^{-5}	HS^-	1×10^{-14}

PROBLEM 4. ■ In Problem 3 the value of the ionization constant for acetic acid was found to be 1.82×10^{-5}. Calculate the $[H_3O^+]$ in a 0.1 molar solution of acetic acid in which the $[CH_3CO_2^-]$ has been increased by adding enough sodium acetate to make the sodium concentration $0.2M$.

SOLUTION
Let

$$[H_3O^+] = x$$

further,

$$[CH_3CO_2^-] = 0.2 + x \quad \text{(Acetate ion comes from two sources: the added sodium acetate and the ionized acetic acid.)}$$

and

$$[CH_3CO_2H] = 0.1 - x$$

Substituting these values in the formula for the ionization constant for acetic acid, we have

$$K_{ion} = \frac{x \times (0.2 + x)}{0.1 - x} = 1.82 \times 10^{-5} \tag{23}$$

The solution to this problem requires that a quadratic equation be solved. However, an approximate solution may be obtained by observing that even in Problem 3 the hydronium-ion concentration was only 0.00134 molar, and that, by the common-ion effect, it will be even less in the present case. Consequently, since x is small, $0.1 - x$ is nearly equal to 0.1, and we may substitute 0.1 for $0.1 - x$; by similar reasoning we may substitute 0.2 for $0.2 + x$:

$$K_{\text{ion}} = \frac{x \times (0.2 + x)}{0.1 - x} \simeq \frac{x \times 0.2}{0.1} = 1.82 \times 10^{-5} \qquad (24)$$

whence

$$x = 0.91 \times 10^{-5} = 0.0000091 \text{ molar}$$

If this value of the hydronium-ion concentration is compared with its value in the absence of the added acetate ion (Problem 3), it can be seen that in this case the common-ion effect has resulted in decreasing the hydronium-ion concentration more than a hundredfold.

Ionization of Weak Bases. What has been said above about the ionization of weak acids can be applied directly to the ionization of weak bases. Here water acts as the acid in the acid-base reaction (Chap. 7):

$$H_2O + NH_3 \rightleftharpoons NH_4{}^+ + OH^- \qquad (25)$$

The ionization constant for ammonia in dilute water solution is written

$$K_{\text{ion}} = \frac{[NH_4{}^+]_{\text{eq}}[OH^-]_{\text{eq}}}{[NH_3]_{\text{eq}}} \qquad (26)$$

The addition of ammonium chloride to the solution will displace the position of equilibrium to the left, since the ammonium ion is common to both ammonium chloride and ammonia solutions.

Ion Equilibrium for Water. Although for many purposes water may be considered an un-ionized compound, it is both an acid [Equation (25)] and a base [Equations (18) and (19)] and undergoes a self-ionization:

$$H_2O + H_2O \rightleftharpoons H_3O^+ + OH^- \qquad (27)$$

The equilibrium constant appropriate to this reaction in dilute solution is known as the ion-product constant:

$$K_w = [H_3O^+]_{\text{eq}}[OH^-]_{\text{eq}} \qquad (28)$$

Exact measurements have shown that in pure water at 25°C the numerical value of $[H_3O^+]_{\text{eq}}$ is 1×10^{-7} molar; according to the mole-for-mole requirement of the chemical equation, this must also be the concentration of $[OH^-]_{\text{eq}}$. Hence, $K_w = 1 \times 10^{-14}$ at 25°C. This value must hold not only for pure water, but for any water solution. If an acid is added to neutral water, $[H_3O^+]$ increases and $[OH^-]$ decreases; if a base is added, $[OH^-]$ increases and $[H_3O^+]$ decreases, but in each case the product, K_w, is 1×10^{-14}. For example, in a $0.01M$ hydrochloric acid solution $[H_3O^+] = 1 \times 10^{-2}$, so $[OH^-]$ must be 1×10^{-12}.

pH Value. Very slight changes in acidity are frequently of great significance, and the values of small concentrations of hydronium ions have to be written often. S. P. L. Sørensen, in 1909, suggested that a more convenient measure of acidity would be obtained if the convention was adopted of using the negative logarithm of the hydronium-ion concentration, for which he used the symbol pH.

$$pH = -\log[H_3O^+] \qquad (29)$$

According to this definition if in a solution $[H_3O^+] = 1 \times 10^{-5}$ molar, the pH of the solution is 5.0, since the logarithm of 1×10^{-5} is -5.00 and the pH is the negative of this; if in a solution $[H_3O^+] = 2 \times 10^{-5}$, the pH is 4.7 since the logarithm of 2×10^{-5} is $\overline{5}.30 = -4.7$. The pH of pure water is 7.0; solutions of pH less than this are acid; those of pH greater than 7.0 are basic.

We now know that Sørensen's definition is not completely satisfactory, especially since modern measurements of the acidity of solutions are commonly made using electrochemical cells (Chap. 23). However, the pH thus measured is approximately equal to $-\log[H_3O^+]$, and for many purposes the older definition is still useful.

Buffer Solutions. Many chemical reactions must be carried out at constant and controlled hydronium-ion concentration. A solution of pH 5.0 can be prepared by making the solution 1×10^{-5} molar in hydrochloric acid, but it cannot readily be maintained at that value, since the accidental entrance of the smallest amount of base will neutralize some of the acid and lower the hydronium-ion concentration, while addition of a small amount of acid will raise it. This difficulty is avoided by using a *buffer solution*, containing relatively high concentrations of a weak acid and a salt of that acid—for example, acetic acid and sodium acetate. This solution contains in it large reservoirs of acetic acid molecules and of acetate ions from the sodium acetate. When a small amount of base is added to the solution, it is true that some of the hydronium ions are removed to form water, but more of the acetic acid molecules then dissociate, to reestablish an equilibrium concentration of hydronium ions only negligibly different from the original concentration. The position of equilibrium in the reaction

$$CH_3CO_2H + H_2O \rightleftharpoons H_3O^+ + CH_3CO_2^- \tag{19}$$

shifts slightly to the right to compensate for the hydronium ions removed by the base. The addition of a small amount of acid simply causes the hydronium ions of the added acid to react with the acetate ions from the sodium acetate, so that again the $[H_3O^+]$ does not change. The solution is thus protected, or *buffered*, against a change in $[H_3O^+]$ on the addition of either acid or base, and maintains a constant pH, regardless of the addition of these substances. Buffer solutions containing weak bases and their salts can also be used.

Human blood is buffered at a pH of 7.2; that is, the hydronium-ion concentration is between 10^{-7} and 10^{-8} molar. It is maintained at this value by buffer mixtures, such as the weak acid, carbonic acid, and its salt, sodium bicarbonate ($NaHCO_3$). If, for any reason, the pH of the blood varies from 7.2 by a significant amount, serious consequences, even death, may follow.

Hydrolysis. It is observed that solutions of many salts have a pH different from 7.0. For example, solutions of sodium acetate, sodium cyanide, or sodium sulfide are basic, while solutions of ammonium chloride, aluminum sulfate, and copper sulfate are acidic.

All of these observations can be explained by assuming that either the cation or the anion (or both) of the salt reacts with water. Such reactions are known as *hydrolysis reactions*. If the anion reacts with water as in

$$H_2O + CH_3CO_2^- \rightleftharpoons CH_3CO_2H + OH^- \qquad (30)$$

or

$$H_2O + CN^- \rightleftharpoons HCN + OH^- \qquad (31)$$

the solution will be basic. Anions that react with water in this way are the anions of weak acids. Hence, they are relatively strong Brønsted bases. If the cation reacts with water as in

$$NH_4^+ + H_2O \rightleftharpoons H_3O^+ + NH_3 \qquad (32)$$

or

$$Al(H_2O)_6^{+3} + H_2O \rightleftharpoons H_3O^+ + Al(H_2O)_5OH^{+2} \qquad (33)$$

the solution will be acidic. Cations that react with water in this way are the cations of weak bases. Hence they are relatively strong Brønsted acids.

If both the cation and anion react with water, as in ammonium acetate,

$$\left. \begin{array}{l} NH_4^+ + H_2O \rightleftharpoons NH_3 + H_3O^+ \qquad (32) \\ H_2O + CH_3CO_2^- \rightleftharpoons CH_3CO_2H + OH^- \end{array} \right\} \longrightarrow 2H_2O \qquad (30)$$

the hydronium and hydroxide ions formed in the separate steps react with one another causing each of the separate equilibria to be displaced toward the products.

Indicators. Indicators are weak acids or weak bases in which the acid form has a color characteristically different from the color of the basic form:

$$\underset{\text{Color } A}{HInd + H_2O} \rightleftharpoons \underset{\text{Color } B}{H_3O^+ + Ind^-} \qquad (34)$$

It is evident from the equation that if $[H_3O^+]$ is small, the position of equilibrium will be far on the right, so that the solution containing the indicator will show color B.

Increase in $[H_3O^+]$ will shift the position of equilibrium to the left, so that color B fades and color A appears.

Equilibria Involving Ionic Compounds of Low Solubility

In a saturated solution of an ionic compound in which an excess of the solid is present, an equilibrium exists between the ions of the dissolved compound and the ions in the crystals of the solid form (Figure 21.3). If the compound has a low solubility, as have silver chloride, barium sulfate, or calcium fluoride, it is found experimentally that the product of the molar concentrations of the ions in solution is equal to a constant, called the solubility-product constant. Table 21.5 gives data for saturated calcium fluoride solutions, and shows the near constancy of the product $[Ca^{+2}][F^-]^2$. The form of this product, containing the square of the fluoride-ion concentration, is suggested by the molar ratios in the equation

$$CaF_2(s) \rightleftharpoons Ca^{+2} + 2F^- \qquad (35)$$

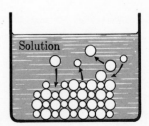

Figure 21.3 Silver ions, Ag^+ (small circles), and chloride ions, Cl^- (large circles), are constantly going into the solution and returning to the crystal of AgCl.

Table 21.5 Concentration of Calcium Ion in a Saturated Solution of Calcium Fluoride which is M Molar in Fluoride Ion

$M = [F^-]$	$[Ca^{+2}]$	$Product\,[Ca^{+2}] \times [F^-]^2$
0.1	1.8×10^{-8}	1.8×10^{-10}
0.01	1.8×10^{-6}	1.8×10^{-10}
0.001	1.7×10^{-4}	1.7×10^{-10}
0.0001	1.7×10^{-2}	1.7×10^{-10}

The complete equilibrium constant for this reaction would be written according to our previous discussions as

$$K_{eq} = \frac{[Ca^{+2}]_{eq}[F^-]^2_{eq}}{[CaF_2(s)]_{eq}} \tag{36}$$

The experimental data show that a constant is obtained when the concentration of solid calcium fluoride is omitted:

$$K_{sp} = [Ca^{+2}]_{eq}[F^-]^2_{eq} \tag{37}$$

This constant is called the solubility-product constant, or the *solubility product*.

The solubility product can be defined in the following manner: In a saturated solution of a slightly soluble electrovalent compound, the product of the molar concentrations of the ions formed, raised to the proper powers as suggested by the chemical equation for the solution process, is constant, and this constant is called the solubility-product constant.*

Determination of K_{sp}. Values of K_{sp} are calculated from the measured molar solubilities of the salts as illustrated by the following problem.

PROBLEM 5. ■ The solubility of calcium fluoride is 2.73×10^{-3} g/100 ml at 25°C. Calculate K_{sp}.

SOLUTION

Solubility in moles/liter $= 2.73 \times 10^{-3} \dfrac{g}{100\,ml} \times \dfrac{1\,mole}{78\,g} \times \dfrac{1,000\,ml}{1\,liter}$

$$= 3.5 \times 10^{-4} \text{ moles/liter}$$

Equilibrium involved:

$$CaF_2 \rightleftharpoons Ca^{+2} + 2F^-$$

$$\text{Solubility} = [Ca^{+2}]_{eq} = 3.5 \times 10^{-4}$$

From the chemical equation two moles of fluoride ion is formed for each mole of calcium ion; hence

$$[F^-]_{eq} = 2[Ca^{+2}]_{eq} = 2 \times 3.5 \times 10^{-4} = 7.0 \times 10^{-4}$$

$$\therefore K_{sp} = [Ca^{+2}] \times [F^-]^2_{eq} = (3.5 \times 10^{-4})(7.0 \times 10^{-4})^2$$

$$= 1.72 \times 10^{-10}$$

---

* The naive interpretation for the omission of $CaF_2(s)$ in the solubility-product expression is that, in the solid, the concentration of calcium fluoride is fixed and unchanging, being determined by the density of the solid, which fixes the number of moles per unit volume. On this basis the fixed value can be incorporated into the equilibrium constant to give a new constant, $K_{sp} = [CaF_2(s)]K_{eq} = [Ca^{+2}][F^-]^2$. The sophisticated explanation is that solid calcium fluoride is in its standard state, where its activity is unity, so that the term for calcium fluoride, being equal to 1, does not appear in the equilibrium-constant expression (cf. footnote, page 419).

Silver chloride, AgCl	1.8×10^{-10}
Silver iodide, AgI	8.7×10^{-17}
Lead chloride, $PbCl_2$	1.6×10^{-5}
Calcium fluoride, CaF_2	1.7×10^{-10}
Magnesium hydroxide, $Mg(OH)_2$	8.9×10^{-12}
Iron(III) hydroxide, $Fe(OH)_3$	6×10^{-38}
Barium sulfate, $BaSO_4$	1.0×10^{-10}
Bismuth sulfide, Bi_2S_3	1×10^{-70}

Table 21.6 K_{sp} Values for Some Common Salts at 25°C

Values for K_{sp} at 25°C for some common salts are given in Table 21.6.

Uses of K_{sp}. The solubility product is often used to: (a) calculate the solubility of a salt; (b) determine whether a precipitate will form if a certain amount of one ion is added to a solution containing the second ion involved in the equilibrium; (c) calculate the concentration of each ion involved in the equilibrium when the ions are present in a solution containing the salt in question and a second salt which contains one of the ions involved in the equilibrium. Examples of each of these uses of K_{sp} follow.

Calculation of Solubility from K_{sp}. This calculation is illustrated in Problem 6.

PROBLEM 6. ■ The K_{sp} for magnesium hydroxide is 8.9×10^{-12} at 25°C. Calculate the molar solubility of magnesium hydroxide.

SOLUTION
Equilibrium involved:

$$Mg(OH)_2(s) \rightleftharpoons Mg^{+2} + 2OH^-$$

$$K_{sp} = [Mg^{+2}]_{eq}[OH^-]_{eq}^2$$
$$\text{Solubility} = [Mg^{+2}]_{eq} = \tfrac{1}{2}[OH^-]_{eq}$$

Let

$$x = [Mg^{+2}]_{eq}$$

Then, from the chemical equation,

$$2x = [OH^-]_{eq}$$

and

$$K_{sp} = [Mg^{+2}]_{eq}[OH^-]_{eq}^2 = (x)(2x)^2 = 4x^3$$
$$4x^3 = 8.9 \times 10^{-12}$$
$$x^3 = 2.2 \times 10^{-12}$$
$$x = \sqrt[3]{2.2} \times 10^{-4} = 1.3 \times 10^{-4} \text{ moles/liter} = \text{solubility}$$

Will a Precipitate Form? A precipitate will form in a solution containing the ions of a slightly soluble salt if the product of the ionic concentrations raised to the appropriate power is greater than K_{sp}. If this ion product is less than K_{sp}, no precipitate will form because the solution is not saturated with respect to these ions.

PROBLEM 7. ■ Will a precipitate form if 500 ml of a $4 \times 10^{-4}M$ $BaCl_2$ solution is mixed with 500 ml of a $4 \times 10^{-4}M$ Na_2SO_4 solution? K_{sp} for $BaSO_4$ is 1.0×10^{-10}.

SOLUTION

The equilibrium involved is $BaSO_4(s) \rightleftarrows Ba^{+2} + SO_4^{-2}$ and

$$K_{sp} = [Ba^{+2}]_{eq}[SO_4^{-2}]_{eq} = 1.0 \times 10^{-10}$$

The final volume of the mixed solutions is 1 liter; hence the actual ionic concentrations upon mixing the solutions is

$$[Ba^{+2}] = 2 \times 10^{-4}; \qquad [SO_4^{-2}] = 2 \times 10^{-4}$$

The product of these is

$$[Ba^{+2}] \times [SO_4^{-2}] = 4 \times 10^{-8}$$

This product is greater than K_{sp}, so precipitation should occur. The amount of precipitate formed will be small, and just sufficient to reduce the product of the concentrations of the ions remaining in the solution to 1.0×10^{-10}.

Solubility and the Common-Ion Effect. Suppose that barium chloride and sulfuric acid solutions containing exactly equivalent amounts, say, 0.01 mole of each substance, are mixed. Barium sulfate will precipitate as a result of the reaction

$$Ba^{+2} + SO_4^{-2} \xrightleftharpoons{\qquad} BaSO_4(s) \tag{38}$$

Then, after the precipitate has settled, a further slight precipitation from the saturated solution can be obtained by adding an excess of either Ba^{+2} or SO_4^{-2}. This is predicted by Le Châtelier's principle, since increasing the concentration of one of the substances on the left of Equation (38) will shift the position of equilibrium to the right. The amount by which the equilibrium will shift can be calculated from the solubility-product constant and the amount of excess ion added, since an increase in $[Ba^{+2}]$, for example, must be compensated for by a decrease in $[SO_4^{-2}]$ if K_{sp} is to remain constant. The only possibility for decreasing $[SO_4^{-2}]$ is for sulfate ions to react with barium ions to precipitate barium sulfate [Equation (38)]. The use of an excess of one of the precipitating ions to remove all but a negligible quantity of the other from the solution is a common laboratory practice; it is another example of the application of the *common-ion effect*.

PROBLEM 8. ■ Calculate the concentration of the sulfate ion in a saturated solution of barium sulfate.

SOLUTION

The K_{sp} for barium sulfate is 1×10^{-10}, or

$$[Ba^{+2}] \times [SO_4^{-2}]_{eq} = 1 \times 10^{-10}$$

Let $[SO_4^{-2}]_{eq} = x$. By the chemical equation (38) the concentration of the sulfate ion must equal the concentration of the barium ion when only barium sulfate is present; so $[Ba^{+2}]_{eq} = [SO_4^{-2}]_{eq} = x$. Substituting in the expression for the solubility-product constant, we get

$$x^2 = 1 \times 10^{-10}$$

Therefore, $x = 1 \times 10^{-5}$, or 0.00001 mole of Ba^{+2} or SO_4^{-2} per liter.

PROBLEM 9. ■ Calculate the concentration of the sulfate ion in a saturated solution of barium sulfate to which barium chloride is added until $[Ba^{+2}] = 0.1M$.

SOLUTION

Let $[SO_4^{-2}]_{eq} = x$. In this case $[Ba^{+2}]_{eq}$ is no longer equal to $[SO_4^{-2}]_{eq}$, since additional barium ion is present; in fact, according to the problem, $[Ba^{+2}]_{eq} = 0.1$ molar. Substituting in the expression for K_{sp},

$$[Ba^{+2}]_{eq} \times [SO_4^{-2}]_{eq} = 1 \times 10^{-10}$$

we get

$$0.1 \times x = 1 \times 10^{-10}$$

Therefore, $x = 1 \times 10^{-9}$, or 0.000000001 mole of SO_4^{-2} per liter.

Thus, the addition of more barium ion has decreased the sulfate-ion concentration from 0.00001 molar (Problem 8) to 0.000000001 molar, as predicted by the common-ion effect.

Dissolving Insoluble Salts. If experiments can be arranged so that the concentration of silver ion or chloride ion is maintained at such a low value that $[Ag^+][Cl^-]$ is always less than K_{sp}, the usually insoluble salt silver chloride may dissolve completely. In some cases this can be accomplished by forming *complex ions* (Chap. 26). Thus, if ammonia is added to a solution containing silver ion, the complex ion $Ag(NH_3)_2^+$ is formed. This reduces the concentration of silver ion and, following Le Châtelier's principle, the position of the solubility equilibrium shifts to the right in the attempt to relieve the "stress" of the decrease in $[Ag^+]$. The shift may be represented by the heavy arrows in the equations

$$AgCl(s) \rightleftharpoons Ag^+ + Cl^- \qquad (39)$$
$$+$$
$$2NH_3$$
$$\updownarrow$$
$$Ag(NH_3)_2^+$$

If the vertical reaction of formation of $Ag(NH_3)_2^+$ goes far enough, by adding excess ammonia, $[Ag^+]$ may be made so small that the silver chloride dissolves completely.

Salts of weak acids, insoluble in pure water, commonly dissolve in solutions of strong acids as a result of removal of the anions of the salts by the formation of undissociated weak acid molecules. Thus, silver acetate will dissolve in nitric acid as a result of the displacement of the following equilibria when $[H_3O^+]$ is made very large by adding nitric acid:

$$CH_3CO_2Ag(s) \rightleftharpoons CH_3CO_2^- + Ag^+ \qquad (40)$$
$$+$$
$$H_3O^+$$
$$\updownarrow$$
$$CH_3CO_2H$$
$$+$$
$$H_2O$$

The positions of the equilibria are displaced in the direction of the heavy arrows.

SUMMARY

The principles of chemical equilibria have been presented in this chapter. Starting with the observation that many chemical reactions do not proceed to completion, the concept of chemical equilibrium is developed. This is followed by a study of chemical equilibrium for a single reaction at a given temperature from which a relation between the equilibrium concentrations of products and reactants is discovered. This relation, the equilibrium-constant expression, is shown to have general applicability for all chemical reactions at equilibrium.

The effect of various stresses such as changes in temperature, in pressure, or in concentration of reactants and products on systems in equilibrium is examined and interpreted in terms of the equilibrium constant, the position of equilibrium, and Le Châtelier's principle.

Application of equilibrium principles to gaseous systems and to reactions occurring in solution is given. This includes equilibria in solutions of weak acids and bases, the water equilibrium, the concept of pH, buffered solutions, hydrolysis, and solubility equilibria.

SOME SPECIAL TERMS

Equilibrium constant
  ionization constant
  ion-product constant
  hydrolysis constant
  solubility-product
    constant

Le Châtelier's principle
  common-ion effect
  mass-action effect
Brønsted acids and bases
Hydrolysis

Extent of reaction
Position of equilibrium
Indicator
Buffer solution
Activity
pH value

QUESTIONS AND PROBLEMS

1. Why must the temperature be specified when indicating the value of an equilibrium constant?

2. Write the expressions for the K_{eq} of the following:
   (a) $H_2(g) + Cl_2(g) \rightleftarrows 2HCl(g)$
   (b) $C(s) + H_2O(g) \rightleftarrows CO(g) + H_2(g)$
   (c) $3H_2(g) + N_2(g) \rightleftarrows 2NH_3(g)$

3. Calculate the value of K_{eq} for the reaction $H_2 + I_2 \rightleftarrows 2HI$ from the following data:

Equilibrium Concentrations at Approximately $700°K$		
mmoles I_2/liter	mmoles H_2/liter	mmoles HI/liter
1.71	2.91	16.5
3.13	1.83	17.7
0.495	0.495	3.66

4. Indicate the effect of the following on (a) the speed of a reaction and (b) the position of equilibrium: (i) catalyst, (ii) pressure, (iii) temperature, (iv) concentration.

5. Show how Le Châtelier's principle can be used in each of the examples in Problem 4.

6. Explain how an increase in temperature may be expected to affect (a) exothermic reactions, (b) endothermic reactions.

7. Using the data of Table 21.4, determine the equilibrium constant for the process

$$H_2S + 2H_2O \rightleftharpoons 2H_3O^+ + S^{-2}$$

and from this calculate the sulfide-ion concentration in a saturated H_2S solution ($0.1M$) to which has been added enough hydrochloric acid to make the hydronium-ion concentration $1M$.

8. Write the expression for the K_{ion} of the following: (a) HCN; (b) H_3PO_4; (c) NH_4OH; (d) $Cu(NH_3)_4{}^{+2}$; (e) H_2S.

9. Suppose a 0.1 molar solution of a base MOH is 2 per cent ionized at 25°C. Calculate the value of the ionization constant of the base.

10. Calculate the value of $[H_3O^+]$ in 500 cc of a $0.050M$ solution of acetic acid to which has been added 0.10 mole of sodium acetate. The value of the ionization constant for acetic acid is $K_{ion} = 1.8 \times 10^{-5}$.

11. Calculate the value of K_w for water if at the neutral point the pH is found to be 7.0.

12. Calculate the pH value of a solution whose $[OH^-]$ concentration is found to be 10^{-8}.

13. Explain how the addition of CH_3CO_2Na to water "buffers" the water and the pH remains almost constant after the first addition of HCl, even though large amounts may be added.

14. Write the hydrolysis equation for a 0.1 molar solution of acetate ion and predict whether the solution will be acidic or basic.

15. The hydrolysis constant for the reaction with water of a salt of a strong base and a weak acid is defined as

$$K_h = \frac{[HA][OH^-]}{[A^-]}$$

from the chemical equation

$$H_2O + A^- \rightleftharpoons HA + OH^-$$

Derive the relationship

$$K_h = \frac{K_w}{K_{ion}}$$

16. (a) Calculate $[H^+]$ in a 0.1 molar solution of NH_4Cl at 25°C. Write the equation for the hydrolysis reaction involved and obtain the necessary data from data tables in this chapter to solve the problem. (b) Calculate the per cent of hydrolysis.

17. Show that an indicator is a weak acid or a weak base and that the indicator action is a shift between the ionized and the un-ionized form.

18. Why does the formula of K_{ion} include the concentration of the undissociated molecule in the denominator while the formula for K_{sp} uses unity as the denominator?

19. The solubility of SrF_2 at 25°C is 1.22×10^{-2} g/100 ml. What is the value of K_{sp} for SrF_2?

20. The value of K_{sp} of $BaCO_3$ is 8.1×10^{-9} at 25°C. What is the solubility of $BaCO_3$ in moles per liter?

21. The value of K_{sp} of Ag_2CrO_4 at 25°C is 9.0×10^{-12}. Calculate the solubility of silver chromate, Ag_2CrO_4, in moles per liter in a $0.25M$ K_2CrO_4 solution.

22. Give examples of dissolving insoluble salts using (a) complexing units, (b) strong acids, (c) oxidation-reduction.

23. At 25°C the K_{sp} for $MgCO_3$ is 1.0×10^{-5} and that for $BaCO_3$ is 8.1×10^{-9}. Assuming both magnesium ions and barium ions are present in solution at $1 \times 10^{-3}M$ concentrations, what is the concentration of carbonate ion that will precipitate the maximum amount of Ba^{+2} ion without precipitating Mg^{+2}?

24. Calculate the pH of a saturated solution of copper hydroxide. Assume the K_{sp} of $Cu[OH]_2$ to be 10^{-20}.

25. (a) Suppose you have a solution of pH 3 and you dilute it a thousandfold, what is the new pH? (b) Suppose you dilute the new solution a thousandfold, what is now the pH?

26. Consider the answers to questions 25(a) and (b) for each of the following assumptions: (a) the original solution is a strong acid, unbuffered, (b) the original solution is buffered.

27. If 1 liter of ozone at 0°C and 760 torr decomposes to O_2 molecules by the equation

$$2O_3 \rightleftarrows 3O_2$$

how much is decomposed when the volume is one-sixth more than the original volume?

28. Suppose you have three beakers under a bell jar, one is half full of water, one is half full of a 0.1 molar sugar solution and the other is half full of a 0.1 molar sodium chloride solution. Allow the system to come to equilibrium. What is the level of liquid in each at equilibrium?

29. Calculate the pH of a 0.1 molar solution of Na_2CO_3. Obtain the necessary data from Table 21.4.

30. Apply Le Châtelier's principle to the equilibrium

$$\text{Solid} \rightleftarrows \text{liquid}$$

represented by the line OC in Figure 13.9, as is done for the liquid $\rightleftarrows$ vapor equilibrium on p. 269. For the substance considered in Figure 13.9, the volume occupied by a given mass of the solid substance is smaller than that occupied by the same mass of the liquid substance. (a) Increase in pressure would then cause the position of equilibrium to shift in which direction? (b) To melt a solid requires the addition of heat (heat of fusion). Considering the answer to (a), would you expect the increase of pressure to have the effect of raising, or lowering, the melting point?

31. The substance water is unusual compared to the vast majority of substances in that the solid form, ice, floats on the liquid; for almost all other substances, the solid would sink to the bottom. (a) What does this information tell you about the relative volume occupied by a given mass of ice and of liquid water (recall Archimedes' principle)? (b) From your answer to (a) what would you predict, from Le Châtelier's principle, would be the effect on the ice $\rightleftarrows$ liquid-water equilibrium of the application of pressure? (c) How would line OC, Figure 13.9, look for the substance water (cf. Problem 12, Chap. 13)? Sketch Figure 13.9 for water; labelling the coordinates of the triple point, O (4.58 mm and 0.0075°C), and those of the critical temperature and pressure (374°C and 218 atm).

32. The substance carbon dioxide has its triple point at −57°C and 5.3 atm. The critical temperature and pressure are 31°C and 73 atm. Solid carbon dioxide is more dense than liquid carbon dioxide. From this information, sketch a diagram for carbon dioxide using the same letters as shown in Figure 13.9, and labelling the coordinates of points O and A. Describe

what would happen as the following experiments are carried out: (a) Liquid carbon dioxide, at 0°C and 60 atm pressure, is gradually heated at constant pressure to 40°C. (b) The pressure on liquid carbon dioxide, originally at 0°C and 60 atm, is gradually reduced at constant temperature to 5 atm. (c) Solid carbon dioxide, originally at −70°C and 15 atm, is heated gradually at constant pressure to 40°C. (d) Solid carbon dioxide, originally at −70°C and 15 atm, is subjected at constant temperature to a gradual pressure reduction to 1 atm. (e) Solid carbon dioxide, originally at −100°C and 1 atm, is allowed to warm to room temperature while exposed to the atmosphere. (f) Solid carbon dioxide, originally at −60°C and 100 atm, is allowed to warm at constant pressure until 40°C is reached.

REFERENCES

BAUMAN, R. P. *An Introduction to Equilibrium Thermodynamics*. Englewood Cliffs, N.J.: Prentice-Hall, 1966.

BUTLER, J. N. *Solubility and pH Calculations*. Reading, Mass.: Addison-Wesley, 1964.

SIENKO, M. J. *Equilibrium*. New York: Benjamin, 1964.

22

Free Energy

The fascination of a growing science lies in the work of the pioneers at the very borderland of the unknown, but to reach this frontier one must pass over well travelled roads; of these one of the safest and surest is the broad highway of thermodynamics.*
Gilbert N. Lewis (1875–1946) and Merle Randall (1888–1950)

Early chemists spent much of their time searching for new elements, determining their properties, studying their reactions, and making compounds of them by a variety of reactions. As they learned more about the fraction of the reactants which was changed to products when a particular reaction took place, and about the changes in the position of equilibrium as reaction conditions were altered, they began to seek the underlying principles that govern the stability and reactivity of chemical systems in general. One avenue of investigation led to the "broad highway" of chemical thermodynamics. Chemical thermodynamics is the branch of physical chemistry which is concerned, among other things, with predicting where the position of equilibrium will be in chemical reactions. It shows that the position often may be calculated from measurements of heat and energy quantities, thus making it possible to choose the best conditions for the largest yield of products from a given amount of material, without performing a large number of experiments to find out, by actual trial of many conditions, which are the best. Equally important, thermodynamics tells the experimenter that some reactions, for which plausible chemical equations can be written, have no chance of success; thus it saves long hours of experimental trials which are foredoomed to failure. The importance of chemical thermodynamics lies just here—it offers an answer to the question: How can you tell whether a reaction can take place?

In this chapter we shall introduce the topic of thermodynamics and discuss the relationship between the thermodynamic quantity called the free energy and the feasibility and yield in chemical reactions.

Heat of Reaction Not the Determining Factor: An Erroneous View. At one time, chemists thought that the requirement for a reaction taking place

---

* From *Thermodynamics* (New York: McGraw-Hill, 1923).

was a release of energy. In other words, all reactions which took place on the mixing of reactants (called *spontaneous* reactions, as contrasted to reactions which were *forced* to proceed, by electrolysis, photolysis, etc., and hence were *not spontaneous*) must be exothermic reactions, and hence must have a negative value of ΔH. We have seen, however, in Equation (16), Chap. 21, that the formation of hydrogen iodide is an endothermic reaction in which heat is absorbed (positive value of ΔH); yet this reaction proceeds spontaneously when hydrogen and iodine, heated separately to 400°C or so, are allowed to mix.* The existence of even this one endothermic spontaneous reaction—there are countless others—is sufficient to show that the hypothesis that only exothermic reactions are spontaneous is incorrect, and must be discarded.

A Spontaneous Process Which Is Neither Exothermic Nor Endothermic—Mixing of Gases. To find out what does control spontaneity of reactions, let us consider a process which proceeds spontaneously with no energy change, namely, the mixing of two perfect gases. A quantity of gas A is placed in flask A (Figure 22.1), and flask B is filled to the same pressure with gas B. On opening the stopcock the two gases will be observed to mix, gradually, so that after a sufficient time each is evenly distributed between the two flasks. The mixing has been a spontaneous process; there has been no temperature change, nor any energy change, and no outside source of stirring was necessary to make the gases mix. There must have been a "natural" tendency causing the system to change from its initial, unmixed, state to the final mixed state. What is the nature of this driving force?

Examination shows that the final state is a more probable one than the initial state of separated gases. If the mixture were before us, we would say that it was unlikely or improbable that the components would separate of themselves; hence we could say that the mixed state had a greater probability of existence than the unmixed state. The driving force in this process is the tendency toward greater "mixed-up-ness," the tendency to go to the less ordered state, to the more random state, to the state of higher probability.

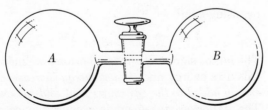

Figure 22.1 Mixing of two perfect gases.

Rule: Spontaneous Processes Go from More Order to Less Order. The mixing of the two gases is a single example of a general and universal rule: All processes which proceed spontaneously from a given initial state to a given final state do so with an increase in randomness, with a decrease in order. This is one form of the statement known as the second law of thermodynamics.

---

* The fact that a reaction is spontaneous does not mean that it will go to completion. It may go almost to completion or some fraction of the way to completion. Spontaneous simply means that *some* reaction will occur.

System and Surroundings. In applying the above rule, one must understand precisely what is meant by the initial and final states. Chemists often distinguish between a *system* and its *surroundings*. By the *system* they might mean the material reacting, or a container and its contents, such as a beaker of reactants on the desk top. The beaker is not *isolated*, but can interchange energy with its *surroundings*—by absorbing heat from the laboratory atmosphere, for example. When the second law of thermodynamics is stated as above, the initial state to be considered is that of the system plus the surroundings, and the final state must also include both the system and surroundings. In the example of the gas mixing, we chose a special kind of gas—a perfect gas—so that no interchange—of energy or stirring—between the system (the two connected flasks) and the surroundings took place, and we needed to consider only the system itself, but this would not be the usual case. The involvement of the surroundings, in the usual case, is unfortunate, since it is not always easy to assess changes in randomness in the surroundings. Hence scientists have sought criteria of spontaneity which involve only the system itself. To separate what happens in the system from what happens in the surroundings, let us first consider the transfer of energy between the two.

Energy Transfer to and from Surroundings and Systems. Energy can be transferred into the system from the surroundings either as heat, denoted by the symbol q, or as work, denoted by w. Any heat transferred to the system will increase its energy. Work done on the system will also increase its energy. (As an example, consider the mechanical work done in compressing a spring; the work done is stored as potential energy in the spring.) Hence we may write for the energy increase in the system

$$\begin{pmatrix}\text{Energy increase in}\\ \text{the system}\end{pmatrix} = \begin{pmatrix}\text{heat absorbed by}\\ \text{the system}\end{pmatrix} + \begin{pmatrix}\text{work done on}\\ \text{the system}\end{pmatrix} \quad (1)$$

Conventional choices prefer the same preposition (by) in both terms on the right, and we write

$$\begin{pmatrix}\text{Energy increase in}\\ \text{the system}\end{pmatrix} = \begin{pmatrix}\text{heat absorbed by}\\ \text{the system}\end{pmatrix} - \begin{pmatrix}\text{work done by}\\ \text{the system}\end{pmatrix} \quad (2)$$

or, using symbols,

$$\Delta E = q - w \quad (3)$$

The minus sign now appears because we measure work done *by* the system; this uses energy and *the net energy increase, ΔE, is the difference between the energy added to the system as heat and the energy used in performing work.* The italicized statement is a consequence of the law of conservation of energy; the specific application to the transfer of heat energy and work energy is known as the first law of thermodynamics.

Let us now look at this equation from a different point of view. Suppose that a process takes place in which there is a decrease in energy, so that $\Delta E = E_{\text{final}} - E_{\text{initial}}$ is a negative quantity. This energy decrease could be transferred to the surroundings in one of several ways: (a) it could go entirely as heat, with no work done, as in a chemical reaction at constant volume; (b) it could be transferred partly as heat and partly as work; and (c) the ratio of the part transferred as heat to the part transferred as work could be varied. Which one of these methods of transfer actually occurs will depend upon the wishes of the experimenter in deciding how much of the energy decrease he wishes to use as work, but only in certain specialized systems can all of the energy change be converted into work. He will find, however, that there is one method which will produce more work than any other, namely, that method in which the work is done in a "reversible" manner.

Thermodynamic Reversibility. The word "reversible" in the last sentence has a special meaning in thermodynamics. A process is being carried out reversibly when an infinitesimal change in the value of a variable can cause the process to proceed in one direction or the other. Consider, for example, gas at pressure P expanding against a piston. If the expansion is allowed to occur against an opposing pressure $P - p$, where p is an infinitesimally small pressure, then raising the opposing pressure to $P + p$ will cause the piston to move in the opposite direction and compress the gas, thus reversing the expansion. The expansion of gas at pressure P against an opposing pressure $P - p$ is thus an example of a reversible expansion; the pressure-volume work for this case is greater than the work which could be done in any other expansion process which allows the gas to undergo the same volume change. Similarly, the work done in *any reversible process* is the *maximum work* obtainable from that process.

Entropy. It is an experimental fact that when the process in which the energy change is ΔE is arranged so as to produce the maximum amount of work, the amount of heat transferred becomes a fixed quantity, which we denote by q_{rev}. Hence for any process carried out reversibly we write

$$\Delta E = q_{rev} - w_{max} \tag{4}$$

The heat transferred, q_{rev}, is now a definite quantity determined only by the initial and final states, and, for processes at constant temperature, we find that q_{rev}, divided by the temperature, is a measure of the change in the "mixed-up-ness," or randomness of the system. The name applied to the randomness is entropy, and it is denoted by the symbol S. In symbols, therefore, for constant temperature processes,

$$\frac{q_{rev}}{T} = \Delta S \tag{5}$$

where the delta symbol again represents the difference between the initial and the final state

$$\Delta S = S_{final} - S_{initial} \tag{6}$$

Thus reversible conditions give the maximum work and make $q_{rev} = T\Delta S$, so

$$\Delta E = T\Delta S - w_{max} \tag{7}$$

Free Energy. In dealing with chemical systems in open beakers, we meet the same situation mentioned in Chap. 20, namely, that we are often obliged to perform pressure-volume work on the atmosphere, whether we wish to or not. This work is included in w_{max}, but often it is not useful work. For the usual constant pressure processes, therefore, it is convenient to add $P\Delta V$ to both sides of the above equation:

$$\Delta E + P\Delta V = T\Delta S - (w_{max} - P\Delta V) \tag{8}$$

We now recognize the left-hand side as ΔH [Equation (7), Chap. 20]; the quantity in parentheses is the maximum *useful* work. Let us conceive that this maximum useful work appeared as the result of a decrease in a store of useful work in the system known as a free energy, G, so that

$$G_{\text{initial}} - G_{\text{final}} = (w_{\text{max}} - P\Delta V) \tag{9}$$

As noted earlier, the delta symbol represents *final minus initial*, so

$$G_{\text{initial}} - G_{\text{final}} = -\Delta G \tag{10}$$

and

$$-\Delta G = (w_{\text{max}} - P\Delta V) \tag{11}$$

Substitution gives

$$\Delta H = T\Delta S + \Delta G \tag{12}$$

The Sign of the Free-Energy Change Is the Criterion of Spontaneity for the System. We now have, in ΔG, the criterion of the *system*, sought for on page 434, which determines whether a change from a specified initial state to a specified final state will be a spontaneous one. Since the decrease in G measures the maximum useful work which can be obtained, only in the case that ΔG is negative can work be obtained.

If the process is to be spontaneous, it must take place of itself, with no work being done on the system. However, if ΔG is positive, work must be done on the system to effect the change; hence the change is not spontaneous if ΔG is positive. If ΔG is negative, work can be obtained, and the process is a spontaneous one. If ΔG is zero, there is no tendency to change at all. Since the free-energy criterion has been developed for systems at constant pressure and constant temperature, the result must be stated: *For spontaneous changes at constant pressure and constant temperature, the change in free energy, $(\Delta G)_{P,T}$, must be negative.* The subscripts indicate that pressure and temperature are constant.

The usefulness of a spontaneity criterion for the *system*, mentioned on page 434, may now be made more clear by considering as an example the freezing of supercooled water at $-10°C$ in contact with a heat reservoir at $-10°C$. (We assume the heat reservoir to be so large that further absorption of heat by it does not make a measurable change in its temperature.) The freezing of water at a temperature below its freezing point is a spontaneous process, yet the entropy of the water decreases, since the random arrangement of water molecules in the liquid changes to the ordered arrangement characteristic of the crystal. These facts seem to contradict the general and universal rule cited on page 433 that in spontaneous processes, the entropy (randomness) must increase. The difficulty arises because we did not include the entropy change of the surroundings (the heat reservoir). In this case it is possible to calculate the entropy change in the surroundings, and it is found that the entropy increase caused by the absorption of the heat of crystallization by the reservoir is greater than the decrease in entropy in the system (the water), so that there *is* a net entropy increase for system *plus* surroundings. No such seeming contradiction arises if we consider the *free-energy change* for the *system* alone; calculation shows that it is negative, as required for a spontaneous process at constant pressure and constant temperature.

Relation of Changes in Enthalpy and Entropy to Changes in Free Energy.

Rearrangement of Equation (12) shows the effect of changes in enthalpy and entropy on ΔG:

$$\Delta G = \Delta H - T\Delta S \tag{13}$$

The first term, ΔH, is a measure of the change in energy in the system; the second term, $T\Delta S$, is a measure of the change in randomness in the system. ΔH is measured by the interchange of heat between system and surroundings when the process is carried out at constant pressure, as in the measurements of heats of reaction in Chap. 20. $T\Delta S$ is measured by the interchange of heat between the system and surroundings, q_{rev}, when the process is carried out in a reversible manner. ΔG is more likely to be negative, that is, the reaction to be spontaneous, the more negative ΔH is. A negative value of ΔH means that energy is given off by the system when the process occurs. ΔG will also more likely be negative if ΔS is positive. A positive ΔS means that the system is changing to a more random state. Both ΔH and ΔS change only little with change in temperature; but $T\Delta S$ is nearly proportional to the temperature, unless there is a change in the physical state of one of the substances, as when the temperature range includes a melting, boiling, or transition point.

Estimating Values of ΔS; Spatial Randomness and Energy Randomness.

Values of ΔH may be directly measured as heats of reaction or estimated from bond energies (Chap. 20). The determination of ΔS from measurements of q_{rev} is not quite so easy, but estimates of ΔS can be made for some cases from the connection of entropy with randomness. Randomness may be considered to be measured by the number of places there are to put molecules without changing the properties of the system. There are more places to put a given number of molecules in a large volume than in a small volume, and the randomness—and hence the entropy—is greater, for any one substance, the larger the volume occupied by the substance. This is the explanation for the increase in entropy (randomness) on opening the stopcock between gases A and B, Figure 22.1; a larger volume becomes accessible to both gases. As another example, the change from solid to liquid always represents an entropy increase, because the molecules of the liquid may occupy many places, and are not restricted to the specific sites of the crystal lattice of the solid. Alternatively, the entropy

---

●●● A MEASURE OF THE DRIVING FORCE OF A REACTION

We have established that the change of order-to-disorder is a driving force in making a process occur. However, the usefulness of this measure of driving force is diminished by the fact that its use requires a knowledge of changes in the surroundings as well as in the system. An *improved* measure of the driving force is found in the ability or inability of the system to perform work under reversible conditions. For constant-pressure and constant-temperature processes, the process is spontaneous only in the case that work can be obtained. The magnitude of the reversible useful work which can be performed, $w_{\text{max}} - P\Delta V$, is measured by the change in free energy. These concepts lead directly to a general indicator for predicting the spontaneity of a constant-temperature process : If the process involves a release of free energy (ΔG is negative), the process is spontaneous ; if, however, work must be done (ΔG is positive) on the system to make the process take place, the process is not spontaneous.

increase on melting may be looked upon as a change to a more disordered state (the liquid) from the ordered, less random state of the solid. This change in order is still more marked in passing from solid to gas or liquid to gas.

Molecules may not only be put in different places in space, as when the volume changes, but also in different "places" in an energy sense. We have seen earlier that an isolated molecule may hold energy in many different ways (Chap. 20): as energy of electronic excitation, as vibrational motion of the atoms in the molecule, as rotational motion of the molecule as a whole, and as kinetic energy of translational motion of the molecule as a whole. Each of these energies is quantized, and the values of each are approximately independent of the values of the others. The difference in energy between one energy level and the next, however, varies greatly among the four kinds. This difference is largest for electronic energies, and decreases in the order listed, being extremely small for translational energies. Consequently, for electronic and vibrational energies there may be accessible to the molecules only a few energy "places," whereas for translational energies there will be many places available to a group of molecules with limited energies. Since there are many more places to put the molecules, energy-wise, in translational motion than there are in other types of motion, the entropy for translational motion will be much larger than for the other types.

Applications to Chemical Reactions. *Solids Reacting to Form Gases.* The reaction of water-gas formation

$$C(s) + H_2O(g) \longrightarrow CO(g) + H_2(g) \tag{14}$$

proceeds with the absorption of heat, the enthalpy change, ΔH, amounting to $+31,400$ cal at $25°C$, when each gas is at 1 atm pressure. The entropy change may be expected to be positive, since a loss of order appears when solid carbon disappears in forming gaseous carbon monoxide; the measured value of ΔS for the reaction written, at $25°C$ and 1 atm for each gas, is 32.0 cal/deg. Hence, at $25°C$,

$$\Delta G = \Delta H - T\Delta S = +31,400 - 298 \times 32.0 = +21,900 \text{ cal} \tag{15}$$

Since ΔG is positive, the reaction will not occur spontaneously at this temperature, when the gases are at 1 atm pressure. At $1000°K$, assuming approximate constancy of ΔH and ΔS, the value of ΔG would be

$$31,400 - 32,000 = -600 \text{ cal}$$

ΔG is negative and the reaction as written is spontaneous.

Since heats of reaction are commonly of the order of tens or hundreds of kilocalories, and entropy changes in reactions are commonly of the order of tens of calories per degree, it is seen that at low temperatures, the sign of the enthalpy change is the factor which controls the sign of ΔG, and hence the spontaneity of the reaction. An exothermic reaction (ΔH negative) will produce a negative value of ΔG, and the reaction will be spontaneous. It is this fact which makes it reasonable to use the value of ΔH alone as a criterion of stability of compounds and spontaneity of reaction, as has been done several times in the preceding chapters. If ΔH

is large and negative (exothermic reaction), ΔG will almost surely be negative at ordinary temperatures, and the reaction will be spontaneous. Similarly, an endothermic reaction (ΔH positive) at low temperatures will produce a positive value of ΔG, and no spontaneous reaction will occur.

The sign and magnitude of ΔS will combine with ΔH and T to determine the actual value of ΔG, through Equation (13). In particular, ΔG may become negative even for an endothermic reaction at high temperatures, if ΔS for the reaction is positive.

The discussion in the last paragraph provides the answer to the question raised in Chap. 20 about the operation of the lime kiln [Equation (54), Chap. 20]. Calcium carbonate is stable at ordinary temperatures, but decomposes at the temperature of the kiln. Note that, again, a solid forms a gaseous product,

$$CaCO_3(s) \longrightarrow CaO(s) + CO_2(g) \qquad \Delta H^\circ_{298} = +42.7 \, kcal$$

and there is an entropy increase amounting to 37.4 cal/deg. Even if ΔH did remain the same with change in temperature, therefore, still amounting to 42,700 calories at 1200°K, the effect of the entropy increase would be sufficient to make the reaction spontaneous (ΔG negative):

$$\Delta G = 42,700 - 1200 \times 37.4 = -2180 \, cal \, at \, 1200°K \qquad (16)$$

Gases Formed from Gases. When all reactants are gases, the sign of the free-energy change is often determined by the relative numbers of molecules in reactants and products, as a result of the overwhelming entropy for translational motion. Consider, for example, the dissociation of nitrogen molecules, which, you recall, are very tightly bound together:

$$N_2(g) \longrightarrow 2N(g) \qquad \Delta H = +225.0 \, kcal \qquad (17)$$

From what has been said above, the electronic terms will make little contribution to the entropy effects. Note, however, that there are two particles in the product, and hence two sources of translational entropy, but only one such source in the reactant. The reactant molecules do have, however, vibrational and rotational entropies, absent in the atomic products. When the change $N_2 \rightarrow 2N$ occurs, molecules are changed to atoms; hence the entropy terms due to rotation and vibration disappear and there is a change from translational entropy for one particle to translational entropy for two. Due to the closeness of quantum-level spacing for the translational energies, the increase in entropy resulting from the added translational term in the product more than compensates for the loss of the rotational and vibrational terms in the reactant, and the overall result is an increase in entropy (ΔS positive). This result is of general application: An increase in the number of particles produces an increase in entropy, so that dissociation processes in gases proceed with an entropy increase.

Since ΔS is positive for dissociation processes, it means that at some temperature all such processes become spontaneous, no matter how much energy the dissociation requires, for at a sufficiently high temperature $T\Delta S$ must become greater than ΔH, so that the difference $\Delta H - T\Delta S$ becomes negative. Every molecule dissociates at high enough temperatures.

Free Energy and Equilibrium

For a reaction which is reversible, the direction in which the reaction will proceed will always be that which can occur with a decrease in free energy. Consider, for example, the simple gas reaction

$$H_2 + I_2 \rightleftarrows 2HI \tag{18}$$

The reaction will proceed from left to right if the free-energy change

$$\Delta G = G_{final} - G_{initial} = G_{2HI} - (G_{H_2} + G_{I_2}) \tag{19}$$

is negative. If the free-energy change for this left-to-right process is positive, then it will be negative for the reverse reaction, by the inequalities

$$G_{2HI} - (G_{H_2} + G_{I_2}) > 0 \tag{20}$$

$$(G_{H_2} + G_{I_2}) - G_{2HI} < 0 \tag{21}$$

and the reverse reaction becomes the spontaneous reaction. If the free-energy change is zero—i.e., if $G_{Products} = G_{Reactants}$,

$$G_{2HI} = (G_{H_2} + G_{I_2}) \tag{22}$$

$$\Delta G = 0 \tag{23}$$

then there is no tendency to go in either direction. This is the situation known as chemical equilibrium, introduced in Chaps. 7 and 21 as the equivalence of forward and reverse rates in a reversible reaction. In those discussions, the tendency to react was related to the concentrations of the reactants, and the arrival of the system at an equality of rates signalled the arrival at fixed values of the concentrations. Since the free-energy change has a nonzero value when reaction occurs and a value zero at equilibrium, it is evident that the free-energy change must be related to the concentrations of reactants and products.

● ● ●   ACTIVITY AND ITS RELATION TO CONCENTRATION

Warning has been given (page 414) that the setting up of equilibrium quotients using concentrations of products at equilibrium divided by concentrations of reactants at equilibrium does not give a constant value for the calculated equilibrium "constant." It would be useful in thermodynamic calculations if equilibrium "constants" were truly constant. In fact, the advantages to be gained if this were the case are so great that chemists have invented a kind of effective concentration known as the *activity*, so that, when activities instead of concentrations are substituted in the mathematical equations of thermodynamics, all these equations are exact. The advantage gained by this procedure is that the whole of the mathematical apparatus of thermodynamics may now be used with complete confidence, since the deviations from exactness which might have arisen because of the peculiar properties of individual substances have been taken care of at the level of the individual substances themselves by the substitution of their activities for their concentrations.

No useful gain will have been made, however, if we do not know how to translate concentrations into activities, or—what amounts to the same thing—how to measure activities as a function of concentrations. Several methods are available for determining this relationship, but most of them share the feature that they require many careful experiments, largely because the activity is a continually changing function of the concentration. Complicating matters further, the activity is not only a changing function of the concentration of a pure substance, as in a gas at varying pressures, or of the concentration of a single solute in

Free Energy of the Standard State. Expression of the relation of ΔG to the concentration of reactants and products requires recognition of the fact that we cannot determine absolutely what the free energy of a given initial or final state is, but only the change between the free energy of the initial and the free energy of the final state. The situation here is similar to that for enthalpy and enthalpy changes, which was resolved by adopting a convention about the values of the enthalpy in some chosen standard state. We proceed for free energy in the same way as for enthalpy, and adopt a standard-state convention. We let the free energy of a substance at each temperature have a fixed, although unknown, value of the free energy, denoted by $G°$, when the substance is at unit activity (Chap. 21). It can then be shown that the free energy, G, for the substance in any other state at the known temperature differs from the value in this standard state by the factor $2.303\,RT \log a$, where $\log a$ is the logarithm of the activity, thus:

$$G = G° + 2.303RT \log a \tag{24}$$

Here G and $G°$ represent free-energy values per mole of substance, and R is the molar gas constant, 1.987 cal/mole/deg. The equation is consistent with the assignment of the value 1 for the activity in the standard state, and in the standard state, $\log a = \log 1 = 0$, so $G = G°$. For an ideal gas, the activity is equal to the pressure, and with some approximation we may equate these two quantities for real gases also, so that the standard state for a gas is 1 atm pressure. With considerably less validity, we may, when discussing solution processes, approximate the activity of a substance with its concentration in the solution. Before making either of these approximations, let us calculate the free-energy change in a chemical reaction.

Free-Energy Change in a Reaction. Suppose we have a reaction with the equation

$$M(a_M) + 2N(a_N) \xrightleftharpoons{} P(a_P) \tag{25}$$

---

solution, but also of the concentration of other solutes which may be in the solutions (gaseous, liquid, or solid solutions), even though these other solutes may have no readily observable chemical effect on the substance whose activity we are trying to measure.

The change in the activity with change in concentration is traced to a change in the interaction between the molecular species; hence it is convenient to establish as a starting point that the activity is equal to the concentration when the molecules do not interact with each other at all. For gases, we already have, in the concept of an ideal gas, such a standard of no interaction, and we may obtain the relation between activity and concentration for a gas in terms of the deviation of its properties from those described by the perfect-gas law (Chap. 13). For solutions, the state of no interaction between solutes can be approached by putting the solute molecules far apart; if we could go to "infinite dilution," there would be an infinite distance between any pair of molecules, and no interaction could occur. While we cannot measure the properties of a solute when its concentration is zero (an infinitely dilute solution), we can make measurements on real solutions of varying concentrations and assess the magnitude of the desired quantity by plotting the measured values against the concentration and extrapolating to zero concentration. This extrapolation gives the standard for no interaction, and comparison of the values for the real solution with those which would be observed if the solutes behaved at all concentrations in the way they behave at infinite dilution gives the required relation between activity and concentration.

in which 1 mole of substance M reacts with 2 moles of substance N to form 1 mole of substance P. The reaction is carried out in solution under conditions such that the activities are a_M, a_N, and a_P respectively. We calculate the free-energy change in this process:

$$\Delta G = G_{final} - G_{initial} = G_P - G_M - 2G_N \qquad (26)$$

The factor 2 appears in front of G_N because 2 moles of N are needed and G_N represents the free energy of 1 mole of N only. Using Equation (24),

$$\Delta G = G_P{}^\circ + 2.303RT \log a_P - G_M{}^\circ - 2.303RT \log a_M \\ - 2G_N{}^\circ - 2(2.303)RT \log a_N \quad (27)$$

Combining terms differently,

$$\Delta G = G_P{}^\circ - G_M{}^\circ - 2G_N{}^\circ + 2.303RT (\log a_P - \log a_M - 2 \log a_N) \qquad (28)$$

$$\Delta G = \Delta G^\circ + 2.303RT \log \frac{a_P}{a_M a_N{}^2} \qquad (29)$$

In the last equation the difference in the standard-state free energies has been expressed in a single term, ΔG°, and the transformation of the terms in the parentheses in the preceding equation comes about by making use of the properties of logarithms.*

If ΔG° and the activities on the right side are such that ΔG on the left side has a negative value, the reaction will proceed from left to right. In fact, the ΔG value calculated will represent the free-energy decrease for a reaction at temperature T when 1 mole of M at activity a_M combines with 2 moles of N at activity a_N to form 1 mole of P at activity a_P under conditions such that the amounts of substances are so large that this change produces no observable change in these activities.

Equilibrium Constant. If ΔG calculated in this way were equal to zero, it would mean that there was no tendency for reaction to take place; that is, the system is at equilibrium, and the activities will be the fixed activities corresponding to the equilibrium conditions. Hence

$$0 = \Delta G^\circ + 2.303RT \log \frac{a_{P,eq}}{a_{M,eq} a_{N,eq}^2} \qquad (30)$$

Solving for ΔG°, we have

$$\Delta G^\circ = -2.303RT \log \frac{a_{P,eq}}{a_{M,eq} a_{N,eq}^2} \qquad (31)$$

Since ΔG° is a properly chosen difference between the fixed values of the free energies in the standard states, it has a fixed (that is, constant) value, and the right-hand side of the equation, which is equal to ΔG°, must also have a fixed and constant value. This means that the quotient of the activities at equilibrium is a constant, which we call the equilibrium constant K:

$$K = \frac{a_{P,eq}}{a_{M,eq} a_{N,eq}^2} \qquad (32)$$

---

* $x \log y = \log y^x;$ $\qquad \log x + \log y = \log xy;$ $\qquad \log x - \log y = \log \left(\frac{x}{y}\right).$

Hence,

$$\Delta G° = -2.303RT \log K \tag{33}$$

Equation (33) makes it possible to calculate the equilibrium constant if $\Delta G°$ is known, or to calculate $\Delta G°$ from measurements of equilibrium activities or the equilibrium constant.

For the general reaction between m moles of M and n moles of N to form p moles of P and q moles of Q,

$$mM(a_M) + nN(a_N) \rightleftharpoons pP(a_P) + qQ(a_Q) \tag{34}$$

Equation (29) would have the appearance

$$\Delta G = \Delta G° + 2.303RT \log \frac{a_P{}^p a_Q{}^q}{a_M{}^m a_N{}^n} \tag{35}$$

where $\Delta G°$ has the form

$$\Delta G° = pG_P° + qG_Q° - mG_M° - nG_N° \tag{36}$$

Setting $\Delta G = 0$ gives us the usual form [Equation (4), Chap. 21] of the equilibrium constant for a reaction of this stoichiometry:

$$K = \frac{a_{P,eq}^p a_{Q,eq}^q}{a_{M,eq}^m a_{N,eq}^n} \tag{37}$$

Concentration Equilibrium Constants. If we make the approximation that the activity is equal to the concentration, the equilibrium-constant expressions (32) and (37) become

$$K_c = \frac{c_{P,eq}}{c_{M,eq} c_{N,eq}^2} \tag{38}$$

$$K_c = \frac{c_{P,eq}^p c_{Q,eq}^q}{c_{M,eq}^m c_{N,eq}^n} \tag{39}$$

These agree with the expressions previously used in Table 21.2. A return to the material on page 442 will show that these are the results which would have been obtained directly if Equation (24) had been written

$$G = G° + 2.303RT \log c \tag{40}$$

This is equivalent to making the approximation that the standard state is that corresponding to unit concentration ($c = 1$). Later (Chap. 23), we shall treat free energies as if that were the case, but it must be remembered that this is an approximation, and often a gross one.

Equilibrium Constants in Terms of Pressure. For gaseous substances, the activity can, with good approximation, be set equal to the pressure, so that Equations (32) and (37) become

$$K_p = \frac{P_{P,eq}}{P_{M,eq} P_{N,eq}^2} \tag{41}$$

$$K_p = \frac{P_{P,eq}^p P_{Q,eq}^q}{P_{M,eq}^m P_{N,eq}^n} \tag{42}$$

Thermodynamics Not Concerned with Rates. It is important to realize that the standard free-energy change is a constant for each reaction at a specified temperature, and that the equilibrium constant is therefore also a constant. This was found experimentally to be the case in the calculations of Table 21.1, and Equation (31) shows that this is a requirement of the thermodynamic approach. An important feature of the thermodynamic approach is that it distinguishes between the equilibrium concept and the concept of rates of reaction. Here we are no longer concerned with the specific values for reaction rates, as we were in Table 7.2, but only with the fact that the free-energy change is zero at equilibrium. Further, the form of the equilibrium-constant quotient is fixed by the over-all stoichiometry of the chemical reaction [Equations (25) and (32); (34) and (37)] and we need not consider the dependence of reaction rates on concentrations or pressures of reactants. This is particularly helpful, because for many reactions this dependence may be very complicated; often it is unknown and, particularly for rapid reactions, difficult to determine.

Positive Values of ΔG°. The value of ΔG° for a reaction refers to the free-energy change when reactants in their standard states are changed to products in their standard states. While a positive value of ΔG° means that the reaction is not spontaneous when the several species are in their standard states, it does not mean that the reaction may not be spontaneous under some other conditions. To consider what may happen let us write Equation (35) for the reaction $A(g) + B(g) \rightleftarrows C(g) + D(g)$, using pressure as the measure of activity. We have

$$\Delta G = \Delta G^\circ + 2.303 RT \log \frac{P_C P_D}{P_A P_B} \tag{43}$$

Substituting Equation (33) for ΔG°,

$$\Delta G = -2.303 RT \log K + 2.303 RT \log \frac{P_C P_D}{P_A P_B} \tag{44}$$

In this equation P_A, P_B, P_C, and P_D represent the pressures of reactants and products under the conditions of the experiment; the quotient

$$\frac{P_C P_D}{P_A P_B}$$

● ● ● ΔG°, ΔG, AND CHEMICAL REACTIONS

Beginning students sometimes say that the value of ΔG°, as calculated for a particular reaction from tables of free-energy values, will tell whether the reaction will take place or not. More mature students, however, will remember that ΔG° refers only to the free-energy change under certain specified conditions, namely, when all the products and all the reactants are present in the reaction mixture, and each in its standard state of unit activity. Under any other conditions, the appropriate criterion of spontaneity is ΔG in Equation (29), not ΔG°.

Let us consider a series of chemical situations involving the reaction described by the equation

$$M(a_M) + 2N(a_N) \rightarrow P(a_P) \tag{A}$$

Case I. All products and reactants are present in the reaction mixture, and ΔG° and the activities a_M, a_N, and a_P have such values that ΔG is negative. Under these conditions the reaction will proceed spontaneously to the right as written, so that the activity of P increases while the activities of M and N decrease. The reaction will continue until a_M, a_N, and a_P reach their equilibrium values $a_{M,eq}$, $a_{N,eq}$, and $a_{P,eq}$. After this, no further change in the activities of products and reactants will occur.

Case II. All reactants and products are in the reaction mixture, and the values of ΔG° and

has the same form as the quotient for the equilibrium constant, but the pressures are not equilibrium pressures. For convenience, let us write

$$Q = \frac{P_C P_D}{P_A P_B}$$

and, using the properties of logarithms, rewrite Equation (44):

$$\Delta G = 2.303 RT \log \frac{Q}{K} \tag{45}$$

Whenever Q/K is less than 1, that is, when the experimental quotient is less than the equilibrium quotient, the logarithm, and hence ΔG, will be negative, and the reaction spontaneous. Ordinarily under these conditions the reaction will proceed until the pressures P_A, P_B, P_C, and P_D have adjusted themselves such that the quotient Q equals the equilibrium constant K. Q/K then equals 1, the logarithm is zero, ΔG is zero, and equilibrium has been established. This sequence of events can occur no matter how small K may be; if, initially, the quotient

$$\frac{P_C P_D}{P_A P_B}$$

is less than

$$\frac{P_{C,eq} P_{D,eq}}{P_{A,eq} P_{B,eq}}$$

a certain amount of spontaneous reaction will occur, until equilibrium is established.

Completion of Reaction. If K is very large, that is, if $\Delta G°$ has a large negative value, the concentration of reaction products at equilibrium will be very large compared to the concentration of reactants at equilibrium, and the reaction has evidently "gone to completion" except for the negligible amounts of reactant left at equilibrium. Even if K is small, however, the reaction can be "driven to completion" by arranging the experimental conditions so that Q remains always less than K. This could be accom-

---

the activities a_M, a_N, and a_P are such that ΔG is positive. Under these conditions the reaction will not proceed spontaneously as written ; that is, it will not proceed from left to right, with an increase in the activity of the product. On the contrary, the reaction will proceed in the reverse direction ; P will be transformed into M and N, moving toward equilibrium ; the final equilibrium activity of the product [in Equation (A) as written] will be less, and the equilibrium activities of the reactants will be greater, than the starting activities.

Case III. Only the reactants M and N are present in the reaction mixture. In this case, since no product is present in the reacting mixture, $a_P = 0$, and the description of the reaction is

$$M(a_M) + 2N(a_N) \longrightarrow P(a_P = 0) \tag{B}$$

Substitution in the free-energy Equation (29) gives

$$\Delta G = \Delta G° + 2.303RT \log \frac{0}{a_M a_N{}^2} \tag{C}$$

The fraction $\frac{0}{a_M a_N{}^2}$ is equal to zero, and the logarithm of zero is minus infinity. Hence,

plished, for example, by continual removal from the scene of the reaction of one of the products of the reaction. If the presence of substance D, say, is kept always very small, as by condensing the gas or absorbing it in some inert solvent, it is evident that Q must always remain small, Q/K always less than 1, and the reaction always spontaneous.

Equilibria in Reactions in Which Solids Are Present. In choosing the standard states for free-energy calculations, the standard state of a solid is chosen as the pure solid at the temperature in question, and the activity of the solid is set equal to 1 in accordance with this choice. Let us consider the free-energy change and the form of the equilibrium constant for the reaction of lime burning:

$$CaCO_3(s) \longrightarrow CaO(s) + CO_2 \text{ (gas, pressure } P_{CO_2}) \tag{46}$$

The free-energy change is

$$\Delta G = G^{\circ}_{CO_2} + 2.3RT \log P_{CO_2} + G^{\circ}_{CaO} - G^{\circ}_{CaCO_3} \tag{47}$$

No terms corresponding to the logarithm of pressure appear for calcium oxide and calcium carbonate because these solids are in their standard states; their activities are 1, and their free energies are equal to their standard-state free energies, $G_{CaO} = G^{\circ}_{CaO}$ and $G_{CaCO_3} = G^{\circ}_{CaCO_3}$. Combining terms, we have

$$\Delta G = \Delta G^{\circ} + 2.3RT \log P_{CO_2} \tag{48}$$

Since $\Delta G = 0$ at equilibrium, we have

$$\Delta G^{\circ} = -2.3RT \log P_{CO_2,eq} \tag{49}$$

Equation (49) shows that when calcium carbonate, calcium oxide, and carbon dioxide are in equilibrium with each other at temperature T, the pressure of carbon dioxide has a fixed value, since ΔG° has a fixed value (Table 22.1). Substitution of Equation (49) back into Equation (48) gives

$$\Delta G = 2.3RT \log \frac{P_{CO_2}}{P_{CO_2,eq}} \tag{50}$$

● ● ● ΔG°, ΔG, AND CHEMICAL REACTIONS *cont.*

ΔG is always negative, no matter whether ΔG° is positive, negative, large, or small, since $\Delta G = \Delta G^{\circ} - \infty$. A negative value of ΔG means that the reaction will proceed spontaneously as written until equilibrium is established. Hence, the activity of M and N will decrease while that of P increases, until equilibrium values are obtained and ΔG is zero :

$$0 = \Delta G^{\circ} + 2.303RT \log \frac{a_{P,eq}}{a_{M,eq}a^2_{N,eq}}, \tag{D}$$

Case IV. All reactants and products are present and their activities are each equal to 1. In this case $\Delta G = \Delta G^{\circ}$, since the activity ratio is equal to 1 and the logarithm of 1 is zero. In this case, and in this case only, the direction of the spontaneous reaction is determined by the sign of ΔG° ; spontaneous to the right if ΔG° is negative, spontaneous to the left if ΔG° is positive. With either sign, reaction will proceed until the equilibrium values of the activities are reached.

Equilibrium Constant Magnitudes. Although Case IV shows that ΔG° is of limited usefulness in determining the spontaneous direction of chemical reaction, being applicable only to the special case where all reactants and products are at unit activities, the value of ΔG° is of great importance as a measure of the magnitude of the equilibrium constant. This may be

ΔG will be negative, and the reaction of Equation (46) will proceed to the right, if P_{CO_2} is less than $P_{CO_2,eq}$ for the temperature of the experiment. Further, ΔG will remain negative if the experimental conditions are kept such that P_{CO_2} is maintained at a value that is less than the equilibrium pressure for that temperature. This condition is met in most lime kilns by blowing air through the kiln to dilute, with nitrogen, the carbon dioxide formed, thus reducing the pressure of carbon dioxide. The carbon dioxide is swept away as fast as it is formed, and its pressure is not allowed to build up to $P_{CO_2,eq}$. The reaction thus goes to completion by removal of a product (p. 445).

Temperature (°C)	Pressure (torr)	Temperature (°C)	Pressure (torr)
550	0.41	850	372
600	1.84	897	760
650	6.90	950	1580
700	22.2	1000	2940
750	63.2	1050	5200
800	167	1100	8740

Table 22.1 Pressure of Carbon Dioxide in Equilibrium with Calcium Carbonate and Calcium Oxide

Equilibrium Constants for Reactions Involving Solids. Comparison of Equation (49) with Equation (33) shows that for the decomposition of calcium carbonate, the equilibrium constant contains only the single term $P_{CO_2,eq}$ and that no terms for the two solids appear in it:

$$K = P_{CO_2,eq} \tag{51}$$

It is generally true for reactions involving solids that the equilibrium constants contains only terms for the gases involved, or for the substances present in solution in contact with the solid. This is the result of the convention that the standard state of a solid is taken as the solid itself. If

shown by considering the two equations

$$\Delta G° = -2.303RT \log K \tag{E}$$

$$\log K = -\frac{\Delta G°}{2.303RT} \tag{F}$$

Case V. $\Delta G°$ is positive. Here log K is negative, corresponding to a value of K less than 1. This means that the experimental result obtained when equilibrium is established is that the position of equilibrium in Equation (A) is to the left as written. Hence the reaction of Equation (A) would not be a good choice for converting M and N into P with large yield unless the special procedures for driving the reaction to completion (p. 445) were applied.

Case VI. $\Delta G°$ is negative. Here log K is positive, corresponding to a value of K greater than 1. This means that the position of equilibrium in the reaction of (A) is to the right as written. Hence this reaction would be useful for converting M and N into P.

Thus the sign and magnitude of $\Delta G°$ is a useful indicator of the degree of completion of a reaction, but not of its spontaneity in the general case. For the latter purpose, ΔG must be used.

Equations (43) and (42) are written for the reaction

$$3\text{Fe}(s) + 4\text{H}_2\text{O}(\text{gas, pressure } P_{\text{H}_2\text{O}}) \underset{\longleftarrow}{\overset{\longrightarrow}{}}$$
$$\text{Fe}_3\text{O}_4(s) + 4\text{H}_2(\text{gas, pressure } P_{\text{H}_2}) \quad (52)$$

the equilibrium constant will be found to be

$$K = \frac{P_{\text{H}_2,\text{eq}}^4}{P_{\text{H}_2\text{O},\text{eq}}^4} \quad (53)$$

in which no terms appear for the solids. Similarly the reaction of dissolving calcium fluoride

$$\text{CaF}_2(s) \longrightarrow \text{Ca}^{+2}(\text{soln}) + 2\text{F}^-(\text{soln}) \quad (54)$$

shows the equilibrium constant [cf. Equation (37), Chap. 21]:

$$K = [\text{Ca}^{+2}]_{\text{eq}}[\text{F}^-]_{\text{eq}}^2 = K_{sp} \quad (55)$$

The standard state of liquids is also chosen as the pure liquid. In consequence, equilibrium constants for reactions of a *pure* liquid (as contrasted to a solution) do not contain terms for the pure liquid. If a solution is involved, the free energy of the liquid differs from that in the standard state by $2.3\,RT$ times the logarithm of the concentration of the liquid in the solution.

Free Energy of Formation; Addition of Free-Energy Values. Just as chemists have found it convenient to speak of an enthalpy of formation, so the concept of free energy of formation is useful. By the free energy of formation, $\Delta G_f{}^\circ$, is meant the free-energy change when one mole of a compound is formed in its standard state from its elements in their standard states; it is usually tabulated for 25°C. Thus the values for $\text{H}_2\text{O}(g)$ and for $\text{AgCl}(s)$ in Table 22.2 represent the free-energy changes in the reactions

$$\text{H}_2(\text{gas, 1 atm}) + \tfrac{1}{2}\text{O}_2(\text{gas, 1 atm}) \longrightarrow \text{H}_2\text{O}(\text{gas, 1 atm})$$
$$\Delta G_{f298}^\circ = -54.64\,\text{kcal} \quad (56)$$

$$\text{Ag}(s) + \tfrac{1}{2}\text{Cl}_2(\text{gas, 1 atm}) \longrightarrow \text{AgCl}(s) \qquad \Delta G_{f298}^\circ = -26.22\,\text{kcal} \quad (57)$$

These values may be added and subtracted in the same way as values of enthalpies of formation are handled, as shown in the following sum:

$$\text{CaCO}_3(s) \longrightarrow \text{Ca}(s) + \text{C}(s) + \tfrac{3}{2}\text{O}_2(g, 1\text{ atm}) \qquad \Delta G_{f298}^\circ = +269.8 \quad (58)$$

$$\text{Ca}(s) + \tfrac{1}{2}\text{O}_2(g, 1\text{ atm}) \longrightarrow \text{CaO}(s) \qquad \Delta G_{f298}^\circ = -144.4 \quad (59)$$

$$\text{C}(s) + \text{O}_2(g, 1\text{ atm}) \longrightarrow \text{CO}_2(g, 1\text{ atm}) \qquad \Delta G_{f298}^\circ = -94.3 \quad (60)$$

$$\text{CaCO}_3(s) \longrightarrow \text{CaO}(s) + \text{CO}_2(g, 1\text{ atm}) \qquad \Delta G_{f298}^\circ = +31.1\,\text{kcal} \quad (61)$$

Effect of Change in Temperature on the Equilibrium Constant and Equilibrium Concentrations. If the equation connecting enthalpy change, entropy change, and free-energy change (13) is written for the standard states

$$\Delta G^\circ = \Delta H^\circ - T\Delta S^\circ \quad (62)$$

and the relationship between the standard free-energy change and the

Substance	ΔG°_{f298}	Substance	ΔG°_{f298}
$H_2O(g)$	-54.6357	$NaCl(s)$	-91.785
$H_2O(l)$	-56.6902	$KCl(s)$	-97.592
$HCl(g)$	-22.769	$CaCl_2(s)$	-179.3
$HBr(g)$	-12.72	$CaCO_3(s)$ (calcite)	-269.78
$HI(g)$	0.31	$AlCl_3(s)$	-152.2
$SO_2(g)$	-71.79	$CaO(s)$	-144.4
$NO(g)$	20.719	$CuO(s)$	-30.4
$NH_3(g)$	-3.976	$Cu_2O(s)$	-34.98
$Br_2(g)$	0.751	$CuSO_4(s)$	-158.2
$Br_2(l)$	0.00	$CuSO_4 \cdot 5H_2O(s)$	-449.3
$CO(g)$	-32.8079	$PbCl_2(s)$	-75.04
$CO_2(g)$	-94.2598	$AgCl(s)$	-26.22
$CH_4(g)$	-12.140	$C_2H_4(g)$	16.282
$CH_3Cl(g)$	-14.0	$C_2H_2(g)$	50.000
$CH_3OH(l)$	-39.73	$C_3H_8(g)$	-5.614
$CHCl_3(l)$	-17.1	$n\text{-}C_4H_{10}(g)$	-4.10
$CCl_4(l)$	-16.4	$n\text{-}C_5H_{12}(g)$	-2.00
$C_2H_6(g)$	-7.860	$iso\text{-}C_5H_{12}(g)$	-3.50
$C_2H_5OH(l)$	-41.77	$neo\text{-}C_5H_{12}(g)$	-3.64
$CH_3CO_2H(l)$	-93.8	$C_6H_6(l)$	29.756
$H^+(aq)$	0.00	$OH^-(aq)$	-37.595
$Na^+(aq)$	-62.589	$Cl^-(aq)$	-31.350
$K^+(aq)$	-67.466	$Br^-(aq)$	-24.574
$Ag^+(aq)$	18.43	$I^-(aq)$	-12.35
$Ca^{+2}(aq)$	-132.18	$S^{-2}(aq)$	20
$Cu^{+2}(aq)$	15.53	$CO_3^{-2}(aq)$	-126.22
$Zn^{+2}(aq)$	-35.184	$SO_4^{-2}(aq)$	-177.34
$H(g)$	48.575	$C(g)$	160.845
$O(g)$	54.994	$N(g)$	81.471

Table 22.2 Standard Free Energies of Formation (ΔG°_{f298} in kcal/mole)

equilibrium constant (33) substituted, we obtain

$$-2.303RT \log K = \Delta H^{\circ} - T\Delta S^{\circ} \tag{63}$$

Division by $2.303RT$ and change of sign gives

$$\log K = -\frac{\Delta H^{\circ}}{2.303RT} + \frac{\Delta S^{\circ}}{2.303R} \tag{64}$$

Since ΔH° and ΔS° are usually nearly constant with temperature, this equation shows that a plot of $\log K$ against $1/T$ should be a straight line. The slope of the line will be positive or negative according as ΔH° is negative (exothermic reaction) or positive (endothermic reaction). For the formation of hydrogen iodide, ΔH° is positive,

$$H_2(g) + I_2(g) \longrightarrow 2HI(g) \qquad \Delta H^{\circ} = 12.4 \text{ kcal} \tag{65}$$

and $\log K$ increases (and K increases) as T increases ($1/T$ decreases). Hence, for a given mixture, the fraction of hydrogen and iodine converted to hydrogen iodide at equilibrium is greater, the higher the temperature. For the formation of ammonia, ΔH° is negative,

$$N_2(g) + 3H_2(g) \longrightarrow 2NH_3(g) \qquad \Delta H^{\circ} = -22.08 \text{ kcal} \tag{66}$$

and log K decreases (K decreases) as T increases ($1/T$ decreases). The effect of the decrease in K is to decrease the percentage of ammonia in the equilibrium mixture as the temperature increases, as shown in each column of Table 21.3.

These conclusions are in accord with the qualitative predictions from Le Châtelier's principle, already discussed (Chap. 21).

SUMMARY

The usefulness of the free-energy concept, and the application of the concept in predicting the direction of spontaneous chemical change and in recording the position of equilibria in chemical reactions, has been studied in this chapter. It is shown that processes take place spontaneously when the measure of randomness known as the entropy increases as the process occurs. The applicability of this criterion of spontaneity is limited by the fact that both the system and its surroundings must be considered. The free-energy change, a measure of the maximum useful work which can be obtained from the system, is then developed as a criterion of spontaneity referring to the system alone. The relationship of free-energy change to change in enthalpy and change in entropy permits the free-energy change to be evaluated for many systems from measurements of the latter two quantities.

In the second part of the chapter, the relationship of free-energy change to standard free-energy change and effective concentrations (activities) of reactants and products leads to a thermodynamic proof of the constancy of that quotient of activities at equilibrium known as the *equilibrium constant*. The relationship of the activities (concentrations) under experimental conditions to those at equilibrium is used to determine the direction of reaction, and the value of the equilibrium constant or the standard free-energy change is shown to be a measure of the degree of completion of the reaction. Finally, the temperature coefficient of equilibrium constants is discussed, and examples are given of the combination of tabulated values for the free energy of formation to obtain free-energy changes for reactions not included in the tabulation.

SOME SPECIAL TERMS

Thermodynamics
Entropy
  spatial randomness
  energy randomness
Enthalpy
System
  surroundings
Reversible (thermodynamic) process
Spontaneous reaction
  exothermic reaction
  endothermic reaction
Activity
  activity of standard state

Free energy
  driving force
  maximum work
  maximum useful work
  free-energy change
  standard free-energy change
  standard-state free energy
  free energy of formation
Equilibrium
  equilibrium constant
Le Châtelier's principle
  completion of reaction

QUESTIONS AND PROBLEMS

1. Explain what causes a reaction to proceed in a system in which no energy is gained or lost and there is no energy change in the system.
2. Show how energy can be transferred into a system as heat; as work. Is such a system an isolated system? A closed system?
3. Explain how work done in a reversible manner gives the maximum work that can be done. Must this be an isolated system? A closed system?
4. How big is an infinitesimal change?
5. Under what conditions can we write $q = T\Delta S$?
6. Under what conditions can we use the change in ΔS as an indication of whether a reaction will go? Under what conditions can the value of ΔG be used?
7. What is the relationship between ΔE and ΔH? Between ΔH and ΔG?
8. How does the value of $T\Delta S$ change with temperature? With this information show that every compound should decompose if the temperature is high enough.
9. A substance undergoes a change in physical state. How can you measure the corresponding free-energy change?
10. In a discussion of atomic structure a statement is often made that atoms react to form compounds because of the tendency to gain, lose, or share pairs of electrons. How do you rationalize that statement with those made in this chapter: "reactions go in the direction of great disorder;" or "an indication of whether a reaction will go is the sign of ΔG"?
11. Given the following data:

$$H_2(g) + \tfrac{1}{2}O_2(g) \rightleftharpoons H_2O(l) \qquad \Delta G° = -56{,}690 \text{ cal}$$

$$H_2O(g) + Cl_2(g) \rightleftharpoons 2HCl(g) + \tfrac{1}{2}O_2(g) \qquad \Delta G° = 9100 \text{ cal}$$

$$H_2O(l) \rightleftharpoons H_2O(g) \qquad \Delta G° = 2053 \text{ cal}$$

calculate the free energy of formation of hydrogen chloride from its elements at 25°C.
12. The standard free-energy change for the reaction

$$2HI \rightleftharpoons H_2(g) + I_2(s)$$

is −630 cal at 25°C. Calculate the value of the equilibrium constant.
13. At 25°C the value of K_{eq} equals 5.65×10^7 for the reaction

$$H_2(g) + C_2H_4(g) \rightleftharpoons C_2H_6(g)$$

Calculate the value of $\Delta G°$.
14. From the following data on the values of ΔH and ΔS calculate the free energy and equilibrium constant at 600°C for the reaction

$$C(s) + 2H_2(g) \rightleftharpoons CH_4(g)$$

The enthalpy change for this reaction is −21,000 cal at 600°C. The entropies of graphite, hydrogen, and methane at 600°C and 1 atm are 4.8, 38.9, and 56.6 cal/mole/deg respectively.
15. The heat of vaporization of benzene (C_6H_6) at 80.2°C and 1 atm is 94.4 cal/g. Calculate the value of ΔH, ΔE, and ΔS for the process at that temperature.
16. Consider the dissolution of two springs in acid: one is a coiled spring of iron under tension; the other is an uncoiled one not under tension. Explain in terms of ΔG why you could predict a difference in the tendency of the dissolution reaction to occur.

17. Explain in terms of order-to-disorder the tendency of ice to melt to form liquid water. Can you use a similar explanation to explain the tendency of water to evaporate to form water vapor?

18. How do you explain the statement "when you boil water you are contributing to the 'running downness' of the universe"?

19. Mercuric oxide dissociates at high temperatures according to the equation

$$2HgO(s) \longrightarrow 2Hg(g) + O_2(g)$$

At 450°C the pressure of the two gases formed is 810 torr but at 420°C the dissociation pressure is only 387 torr. (a) Calculate the partial pressures of mercury and of oxygen, and from these, the value of the equilibrium constant, in pressure units, at each temperature. (b) If 10.0 g HgO is placed in a 1.0 liter evacuated vessel and the temperature raised to 450°C, how many grams of mercuric oxide will remain undecomposed?

20. Using the data in Table 22.1, calculate the weight of solid matter present if 10 g $CaCO_3$ is placed in an evacuated 1.0 liter container and heated to 900°C. How much solid will remain if the container is opened to the atmosphere at that temperature?

21. Plot the data of Table 22.1 in an appropriate fashion, and from the graph determine $\Delta H°$ for the reaction

$$CaCO_3(s) \longrightarrow CaO(s) + CO_2(g)$$

Compare the result with that obtained in Problem 15, Chap. 20.

22. From the information given in Problem 19 above, estimate the value of $\Delta H°$ for the decomposition of mercuric oxide.

REFERENCES

Macwood, G. E., and F. H. Verhoek. "How Can You Tell Whether a Reaction Will Occur?" *J. Chem. Educ.*, 38 (1961), p. 334.

Mahan, B. H. *Elementary Chemical Thermodynamics.* New York: Benjamin, 1964.

Strong, L. E., and W. A. Stratton. *Chemical Energy.* New York: Reinhold, 1965.

23

Electrochemical Cells—The Measurement of Free Energy

*Die Vorgänge in einem constanten galvanische Elemente, welche bei
verschwindend kleiner Stromintensität vor sich gehen, wobei man
die dem Widerstand und dem Quadrat dieser Intensität propor-
tionale Wärmeentwicklung in Schliessungsdrahte als verschwin-
dende Grössen zweiter Ordnung vernachlässigen kann, sind
vollkommen reversible Prozesse und müssen den thermodynamis-
chen Gesetzen der reversiblen Prozesse unterliegen.**
Hermann Ludwig Ferdinand von Helmholtz (1821–1894)

An electrochemical cell is a device in which a chemical reaction is caused
to take place as the result of the passage of an electric current (electrolysis
cell), or in which a chemical reaction takes place and causes an electric
current to be produced (galvanic cell). In this chapter we shall discuss
both types of cell and refer particularly to the measurements with galvanic cells which provide the data on oxidation potentials. It will be recalled that we have used such data in previous chapters to arrange elements
and compounds in the order of their oxidizing or reducing strength in
aqueous solution. The voltages of galvanic cells are a direct measure of the
free-energy changes in the chemical reactions in the cells. We shall also
study the variation of cell voltage with the concentrations of reactants
and products, the use of cell voltage in predicting equilibrium concentrations, and application of electrochemical cells in chemical analysis.

Let us first examine the nature of electrical conduction in solution, and
the reactions that occur in some cells.

---

* "The reactions in a given galvanic cell which take place at vanishingly small currents,
where one can neglect, as a second-order correction, the heat evolved (proportional to the
resistance and the square of this small current), are completely reversible processes, and
must obey the thermodynamic laws of reversible processes." (The quotation is from *Monats-
berichte der königlichen preussischen Akademie der Wissenschaften* (1877), p. 713.)

Conduction of Electricity in Solution. A solution of an electrovalent compound, such as sodium chloride, contains sodium ions, positively charged, and chloride ions, negatively charged. When two electrodes are placed in the solution, and connected each to one of the poles of a battery, the positive sodium ions will be drawn toward the negative electrode, and the negative chloride ions will be drawn toward the positive electrode (Figure 23.1). This migration of charged particles through the solution results in a transfer of electric charge; we recognize this as an electric current and say that the solution conducts a current. This type of conduction, which results from the motion of ions through the solution, is called *electrolytic conduction*, distinguishing it from *metallic conduction*, which occurs when electrons flow along a wire.

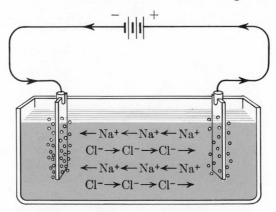

Figure 23.1 Migration of ions in electrolytic conduction.

The changeover from metallic conduction along the wires from the battery to electrolytic conduction in the solution occurs at the surface of the electrodes, and always results in chemical reaction, most often forming atoms from ions or ions from atoms or molecules. The exact nature of the electrode reactions depends upon the nature of the dissolved salt and its concentration, the nature of the electrodes, the relative ease of reaction of solute species and solvent at the electrode surfaces, the temperature, etc. The reactions are those of oxidation and reduction and may be written as *half-reactions*, in which electrons are treated as if they were reactants or products. In the case of sodium chloride solution, for example, the half-reactions are

$$2Cl^-(aq) \longrightarrow Cl_2(g) + 2e^- \text{ oxidation, at the anode} \tag{1}$$

$$2H_2O(l) + 2e^- \longrightarrow H_2(g) + 2OH^-(aq) \text{ reduction, at the cathode} \tag{2}$$

The first reaction gives electrons to one of the electrodes; the second takes electrons away from the other. The electric circuit is completed by the battery, which serves much as an electron pump, taking electrons away from the first electrode and pumping them along to the other, where they are released (Figure 23.2).

Of course electrons are not observable products and reactants, as Equations (1) and (2) seem to show; rather, electrons are simply transferred from chloride ions to water molecules. The observed reaction, therefore, is the sum of the two half-reactions above.

$$2H_2O(l) + 2Cl^-(aq) \longrightarrow H_2(g) + Cl_2(g) + 2OH^-(aq) \tag{3}$$

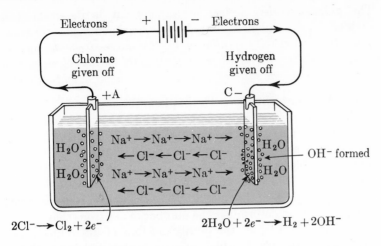

Figure 23.2 Electrode reactions in the electrolysis of sodium chloride solutions.

The arrangement of solution and electrodes does, however, permit the *oxidation* to take place at one electrode (called the anode) and the reduction to take place at the other (called the cathode). Thus the chlorine and hydrogen gases appear at different places, and may be collected separately if desired. The sodium ions of the sodium chloride remain unchanged in quantity and may be removed from the solution as sodium hydroxide. The industrial preparation of sodium hydroxide and chlorine by this electrolysis process has already been mentioned (Figure 8.7).

Electrolysis Cell. The arrangement of electrodes dipping into a solution of an electrolyte is known as a cell. In the use just described, it is an *electrolysis cell*, in which an oxidation-reduction reaction is caused to take place by passing a current from an external source through the cell. Such cells are widely used in industry (a) in winning certain metals from their ores, as in the Hall process for aluminum, (b) in refining of crude metals, as in the refining of copper, (c) in the preparation of elements and compounds, as for chlorine and sodium hydroxide, just mentioned, (d) in electroplating, usually for combating corrosion, as in the protection of automobile bright-work with chromium plate, and (e) in the preparation of certain organic compounds.

Faraday's Laws. The laws governing the amount of material undergoing reaction in an electrolysis were discovered by Faraday in his early researches on electrolytic conduction. Faraday observed that the weight of hydrogen or oxygen or silver or other elements liberated at an electrode depends *solely* on the *quantity of electricity* that flows through the solution undergoing electrolysis. It does not depend at all on the temperature or the concentration of the solution, or the rate at which the charge flows, but only on the *quantity of electricity*. This fact constitutes Faraday's first law: *The amount of electrochemical change is directly proportional to the quantity of electricity that flows* (Figure 23.3). The quantity of electricity, measured in coulombs, is the product of the current in amperes times the time in seconds.

Faraday's second law has to do with the relation between the relative weights of the *different elements* liberated at the electrodes by the *same* quantity of electricity, and the gram-equivalent weights of those elements.

The *gram-equivalent weight* of an element is its gram-atomic weight divided by its valence. Faraday's experiments proved that if *a given quantity of electricity is allowed to flow successively through a number of different solutions in series, the weights of the various elements liberated at the electrodes are in the ratio of their gram-equivalent weights* (Figure 23.4).

The Avogadro Number. The explanation of Faraday's laws can now be made in the light of our knowledge that an electric current is a flow of electrons. Since the electrode reactions involve gain or loss of electrons, it is evident that the amount of material deposited depends only upon the number of electrons which pass around the circuit—that is, upon the quantity of electricity which passes around the circuit—and not upon the temperature or other conditions of the electrolysis. Further, since the charge on an ion determines the number of electrons that need to be gained or lost to neutralize it, the number of ions of different elements, such as Ag^+, Ni^{+2}, and Cr^{+3}, which can be neutralized by a given number of electrons, will vary inversely as the number of charges on the ions. Thus for the passage of y electrons, there will be neutralized y atoms of silver, $y/2$ atoms of nickel, and $y/3$ atoms of chromium. The weights of the elements deposited (Figure 23.4) at the electrode will equal the number of atoms deposited times the weight of the atom. Thus if there are N atoms in a gram-atomic weight, there will be deposited $y \times 108/N$ g of silver, $y/2 \times 59/N$ g of nickel, and $y/3 \times 52/N$ g of chromium. The weights of the elements deposited will therefore be in the ratio of their equivalent weights (atomic weights divided by electrovalence); the actual weights are: $y/N \times 108$ g Ag, $y/N \times 59/2$ g Ni, $y/N \times 52/3$ g Cr, and their ratio is

$$108 : \frac{59}{2} : \frac{52}{3}$$

An electrolysis, in other words, is essentially a counting process. The number of electrons which pass through the circuit is measured by the quantity of material deposited. This fact makes it possible to calculate the Avogadro number from electrolysis experiments. It is found experimentally that a quantity of electricity amounting to 96,487 coul is required to liberate 1 g-equiv. wt. of an element. This quantity (called a faraday) is the same for any element, by Faraday's second law. For a

Figure 23.3 The quantity of hydrogen produced in the electrolysis of sodium chloride solution is proportional to the quantity of electricity which flows through the solution—i.e., to the product of the current times the time.

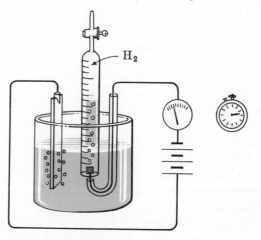

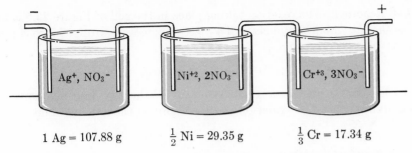

$1\ Ag = 107.88\ g \qquad \frac{1}{2}\ Ni = 29.35\ g \qquad \frac{1}{3}\ Cr = 17.34\ g$

Figure 23.4 Illustration of Faraday's second law. To deposit the metallic *atoms* silver, nickel, and chromium from the solutions of the salts in which they occur as the ions Ag^+, Ni^{+2}, and Cr^{+3}, each Ag^+ ion must recover one electron, each Ni^{+2} ion two electrons, and each Cr^{+3} ion three electrons. One faraday of electricity passing through the circuit furnishes enough electrons to deposit 1 mole of silver at the left electrode of the left-hand cell. A corresponding number of electrons is introduced to the circuit at the right electrode but deposits only $\frac{1}{2}$ mole of nickel in the center cell. The like number of electrons released at the right hand electrode in the center cell will deposit $\frac{1}{3}$ mole of chromium, and the circuit is completed when the faraday of electrons returns to the battery from the right-hand electrode of the chromium nitrate cell. A given current will deposit these three metals from solution in the *ratio* of their gram-equivalent weights (107.88 g Ag ; 29.35 g Ni ; 17.34 g Cr), whether the quantity of current passing consists of 100 or of 100 billion electrons.

univalent element such as silver, the gram-equivalent weight is equal to the gram-atomic weight, and it follows that the passage of 96,487 coul will produce 1 mole of silver. The charge on an electron is 1.6021×10^{-19} coul; hence the passage of 96,487 coul represents the passage of

$$\frac{96487}{1.602 \times 10^{-19}} = 6.0225 \times 10^{23}\ \text{electrons}$$

around the circuit. Each electron neutralizes one silver ion,

$$Ag^+ + e^- \longrightarrow Ag \tag{4}$$

so that the number of silver atoms in a gram-atomic weight is 6.02×10^{23}.

Galvanic Cells. In addition to the use of a cell for electrolysis, it is possible to arrange the electrodes and electrolytes in such a fashion that the electrons transferred, when an oxidation-reduction reaction takes place spontaneously within a cell, will serve as a source of electric current in an external circuit. Such a cell is called a *galvanic* cell.

A typical galvanic cell might consist of a metal rod (such as zinc) dipping into a solution of its ions (zinc ions); this solution is separated mechanically, but not electrically, from a solution of ions of a different metal (such as copper ions) into which dips a rod of the second metal (copper). The connection between the two solutions might be made with a "salt bridge"—typically, a solution of potassium chloride—which conducts a current but keeps the two solutions separate. A diagram of such a cell is shown in Figure 23.5, and the conventional representation is

$$Zn \mid Zn^{+2} \parallel Cu^{+2} \mid Cu$$

The single vertical lines represent separations of phases between the solid metals and the solutions of their ions, and the double vertical line represents the separation of the two halves of the cell.

Cell Reaction. The reaction taking place in the cell of Figure 23.5 is the same as that which would occur if a piece of zinc were dropped into copper sulfate solution, namely,

$$Zn(s) + Cu^{+2}(aq) \longrightarrow Zn^{+2}(aq) + Cu(s) \tag{5}$$

With the salt-bridge arrangement, however, the two half-reactions are separated, so that the oxidation process occurs at the left electrode

$$Zn(s) \longrightarrow Zn^{+2}(aq) + 2e^- \tag{6}$$

and the reduction at the right

$$Cu^{+2}(aq) + 2e^- \longrightarrow Cu(s) \tag{7}$$

Thus the zinc rod dissolves, forming zinc ions, and copper ions deposit on the copper rod. The electrons released by the zinc atoms in forming ions displace electrons in the wire toward the copper rod, where copper ions are neutralized. Since the formation of zinc ions in the left beaker would, if that were the only change there, give that solution a positive charge, electrical neutrality requires the diffusion of some positive ions from the left beaker toward the right, or of some negative ions into the left beaker, or both. These ions are exchanged for ions of similar charge in the salt bridge, which releases any oversupply or makes up any deficiency by diffusion to or from the right-hand beaker, which would otherwise acquire a negative charge as copper ions are removed.

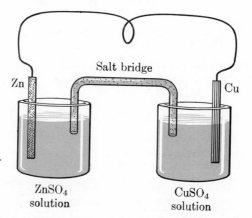

Figure 23.5 The zinc-copper galvanic cell.

Electrical Work. The net result of using a galvanic cell such as that shown in Figure 23.5 is that the electron-transfer process of Equation (5), which changes zinc atoms to zinc ions while changing copper ions to copper atoms, has been used to transfer these electrons along a wire. If an "engine" is placed in the external circuit, the expenditure of energy in the movement of these electrons through the difference in potential (difference in voltage) between the two electrodes can be made to do work. This work will be a maximum when the whole process occurs reversibly (page 435). Reversibility is easy to arrange with a cell, because the cell can be made to

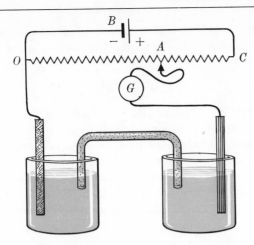

Figure 23.6 Potentiometric measurement of cell voltage. The current from a source of known voltage, *B*, is passed through a wire of uniform resistance per unit length, *OC*. The leads from the cell are connected through a galvanometer, *G*, to the uniform wire at a point *A* which is moved along *OC* until the galvanometer shows no deflection. Slight movement from this setting toward *O* will cause the galvanometer to deflect in one direction, showing the cell to be a source of current; movement toward *C* will cause deflection in the other direction, showing that current is passing through the cell from the battery. When the point of no deflection *A* has been found, the ratio of length *OA* to length *OC* gives the fraction of the voltage of *B* being produced by the cell.

buck against another current source whose voltage is adjusted until a further infinitesimal change in voltage will cause the current to flow through the cell in the opposite direction. The work of electron transfer done under these conditions measures the free-energy change in the process, since it is reversible work which does not include pressure-volume work. The voltage needed to produce reversible operation is measured on the bucking source (Figure 23.6).

When an electron moves through a difference in potential, electrical work is done equal to the product of the charge on the electron by the difference in potential, $w = \varepsilon E$, where ε is the charge and E the potential difference. If a mole of electrons moves under these conditions, the work done will be $N\varepsilon E$. The charge carried by a mole of electrons, $N\varepsilon$, is the faraday, F, and is equal to 96,487 coul. Since the reaction of a mole of zinc atoms with a mole of copper ions requires the transfer of two moles of electrons [Equations (6) and (7)], the work done will be $2FE$, or, in general, nFE, where n is the number of moles of electrons transferred when the cell reaction takes place according to the equation written. This is equal to the negative of the free-energy change [Equations (9) and (11), Chap. 22].

$$(w_{\max} - P\Delta V) = G_{\text{initial}} - G_{\text{final}} = -\Delta G$$

and

$$\Delta G = -nFE \qquad (8)$$

If E is the voltage of the cell when the zinc and copper are in their standard states—as they must be, since they are solids—and the zinc and copper ions are at concentrations $c_{\text{Zn}^{+2}}$ and $c_{\text{Cu}^{+2}}$, ΔG, with $n = 2$, will measure the free-energy change when 1 mole of solid zinc reacts with 1 mole of copper ions at concentration $c_{\text{Cu}^{+2}}$ to form 1 mole of zinc ions at concentration $c_{\text{Zn}^{+2}}$ and 1 mole of copper metal, according to the equation*

$$\text{Zn}(s) + \text{Cu}^{+2}(c_{\text{Cu}^{+2}}) \longrightarrow \text{Cu}(s) + \text{Zn}^{+2}(c_{\text{Zn}^{+2}}) \qquad (9)$$

---

* Actually, the measured E for a cell constructed as in Figure 23.5 will not correspond exactly to Equation (9), since there will be "liquid junction potentials" at the two ends of the salt bridge where a solution of potassium and chloride ions comes in contact with solutions of other ions. Often, extended experiments are needed to obtain the precise value, but the simple apparatus gives values precise enough for all but the most exacting work.

If all substances are in their standard states and all ions in solution are at the concentrations chosen as their standard states, we write Equation (8) in the form

$$\Delta G^\circ = -nFE^\circ \qquad (10)$$

The galvanic cell is thus of particular importance to chemistry, because, in contrast to most devices, it can be used easily to measure the work of a chemical reaction, excluding the pressure-volume work, and the value obtained is that for reversible operation. Thus the result of the measurement is a direct measure of the free-energy change in the chemical reaction taking place in the cell. Since ΔG° differs from E° only by the constant term $-nF$, either of the two quantities, E° or ΔG°, can serve as measures of spontaneity. When working mainly with solutions and cells, E° is the more convenient.

Electrode Potentials. Just as the reaction taking place in a cell such as that shown in Figure 23.5 can be separated into two electrode reactions at the cathode and anode [Equations (6) and (7)], so also the voltage of the cell is by convention considered to be the sum of a voltage associated with the cathode reaction and a voltage associated with the anode reaction. It is not possible to measure these voltages separately, since every cell must contain both an anode and a cathode; however, numerical values can be assigned to the individual electrode reactions by assigning an arbitrary value to some electrode reaction chosen as a standard. The convention adopted is that the voltage corresponding to the reaction

$$H_2(g, 1\ \text{atm}) \xrightleftharpoons{(H_2O)} 2H_3O^+(a = 1) + 2e^- \qquad E^\circ = 0 \qquad (11)$$

is assumed to be zero for the reaction proceeding in either direction. Here we have used the precise expression for the standard state of the hydronium ion, namely, unit activity, to indicate that our usual procedure, in which the free energy or cell potential is expressed in terms of concentrations rather than activities, is an approximation (page 414). In dilute solutions it is found that both concentrations and activities increase or decrease together, and we can, without major loss of validity in our calculations, replace activities with concentrations in our mathematical equations at low concentrations. Because the molality of a solution is temperature independent, it is usually more convenient to use molalities rather than molarities in thermodynamic measurements. We shall often proceed as if the standard state for ions in solutions is a 1-molal solution, while recognizing that the actual concentration of a solution of unit activity probably is not 1 molal.

With the adopted convention that the half-reaction

$$H_2(g, 1\ \text{atm}) \xrightleftharpoons{(H_2O)} 2H_3O^+(a = 1) + 2e^- \qquad (11)$$

has zero voltage, we may now find values for other half-reactions by making cells with hydrogen as one of the electrodes. Since hydrogen, being gaseous, cannot of itself serve as a conducting electrode, a chemically inert electrode, such as platinum, which absorbs hydrogen readily, is used, and, while in use, is kept bathed in an atmosphere of hydrogen.

The electron-transfer reaction between zinc metal and hydronium ions can be used under the above convention to measure the potential for the oxidation of zinc to zinc ions. A cell is constructed in which a zinc rod is immersed in a solution of zinc ions at "1-molal" concentration, and this connected through a salt bridge to a standard hydrogen electrode (Figure 23.7). The reaction taking place is known from experiments in dipping zinc into acid solutions, namely,

$$Zn + 2H_3O^+ \longrightarrow Zn^{+2} + H_2 + 2H_2O \tag{12}$$

Hence the half-reactions are

$$Zn(s) \longrightarrow Zn^{+2}(a = 1) + 2e^- \tag{13}$$

$$2H_3O^+(a = 1) + 2e^- \xrightarrow{\text{H}_2\text{O}} H_2(g, 1 \text{ atm}) \tag{14}$$

a fact which is readily confirmed by electrical measurements showing that electrons flow through the meter M *from* the zinc *to* the hydrogen electrode. The voltage of the cell is measured as 0.762 volt. According to our convention this is the sum of the voltages of the two half-cells.

$$0.762 \text{ volt} = E^\circ_{cell} = E^\circ_{Zn \to Zn^{+2}} + E^\circ_{2H_3O^+ \to H_2} = E^\circ_{Zn \to Zn^{+2}} + 0 \tag{15}$$

Since the cell has been constructed with all components in their standard states, the measured voltage is a standard voltage, as indicated by the superior zeros on the E° symbols. Further, since by convention the E° value for hydrogen is chosen as zero, the voltage of the cell, 0.762 volt, is the standard potential for zinc. It is called the *standard oxidation potential*, and corresponds to the oxidation half-reaction

$$Zn(s) \longrightarrow Zn^{+2}(a = 1) + 2e^- \qquad E^\circ = 0.762 \text{ volt} \tag{16}$$

By a series of measurements of this sort a table (Table 23.1) of standard oxidation potentials can be obtained, not only for the formation of ions from metals but for other electrode reactions as well. All the values in the table are for 25°C and standard states: 1-molal concentrations (more precisely, unit activity) of all reacting ions in water solution, and hydrogen and other gases at 1 atm pressure.

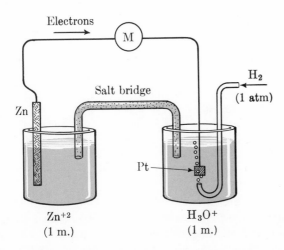

Figure 23.7 The cell $Zn|Zn^{+2}\|H_3O^+|H_2|Pt$.

Table 23.1   Standard Oxidation
Potentials at 25°C

Half-reaction	$E°$(volts)
$Li(s) \rightarrow Li^+ + e^-$	+3.05
$K(s) \rightarrow K^+ + e^-$	2.93
$Rb(s) \rightarrow Rb^+ + e^-$	2.93
$Cs(s) \rightarrow Cs^+ + e^-$	2.92
$Ba(s) \rightarrow Ba^{+2} + 2e^-$	2.90
$Sr(s) \rightarrow Sr^{+2} + 2e^-$	2.89
$Ca(s) \rightarrow Ca^{+2} + 2e^-$	2.87
$Na(s) \rightarrow Na^+ + e^-$	2.71
$Mg(s) \rightarrow Mg^{+2} + 2e^-$	2.37
$Al(s) \rightarrow Al^{+3} + 3e^-$	1.66
$Mn(s) \rightarrow Mn^{+2} + 2e^-$	1.18
$Zn(s) \rightarrow Zn^{+2} + 2e^-$	0.76
$Cr(s) \rightarrow Cr^{+3} + 3e^-$	0.74
$Fe(s) \rightarrow Fe^{+2} + 2e^-$	0.44
$Cd(s) \rightarrow Cd^{+2} + 2e^-$	0.40
$Pb(s) + SO_4^{-2} \rightarrow PbSO_4(s) + 2e^-$	0.36
$Co(s) \rightarrow Co^{+2} + 2e^-$	0.28
$Ni(s) \rightarrow Ni^{+2} + 2e^-$	0.250
$Ag(s) + I^- \rightarrow AgI(s) + e^-$	0.151
$Sn(s) \rightarrow Sn^{+2} + 2e^-$	0.136
$Pb(s) \rightarrow Pb^{+2} + 2e^-$	0.126
$H_2(g, 1\ atm) \rightarrow 2H_{aq}^+ + 2e^-$	0.000
$Ag(s) + Br^- \rightarrow AgBr(s) + e^-$	−0.095
$H_2S(g) \rightarrow 2H_{aq}^+ + S(s) + 2e^-$	−0.14
$Sn^{+2} \rightarrow Sn^{+4} + 2e^-$	−0.15
$Cu^+ \rightarrow Cu^{+2} + e^-$	−0.153
$Ag(s) + Cl^- \rightarrow AgCl(s) + e^-$	−0.222
$Cu(s) \rightarrow Cu^{+2} + 2e^-$	−0.34
$Ti^{+2} + 2H_2O \rightarrow TiO_2 + 4H_{aq}^+ + 2e^-$	−0.37
$S(s) + 3H_2O \rightarrow H_2SO_3 + 4H_{aq}^+ + 4e^-$	−0.45
$2I^- \rightarrow I_2(s) + 2e^-$	−0.536
$MnO_4^{-2} \rightarrow MnO_4^- + e^-$	−0.56
$H_2O_2 \rightarrow O_2(g) + 2H_{aq}^+ + 2e^-$	−0.68
$Fe^{+2} \rightarrow Fe^{+3} + e^-$	−0.77
$2Hg(l) \rightarrow Hg_2^{+2} + 2e^-$	−0.79
$Ag(s) \rightarrow Ag^+ + e^-$	−0.80
$NO + 2H_2O \rightarrow NO_3^- + 4H_{aq}^+ + 3e^-$	−0.96
$Au(s) + 4Cl^- \rightarrow AuCl_4^- + 3e^-$	−1.00
$2Br^- \rightarrow Br_2(l) + 2e^-$	−1.09
$2H_2O \rightarrow O_2 + 4H_{aq}^+ + 4e^-$	−1.23
$Mn^{+2} + 2H_2O \rightarrow MnO_2(s) + 4H_{aq}^+ + 2e^-$	−1.23
$2Cr^{+3} + 7H_2O \rightarrow Cr_2O_7^{-2} + 14H_{aq}^+ + 6e^-$	−1.33
$2Cl^- \rightarrow Cl_2(g) + 2e^-$	−1.36
$Pb^{+2} + 2H_2O \rightarrow PbO_2 + 4H_{aq}^+ + 2e^-$	−1.455
$Au(s) \rightarrow Au^{+3} + 3e^-$	−1.50
$PbSO_4(s) + 2H_2O \rightarrow PbO_2(s) + 4H_{aq}^+ + SO_4^{-2} + 2e^-$	−1.69
$MnO_2(s) + 2H_2O \rightarrow MnO_4^- + 4H_{aq}^+ + 3e^-$	−1.70
$2H_2O \rightarrow H_2O_2 + 2H_{aq}^+ + 2e^-$	−1.77
$2F^- \rightarrow F_2 + 2e^-$	−2.87

The electrode reactions are all written as oxidation reactions. In this
book we use the positive sign to indicate that the element is oxidized more
readily than hydrogen and the negative sign to indicate that the element
is oxidized less readily than hydrogen. Thus for the cell of Figure 23.7,

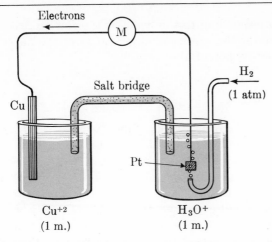

Figure 23.8 The cell $Cu|Cu^{+2}\|H_3O^+|H_2|Pt$.

containing zinc and hydrogen, the oxidation potential of zinc is given a plus value.

If a cell using copper and copper ions (Figure 23.8) instead of zinc and zinc ions

$$Cu \mid Cu^{+2}(1 \text{ m.}) \parallel H_3O^+(1 \text{ m.}) \mid H_2$$

is constructed for measuring the standard oxidation potential of copper, the direction of flow of current shows that electrons are flowing *toward* the copper *from* the hydrogen electrode. The half-reactions are

$$H_2(g, 1 \text{ atm}) \xrightarrow{(H_2O)} 2H_3O^+(a = 1) + 2e^- \tag{11}$$

$$Cu^{+2}(a = 1) + 2e^- \longrightarrow Cu(s) \tag{17}$$

and the voltage is

$$E^\circ_{cell} = E^\circ_{H_2 \to 2H_3O^+} + E^\circ_{Cu^{+2} \to Cu} \tag{18}$$

Again the hydrogen voltage is assigned the value zero; the total voltage of the cell, 0.345 volt, is assigned to the copper electrode.

$$0.345 \text{ volt} = E^\circ_{cell} = 0 + E^\circ_{Cu^{+2} \to Cu} \tag{19}$$

● ● ●   SIGN CONVENTIONS

The procedure adopted in this book, namely, that potential values shall be strictly related to a half-reaction written as an oxidation reaction and shall be positive for substances more easily oxidized than hydrogen but negative if less easily oxidized, is that used by most physical chemists in the U.S., though not necessarily by most electrochemists. The International Union of Pure and Applied Chemistry focuses attention on the *electrode* rather than on the *electrode reaction* and recommends that the sign of the electrode potential be determined by the electrical behavior of the electrode when in a cell with the hydrogen electrode; hence negative for negative electrodes and positive for positive electrodes. This has the effect of making the *electrode* potentials exactly opposite in sign to those of the *oxidation* potentials in Table 23.1. One of the easiest ways to make use of either system is to associate the electrode potentials of the IUPAC system with *reduction half-reactions* and use them as such in calculations.

$Cu^{+2}(a = 1) + 2e^- \to Cu(s)$ Electrode potential (IUPAC) $= +0.345$ volt

$Cu(s) \to Cu^{+2}(a = 1) + 2e^-$ Oxidation potential $= -0.345$ volt

The half-reaction corresponding to this value is a *reduction* reaction; the oxidation half-reaction is the reverse of this, and gives the negative sign to the standard oxidation potential of copper.

$$E^{\circ}_{Cu \to Cu^{+2}} = -0.345 \text{ volt} \tag{20}$$

$$Cu(s) \longrightarrow Cu^{+2}(a=1) + 2e^{-} \qquad E^{\circ} = -0.345 \text{ volt} \tag{21}$$

Reducing Agents and Oxidizing Agents. Since $\Delta G^{\circ} = -nFE^{\circ}$, and ΔG° is negative for spontaneous reactions, those half-reactions will have the greatest driving force which have the most positive values of E°. Hence the strongest reducing agents are the substances appearing as *reactants* in the half-reactions near the top of Table 23.1. At the bottom of the table, the half-reactions will give a negative value of ΔG° when written in the reverse direction. Hence the strongest oxidizing agents are the substances appearing as *products* in the half-reactions near the bottom of the table. Thus, of the substances listed, lithium is the best reducing agent, and fluorine the best oxidizing agent. Fluoride ion, on the other hand, is the poorest reducing agent, and lithium ion, the poorest oxidizing agent.

Cell Voltage from Oxidation Potentials. From the data in Table 23.1, we can now calculate the voltage of a cell containing any pair of electrodes. The voltage of the zinc-copper cell of Figure 23.5, for example, for 1-molal concentrations of zinc and copper ions, would simply be the sum of the potentials corresponding to the half-reactions taking place in the electrode compartments. These are

$$Zn(s) \longrightarrow Zn^{+2}(1 \text{ m.}) + 2e^{-} \tag{13}$$

$$Cu^{+2}(1 \text{ m.}) + 2e^{-} \longrightarrow Cu(s) \tag{17}$$

The second half-reaction given is the reverse of that given for the copper electrode in the table; to get the value for it we must change the sign of the tabulated value:

$$\begin{aligned} E^{\circ}_{cell} &= E^{\circ}_{Zn \to Zn^{+2}} + E^{\circ}_{Cu^{+2} \to Cu} = E^{\circ}_{Zn \to Zn^{+2}} - E^{\circ}_{Cu \to Cu^{+2}} \\ &= 0.762 - (-0.345) = 1.107 \text{ volt} \end{aligned} \tag{22}$$

The value of 1.107 corresponds to the cell voltage when the components are in their standard states.

The sign of the oxidation potential does not show whether the electrode is the positive or negative pole of a cell; this depends upon what the other electrode is. Thus if a zinc electrode is placed in a cell with the copper electrode,

$$Zn \mid Zn^{+2}(1 \text{ m.}) \parallel Cu^{+2}(1 \text{ m.}) \mid Cu$$

electrons flow from the zinc to the copper, and the zinc rod must be connected as the negative pole. However, in a cell containing a zinc and a magnesium electrode,

$$Zn \mid Zn^{+2}(1 \text{ m.}) \parallel Mg^{+2}(1 \text{ m.}) \mid Mg$$

electrons flow toward the zinc from the magnesium, and the zinc rod must be connected as the positive pole. The half-reactions in the zinc-magnesium cell are

$$Zn^{+2}(1 \text{ m.}) + 2e^- \longrightarrow Zn(s) \qquad (23)$$

$$Mg(s) \longrightarrow Mg^{+2}(1 \text{ m.}) + 2e^- \qquad (24)$$

and the voltage is

$$E^\circ_{\text{cell}} = E^\circ_{Zn^{+2} \to Zn} + E^\circ_{Mg \to Mg^{+2}} = -E^\circ_{Zn \to Zn^{+2}} + E^\circ_{Mg \to Mg^{+2}}$$
$$= -(+0.762) + 2.37 = 1.61 \text{ volt} \qquad (25)$$

The reaction taking place in the cell will be that which makes the cell voltage positive (ΔG negative).

Relationship Between Cell Voltage and Concentration. Up to this point all the cells we have dealt with have been made with solutions of ions in their standard states of "1-molal" concentration. The voltages for other concentrations may be readily obtained by making use of Equation (40) of Chap. 22 to obtain an equation similar to Equation (35) of that chapter, but written in terms of the concentration approximation. The result,

$$\Delta G = \Delta G^\circ + 2.3RT \log \frac{c_P{}^p c_Q{}^q}{c_M{}^m c_N{}^n} \qquad (26)$$

records the effect of change in concentration on the change in free energy for the general reaction

$$m\text{M}(c_M) + n\text{N}(c_N) \rightleftarrows p\text{P}(c_P) + q\text{Q}(c_Q) \qquad (27)$$

The relationship between cell potential and free-energy change is given by Equations (8) and (10):

$$\Delta G = -nFE \qquad (8)$$

$$\Delta G^\circ = -nFE^\circ \qquad (10)$$

Substitution in Equation (26) gives

$$E = E^\circ - \frac{2.3\,RT}{nF} \log \frac{c_P{}^p c_Q{}^q}{c_M{}^m c_N{}^n} \qquad (28)$$

This equation makes it possible to calculate E° from measurements of the potential E of the cell at concentrations other than 1 molal and to calculate the voltages of cells from tabulated E° values when the ion concentrations are not 1 molal. The following is an example of the second calculation.

PROBLEM. ■ Calculate the voltage of the cell of Figure 23.5 at 25°C when the zinc sulfate solution is 0.1 molal and the copper sulfate solution is 0.001 molal.

SOLUTION
Substitution of the concentrations in Equation (28) gives

$$E = 1.107 - \frac{RT}{2F} 2.303 \log \frac{0.1}{0.001} = 1.048 \text{ volt}$$

The cell voltage is less than the voltage when the concentrations were equal, and the free-energy change is less negative ($\Delta G = -nFE = -24.2$ kcal as compared to -25.3 kcal in the equal concentrations case). This is to be expected, since the relatively greater decrease in the copper-ion concentration as compared to the decrease in the zinc-ion concentration decreases the driving force in the reaction from left to right.

$$Zn(s) + Cu^{+2}(0.001 \text{ m.}) \longrightarrow Cu(s) + Zn^{+2}(0.1 \text{ m.}) \qquad \Delta G = -24.2 \text{ kcal}$$

$$Zn(s) + Cu^{+2}(1 \text{ m.}) \longrightarrow Cu(s) + Zn^{+2}(1 \text{ m.}) \qquad \Delta G = -25.3 \text{ kcal}$$

Cell Voltage and Equilibrium Constant. The relations obtained from Equation (10)

$$\Delta G^\circ = -nFE^\circ \tag{10}$$

and from Equation (33) of Chap. 22

$$\Delta G^\circ = -2.303RT \log K$$

permit the immediate calculation of the equilibrium constant for any reaction for which E° is known.

PROBLEM. ■ Calculate, from electrode potential data, the equilibrium constant at 25° C for the reaction represented by Equation (A).

$$Br_2(l) + 2Fe^{+2}(1 \text{ m.}) \rightleftharpoons 2Br^-(1 \text{ m.}) + 2Fe^{+3}(1 \text{ m.}) \tag{A}$$

SOLUTION

Since the ions are in their standard states (approximation!), the data of table 23.1 may be used directly. The half-reactions are

$$Br_2(l) + 2e^- \longrightarrow 2Br^-(1 \text{ m.}) \qquad E^\circ = 1.09$$

$$Fe^{+2}(1 \text{ m.}) \longrightarrow Fe^{+3}(1 \text{ m.}) + e^- \qquad E^\circ = -0.771$$

The E° value for the first reaction is given the positive sign, since the equation is the reverse of that in Table 23.1. The voltage of a cell in which reaction (A) took place would then be

$$E_{cell} = E^\circ_{Br_2 \to 2Br^-} + E^\circ_{Fe^{+2} \to Fe^{+3}} = +1.09 - 0.771 = +0.32 \text{ volt}$$

The positive voltage means that the reaction is spontaneous as written. The free-energy change is

$$\Delta G^\circ = -nFE^\circ = -2 \times 96,487 \times (+0.32) = -61,800 \text{ joules or } -14.8 \text{ kcal}$$

Note that the cell voltage is obtained by direct use of oxidation-potential data obtained from Table 23.1; no alteration of those values is necessary to take account of the fact that the bromine molecule gains two electrons, while the iron(II) ion loses only one. Account of this difference *has* been taken in balancing the chemical equation for the oxidation-reduction process. The balanced equation shows that two electrons have been transferred, and hence the value $n = 2$ has been assigned in calculating the standard free-energy change as $-nFE^\circ$.

From the equation relating to the equilibrium constant

$$\log K = -\frac{-14,800}{2.3 \times 1.987 \times 298}$$

and

$$K = 7.3 \times 10^{10} = \frac{[Br^-]^2_{eq}[Fe^{+3}]^2_{eq}}{[Fe^{+2}]^2_{eq}}$$

The large value of the equilibrium constant in the problem tells us, it will be remembered (page 413), that when equilibrium is established in the

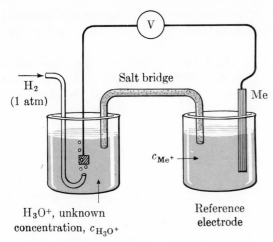

Figure 23.9 Measurement of hydronium-ion concentration.

bromine, bromide, ferrous ion, ferric ion system, the ferrous-ion concentration will be low, or, the position of equilibrium is well toward the right.

Galvanic Cells and Hydronium-Ion Concentration. An important application of the galvanic cell in the laboratory is its use in measuring the concentration of hydronium ions in a solution. Suppose that a cell is set up as in Figure 23.9. Here one electrode is a hydrogen electrode and the other a "reference electrode," and the two are connected by a salt bridge. The voltage of the cell can be measured, using a potentiometer, or, typically, a vacuum-tube voltmeter, V, which draws negligible current and allows the *reversible* potential difference to be measured. The voltage will be found to depend upon the concentration of hydronium ions and of the metal ions (Me^+) of the reference electrode:

$$E = E^\circ - 2.303 \frac{RT}{F} \log \frac{c_{Me^+}}{c_{H_3O^+}} \qquad (29)$$

If the concentration of hydronium ion in the left-hand beaker is now changed to $c'_{H_3O^+}$, while leaving the reference half-cell unchanged, the voltage will be

$$E' = E^\circ - 2.303 \frac{RT}{F} \log \frac{c_{Me^+}}{c'_{H_3O^+}} \qquad (30)$$

Thus the magnitude of the voltage, E or E', is a correct measure of the hydronium-ion concentration $c'_{H_3O^+}$ or $c'_{H_3O^+}$. The nature of the reference half-cell is unimportant except that it be unchanged from experiment to experiment, so that it makes a constant contribution to the over-all cell voltage. The arrangement of Figure 23.9 can be calibrated by measuring the voltage for a known hydronium-ion concentration; measured changes in voltage can then be translated into hydronium-ion concentrations through the logarithmic term of Equation (30).

In practice, a *glass electrode*, consisting of a thin glass bulb containing, typically, an electrode of silver coated with silver chloride dipping into hydrochloric acid solution (Figure 23.10), is used in place of the hydrogen electrode, for convenience. This device, when combined with a reference electrode, shows differences in potential which depend upon the hydronium-ion concentration in the same way that the hydrogen electrode does.

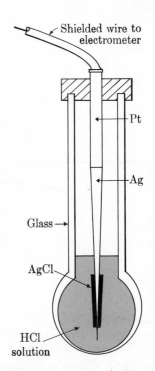

Figure 23.10 Diagram of a glass electrode.

pH Value. We are now in position to explain the present convention defining the quantity pH, for which the historical definition was introduced on page 421.

The pH of a solution, pH(X), is precisely defined in terms of the voltages of two cells, each similar to the one shown in Figure 23.9, one of which contains a carefully chosen solution which we may call the standard, S, and the other the unknown solution X. The pH of the unknown is then defined by the equation

$$pH(X) = pH(S) + (E_x - E_s)\frac{F}{2.3RT} \tag{31}$$

where E_x and E_s are the voltages of the two cells and pH(S) is the value assigned to the standard solution. In the United States a commonly used standard is a 0.05 molal solution of potassium acid phthalate, to which the National Bureau of Standards has assigned the value pH(S) = 4.008 at 25°C. For measurements in dilute solutions which do not claim a precision greater than about 0.1 pH unit we may safely consider that the pH value of a solution is equal to $-\log[H_3O^+]$.

In practice, the pH of a solution is measured on a "pH meter," which measures the voltage of cells consisting of a glass electrode and an electrode of mercury in contact with a saturated solution of mercury(I) chloride, connected through a potassium chloride salt bridge. The meter is first set at a particular value E_s by measurement on a standard solution of known pH(S), and the difference $E_x - E_s$ between that value and the voltage measured for the unknown solution is read off a scale marked directly in pH units.

Potentiometric Titration. Suppose that, instead of changing from one solution to another in the left half-cell of Figure 23.9, the experimenter repeatedly adds to the acid solution measured amounts of a solution of a strong base. This will neutralize the acid, changing the hydronium-ion concentration, and changing the voltage of the cell. From the form of Equation (29), it can be seen that the change in $c_{H_3O^+}$ from, for example, 0.1 m. to 0.01 m., will make the same change in voltage as the change from 0.00001 m. to 0.000001 m. It will require, however, only one ten-thousandth as much base solution to produce the latter change as would be required for the former. Consequently, a plot of the change in voltage per milliliter of base solution added will show a rise at first, followed by a very rapid change near the neutral point and a slow change on the basic side (Figure 23.11). The volume of base added to reach the most rapidly rising portion of the curve represents the amount needed to neutralize the acid.

The experiment thus constitutes a *titration* of the acid with the base, using a potentiometric (*potential measurement*) procedure for determining the end-point of the titration. Obviously, in order for the procedure to be usable, the cation present in the solution of the base used must not react with any compounds in the cell solution in such a way as to change the cell voltage.

Curves exactly similar to that of Figure 23.11 will appear in other half-cells when a titrating solution is added which removes the ion in the cell.

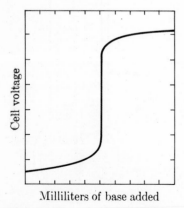

Figure 23.11 Change of cell voltage upon addition of base to an acid solution.

For example, silver ion in the cell

$$Ag \mid Ag^+ \parallel \text{reference electrode}$$

may be removed by adding sodium chloride solution to precipitate silver chloride.

SUMMARY

This chapter is an introduction to the topic of electrochemistry of solutions. Herein are discussed the principles underlying the operation of electrolysis cells (cells in which electricity is used to bring about a chemical reaction) and galvanic or voltaic cells (cells in which a chemical reaction is allowed to proceed so that an electric current is produced).

In electrolytic cells, the battery or generator, operating as an electron pump, charges one electrode negatively (cathode) and the other positively (anode) and creates a potential difference across the electrodes. Positive ions are attracted to the cathode, negative ions to the anode, and this movement of ions constitutes the electrical conductivity of the solution. At each electrode a chemical change occurs—an oxidation at the anode and a reduction at the cathode. The over-all chemical reaction of the cell is the sum of the electrode reactions. Faraday's laws establish a quantitative relationship between the quantity of electricity passed through the cell and the amount of reaction occurring at the electrodes.

In galvanic cells, a spontaneous process is allowed to occur in such a way that reactants are not in direct contact but are connected by an external electric circuit. Transfer of electrons takes place from one reactant to another through the wire thereby creating an electric current as the reaction proceeds. The voltage of the cell depends upon the nature of the reactants, the concentrations (activities) of ions in solution and on the temperature. The work obtained from a galvanic cell operating under reversible conditions is a precise measure of the free-energy change for the chemical process occurring in the cell. Assuming the cell voltage is the sum of contributions from each electrode, it is possible to obtain a set of relative potentials (oxidation potentials) for each electrode immersed in a solution of its ions. These relative values, based on the arbitrary standard of zero voltage for the hydrogen electrode in a solution of hydronium ions at unit activity, give a quantitative measure of chemical reactivity for these systems.

Applications of standard oxidation potentials to problems of chemical reactivity and equilibrium are given.

SOME SPECIAL TERMS

Electrochemical cell	**Cell reaction**	**Hydrogen electrode**
electrolysis cell	half-reaction	reference electrode
galvanic cell	**Reversible potential**	glass electrode
Electrolytic conduction	electrode potential	**Electrical work**
metallic conduction	oxidation potential	**Salt bridge**
Anode	standard potential	**Potentiometric titration**
cathode	**Faraday's laws**	**pH value**

QUESTIONS AND PROBLEMS

1. What is the difference in the manner in which electricity is conducted through a solution and through a metal?
2. Does metallic conduction produce chemical changes in the metal? Explain.
3. Define anode and cathode in terms of oxidation and reduction and in terms of change in oxidation number.
4. Describe some industrial applications of electrolysis.
5. Explain how the Avogadro number might be determined by electrolysis.
6. If a current of 0.20 amp is passed through a copper sulfate solution for 10 minutes, calculate the following: (a) the number of grams of copper deposited; (b) the number of atoms of copper deposited.
   (*Note:* Recall that the charge on an electron is 1.60×10^{-19} coul; 96,487 coul is required to reduce 1 gram-ionic weight of a univalent metal, and an ampere is a rate of current flow equal to 1 coul/sec.)
7. A weight 3.974 g of copper is deposited when 12,062 coul of electricity is passed through a copper sulfate solution using platinum electrodes. Calculate the number of atoms in a gram-atomic weight of copper.
8. Trace the ionic and electron processes in the solution and at the electrodes in the electrolysis of a water solution containing an acid such as HCl; such as H_2SO_4.
9. Trace the ionic and electron processes in solution and at the electrodes in a battery made of copper and zinc electrodes immersed in copper sulfate and zinc sulfate respectively.
10. Write the equations for the half-reaction occurring at each electrode in Problem 9. Calculate the $E°$ for the cell from the $E°$ for each half-reaction.
11. Under what conditions can we write $\Delta G° = -nFE°$?
12. What is the basis for assuming $E° = 0$ for the reaction

$$H_2 \text{ (1 atm)} \xrightleftharpoons{\text{(H}_2\text{O)}} 2H_3O^+ \text{ (1 m.)} + 2e^-$$

13. Calculate the electromotive force at 25° C for a zinc-copper cell in which the zinc sulphate concentration is 0.01 molar and the copper sulfate concentration is 0.1 molar.
14. Calculate the value of ΔG for the cell in Problem 13.
15. Calculate the value of the equilibrium constant at 25°C for the reaction

$$Zn + 2H^+_{aq} \longrightarrow Zn^{+2} + H_2$$

using the information that $E°$ for the zinc half-cell is -0.76 and for the hydrogen electrode is 0.
16. Under what conditions can we write $\Delta G = -2.303RT \log K$?
17. Explain how the pH value of a solution can be determined from voltage measurement.
18. Explain how you might determine the end-point of a titration of Ag^+ with Cl^- using a silver rod as one electrode in a cell whose voltage is measured as the solution is titrated.
19. Look up the oxidation potentials of zinc and iron in Table 23.1. Which metal is more active? Explain why zinc can be used as a protective coating for iron (galvanizing iron) even though its $E°$ is higher than the $E°$ of iron.
20. Diagram a lead storage cell on discharge; draw another diagram of the same cell on charge. Label the electrode *anode*, *cathode*, *positive*, and *negative* in each process.

21. Metallic tin placed in silver nitrate solution will precipitate metallic silver. If tin is added to a suspension of silver chloride in 1.0 molal sodium chloride solution, will silver be formed? Will silver form if tin is added to a suspension of silver iodide in 1.0 molal sodium iodide solution? Explain why or why not.

REFERENCES

SANDERSON, R. T. "On the Significance of Electrode Potentials," *J. Chem. Educ.*, *43* (1966), p. 584.

WASER, J. *Basic Chemical Thermodynamics*. New York: Benjamin, 1966.

24

Chemical Kinetics

The rate of the observed reaction depend[s] on the numbers of collisions per second which take place between active molecules of the participating substances.* W. C. McC. Lewis (1885–1956)

The present theory of rates reduces the problems of kinetics to a thermodynamic calculation of an equilibrium constant for the activated complex . . . . The equilibrium constant must be multiplied by the frequency kT/h . . . to give the absolute rate.*
Henry Eyring (1901—) and W. F. K. Wynne-Jones (1903—)

Chemical *kinetics* deals with the rates of chemical reactions. It is often contrasted with chemical *thermodynamics* (Chaps. 21–23) by saying that the time is not a variable in thermodynamic treatments, while kinetics investigates how the state of the system is changing with time. Thermodynamics examines only the differences between initial and final states; its major concern is with systems at equilibrium, but it does not concern itself with the rates at which systems approach the equilibrium condition, nor the pathways which they take as they do so. These problems of rates and pathways make up the subject of chemical kinetics.

Some of the most interesting and important facts about chemical reactions have been obtained from the study of chemical kinetics. For example, it might be supposed that the reaction of hydrogen with gaseous bromine

$$H_2 + Br_2 \longrightarrow 2HBr$$

is the result of a simple collision of a hydrogen molecule with a bromine molecule, resulting in a switch of partners to form two hydrogen bromide molecules. The study of the rate of the reaction, however, shows that the path from hydrogen and bromine to hydrogen bromide involves several reaction steps, in which free atoms of bromine and of hydrogen are involved, as well as hydrogen and bromine molecules. In contrast, rate studies of the reaction between hydrogen and gaseous iodine,

$$H_2 + I_2 \longrightarrow 2HI$$

---

* The quotations are from *J. Chem. Soc., 113* (1918), p. 471 and *J. Chem. Phys., 3* (1935), p. 502.

long thought to result from a simple collision and shift of partners, show that the path from reactants to products involves a collision between two iodine atoms and a hydrogen molecule. How does the study of reaction rates enable us to get such information about reaction pathways?

Rate and Mechanism of Reaction

Rate of Reaction. By the rate of a reaction we mean the quantity of material per unit volume undergoing transformation in a unit of time (second, minute, hour, day). Usually the rate is a rapidly changing quantity, since, as reaction proceeds, the reactants are used up, and there remains progressively less and less material to undergo reaction. Such a change in rate with change of time and concentration of reactants is shown in the graphs for the hydrogen iodide reaction in Chap. 9. The rate must, therefore, be looked upon as an instantaneous quantity determined by plotting the quantity of reactant per unit volume (that is, by plotting the concentration) against the time, and measuring the small change in concentration Δc in a brief instant Δt. The change per unit time (that is, the rate of reaction) is then $\Delta c/\Delta t$. It is evident from the graph that $\Delta c_1/\Delta t$ is larger than $\Delta c_2/\Delta t$, showing that the rate decreases as the reaction proceeds (Figure 24.1).

Neither $\Delta c_1/\Delta t$ nor $\Delta c_2\Delta t$ corresponds to any particular instant of time, but rather to the intervals of time covered by the Δt values. The instantaneous quantity, the rate of the reaction at any given time, is obtained by imagining the time interval, Δt, to become smaller and smaller. As Δt becomes very small and approaches 0, $\Delta c/\Delta t$ becomes

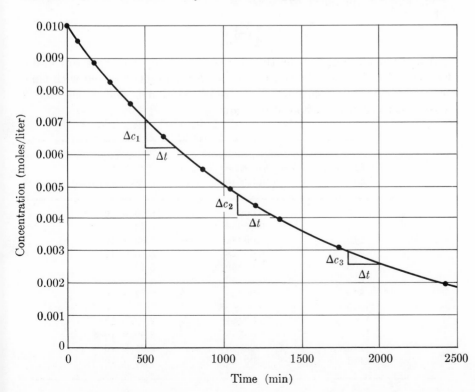

Figure 24.1 Change of concentration of trinitrobenzoic acid as a function of time showing change in $\Delta c/\Delta t$ as reactant is used up.

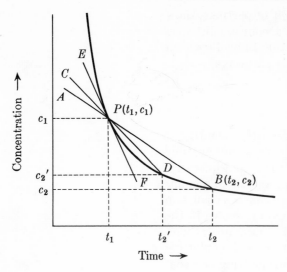

Figure 24.2 Finding the slope of the curve dc/dt at the precise instant t_1. The line AB is drawn from B, where the measured coordinates are (t_2, c_2) through (t_1, c_1) ; the approximate measure of the rate is given by the slope of this line, $(c_2 - c_1)/(t_2 - t_1)$. Now if we take another point D, with coordinates (t_2', c_2'), a line CD drawn from it through P will have the slope $(c_2' - c_1)/(t_2' - t_1)$. Moving from P to D corresponds to making the interval $t_2 - t_1$ smaller, and if we continue to make the interval smaller, the points corresponding to B and D move up the curve closer and closer to P. At the same time the slopes of the lines corresponding to BP, DP, etc., become steeper and steeper, until at the limit where t_2 and t_1 are the same, they have the slope corresponding to the line EF which is tangent to the curve at P. One way to determine the rate of a reaction, therefore, is to determine by experiment the shape of a concentration-time curve, such as that shown in Figure 24.1, and then to determine the slope of a tangent to that curve at a particular concentration.

equal to the slope of the curve at that particular time (Figure 24.2). It is this value of the slope of the curve at the time in question which is the true value of the reaction rate at that time and at the concentration of the reactants existing at that instant. Thus on the graph (Figure 24.1) the reaction rate 172 min after the beginning of the reaction is the slope of the curve at 172 min; this slope has the value 5.89×10^{-6} mole/liter/min, and this is the value of the reaction rate at that time. At 405 min after the start of the reaction, the rate is 5.19×10^{-6} mole/liter/min.

The slope of the curve expressed as

$$\left(\frac{\Delta c}{\Delta t}\right)_{\Delta t \to 0}$$

is defined in mathematics as the derivative of c with respect to t and is written dc/dt. Because the concentration of reactants decreases with time, dc/dt (the slope) is negative. The rate of reaction is defined as $-dc/dt$, where c is the concentration of reactant.

Table 24.1 Decomposition of Trinitro-benzoic Acid in Water at 70°C

Time (min)	Concentration of Trinitrobenzoic Acid (moles/liter)	Rate (moles/liter/min)
0	0.00998	6.69×10^{-6}
58	0.00959	6.42×10^{-6}
172	0.00888	5.89×10^{-6}
275	0.00828	5.55×10^{-6}
405	0.00759	5.19×10^{-6}
618	0.00658	4.51×10^{-6}
870	0.00555	3.72×10^{-6}
1040	0.00495	3.21×10^{-6}
1200	0.00444	2.90×10^{-6}
1360	0.00398	2.69×10^{-6}
1740	0.00308	2.05×10^{-6}
2425	0.00196	1.35×10^{-6}

Measurement of Reaction Rates. From what has been said above, it is seen that the measurement of reaction rate demands the collection of data from which the concentration-time curve of Figure 24.1 may be plotted. The data may be obtained in a variety of ways, depending upon the system under investigation. Some procedures frequently used are described in the following paragraphs.

If the reaction involves the removal of an acid or a base, for example, samples may be pipetted from the reaction mixture at measured times $(t_1, t_2, t_3,$ etc.) and the concentrations of acid $(c_1, c_2, c_3,$ etc.) determined in each sample. This was the procedure used in obtaining the data in Table 24.1. Here the reaction is

Trinitrobenzoic acid   Trinitrobenzene

Samples of the reacting solution were removed at the times recorded, and titrated with standard base to determine the concentration of the acid remaining unchanged at that instant. A graph such as Figure 24.1 was plotted, showing the change of concentration of the acid as a function of time. Tangents to the curve were then drawn; the slopes of these tangents represent the instantaneous values of the rates $(-dc/dt)$ at the concentrations and times corresponding to the points of tangency, and are recorded in the third column of the table.

For a reaction involving gases, the pressure of the gas is a measure of concentration (from $P = n/V \times RT$), and a pressure measurement at known times will give data for the curve.

In another method the formation or disappearance of a colored substance as a result of the reaction may be observed by watching the changing depth of color as a function of time.

Factors Determining the Rate of Reaction. When data on reaction rates are examined it is found that the rates depend upon four major quantities: (a) the nature of the reactants, (b) the presence or absence of a catalyst, (c) the temperature, and (d) the concentration of the reactants. Let us discuss each of these.

Nature of the Reactants. In the discussions of ionic equilibria in Chap. 21, no question needed to be raised as to whether the systems under consideration were at equilibrium, since most reactions between simple ions in solution are so fast that their rates cannot be observed by ordinary methods. Hence many reactions of ions reach equilibrium almost instantaneously. This is not true for most reactions involving covalent bonds such as those in organic molecules, and the rates of reactions involving these substances can often be conveniently measured by methods similar to those described earlier. A useful rule then is that reactions involving simple ions are rapid, and reactions of most covalent substances are slow. There are exceptions to both generalizations. Further, within each class there are individual variations, so that some "slow" reactions are slower than others, and the same covalent substance, or even the same functional group on an organic molecule, may react faster with a given functional group on one type of molecule than with the functional group on another type. It is one of the tasks of the organic chemist to interpret such a difference in rates in terms of the changing structure of the molecules or the difference in the electronic environment in which the functional group finds itself in the two molecules of different reactivity (Chap. 30).

Catalysis. The rates of many reactions are changed when the reaction mixture is permitted to include a substance known as a catalyst, which itself remains unchanged in quantity and chemical composition at the end of the reaction. For example, the decomposition of hydrogen peroxide in water solution

$$2H_2O_2 \longrightarrow 2H_2O + O_2 \tag{1}$$

proceeds much faster when bromide ion is present than when the solution contains only hydrogen peroxide. The bromide ion is still in the solution, unchanged in amount, at the end of the reaction; *apparently* it has changed the reaction rate somehow by being present! Chemists do not accept an interpretation that catalysis is due to the mere presence of a catalyzing substance, however, and seek an explanation in terms of a preliminary reaction of the catalyst with the reactant, followed by another reaction which regenerates the catalyst while forming the final product. Thus, the catalyst actually takes some part or a part in the reaction.

The bromide ion catalysis of hydrogen peroxide decomposition is an example of *homogeneous* catalysis, since only one phase (the solution) is present. The reactions in many biological systems involve such homogeneous catalysis, by complex substances known as *enzymes*. More usual in chemical industries are cases of *heterogeneous* catalysis, in which a gas or liquid phase containing the reactants is in contact with a solid catalyst. Thus the ammonia synthesis (Chap. 17 and Table 21.8) uses iron containing small amounts of potassium and aluminum oxides as a catalyst; the oxidation of sulfur dioxide to sulfur trioxide (Chap. 16) uses divandium pentoxide; and catalytic cracking of hydrocarbons uses silica-alumina mixtures. In each of these cases the reaction proceeds more rapidly than it would in the absence of the catalyst at the same temperature; this permits the ammonia synthesis, for example, to operate profitably at 500°C instead of going to the higher temperatures which would otherwise be required (see paragraphs on "Temperature," below) to bring the reaction rate to a high enough value for profitable operation.

It has been noted (Figure 21.1) that the presence of a catalyst has no effect on the position of equilibrium, which is determined only by the free-energy change in passing from the initial to the final state. Since the catalyst is a component of both the initial and the final states, it makes the same contribution to both, and the terms involving it disappear when the free-energy difference is taken between the two states.

Temperature. With a few exceptions, the rate of a chemical reaction, under fixed conditions of concentration, increases with increase in temperature. The increase is more than proportional to the increase in temperature: for many reactions in solution, for example, the rate more than doubles for each 10° rise in temperature. Thus a reaction proceeding at a given rate at 50° will go more than twice as fast at 60°, and more than twice as fast again at 70°, making the rate at 70° more than four times as fast as at 50°. Data for the decomposition of trinitrobenzoic acid at 0.00800 moles/liter are shown in Figure 24.3.

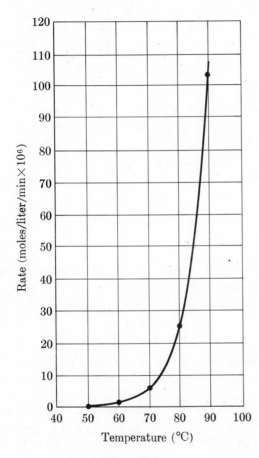

Figure 24.3 The rate of decomposition of trinitrobenzoic acid as a function of temperature. The rates are determined for the concentration 0.0080 moles/liter.

Exact measurements show that the logarithm of the rate is proportional to the reciprocal of the absolute temperature, as expressed by the following relation

$$\log (\text{Rate}) = -\frac{A}{T} + \log B \tag{2}$$

where A and B are constants which differ for each reaction and, for B, for each of the constant concentrations of reactants used in the measurements at the different temperatures (Figure 24.4).

Concentration. It is a general rule that the reaction rate increases with increase in the concentration of reactants. This is what we ought to expect, since a reaction between two molecules such as hydrogen and iodine can only occur when they are in contact, or at least close together, so that new

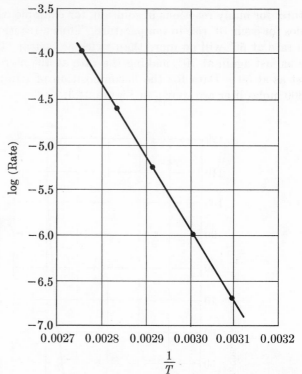

Figure 24.4 The logarithm of the rates of decomposition of trinitrobenzoic acid given in Figure 24.3 plotted according to Equation (2). From Figure 24.3 it is seen that the rate at 70° C is 5.36×10^{-6} moles/liter/min. The logarithm of this is $\bar{6}.730$ or -5.270 as plotted above for $1/T = 1/(273 + 70) = 0.00292$ (deg K)$^{-1}$.

bonds may form between certain atoms, while existing bonds between other atoms are broken.

$$
\begin{array}{ccc}
\text{H} & \text{I} & \text{H—I} \\
| \; + \; | & \longrightarrow & \\
\text{H} & \text{I} & \text{H—I}
\end{array}
$$

The numbers of such contacts in unit time will depend upon how intensively the molecules are crowded together, that is, upon the concentration, just as the number of collisions between couples on a dance floor depends upon how crowded the dancing area is. The number of contacts between the *two* kinds of molecules H_2 and I_2 will be proportional to the concentration of *each* and hence to the product of their concentrations, and we might predict that the rate would be given by an equation of the sort

$$\text{Rate} = k c_{H_2} c_{I_2} \tag{3}$$

If this is found to be the case, k, the proportionality constant, is known as the rate constant for the reaction. Its value depends upon the temperature at which the rate is measured.

We can also conceive that a reaction might involve only one substance in decomposition, and that the rate of the reaction—that is, the amount decomposing per unit volume per unit time—would depend upon the amount of reactant present in unit volume, so that a rate equation of the form

$$\text{Rate} = kc \tag{4}$$

might appear. This is experimentally the case for the trinitrobenzoic acid decomposition plotted in Figure 24.1 (see Table 24.2).

Reactions which have a rate equation like Equation (4) whose rates depend mathematically upon the concentration of only one substance raised to the first power are known as *first-order reactions*. Those following an equation like Equation (3) are known as *second-order reactions*, because they involve the product of *two* concentration terms. An equation corresponding to the reaction of two molecules of the same substance

$$\text{Rate} = kc_A{}^2 \tag{5}$$

is also an equation for a second-order reaction; an example would be that of the reverse of hydrogen iodide formation

$$2HI \longrightarrow H_2 + I_2 \tag{6}$$

$$\text{Rate} = kc_{HI} \times c_{HI} = kc_{HI}{}^2 \tag{7}$$

A few third-order reactions are also known, for example,

$$2NO + O_2 \longrightarrow 2NO_2 \tag{8}$$

with the rate equation

$$\text{Rate} = kc_{NO}{}^2 \times c_{O_2} \tag{9}$$

There are many additional examples of the dependence of reaction rate on concentrations giving rate equations similar to those given, and a general law, known as the *law of mass action*, can be formulated: *The rate of a chemical reaction is proportional to the concentration of each of the reacting substances*. The *order* of the reaction is equal to the sum of the exponents which appear on the concentration terms in the equation expressing the rate in terms of concentrations.

Complex Rate Equations. The rate equations given in the preceding section have the exponents in the rate equation identical to the coefficients in the chemical equation. It becomes quickly evident, however, that this connection between the chemical equation and the rate equation, which seems to emerge from the results of the preceding paragraphs, is not correct for many reactions. The reason is that reactions often involve

Concentration (moles/liter)	Rate (moles/liter/min)	Rate Constant $\left(\dfrac{\text{rate}}{\text{concentration}}\right)$*
0.00998	6.69×10^{-6}	6.70×10^{-4}
0.00959	6.42×10^{-6}	6.69×10^{-4}
0.00888	5.89×10^{-6}	6.63×10^{-4}
0.00828	5.55×10^{-6}	6.70×10^{-4}
0.00759	5.19×10^{-6}	6.83×10^{-4}
0.00658	4.51×10^{-6}	6.85×10^{-4}
0.00555	3.72×10^{-6}	6.70×10^{-4}
0.00495	3.21×10^{-6}	6.48×10^{-4}
0.00444	2.90×10^{-6}	6.53×10^{-4}
0.00398	2.69×10^{-6}	6.75×10^{-4}
0.00308	2.05×10^{-6}	6.66×10^{-4}
0.00196	1.35×10^{-6}	6.88×10^{-4}

Table 24.2 Rate Constant for the Decomposition of Trinitrobenzoic Acid at 70°C

* See Equation (4).

several steps, some of which are slow and others fast and require rate equations that have exponents quite different from the coefficients of the chemical equation. For example, consider the following three reactions and their rate equations.

$$2N_2O_5 \longrightarrow 2N_2O_4 + O_2 \tag{10}$$

$$\text{Rate} = k_{obs}\, c_{N_2O_5} \tag{11}$$

$$Br^- + OCl^- \longrightarrow OBr^- + Cl^- \tag{12}$$

$$\text{Rate} = k_{obs}\, \frac{c_{Br^-}c_{OCl^-}}{c_{OH^-}} \tag{13}$$

$$H_2 + Br_2 \longrightarrow 2HBr \tag{14}$$

$$\text{Rate} = k_{obs}\, \frac{c_{H_2}c_{Br_2}^{1/2}}{1 + k'\,\dfrac{c_{HBr}}{c_{Br_2}}} \tag{15}$$

In the first case, the chemical equation shows that two molecules are required in the over-all reaction, but the rate equation shows that the rate does not depend upon the number of contacts (collisions) between pairs of molecules, which would require a c^2 term, but that the reaction apparently involves only a single, isolated molecule (c^1). In the case of the oxidation of bromide by hypochlorite, the rate depends upon the concentration of a substance (the hydroxyl ion) which does not even appear in the chemical equation for the reaction. In the third case, the rate equation is quite complicated, in spite of the fact that the chemical equation seems very similar to that for the combination of hydrogen and iodine, which has a simple rate equation involving only a product of concentrations.

Mechanism of Reaction. Rate equations, such as those given, are established by experiment, by finding what concentration changes change the rate of reaction, and whether the concentrations should appear as the first power or the square, etc., in the rate equation. The experimental nature of the rate equation has been indicated by labeling the rate constant $k_{observed}$. The chemist then proceeds to suggest a *mechanism* for the reaction, which will explain how a particular rate equation can arise. A complex rate equation such as (13) or (15) indicates that the over-all reaction is taking place with more than one step, so that an intermediate first formed reacts further in subsequent steps to form the final product. Even a simple rate equation may represent a multi-step mechanism, as shown in the next section.

Determination of the Mechanism of a Reaction of Simple Order: The Conversion of Ammonium Cyanate to Urea. Consider, as an example of a mechanism study, the transformation of ammonium cyanate (NH_4OCN) to urea:

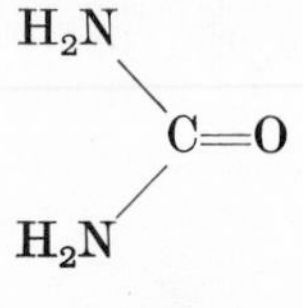

$$\begin{array}{c} H_2N \\ \diagdown \\ C{=}O \\ \diagup \\ H_2N \end{array}$$

a reaction which takes place in water solution

$$NH_4OCN \longrightarrow \begin{matrix} H_2N \\ \diagdown \\ C{=}O \\ \diagup \\ H_2N \end{matrix} \tag{16}$$

Some data for this reaction are given in Table 24.3.

The Rate Equation. The reaction represented by Equation (16) seems to require only the rearrangement of a single molecule, and suggests that a first-order process is involved. It is evident from column 7 of the table, however, that a rate "constant" calculated for an assumed first-order rate equation shows a definite trend as the concentration decreases, whereas that calculated for a second-order rate equation is constant (column 8). The rate of the reaction is thus expressed by

$$\text{Rate} = k_{\text{obs}}\, c_{\text{NH}_4\text{OCN}}^2 \tag{17}$$

Application of Chemical Information. Equation (17) is simply explained if two molecules of ammonium cyanate are involved in the reaction

$$2\text{NH}_4\text{OCN} \longrightarrow 2(\text{H}_2\text{N})_2\text{CO} \tag{18}$$

But there seems no compelling chemical reason why the reaction should require two molecules of reactant, and we seek some other explanation of the second-order rate equation. If we remember that ammonium cyanate is a salt, and therefore completely ionized, we recognize that no substance of the formula NH_4OCN can be present in water solution; dissociation into NH_4^+ and OCN^- must occur. When we dissolve 0.1 mole of ammonium cyanate in one liter of solution, therefore, we are really dissolving 0.1 mole of ammonium ions and 0.1 mole of cyanate ions.

Table 24.3 Rate of Disappearance of Ammonium Cyanate in the Formation of Urea in Water Solution at 50°C*

Time (min)	Concentration (mole/liter)	Δc	Δt	Rate	Average Concentration	$\dfrac{\text{Rate}}{\text{Concentration}}$	$\dfrac{\text{Rate}}{(\text{Concentration})^2}$
0	0.1000						
		−0.0192	45	0.000427	0.0904	0.00472	0.0523
45	0.0808						
		−0.0092	27	0.000341	0.0762	0.00448	0.0587
72	0.0716						
		−0.0078	35	0.000223	0.0677	0.00329	0.0487
107	0.0638						
		−0.0079	50	0.000158	0.0599	0.00263	0.0440
157	0.0559						
		−0.0096	73	0.000132	0.0511	0.00258	0.0506
230	0.0463						
		−0.0083	82	0.000101	0.0422	0.00239	0.0567
312	0.0380						
		−0.0131	288	0.000045	0.0315	0.00143	0.0455
600	0.0249						

* The rates are approximated as $-(c_2 - c_1)/(t_2 - t_1) = -\Delta c/\Delta t$, and these rates are attributed to the average concentration $(c_1 + c_2)/2$ of the change from c_1 to c_2.

If these are the reactants, so that the equation for the reaction is written

$$NH_4^+ + OCN^- \longrightarrow (H_2N)_2CO \tag{19}$$

then the rate equation would become

$$\text{Rate} = kc_{NH_4^+} \times c_{OCN^-} \tag{20}$$

But the concentrations of the two ions are equal, since we dissolved them pair-wise at the start, and they remain equal throughout the reaction, since the chemical equation uses one of each. Hence $c_{NH_4^+} = c_{OCN^-} = c$, and Equation (20) becomes

$$\text{Rate} = kc \times c = k_{\text{obs}}c^2 \tag{21}$$

as observed in the experimental data of Table 24.3.

Test of the Mechanism. Equation (19) represents a suggested mechanism; it represents a possible explanation for the second-order rate equation found by experiment. In this particular case, the suggestion can be further tested by adding ammonium ion which is not paired up with cyanate ion. Table 24.4 gives data for such an experiment. Here ammonium nitrate (NH_4^+, NO_3^-) has been added to an ammonium cyanate solution and the rate equation examined by applying the law of mass action to Equation (19). It is evident that the reaction in the presence of additional ammonium ion is faster than before, and that a constant value of k is obtained when Equation (20) is applied to the data.

Alternative Mechanism. It might be supposed that Equation (19) is now confirmed as the mechanism. Ammonium cyanate, however, is the salt of a weak acid, HOCN, and a weak base, NH_3. Ammonium ions and cyanate ions in water solution therefore will react according to the equation

Table 24.4 Rate of Disappearance of Cyanate in a Solution 0.1 Molar in Ammonium Cyanate and 0.1 Molar in Ammonium Nitrate in Water at 50°C*

$$NH_4^+ + OCN^- \rightleftharpoons HOCN + NH_3 \tag{22}$$

Furthermore, equilibrium will be rapidly established in this reversible

Time (min)	Concentration of OCN^- (mole/liter)	Concentration of NH_4^+ (mole/liter)	Δc	Δt	Rate	Average c_{OCN^-}	Average $c_{NH_4^+}$	Rate $\overline{c_{OCN^-} \times c_{NH_4^+}}$
0	0.1000	0.2000						
			0.0150	16	0.000912	0.0925	0.1925	0.0526
16	0.0850	0.1850						
			0.0218	34	0.000641	0.0741	0.1741	0.0497
50	0.0632	0.1632						
			0.0131	28	0.000468	0.0566	0.1566	0.0528
78	0.0501	0.1501						
			0.0078	23	0.000342	0.0462	0.1462	0.0502
101	0.0423	0.1423						
			0.0112	46	0.000243	0.0367	0.1367	0.0484
147	0.0311	0.1311						
			0.0078	42	0.000186	0.0272	0.1272	0.0537
189	0.0233	0.1233						

* The rates are approximated as $-(c_2 - c_1)/(t_2 - t_1) = -\Delta c/\Delta t$, and these rates are attributed to the average concentration $(c_1 + c_2)/2$ of the change from c_1 to c_2.

acid-base reaction, so that every solution containing ammonium ion and cyanate ion contains ammonia and cyanic acid. The reaction forming urea might then be

$$NH_3 + HOCN \longrightarrow (H_2N)_2CO \tag{23}$$

The rate of this reaction should be expressed by

$$\text{Rate} = k'c_{NH_3} \times c_{HOCN} \tag{24}$$

But the equilibrium in Equation (22) requires that

$$K = \frac{c_{NH_3} \times c_{HOCN}}{c_{NH_4^+} \times c_{OCN^-}} \tag{25}$$

so that

$$c_{NH_3} \times c_{HOCN} = Kc_{NH_4^+} \times c_{OCN^-} \tag{26}$$

which, on substitution in Equation (24), gives

$$\text{Rate} = k'Kc_{NH_4^+} \times c_{OCN^-} \tag{27}$$

This is of the same form as Equation (20) if $k = k'K$, so that the observed rate equation, Equation (20), agrees with both Equations (19) and (23), and we don't know whether the constant multiplying the concentration term $c_{NH_4^+} \times c_{OCN^-}$ is the single constant k or the product of two constants $k'K$. There are thus two explanations for the same data, and kinetic experiments cannot distinguish which of the two is correct. From other considerations, and by analogy with similar reactions between amines and organic isocyanates, it seems that the mechanism represented by Equation (23) is the more likely.

Rate-Determining Step. The two explanations for the formation of urea represent two mechanisms:

$$NH_4^+ + OCN^- \longrightarrow (H_2N)_2CO \qquad \begin{array}{l} NH_4^+ + OCN^- \rightleftharpoons HOCN + NH_3 \\ HOCN + NH_3 \longrightarrow (H_2N)_2CO \end{array} \tag{28}$$

Mechanism I   Mechanism II

each of which leads to the experimental rate equation. The individual reactions in the mechanisms are known as the *elementary reactions*. In the second mechanism, the first of the elementary reactions is very fast, while the rate of the second reaction is small. The rate of this second reaction determines the over-all rate of production of urea, through Equation (24); it is called the *rate-determining step*. It is often true, even in more complex cases, that one of the reactions in a mechanism involving several elementary reactions is much slower than the others, so that the over-all rate is determined by the rate of the slow, rate-determining step.

Although, for many reactions, only one of the proposed mechanisms seems to offer a reasonable explanation of the experimental facts, the possible existence of other applicable mechanisms cannot be excluded. The student will not be far wrong if he treats a mechanism as a *theory* for interpreting the experimental results. As seen earlier in the book, the same experimental data can often be interpreted by more than one theory. This is also true of the theories governing the rates of chemical reaction in general, as discussed in the next sections.

Theories of Reaction Rates

The form of the rate equation, the mechanism of the over-all reaction, the orders of the elementary reactions and the change of their rates with temperature have been determined from experimental data for many reactions. It remains to construct a theory to explain, in terms of our knowledge about atoms and molecules, why elementary reactions behave as they do. Actually two theories have proved useful: the *collision theory* and the *activated-complex theory*. The collision theory suggests that reaction between two molecules takes place on collision of the two, provided that the collision is at least of a certain minimum violence, and that the rate is determined by the number of such violent collisions in unit volume in unit time. The activated-complex theory suggests that an equilibrium is set up in which the reacting molecules form a high-energy association complex containing both of them, and that the rate is determined by the concentration of this complex at equilibrium and by the rate at which it decomposes.

Collision Theory. We have already suggested, in the introductory paragraphs of this chapter, that in order for reaction to occur between two molecules, the two must come together, that is, a *collision* must occur. If this were the only requirement, then a calculation of the number of collisions per unit volume per unit time between molecules A and B should give the rate of reaction between A and B. On the basis of the kinetic theory of gases it is possible to make such a calculation of the collision rate for gaseous molecules, and it is found that the observed reaction rates are less than the collision rate by many powers of ten. Further, the increase of the calculated collision rate for a 10° rise in temperature is only one per cent or less, whereas the observed increase in reaction rate is 100 per cent or more.

The collision theory explains this by suggesting that it is not sufficient for reaction simply that a collision occur, but that the collision must be a violent one, involving an energy amounting at least to 10–60 kilocalories for a mole of such collisions. If it be assumed that the effective energy is that obtained from the head-on components of the ordinary kinetic theory velocities of the molecules (Figure 24.5), an equation of the following form is derived.

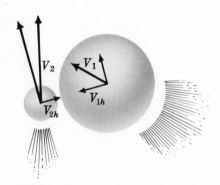

Figure 24.5 In collision theory the energy available for reaction is assumed to be that associated with the head-on components V_{1h} and V_{2h} of the velocities V_1 and V_2 of the two colliding molecules.

$$\log \begin{bmatrix} \text{number of collisions} \\ \text{per} \cdot \text{cubic centimeter} \\ \text{per second with energy} \\ \text{in head-on component} \\ \text{greater than } E_a \end{bmatrix} = -\frac{E_a}{2.3RT} + \log \begin{bmatrix} \text{total number of colli-} \\ \text{sions per cubic centi-} \\ \text{meter per second for} \\ \text{the concentration and} \\ \text{temperature of the} \\ \text{experiment} \end{bmatrix}$$

(29)

Here R is the gas constant, 1.987 cal/deg/mole, and E_a is the minimum energy in the head-on component of collision which will lead to reaction, known as the *energy of activation*. Equation (29) is of the same form as the experimental equation, Equation (2), and if $E_a/2.3R$ is set equal to the experimental constant A in Equation (2), it is found that, for many second-order reactions, B is equal to the calculated logarithmic term on the right of Equation (29) when it is assumed, in accordance with the theory, that the rate of reaction is given by the number of collisions with energy greater than E_a. For these reactions, the theory is thus confirmed.

For some second-order reactions, the number of violent collisions calculated on this basis is greater than the observed rate, suggesting that requirements other than a collision of minimum violence are necessary. One such requirement might be that the molecules must collide with a specific orientation at the moment of collision; since this orientation would be only one of many possible orientations, the reaction rate would be lessened considerably.

The minimum energy E_a, the activation energy, provides an interpretation of the empirical constant A in Equation (2), as shown by the comparison of Equations (29) and (2). To understand its effect in producing the marked increase in reaction rate as a function of temperature, it is helpful to consider Figure 24.6. This figure shows the number of collisions in which the energies of the collisions lie in the narrow energy range between the energy E and $E + dE$, plotted as a function of E. Each curve shows that the number of collisions with very little energy is small, but that this number increases as the energy of the collision increases, and then decreases again. Note that the curves for the two temperatures cross; at the higher temperature T_2 the number with any particular energy is smaller than at the lower temperature T_1 for low energies, but larger than for T_1 at high energies. Hence the number of violent collisions, represented by the sum of all collisions with energies greater than that marked by the line M, is markedly increased as the temperature is increased. On the average, half of the collision energy will be available for reaction (the other half, corresponding to the component of relative velocity perpendicular to the line of centers, represents a glancing blow which does not lead to reaction); hence the increase of the reaction rate with temperature corresponds closely to the ratio of the area to the right of M under curve T_2 to the corresponding area under T_1, where M represents the minimum collision energy necessary to provide the activation energy E_a.

First-Order Reactions. The collision theory in its simple form makes no allowance for the possibility of first-order reactions, since a collisional process is of necessity second-order, involving *two* molecules. As a way

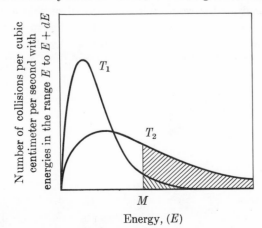

Figure 24.6 Numbers of collisions with specified total energies as a function of the energy of the collision.

out of this difficulty it was suggested that activation by a violent collision did not necessarily lead immediately to decomposition, but that the decomposition occurred only after a time delay in which the energy acquired by the molecule in the collision rearranged itself among the various modes of vibrational motion in the molecule until it reached the one particular vibration which would lead to bond breaking and reaction. Since the rearrangement of energy could take place in an isolated molecule, the collisional history of the *acquisition* of the energy would no longer affect the concentration dependence of the actual decomposition (Figure 24.7).

Since the mechanism postulates a time lag between the acquisition of energy and its arrival at the vibration leading to reaction, it would be expected that first-order processes would be more likely, the more complex the molecule and hence the more vibrational modes of motion it had. This prediction is verified experimentally, and first-order reactions of gaseous molecules are mainly confined to large and complex species. In the simplest case of a diatomic molecule there is only one possible vibration, and dissociation of diatomic molecules is never observed to be first order.

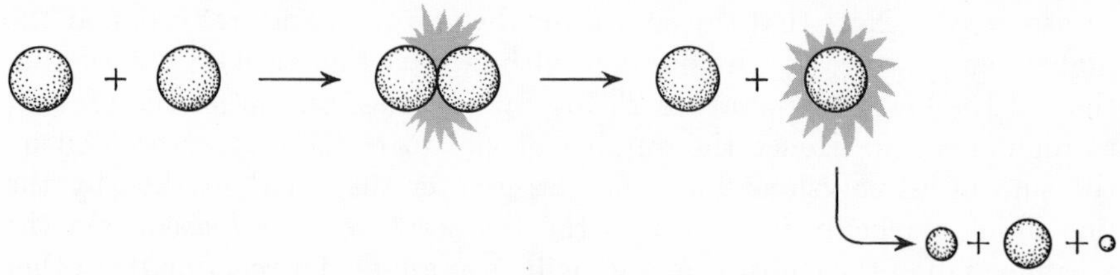

Figure 24.7 In a first-order reaction in gases the acquisition of energy does not immediately lead to reaction; this is a separate event involving only one energy-rich molecule.

Three-Body Processes. A further consequence of the single vibrational degree of freedom in a diatomic molecule X_2 is that the combination of two atoms to form such a molecule must always be a three-body collision:

$$X + X + M \longrightarrow X_2 + M \qquad (30)$$

The "third body," molecule M, must act as a sink to remove excess energy from X_2 (Figure 24.8). If M were not there, all the bond energy of forming X_2 would be stored as vibrational energy in the newborn molecule, and it would dissociate in the first vibration after forming. Different substances have different capacities for removing some or all of this excess energy, and molecules M may be classified according to their efficiencies as third bodies. Larger molecules are more efficient than smaller ones, because they are more capable of storing energy among their many degrees of vibrational freedom.

Figure 24.8 Combination of two atoms to form a diatomic molecule requires the presence of a third body to carry off the energy produced when the two atoms combine.

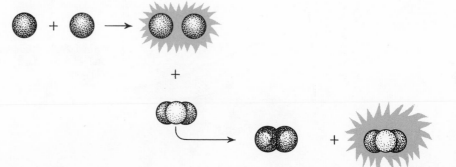

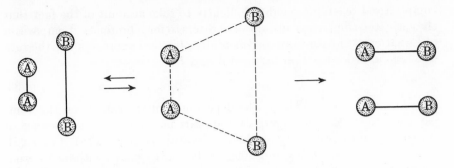

Figure 24.9 Formation and decomposition of an activated complex in the reaction of molecules A_2 and B_2 to form AB molecules.

Activated-Complex Theory. This theory presumes that the reacting molecules in an elementary reaction combine to form a transient intermediate known as an activated complex (Figure 24.9). The concentration of the activated complex is assumed to be calculable on the basis of an equilibrium between it and the reactants,

$$A + B \rightleftharpoons M^{\ddagger} \tag{31}$$

and the observed rate of reaction is proportional to this concentration. An important property of this equilibrium is that the activated complex is presumed to be at a much higher energy level than that of the reactants. Thus in the passage from the initial state to the final state, which results in the enthalpy change for the reaction, ΔH, the individual molecules must acquire a high energy to put them into the state represented by the activated complex. The difference in energy, per mole of complexes, between the initial state and the state representing the activated complex is approximately equal to the energy E_a of Equation (29) and reproduces

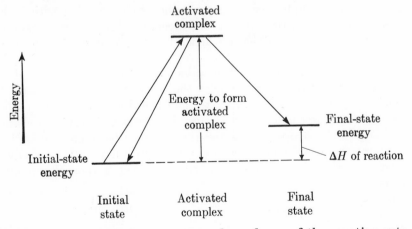

Figure 24.10 Energy relationships in the formation of the activated complex and in the over-all reaction.

in the theory the observed temperature dependence of the reaction rate (Figure 24.10).

Application of thermodynamic principles to these concepts predicts that the rate of a second-order reaction between molecules A and B should be given by

$$\text{Rate} = \frac{kT}{h} K^{\ddagger}[A][B] \tag{32}$$

Here k is Boltzmann's constant, h is Planck's constant, and $K^{\ddagger}$ is an equilibrium constant for the assumed equilibrium between activated complex and reactants, modified slightly to take account of the fact that the activated complex is unstable and reacts to form products. Comparison of Equation (32) with the experimentally observed expression for the rate of a second order reaction between A and B

$$\text{Rate} = k_{\text{obs}}[\text{A}][\text{B}] \tag{33}$$

shows that $k_{\text{obs}} = (kT/h)K^{\ddagger}$. The dependence of the rate upon the temperature exemplified in Figure 24.3 appears mainly as the dependence of the equilibrium constant $K^{\ddagger}$ on the temperature [Equation (64), Chap. 22]. If molecules A and B are presumed to be hard spheres without internal structure as assumed in collision theory, and if the energy level difference between them and the activated complex is set equal to the activation energy E_a of collision theory, the rate of reaction calculated from Equation (32) is the same as that calculated from the collision theory. For this special case, therefore, the two theories give identical results.

An important feature of the activated complex theory is that the term kT/h appears in all rate equations for elementary reactions, no matter what the reactants or order, and that $K^{\ddagger}$ can (in principle) be calculated from the structures and energy levels in the reacting molecules and the activated complex. The parenthesis "in principle" is necessary, because although we can obtain the necessary experimental data on structures and levels in the reactants, which, being stable, permit experimental examination of their spectra, dipole moments, etc., such experimental examination for the transient activated complex is not possible, and various estimates, analogies, semiquantitative calculations, etc., must be used to guess at its structure and energy levels. These difficulties prevent us from carrying out the precise calculation of the rate which the theory seems to promise except in the simplest cases of hydrogen atoms reacting with hydrogen molecules. In this case, however, the theory does give correct answers, and encourages us to believe that the general postulates of the theory are valid.

Enthalpy and Entropy of Activation. The presence of the equilibrium constant, $K^{\ddagger}$, in the expression for the reaction rate on the basis of the activated complex theory suggests the extension to free-energy changes. The change in free energy can, in turn, be expressed in terms of changes in enthalpy and entropy. Recalling the relations between the equilibrium constant and these quantities [Equation (63), Chap. 22], we apply these relations to the postulated equilibrium between activated complex and reactants:

$$-2.303RT \log K^{\ddagger} = \Delta G^{\ddagger} = \Delta H^{\ddagger} - T\Delta S^{\ddagger} \tag{34}$$

$\Delta H^{\ddagger}$, the "enthalpy of activation," represents the difference in energy between reactants and activated complex, and can be related to the experimentally determined energy of activation E_a [Equation (29)] obtained from A in Equation (2) and to the energy level difference between the initial state and the activated complex shown in Figure 24.10. $\Delta S^{\ddagger}$ is the "entropy of activation" which can also be determined from experiment, and is related to B in Equation (2). Thus, meanings, in terms of concepts of enthalpy and entropy, are given to the purely empirical quantities A and B of the earlier equation, and chemists are led to think of variations from reaction to reaction in terms of these concepts. The enthalpy of activation is always positive; the entropy of activation may be positive or negative. The *larger the enthalpy of activation* and the *smaller or more negative the entropy of activation*, the *smaller* the reaction rate, and conversely.

In general the enthalpy of activation will depend upon the strengths of the bonds to be broken and the bonds to be formed in producing the activated complex, and we can make predictions as to the expected changes in rate when a change is made in these bond strengths. A substitution on an organic molecule, for example, which changes the bond strength in the reacting functional group, will be expected to change the reaction rate in the direction corresponding to the change in bond strength. The entropy of activation is a measure of the change in randomness in forming the activated complex. If the activated complex is more loosely joined together than the reactants, there will be an increase in disorder, and consequently a positive value for $\Delta S^{\ddagger}$. If, on the other hand, the complex is more ordered than the reactants, as might happen, for example, if a ring structure were produced from chain structures, the entropy of activation will be negative, and the predicted reaction rate less than it would be if $\Delta S^{\ddagger}$ were zero or positive. The concepts of enthalpy and entropy of activation have been particularly useful to organic chemists in interpreting and predicting reaction rates on the basis of the structures and bonding in the reacting compounds. No such relationship to internal structure is available from collision theory, which treats molecules essentially as if they were hard spheres, colliding like billiard balls with no internal "softness" to absorb or transfer energy.

Chain Reactions and Explosions

Chain Reactions. The formation of hydrogen bromide from hydrogen and bromine is an example of one of the class of reactions known as chain reactions. A mechanism leading to the experimental rate equation

$$\text{Rate} = k_{\text{obs}} \frac{c_{\text{H}_2} c_{\text{Br}_2}^{1/2}}{1 + k' \dfrac{c_{\text{HBr}}}{c_{\text{Br}_2}}} \tag{15}$$

is

$$
\begin{array}{lll}
\text{(a)} & \text{M} + \text{Br}_2 \longrightarrow 2\text{Br} + \text{M} & \\
\text{(b)} & \text{Br} + \text{H}_2 \longrightarrow \text{HBr} + \text{H} & \\
\text{(c)} & \text{H} + \text{Br}_2 \longrightarrow \text{HBr} + \text{Br} & \text{(35)} \\
\text{(d)} & \text{H} + \text{HBr} \longrightarrow \text{H}_2 + \text{Br} & \\
\text{(e)} & \text{M} + \text{Br} + \text{Br} \longrightarrow \text{Br}_2 + \text{M} &
\end{array}
$$

Note that, in this mechanism, a bromine atom is a reactant in reaction (b) of Equation (35) and a product in reaction (c). A combination of elementary reactions such as these two, in which a reactive species serving as reactant in one of the steps is regenerated in a subsequent step, is known as a *chain reaction*, and the reactive species—here, the bromine atom—is known as the *chain carrier*. It is evident that, *if no other processes intervened*, the chain could continue indefinitely until all the hydrogen or bromine was used up. A single bromine atom, if introduced into a mixture of hydrogen and bromine, could cause all the material to change to hydrogen bromide, by repetition of reaction (b) followed by (c), and that in turn by (b), then by (c), etc. Actually such extensive reaction does not occur, because reactions such as (e), which remove chain carriers, intervene.

It is characteristic of a chain reaction that there must be (1) a *chain-initiating step* which produces chain carriers [here, reaction (a)]; (2) *chain-propagating steps*, which bring about the actual transformation to reaction products [here, reactions (b) and (c)]; and (3) *chain-breaking steps*, which remove chain carriers [here, reaction (e)]. The chain-breaking steps "shorten the length of the chain," because whenever a chain carrier is removed, all the reactions of the subsequent chain steps which would have been built up on that chain carrier are prevented from taking place. We can, in fact, prevent a chain reaction from taking place by adding to the reaction mixture a substance which will react with chain carriers as they are formed, and keep the chain from propagating. A substance used for this purpose is known as an *inhibitor* for the chain reaction.

Reaction (d) is somewhat special to the hydrogen-bromine reaction, and serves to explain the presence of the concentration of hydrogen bromide in the denominator of the rate equation (15). As the hydrogen bromide concentration increases, hydrogen atoms, which are also chain carriers, disappear wastefully in reaction (d), without producing HBr as the reaction product.

The Steady-State Approximation. Chain carriers are extremely reactive; hence under normal conditions it can be presumed that their rates of reaction with molecules are so much greater than their rates of formation or rates of removal by reaction with each other that their concentrations reach a constant value characteristic of a *steady state* in which the rate of formation of chain carriers is equal to the rate of their disappearance. Making use of this hypothesis, we apply the law of mass action to all the elementary reactions producing bromine atoms and all those removing bromine atoms, and set the two expressions equal to each other.

$$\text{Rate of production of bromine atoms} = k_a[\text{Br}_2][\text{M}] + k_c[\text{H}][\text{Br}_2] + k_d[\text{H}][\text{HBr}] \tag{36}$$

$$\text{Rate of removal of bromine atoms} = k_b[\text{Br}][\text{H}_2] + k_e[\text{Br}]^2[\text{M}] \tag{37}$$

Equating the two in the steady state,

$$k_a[\text{Br}_2][\text{M}] + k_c[\text{H}]_{ss}[\text{Br}_2] + k_d[\text{H}]_{ss}[\text{HBr}] = k_b[\text{Br}]_{ss}[\text{H}_2] + k_e[\text{Br}]_{ss}^2[\text{M}] \tag{38}$$

A similar equation representing the steady-state concentration of hydrogen atoms can be obtained:

$$k_b[\text{Br}]_{ss}[\text{H}_2] = k_c[\text{H}]_{ss}[\text{Br}_2] + k_d[\text{H}]_{ss}[\text{HBr}] \tag{39}$$

We now have two equations in two unknowns, $[\text{Br}]_{ss}$ and $[\text{H}]_{ss}$, which may be solved, and the resultant solutions substituted in Equation (40), which gives the net rate of production of hydrogen bromide [reaction (b) plus reaction (c) minus reaction (d)].

$$\text{Rate of HBr production} = k_b[\text{Br}]_{ss}[\text{H}_2] + k_c[\text{H}]_{ss}[\text{Br}_2] - k_d[\text{H}]_{ss}[\text{HBr}] \tag{40}$$

The final result is

$$\text{Rate} = \frac{2k_a^{1/2}k_b}{k_e^{1/2}} \frac{[H_2][Br_2]^{1/2}}{1 + \dfrac{k_d[HBr]}{k_e[Br_2]}} \qquad (41)$$

This has the same form as the observed rate equation, Equation (15).

Branched-Chain Reactions. In the chain-propagating steps of some chain reactions, the reaction of one chain carrier leads to the formation of more than one chain carrier. This, for example, is the case in the reaction of hydrogen and oxygen to form water. Here the chain-propagating steps are

$$\begin{aligned} H + O_2 &\longrightarrow OH + O \\ O + H_2 &\longrightarrow OH + H \\ OH + H_2 &\longrightarrow H_2O + H \qquad (42) \\ \underline{OH + H_2 \longrightarrow H_2O + H} \\ H + O_2 + 3H_2 &\longrightarrow 2H_2O + 3H \end{aligned}$$

The summation of these equations shows that from one chain carrier hydrogen atom, three are produced. The chain is said to *branch*. Since each new hydrogen atom can initiate new chains, which can also branch, the net production of water goes on faster and faster. If sufficient hydrogen and oxygen are present to permit the attainment of enormously high rates of reaction before all the reactants are used up, an explosion will occur.

Thermal Explosions. Not all explosive chemical reactions result from a chain-branching mechanism. In highly exothermic reactions, even of a nonchain type, the heat of reaction may not be carried away fast enough to maintain a constant temperature. Hence the temperature of the reaction mixture rises. As a result of the temperature effect on reaction rates, this causes the reaction to proceed more rapidly, liberating heat at a still faster rate with still less chance that it will be conducted away. Thus the temperature continues to rise and the reaction rate to increase, until it becomes so great that an explosion occurs.

SUMMARY

Rates of chemical reactions, their measurement, factors which affect them, theories concerning them, and uses of rate data in elucidating mechanisms of reactions are summarized in this chapter.

The rate of a reaction, defined as the quantity of material per unit volume undergoing transformation in a unit time and expressed mathematically as $-dc/dt$ where c is the concentration of a reactant and t is the time, is found by experiment to be dependent upon the nature of the reacting substances, their concentrations, and the temperature. A quantitative relation showing the dependence of the reaction rate on the concentrations of reactants can be obtained by studying the rate at a series of reactant concentrations. From this the order of the reaction is obtained. The order of the reaction often provides information about the number and kind of species involved in the rate-determining step of the reaction.

Studies of the effect of temperature on rate give data for calculation of the activation energy of the reaction—the energy, above the average, needed for reaction.

Two theories of reaction rates, the collision theory and the activated-complex theory, are presented. The collision theory focuses attention on the collisions which result in reaction, on their number, and their energy. The activated-complex theory emphasizes the nature of the chemical intermediate formed in a successful collision, on its geometry, bonding, and structure.

Applications of rate studies to mechanisms of molecular and ionic reactions and to chain reactions including explosions are given.

SOME SPECIAL TERMS

Mechanism of reaction
  complex reaction
  rate-determining step
Slope of a curve
  negative slope
  linear equation
  dc/dt
Catalysis
  heterogeneous
  homogeneous
  enzyme

Rate of reaction
  law of mass action
  first-order reaction
  second-order reaction
  reaction-rate constant
Collision theory
  activated-complex
    theory
Energy of activation
  enthalpy of activation
  entropy of activation

Chain reaction
  chain carrier
  chain-initiating step
  chain-propagating step
  chain-breaking step
  steady state
  inhibitor
  branched-chain reaction
Thermal explosion
  branched-chain
    explosion
Three-body process

QUESTIONS AND PROBLEMS

1. Distinguish between (a) chemical kinetics and thermodynamics; (b) unimolecular and bimolecular reactions; (c) first-order and second-order reactions; (d) enthalpy of activation and enthalpy of reaction; (e) rate constant and equilibrium constant; (f) branching chains and nonbranching chains; and (g) activity and concentration.
2. Describe five methods of following the rate of a reaction.
3. Show that the equation, $\log (\text{Rate}) = -(A/T) + \log B$, can be cast into the form of an equation for a straight line. What is the interpretation of the quantity A? Of the quantity B?
4. How do you explain the fact that "a catalyst affects the rate of a reaction but it does not affect the position of equilibrium"?
5. The half-life of a reaction is the time required for one-half the original material to be used up. What is the half-life of the reaction of Figure 24.1?
6. A substance A undergoes reaction to form substances B and C. At a fixed temperature the concentration of A is observed to change with time according to the measurements recorded in the table. Plot these data and determine the rate of reaction at 50, 100, 200, 400, and 700 min, and the

concentration of A at those times. From these corresponding values of rate and concentration, determine the order of the reaction and the value of the rate constant for the fixed temperature of the experiment.

Time (min)	Concentration (moles/liter)	Time (min)	Concentration (moles/liter)
0	0.1000	180	0.0597
20	0.0930	240	0.0526
40	0.0870	300	0.0471
60	0.0817	400	0.0400
80	0.0769	500	0.0348
100	0.0727	700	0.0276
125	0.0696	1000	0.0210
150	0.0640		

7. Assuming that Equations (3) and (7) are formally correct expressions for the rates of formation and decomposition of hydrogen iodide, derive the expression for the equilibrium constant of the reaction of hydrogen iodide formation.

8. Distinguish between a steady-state process and an equilibrium process.

9. How can the values of $K^{\ddagger}$, $\Delta G^{\ddagger}$, $\Delta H^{\ddagger}$, and $T\Delta S^{\ddagger}$ be determined?

10. Discuss the effect of a change of temperature on the values of k, K, ΔG, ΔH, and $T\Delta S$.

11. What is the difference in the assumptions on which the following theories are based: (a) the collision theory; (b) the activated-complex theory?

12. How are (a) the energy of activation of the reaction $A + B \rightarrow C + D$, (b) the energy of activation of the reaction $C + D \rightarrow A + B$, and (c) the enthalpy of the reaction $A + B \rightarrow C + D$ related, if both the reactions written are elementary reactions?

13. How are chain reactions related to explosions? How can explosions be avoided in such reactions?

14. How do reactions in solution differ from those in the gaseous state?

15. A substance Q undergoes a reaction in water solution. Analyses of the products of the reaction indicate that they contain hydrogen and oxygen which must have come from the water. Analyses of the concentration of Q as a function of time gave the following results for an experiment carried out at a constant temperature. Determine, from these data, the order of the reaction with respect to Q. What can you say about the number of molecules involved in the chemical equation for the rate-determining step?

Time (min)	Concentration (moles/liter)	Time (min)	Concentration (moles/liter)
0	0.200	150	0.088
20	0.178	190	0.071
40	0.161	200	0.057
60	0.144	275	0.045
80	0.129	310	0.037
100	0.116	350	0.030
125	0.101		

16. If you assume that rates of chemical reactions are affected by a change of temperature and also assume that atomic nuclei are made of particles which interact with each other to give nuclear reactions, how do you account for the validity of the statement found in many textbooks that "the radio-chemical process occurs at the same rate at the temperature of liquid air as it does at the temperature of boiling iron"? If this is true, does it therefore follow that the rate of the nuclear disintegration process is independent of temperature? Defend your answer.

REFERENCES

KING, E. L. *How Chemical Reactions Occur*. New York: Benjamin, 1963.
LATHAM, J. L. *Elementary Reaction Kinetics*. London: Butterworth, 1962.
PATTON, A. R. *Biochemical Energetics and Kinetics*. Philadelphia: Saunders, 1965.

PART SIX

NUCLEAR
CHEMISTRY

25

Nuclear Chemistry

*Scientific work must not be considered from the point of view of the
direct usefulness of it. It must be done for itself, for the beauty of
science and then there is always the chance that a scientific discovery may become, like radium, a benefit for all humanity.*
Marie Curie (1867–1934)

Nuclear Phenomena. The search for understanding of the atomic
nucleus is taking place in chemistry and physics laboratories around the
world, where both experimental and theoretical tools of great sophistication
often are used. Such experimental tools include the cyclotron, the syn-
chrotron, the linear accelerator, and the Van de Graaff generator—devices
for exciting nuclei by bombardment with high-energy particles. By
following the nuclear changes which occur or the radiation emitted as
an excited nucleus returns to a stable state, much knowledge about properties of the atomic nucleus has been gathered. The theoretical tool is
quantum mechanics, for it is found that in nuclear phenomena, as with
atomic structure, essential insight into observed behavior is provided by
this powerful mathematical approach which relates energy to shape and
symmetry.

Yet the nature of the atomic nucleus remains one of the great mysteries
of modern science. To date, no comprehensive theory which explains all
observed nuclear phenomena has been developed, and we are just beginning
to understand the nature of nuclear forces. Several kinds of symmetry
factors known as spin, parity, and strangeness have been used successfully to interpret various aspects of nuclear behavior, but even here the
picture remains cloudy and somewhat obscure.

Various theories of the nucleus have emerged: a liquid-drop model, a
shell theory, a unified theory, a cluster theory. All of these account
reasonably well for important nuclear properties such as mass, charge,
spin, magnetic moment, binding energy, and energies of nuclear excited
states. It appears that neutrons and protons are very similar, and the
general term *nucleon* is used for both. Nuclear structure often is described
in a manner similar to atomic structure—as an assembly of protons and
neutrons existing in definite energy levels analogous to the electron energy

497

levels of the atom. An ideal theory would enable us to calculate the various properties of a given nucleus from quantum mechanical principles and the charge and mass of the nucleons present. To do this the forces between two nucleons must be known exactly. Unfortunately, the nucleon-nucleon force does not appear to be as simple as the electrostatic force and at present it is not known with accuracy. Nevertheless, considerable progress has been made in understanding nuclear structure, and even the incomplete picture developed here will enable us to predict reliably certain nuclear properties.

Unstable Nuclei. Unstable or energy-rich nuclei throw off their excess energy and drop to more stable energy states by emitting various high-energy particles and radiations; some nuclei split or fission in this process. These processes of nuclear change have become known as radioactive processes, or radioactivity. The more general term *nuclear processes*, or nuclear chemistry, is now used to refer to (a) the reactions in the nucleus in which particles or radiations are emitted and to (b) the opposite process in which the nucleus is bombarded by particles or radiations and captures them; the new nucleus formed may exist for infinite time, or it may disintegrate instantly or slowly. Examples of these emission and capture processes are given below.

Emission Process. Radium emits helium nuclei (called alpha particles) and changes to radon. This reaction is described by the *nuclear* equation

$$_{+88}^{222}\text{Ra} \longrightarrow {}_{+2}^{4}\text{He} + {}_{+86}^{218}\text{Rn}$$

The masses of the nuclei are indicated with superscripts and the atomic numbers are given in subscripts. A nuclear equation such as this is "balanced" when the sum of the subscripts on the left side of the equation equals the sum of the subscripts on the right side of the equation ($88 = 2 + 86$), and when the same equality holds for the superscripts ($222 = 4 + 218$). This indicates that there is no loss in the number of nucleons or in total charge in a nuclear reaction.

Capture Process. In α-particle bombardment, nitrogen nuclei capture helium and then immediately emit protons and are changed to oxygen nuclei, as shown by the equation

$$_{+7}^{14}\text{N} + {}_{+2}^{4}\text{He} \longrightarrow {}_{+1}^{1}\text{H} + {}_{+8}^{17}\text{O}$$

Historical. The discovery of radioactivity dates back to 1895 when the French scientist Antoine Henri Becquerel was studying the fluorescence of uranium compounds (Chap. 2). He had heard of Wilhelm Conrad Roentgen's discovery of X-rays in 1895 and incorrectly interpreted Roentgen's work as the transformation of cathode rays into a high-energy, deeply penetrating radiation which caused fluorescence. Becquerel reasoned that the fluorescence and the high-energy radiation were somehow tied together, and he hoped that he might also cause sunlight to be transformed into a high-energy radiation by causing it first to produce fluorescence.

Becquerel planned a series of experiments to test his theory. Since neither sunlight nor fluorescent light will go through paper, but a high-energy radiation should penetrate it, he wrapped a photographic plate in paper to protect it from the action of the sunlight. On this he placed a sample of uranium ore which he exposed to sunlight to cause fluorescence. After a reasonable exposure time he then removed the photographic plate and developed it. True to his expectation he found the plate contained streaks caused by a deeply penetrating radiation which had passed through the paper in which the plate was wrapped. But the sun did not shine for several days so Becquerel decided to do some control experiments. He repeated the identical experiment but in the absence of sunlight and to his surprise he obtained results identical with those with sunlight. At this point he was forced to revise his theory and to conclude that there must be an element or elements heretofore undiscovered that were emitting these deeply penetrating radiations which would pass through thick layers of paper. This was reported in February, 1896; the phenomenon was called *radioactivity*.

Not only did Becquerel's work open the great new frontier known as nuclear science, but it also called the attention of scientists to a source of high-energy particles that were useful in some of the early work in the study of the structure of atoms.

Madame Curie. Following his discovery, Becquerel assigned Marie Sklodowska (Madame Curie), as her graduate research thesis, the research on the analysis of uranium ore to determine what element or elements were present in the ore which produced these deeply penetrating radiations. In her work in 1898 she and her husband isolated a compound of a new element polonium, which she named after her native country, Poland, and also a compound of another new element which she named radium. Both of these were much more radioactive than uranium. In fact, radium proved to be so radioactive that its salts glow in the dark.

Ernest Rutherford. Another young scientist whose interest was aroused by the discovery of radioactivity was Ernest Rutherford. He and his associates showed that natural radioactivity resulted from a disintegration of atoms, or rather a series of disintegrations, in which elements were transmuted into other elements. His first experiments had to do with the nature and properties of the rays emitted by naturally radioactive elements.

The Nature and Properties of the Rays

Alpha, Beta, and Gamma Rays. In a very simple experiment Rutherford identified three kinds of rays that may be emitted in the radioactive process. He named them alpha (α), beta (β), and gamma (γ) rays. He placed a small quantity of a material containing radium at the bottom of a hole bored in a piece of lead (Figure 25.1). The intensity of all the rays, except those traveling directly upward, was severely reduced by the shielding power of the lead. He then placed the radium between the poles of a magnet, as shown, with a photographic plate (protected from light) arranged above to receive the rays. The alpha rays were bent to the extent and in the direction that one would expect for relatively heavy, positively charged particles passing through a magnetic field; and further study proved them to be helium nuclei, He^{+2}. The beta rays, deflected in the

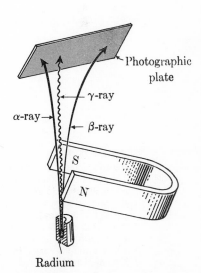

Figure 25.1 Gamma rays are not bent, but alpha and beta rays are bent to the left and to the right, respectively, in a magnetic field with the orientation as shown.

opposite direction and to a much greater extent, behaved like negatively charged particles of very small mass; they are electrons. The gamma rays, not deflected at all, are waves of light, similar to X-rays but most of them are of shorter wavelength and hence of higher energy.

Speed and Energy of the Rays. The speed of the gamma rays is the same as that of light, 3×10^{10} cm/sec, or 186,000 miles/sec. The speed of the alpha particles depends on the kind of nucleus from which they are ejected, but ranges from 9,000 to 14,000 miles/sec. Likewise, the beta particles travel at various speeds that can be as fast as 100,000 miles/sec.

The energy of these rays is given in units of electron volts and is usually several million electron volts (Mev). This is about 1,000,000 times more energy than that required to remove the outside electron from an atom of sodium (5.1 ev). The energies of the alpha and beta particles result from their high velocities and are the kinetic energy ($\frac{1}{2} mv^2$) of the particle; the energy of the gamma rays is calculated by Planck's equation, $E = h\nu$.

The alpha particles from a given isotope either all have the same energy or their energies are distributed in a few energy groups, one of a few specific energy values characteristic of that isotope. This monoenergetic character of the alpha particles is evidence of energy levels in the nucleus.

Beta particles, in contrast to alpha particles, are emitted with a continuous energy distribution extending from near zero energy to a maximum energy which may be as high as 15 Mev (Figure 25.2). If energy levels exist in nuclei, one is puzzled to find that alpha particles from a given isotope are monoenergetic but beta particles appear not to be. To explain this paradox as well as several other problems, the existence of another particle, the neutrino, has been postulated. Neutrinos are assumed to be ejected at the same time as the beta particles and to carry away varying amounts of energy. The resulting energy of the observed beta radiation is thus distributed over a range of values, although the sum, (beta-particle energy) + (neutrino energy), is a constant for any one beta emission.

Gamma rays from a given nucleus are in single or in a few energy groups. The scheme for the decay of ^{60}Co to ^{60}Ni is shown in Figure 25.3, indicating the gamma-rays that are observed when the excited nickel nucleus first formed loses energy in dropping to the ground state. The overwhelming fraction (99.9 per cent) of the beta particles have the maximum energy

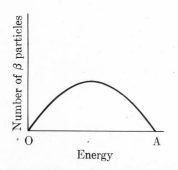

Figure 25.2 A β-decay energy spectrum. Here the energies of the β-rays emitted from a given element are plotted along the abscissa with the number of such emissions having each energy recorded along the ordinate. In contrast to α- and γ-radiations, β-radiation is emitted with a wide range of energies.

Figure 25.3 An excited ^{60}Co nucleus emits a β-ray and is transformed into an excited nickel nucleus. The excited nickel nucleus emits a 1.173 Mev γ-ray and falls into a lower energy state. Before reaching the ground state the nickel nucleus emits a second γ-ray (1.332 Mev). From this it is suggested that two excited states for the nickel nuclei lie at 1.332 and 2.505 Mev above the ground state. There is some evidence for still a third excited state of the ^{60}Ni nucleus.

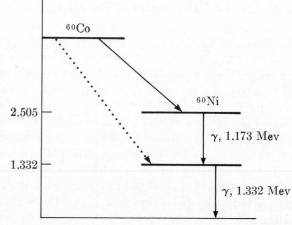

0.31 Mev; a very few, as indicated by the dotted line, have an energy maximum 1.48 Mev leading to another energy state of the nickel nucleus. Direct beta emission to the ground state of nickel is not observed.

Penetrating Power of the Rays. The alpha particles penetrate only the thinnest sheets of metal, and are stopped by even an ordinary piece of paper. The beta particles have greater penetrating power than the alpha particles, but are stopped by relatively thin sheets of metal. The gamma rays can penetrate thick layers of metal, and can be detected after traversing 8 or 10 in. of lead. The *relative* penetrating power of the three types of particles, tested toward aluminum, are approximately as follows: alpha particles, 1; beta particles, 100; gamma rays, 10,000.

Ionizing Power of the Rays. As they pass through air or other gases, all three kinds of rays have the power to *ionize* gas molecules by knocking off electrons from the outer regions of the atoms of which the gas molecules are composed. Gas or air in the neighborhood of a radioactive substance is thus made electrically conducting. On an average, about 35 ev are required to produce an ion pair (a positive ion and an electron) when the radiations pass through gases, liquids, or solids. Hence an alpha particle of 3.5 Mev of energy will produce at least 100,000 pairs of ions before its speed is reduced to that of a normal gas particle.

Some Properties of the Nucleus

Radius. From Rutherford's early experiments in which he bombarded metal foil with alpha particles (see Chap. 2) he calculated the nuclear radius of atoms of light elements to be about 3×10^{-13} cm. The equation now used to calculate nuclear radii is

$$r = A^{1/3} \times 1.4 \times 10^{-13} \text{ cm}$$

where r is the nuclear radius and A is the sum of the protons and neutrons in the nucleus.

Binding Energy. For the nucleus to remain intact, the nucleons must be bound together by attractive forces strong enough to overcome the repulsive electrostatic forces between protons. Calculations of the binding energy of the particles in the nucleus indicate that the particles of most nuclei, except deuterium, are held to each other with a binding energy of about 7 Mev per particle; the range is from 2 Mev for deuterium to 8 Mev for the most stable nuclei. This is about 100,000 to 1,000,000 times greater than the ionization energy required to remove outside electrons from atoms. The binding energy can be calculated from the mass lost when nuclei of light atoms fuse together to form heavier nuclei.

PROBLEM ■ Calculate the binding energy per particle in a nucleus of helium.

SOLUTION
Assume

$$2p + 2n \xrightarrow{\text{fuse}} \text{helium nucleus} + \text{binding energy}$$

The sum of the atomic mass units is $2 \times 1.007825 + 2 \times 1.008665$, or

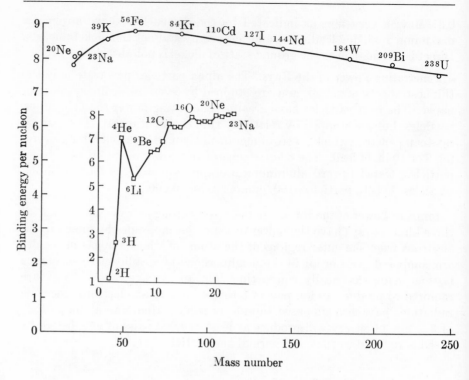

Figure 25.4 Binding energy per nucleon as a function of mass number. The inset shows the light nuclei on an expanded mass number scale. Note the stability of ^{4}He, ^{12}C, ^{16}O, ^{20}Ne.

4.032980. The mass of the helium nucleus is 4.00258 g/mole. This means that 4.032980 − 4.00258 or 0.0304 g/mole of mass is lost on fusion. Hence the binding energy of the particles of the nucleus is equal to the energy equivalent to this mass lost, or

$$\frac{0.0304 \text{ g/mole}}{6.02 \times 10^{23} \text{ atoms/mole}} = 5.05 \times 10^{-26} \text{ g lost/atom}$$

when two protons and two neutrons fuse to form one helium nucleus.

$$E = mc^2 = (5.05 \times 10^{-26})(3.0 \times 10^{10})^2 = 45.4 \times 10^{-6} \text{ ergs}$$

Since

$$1 \text{ Mev} = 1.6 \times 10^{-6} \text{ erg}$$

$E = 28.4$ Mev for the nucleus containing four particles, or 7.1 Mev per particle

This means that in the fusion process the excess energy of 7 Mev per particle is emitted, hence the nucleus is *more stable* by 7 Mev per particle than it would be if this energy were not released. This energy is called the *binding energy* of each particle. Figure 25.4 is a plot of binding energy as a function of atomic number illustrating that very light and heavy nuclei are less stable than nuclei of intermediate mass.

Neutron-Proton Ratio. The stability of nuclei seems to be associated with the ratio of the number of neutrons to the number of protons in the nucleus (Figure 25.5). The graph shows the neutron-proton ratio in the stable nuclei which occur naturally. If the n/p ratio is above the curve of the graph, the nucleus tends to stabilize itself by converting a neutron to a proton and a beta particle (this process is called β-decay) [(a), Figure 25.5].

$$n \longrightarrow p + \beta^-$$

If the n/p ratio is too low, a proton will be converted to a neutron and a positron [(b), Figure 25.5].

$$p \longrightarrow n + \beta^+$$

Note that the number of neutrons is greater than the number of protons (a straight line at 45° angle through the origin would represent systems with $n = p$). This indicates that a few "extra" neutrons are required to provide additional binding energy to overcome the electrostatic proton-proton repulsion.

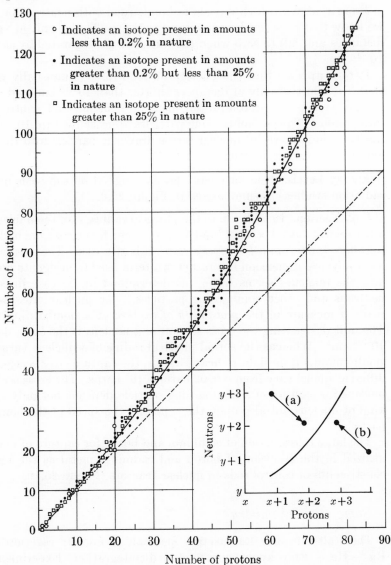

Figure 25.5 Neutron-proton ratio of naturally occurring elements; dashed line is for a neutron-proton ratio of one.

Nucleon-Nucleon Force. An important conclusion concerning nuclear forces follows from a comparison of the binding energies of certain pairs of light nuclei. Consider, for example, the nuclei ^{3}H and ^{3}He. Tritium, $^3_1$H, consists of two neutrons and one proton; helium 3 consists of two protons and one neutron. The binding energies of these nuclei are similar, differing only by an amount comparable to the electrostatic repulsion energy in helium 3. Corresponding observations can be made with other pairs of light nuclei such as ^{7}Li and ^{7}Be, or ^{11}C and ^{11}B. Such comparisons compel us to conclude that the nucleon-nucleon force remains unchanged when replacing neutrons by protons or protons by neutrons. The strength of these forces is at least one million times greater than in the chemical bond. Compare H—H bond energy (4.48 ev/molecule) with binding energy (7 Mev/particle).

From studies in which nuclei are bombarded with neutrons or protons, we know that these nucleon-nucleon forces are effective only at very short distances and fall to zero when the nucleons are separated by as much as 10^{-12} cm.

It thus appears that the nucleon-nucleon force is unusually powerful, that it is effective only at distances shorter than 10^{-12} cm, and that it is equally strong for proton-proton, neutron-neutron, and neutron-proton interactions. Thus if bombarding particles approach within 10^{-12} cm of a nucleus, these powerful nuclear forces draw the particle into the nucleus and cause a fusion reaction to occur.

Energy Levels. Nuclear energy levels assigned on the basis of nuclear radiation studies are summarized in Figure 25.6.

Cross Section. In addition to the physical radius, r, of the nucleus which is between about 1.4×10^{-13} and 6×10^{-13} cm, for atoms from hydrogen to uranium, the term *nuclear cross section*, σ, is also used. The cross section is *not* a physical dimension but rather is a term used to designate how big in area the nucleus "seems to be" as determined by its ease in capturing neutrons and other bombarding particles. The nuclear cross section is really a measure of the *probability of capture* of a bombarding particle. The unit designating the cross section of a nucleus is the *barn*, defined as 10^{-24} cm^2. Whereas the actual physical radius of a nucleus varies only a small amount from light to heavy atoms, the capture cross sections of the different nuclei vary from 0.0002 barn to 10^5 barns. The cross section of a nucleus for capture of a bombarding particle depends not only upon the kind of nucleus but also upon the type and the speed of the bombarding particle.

The large cross section of cadmium and boron for capture of neutrons is utilized in the adoption of boron and cadmium metal as the important constituents of control rods in nuclear reactors (Figure 25.10).

Some Radiochemistry

The Half-Life of a Radioactive Element. A nuclear reaction such as Ra → He + Rn is known as a nuclear disintegration. Experiments show that the number of nuclei of a given element disintegrating in unit time is proportional to the number of atoms of that element present at the particu-

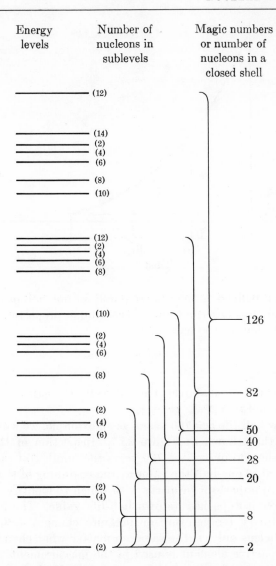

Energy levels	Number of nucleons in sublevels	Magic numbers or number of nucleons in a closed shell

Figure 25.6 Schematic diagram of energy levels in a nucleus. The numbers in parentheses on each level indicate the number of sublevels contained in each main level and hence the number of nucleons of each kind that can occupy that main level. The numbers in the right-hand column are often called "magic numbers": They correspond to a closed shell and are analogous to the completed octet of electrons in the noble gas structure of atoms. A magic number appears whenever the jump between adjacent levels is particularly large. These numbers represent the number of nucleons required to fill the indicated level and all lower-lying levels.

lar moment at which the measurement is made (first-order reaction, Chap. 24). Since the parent nucleus disappears in the disintegration, the number of nuclei of the original element steadily decreases. The experimental curve for nuclear disintegrations has a shape similar to that shown in Figure 25.7, which shows the decrease in the number of atoms of a radioactive substance as a function of the time. This decrease may also be represented by the logarithmic equation

$$\log A/A_0 = -\frac{\lambda t}{2.303}$$

where A_0 is the number of atoms at the beginning of the measurements, A is the number at time t, and λ is a constant called the disintegration constant which depends upon the radioactive isotope being studied.

The decay curve is of such a nature that the number of atoms decrease to zero only after an infinite time. Hence it is meaningless to speak of the time of complete decay (full-life) of a radioisotope. However, the term

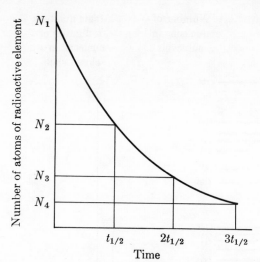

Figure 25.7 Radioactive decay.

half-life is used; it is defined as the time required for one-half of the atoms to disintegrate and thus describes one of the unique properties of radioisotopes. The equation for the half-life is

$$t_{1/2} = \frac{0.693}{\lambda}$$

where λ is the constant given above. The values for the half-life of several isotopes are given in Table 25.1.

Using ^{14}C, whose half-life is 5,760 years, as an example, we would find a decay curve like that shown in Figure 25.7. Inspection of this graph indicates that at the end of every 5,760 years the number of radioactive atoms has decreased to one-half the value at the beginning of that period.

The half-life is an important property with which to identify elements, for each radioactive isotope has its own half-life value. The half-life is unaffected by ordinary temperature or pressure changes and, being a property of the nucleus only, is the same no matter what chemical compound of the radioactive element is used in the measurement. Furthermore, half-life values have become a very useful means of dating geological time periods and archaeological objects.

Radioactivity and Change in Atomic Weight and Number. The loss of one alpha particle, He^{+2}, by the nucleus of an atom results in a lowering of atomic weight by four units; at the same time it produces a lowering of the positive charge on the nucleus, and hence a lowering of the atomic number, by two units. With beta-particle emission there is no change in atomic weight, but there is a gain of $+1$ in the atomic number. For example,

$$^{238}_{92}\text{U} \longrightarrow {}^{4}_{2}\text{He} + {}^{234}_{90}\text{Th}$$

and

$$^{234}_{90}\text{Th} \longrightarrow {}_{-1}\beta + {}^{234}_{91}\text{Pa}$$

This information makes it possible to predict the product of a nuclear reaction if the type of radiation that is emitted is known.

Table 25.1 The Half-Life of Several Isotopes

Isotope	Half-Life
^{3}H	12.5 yr
^{14}C	5760 yr
^{24}Na	15 hr
^{60}Co	5.2 yr
^{90}Sr	20 yr
^{235}U	4.5×10^{9} yr
^{15}O	118 sec
^{11}C	20 min

Isotopes—Historical. In the early research on these disintegrations a much larger number of elements was found in the disintegration products than there were places for these elements in the periodic table; they were given such odd designations as UX_1, UX_2, I_0, RaA, RaC, etc. In 1913 the English scientist Frederick Soddy found that many of these "different elements" had such similar properties that they could not be separated by chemical means even though each had its own unique half-life. This led Soddy to the conclusion that contrary to Dalton's atomic theory (Chap. 2) atoms of the same element could have different weights; he named such different species of a given element *isotopes*. Direct proof of the existence of isotopic atoms of the same element was obtained in 1919 by F. W. Aston using the mass spectrograph to measure atomic masses. Thus the problem of the larger number of elements found in radioactive disintegration was solved—many of these "new elements" were isotopes of known elements.

In Figure 25.8 is given the decay of ^{238}U and its daughter elements showing the different products formed.

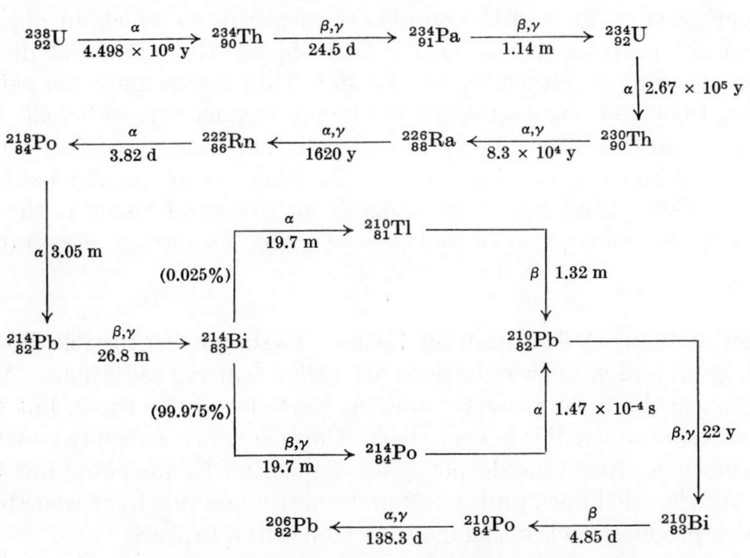

Figure 25.8 The uranium-238 disintegration series.

$$y = years, \quad d = days, \quad m = minutes, \quad s = seconds$$

The Radioactive Elements in Nature. The naturally occurring radioactive elements are limited almost exclusively to the heavy elements above lead, with the exceptions of

$$^{40}K, \ ^{87}Rb, \ ^{115}In, \ ^{138}La, \ ^{144}Nd, \ ^{147}Sm, \ ^{176}Lu, \ ^{187}Re, \ and \ ^{190}Pt$$

Four disintegration series of the heavy elements are known in which the parent substances of each series are ^{232}Th, ^{241}Pu, ^{238}U, and ^{235}U, respectively. The end product of the ^{241}Pu series is ^{209}Bi; the end product of ^{232}Th is ^{208}Pb; of ^{238}U it is ^{206}Pb; and of ^{235}U it is ^{207}Pb.

Some radioactive isotopes found in nature are being continually produced by bombardment with cosmic rays. Most likely the carbon-14 in the atmosphere is produced by this process.

Units of Radioactivity. In addition to the energy of radiation and the half-life of isotopes we are also interested in the number of radiations emitted per unit weight of a radioactive isotope per unit time and the effect of these radiations as they impinge on matter, especially on biological tissue.

The *curie* is the unit now used to indicate the number of radioactive atoms disintegrating per second. It is defined as the quantity of any radioactive substance in which the number of disintegrations per second is 3.7×10^{10}. Since the total effect of these particles as they strike other molecules depends upon the energy of the particle as well as the *number* of particles, another term or unit is required to describe the effect resulting from the bombardment of matter with the high-energy particles.

The destructive power of radiation is difficult to measure, but it can be presumed to be proportional to the number of ions formed in passing through tissue, and this in turn presumed to be proportional to the number of ions formed in passing through air. The *roentgen* (r) is defined as the amount of gamma or X-radiation that will produce 1.7×10^{12} ion pairs per gram of air, and the number of roentgens to which an object is exposed is known as the *dosage* for that object. One thousand disintegrations producing gamma rays of 3.5 Mev will cause as many ion pairs to form as 1,000,000 disintegrations producing gamma rays of 0.0035 Mev. Hence, the dosage from absorption of radiation from these two sources would be the same (about 6×10^{-5} r). Another unit frequently used as a measure of potential radiation damage in biological tissue is the *rad*, defined as the absorption of 100 ergs of radiation energy per gram of tissue.

Effect of Ionizing Radiation on Tissue—Maximum Permissible Dosage. Alpha, beta, and gamma radiations are called *ionizing* radiations. Alpha particles are the most powerful ionizing particles of the three, but their path in liquids and solids is very short. Gamma rays are deeply penetrating radiations. Neutrons do not cause ionization by knocking out electrons, but they do knock protons off molecules containing hydrogen atoms; they also produce nuclear changes due to neutron capture.

The ions that are formed by these radiations are very reactive in body tissue. The result may be a deep burn in tissue, or a reduction in the number of blood cells or even destruction of genes. Excessive radiation will cause death. Moderate doses of radiation may retard the growth of cancer cells, while heavy doses may produce cancer.

The maximum permissible dosage of full-body radiation that a person may receive with safety is 0.1 roentgen in an eight-hour day, or 0.3 r per week. The lethal dosage is about 600 r of full-body radiation. Great care must be observed when working near radioactive substances in order to protect against the tissue damage due to large doses of radiation. Workers should use proper shielding material, such as lead or concrete; they should work as far away from the radioactive material as possible, and should keep the time of exposure to a minimum. They should avoid inhaling or swallowing radioactive material except under supervision of a physician for medical purposes.

Daily Human Exposure to Radiation. We are constantly bombarded by radiations from radioactive substances. The deeply penetrating radiations from interstellar space and the radiations from natural radioactive substances in the dust, the air, and building materials are bombarding us at the rate of about 20 radiations per square centimeter per second and represent a dosage of about 0.0003 r per day of full-body radiation. This is called background radiation. In the body tissue the radioactive elements present also produce radiations; for example, a person weighing 150 pounds has enough radioactive carbon, ^{14}C, and potassium, ^{40}K, to give a total of over 300,000 beta particles per minute. Fallout from atomic bomb explosions can cause considerable radiation damage.

The Artificially Produced Radioactive Isotopes. Ernest Rutherford, in 1919, had showed that hydrogen and oxygen are formed when alpha particles bombarded nitrogen atoms:

$$^{14}_{7}N + ^{4}_{2}He \longrightarrow ^{1}_{1}H + ^{17}_{8}O$$

This was the first artificial transmutation, or synthesis, of elements ever reported—a feat tried without success for over 1,000 years by the alchemists.

Continuing experiments on the bombarding of elements with alpha particles, Madame Curie's older daughter, Irène Joliot-Curie, and her husband, Frédéric, bombarded magnesium and aluminum with alpha particles. In one of these experiments in 1934, they accidently covered up the bombarding source and found that the metal they had been bombarding was radioactive. This was the first radioactive material ever produced artificially. Since that time all elements have been made radioactive. Today there are a variety of bombarding particles used to make elements radioactive.

Types of Bombarding Particles. The two general types of bombarding particles are charged particles and neutrons. It is believed that either type of particle will be drawn into the nucleus by the powerful nuclear forces if it comes within about 10^{-12} cm of the nucleus. With neutrons capture occurs readily if the velocity of the neutron can be reduced sufficiently so the nuclear forces can be effective. Hence, substances such as graphite, called moderators, are used in nuclear reactors to slow down neutrons. Figure 25.9 shows the relative number of low-energy (low-speed) neutrons and high-energy neutrons captured by nuclei.

Positively charged bombarding particles, He^{+2}, H^{+}, D^{+}, and so on, are repelled by the positive charge on nuclei. Hence, in order to bring positively charged particles to within 10^{-12} cm of a nucleus so that they can be drawn into the nucleus by the nuclear forces, the particle must be traveling at a very high velocity—i.e., with a high energy. A high velocity can be obtained by accelerating the particle in an apparatus called a cyclotron, or heating the particle to a high temperature. In the sun, stars, and the hydrogen bomb where the temperature is 10,000,000°K or higher, protons have a sufficiently high velocity to come within 10^{-12} cm of each other and fuse together.

Mechanisms of the Process of Induced Radioactivity. When high-energy charged particles are captured by nuclei, they invariably carry a large

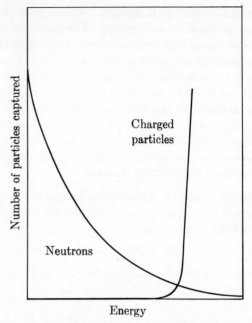

Figure 25.9 Particle capture as a function of energy. These curves indicate that low-energy neutrons are captured more readily than high-energy neutrons but that positively charged bombarding particles must have an energy great enough to overcome electrostatic repulsion with the nucleus in order to be captured.

amount of energy with them into the nuclei. Very likely this energy is then distributed among the particles of the nucleus and is eventually thrown off again by one or more nuclear processes.

When a neutron is captured by a nucleus, an unfavorable balance of protons to neutrons usually results. A common process of emitting the excess energy is for a neutron to change into a proton and a beta particle, which is emitted.

$$_0^1 n \longrightarrow {}_1^1H + \beta^-$$

The excited nucleus remaining can drop to a lower energy level and emit energy as a gamma ray.

This process, a very common one, is known as "neutron capture followed by beta decay." A second process by which a nucleus, made unstable by neutron capture, can return to a stable state is fission—fragmenting of the nucleus into two smaller and more stable nuclei.

Neutron Sources—Nuclear Reactors. The nuclear reactor (Figure 25.10) is the main neutron source today. The usual fuel is uranium-235 which undergoes fission when struck with a neutron, producing on the average three neutrons and fission fragments of near but not equal mass and much energy.

$$_{92}^{235}U + n \longrightarrow \text{fission products} + 3n + 200 \text{ Mev}$$

Note that this is a chain reaction with chain-branching [Equation (42), Chap. 24], since the neutrons produced can produce fission in other uranium-235 atoms. If uncontrolled, explosion will result. The function of the control rods in the reactor is to remove chain carriers by absorbing the neutrons.

Much research remains to be done to understand fully the mechanism of the fission process. Altogether about sixty different elements have been identified in fission fragments of uranium-235.

Another common source of neutrons is from the bombardment of the nuclei of light elements with alpha particles. Beryllium and boron are particularly effective as neutron emitters.

$$\,^{9}_{4}Be + \,^{4}_{2}He \longrightarrow \,^{1}_{0}n + \,^{12}_{6}C$$

Applications of Nuclear Science

Manufacture of Elements. A large number (over 1,200) artificially radioactive isotopes have now been made. In addition to the artificially radioactive isotopes of elements already known, many new elements, the transuranic elements (lying beyond uranium), have been made. These include the elements neptunium (Np), 93; plutonium (Pu), 94; americium (Am), 95; curium (Cm), 96; berkelium (Bk), 97; californium (Cf), 98; einsteinium (Es), 99; fermium (Fm), 100; mendelevium (Mv), 101; nobelium (No), 102; and lawrencium (Lw), 103. These elements are placed in the periodic table in the *actinide series*, which contains also the previously known elements actinium, thorium, protactinium, and uranium. They are formed artificially by several processes but chiefly as a result of a sequence of reactions starting with the capture of a neutron by the nucleus of $\,^{238}U$. The $\,^{239}U$ thus formed is radioactive (with a half-life of 23 min) and loses a beta particle to form neptunium, which (with a half-life of 2.3 days) in turn loses a beta particle to give an atom of plutonium (which decays, with a half-life of 24,000 years, giving off alpha particles). The sequence of results is represented as follows:

$$\,^{238}_{92}U + \,^{1}_{0}n \longrightarrow \,^{239}_{92}U + \text{gamma rays}$$

$$\,^{239}_{92}U \longrightarrow \,^{239}_{93}Np + \,_{-1}^{0}e \text{ (beta)}$$

$$\,^{239}_{93}Np \longrightarrow \,^{239}_{94}Pu + \,_{-1}^{0}e \text{ (beta)} + \text{gamma rays}$$

By similar nuclear reactions between $\,^{4}_{2}He$ and the successively heavier nuclei of the actinides as they are created, the next higher members of the

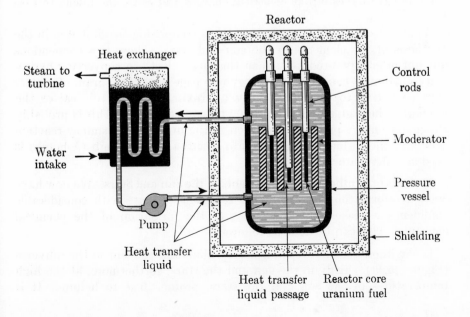

Figure 25.10 The fuel box of a nuclear reactor used for power generation. The control rods regulate the number of neutrons that can cause fission and hence control the rate of the fission process. This in turn controls the amount of energy produced. (Adapted from an AEC figure from Argonne Laboratory.)

series have been synthesized. Three elements, *technetium* (43), *astatine* (85), and *promethium* (61), missing from earlier versions of the periodic table, have been made by the particle-bombardment technique.

Atomic Energy by Fission and by Fusion. We know now that atomic energy can be released by the fusion of nuclei of light elements and also by the fission of the nuclei of heavy elements. In both processes the mass of the products is less than the mass of the reactants. The mass "lost" is converted to energy. Such reactions are exothermic (called exoergic). Nuclear reactions also occur in which the mass of the products is *greater* than the mass of the reactants. For such reactions a large amount of energy must be added; these are endothermic reactions (called endoergic reactions). For atomic-fuel purposes we are interested in the exothermic reaction; a study of this type of reaction also gives us information about the binding energy of nuclei.

A plot of the binding energy of nuclear particles against the atomic weight is given in Figure 25.4.

From this graph several conclusions can be drawn:

1. The most stable nuclei—i.e., those with greatest binding energy per particle in the nucleus—are those in the range of atomic weight 50 to 60.
2. Exothermic reactions (those with mass loss) can occur by either of two processes: (a) fusion of light nuclei (hydrogen, helium, etc.) to heavier nuclei, or (b) fission of heavy nuclei.
3. Since energy is released in fusion of many light elements and in fission of many heavy elements, atomic fuels should be available among the light elements as well as among the heavy ones.

The Fusion Reaction of Hydrogen. At temperatures of 10,000,000 to 50,000,000°K, such as might be expected on the surface of the sun, protons are traveling at high enough velocities to approach each other within 10^{-12} cm. At this distance the powerful nuclear forces overcome the repulsive forces of like electrical charges and cause the nuclei to fuse together.

As protons fuse, helium is formed, thus comprising the first step in the synthesis of the elements in the sun and stars. There is a tremendous amount of energy produced when the mass "lost" in converting hydrogen to helium is converted to energy (see page 501). One gram of matter thus converted to energy produces approximately 2×10^{13} cal or the amount of heat given off when 3,000 tons of coal burn. This is probably the major energy-producing reaction in the universe. A similar reaction occurs in the fusion bomb (H-bomb) where a fission bomb (A-bomb) is used as a detonator.

Methods of Synthesis of the Elements in the Sun and Stars. We now have enough information about nuclear reactions to state with considerable confidence a reasonable hypothesis of the formation of the chemical elements. This can be done as follows:

1. We know that hydrogen is a very abundant element in the universe (Figure 25.11), chiefly in the sun and the stars; furthermore, at the high temperatures of the sun and the stars, protons fuse to helium. It is

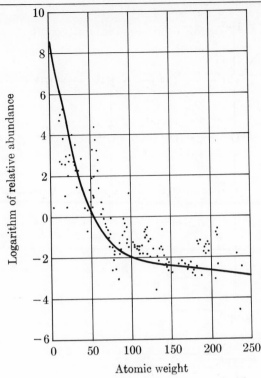

Figure 25.11 The relative abundance of the elements. About 92 per cent of the elements of the universe are hydrogen atoms, and about 7 per cent are helium atoms.

reasonable to assume that the light elements probably are synthesized by a series of successive fusion reactions. As indicated, helium nuclei undoubtedly are the first of these new nuclei to be formed.

2. Laboratory experiments show that the bombardment of light elements, such as beryllium and boron, with α-particles produces neutrons. Similar reactions probably are a main source of neutrons in the sun and stars.

3. With such neutron sources, the heavier elements can be synthesized by the well-known process of neutron capture followed by β-decay, and this process probably constitutes the second step in the synthesis of the elements.

4. According to present theory, these two main processes, fusion and neutron capture followed by beta decay, can account for the formation of most of the elements (Figure 25.12). It is known that several other secondary processes may occur but fusion and neutron capture are certain to occur to a large extent in the great hot mass of hydrogen in the sun and stars.

The Energy Scale of the Universe. It is significant that our present knowledge of kinetic theory and of nuclear processes now makes it possible for us to gain a fairly complete picture of the types of chemical entities and the reactions they undergo in the various temperature regions of the entire universe (Figure 25.13).

At low temperatures both atoms and molecules are stable, but as the total energy increases with increasing temperature, the vibrational energy becomes sufficiently large to cause the molecules to dissociate into atoms; then as the temperature drops, molecules are formed again. Above 10,000°K few, if any, molecules can exist.

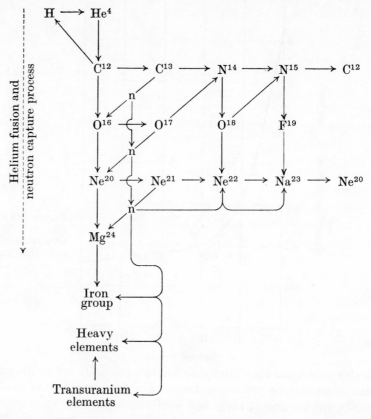

Figure 25.12 This diagram is a simplified explanation of how the elements may have been formed. Hydrogen is believed to be the starting point. The light elements are formed by fusion and neutron capture; the heavier elements are formed mainly by neutron capture. (Adapted from E. M. Burbidge, *et. al. Rev. Mod. Physics, 29* (1957), p. 547.)

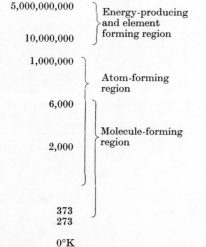

Figure 25.13 The probable temperature scale of the universe showing the element-forming region.

Above these temperatures the kinetic energy and electronic energy of atoms becomes greater and greater, causing electrons to move to higher energy levels and finally ionization occurs. At 1,000,000°K probably all atoms are stripped of their electrons; but should the temperature drop, the atom systems would be formed again.

As the temperature rises above 1,000,000°K, the kinetic energies of the particles increase and finally become so great that they can overcome the repulsion forces between nuclei and fusion occurs. This is accompanied by massive energy release. Hence, above 10,000,000°K we identify a third region as the element-forming region of the universe—it is also the energy-producing region and it is found in the sun and the stars.

SUMMARY

Energy-rich nuclei emit high-energy particles or radiations and become stabilized. This process has been known as radioactivity. Natural radioactive materials usually emit high-energy radiations called alpha, beta, or gamma rays. Stable nuclei can be made energy-rich by bombardment with neutrons or high-energy particles.

Nuclear forces are extremely strong forces but they are effective only at very short distances, dropping to zero at about 10^{-12} cm. Charged particles, when accelerated to high velocities (energies), can overcome the coulomb repulsion of the charged nucleus and approach the nucleus closely enough (10^{-12} cm) to be drawn in by these forces and be captured.

Bombarding particles to produce nuclear changes may be neutrons or charged particles of atomic weight ranging from 1 to approximately 20.

Atomic energy can be produced by mass loss in fusion reactions or in fission reactions.

We can describe with considerable confidence the reactions that, given the proper conditions of nuclear abundance and temperature, must take place to form the various elements of the universe. These nuclear processes have been observed to occur in nuclear reactors, cyclotrons, betatrons, and in the hydrogen bomb. They can be expected to be taking place in the sun and stars—hence, producing the chemical elements.

Undoubtedly the hydrogen fusion reaction is the initial step in the element-forming process and is probably the main energy-forming step in the universe.

SOME SPECIAL TERMS

Alpha particle
Barn
β-decay process
Beta particle
Binding energy of nucleons
Curie
Gamma ray
Half-life
Ionizing radiation

Isotopes
Magic number nuclei
Maximum permissible dosage
Nuclear cross section, σ
Nuclear process
Nucleon
Radioactivity
Roentgen

QUESTIONS AND PROBLEMS

1. What is the status of theories about the structure of the nucleus?
2. Describe the experiments leading to the discovery of radioactivity.
3. Write nuclear equations representing an emission process and a capture process.
4. What property of nuclei is indicated by the fact that alpha particles and gamma rays are monoenergetic? Why do beta particles not show monoenergetic properties?
5. How can the magnitude and sign on alpha particles and beta particles be demonstrated?
6. Assume an alpha particle of 4.5 Mev passes through a gas. How many positive ions will be formed along its path if approximately 35 ev are required to form an ion pair (a positive ion and an electron)?
7. Calculate the relative size of the nucleus of a helium atom and a uranium atom.
8. The energy emitted when nucleons fuse to form an atomic nucleus is called the binding energy of the nucleus. What is the justification for labeling the emitted energy "binding energy"?
9. What is the relationship between the neutron-proton ratio and the stability of a nucleus?
10. How do you account for the fact that most particles emitted from the nucleus have very high energies rather than just enough to get out of the nucleus?
11. Cite evidence which indicates that energy levels exist in nuclei.
12. What is the significance of the term "nuclear cross section for capture"?
13. How is ^{14}C used as a method of determining the age of a wooden relic?

14. Fill in the proper mass and charge numbers in the nuclear equations:

$$^{238}_{92}U + n \longrightarrow U \longrightarrow Np + \beta$$
$$\phantom{^{238}_{92}U + n \longrightarrow U \longrightarrow Np}\quad\longrightarrow Pu + \beta$$

15. Calculate how much higher the maximum permissible dosage is above the amount of natural daily radiation received by each person.

16. What was a significant contribution of Rutherford and of Joliot to radiochemistry?

17. What types of bombarding particles are used to produce nuclear changes?

18. How does a captured particle "create" an energy-rich nucleus?

19. If element 104 were prepared, where would it be located in the periodic table? What are several nuclear processes that could be used to produce element 104?

20. Assume that a reaction that may be used in a hydrogen bomb is $^6Li + {}^2H \to 2\,{}^4He$. From the mass differences in the reactants and products, calculate the number of kilocalories produced when 100 g of lithium reacts by this process. Isotopic masses ^6_3Li, 6.015126; ^2_1H, 2.014102 atomic mass units.

21. When Lise Meitner interpreted the fission process, she at once realized that this could be an important source of high energy. Show by means of Figure 25.4 how she could have arrived at this conclusion.

REFERENCES

CHOPPIN, G. *Nuclei and Radioactivity*. New York: Benjamin, 1964.

FOWLER, W. A. "Theory of the Origin of the Elements," *Scientific American*, vol. *195*, no. 3 (1956), pp. 82–91; *Chem. Eng. News, 42* (1964), pp. 90–104.

GARRETT, A. B. *The Flash of Genius*. Princeton, N.J.: Van Nostrand, 1962. (Useful for stories of the discoveries in radioactivity by Rutherford, Becquerel, Libby, Curie, Joliot, Soddy, Chadwick, Meitner, and de Hevesy.)

SEABORG, G. T. "Some Recollections of Early Nuclear Age Chemistry," *J. Chem. Educ., 45* (1968) pp. 278–289.

PART SEVEN

THE TRANSITION
ELEMENTS

26

Overview of the Transition Elements— Coordination Chemistry

Über die räumliche Lagerung habe ich . . . die Vorstellung entwickelt, dass die sechs Gruppen in der relativen Stellung der Ecken eines Oktaeders um das Zentralatom angeordnet sind. Diese Vorstellung führt zu verschiedenen Folgerungen . . . Einige derselben haben die experimentelle Prüfung schon bestanden, so z.B. diejenige, dass Verbindungen mit komplexen Radikalen [MeA₅B] nur in einer Form auftreten können, und ebenso die wichtige Folgerung, dass die Verbindungen mit komplexen Radikalen [MeA₄B₂] oder [MeA₄BC] in zwei stereoisomeren Reihen bestehen können.* Alfred Werner (1866–1919)

The group of metals in the middle of the periodic table whose inner d or f orbitals are not completely filled are called the transition elements. There are about fifty-five such elements—a majority of all known elements. The transition elements have certain common properties:

1. All are metals.
2. They are hard, high melting, brittle, and good conductors of heat and electricity.
3. With few exceptions, their ions and compounds are colored.
4. With few exceptions, they exhibit multiple oxidation states.
5. Many of these elements and their compounds act as catalysts for chemical reactions.
6. Most of their compounds are paramagnetic—they are attracted by a magnetic field.

---

* "With regard to the spatial arrangement I have developed the postulate that the six groups are arranged in the relative positions of the corners of an octahedron about the central atom. This postulate leads to various consequences. Several of these have already been confirmed experimentally, for example, the conclusion that compounds with complex radicals [MeA₅B] can appear only in one form, and the important conclusion that compounds with complex radicals [MeA₄B₂] or [MeA₄BC] can exist in two stereoisomeric forms." (The quotation is from *Berichte*, *44* (1911) p. 1887.)

7. Finally, one of their most general properties is the property of forming complex ions, especially for that group known as the *d*-electron group. Much of the chemistry of the transition elements is associated with the use of *d* as well as *s* and *p* orbitals in forming complex ions.

The *d*-electron group includes those elements which have partially filled *d* orbitals (but either completely empty or completely filled *f* subshells); the second group, called the *f*-electron group, has partially filled *f* orbitals. The *d*-group elements are:

First transition series		Sc	Ti	V	Cr	Mn	Fe	Co	Ni	Cu
Electron	$4s$	2	2	2	1	2	2	2	2	1
configuration	$3d$	1	2	3	5	5	6	7	8	10
Second transition series		Y	Zr	Nb	Mo	Tc	Ru	Rh	Pd	Ag
Third transition series		La	Hf	Ta	W	Re	Os	Ir	Pt	Au

The *f*-group elements are:

Lanthanides

| La | Ce Pr Nd Pm Sm Eu Gd Tb Dy Ho Er Tm Yb Lu

Actinides

| Ac | Th Pa U Np Pu Am Cm Bk Cf Es Fm Md No Lw

An important distinction between the *d* and *f* groups of elements arises because the electron cloud of the partially filled *d* orbitals apparently projects well out to the periphery of the atoms and ions so that the electrons in these orbitals introduce or accentuate several important properties of these elements. By contrast the *f* orbitals are believed to be buried rather deeply in the atom or ion and hence do not have a profound effect on its properties. As a consequence, *d*-group elements, while showing the common properties listed above, show a much wider variation in properties than do *f*-group elements.

Properties of Transition Elements

Metallic Properties. Since the outermost shell of these elements contains only one or two electrons, it is not surprising that they are all metals. Moreover, because most of the atoms are relatively small and because some covalent binding between atoms may occur, these metals are high melting and brittle.

Oxidation States. Most of these elements show several oxidation states because some or all of the electrons in *d* orbitals may be used along with the valence shell *s* electrons in compound formation. For example, vanadium ($3d^3\,4s^2$) exhibits oxidation states of V, IV, III, and II corresponding to the use of the two $4s$ as well as 3, 2, 1, or 0 *d* electrons, respectively.

Color. Color in the ions of these elements arises because the electronic energy levels lie close enough to one another so that electrons can move to higher energy levels by absorbing visible light. The color of the compound is the complement of the color absorbed. (Figures 26.1 and 26.2.)

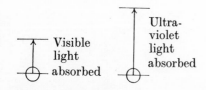

Figure 26.1 Visible and ultraviolet light absorption. Visible light may be absorbed when an electron moves to a slightly higher energy level; ultraviolet light is absorbed when energy levels are more widely separated.

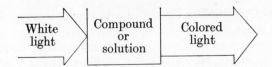

Figure 26.2 Color as a consequence of absorption. White light, a mixture of all colors, passes through a solution and appears as colored light. This is the result of absorption of one or more wave lengths of light from the white light by the compound or its ions.

Magnetic Properties. The presence of unpaired electrons in the atoms or ions of the transition elements gives rise to paramagnetism. It is possible to measure the paramagnetism of a compound and from this to estimate the number of unpaired electrons present. This is often useful in determining the structure of the compound.

Complex Ions. A complex ion is one that contains more than one atom. Complex ions may contain either a metal ion or a nonmetal atom or ion as the central ion. Some examples are given in Table 26.1.

The deep blue color of a solution of copper sulfate containing ammonium hydroxide is due to the $Cu(NH_3)_4^{+2}$ ions. In nature we find that the red coloring matter in blood, hemoglobin, is a complex ion of iron; the green coloring matter in plants, chlorophyll, is a complex ion of magnesium; and vitamin B_{12}, a constituent of the vitamin-B group, is a complex ion of cobalt. Because water tends to hydrate ions readily, most ions in aqueous solution may be considered to be complex ions. Complex ions occur in both the solid state and in solution.

The transition elements are not the only metals whose ions form complex ions, but the tendency is very pronounced among the transition elements. A principal reason why complex ions are formed by the transition elements is the presence of unfilled d orbitals that can be used to form rather strong bonds. Hence, we shall discuss the chemistry of complex metal ions with the chemistry of the transition elements in this chapter.

Table 26.1 Some Complex Ions

Complex Metal Ions	Complex Nonmetal Ions
$Cu(NH_3)_4^{+2}$	ClO_3^-
$Cu(H_2O)_4^{+2}$	SO_4^{-2}
$Co(NO_2)_6^{-3}$	NO_3^-
$Co(NH_3)_6^{+3}$	CO_3^{-2}
$Fe(CN)_6^{-3}$	PO_4^{-3}
$Ag(NH_3)_2^+$	
$Al(H_2O)_6^{+3}$	
$Zn(H_2O)_6^{+2}$	
CrO_4^{-2}	

Properties and Bonding in Complex Ions

Ion-Dipole Interaction. Hydration of ions in solution is a familiar example of complex ion formation. In many cases the bonding is of the ion-dipole type; however, some hydrates may be formed by use of coordinate covalent bonds. Water is a polar covalent molecule. Hence, it will "stick" to ions of all kinds in solution due to the attraction of the + or − end of the water molecule to the negative or positive ion. Examples are shown in Figure 26.3.

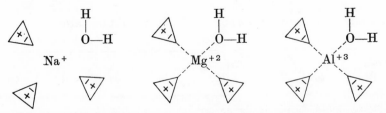

Figure 26.3 Hydration of positive ions; the negative end of the water dipole is near the positive charge on the ion. Whether this is purely electrostatic attraction or partially coordinate covalent bond formation is not known in most cases. All of the transition metal ions in solution form complex ions by hydration.

Historical: Werner Coordination Theory. Early chemists recognized such compounds as $Cu(NH_3)_4SO_4$, $Co(NH_3)_6Cl_3$, and $K_3Fe(CN)_6$, but they could not account for the formation of such compounds in terms of the theories of valency then known. A German chemist, Alfred Werner, in a series of researches between 1893 and 1918, described a theory to account for such compounds, which have become known as Werner complexes. He was able to show that such groups as NH_3 and CN^- assumed fixed positions around the central ion in regular geometric patterns. (Figure 26.4.)

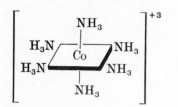

Figure 26.4 Structure of octahedrally shaped $Co(NH_3)_6^{+3}$ ion.

Werner suggested that two kinds of valence forces seem to be present: principal and auxiliary forces. He coined a new term, *coordination number*, to indicate the number of the "extra" ions or molecules that surrounded the metal ion. In the ion $Co(NH_3)_6^{+3}$, the coordination number of the central cobalt ion is six (six ammonia molecules surround the metal ion). With the advent of the electron theory of chemical bonds the actual bonding of the groups to the central ion in Werner complexes was thought to involve the formation of coordinate bonds with the group supplying a pair of electrons and the metal ion providing empty orbitals.

The Atomic Orbital Theory (Coordinate Covalent Bonds). An early explanation of the bonding in Werner complexes became available in the 1920's. The concept developed by G. N. Lewis of bonding as the result of the sharing of pairs of electrons, as extended to coordinate covalent bonding, was combined with the concept of atomic orbitals to provide the explanation known as the *atomic orbital theory* of bonding in complex ions. In the theory, we assume that the formation of the complexes depends upon: (a) the orbitals available for coordinate covalent bond formation; (b) the tendency of the ions or groups to share a pair of electrons; and (c) the number of molecules or ions that can be placed around a central ion.

These factors can be illustrated with three complex ions of the transition elements: $MnCl_4^{-2}$, $Fe(CN)_6^{-3}$, $Co(NH_3)_6^{+3}$.

The atomic orbitals of the *atoms* of manganese, iron and cobalt are:

Atomic Number	Atom	Orbitals Filled	3d	4s	4p
25	Mn	$1s^2\ 2s^2\ 2p^6\ 3s^2\ 3p^6$	↓ ↓ ↓ ↓ ↓	↓↑	_ _ _
26	Fe	$1s^2\ 2s^2\ 2p^6\ 3s^2\ 3p^6$	↓↑ ↓ ↓ ↓ ↓	↓↑	_ _ _
27	Co	$1s^2\ 2s^2\ 2p^6\ 3s^2\ 3p^6$	↓↑ ↓↑ ↓ ↓ ↓	↓↑	_ _ _

The atomic orbitals of the *ions* of Mn^{+2}, Fe^{+3} and Co^{+3} are:

Atomic Number	Ion	Orbitals Filled	3d	4s	4p
25	Mn^{+2}	$1s^2\ 2s^2\ 2p^6\ 3s^2\ 3p^6$	↓ ↓ ↓ ↓ ↓	_	_ _ _
26	Fe^{+3}	$1s^2\ 2s^2\ 2p^6\ 3s^2\ 3p^6$	↓ ↓ ↓ ↓ ↓	_	_ _ _
27	Co^{+3}	$1s^2\ 2s^2\ 2p^6\ 3s^2\ 3p^6$	↓↑ ↓ ↓ ↓ ↓	_	_ _ _

The ionization process produces the *principal valence* described by Werner; these ions can now take part in forming electrovalent bonds as in $MnCl_2$, $FeCl_3$, or $CoCl_3$.

But a second type of bond can also be formed with these ions, due to the *auxiliary valence force* described by Werner. This second type of bond can be formed if the ligands (the combining ions or molecules) have a pair of electrons which can enter the unfilled d, s, or p orbitals. According to the atomic orbital theory such a bond is of the coordinate covalent type, and the reaction that occurs to form this bond is a Lewis acid-base type of reaction. The number of ligands that will combine this way depends on the relative size of the central ion, the nature of the combining groups, and to a certain extent, upon the number of orbitals available for bond formation. Let us illustrate these factors with examples.

Example: $Mn^{+2} + 4Cl^- \longrightarrow MnCl_4^{-2}$

$MnCl_4^{-2}$

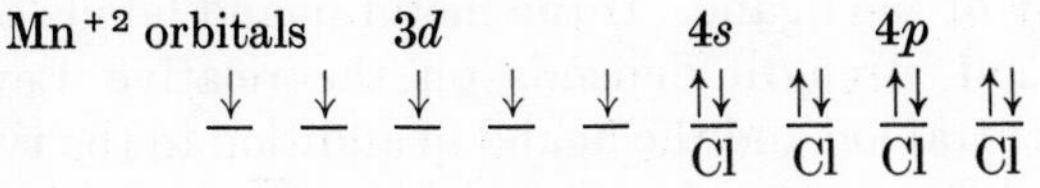

| Mn^{+2} orbitals | 3d | 4s | 4p |

One pair of electrons on each chloride ion can form a covalent bond with the $4s$ and each of the $4p$ orbitals on the manganese ion. The Mn^{+2} ion is now surrounded by chloride ions. This probably is an sp^3 type of complex. The configuration is tetrahedral.

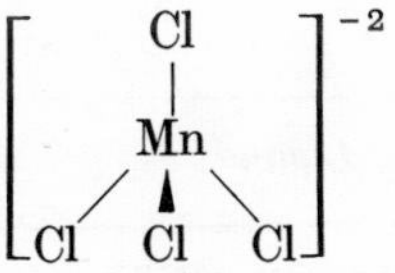

Example: $Co^{+3} + 6NH_3 \longrightarrow Co(NH_3)_6^{+3}$

$Co(NH_3)_6^{+3}$

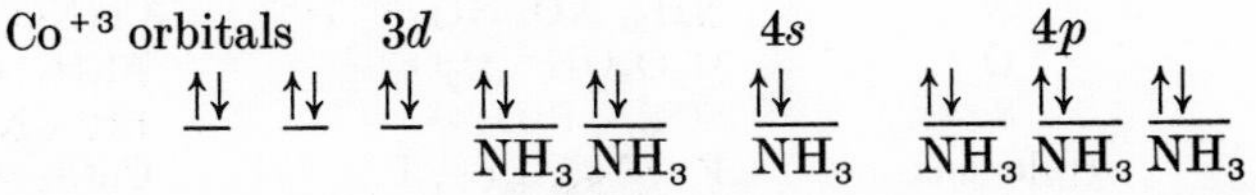

| Co^{+3} orbitals | 3d | 4s | 4p |

Here the extra pairs of electrons from the various ammonia molecules are said to be bonded in two d, one s, and three p orbitals of the metal ion. The Co^{+3} is now surrounded by six ammonia molecules. This is called a d^2sp^3 type of complex. The configuration is octahedral.

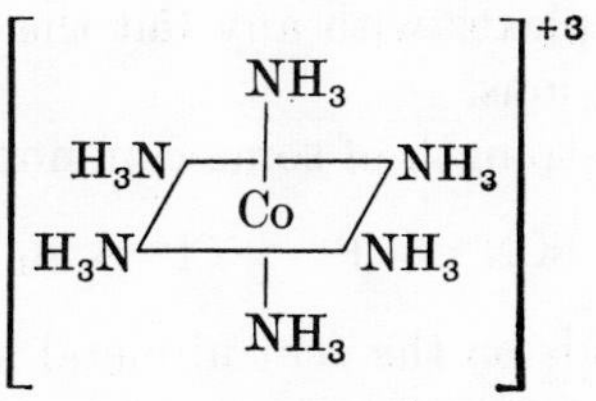

● ● ●   WERNER STATEMENT

"Even when, to judge by the valence number, the combining power of certain atoms is exhausted, they still possess in most cases the power of participating further in the construction of complex molecules with the formation of very definite atomic linkages. The possibility of this action is to be traced back to the fact that, besides the affinity bonds designated as *principal* valences, still other bonds, called auxiliary valences, may be called into action."

Example: $Fe^{+3} + 6CN^- \longrightarrow Fe(CN)_6^{-3}$

Fe^{+3} orbitals $3d$ $4s$ $4p$

$Fe(CN)_6^{-3}$

$\uparrow\downarrow$	$\uparrow\downarrow$	$\uparrow$	$\uparrow\downarrow$	$\uparrow\downarrow$	$\uparrow\downarrow$	$\uparrow\downarrow$	$\uparrow\downarrow$	$\uparrow\downarrow$
		CN	CN	CN	CN	CN	CN	CN

Here the extra pairs of electrons of the cyanide ions are shared with in the d, s, and p orbitals of the metal ion. The Fe^{+3} is now surrounded by six CN^- ions. This type of complex also is the d^2sp^3 type. The configuration is octahedral.

Ligands and Bond Strength. The ion or molecule that attaches itself to a central ion to form a complex ion is called a *ligand*. Table 26.2 gives the formulas of some simple ligands. The strength of the ligand-metal bond depends upon the bond type. If the bonds are of the ion-dipole type, the bond strength depends upon the size and charge of the central ion as well as on the polarity of the ligand. If the metal-ligand bonds are coordinate covalent, the bond strength depends on the relative Lewis acid-base strength of the central ion and the ligand in addition to the type of orbitals available for bond formation. In general, the use of inner d orbitals gives stronger bonds than those formed when only the s and p orbitals of the next higher quantum number are used. For example, complexes in which metals use d^2sp^3 hybridization are often more stable than those in which sp^3 hybridization occurs.

Table 26.2 Some Simple Ligands

Donor Atom	Ligand	Example
C	CN^-, CO, CNS^-	$Cd(CN)_4^{-2}$ $Co(CO)_4$
N	NH_3, NO, NO_2^-	$Co(NO_2)_6^{-3}$
O	H_2O, OH^-, $C_2O_4^{-2}$	$Al(H_2O)_6^{+3}$
S	SCN^-, $S_2O_3^{-2}$	$Pt(SCN)_6^{-2}$
Halogens	F^-, Cl^-, Br^-, I^-	$CuCl_4^{-3}$, HgI_4^{-2}

The strongest coordinating ions with most ligands are the small cations of the transition elements such as Co^{+3}, Cr^{+3}, Fe^{+3}. Of intermediate stability are the nontransition ions such as Cd^{+2} and Zn^{+2}; and those least likely to form complexes with any but the strongest ligand are the alkali and alkaline earth ions.

The relative bonding strength of some common ligands is

$$CN^- > SCN^- > F^- > Cl^- > Br^- > I^-$$

although this also depends on the central metal ion.

Ring formation is an important factor in giving stable complexes. Hence ligands with more than one attaching group can be strong complexing agents.

Ligands with More Than One Attaching Group. Large molecules may have more than one basic group that can donate a pair of electrons to a central ion. For example, the molecule $H_2\overset{..}{N}CH_2CH_2\overset{..}{N}H_2$ (ethylenediamine) contains two NH_2 groups each of which can share a pair of electrons. Hence, if ethylenediamine is added to a solution containing cobalt(III) ions, three of these $\ddot{N}H_2CH_2CH_2\ddot{N}H_2$ molecules will attach themselves to the cobalt(III) ions as shown in Figure 26.5.

Each ethylenediamine molecule forms, with the central ion, a ring of five atoms. Complex ions containing ring structures such as this, with five or six atoms in the ring, are particularly stable. Ligands with two attaching groups are called *bidentate* ligands. It is possible to synthesize more complex organic molecules that contain three, four, or more attaching groups. These are called tridentate, tetradentate, and polydentate ligands (Figure 26.6). Chlorophyll and hemoglobin contain tetradentate ligands.

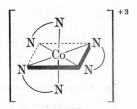

Figure 26.5 A complex ion containing bidentate ligands such as ethylene diamine, $H_2N—CH_2—CH_2—NH_2$.

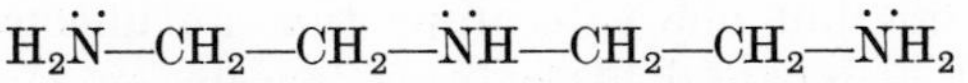

$$H_2\ddot{N}—CH_2—CH_2—\ddot{N}H—CH_2—CH_2—\ddot{N}H_2$$
Diethylenetriamine, a tridentate ligand

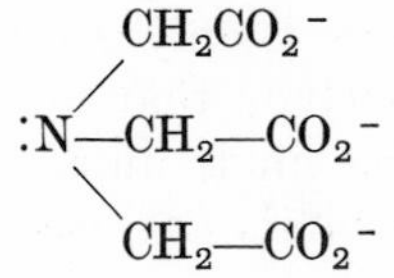

$$:N \begin{matrix} ^{\nearrow CH_2CO_2{}^-} \\ —CH_2—CO_2{}^- \\ _{\searrow CH_2—CO_2{}^-} \end{matrix}$$

Anion of nitrilotriacetic acid, a tetradentate ligand

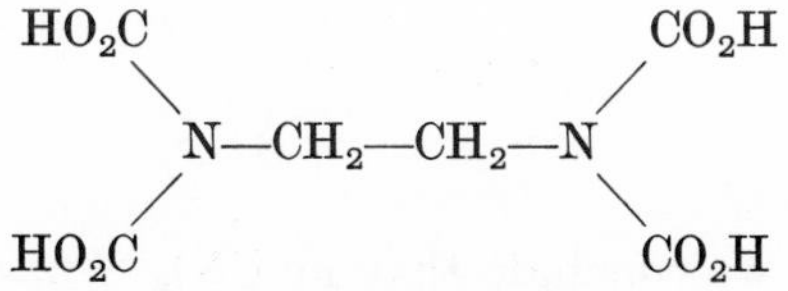

$$\begin{matrix} HO_2C & & CO_2H \\ {}^{\searrow} & & {}^{\swarrow} \\ & N—CH_2—CH_2—N & \\ {}^{\nearrow} & & {}^{\searrow} \\ HO_2C & & CO_2H \end{matrix}$$
Ethylenediaminetetraacetic acid, a sexadentate ligand

Figure 26.6 Some polydentate ligands.

Chelation. The formation of complex ions with ligands that are bidentate, tridentate, tetradentate, etc., give complex ions that are called *chelates* and the process of forming these ions is called *chelation*. The term chelate means *claw*, and is derived from the analogy of the attachment of a crab to an object with its claws. Many chelates are known. Chlorophyll and hemoglobin are examples of chelates.

Magnetic Criterion of Bond Type. Information on the pairing of electrons in the metal-ligand complex is obtained from data on the magnetism of the compound containing the ion in question: *diamagnetism* if all electrons are paired and *paramagnetism* if one or more electrons is unpaired. Diamagnetism causes a sample of a compound to be pushed out of a magnetic field whereas paramagnetism causes a sample to be drawn into a magnetic field (Figure 26.7). The type of magnetism and the amount of paramagnetism can be determined by weighing a sample in the presence and in the absence of a magnetic field (Figure 26.7). The magnetic susceptibility of an ion, which is related to the magnetic moment, is a measure of the strength of interaction with the magnetic field. The larger the magnetic moment, the greater the number of unpaired electrons present. For example, the hydrated nickel(II) ion contains two unpaired electrons whereas the hydrated copper(II) ion contains only one unpaired electron.

The magnetic moment of the nickel(II) ions is 3.2 magnetons whereas that of copper(II) ions is 1.9 magnetons.*

An example of how the metal-ligand bond type can be determined by the magnetic method is given by comparing the magnetic moments of the ions $Fe(CN)_6^{-3}$ and FeF_6^{-3}.

Ion Magnetic Moment (observed)	
$Fe(CN)_6^{-3}$	1.7 magnetons
FeF_6^{-3}	5.9 magnetons

These moments show that FeF_6^{-3} contains five unpaired electrons whereas $Fe(CN)_6^{-3}$ contains but one. Recalling that an uncomplexed iron(III) ion should have five unpaired $3d$ electrons, it seems evident that in FeF_6^{-3} the $3d$ electrons are not rearranged. Evidently either the $4d$ orbitals are used or else ion-dipole or ion-ion type of bonding occurs. By contrast, since the magnetic data indicate that there is only one unpaired electron in $Fe(CN)_6^{-3}$ it seems reasonable to conclude that here the $3d$ orbitals *are* used in bond formation. Indeed, the single unpaired electron leads to the conclusion that two of the $3d$ orbitals are used by the bonding ligands so that the $3d$ configuration changes from $\downarrow\ \downarrow\ \downarrow\ \downarrow\ \downarrow$ in the uncomplexed ion to

$$\underline{\uparrow\downarrow}\ \underline{\uparrow\downarrow}\ \underline{\downarrow}\ \underline{\uparrow\downarrow}\ \underline{\uparrow\downarrow}$$
$$\qquad\qquad\text{CN}\quad\text{CN}$$

in the complex ion.

From these data we conclude that $Fe(CN)_6^{-3}$ has coordinate covalent metal-ligand bonds; this is called a "low-spin" complex because most of the electron spins are paired, cancelling each other. FeF_6^{-3} must have either ionic bonds, or the iron(III) ion must use $4d$ rather than $3d$ orbitals for covalent bonding. Due to the high electronegativity of the fluoride

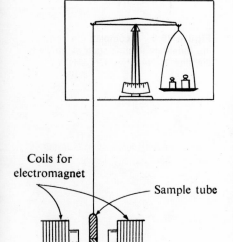

Coils for electromagnet

Sample tube

Pole faces

Figure 26.7 Determination of paramagnetic susceptibility. The sample is placed in a tube suspended from one arm of a balance, and the apparent weight of the sample is measured in the presence of a magnetic field and in its absence. Paramagnetic material will be pulled into the field and will appear to weigh more with the field on. (From Douglas and McDaniel, *Concepts and Models in Inorganic Chemistry.* Waltham, Mass.: Blaisdell, 1965.)

• • •   NOMENCLATURE FOR COMPLEX IONS

A system for naming complexes is in common use and can be illustrated by the following examples:

Case	Formula	Name
I	$Ni(H_2O)_6^{+2}$	Hexaaquonickel(II) ion
II	$Co(NH_3)_6(NO_3)_3$	Hexaamminecobalt(III) nitrate
III	$Cu(NH_3)_4(H_2O)_2^{+2}$	Diaquotetraamminecopper(II) ion
IV	$Pt(NH_3)_4ClNO_2^{+2}$	Chloronitrotetraammineplatinum(IV) ion
V	$Fe(CN)_6^{-4}$	Hexacyanoferrate(II) ion
VI	VCl_4^-	Tetrachlorovanadate(III) ion

These examples bring out both the general pattern and the more common rules in this

---

* It can be shown that the equation relating the magnetic moment in magnetons to the number of unpaired electrons is $M = \sqrt{n(n+2)}$ where M is the number of magnetons and n is the number of unpaired electrons on the ion. A magneton is defined by the equation $eh/4\pi mc$, where e is the charge on the electron, h is Planck's constant, m is the mass of the electron, and c is the velocity of light.

ion, the bonds are probably ionic, and the metal and nonmetal ions are held to each other with electrostatic forces. This is called a "high-spin" complex since a number of the electrons are not paired and their spins, added together, give a high value to the magnetic moment.

The Coordination Number. The coordination number is defined as the number of monodentate ligands surrounding a central ion. This number depends primarily upon the relative sizes of the central ion and the ligand. The more common coordination numbers are four and six as in the ions $MnCl_4^{-2}$ and $Fe(CN)_6^{-3}$. Some coordination numbers of complex ions are given in Table 26.3. The term coordination number is also used to designate the number of nearest neighbors of an atom or ion in a crystal (Chap. 15).

Table 26.3 Coordination Numbers of Some Complex Ions

Ion	*Coordination Number*	*Ion*	*Coordination Number*	*Ion*	*Coordination Number*
$Ag(NH_3)_2^+$	2	$Fe(CN)_6^{-3}$	6	$Fe(CO)_5$	5
$Cd(NH_3)_4^{+2}$	4	$Fe(C_2O_4)_3^{-3}$	6	$CuCl_5^{-3}$	5
$Ni(CN)_4^{-2}$	4	$Cr(H_2O)_6^{+3}$	6	$Re(CN)_8^{-2}$	8

The Ligand Field Theory. As the research on complex ions progressed, another bonding theory called the *ligand field theory* was devised to account for the colors of the ions and for observed properties of the bond between the central metal ion and the ligand. This is also extended to crystal-like arrangements because the central ion-ligand bond may be considered to be similar to the bonds between a central ion and surrounding ions in a crystal; hence, a simpler form of the theory is sometimes called the *crystal field theory.*

The ligand field theory takes into consideration the fact that the near

system of nomenclature. As is apparent from the examples given, the general pattern for this nomenclature is:

Number and name of ligand—name of metal—oxidation state of metal

In Case I, $Ni(H_2O)_6^{+2}$, there are six water molecules surrounding the metal ion. The name given the ligand H_2O is aquo. Hence, hexaaquonickel(II) ion indicates six water molecules surrounding a nickel ion in the (II) oxidation state.

Water and negatively charged ligands are given names ending in *o* as chloro, cyano (CN^-), and sulfato (SO_4^{-2}); ammonia, NH_3, is called ammine.

In Case II, the complex salt of cobalt nitrate is named so the cation name comes first—hexaamminecobalt(III)—followed by the name of the anion—nitrate.

Case III illustrates a complex ion with two neutral ligands, $Cu(NH_3)_4(H_2O)_2^{+2}$. The least complex ligand is named first, hence, diaquotetraamminecopper(II) ion.

The ion $Pt(NH_3)_4ClNO_2^{+2}$ has two negatively charged ligands—chloro and nitro—NO_2^-, and a neutral ligand. The negative ligands are named first in alphabetical order followed by the name of the neutral ligand. Hence the name chloronitrotetraammine platinum(IV) ion.

Anions containing the metal ion end in *ate* as in chromate, permanganate, etc. Hence the ions $Fe(CN)_6^{-4}$ and VCl_4^- are hexacyanoferrate(II) ion [where ferrate(II) means iron(II) in an anion] and tetrachlorovanadate(III) ion.

approach of a ligand molecule or ion to a charged particle causes disturbances, called perturbations, in the electron cloud of both the ion and the ligand. These perturbations in the electric field affect the orientation and energies of the d-electron orbitals in the metal ions attached to the ligand and hence produce a new set of unequally spaced energy states in the complex ion. This in turn affects some properties of the ion such as color, bond strength, reactivity, etc.

In general we can understand that different arrangements (square planar, tetrahedral, octahedral, etc.) of the ligands around a central ion will change the symmetry of the electrical field around the ion and hence will have different perturbation effects; this change in symmetry should cause different orientations of the d orbitals and hence produce different energy-state patterns. Let us consider first the case of the free atom.

It is known that the d electrons in a free atom in the absence of an electric field are in orbitals all of which have the same energy; they are then said to be five-fold degenerate. (This is represented in Case I, Table 26.4.) In the presence of an electric field the energies of these orbitals is changed, but if the field is spherically symmetrical about the ion (of the same strength at a given distance, no matter in what direction from the central ion), the degeneracy of the five orbitals remains. This is shown in Case II. However, if the field produced by the attached ligands is concentrated in particular directions from the central ion, the degenerate levels are separated into two or more sets of levels. The magnitude of the separation, and the number of orbitals in the new levels, depend upon the type of arrangement of the ligands around the central ion, and will be different according as they are arranged in a square planar, tetrahedral, octahedral, etc., manner. The result for octahedral arrangement is shown in Case III.

Had the ligands been arranged in a tetrahedral pattern around the central ion, the separation in Case III would have been in general less than for the octahedral arrangement, and would have been in a triply degenerate upper level and a doubly degenerate lower level as illustrated in Case IV.

If the transition metal ion has electrons in the d orbitals, the electrons will enter the split d orbitals so that the lowest levels fill first and will

Table 26.4 Relative Energies of Metal Ion d Levels in Various External Fields

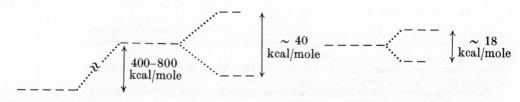

Case I. Free metal ion showing degenerate d orbitals all at the same energy, e.g., Ti^{+3}.

Case II. Showing change in energy produced by a spherically symmetric electric field. The degeneracy remains.

Case III. Separation of the degenerate levels into a doubly degenerate upper level and a triply degenerate lower level by an octahedral field as in TiF_6^{-3}.

Case IV. Separation of the degenerate levels of the spherically symmetric system by a tetrahedral field, as in $TiCl_4^-$.

pair only when there is an energy advantage as described below. For example, consider the ions $Ti(H_2O)_6^{+3}$, $Fe(H_2O)_6^{+3}$, and $Co(NH_3)_6^{+3}$.

Since all are octahedral complexes, the d orbitals are split as shown in Figure 26.8.

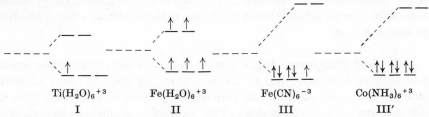

| $Ti(H_2O)_6^{+3}$ | $Fe(H_2O)_6^{+3}$ | $Fe(CN)_6^{-3}$ | $Co(NH_3)_6^{+3}$ |
| I | II | III | III′ |

Figure 26.8 Relative energies of d levels in some ions with octahedral fields.

High-Spin and Low-Spin Complexes. The reason the electrons are all placed in the lower levels in $Co(NH_3)_6^{+3}$ is that the ammonia ligands produce a strong field, which causes a rather large separation between the lower and higher d energy levels. Hence, less energy is expended in overcoming the repulsion of another electron in two of the lower orbitals than would be required to promote two electrons to the two higher orbitals; therefore the electrons pair in the lower orbitals. In $Fe(H_2O)_6^{+3}$, on the other hand, the water molecules produce a rather weak field around the iron(III) ion, and the separation between the lower and higher d energy levels is less than in the cobalt-ammonia case. Hence the electrons remain unpaired, since the energy expended in promoting two electrons to the higher levels is less than that which would be needed to overcome the repulsion of another electron in two lower levels in order that pairing might occur. The $Co(NH_3)_6^{+3}$ ion is thus a "low-spin" complex, while $Fe(H_2O)_6^{+3}$ is a "high-spin" complex.

Whether a low-spin or high-spin complex will form depends upon (a) the relative strength of the field established by the ligands surrounding the central ion and the energies of the d orbitals of the central ion, and (b) the overlap between the orbitals of the central ion and the ligand. In general, water as a ligand produces a smaller difference between the two octahedral d levels than ammonia and is more prone to produce high-spin complexes. Cyanide ion has the most effect in increasing the separation, and appears at the extreme of the "spectro-chemical series" which lists ligands in the order in which they increase the separation between the two d levels:

$$I^- < Br^- < Cl^- < F^- < C_2O_4^{-2} < H_2O < NH_3 < NO_2^- \ll CN^-$$

The position of F^- in this series shows that the theory would predict a high-spin complex, FeF_6^{-3}, and thus provides an alternative explanation for the high magnetic moment of FeF_6^{-3}, mentioned earlier.

Color of Complex Ions. The color of transition metal complex ions is readily explained in terms of the ligand field theory by assuming that electrons in the lower d levels may absorb photons and move to higher levels. Thus, for example, the violet color of the $Ti(H_2O)_6^{+3}$ ion arises when the single d electron absorbs a photon of wavelength 5,000 A and moves to one of the higher d levels. The light transmitted by the solution containing many $Ti(H_2O)_6^{+3}$ ions will be white light minus the yellow photons of wavelengths 5,000–6,700 A. Such light is violet to the eye. The difference in energy between the energy levels is obtained in this and other cases by measuring the wavelength of the light absorbed and applying the equation $E_2 - E_1 = h\nu$.

Further discussion of the ligand field theory is beyond the scope of this book. Suffice it to say that the theory appears to be a satisfactory extension of the atomic orbital theory to aid in a better understanding of bonding in complex ions.

π-Bonding Complexes. Ligands such as carbon monoxide, nitric oxide, and sulfides form complexes with transition metals. In many of these complexes the metals are in the zero oxidation state or in low-negative or low-positive oxidation states. For example in nickeltetracarbonyl, $Ni(CO)_4$, nickel is in the zero state since carbon monoxide is neutral; in $V(CO)_6^{-1}$ vanadium is in the $-I$ state.

The metal-ligand bonding in these cases is believed to involve both σ and π bonds. The σ bonding involves a coordinate covalent bond, in which the ligand supplies a filled orbital for end-to-end overlap with an empty orbital on the metal atom. The π bond involves a filled metal orbital overlapping sideways with an empty orbital on the ligand. A comparison between σ and π bonding in complexes is given in Figure 26.9.

Carbon monoxide complexes are the most common of the π complexes, and carbonyl compounds of all but two of the transition elements are known.

A wide variety of π-bonded complexes exist as illustrated by the following examples: $Cr(CO)_6$, $Mn_2(CO)_{10}$, $Na[Co(CO)_4]$, $Mo(CO)_5I^-$, $[Re(CO)_4Cl]_2$, $Ni(PF_3)_4$, $Co(CO)_3NO$, $HMn(CO)_5$.

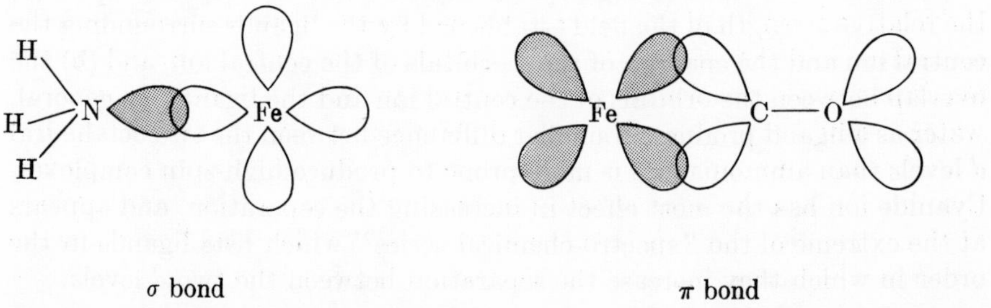

Figure 26.9 σ and π bonding in complexes.

σ bond π bond

Shapes of Complex Ions—Isomerism. The shapes, or stereochemistry, of complex ions is determined by the coordination number of the central ion and by the strength of the interaction between the metal ion and the ligands. The base strength of the ligand, the size and charge on the metal ion, and the orbitals available for forming bonds may all be involved in determining the shape. However, a good general rule is: the shape will be that resulting from the most efficient packing of ligands around the central ion.

Ions having a coordination number of six occur only in octahedral arrangements, although large distortions are often found. Two geometrical arrangements are possible when the coordination number is four—i.e., tetrahedral and planar. The planar configuration is important in complexes of nickel(II), copper(II), gold(III), and platinum(II) as illustrated in Figure 26.10. Many halogen complexes of the first-row transition elements are tetrahedral. These include $FeCl_4^{-1}$, $CoCl_4^{-2}$, CoI_4^{-2}, $MnCl_4^{-2}$.

Coordination numbers of three and five are not common, but, when they occur, the shapes are often either planar or pyramidal when three groups surround the central ion, and trigonal bipyramidal when the coordination number is five.

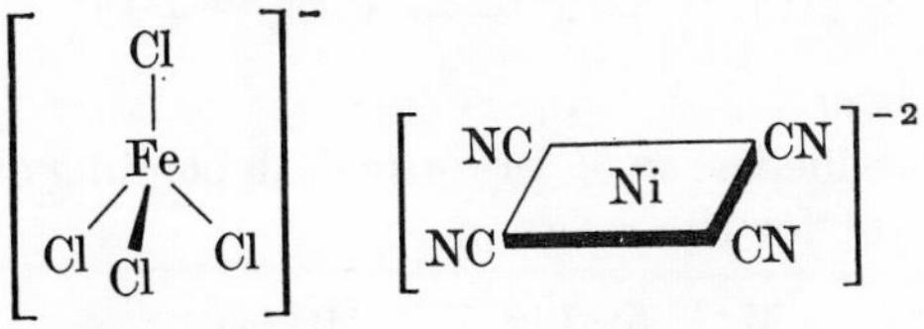

A tetrahedral
iron(III)
complex ion

A square-planar
nickel(II)
complex ion

Figure 26.10 Tetrahedral and planar complex ions.

Isomeric Complex Ions. Both geometrical (Chap. 10) and optical (Chap. 32) isomerism are found among complex ions. Geometrical isomerism is of special importance in square and octahedral complexes.

Two isomers of the square-planar complex $Pt(NH_3)_2Cl_2$ are known. These have been assigned the structures

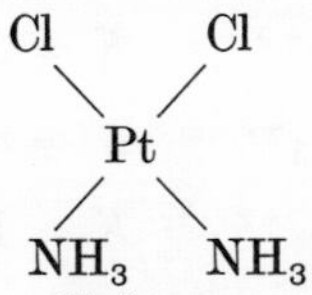

Cis isomer

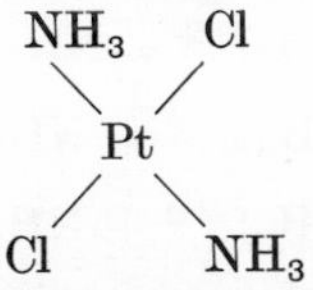

Trans isomer

Two such isomers are possible with any square-planar complex of the type MA_2B_2 where M is the metal ion and A and B are ligands.

Geometrical isomers in octahedral complexes are illustrated by the complex $Co(NH_3)_4Cl_2^+$. Here the isomers have the structures

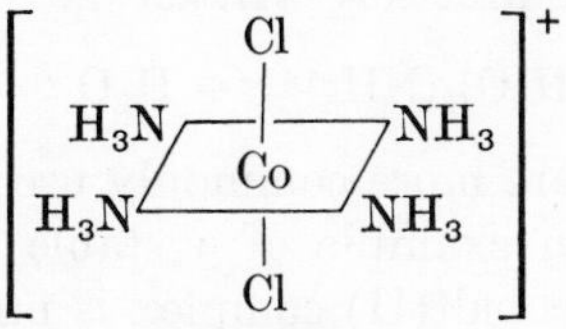

Trans isomer

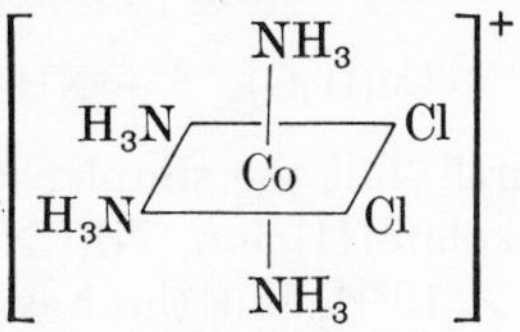

Cis isomer

Optical isomers (structures which are nonsuperimposable mirror images) are possible with polydentate ligands as illustrated with $Co(en)_3^{+3}$ where en represents ethylenediamine (NH_2—CH_2—CH_2—NH_2). The following two structures are not identical. They are nonsuperimposable mirror images and hence are known as optical isomers.

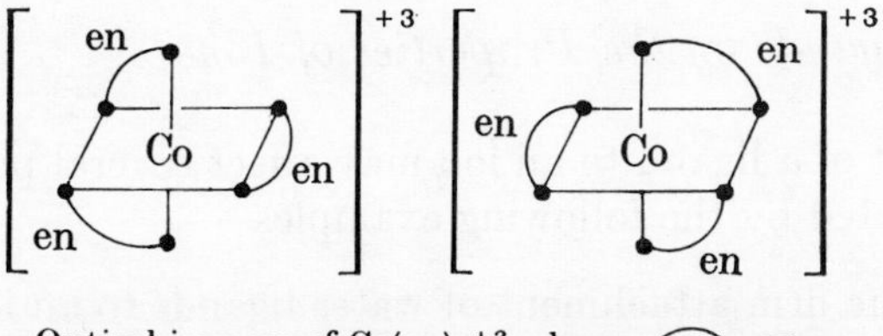

Optical isomers of $Co(en)_3^{+3}$ where ⚬—⚬ ≡ en

Stability and Lability in Complex Ions. Complexes in which ligands are rapidly replaced by other ligands are known as *labile complexes* while those in which such replacement is slow are called *inert*. For example, the exchange

$$NiCl_4^{-2} + Cl^- \longrightarrow NiCl_4^{-2} + Cl^-$$

is very rapid, while the corresponding exchange

$$PtCl_4^{-2} + Cl^- \longrightarrow PtCl_4^{-2} + Cl^-$$

is considerably slower.

A complex is classified as *stable* or *unstable* depending on the value of the equilibrium constant for the reaction

$$M^{+x} + n\text{Lig} \rightleftharpoons M(\text{Lig})_n^{+x}$$

If the equilibrium constant is large, the complex is said to be stable; if the equilibrium constant is small, the complex is unstable. The evidence is that the formation of the complex occurs in steps, so that in addition to the equilibrium constant for the equation written, constants for the individual steps can be determined. For the tetraammine copper(II) ion, for example, these are

$$Cu^{+2} + NH_3 \rightleftharpoons Cu(NH_3)^{+2} \qquad K = 1.4 \times 10^4$$

$$Cu(NH_3)^{+2} + NH_3 \rightleftharpoons Cu(NH_3)_2^{+2} \qquad K = 3 \times 10^3$$

$$Cu(NH_3)_2^{+2} + NH_3 \rightleftharpoons Cu(NH_3)_3^{+2} \qquad K = 8 \times 10^2$$

$$Cu(NH_3)_3^{+2} + NH_3 \rightleftharpoons Cu(NH_3)_4^{+2} \qquad K = 1.4 \times 10^2$$

The equilibrium constant, K_n, for the over-all reaction

$$Cu^{+2} + 4NH_3 \rightleftharpoons Cu(NH_3)_4^{+2}$$

has the value 4.7×10^{12}. This would be considered a moderately stable complex. Since the copper ion is undoubtedly hydrated in water solution, these equations should probably be more precisely written

$$Cu(H_2O)_4^{+2} + NH_3 \rightleftharpoons Cu(H_2O)_3(NH_3)^{+2} + H_2O$$

and so forth, but the simpler equations are more commonly used. Tetra-cyanonickelate(II) ion, $Ni(CN)_4^{-2}$, is an example of a stable complex, ($K_n = 1 \times 10^{22}$); but the hexaammine cobalt(II) complex is unstable in water solution ($K_n = 1.3 \times 10^5$).

While the $Ni(CN)_4^{-2}$ ion is stable, it also is labile. Addition of ^{14}C-labeled cyanide ion to an aqueous solution of the complex gives almost instantaneously a complex of the same formula containing radioactive carbon.

Effect of Ligands on the Properties of Ions

The attachment of a ligand to an ion may affect several properties of the ion as is illustrated by the following examples.

Solubility. The firm attachment of water ligands to an ion presumably is the main reason that ions of solids such as sodium chloride go into solution. Some compounds which are insoluble in water will dissolve in the presence of other complexing agents. For example, silver chloride is insoluble in water but dissolves in solutions of ammonia because of the formation of the $Ag(NH_3)_2{}^+$ complex ion.

Oxidation-State Stabilization. The attachment of six monodentate ligands to a cobalt(III) ion fills the two empty $3d$ orbitals as well as the $4s$ and the $4p$ orbitals; hence, there is very little tendency for cobalt(III) to pick up an electron and be reduced to cobalt(II) ions. However, this reduction can be readily accomplished in the following reaction:

$$Co(NH_3)_5Cl^{+2} + Cr(H_2O)_6{}^{+2} + 5H_3O^+ \longrightarrow$$
$$Co(H_2O)_6{}^{+2} + Cr(H_2O)_5Cl^{+2} + 5NH_4{}^+$$

Here the electron is believed to be transferred through the chloride ion in a complex of the type

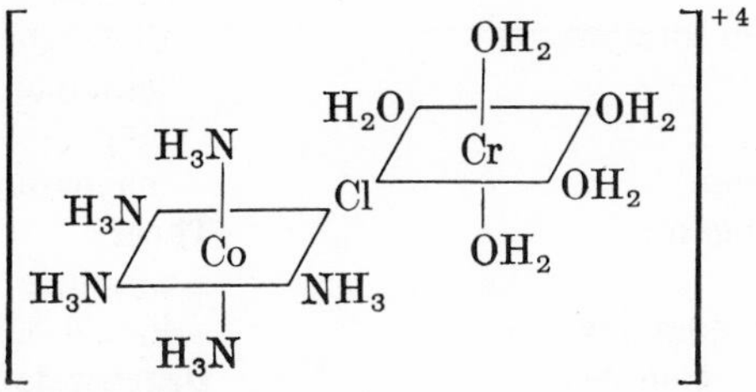

Color. The color of $Cu(H_2O)_6{}^{+2}$ is blue-green, $Cu(NH_3)_4{}^{+2}$ is deep blue, and $CuCl_4{}^{-2}$ is green. These are only several of many examples that can be cited to show the effect of the ligand on the color of the ion as explained earlier.

Reactivity. Iron(II) ions react with sulfide ions; but iron(II) ions in $Fe(CN)_6{}^{-4}$ complex ions do not react with sulfide ion. Silver(I) ions precipitate with chloride ions, but $Ag(NH_3)_2{}^+$ complex ions do not form an insoluble compound with chloride ions. The standard oxidation potential of the metal ion also is dependent on the ligands present as illustrated in the following examples:

$$Fe(H_2O)_6{}^{+2} \longrightarrow Fe(H_2O)_6{}^{+3} + e^- \qquad E^\circ = -0.77 \text{ volt}$$
$$Fe(CN)_6{}^{-4} \longrightarrow Fe(CN)_6{}^{-3} + e^- \qquad E^\circ = -0.36 \text{ volt}$$

Many other examples can be given to show how the reactivity of an ion may be altered by forming a complex ion.

Importance of Complex Ions. A knowledge of the structure, type of bonding, and properties of complex ions is becoming more and more important to the chemist as he studies enzymes containing zinc and other metal ions such as manganese, cobalt, copper and molybdenum, hemoglobin containing iron (and sometimes copper or vanadium), and chlorophyll containing magnesium. These are but a few of the many compounds in which complex ions occur.

SUMMARY

In this chapter the composition, bonding, structure, and energies of the complex ions of the metallic elements of the first transition series have been discussed. It is shown that the bonding in these compounds is interpreted as covalent bonding, frequently involving d orbitals. The magnetic properties depend upon the number of unpaired electrons in the complex ions, which in turn depends upon the total number of electrons and the distance between energy levels, as determined by the nature of the transition metal and the nature of the ligand. Isomerism, stability, and lability of complex ions are introduced.

SOME SPECIAL TERMS

Transition elements
  first (second, third) transition series
  lanthanides
  actinides
Complex ions
  coordination number
  ligand
  sp^3 complex
  d^2sp^3 complex
  bidendate ligand
  chelation
  "low-spin" complex
  "high-spin" complex
  π-bonding complex
  tetrahedral complex
  square-planar complex
  octahedral complex
  stable complex
  labile complex

Isomers
  optical
  geometrical
  substitutional
Magnetic
  diamagnetic
  paramagnetic
  magnetic moment
  magneton
Theory
  atomic orbital theory
  ligand field theory
Degenerate level
Spectrochemical series
Oxidation-state stabilization

QUESTIONS AND PROBLEMS

1. In what ways do the transition elements differ from the representative metals of periodic Groups I and II?
2. How do you explain the fact that transition elements commonly exhibit several oxidation states?
3. List, by name and formula, fifteen examples of complex ions.
4. What is the coordination number of the central atom in the following ions and molecules: $Cu(NH_3)_4^{+2}$, $Co(NO_2)_6^{-3}$, SF_6, $Sb(OH)_6^-$, $Ag(NH_3)_2^+$?
5. Indicate the electronic structures of nickel atoms, Ni, nickel ions, Ni^{+2}, the hydrated ion, $Ni(H_2O)_6^{+2}$, the ion $Ni(CN)_4^{-2}$, and the compound $Ni(CO)_4$.
6. Show by diagrams that there can be (a) one and only one complex of the formula $Co(NH_3)_5(NO_2)^{+2}$, (b) two and only two complexes of the formula $Co(NH_3)_4(H_2O)(NO_2)^{+2}$, and (c) two complexes of formula $Co(NH_3)_3(NO_2)_3$. Explain the magnitude of the electrical charges on these species.
7. How many isomers can there be of the compound $Co(en)_2(NO_2)_2^+$, where en represents ethylene diamine, $H_2NCH_2CH_2NH_2$?
8. Discuss the interpretations of the magnitudes of the magnetic moments of $Fe(H_2O)_6^{+3}$ and FeF_6^{-3} and $Fe(CN)_6^{-3}$. Draw an energy-level diagram to illustrate how $Fe(H_2O)_6^{+3}$ can be a high-spin complex, while $Fe(CN)_6^{-3}$ is a low-spin complex.
9. Show, by means of an energy-level diagram, what happens when $Ti(H_2O)_6^{+3}$ absorbs a photon in the 5,000 A region of the spectrum.

10. Calculate the concentration of copper ion in a solution prepared by adding 50 ml of $0.40M$ molar copper nitrate solution to 150 ml of $0.40M$ molar ammonia solution.

11. Explain, using chemical equations and applying Le Châtelier's principle, why silver chloride dissolves in ammonia solutions.

12. Will the addition of sodium sulfide until the solution becomes 0.1 molar in sulfide ion precipitate NiS from a 0.1 molar solution of $K_2Ni(CN)_4$? CoS from a 0.1 molar solution of $Co(NH_3)_6^{+2}$? The solubility product constants are 1×10^{-22} for NiS and 5×10^{-22} for CoS.

13. Spots of rust or ink can often be removed from cloth by treatment with oxalic acid solution. Can you suggest what chemical reaction makes this treatment effective?

REFERENCES

BASOLO, F., and R. JOHNSON. *Coordination Chemistry*. New York: Benjamin, 1964.

DOUGLAS, B. E. "Stabilization of Oxidation States Through Coordination," *J. Chem. Educ.*, *29* (1952), p. 119.

GRAY, H. B. "Molecular Orbital Theory for Transition Metal Complexes," *J. Chem. Educ.*, *41* (1964), p. 2.

KIRSCHNER, S. "Inorganic Coordination Compounds in General Chemistry," *J. Chem. Educ.*, *35* (1958), p. 139.

LIEHR, A. D. "Molecular Orbital, Valence Bond, and Ligand Field," *J. Chem. Educ.*, *39* (1962), p. 135.

MURMANN, R. K. *Inorganic Complex Compounds*. New York: Reinhold, 1964.

TAUBE, H. "Mechanisms of Oxidation-Reduction Reactions," *J. Chem. Educ.*, *45* (1968), p. 452.

27

The First Row of Transition Elements

*Jag gienom mine experimenter haft den lycken, att jag är förste
upfinnaren af en ny half-metall, neml. cobolt-regulus, som
tilförene med wismuth blifwit confunderad.**

Georg Brant (1694–1768)

The nine elements having atomic numbers 21 to 29 are all in one row of the periodic table,

Symbol	Sc	Ti	V	Cr	Mn	Fe	Co	Ni	Cu
Atomic number	21	22	23	24	25	26	27	28	29

and are called the first-series transition elements. They are all metals and differ much less in properties (Table 27.1) than do the eight elements in the first two rows of the periodic table.

Li	Be	B		C	N	O	F		Ne
Na	Mg	Al		Si	P	S	Cl		Ar
	(metals)				(nonmetals)				(noble gases)

The purpose of this chapter is to explore the properties of this first series of transition elements and to apply the principles of the theories of atomic and molecular structure to explain observed similarities and differences in properties. A study of the transition metals covers some of the most interesting principles of chemical combination, chemical bonding, and general properties that can be collected for any groups of elements.

A Summary of Properties

Electron Structure of the Transition Elements. The reason that the properties of the transition elements change only gradually with change in atomic number, in contrast to the extreme change in properties from column to column for the elements in the first two rows of the periodic

---

* "I had the good fortune, through my experiments, that I am the first discoverer of a new half-metal, namely, cobalt-regulus, which earlier was confused with bismuth." (The quotation is from *Diarium chymicum*, 1741.)

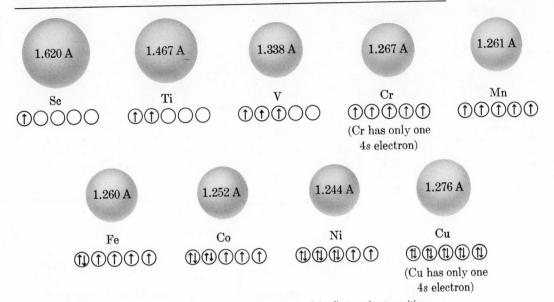

Figure 27.1 Atomic size and 3*d* orbital configurations of the first-series transition elements.

table, is attributed to the gradual filling of the 3*d* orbitals and the nearly constant atomic radius. The atomic radius and the *d*-orbital population is shown pictorially in Figure 27.1 (recall that chromium and copper have only one 4*s* electron).

Electron Configuration and Oxidation States. The oxidation states exhibited by these elements in compounds are given in Figure 27.2.

The multiplicity of positive states has been explained in Chap. 26 as arising because not only the 4*s* electrons but also some or all of the electrons in the *d* orbitals may be used in compound formation. For the elements scandium, Sc, to manganese, Mn, the highest oxidation state formed is the sum of the electrons in the 4*s* and 3*d* orbitals of the atom. It increases from III for scandium to VII for manganese. The stability of the highest oxidation state decreases from Ti^{IV} to Mn^{VII}. Beyond manganese

Table 27.1 Properties of the First Transition Series of Metals

Element	Density (25°C, g/cc)	Melting Point (°C)	Electrical Conductance (microhms^{-1} cm^{-1} between 0 and 25°C)	Thermal Conductivity (25°C cal/gm/sec/deg)	Tensile Strength of Hard-Drawn Wire (1000 lb/ sq in.)
Sc	2.5	1423			
Ti	4.5	1677	1.3×10^{-2}		
V	5.96	1917	3.8×10^{-2}		
Cr	7.1	1900	7.7×10^{-2}	0.16	
Mn	7.2	1244	5×10^{-3}		
Fe	7.86	1528	1.02×10^{-1}	0.11	80–120
Co	8.9	1490	1.6×10^{-1}	0.16	33
Ni	8.9	1452	1.5×10^{-1}	0.14	155
Cu	8.92	1083	6×10^{-1}	0.99	60–70

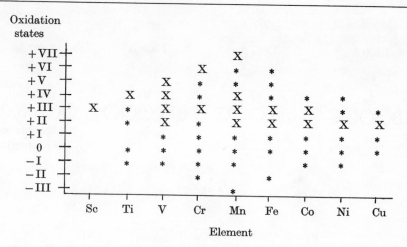

Figure 27.2 Oxidation states of the elements scandium through copper in compounds. X designates the most common states. The * designates a state known to exist but which may not be very stable.

the stability of the very high states is so low that they are difficult to obtain.

Certain peculiar conditions appear with several of the elements. Negative and zero oxidation states are found in certain compounds, for example, in nickel tetracarbonyl, $Ni(CO)_4$, or potassium pentacarbonyl manganate, $KMn(CO)_5$. In the former compound nickel is in its zero oxidation state since the carbon monoxide ligands are all neutral. In the manganese compound, the manganese atom with the five carbon monoxide ligands complexed to it carries a -1 charge. Presumably this charge is associated with the manganese atom thereby giving it a $-I$ oxidation state. These negative and zero oxidation state species are formed when certain π-bonding ligands, such as carbon monoxide, complex with the metal atom. Under these conditions the metal atom may be stabilized as a neutral species as in $V(CO)_6$ or the complex may actually pick up one or more electrons as in $V(CO)_6{}^-$, $Mn(CO)_5{}^-$, or $[Fe(CO)_4]^{-2}$.

Colors of the Ions. The transition elements are the only metals that form colored ions. The color, as explained in Chap. 26, is attributed to the absorption of photons from white light to raise the d electrons from the ground state to higher energy levels. The transmitted light will then be colored—the color being the complement of the absorbed color. Figure 27.3 illustrates the electronic transition responsible for the green color of $V(H_2O)_6{}^{+3}$. The colors of some of the ions of these elements in the various oxidation states in water are given in Table 27.2.

Table 27.2 Colors of Aquo or Oxo Ions of the First Transition Series

Sc	Ti	V	Cr	Mn	Fe	Co	Ni	Cu
III, colorless	II, violet III, violet (green) IV, colorless	II, violet III, green IV, blue V, colorless	II, blue III, gray VI, yellow	II, pink III, red-brown VI, green VII, purple	II, green III, orange	II, pink III, blue	II, green	I, colorless II, blue

Note: The aquo ion is the hydrated ion; the oxo ion is the oxygen-bonded type represented by $CrO_4{}^{-2}$, $MnO_4{}^-$, etc.

The color of the ion is also dependent upon the ligand or ligands present as illustrated in Table 27.3. Here the Co^{+2} ion, complexed with three different ligands, exhibits three different colors. The shift in color is explained by the fact that the strength of the metal-ligand bond changes when the ligand is changed. This brings about a change in the separation of the two groups of d orbitals in the ligand field. As this separation changes, the energy (color) of the photon needed to promote the electron from the lower to the higher level also changes. The result is a shift or change in color. In the complex ions in Table 27.3 water is the ligand showing the weakest metal-ligand interaction, while ethylene diamine interacts most strongly. Consequently, the separation between d levels is least in the hydrated ion, greatest in the ethylene diamine complex. In these cases the hydrated ion is absorbing in the yellow region of the spectrum while the ethylene diamine complex is absorbing close to the green region of the visible spectrum.

Some Trends in Properties. Before discussing the chemistry of each element in this series, we shall list some general trends in properties that may help in developing a broad view of the chemistry of these elements.

1. The densities of the metals are relatively high, and they increase regularly from scandium to copper. Undoubtedly this is a consequence of decreasing atomic diameter and increasing atomic mass in proceeding across the series. The melting points are very high, reflecting the added stability resulting from participation of d and s electrons in the bonding of the metals. The melting-point trends appear to be related to the number of unpaired electrons in the atoms—increasing from scandium to vanadium, decreasing from iron to copper.

2. From titanium to manganese the highest oxidation states are usually found only in the presence of oxygen, fluorine, or chlorine—the most electronegative elements.

3. In the presence of oxyligands, the metal ions usually exhibit tetrahedral coordination in oxidation states IV to VII as in VO_4^{-3}, CrO_4^{-2}, MnO_4^-. In oxidation states up to IV, the metal ions are usually octahedrally coordinated as in $Mn(H_2O)_6^{+2}$, ScF_6^{-3}, $V(CN)_6^{-4}$ or tetrahedrally coordinated as in $MnCl_4^{-2}$.

4. The oxides of a given element usually produce stronger acids as the oxidation state increases. The halides become more covalent and more susceptible to hydrolysis as the oxidation state increases. For example, Mn_2O_7 is acidic (forming salts in which the manganese appears in the anion, such as $K^+MnO_4^-$) while MnO is basic (forming salts in which the manganese is a cation, such as $Mn^{+2} 2Cl^-$); $TiCl_4$ is so sensitive to hydrolysis that it forms white fumes of TiO_2 on exposure to air while $TiCl_2$ reacts only slowly with water.

The Chemistry of the Elements

3d orbitals

Scandium. $1s^2, 2s^2, 2p^6, 3s^2, 3p^6,$ ①〇〇〇〇, $4s^2$

The element following calcium is scandium whose atoms have an electron configuration similar to calcium except for an electron in the $3d$ shell.

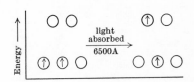

Figure 27.3 Electronic transition responsible for the green color of $V(H_2O)_6^{+3}$. Circles represent d levels which are split by the octahedral ligand field.

Table 27.3 Dependence of Color on the Ligand Present

Ion	Color
$Co(H_2O)_6^{+2}$	pink
$Co(NH_3)_6^{+2}$	blue
$Co(en)_3^{+2}$	violet

Thus scandium is the first element in the first transition series. The electron levels of the $4s$ and $3d$ electrons are close together; hence we find that scandium, like calcium, reacts vigorously with water to form hydrogen. In this reaction colorless scandium(III) ions are produced. The III oxidation state is the only stable oxidation state of scandium, other than the zero oxidation state, exhibited by the metal. In many ways scandium is similar to aluminum. However, scandium oxide, Sc_2O_3, is more basic than aluminum oxide, Al_2O_3.

Scandium chemistry was of only little interest until scandium was found to be one of the fission products of atomic fuels. Its chemistry then became important in the working out of methods of separation of scandium from uranium in the purification of atomic fuels. Scandium occurs in nature in the minerals monazite (a phosphate) and gadolinite (a silicate). It is as abundant as arsenic and about twice as abundant as boron.

3d orbitals

Titanium. $1s^2$, $2s^2$, $2p^6$, $3s^2$, $3p^6$, ⟨↑⟩ ⟨↑⟩ ◯ ◯ ◯, $4s^2$

The second transition element is titanium with two $3d$ electrons. These two $3d$ electrons and the two $4s$ electrons are easily removed or used in bonding. Thus we find the IV oxidation state a common and stable one. This is illustrated by such compounds as the dioxide, TiO_2, a white solid, and the tetrachloride, $TiCl_4$, a colorless, fuming liquid which boils at 136.4°C.

TiO_2 is used as a pigment because of its good covering power; $TiCl_4$ reacts with moist air, forming a smoke, and with water to give titanium dioxide. The liquid character of $TiCl_4$ at room temperature indicates that the bonds are predominantly covalent.

$TiCl_4$ and $TiBr_4$ use $3d$ orbitals as electron acceptors and hence act as Lewis acids toward such compounds as alcohols, ethers, and other oxygen compounds.

$$\begin{matrix} R \\ \diagdown \\ \quad \quad O + TiCl_4 \longrightarrow \\ \diagup \\ R \end{matrix} \qquad \begin{matrix} R \\ \diagdown \\ O-TiCl_4 \\ \diagup \\ R \end{matrix}$$

There is a sufficient difference in the energy levels of the $4s$ and $3d$ electrons so that titanium forms compounds in the II and III oxidation states, using or losing only two or three electrons, as well as in the IV oxidation state. It has unusual tendency to go to the IV state. As a result the compounds in the II and III states are reducing agents; titanium(II) ion, Ti^{+2}, is a better reducing agent than hydrogen. Titanium(III) hydroxide, $Ti(OH)_3$, gradually changes to titanium dioxide, TiO_2 (white), on standing.

$$2Ti(OH)_3(s) \rightleftharpoons 2TiO_2(s) + 2H_2O + H_2(g)$$

In the trivalent state, titanium forms salts of which $Ti_2(SO_4)_3$ and $TiCl_3$ are examples. $Ti(H_2O)_6^{+3}$ is violet and paramagnetic because of the presence of the unpaired d electron. At high temperatures the yellow nitride TiN is formed by the action of nitrogen on titanium.

Titanium has been known for many years but it has not been used as a metal for structural purposes because the common methods of metallurgy produced a brittle product. Recent research has shown that the metal can be worked in a controlled atmosphere which produces a product that is useable for many purposes because it is stronger than iron. The metal is hard, refractory (m.p. 1680°C), a good conductor but of quite low density, and unusually resistant to corrosion (due to a surface coating of oxide and nitride). These properties are responsible for its use in spacecraft and marine equipment.

Titanium, while resistant to corrosion and unreactive with most elements at ordinary temperatures, reacts at high temperatures with hydrogen, oxygen, sulfur, the halogens, nitrogen, carbon, and boron and with hot steam; it reacts readily with cold sulfuric acid and hot hydrochloric acid to give titanium(III) salts and hydrogen.

Titanium is the tenth most abundant element in the earth's crust.

$$3d \text{ orbitals}$$

Vanadium. $1s^2, 2s^2, 2p^6, 3s^2, 3p^6,$ ⊕ ⊕ ⊕ ○ ○, $4s^2$

Vanadium exists in $-I$, 0, II, III, IV, and V oxidation states. In the V state V_2O_5 is formed; this is probably the most important compound of vanadium. It is an excellent catalyst for the oxidation of sulfur dioxide to sulfur trioxide.

V_2O_5 is amphoteric. In bases it forms vanadate ion, VO_4^{-3}, and in strong acids it forms such ions as $VO_2(OH)_3^{-2}$ and $VO(OH)_4^{-1}$. Vanadium in the V state can be reduced with zinc to ions in the IV, III, and II states successively.

Pure vanadium is difficult to prepare. It is an important alloy metal used to give toughness and elasticity to steel. Such steels are used to make the jaws of steam shovels, the burrs for rock crushers, and some gears. Vanadium also reacts with oxygen and nitrogen in molten iron. In nature, vanadium occurs as patronite (V_2S_5), vanadinite ($Pb_5V_3O_{12}Cl$), and carnotite ($KUVO_6$).

$$3d \text{ orbitals}$$

Chromium. $1s^2, 2s^2, 2p^6, 3s^2, 3p^6,$ ⊕ ⊕ ⊕ ⊕ ⊕, $4s^1$

Chromium forms compounds in all states between $-II$ and VI. The III state is probably the most stable, existing as $Cr(H_2O)_6^{+3}$ ions of deep blue-gray color in water solution. The chromium(III) ion stands midway in the reducing-oxidizing properties among the III ions of the first transition series:

$$Sc^{+3} \quad \underbrace{Ti^{+3} \quad V^{+3} \quad Cr^{+3}} \quad \underbrace{Mn^{+3} \quad Fe^{+3} \quad Co^{+3}}$$

Reducing ions   Oxidizing ions

(Usually tend to   (Usually tend to
lose electrons to   gain or share
give noble gas   electrons to fill
configuration)   3d shell)

The II state is formed by reduction of chromium(III) ion, Cr^{+3}, with zinc but the II ion is unstable in aqueous solution in the presence of oxygen and is readily oxidized back to the III state. Chromium(II) ion is the strongest reducing agent known in aqueous solution. It is an excellent absorbent for oxygen. Chromate ion, CrO_4^{-2}, and dichromate ion, $Cr_2O_7^{-2}$, are the common ions of chromium in the VI state.

Either of the two ions of chromium in the VI state can be changed from one to the other by changing the acidity of the solution,

$$2CrO_4^{-2} + 2H_3O^+ \longrightarrow Cr_2O_7^{-2} + 3H_2O$$

$$Cr_2O_7^{-2} + 2OH^- \longrightarrow 2CrO_4^{-2} + H_2O$$

The following formulas show the relationship between these two ions:

Chromate ion   Dichromate ion

Since these ions are in equilibrium with each other in aqueous solution either can react with added ions; for example,

$$2Pb^{+2} + Cr_2O_7^{-2} \text{ (acid solution)} + 3H_2O \longrightarrow 2PbCrO_4 + 2H_3O^+$$

The factor that determines whether $PbCr_2O_7$ or $PbCrO_4$ is formed is the much lower solubility of $PbCrO_4$. Low solubility of a product is a driving factor for many reactions.

The main property of chromates and dichromates is their strong oxidizing properties. With these oxidizing agents chromium(III) ions are formed if the oxidizing medium is acidic, and chromium(III) hydroxide, $Cr(OH)_3$, is formed if the solution is alkaline.

$$Cr_2O_7^{-2} + 14H_3O^+ + 6Fe^{+2} \longrightarrow 6Fe^{+3} + 2Cr^{+3} + 21H_2O$$

$$CrO_4^{-2} + 3Fe(OH)_2 + 4H_2O \longrightarrow 3Fe(OH)_3 + Cr(OH)_3 + 2OH^-$$

Chromic acid, H_2CrO_4, cannot be crystallized. If dilute solutions are concentrated, deep purple-red crystals of chromic anhydride, CrO_3, are formed.

Chromium metal is produced from chromite, $FeCr_2O_4$, by successive conversion of chromite to chromate, then to the oxide and finally to the metal by the Goldschmidt process using aluminum as the reducing agent. Chromium is a white, hard, lustrous, and brittle metal which melts at 1890°C. Chromium metal is notorious for being passive, a condition that makes it highly corrosion resistant, and hence an excellent metal for protecting metal surfaces or for making stainless steel. The cause of passivity is attributed to a thin oxide film that protects the metal from corrosion and/or electrochemical action. Some chromium alloys are described in Table 27.4.

Chromium does react slowly in cold dilute hydrochloric and sulfuric acids and rapidly in hot hydrochloric acid and hot concentrated sulfuric acid. However, it does not react with nitric acid. It also reacts with chlorine or bromine, on heating, and with oxygen and water at high temperatures.

With sulfur, chromium forms a number of nonstoichiometric compounds. These vary in composition from $CrS_{0.95}$ to $CrS_{1.5}$.

Alloy	Composition	Use
Chrom steel	4–10% Cr; Fe	Corrosion-resistant and high-temperature uses
Stainless steel	17–19% Cr; 7–9.5% Ni; Fe	Rollers; furnace parts; plant, medical, and restaurant equipment
Nichrome	20% Cr; 80% Ni	Electrical heating elements

Table 27.4 Some Alloys of Chromium

$3d$ orbitals

Manganese. $1s^2, 2s^2, 2p^6, 3s^2, 3p^6,$ ⟨↑⟩ ⟨↑⟩ ⟨↑⟩ ⟨↑⟩ ⟨↑⟩, $4s^2$

Manganese forms compounds in $-$III, $-$I, 0, I, II, III, IV, V, VI, and VII states. The VII state is the highest exhibited by any of the elements in this series. The I and V states are very unstable. The II state of manganese in contrast to the II state of chromium is quite stable in neutral and acid solutions. In alkaline solutions, however, manganese(II) as $Mn(OH)_2$ is quickly oxidized to the III state in the presence of oxygen. In fact, a slurry of $Mn(OH)_2$ is an excellent absorber for oxygen.

The III state of manganese is stable only in the solid or as a complex ion. Manganese(III) ion, like chromium(III) ion, readily forms complex ions of the high-spin type with fluoride ions, and the low-spin type with ligands such as $C_2O_4^{-2}$ and PO_4^{-3}. Unlike chromium(III), manganese(III) is a powerful oxidizing agent; left alone it disproportionates into manganese(II) and manganese(IV).

$$2Mn^{+3} + 6H_2O \rightleftarrows Mn^{+2} + MnO_2 + 4H_3O^+$$

$$2MnF_3 + 2H_2O \rightleftarrows MnF_2 + 4HF + MnO_2$$

Manganese Dioxide. In the IV oxidation state the chemistry of manganese is largely that of manganese dioxide, MnO_2. Treated with acids, manganese dioxide undergoes reduction to give salts of bivalent manganese. With hydrochloric acid the primary action seems to be

$$MnO_2 + 4H_3O^+ + 2Cl^- \longrightarrow Mn^{+2} + Cl_2 + 6H_2O$$

Manganese dioxide is an excellent catalyst for reactions involving the preparation of oxygen. It is used in the paint and varnish industry to catalyze the reaction of oxygen with the drying oil and thus helps to harden the paint. In the battery industry great quantities of manganese dioxide are used as the oxidizing agent (cathode material).

The Manganates and Permanganates. The manganate ion, MnO_4^{-2}, is green. It is an example of manganese in the VI state. However, it is unstable, being transformed in water by a disproportionation reaction to permanganate ion and manganese dioxide

$$3MnO_4^{-2} + 2H_2O \longrightarrow 2MnO_4^- + MnO_2 + 4OH^-$$

Permanganates, as well as free permanganic acid, can be prepared by electrolysis of solutions of the manganate under conditions such that the manganate ions are oxidized to permanganate ions (MnO_4^-) at the anode of a suitable cell.

Permanganate ion has a deep purple color. It is a strong oxidizing agent, and the products formed both from the permanganate and from the oxidation of the reducing agent have very little color as a rule. Thus the end-point of a reaction in which a permanganate is used as an oxidizing agent is sharply marked by the first appearance of color, which makes potassium permanganate a valuable reagent in chemical analysis.

When reduced in *acid* solution the manganese in the permanganate ion is converted to the II oxidation state. For example, if an oxidizable substance such as oxalic acid (HO_2C—CO_2H or $H_2C_2O_4$) is added to an acidified solution of a permanganate, the following reaction occurs:

$$2MnO_4^- + 5H_2C_2O_4 + 6H_3O^+ \longrightarrow 2Mn^{+2} + 10CO_2 + 14H_2O$$

In *neutral* or *alkaline* solution in the presence of an oxidizable substance, the oxidation state of manganese drops only to IV, and the product formed is $Mn(OH)_4$, or its dehydration product, MnO_2. The reason this occurs appears to be associated with the very low solubility of these substances.

Manganese is widely distributed in nature, chiefly as manganese dioxide, MnO_2 (pyrolusite). Metallic manganese is made by electrolysis of manganese sulfate solution or by reduction of MnO_2 with aluminum (Goldschmidt process). It is harder, more brittle, and less refractory than iron. The major use of manganese is as a scavenger of sulfur and oxygen in steel, and as an alloying element in steel.

$$3d \text{ orbitals}$$

Iron. $1s^2$, $2s^2$, $2p^6$, $3s^2$, $3p^6$, (⇅) (↑) (↑) (↑) (↑), $4s^2$

Iron exhibits oxidation states of $-II$, 0, I, II, III, IV, V, and VI; however, the states above III are unstable and oxyanions such as ferrate, FeO_4^{-2}, rarely form. The II and III states have almost equal stability; only mild oxidizing and reducing agents are required to go from the II to the III or back from the III to the II state. Like chromium, the II state in alkaline solution is readily oxidized to the III state. In both the II and III states, iron forms complex ions of coordination number six readily; many of these complexes have high spin.

Reactions of Iron. Iron is a strong enough reducing agent to reduce hydrogen ions to hydrogen; hence, iron reacts with dilute and concentrated hydrochloric and dilute sulfuric acids to give hydrogen. With concentrated sulfuric acid, sulfur dioxide is produced. Concentrated nitric acid causes iron to become passive, probably forming a layer of oxide over the surface. Iron, when heated, reacts with most of the nonmetals; with oxygen it forms the oxides FeO, Fe_2O_3, and Fe_3O_4.

Pure FeO is unknown. Successive replacement of iron(II) ions with iron(III) ions gives Fe_3O_4 which may be a compound $Fe^{II}(Fe^{III}O_2)_2$. Further replacement of iron(II) ions with iron(III) ions gives γ-Fe_2O_3. γ-Fe_2O_3 changes to the stable crystalline form of iron oxide, α-Fe_2O_3, the familiar hematite.

With sulfur, iron forms FeS, FeS_2, and Fe_2S_3, but Fe_2S_3 is unstable. Iron monosulfide, FeS, actually is a nonstoichiometric compound. Samples of this material in which the Fe:S ratio is exactly 1 are seldom found. Usually the Fe:S ratio is less than 1, most often 0.858, evidence that some of the iron atom positions in the crystal lattice are vacant.

The anhydrous halides, $FeCl_2$ and FeF_2, are made by the direct action of HCl and H_2F_2 on the heated metal; the halides, $FeCl_3$ and FeF_3, are made by direct combination with Cl_2 and F_2. In the presence of moisture, the halides become hydrated giving $FeX_3 \cdot 6H_2O$. Heating the hydrates gives iron oxide and the hydrogen halide.

Complexes of Iron. Iron forms complexes in both the II and III oxidation states. They are octahedral; most are high spin, but a few are low spin; $Fe(NH_3)_6{}^{+2}$ has high spin, but with the stronger bonding CN^- ion, iron forms $Fe(CN)_6{}^{-4}$ which is a diamagnetic complex.

One of the most important complexes of iron is that formed with the porphyrin structure called *heme* which exists in hemoglobin. Heme is an iron(II) complex of porphyrin as shown in Figure 27.4.

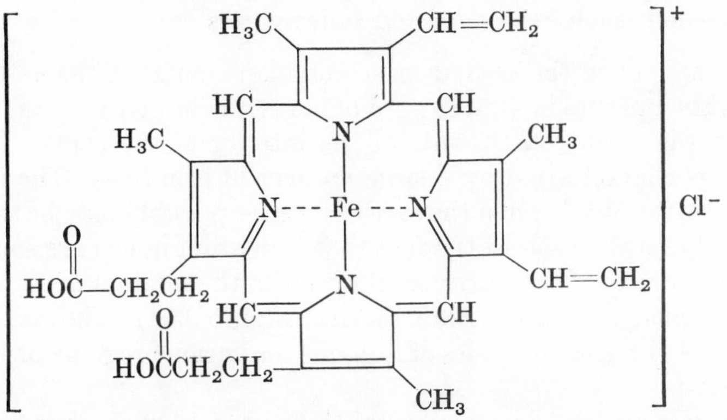

Figure 27.4 Hemin showing the iron(II) complexed to the four nitrogen atoms of the porphyrin ring structure. Oxygen, coordinated to the iron(II) in this structure, is carried throughout the circulatory system.

As illustrated, four of the coordination positions on the iron ion are occupied by nitrogen atoms from the porphyrin. A fifth position appears to be occupied by a nitrogen atom from the protein. The sixth coordination position is undoubtedly occupied by a water molecule but when exposed to oxygen, an oxygen molecule displaces the water molecule. The complex has four unpaired electrons when water is a ligand but when oxygen is present there are no unpaired electrons. The oxygen-containing complex is the substance that carries oxygen throughout the bodies of animals with circulating systems. If the water molecules are displaced by a strongly complexing ligand such as cyanide ion, CN^-, or carbon monoxide, CO, the oxygen molecule cannot enter the complex. This accounts for the poisonous nature of certain substances which contain strongly bonding ligands.

An unusual type of complex recently discovered is the ferrocene type made by complexing the unsaturated hydrocarbon, cyclopentadiene, with Fe^{+2} ions giving a complex of the type

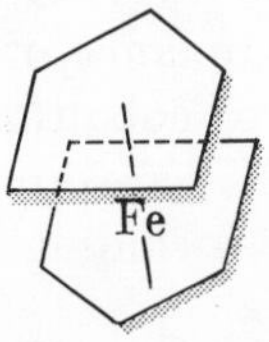

The complex is diamagnetic and so stable that it is unaffected by sodium hydroxide or hydrochloric acid at the boiling point.

Hydrolysis. Ferric salts are readily hydrolyzed, undergoing the reaction

$$Fe(H_2O)_6^{+3} + H_2O \rightleftarrows H_3O^+ + Fe(H_2O)_5OH^{+2}$$

Ferric chloride solution gives a brown color, probably due to $Fe(H_2O)_4(OH)_2^+$. Ferrous salts are less readily hydrolyzed than ferric salts, but are readily oxidized.

Important Iron Compounds. When ferric hydroxide is strongly heated, it forms ferric oxide, (Fe_2O_3), which is an insoluble red material occurring in nature in various forms of hematite, which range in color from red to black. The same compound is obtained by burning pyrite (FeS_2) and, when carefully prepared, constitutes the pigment called *Venetian red*. Owing to its permanency, this is much used for painting structures that are exposed to the weather, such as bridges and railway cars.

The Metal. Iron, the second most abundant metal in the earth's crust (4.7 per cent), occurs in almost pure oxide forms in many areas, and may be one of the main constituents of the interior of the earth. The solar spectrum is characterized by a large number of iron lines. The indicated high concentration of iron in the earth's interior possibly may be accounted for partially on the basis of the fact that iron atom nuclei are some of the most stable nuclei of the universe; they are in the maximum on the graph of binding energy against atomic masses (Figure 25.4). The cause of the formation of the great deposits of iron ores in various regions of the earth is not known.

Pure iron is a white, lustrous metal melting at 1528°C. It is not a hard metal and it is quite reactive. In a finely divided state it is pyrophoric. At temperatures up to 906°C the metal has a body-centered crystal structure; from 906°C to 1401°C it has a cubic close-packed structure. Above 1401°C it again becomes body-centered. It is ferromagnetic up to 768°C.

Iron is obtained from its ore (usually the oxide) chiefly by reduction with hot carbon in the blast furnace. For industrial purposes it is purified in basic oxygen furnaces, in Bessemer converters, basic open-hearth furnaces, or in electric furnaces. The metallurgy and manufacture of iron and steel is one of the world's greatest industries.

3d orbitals

Cobalt. $1s^2, 2s^2, 2p^6, 3s^2, 3p^6,$ (⇅) (⇅) (↑) (↑) (↑)$, 4s^2$

Although the II and III states in iron have about equal stability, in cobalt the II state is stable in water and in the presence of other weak complexing agents, but the III state is stable only in the presence of strong complexing agents. There are also some important complexes of cobalt in the I state.

Because the uncomplexed cobalt(II) ion is the most stable of the uncomplexed ions, there is an abundance of simple salts and binary compounds of cobalt(II) but those of cobalt(III) are rare. In fact, only the fluoride and sulfate of cobalt(III) are known while cobalt(II) forms an extensive group of compounds including the oxide, hydroxide, several sulfides, halides, etc.

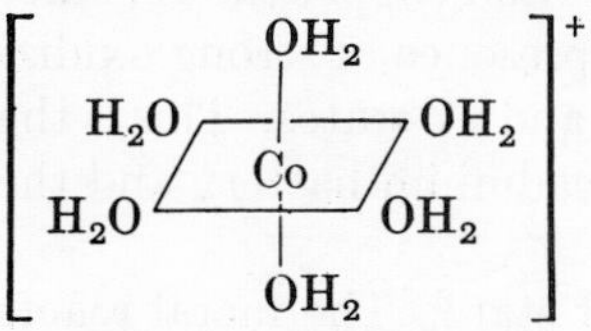

Hexaaquocobalt(II) ion,
pink

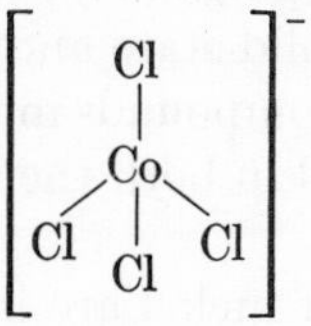

Tetrachlorocobaltate(II)
ion, blue

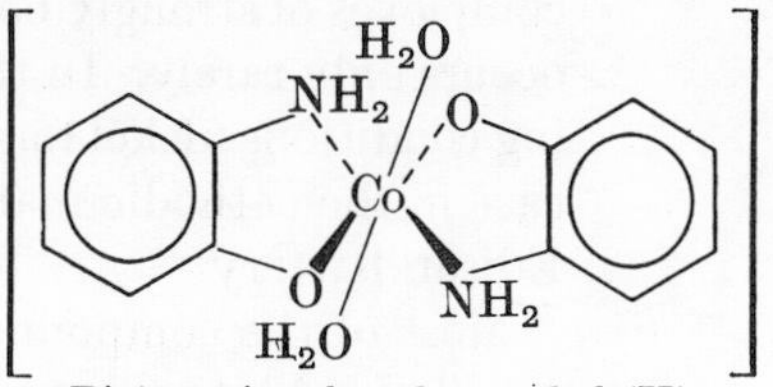

Bis(o-aminophenolato)cobalt(II)

Figure 27.5 Complexes of cobalt(II).

Cobalt Complexes. A large number of complexes of cobalt ions are known; a few are illustrated in Figures 27.5 and 27.6. All cobalt(II) complexes have high spin—even those formed with strongly bonded ligands. Nearly all cobalt(III) complexes have low spin. An exception is CoF_6^{-3}.

Cobalt(II) ions are oxidized only with extreme difficulty in water solution; the standard oxidation potential for the reaction

$$Co^{+2} \longrightarrow Co^{+3} + e^-$$

in aqueous acid solution is -1.82 volt. However, in the presence of strongly complexing ligands such as ammonia or cyanide ion, cobalt(II) is easily oxidized to cobalt(III) ion by air or by hydrogen peroxide.

$$2Co(NH_3)_6^{+2} + H_2O_2 + 2H_3O^+ \longrightarrow 2Co(NH_3)_6^{+3} + 4H_2O$$

This is a good example of the ability of ligands to alter the properties of the ion with which they are complexed. Presumably in this case the ammonia or cyanide ligands make the III state much more stable by bonding so tightly that a low-spin complex is formed.

The Metal. Cobalt occurs in nature principally as $CoAs_2$ and $CoAsS$. Such minerals are found sparingly in many localities; the richest known deposits are those located at Cobalt, Ontario, and in Africa. These are very rich in silver, and cobalt is worked up as a by-product, together with nickel and arsenic trioxide. In the Congo, cobalt is a by-product of copper-refining. The metal is obtained by roasting to the oxide, Co_3O_4, and reducing it with aluminum by the Goldschmidt process. It is a malleable, magnetic, silvery metal, which soon takes on a reddish tint upon exposure to the air. It melts at 1490°C and is relatively unreactive. The metal is used chiefly in the form of alloys.

Cobalt Chromium Steels. Collectively known as Stellite, cobalt chromium steels are used extensively in making high-speed cutting tools, since they retain their temper at high temperatures and are important rust-resisting alloys. They are often modified by additions of tungsten, molybdenum, and nickel. An alloy called Konel contains cobalt, nickel, and ferrotitanium, and is harder than steel even when very hot. Metallic cobalt is used as a binding material for crystals of tungsten carbide in making the hard-cutting material Carboloy.

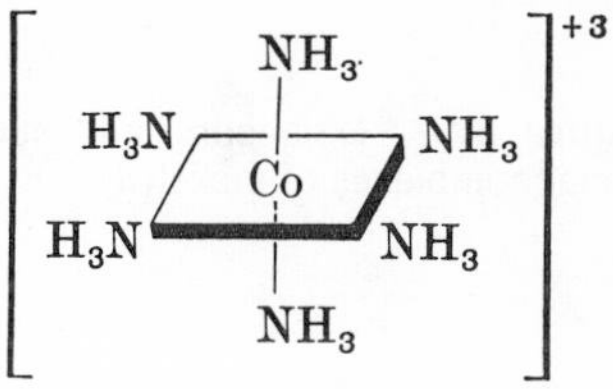

3d orbitals

Nickel. $1s^2, 2s^2, 2p^6, 3s^2, 3p^6,$ (⇅) (⇅) (⇅) (↑) (↑), $4s^2$

The III oxidation state becomes progressively less stable in the sequence $Fe^{+3} \rightarrow Co^{+3} \rightarrow Ni^{+3}$. With iron the III and II states are of approximately the same stability; with cobalt, the III state is stable only in

Hexaaminecobalt(III) ion

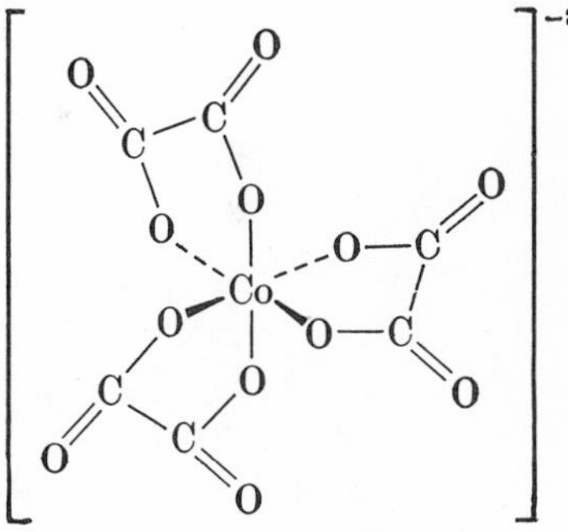

Trisoxalatocobaltate(III) ion

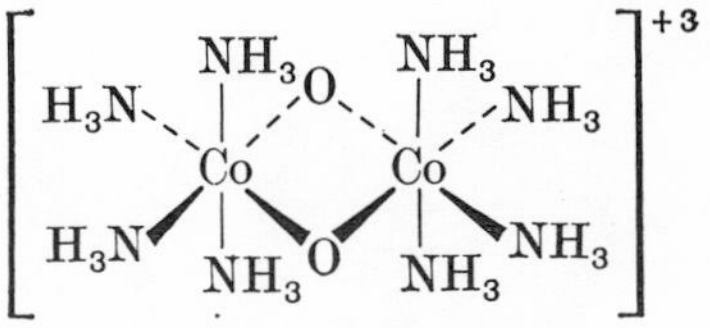

Example of oxygen ligands
bridging two cobalt ions

Figure 27.6 Complexes of cobalt(III).

complexes of strongly bonding ligands; with nickel and copper the III state occurs only rarely. In the solid state and in the presence of strong oxidizing conditions nickel forms compounds in the III and IV states. This is the case in the cathodic material in both the nickel-cadmium battery and the Edison battery.

Most of the compounds of nickel are in the II state. The metal reacts readily in dilute mineral acids to give binary nickel(II) compounds from which a wide variety of both simple and complex salts of the metal in the II state can be made. Thus the oxide, the hydroxide, all the halides, the sulfide, cyanide, sulfate, nitrate, etc., are well known. A few nonstoichiometric compounds of nickel with the heavier nonmetals, including tellurium, are known.

The complexes of nickel(II) are octahedral, tetrahedral, or square-planar (Figure 27.7).

Figure 27.7 Octahedral and square planar complexes of nickel(II).

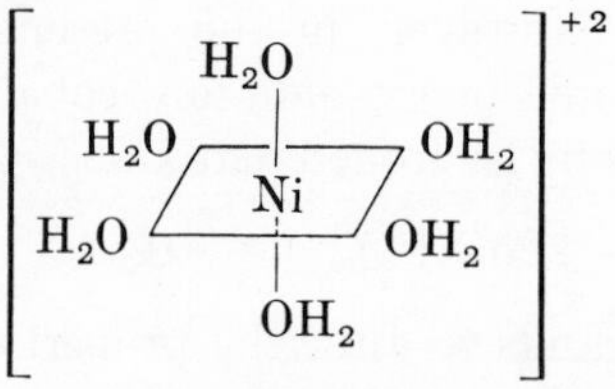

Hexaaquonickel(II) ion, green
(an octahedral complex)

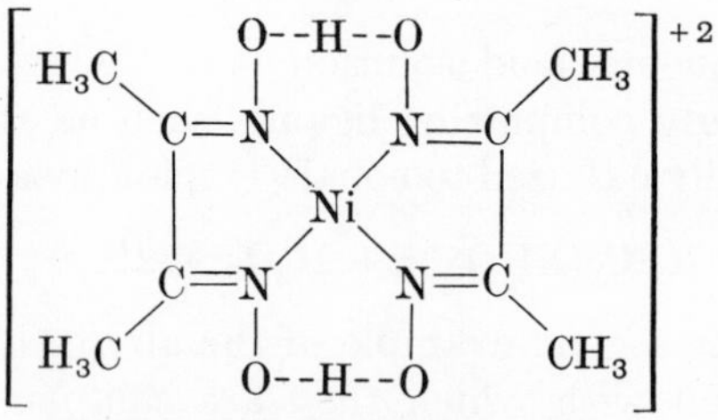

Bis(dimethylglyoximato)nickel(II) ion
(a square-planar complex)

The octahedral complexes have high spin—two of the d electrons are unpaired. The square-planar complexes may be either low or high spin depending on the ligand. A very few tetrahedral complexes are known.

Nickel Carbonyl, $Ni(CO)_4$. When carbon monoxide is passed over metallic nickel at a temperature between 30°C and 50°C, the two unite to form a compound of the formula $Ni(CO)_4$, known as nickel carbonyl. It is a colorless liquid boiling at 43.2°C, and freezing at $-25°C$ to colorless, needle-shaped crystals. When the vapor of the compound is passed through a tube heated to above 100°C, the compound dissociates into the metal and carbon monoxide. Advantage is taken of this reaction in the Mond process for purifying nickel. Iron and cobalt also form carbonyls.

The Metal. Nickel is almost always associated with cobalt in nature. Like the latter element, it occurs in combination with sulfur and arsenic and is often associated with copper, silver, and iron. Most of its ores are very complex. It was formerly obtained, chiefly as a by-product, in the metallurgy of copper and silver. At present most of the world's supply of nickel comes from the Sudbury district in Ontario, Canada. There the nickel occurs in the mineral pyrrhotite (a sulfide of iron) and is associated with chalcopyrite, the nickel-copper content being from 10 to 20 per cent. The Sudbury minerals contain small percentages of platinum, palladium, and iridium, and are a large source of these rare metals. The extraction of nickel from the mineral ores is a complicated process.

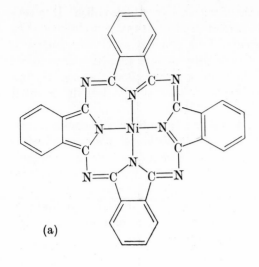

(a)

Figure 27.8 The nickel phthalocyanine complex. (a) Structural formula showing the coordination bonding with nickel. (b) The electron density profile obtained from X-ray diffraction data showing the arrangement of the atoms in the complex. Each contour line represents a density increment of one electron per A^2, except on the central nickel atom where the increment is five electrons per A^2 for each line. (c) Enlargement of the central portion of the electron density profile. [Parts (b) and (c) courtesy of Robertson and Woodward, *Journal of the Chemical Society* (1937), pp. 220 and 222.]

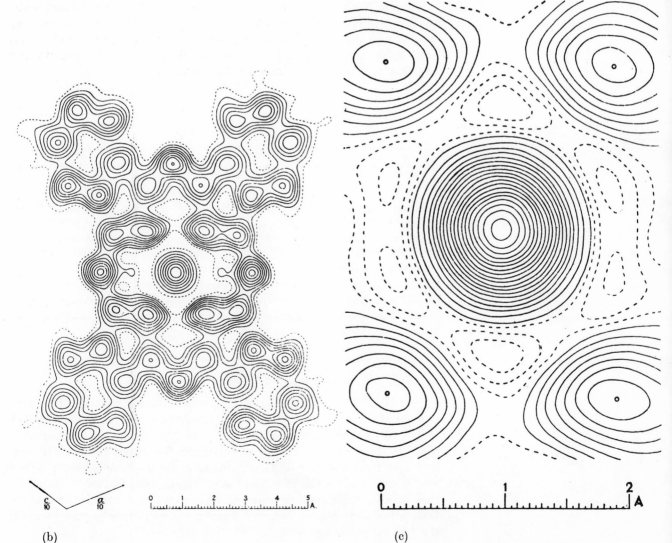

(b)

(c)

Nickel is a silvery metal capable of taking a very high polish. It is very hard, but is quite malleable and melts at 1452°C. It can be welded on iron, and the two can be rolled into sheets. Like iron and cobalt, it is magnetic but less so than iron. It is not attacked by melted alkalies; hence nickel crucibles are often employed in the laboratory for alkali fusions. Hydrochloric acid with nickel evolves hydrogen very slowly, but dilute nitric acid dissolves nickel readily.

In many countries, pure nickel is used for subsidiary coinage for a total of several billion coins. In the form of a fine powder it is a most effective catalyst in reactions in which hydrogen is added to unsaturated organic compounds, as in the hydrogenation of oils. It has been used extensively for electroplating on other metals, such as iron, brass, or copper, to prevent tarnishing. Chromium plating is largely replacing it, but a preliminary plating with nickel usually precedes plating with chromium. For nearly all other purposes it is used as an alloy metal.

Alloys of Nickel. The older alloys were (a) for coinage, the United States using a five-cent piece containing 25 per cent nickel and 75 per cent copper, and (b) for German silver, containing 20 per cent nickel, 55 per cent copper, and 25 per cent zinc. The nickel alloys, a great many of which have special trade names, may be classified as in Table 27.5.

Table 27.5 Commercial Alloys of Nickel

Alloy	Composition	Use
Low nickel steel and cast iron	1.5–5% Ni; Fe	Structural purposes, castings, and machinery parts
Ferronickel alloys	35–80% Ni; Fe	Electrical and magnetic uses
Nickel-chromium-iron structural steel	1.5–5% Ni; Fe	Automobiles and heavy machinery
Noncorrosive (stainless) steel	Cr; 7–35% Ni; Fe	
"Nonferrous" alloys	70% Ni; 28% Cu; 2% Fe	

3d orbitals

Copper. $1s^2$, $2s^2$, $2p^6$, $3s^2$, $3p^6$, ⇅ ⇅ ⇅ ⇅ ⇅, $4s^1$

Copper atoms have only one $4s$ electron over a filled $3d$ subshell. However, in spite of its single valence electron, copper does not resemble the alkali metals in most of its properties. For example, copper is a much more noble metal than any member of the alkali family—it does not liberate hydrogen from water or acids, it oxidizes in air much more slowly, and it reacts with nonmetals at considerably higher temperatures. Moreover, the common stable state of copper in its aqueous chemistry is the II state. Only a few examples of complex compounds containing copper atoms in the I or III states are known.

The nobility of copper is attributed to (a) the very high lattice energy of the copper crystal, where the $3d$ and $4s$ electrons are involved in the metallic bonds, and (b) the poor shielding of the $4s$ electron by the $3d$ subshell.

The stability of the II state over the I state for copper in water solution is believed to be due to the very high hydration energy in forming the $Cu(H_2O)_6^{+2}$ ion. This is probably the driving force for the very common and rapid disproportionation reaction of copper(I) in water solution:

$$2Cu(H_2O)_6^+ \rightleftharpoons Cu(H_2O)_6^{+2} + Cu + 6H_2O$$

The equilibrium between copper(I) and copper(II) may be displaced in either direction if various ligands are added to the solution. Thus if cyanide ion or iodide ion is added, the copper(I) species is favored, while perchlorate or sulfate favor copper(II). Both cyanide and iodide ions are capable of forming covalent bonds with the metal ion while the sulfate and perchlorate ions do not. Here again the less stable oxidation state may be stabilized by strongly bonding ligands.

Common complexes of copper(II) have a distorted octahedral or tetragonal structure (Figure 27.9). In the distorted octahedral structure four bonds are of equal lengths, but the remaining two are longer than the others. The long bonds are located opposite one another as shown in the figure. For ions such as the diaquotetraammine copper(II) ion, the formula $Cu(NH_3)_4^{+2}$ is often used to indicate that the four ammonia molecules are attached by the shorter bonds. The complex may be described as a tetragonal structure.

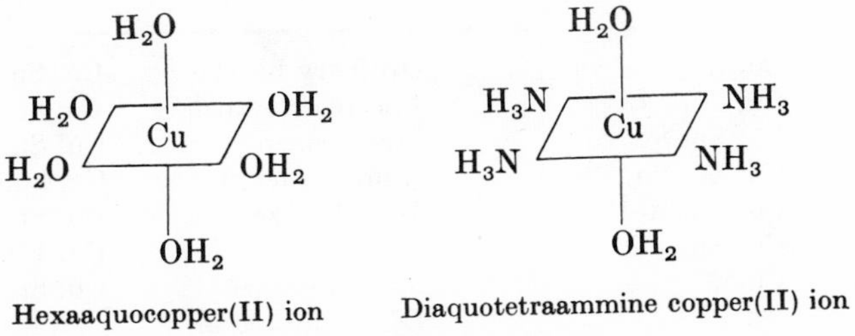

Hexaaquocopper(II) ion   Diaquotetraammine copper(II) ion

Figure 27.9 Complexes of copper(II) showing distorted octahedra.

Occurrence. Metallic copper has been known from the earliest times and was probably the first metal to come into any considerable use. This is explained by its native occurrence in large pieces and by the ease with which its oxygen compounds are reduced. Well-fashioned copper articles that are at least six thousand years old have been found.

Large quantities of native copper are known; in combination copper is found in a wide variety of forms, especially as sulfides, oxides, carbonates, and silicates. In small quantities it is present in the great majority of sulfide minerals, and in traces it is very widely distributed in nature. To some extent it is absorbed by plants growing in copper-bearing regions. Traces of copper are found in the human body.

The metallurgy of copper is complicated. It is done by processes of leaching or reduction; the metal is usually refined by electroplating.

Table 27.6 Some Ores of Copper

Sulfide Ores	Oxygen Ores
Chalcopyrite, $CuFeS_2$	Cuprite, Cu_2O
Chalcocite, Cu_2S	Melaconite, CuO
Bornite, $CuFeS_4$	Malachite, $CuCO_3 \cdot Cu(OH)_2$

The Metal. Copper is a heavy metal of characteristic ruddy color. It is rather soft and is very ductile, malleable, and flexible, yet tough and fairly strong. It melts at 1083°C and has a density at 25°C of 8.9 g/cc. As an electrical conductor it is second only to silver. It is not attacked by hydrochloric acid (unless oxygen is present) or by fused alkalies, but strong oxidizing acids convert it into the corresponding salts. In the presence of air most acids slowly act upon it; even carbon dioxide in moist air gradually covers its surface with a greenish coating of a basic carbonate, patina. When heated in the air, it is oxidized to black copper oxide, CuO. Sulfur and the halogens attack it much more readily than does oxygen.

Uses of Copper. About one-fourth of all the copper produced is used for electrical purposes.

A second very great use of copper is in the making of alloys. More than a thousand varieties of these alloys are recognized commercially, and the more familiar names, such as *brass* and *bronze*, now indicate merely the *type* of the alloy, since their composition is subject to wide variation. Some alloys, however, have rather definite compositions.

Table 27.7 Some Alloys of Copper

Class	Components	Class	Components
Simple brasses	Cu, Zn	Ordinary bronze	Cu, Sn
Leaded brasses	Cu, Zn, Pb	Phosphor bronze	Cu, Sn, P
Tin brasses	Cu, Zn, Sn	Zinc bronze	Cu, Sn, Zn, (P)
Leaded tin brasses	Cu, Zn, Sn, Pb	Leaded zinc bronze	Cu, Sn, Zn, Pb
High-tensile	Cu, Zn, Al	Lead bronze	Cu, Sn, Pb, (Zn)
brasses	Cu, Zn, Fe		Cu, Pb, Sn, (Zn)
Nickel coin	Cu(75%), Ni	Special bronze (X = any metal)	Cu, Sn, X
		Aluminum bronze	Cu, Al, (Fe, Mg, Mn, Ni, Pb, Si)
18-carat gold	Au(75%), Cu, Ag	Sterling silver	Ag(92.5%), Cu
Beryllium copper	Cu, Be	Duraluminum	Cu, Al

Note: The elements other than copper are given in the order of their percentages, except where the percent is given.

SUMMARY

The discussion of the first-row transition elements in this chapter has shown that most share the typical properties of transition metal elements (high melting point, many oxidation states, colored compound formation, and formation of complex ions). Several are shown to be of commercial importance as the pure metal or in alloys.

SOME SPECIAL TERMS

Ion
  aquo ion
  oxo ion
  oxyanion
Metal-ligand bond
Metal-ligand interaction
Oxy-ligand
Tetrahedrally oriented
Fission product
Passive metal
Alloy

High-spin complex
Low-spin complex
Heme
Ferrocene-type complex
Body-centered crystal lattice
Cubic close-packed
Metallurgy
  blast furnace
  Bessemer converter
  basic open-hearth furnace
  basic oxygen process

QUESTIONS AND PROBLEMS

1. Give the electron configuration or electron-dot formulas of the following atoms and ions:
   Sc, Sc^{+3}, V, Cr, Cr^{+3}, $Cr(NH_3)_6^{+3}$, Co, Co^{+2}, Co^{+3}, $Co(NH_3)_6^{+3}$, MnO_4^{-2}, $Cr_2O_7^{-2}$.

2. Write equations for the following reactions: (a) The transformation of chromate ion to dichromate ion in water solution. (b) The oxidation of ferrous ion by chromate ion in acid solution. (c) The oxidation of ferrous ion by permanganate ion in acid solution. (d) The reaction of manganese dioxide with bromide ion in acid solution. (e) The reduction of ferric ion with sulfide ion in acid solution; ferrous sulfide precipitates. (f) The reaction of iron with oxygen. (g) The reaction of nickel sulfide with nitric acid; free sulfur is formed.

3. How do you explain the fact that copper(I) oxide and sulfide are common ores of copper in nature, but that Cu^+ ions are rarely found in solution?

4. Make a table to summarize information about the first-row transition elements with regard to (a) occurrence in nature, (b) melting point, (c) oxidation states, (d) formulas of typical compounds in each oxidation state.

5. Suggest an explanation for the fact that for the compounds of any one element which contain hydrogen and oxygen the acidity increases with increasing oxidation state.

6. Using the standard oxidation potentials listed in Table 23.1 and in the appendix, would you expect that it would be easy to: (a) Oxidize ions of Fe(II) with ions of Cr(VI) in acid solution? (b) Oxidize ions of I^- with ions of Fe(III) in acid solution? (c) Reduce MnO_2 with Cl^- in acid solution? (d) Oxidize ions of Cr(III) with H_2O_2 in acid solution? (e) Oxidize ions of Cr(III) with H_2O_2 in basic solution? (f) Prepare chlorine by reaction of hydrochloric acid on TiO_2?

7. What would you predict as the limiting value of the freezing-point depression per mole of solute at extremely low concentrations for the salts $Na_4Fe(CN)_6$, $KMnO_4$, $K_2Cr_2O_7$, $K_3Fe(CN)_6$, $Co(NH_3)_6Cl_3$, $[Co(NH_3)_4(NO_2)_2]_3[Co(NO_2)_6]$?

REFERENCES

BASOLO, F., and R. C. JOHNSON. *Coordination Chemistry.* New York: Benjamin, 1964.

DOUGLAS, B. E., and D. H. MCDANIEL. *Concepts and Models of Inorganic Chemistry.* Waltham, Mass.: Blaisdell, 1965.

FACKLER, J. P., Jr. *Transition Elements.* New York: Reinhold, 1966.

LARSEN, E. M. *The Transitional Elements.* New York: Benjamin, 1965.

28

The Remaining Transition Elements; Zinc, Cadmium, and Mercury

Just as lanthanum is the prototype element for the rare-earth series, so actinium is the prototype for the heavy-element series. Hence the new group may be called the actinide series.*

Isadore Perlman (1915—) and Glenn T. Seaborg (1912—)

In the previous chapter, the chemistry of the first transition series elements was summarized. In this chapter the chemistry of the remaining transition elements and three neighboring elements—zinc, cadmium, and mercury—will be presented. Included among the remaining transition elements are two *d*-electron groups and two *f*-electron groups.

The *d*-electron groups, the second and third transition series, include the elements in the two rows lying immediately below the elements scandium through copper in the periodic table. In presenting the chemistry of these elements we shall attempt to show the similarities and differences between the first-row and the second- and third-row metals. Viewed broadly, then, Chap. 27 emphasizes what may be termed horizontal relationships among *d*-group transition elements while a portion of this chapter will emphasize vertical relationships among such elements.

The *f*-electron groups include the lanthanides, elements 57 through 71, and the actinides, elements 89 through 104. These two series are closely related to the first family of the *d*-electron elements. Their first members are lanthanum and actinium, which are the third and fourth members of the scandium-yttrium family. All of the elements in this family and in the lanthanum and actinium series have similar valence-electron configurations.

In many ways the elements in the second and third transition series have

Table 28.1 The Second and Third Transition Series

Sc	Ti	V	Cr	Mn	Fe	Co	Ni	Cu
Y	Zr	Nb	Mo	Tc	Ru	Rh	Pd	Ag
La	Hf	Ta	W	Re	Os	Ir	Pt	Au
Ac								

* From "The Synthetic Elements," *Scientific American* (April 1950), p. 38.

chemical properties similar to the corresponding element in the first transition series. However, there are also important differences which may be generalized as follows:

1. The radii of the second- and third-series atoms and ions in any family are about the same (due to the lanthanide contraction) and somewhat larger than the corresponding member of the first series; e.g., Zr and Hf atoms have radii of 1.45 A and 1.44 A respectively; Zr^{+4} and Hf^{+4} ions have radii of 0.74 A and 0.75 A respectively. Compare these with the titanium atom, 1.32 A, and the Ti^{+4} ion, 0.68 A. The consequence of this is that, in general, the second and third members of a family of transition elements will have more in common with each other than with the first member of each family.

2. The higher oxidation states for second- and third-series elements are usually the most stable states while the lower states are often the stable ones for the first-series elements. For example, the molybdate ion, MoO_4^{-2}, is very stable while the chromate ion, CrO_4^{-2}, is a powerful oxidizing agent.

3. In general the lower oxidation states of the second and third series elements are not stable.

$_{21}Sc$	**Elements Below Scandium.**
$_{39}Y$	
$_{57}La$	Lanthanides
$_{89}Ac$	Actinides

Yttrium. Yttrium, like scandium (and calcium), is quite reactive. It forms colorless nonparamagnetic compounds in the III oxidation state. One of the best known compounds is the oxide Y_2O_3, yttria, a white powder.

In 1794 Johann Gadolin discovered a new mineral, now called gadolinite, in the mines of Ytterby, near Stockholm, and found it to contain an oxide unlike any known at that time; this was named yttria. This same material has since been found in a great many minerals. Almost at once yttria was recognized as a complex substance, and from the time of its discovery to the present day many chemists have been engaged in determining its composition. Seventeen very similar elements are now clearly recognized to be present in yttria. Two, scandium and yttrium, fall into regular places in the periodic table. The other fifteen have consecutive atomic numbers, 57–71. Their oxides are known collectively as the *rare earths*, and the elements are called the *rare-earth elements*.

Lanthanum. Lanthanum is the most common member of this family. It is a soft metal, quite reactive, and it forms compounds in the III oxidation state. Like yttrium, lanthanum forms the oxide La_2O_3. This is the most basic oxide of the first three elements of this family.

Lanthanum is considered to be the first element in the series of rare-earth elements, also known as the lanthanides.

Actinium. This element exists in nature in small amounts in all uranium ores. Like lanthanum, actinium is the first element in a series known as the actinides. Also like lanthanum, it is an active metal and forms compounds in the III state only. Unlike the other members of the scandium family, actinium is radioactive. The most common isotope of actinium is that of mass 227, $^{227}_{89}Ac$, which has a half life of 21.7 years, decaying mainly by β-emission.

The oxide Ac_2O_3 is the most basic of the scandium family oxides.

Following lanthanum is a series of 14 elements whose $4f$ subshell is filling to 14 electrons. The gradual filling of the $4f$ shell results in a shrinkage of the atomic radius (Figure 28.1), giving the lanthanide contraction (Chap. 11). This contraction is believed to arise because the $4f$ electrons interact more strongly with the nucleus than with one another. Thus as more electrons are added to the $4f$ subshell, the nucleus-electron interaction becomes greater, and the atom or ion shrinks. The consequences of the strong interaction of f electrons with the nucleus are that (a) the three valence electrons in all lanthanides, i.e., the $5d^1 6s^2$ electrons, are less tightly held than expected; consequently the lanthanides are all relatively reactive metals, forming the III state easily; (b) the chemistry of the lanthanides does not directly involve $4f$ electrons. Apparently these electrons are so deep in the atom or so strongly bound to the nucleus that they are not available for bonding. As a result, the lanthanides (which differ only in the number of f electrons and in atomic size) have almost identical chemistry—chemistry related to the III state.

An important aspect of the lanthanide contraction is that the size of atoms and ions of the elements following lanthanum are smaller than might have been expected. The usual trend in atomic sizes down a column in the periodic table is that they increase as the number of electron shells increases from one row to the next. However, the lanthanide contraction intervenes between the fifth and sixth periods, so that little or no increase in size occurs between the fifth and sixth periods for the elements following lanthanum, or between the sixth and seventh periods in Groups I and II. The effect of this is that the atoms and ions of, for example, hafnium are nearly identical to those of zirconium, in spite of the fact that these elements differ by 32 atomic numbers. Since their valence electron con-

Table 28.2 The Lanthanides (Rare Earths) and Actinides

Sc														
Y														
La	Ce	Pr	Nd	Pm	Sm	Eu	Gd	Tb	Dy	Ho	Er	Tm	Yb	Lu
Ac	Th	Pa	U	Np	Pu	Am	Cm	Bk	Cf	Es	Fm	Md	No	Lw

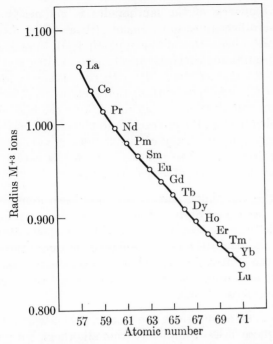

Figure 28.1   Illustrating the lanthanide contraction.

figurations are also the same, the chemistry of these elements shows a similarity almost without parallel elsewhere in the periodic table. Similarly, the elements niobium and tantalum are very alike, as are those of the second- and third-series elements of each of the transition-element families.

General Properties of the Lanthanides.   The lanthanide metals are silvery white and are comparable to the alkali metals (Group I) in their reactivity. Their ionization energies are of the order five or six electron volts and the standard oxidation potentials for the reaction

$$M(s) \longrightarrow M^{+3} + 3e^-$$

are of the order 2.5 volts. Hence the free metals are strong reducing agents. They all burn in air to give oxides of the type M_2O_3, except cerium which forms CeO_2. At temperatures below 250°C they all react with hydrogen to give hydrides such as MH_3 or MH_2, and all react with hot water to give hydrogen. The halogens, sulfur, phosphorus, silicon, nitrogen, carbon, and other nonmetals react readily with these elements at elevated temperatures.

Important compounds of the lanthanides include the oxides, the hydroxides ($M(OH)_3$), fluorides, carbonates, phosphates, and oxalates, which are insoluble in water; and chlorides, bromides, sulfates, nitrates, and perchlorates, which are soluble in water. Double salts such as

$$M(NO_3)_3 \cdot 2NH_4NO_3 \cdot 4H_2O$$

are common. Most of these compounds are colored—a consequence of the $4f$ electrons being excited (Figure 28.2). The basicity of the hydroxides decreases as the atomic number increases.

The complexing tendency of the lanthanides is *not* nearly as pronounced as with the other transition elements (those filling *d* orbitals). Complexes are formed with water of the type $M(H_2O)_n^{+3}$ and with the strongest of oxygen-containing chelating agents such as citric and tartaric acids. There is a much greater similarity with the alkaline earth metal ions than with the *d* electron type of transition metals. Apparently, the low tendency to form complex ions is associated with the high shielding of the *f* electrons which reduces the interaction to form bonds as *d* orbitals do. Hence, the complexing tendency of lanthanides is very low and is associated almost entirely with strong electrostatic forces between metal ion and ligand rather than by use of *d* or *f* orbitals.

Occurrence. Minerals containing lanthanides have been found in many countries, including the United States. Some of these elements, for which delicate spectroscopic tests are known, are found to be widely distributed in many minerals, but they are found in appreciable quantities only in Scandinavia, India, the United States, and the Soviet Union. As far as is known, none of them ever occurs by itself, and a mineral which contains one is likely to contain most of them.

Separation. A number of reactions are known which separate these elements as a group more or less completely from all others, but no one of the rare earths, with the exception of cerium, can be separated from the others by a single precipitation of the usual kind. Separation was done originally by long laborious processes involving fractional recrystallizations or precipitations repeated hundreds and often thousands of times. The method commonly used at present involves ion-exchange reactions similar to those used in water purification.

The Actinides. The series of elements with the $5f$ shell filling to 14 electrons includes elements 89 to 103. These elements are similar to the corresponding elements in the lanthanide series.

The actinide series was not identified until several of the transuranium elements were prepared. After a careful study of the properties of elements

$_{63}Eu^{+3}$	$_{64}Gd^{+3}$	Colorless
	Pink	$_{65}Tb^{+3}$
$_{62}Sm^{+3}$	Yellow	$_{66}Dy^{+3}$
$_{61}Pm^{+3}$	Pink; Yellow	$_{67}Ho^{+3}$
$_{60}Nd^{+3}$	Red	$_{68}Er^{+3}$
$_{59}Pr^{+3}$	Green	$_{69}Tm^{+3}$
$_{58}Ce^{+3}$	Colorless	$_{70}Yb^{+3}$
$_{57}La^{+3}$	Colorless	$_{71}Lu^{+3}$

Figure 28.2 Colors of lanthanide(III) ions.

Element	5f	6d	7s
Actinium, $_{89}$Ac		1	2
Thorium, $_{90}$Th		2	2
Protactinium, $_{91}$Pa	2	1	2
Uranium, $_{92}$U	3	1	2
Neptunium, $_{93}$Np	4	1	2
Plutonium, $_{94}$Pu	6		2
Americium, $_{95}$Am	7		2
Curium, $_{96}$Cm	7	1	2
Berkelium, $_{97}$Bk	9		2
Californium, $_{98}$Cf	10		2
Einsteinium, $_{99}$Es	11		2
Fermium, $_{100}$Fm	12		2
Mendelevium, $_{101}$Md	13		2
Nobelium, $_{102}$No	14		2
Lawrencium, $_{103}$Lw	14	1	2

Table 28.3 Outer Electron Configuration of Actinide Atoms

90 to 96 and additional evidence from paramagnetic and spectroscopic techniques provided evidence for the presence of f electrons, a suggestion was made by the American chemist Glenn Seaborg that they are all a part of a new transition series similar to the rare earths (Table 28.3).

Of this series, only the first four members (actinium through uranium) are found in nature in amounts sufficient to be extracted economically; traces of plutonium are found in uranium minerals. Elements 92 through 103 are made by nuclear transmutation processes which bombard elements with neutrons, protons, alpha particles, and nuclei of heavier elements. All of these elements are radioactive. Most of the isotopes of the heavier members have very short half-lives.

The chemical properties of the actinides are very similar to those of the lanthanides; however, besides the common III oxidation state, they also have states of IV, V, and VI. Like the lanthanides, a number of the actinides form colored ions (Figure 28.3). The actinide ions are only slightly larger than the analogous lanthanide ions. Similar to the lanthanide contraction is the analogous predicted and observed *actinide* contraction which shows the same general trends.

Actinium was discovered by Andre Debierne in 1899 in *pitchblende*. It precipitates with the rare-earth elements when they are separated from uranium ores and is difficult to remove from them. The properties of several of its compounds are known.

Thorium was discovered by J. J. Berzelius in 1828 and named in honor of the Scandinavian god Thor. For the most part, it is found in very small percentages in various minerals, especially those that are rich in the rare earths. Industrially, its compounds are obtained from *monazite sand*. This is a heavy sand that consists of cerium phosphate associated with the phosphates of other rare earths and of thorium. The best quality of monazite sand comes from India and Brazil.

Compounds of thorium are obtained from monazite for the manufacture of gas mantles, which consist of 99 per cent of thorium oxide, ThO_2, and

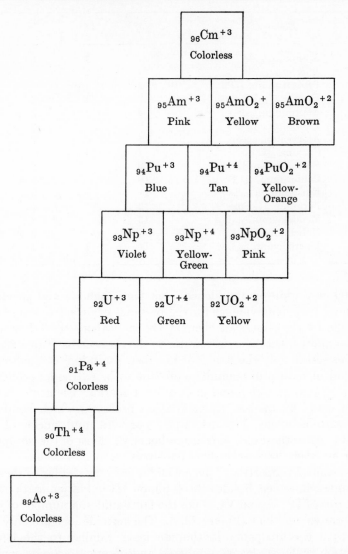

Figure 28.3   Colors of actinide ions.

1 per cent of cerium oxide, Ce_2O_3. The chief scientific interest in thorium lies in the fact that the element and all its compounds are radioactive (Chap. 25), like uranium and its compounds. In its chemistry thorium exhibits the IV state in all its compounds, and solutions of its salts are basic. The metal itself is very difficult to obtain in really pure form.

Protactinium is present in all uranium ores. It was discovered in 1917 by Otto Hahn and Lisa Meitner and by Frederick Soddy and John Cranston. A number of its compounds have been described. Oxides ranging from PaO_2 to Pa_2O_5 have been prepared.

Uranium was discovered in 1789 by Martin H. Klaproth in the ore pitchblende. In that ore it occurs as the oxide U_3O_8. Uranium ores are now found in the United States, Canada, Africa, Czechoslovakia, Russia, the Scandinavian peninsula, and the Far East. The metal is difficult to prepare in pure condition. It resembles nickel in appearance. As an acid-forming element uranium is similar to chromium, in that it forms salts of the formulas M_2UO_4 and $M_2U_2O_7$, but ordinarily it plays the part of a base-forming element. In this capacity it forms a great variety of salts, the best known of which are a series in which the complex ion UO_2^{+2}, known as *uranyl*, is the cation. Examples of these salts are uranyl nitrates, $UO_2(NO_3)_2 \cdot 6H_2O$, and uranyl acetate, $UO_2(CH_3CO_2)_2 \cdot 2H_2O$. The oxides of uranium have long been used in making greenish-yellow fluorescent glass and in glazes. The greatest use for uranium is in the production of atomic energy (Chap. 25).

Plutonium has been prepared in large amounts for atomic fuels by neutron capture reactions of uranium-238. The other actinides have been prepared in only small amounts; for some of them only a few atoms have been prepared.

Elements Below Titanium. In contrast to the scandium group which forms compounds in the III state only, this family forms compounds in the IV state (due to the d^2s^2 configuration). While titanium also forms compounds in the II, III, and IV states, zirconium and hafnium have stable compounds only in the IV state. This is in accordance with the general trend of higher oxidation-state stability for the elements in the second and third transition series.

$_{22}$Ti

$_{40}$Zr

$_{72}$Hf

Elements Below Vanadium. Vanadium, niobium, and tantalum show the variation in oxidation states to be expected in a family of the transition elements—the highest oxidation state (V for these elements) becomes more stable as the atomic weight increases. The chemistry of niobium and tantalum is similar in many ways to that of phosphorus and arsenic. These two transition elements form anionic species predominately. The most common compounds are the oxides, Ta_2O_5 and Nb_2O_5, which can be formed by heating the finely divided metal in air or in oxygen.

$_{23}$V

$_{41}$Nb

$_{73}$Ta

Elements Below Chromium. These are known as alloy metals for they are very important in the manufacture of high-grade, special-purpose steels. The metals have small atomic volumes and correspondingly high melting points, high resistance to corrosion, and great hardness. They all form compounds in the VI oxidation state; chromium also exhibits the II and III states, and molybdenum the III and IV states. They all form oxyanions and many other complex ions. An important feature of molybdenum and tungsten chemistry is the formation of a large number of polymolybdate(VI) and polytungstate(VI) acids and salts. These are polymeric structures similar to those formed by selenium and tellurium (Chap. 16). The chemistry of these elements is among the most diverse and complicated of any of the metals.

$_{24}$Cr

$_{42}$Mo

$_{74}$W

Table 28.4 Some Properties of the
Heavy Platinum Metals

Element	Density (g/cc, 25°C)	Melting Point (°C)	Boiling Point (°C)
Osmium	22.7	2700	5300
Iridium	22.6	2450	4800
Platinum	21.5	1774	4100

$_{25}$Mn

$_{43}$Tc

$_{75}$Re

Elements Below Manganese. Technetium and rhenium resemble manganese in forming anions in the VII oxidation state such as ReO_4^{-1} and TcO_4^{-1} and in forming some complexes with π-bonding ligands. However, unlike manganese, the lower (II and III) oxidation states are not stable.

$_{26}$Fe

$_{44}$Ru

$_{76}$Os

Elements Below Iron. Ruthenium and osmium are the first of a group of six transition elements known as the platinum metals. These metals are

Ru   Rh   Pd
Os   Ir   Pt

Of this group, osmium, iridium, and platinum are the most dense metal elements and are commonly called the heavy platinum metals. Some of their properties are given in Table 28.4.

$_{27}$Co

$_{45}$Rh

$_{77}$Ir

Elements Below Cobalt. Rhodium and iridium are unusual in that they form no oxy-anions or high oxidation states. Their stable states are the III and IV, and the III state is the most common for rhodium. Complexes, such as $RhCl_6^{-3}$ and $Ir(C_2O_4)_3^{-3}$, are formed by these elements; and in many ways they resemble cobalt more closely than the other members of the second and third transition series elements resemble their opposite element in the first transition series.

Both metals have high melting points and both are silvery white. Iridium is hard and brittle while rhodium is relatively soft and ductile. Neither metal is attacked by acids; both are oxidized by chlorine at red heat and by sodium chlorate in hot concentrated hydrochloric acid.

$_{28}$Ni

$_{46}$Pd

$_{78}$Pt

Elements Below Nickel. Palladium and platinum form compounds in the II and IV states with the latter being more important in commonly occurring compounds, and the II state being of importance in complexes. Unlike nickel these elements do not form carbonyls readily and their complexes are often square planar and inert.

The metals are malleable and ductile, lustrous and grey-white in appearance. Both are inert chemically but hot nitric acid will oxidize palladium and hot aqua regia will oxidize platinum. Fusion with sodium peroxide will produce oxides of both elements. Fluorine and chlorine will attack the metals at red heat. Palladium has the unusual property of absorbing large volumes of hydrogen.

Elements Below Copper. Copper, silver, and gold are sometimes known as "coinage" metals. Their Latin names give the sources for their symbols:

Copper	*Cuprum*	Cu
Silver	*Argentum*	Ag
Gold	*Aurum*	Au

Silver and gold are found in nature in the free state and as sulfides and arsenides. Gold is sometimes found as the telluride and silver as the chloride. The elements usually are extracted from the ores by treatment with cyanide solutions in the presence of air. Here the combination of oxidation and complex ion formation serves to get the metal ions into solution according to the equation

$$4Ag(s) + 8CN^- + 2H_2O + O_2(g) \longrightarrow 4Ag(CN)_2^- + 4OH^-$$

Pure silver and gold are obtained by electrode deposition.

Silver is white, lustrous, soft, and malleable with the highest electrical and thermal conductivity of any element. It is less reactive chemically than copper except toward hydrogen sulfide and sulfur. Silver dissolves in strong oxidizing acids including nitric and sulfuric acid. At room temperature it does not react readily with oxygen, hydrogen, carbon, or nitrogen or with dilute acids or fused alkalies. It does react with ozone to give AgO, and it tarnishes readily in air containing sulfur or hydrogen sulfide.

Gold is soft, yellow, a good conductor of electricity, and is the most malleable and ductile of the metals. It forms alloys with most metals. Chemically unreactive, gold is not attacked by any of the common acids. It is easily dissolved by solutions containing aqua regia, by sodium cyanide in the presence of air, and by solutions containing chlorine or bromide. It does not react with oxygen or sulfur at room temperature.

Table 28.5 is a summary of some physical properties of these metals.

Element	Density (g/cc, 25°C)	Atomic Volume	Melting Point (°C)	Boiling Point (°C)
Copper	8.9	7.1	1083	2310
Silver	10.5	10.3	960	1950
Gold	19.3	10.2	1062	2600

Table 28.5 Some Physical Properties of Copper, Silver, and Gold

Both silver and gold form ions in the I state; silver also appears in the II state, and gold exhibits the III state. The II state of silver is formed only in the presence of strong oxidizing agents such as fluorine, and the I state of gold disproportionates in solution to give the equilibrium

$$3Au^+(aq) \rightleftharpoons 2Au(s) + Au^{+3}(aq)$$

Both elements in the I state form insoluble oxides, sulfides, and halides (except AgF). Nearly all of these compounds are polymeric. Water-soluble compounds of silver and gold usually contain complex ions such as $Ag(CN)_2^-$, $Ag(NH_3)_2^+$, and $Au(CN)_2^-$. These complexes have linear geometry.

In the III state gold usually forms square-planar complexes as in $AuCl_4^-$, Au_2Cl_6, but a few octahedral complexes, such as $AuBr_6^{-3}$, are known. Gold(III) is a strong oxidizing agent.

Zinc, Cadmium, and Mercury

Zn
Cd
Hg

The family of elements consisting of zinc, cadmium, and mercury has two s electrons beyond filled d subshells. Because the d subshells are filled, these elements are not usually considered transition elements. The common oxidation state is II; there is no evidence for higher states and the I state is known in solution only for mercury which forms the unique Hg_2^{+2} ion ($^+Hg—Hg^+$). These metals differ from transition metals in several ways. For example, they are softer, lower melting, and considerably more reactive than their nearest neighbors in the transition series. However they resemble transition elements in their ability to form complexes with ligands such as ammonia, and with cyanide and halide ions.

Zinc and cadmium are very similar in their properties, and their ions resemble the magnesium ion in many ways. Mercury is much less reactive than zinc or cadmium and its complexes are much more stable. All three elements have a greater-than-expected tendency to form covalent compounds, possibly because of the polarizability of the electron cloud around the nucleus. Organometallic compounds of the type R_2Hg, R_2Zn, and R_2Cd are well-known covalent substances.

Some important properties of these elements are given in Table 28.6. Mercury* is the only liquid metal at room temperature; zinc and cadmium are white and shiny but easily tarnished. Zinc and mercury react with non-oxidizing acids like hydrochloric acid to liberate hydrogen; mercury is inert to these acids. Zinc reacts with strong bases to form the zincate ion, $Zn(OH)_4^{-2}$. Cadmium and mercury do not react with bases presumably because their tetrahydroxo complexes are unstable.

Table 28.6 Some Properties of Zinc, Cadmium, and Mercury

Element	Density (g/cc, 25°C)	Melting Point (°C)	Boiling Point (°C)	Heat of Vaporization (kcal/mole)	Standard Oxidation Potential (E° volts)	Radius of M^{+2}
Zinc	7.4	419	907	31.2	0.762	0.69
Cadmium	8.65	321	767	26.8	0.402	0.92
Mercury	13.55	−39	357	14.7	−0.854	0.93

* Mercury is volatile and toxic. Particular care should be taken not to leave its surface exposed so that evaporation can occur; hence it should be stored in closed containers, and any spilled droplets should be searched out and cleaned up immediately.

Zinc and cadmium react readily with oxygen on heating to give the oxides; mercury reacts with oxygen very slowly at temperatures between 300°C and 350°C.

SUMMARY

This chapter discusses the elements which are filling a d shell after arriving at the electron configuration of strontium and barium, and an f shell in the energy level of next lower principal quantum number. The d shell filling elements are similar to those discussed in Chap. 27, modified by the increase in nuclear charge and size, but the change in nuclear charge has less effect on those elements following lutetium than might have been expected, because of the lanthanide contraction. The usefulness of several of these metals in industry, as the free metal or as components of alloys, is indicated since this use is generally more important than the use of compounds of these elements.

SOME SPECIAL TERMS

Rare-earth elements
  lanthanides
  actinides
Platinum metals

Lanthanide contraction
Fractional crystallization
Ion-exchange process

QUESTIONS AND PROBLEMS

1. For each of the groups mentioned, prepare tables listing the following for each element in the group: a source of the element from a compound found in nature; the formulas of two compounds of the element; the electron configuration of the element; a compound or alloy of the element used commercially, and a descriptive adjective or phrase to indicate what property of the compound or alloy makes it useful. (a) The elements below titanium, (b) the elements below vanadium, (c) the elements below chromium, (d) the elements below copper, (e) the heavy platinum metals, (f) ruthenuim, rhodium, palladium, and (g) the elements below zinc.
2. List the consequences of the lanthanide contraction and present experimental facts to show that your statements are correct.
3. Compare the complexing tendency of the lanthanides with that of the elements of the first-row transition elements and that of the alkaline earth elements. How do you account for similarities and differences?
4. Palladium will not absorb nitrogen to any appreciable extent. Can you design a procedure, using palladium, to purify hydrogen from a hydrogen-nitrogen mixture?
5. Give the structure and electronic configuration of (a) a platinum(II) complex, (b) a platinum(IV) complex.
6. Explain why gold will not dissolve in nitric acid, but will dissolve in the seemingly much less corrosive reagent, sodium cyanide, when air is present.
7. Discuss the use and reactions of silver salts in the photographic process, writing equations for all chemical reactions which occur.

8. Compare the melting points of zinc, cadmium, and mercury with those of their neighbors in the periodic table, and with the alkaline earth elements. What factors, such as electronic configuration, ion size, ionization energy, etc., can be used to help account for the difference, and how do they account for it (if they do)?

9. The following transformations can be carried out consecutively in the same beaker:

$$Ag^+(aq) \longrightarrow Ag_2O(s) \longrightarrow AgCl(s) \longrightarrow Ag(NH_3)_2^+(aq) \longrightarrow$$

$$AgBr(s) \longrightarrow Ag(S_2O_3)_2^{-3}(aq) \longrightarrow AgI(s) \longrightarrow Ag(CN)_2^- \longrightarrow Ag_2S(s)$$

(a) At each arrow, list the reagent solution you would add to effect the transformation. (b) Write equations for each of the reactions. (c) Explain, in terms of solubility product equilibria, why precipitation or solution occurs in each of the reactions.

10. (a) Would you expect silver chloride to precipitate (i) from ammonia solution, (ii) from sodium cyanide solution? (b) Would you expect silver oxide to change to silver bromide on shaking with potassium bromide solution? (c) Would you expect silver sulfide to change to silver bromide on shaking with potassium bromide solution? Explain your answer in each case.

REFERENCES

HINDMAN, J. C., B. B. CUNNINGHAM, T. K. KEENAN, and G. T. SEABORG. "The New Elements," *J. Chem. Educ., 36* (1959) pp. 2–44.

KATZ, J. J., and G. T. SEABORG. *The Chemistry of the Actinide Elements.* London: Meuthen, 1957.

MOELLER, T. *The Chemistry of the Lanthanides.* New York, Reinhold, 1963.

SHELTON, S. M. "Zirconium," *Scientific American*, Vol. *184*, No. 6 (1951), p. 18–24.

WALLMAN, J. C. "The First Isolations of the Transuranium Elements," *J. Chem. Educ., 36* (1959), p. 340.

PART EIGHT

ORGANIC CHEMISTRY

29

Organic Chemistry I: Structures and Nomenclature

*By showing on the one hand the atomic groups which remain
unaffected by certain reactions, and on the other hand those which
play a role in frequently recurring metamorphoses, such structural
formulae give a picture of the chemical nature of the substance . . .*
Kekulé von Stradonitz (1829–1896)

In Chap. 10 we presented a very brief introduction to organic chemistry
as a part of the overview of the classes of elements. Our primary concern
in that chapter was to show how the many and varied kinds of carbon-
containing structures arise, and to relate these structures to the electron
configuration of the carbon atom. The question we now ask is: How does
the structure of an organic molecule affect its properties? In this and in the
following three chapters we shall study the correlation of the physical and
chemical properties of organic compounds with their structural features.

Organic compounds exhibit a remarkable variation in properties. They
constitute products which vary widely: plastics and elastomers like polystyrene and rubber; fibers like cotton and nylon; gasolines, greases, and
lubricating oils; drugs, dyes, insecticides, weed killers, explosives, photographic film, varnishes, lacquers, and many other useful and essential
items of our economy. Moreover, the knowledge of organic chemistry has
developed to the point that it is now possible in many cases to synthesize
compounds meeting the specifications required for a specific use. For
example, nylon was synthesized as a substitute for silk, demerol was prepared in a quest for a pain-killer of the caliber of morphine but without
the habit-forming quality of that drug, and the new rubbers now being
used in space ships are prepared to withstand the extremely wide temperature variation experienced during space flight.

Organic compounds and their reactions constitute the foundation of
modern biology and are, in fact, the basis of life itself.

We shall begin this series of chapters with an illustration of the age-
old technique of the scientist known as simplification by classification.
Starting with the more than two million known organic compounds, we
shall classify them into broad groups and then into smaller families or

series of compounds according to their properties and structure. Following this, some important properties, structural features, and a system of nomenclature will be given for ten series of organic compounds. Physical properties will receive more attention than chemical properties in this chapter; the following chapter is devoted entirely to chemical reactions of organic compounds. Topics in organic chemistry to be presented in the remaining chapters are: Chap. 31, Polymers and Other Complex Molecules, and Chap. 32, Some Physical Organic Chemistry.

Classification of Organic Substances

The early chemists classified organic compounds into two broad divisions: (a) the aliphatic division, made up of fats and waxes, and compounds related to them; and (b) the "aromatic" division, consisting of the essential oils from plants such as the oil of wintergreen and other flavoring compounds. While the names aliphatic and aromatic are still used for the two chief divisions of organic compounds, neither the fatty character nor the aroma of a compound is any longer used as a basis of its classification. Structurally, aromatic compounds are those containing aromatic rings such as benzene, naphthalene, pyridine, and many others, some of which are discussed in Chap. 10. Aliphatic compounds contain chains or nonaromatic rings of carbon atoms.

Within both the aliphatic and aromatic divisions further subdivision into various series of compounds, known as *homologous series*, is made. An homologous series is defined as a group of compounds containing the same functional group or groups in which each member in the series differs from the member of next higher molecular weight by a methylene group, CH_2. For example, the compounds

$$CH_3—CH_2—CH_3 \qquad CH_3—CH_2—CH_2—CH_3$$
$$\text{Propane} \qquad\qquad\qquad \textit{n}\text{-Butane}$$

$$CH_3—CH_2—CH_2—CH_2—CH_3$$
$$\textit{n}\text{-Pentane}$$

are members of the homologous series known as *alkanes*; pentane has one more and propane has one less methylene group than butane. Other examples of homologous series in the aliphatic division are given in Table 29.1.

All members of an homologous series contain the same functional group. For example, all alkenes have the carbon-carbon double bond in their molecules; all alkanols (alcohols) have the hydroxyl group in their molecules; all carboxylic acids contain the carboxyl group

$$—\underset{\underset{O}{\|}}{C}—OH$$

Table 29.2 gives the generalized structural formulas and names for a number of homologous series not given in Table 29.1. In the generalized structural formula the symbol R is used to represent any aliphatic hydrocarbon group and Ar is used to represent any aromatic hydrocarbon group.

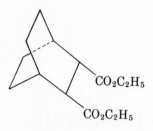

Figure 29.1 Structures of some organic substances.

Name of Series	Structural Features	Several Representative Members
Alkanes	Hydrocarbons containing single bonds	$CH_3\text{—}CH_3$, ethane $CH_3\text{—}CH_2\text{—}CH_3$, propane
Alkenes	Hydrocarbons containing one double bond between carbon atoms	$CH_2\text{==}CH_2$, ethene (ethylene) $CH_3\text{—}CH\text{==}CH_2$, propene
Alkynes	Hydrocarbons containing one triple bond between carbon atoms	$CH\text{≡}CH$, ethyne (acetylene) $CH_3\text{—}C\text{≡}CH$, propyne
Alkanols (alcohols)	Alkanes with one hydrogen atom replaced by a hydroxyl group	$CH_3\text{—}CH_2\text{—}OH$, ethanol $CH_3\text{—}CH_2\text{—}CH_2\text{—}OH$, propanol
Alkanals (aldehydes)	Compounds containing the group $\overset{\displaystyle —C—H}{\underset{\displaystyle O}{\|\|}}$	$CH_3\text{—}\overset{\|\|}{\underset{O}{C}}\text{—}H$, ethanal (acetaldehyde) $CH_3\text{—}CH_2\text{—}\overset{\|\|}{\underset{O}{C}}\text{—}H$, propanal
Alkanones (ketones)	Compounds containing the group $\overset{\displaystyle C—C—C}{\underset{\displaystyle O}{\|\|}}$	$CH_3\text{—}\overset{\|\|}{\underset{O}{C}}\text{—}CH_3$, propanone (acetone) $CH_3\text{—}CH_2\text{—}\overset{\|\|}{\underset{O}{C}}\text{—}CH_3$, butanone
Alkanoic acids (carboxylic acids)	Compounds containing the group $\overset{\displaystyle —C—OH}{\underset{\displaystyle O}{\|\|}}$	$CH_3\text{—}\overset{\|\|}{\underset{O}{C}}\text{—}OH$, ethanoic acid (acetic acid) $CH_3\text{—}CH_2\text{—}\overset{\|\|}{\underset{O}{C}}\text{—}OH$, propanoic acid
Amines	Derivatives of ammonia containing a nitrogen atom bonded to at least one carbon atom	$CH_3\text{—}CH_2\text{—}NH_2$, ethanamine (ethylamine)
Alkyl halides	Aliphatic hydrocarbons with one hydrogen atom replaced by a halogen atom	$CH_3\text{—}CH_2\text{—}CH_2\text{—}Cl$, 1-chloropropane $CH_3\text{—}CH_2\text{—}\overset{\|}{\underset{F}{CH}}\text{—}CH_2\text{—}CH_3$, 3-fluoropentane

Some Important Homologous Series

The Alkanes, RH. The alkanes are hydrocarbons with single bonds between carbon atoms. They are also known as *saturated hydrocarbons* because their molecules contain the maximum number of hydrogen atoms possible with tetravalent carbon. The formulas, names, and some of the properties and uses of some members of this series are given in Table 29.3. The alkanes are present in natural gas and petroleum and are among our most important fuels and lubricants.

Table 29.2 Generalized Structural Formulas for Some Homologous Series

Name of Series	General Formula	Name of Series	General Formula
Phenols	Ar—OH	Aliphatic ethers	R—O—R
Nitroaryls	Ar—NO$_2$	Aromatic ethers	Ar—O—Ar
Nitroalkyls	R—NO$_2$	Alkylsulfonic acids	$R-\overset{\displaystyle O}{\underset{\displaystyle O}{\overset{\|}{\underset{\|}{S}}}}-OH$
Aromatic esters	$Ar-\overset{}{\underset{\displaystyle O}{\overset{}{C}}}-O-Ar$		
Aliphatic esters	$R-\overset{}{\underset{\displaystyle O}{\overset{}{C}}}-O-R$	Arylsulfonic acids	$Ar-\overset{\displaystyle O}{\underset{\displaystyle O}{\overset{\|}{\underset{\|}{S}}}}-OH$
Mixed esters	$Ar-\overset{}{\underset{\displaystyle O}{\overset{}{C}}}-O-R,$ or $R-\overset{}{\underset{\displaystyle O}{\overset{}{C}}}-O-Ar$	Alkylthiols (mercaptans)	R—S—H
		Arylthiols	Ar—S—H
Aliphatic amides	$R-\overset{}{\underset{\displaystyle O}{\overset{}{C}}}-NH_2$	Alkandioic acids	$\overset{\displaystyle CO_2H}{\underset{\displaystyle CO_2H}{(CH_2)_n}}$
Aliphatic anhydrides	$R-\overset{}{\underset{\displaystyle O}{\overset{}{C}}}-O-\overset{}{\underset{\displaystyle O}{\overset{}{C}}}-R$	Alkandiols	$\overset{\displaystyle OH}{\underset{\displaystyle OH}{(CH_2)_n}}$
Alkanoyl chlorides (acyl chlorides)	$R-\overset{}{\underset{\displaystyle O}{\overset{}{C}}}-Cl$	α-Amino acids	$R-\underset{\displaystyle NH_2}{CH}-CO_2H$

Table 29.3 Formulas, Names, and Boiling Points of Representative Alkanes

Formula	Chemical Name	Physical State	Boiling Point (°C)	Uses
CH$_4$	Methane	Gas	−161 ⎫	
C$_2$H$_6$	Ethane	Gas	−88 ⎪	Natural gas
C$_3$H$_8$	Propane	Gas	−46 ⎬	
C$_4$H$_{10}$	Butane	Gas	−1 ⎭	
C$_5$H$_{12}$	Pentane	Liquid	36 ⎫	High-grade naphtha
C$_6$H$_{14}$	Hexane	Liquid	69 ⎭	
C$_7$H$_{16}$	Heptane	Liquid	98 ⎫	
C$_8$H$_{18}$	Octane	Liquid	126 ⎪	
C$_9$H$_{20}$	Nonane	Liquid	150 ⎬	Gasoline
C$_{10}$H$_{22}$	Decane	Liquid	174 ⎪	
C$_{11}$H$_{24}$	Undecane	Liquid	195 ⎭	
C$_{12}$H$_{26}$	Dodecane	Liquid	215	Kerosene (C$_{12}$H$_{26}$ to C$_{18}$H$_{38}$)
C$_{14}$H$_{30}$	Tetradecane	Liquid	253	Lubricating oil (mixtures of higher hydrocarbons)
C$_{20}$H$_{42}$	Eicosane	Solid		Paraffin (C$_{20}$H$_{42}$ to C$_{30}$H$_{62}$)

Note: The data given here are for the normal, or straight-chain, hydrocarbons.

The alkanes can be thought of as derived from methane by increasing the number of carbon atoms in the chain. In this way it is possible to account for both the straight- and branched-chain members of the series discussed in Chap. 10. The first alkanes—methane, ethane, and propane—are straight-chain compounds, but for the fourth member of the series, butane, C_4H_{10}, there are two position isomers—a straight-chain compound and a branched-chain compound.

As the number of carbon atoms increases, the possibilities for chain branching also increases and the number of isomers increases rapidly. Thus the hydrocarbon with 7 carbon atoms has 9 possible isomers, that with 10 carbon atoms has 75 possibilities, with 14 carbon atoms, 1,858 possibilities, etc. Table 29.4 gives the formulas for the position isomers of the four-, five-, and six-carbon atom alkanes. As indicated in Chap. 10 the correlation between the number of isomers found and the number predicted from our structural theory is exact. Consequently, it is possible to use this theory —which encompasses the covalent bond, the tetravalency of carbon, the univalency of hydrogen, and the idea that carbon-carbon bonds are especially stable—not only to predict the number of isomers corresponding to a given carbon content but also to write structural formulas for each isomer.

Table 29.4 Isomers of Butane, Pentane, and Hexane

Butanes

$CH_3—CH_2—CH_2—CH_3$
n-Butane
(b.p., $-0.5°C$)

$CH_3—CH—CH_3$
       |
      CH_3
2-Methylpropane
(b.p., $-10.2°C$)

Pentanes

$CH_3—CH_2—CH_2—CH_2—CH_3$
n-Pentane
(b.p., $36.1°C$)

$CH_3—CH—CH_2—CH_3$
       |
      CH_3
2-Methylbutane
(b.p., $27.9°C$)

$$CH_3—\overset{\displaystyle CH_3}{\underset{\displaystyle CH_3}{\overset{|}{\underset{|}{C}}}}—CH_3$$
2,2-Dimethylpropane
(b.p., $9.5°C$)

Hexanes

$CH_3—CH_2—CH_2—CH_2—CH_2—CH_3$
n-Hexane
(b.p., $68.7°C$)

$CH_3—CH_2—CH_2—CH—CH_3$
                  |
                 CH_3
2-Methylpentane
(b.p., $60.3°C$)

$CH_3—CH_2—CH—CH_2—CH_3$
              |
             CH_3
3-Methylpentane
(b.p., $63.3°C$)

$$CH_3—\overset{\displaystyle CH_3}{\underset{\displaystyle CH_3}{\overset{|}{\underset{|}{C}}}}—CH_2—CH_3$$
2,2-Dimethylbutane
(b.p., $49.7°C$)

$$CH_3—\overset{\displaystyle CH_3}{\overset{|}{CH}}—\overset{\displaystyle CH_3}{\overset{|}{CH}}—CH_3$$
2,3-Dimethylbutane
(b.p., $58.0°C$)

PROBLEM. ■ Write the carbon skeletons for the isomeric heptanes.

SOLUTION

The first isomer will be the straight-chain compound:

$$\text{I} \qquad \text{C—C—C—C—C—C—C}$$

In the next group of isomers one carbon atom is attached at various places along a chain of six carbon atoms. The two different structures are:

$$\text{II} \quad \begin{array}{c} \text{C—C—C—C—C—C} \\ | \\ \text{C} \end{array} \qquad \text{III} \quad \begin{array}{c} \text{C—C—C—C—C—C} \\ | \\ \text{C} \end{array}$$

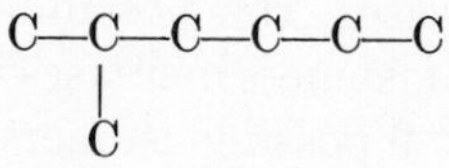

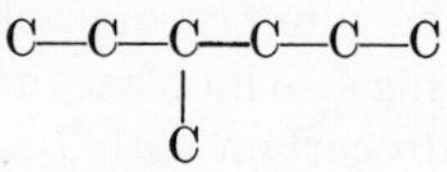

In the third group two carbon atoms are attached at various points along a chain of five carbon atoms. The five possible structures are:

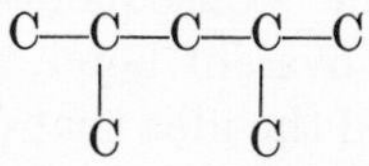

$$\text{IV} \begin{array}{c} \text{C—C—C—C—C} \\ |\ \ | \\ \text{C}\ \text{C} \end{array} \quad \text{V} \begin{array}{c} \text{C—C—C—C—C} \\ \ |\ \ \ | \\ \ \text{C}\ \ \text{C} \end{array} \quad \text{VI} \begin{array}{c} \text{C} \\ | \\ \text{C—C—C—C—C} \\ | \\ \text{C} \end{array}$$

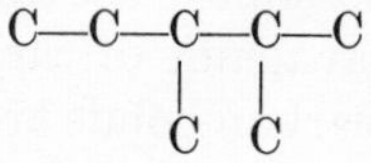

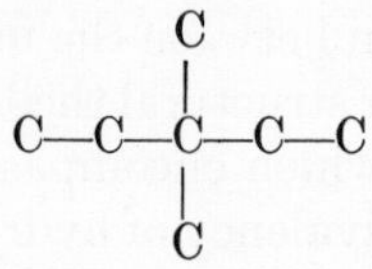

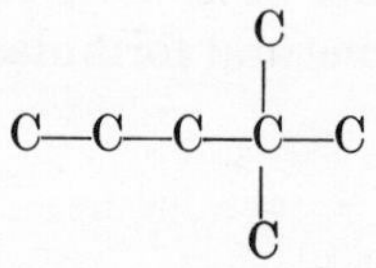

$$\text{VII} \quad \begin{array}{c} \text{C} \\ | \\ \text{C—C—C—C—C} \\ | \\ \text{C} \end{array} \qquad \text{VIII} \quad \begin{array}{c} \text{C—C—C—C—C} \\ | \\ \text{C} \\ | \\ \text{C} \end{array}$$

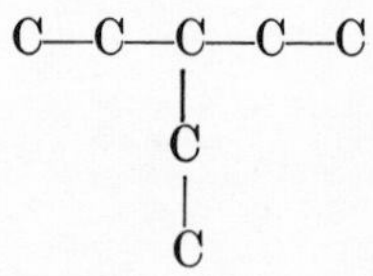

The last isomer consists of a chain of four carbon atoms with three carbon atoms attached to it:

$$\text{IX} \qquad \begin{array}{c} \text{C} \\ | \\ \text{C—C—C—C} \\ |\ \ | \\ \text{C}\ \text{C} \end{array}$$

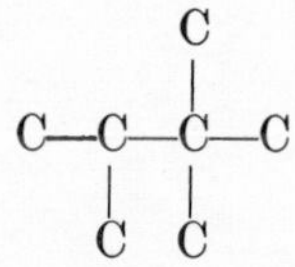

Nomenclature. The large number of isomers poses the problem of naming organic compounds. The nomenclature of organic chemistry involves both common and systematic names. The former are usually applied to simple compounds, the latter to more complex substances. While both the simple and systematic names will be used in this text, we shall develop the systematic nomenclature at this point in order to facilitate communication.

The systematic names are the outgrowth of an international system of nomenclature devised and used by organic chemists throughout the world and recommended by the International Union of Pure and Applied Chemistry (IUPAC). The rules for the IUPAC system are few and simple to use:

1. Straight-chain alkanes are given the names listed in Table 29.3. (It is important that the names of the first ten alkanes in the table be memorized in order to use the rules that follow.)

2. For branched-chain hydrocarbons, determine the longest *continuous* chain of carbon atoms in the molecule. Use the name of the straight-chain alkane corresponding to this number of carbon atoms as the basis

for the name of the compound. Thus in the structure

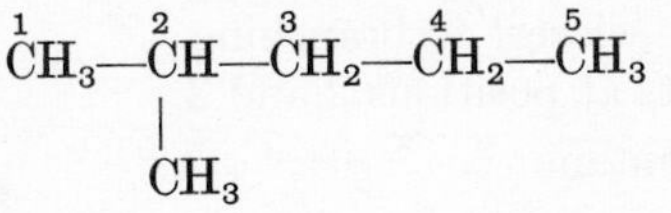

$$\overset{1}{CH_3}-\overset{2}{CH}-\overset{3}{CH_2}-\overset{4}{CH_2}-\overset{5}{CH_3}$$
$$|$$
$$CH_3$$

the longest continuous chain of carbon atoms is five. Therefore this is known as a *pentane*.

3. Number the carbon atoms of the continuous chain, beginning at the end closest to the branching. In the formula above, numbering starts at the left.

4. Name and number the substituents other than hydrogen atoms attached to the chain. The name of the substituent is taken from the alkane with the same number of carbon atoms but the *ane* ending is replaced by a *yl* ending. Thus a CH_3— or

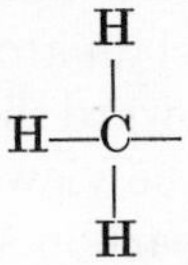

$$\begin{array}{c} H \\ | \\ H-C- \\ | \\ H \end{array}$$

is a *methyl* group because it is derived from methane. Names of other substituents are given in Table 29.5. The number of the substituent is taken from the number of the carbon atom to which it is attached. *Each substituent receives a name and a number.* The name of the compound above is 2-methylpentane.

5. Where alternatives exist, numbering of the longest chain is done so that the substituents will have the lowest possible numbers.

PROBLEM. ■ Name the following compounds:

1. 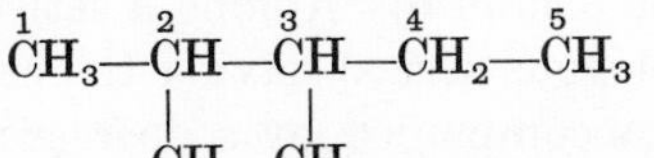
$$\overset{1}{CH_3}-\overset{2}{CH}-\overset{3}{CH}-\overset{4}{CH_2}-\overset{5}{CH_3}$$
$$|\quad\ |$$
$$CH_3\ CH_3$$

Formula	Name	Formula	Name
CH_3—	Methyl	$CH_2{=}CH$—	Ethenyl
$CH_3{-}CH_2$—	Ethyl	$CH{\equiv}C$—	Ethynyl
$CH_3{-}CH_2{-}CH_2$—	*n*-Propyl	Cl—	Chloro
$CH_3{-}CH$—$\!\!\underset{CH_3}{\big|}$	Isopropyl	F—	Fluoro
		HO—	Hydroxy
$CH_3{-}\underset{CH_3}{\overset{CH_3}{C}}$—	*tert*-Butyl	CH_3O—	Methoxy
		$CH_3{-}CH_2{-}O$—	Ethoxy
		—CF_3	Trifluoro-methyl
		—NH_2	Amino
Phenyl		—NO_2	Nitro
		—SH	Mercapto

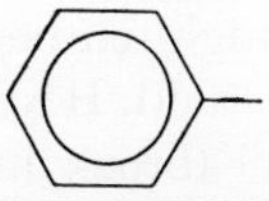

Table 29.5 Formulas and Names of Substituents

SOLUTION
(a) Longest continuous chain, five: pentane.
(b) Number from left—closest to branching.
(c) Methyl substituents at positions 2 and 3.
Name: 2,3-dimethylpentane

2. $\overset{1}{CH_3}-\overset{2}{CH}-\overset{3}{CH}-\overset{4}{CH_2}-\overset{5}{CH_3}$
$\underset{Cl}{|}$

SOLUTION
Refer to Table 29.5 for names of substituents.
Name: 2-chloro-3-phenylpentane

Bonding and Structure in Alkanes. The carbon atoms in alkanes exhibit sp^3 hybridization so that each carbon atom may be represented as having its four covalent bonds directed toward the corners of a regular tetrahedron. Carbon-carbon single bonds may be viewed as two tetrahedra which have a corner in common. A chain of carbon atoms might be pictured as a zig-zag arrangement of tetrahedra as shown in Figure 29.2. Rotation around the single bonds in hydrocarbon chains (Chap. 10) occurs easily at room temperature; however, there is a preference for the staggered conformations over the eclipsed ones. In cyclic alkanes, rotation around the bonds in the rings is restricted as demonstrated in Chap. 10.

Physical Properties of Alkanes. Within an homologous series of organic compounds the melting and boiling points increase in a regular way as the carbon content increases as illustrated in Table 29.3. This is consistent with the idea that van der Waals forces increase as the number of electrons in the molecule increase (Chap. 6). Among a series of homologues (members of the same homologous series) having the same molecular formula, increased branching is accompanied by a decrease in boiling point. This is illustrated in Table 29.4 where the boiling points of the various isomeric compounds are given.

Alkanes containing four carbon atoms or less are gases; the straight-chain homologues containing from five to sixteen carbon atoms are liquids, and the higher members of the series are waxlike solids.

The densities of alkanes are always less than 1.0 g/cc; and they increase as the carbon content increases, a consequence of the fact that as the chain lengthens, the ratio of molecular weight to molecular volume increases. Because they are nonpolar, the alkanes are not soluble in (or miscible with) water. Liquid alkanes are good solvents for paraffin and other hydro-carbons.

Chemical Properties of Alkanes.   The alkanes are relatively inactive; they do not react with acids or bases or with oxidizing agents such as potassium permanganate, $KMnO_4$, or potassium dichromate, $K_2Cr_2O_7$. They do react with oxygen, when heated; with halogens, at high temperatures, or in the presence of light; and with concentrated nitric acid, HNO_3.

In the absence of air, alkanes can be caused to "*crack*" (break into smaller fragments) at high temperatures or in the presence of catalysts.

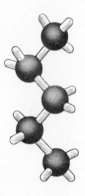

Figure 29.2 Model of a chain of carbon atoms.

The cracking reaction is used extensively in the petroleum industry to convert hydrocarbons of high molecular weight (C_{15} to C_{18}) to gasoline hydrocarbons (molecules having five to twelve carbon atoms).

Catalysts, such as aluminum chloride or sulfuric acid, can be used to facilitate conversion of straight-chain alkanes to branched-chain or to aromatic hydrocarbons. Both branched-chain and aromatic hydrocarbons have higher octane ratings as gasolines than do their straight-chain derivatives.

Uses of Alkanes. Readily available from petroleum, the alkanes serve as the basis for the petroleum and petrochemical industries. Table 29.6 gives some uses of alkanes.

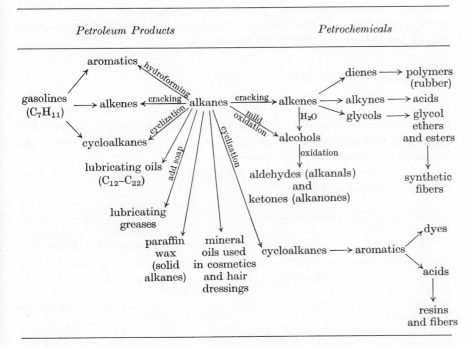

Table 29.6 Uses of Alkanes in the Petroleum and Petrochemical Industries

Cycloalkanes. Compounds containing rings of saturated carbon atoms are known as the cycloalkanes. Examples are shown in Figure 29.3. These compounds have higher boiling points and densities than the alkanes containing the same number of carbon atoms. Their chemical properties are similar to those of the alkanes except that the small-ring compounds are more reactive than the corresponding alkanes. This is because the C—C—C bond angles in the small rings are considerably less than the tetrahedral angle, resulting in a *strained* structure—one that reacts by

Cyclopropane
(b.p., −34°C)

Cyclobutane
(b.p., 12°C)

Cyclopentane
(b.p., 49.2°C)

Cyclohexane
(b.p., 80.8°C)

Figure 29.3 Some cycloalkanes.

Figure 29.4 The chair conformation of cyclohexane.

allowing the ring to open as illustrated by the reaction

$$\text{CH}_2\text{—CH}_2 + \text{Br}_2 \longrightarrow \underset{\underset{\text{Br}}{|}}{\text{CH}_2}\text{—CH}_2\text{—}\underset{\underset{\text{Br}}{|}}{\text{CH}_2}$$
$$\underset{\text{CH}_2}{\diagdown}$$

Note that cyclohexane is not planar, as benzene is. There is less strain and less interference of the hydrogen atoms with each other, if the molecule adopts the *chair* form (Figure 29.4).

Alkenes, RCH═CHR

Hydrocarbons containing one double bond between carbon atoms are known as alkenes or *olefins*. The formulas, names, and some properties of some members of this series are given in Table 29.7. The nature of the double bond between carbon atoms was discussed in Chaps. 6 and 10. The alkenes are the starting materials for many plastics and synthetic fibers and for numerous alcohols.

Table 29.7 Names, Formulas, and Physical Constants of Some Alkenes

Name	*Formula*	*Melting Point* (°C)	*Boiling Point* (°C)
Ethene (ethylene)	$\text{CH}_2\text{═CH}_2$	-169.4	-103.8
Propene (propylene)	$\text{CH}_3\text{—CH═CH}_2$	-185.2	-47
1-Butene	$\text{CH}_2\text{═CH—CH}_2\text{—CH}_3$	—	-6.3
2-Butene	$\text{CH}_3\text{—CH═CH—CH}_3$	$-127*$	$1.4*$
Methylpropene	$\underset{\overset{|}{\text{CH}_3}}{\text{CH}_3\text{—C═CH}_2}$	-140.7	-6.9
1-Pentene	$\text{CH}_2\text{═CH—CH}_2\text{—CH}_2\text{—CH}_3$	-138	30.1

* Mixture of cis and trans isomers. See Chap. 10.

Similar to the alkanes in physical properties, the alkenes are considerably more reactive. The characteristic reaction of these compounds involves addition to the double bond as illustrated by the equations

$$\text{CH}_3\text{—CH═CH}_2 + \text{Br}_2 \longrightarrow \text{CH}_3\text{—}\underset{\underset{\text{Br}}{|}}{\text{CH}}\text{—}\underset{\underset{\text{Br}}{|}}{\text{CH}_2}$$

$$\text{CH}_2\text{═CH}_2 + \text{H}_2\text{O} \xrightarrow{\text{catalyst}} \underset{\underset{\text{H}}{|}}{\text{CH}_2}\text{—}\underset{\underset{\text{OH}}{|}}{\text{CH}_2}$$

Perhaps the most important reaction of alkenes is *polymerization*, or self-addition. In this process, small molecules unite to form giant molecules known as *polymers*. The reaction of ethylene molecules to form polyethylene—molecules containing more than 100,000 ethylene molecules—may be illustrated by the equations

$$CH_2{=}CH_2 + CH_2{=}CH_2 \longrightarrow -CH_2{-}CH_2{-}CH_2{-}CH_2{-}$$

$$nCH_2{=}CH_2 \longrightarrow -CH_2{-}CH_2{-}(-CH_2{-}CH_2{-})_{n-2}{-}CH_2{-}CH_2{-}$$

where $n = 10^5$ and higher.

Polyethylene may be waxlike, tough but flexible, or rigid, depending upon how the polymerization reaction is carried out. The uses of polyethylene range from electrical insulation and plastic pipe or tubing to bread wrapping or heavier construction sheeting. Many other alkenes can be polymerized to give plastics, elastomers, or fibers. Various kinds of polymers are discussed in Chap. 31.

Nomenclature of Alkenes. Rules of the IUPAC nomenclature system apply to alkenes with the following additions to the rules for alkanes:

1. The ending *-ene* is used (instead of *-ane*) to indicate that one carbon-to-carbon double bond is present.
2. The *longest continuous chain of carbon atoms containing the double bond* forms the base for the name and the chain is numbered so that the carbon atoms of the double bond have the lowest possible numbers.
3. The position of the double bond is indicated by the smaller of the numbers of the carbon atoms involved in the double bond. For example: $CH_2{=}CH{-}CH_2{-}CH_3$ is 1-butene. The 1- indicates that the double bond is situated between the first and second carbon atoms.

PROBLEM. ■ Name the following alkenes:

1.

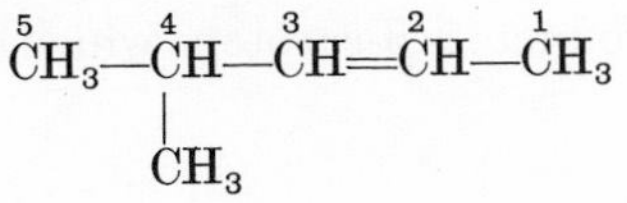

$$\overset{5}{C}H_3{-}\overset{4}{C}H{-}\overset{3}{C}H{=}\overset{2}{C}H{-}\overset{1}{C}H_3$$
$$|$$
$$CH_3$$

SOLUTION
4-methyl-2-pentene

2.

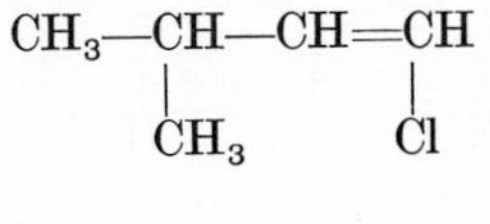

$$CH_3{-}CH{-}CH{=}CH$$
$$| \qquad |$$
$$CH_3 \qquad Cl$$

SOLUTION
1-chloro-3-methyl-1-butene

3.

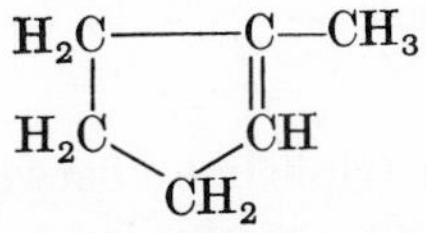

$$\begin{array}{c} H_2C{-\!-\!-\!-}C{-}CH_3 \\ |\qquad\ \| \\ H_2C\ \ \ \ CH \\ \diagdown\ \diagup \\ CH_2 \end{array}$$

SOLUTION
1-methyl-1-cyclopentene

Isomerism Among Alkenes. In addition to position isomerism, which arises because of the position of the double bond along the chain as in 1-pentene and 2-pentene, there is also *geometrical isomerism*, discussed previously in Chap. 10, and illustrated by the cis and trans isomers of 2-pentene:

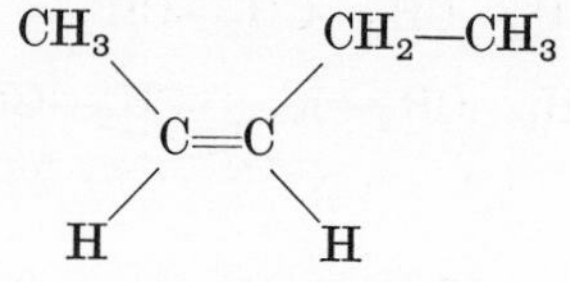

$$
\begin{array}{ccc}
CH_3 & & CH_2\text{---}CH_3 \\
 & C{=}C & \\
H & & H \\
\end{array}
\qquad
\begin{array}{ccc}
CH_3 & & H \\
 & C{=}C & \\
H & & CH_2\text{---}CH_3 \\
\end{array}
$$

cis-2-Pentene 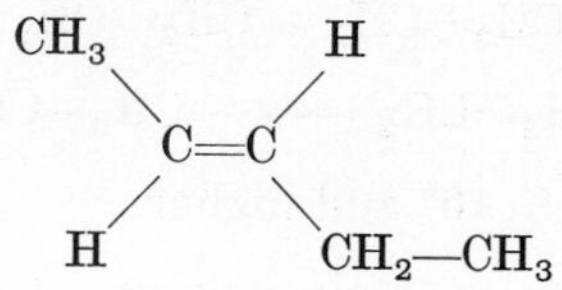   *trans*-2-Pentene

This isomerism arises because of restricted rotation around the double bond as shown in Chap. 10.

Alkadienes, Alkapolyenes. Hydrocarbons containing two or more carbon-to-carbon double bonds belong to these homologous series. Examples are:

$$CH_2{=}CH\text{---}CH{=}CH_2 \qquad CH_2{=}C\text{---}CH{=}CH_2$$

1,3-Butadiene

$$\underset{\displaystyle CH_3}{\big|}$$

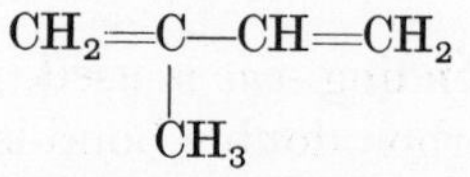

2-Methyl-1,3-butadiene
(isoprene)

$$CH_2{=}CH\text{---}CH{=}CH\text{---}CH{=}CH\text{---}CH_3$$

1,3,5-Heptatriene

The two alkadienes given above are raw materials for synthetic rubber. Compounds having more than two double bonds are often found in nature where they supply the coloring matter for many fruits and vegetables such as tomatoes, carrots, corn, and red peppers. The formula for the yellow coloring matter in eggs, carrots, butter, and other yellow-colored vegetables and animal products is β-carotene which has the structure shown in Figure 29.5.

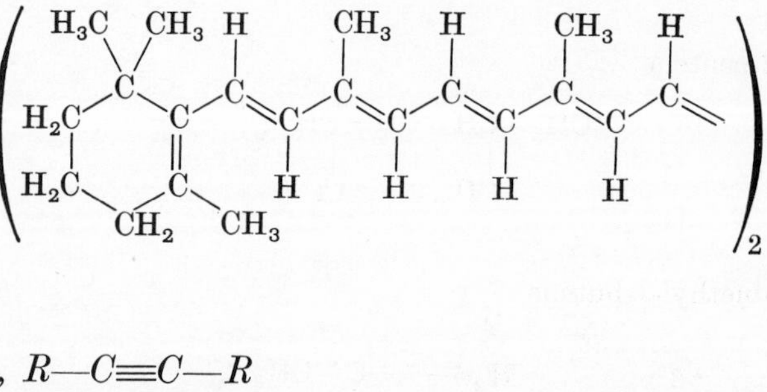

Figure 29.5 β-Carotene.

Alkynes, $R\text{---}C{\equiv}C\text{---}R$

Hydrocarbons containing one triple bond between carbon atoms are known as alkynes. These compounds are similar to the alkenes in both their chemical and physical properties, except that the alkynes can add two moles of reagent per mole of hydrocarbon as illustrated by the reaction

$$H—C{\equiv}C—H + 2Br_2 \longrightarrow H—\overset{\overset{\displaystyle Br}{|}}{C}—\overset{\overset{\displaystyle Br}{|}}{\underset{\underset{\displaystyle Br}{|}}{C}}—H$$

1,1,2,2-Tetrabromoethane

The nomenclature for the alkynes is identical to that of the alkenes except the ending *-yne* is used to denote the presence of the triple bond. Table 29.8 gives the names, formulas, and some physical properties of representative members of the series.

Name	Formula	Melting Point (°C)	Boiling Point (°C)
Ethyne (acetylene)	H—C≡C—H	—	−83.6
Propyne	CH₃—C≡C—H	−104.7	−27.5
1-Butyne	HC≡C—CH₂—CH₃	−130	8.6
2-Butyne	CH₃—C≡C—CH₃	−32.2	27.1
1-Pentyne	HC≡C—CH₂—CH₂—CH₃	−95	40
1-Hexyne	H—C≡C—CH₂—CH₂—CH₂—CH₃	−132	71.5

Table 29.8 Names, Formulas, and Physical Properties of Some Alkynes

The nature of the carbon-to-carbon triple bond was discussed in Chaps. 6 and 10. Ethyne, or acetylene, is a linear molecule in which the carbon atoms use *sp* hybrid orbitals to form σ bonds. The two π bonds between carbon atoms are oriented as shown in Figure 29.6.

Used primarily as intermediates for the synthesis of other organic compounds, including the starting materials for the synthetic fibers Orlon, Acrilan, and Dynel, and in the manufacture of benzene, ethyne is currently the most important member of this family.

Alkyl Halides, RX

When a hydrogen atom on an alkane or cycloalkane molecule is replaced by a halogen atom, the resulting compound is known as an alkyl halide, often represented by the formula RX. Since any of the halogens and any straight, branched or saturated cyclic compounds may be used, the number of possible alkyl halides is large. The alkyl halides are especially useful in the preparation of a variety of aliphatic compounds and as solvents. Table 29.9 gives the common names, formulas, and boiling points of some fluorides, chlorides, bromides, and iodides.

The IUPAC names for alkyl halides are derived from the rules given on page 574. The compound is named for the normal alkane having the same number of carbon atoms as are present in the longest continuous chain of carbon atoms in the compound under consideration.

Figure 29.6 Orbital model of ethyne (acetylene).

$$\underset{\underset{\underset{\displaystyle \text{2-Chloropropane}}{}}{\overset{\displaystyle |}{Cl}}}{CH_3—CH—CH_3} \qquad \underset{\displaystyle \text{1-Iodopropane}}{CH_3—CH_2—CH_2—I}$$

Alkyl halides also may be subclassified into primary, secondary, or tertiary series depending upon the number of hydrocarbon groups attached to the carbon atom bonded to the halogen atom.

$$
\begin{array}{ccc}
\text{H} & \text{R} & \text{R} \\
| & | & | \\
\text{R---C---H} & \text{R---C---H} & \text{R---C---R} \\
| & | & | \\
\text{X} & \text{X} & \text{X}
\end{array}
$$

| A primary halide (the carbon atom attached to the halogen atom holds only one hydrocarbon group) | A secondary halide (two hydrocarbon groups) | A tertiary halide (three hydrocarbon groups) |

Physical Properties of Alkyl Halides. Among the alkyl halides the alkyl iodides have the highest boiling points, followed by the alkyl bromides, chlorides, and fluorides in that order. Since the iodine atom is the most polarizable and the fluorine atom is the least polarizable of the halogens, the order of boiling points can be explained in terms of van der Waals forces associated with the respective halogen atoms. The observed order is opposite to that expected if dipole forces were of primary importance, for these are greatest in the alkyl fluorides and least in the alkyl iodides. Increasing the carbon content also increases the boiling points of the alkyl halides, as shown in Table 29.9.

Alkyl halides are nearly insoluble in or immiscible with water.

Chemical Properties of Alkyl Halides. An especially important use of alkyl halides is in the synthesis of a large number of organic compounds. The versatility of the halides in such syntheses is due to the ease with which the halogen atom is replaced by a number of other functional groups. The general reaction involves the replacement of the halide ion by some other negative ion:

$$ B^- + R\text{---}X \longrightarrow B\text{---}R + X^- $$

Examples of such replacements and of the kinds of compounds that can be synthesized from alkyl halides are given in Chap. 30.

Polyhalogen Compounds. A large number of polyhalogen compounds are known and some of these are of industrial importance. Examples of such compounds and their uses are given in Table 29.10.

Table 29.9 Formulas, Names, and Boiling Points of Some Alkyl Halides

General Formula	Name	Fluoride	Chloride	Bromide	Iodide
			BOILING POINT (°C)		
CH_3---X	Methyl halide	−78.0	−23.7	4.6	42.6
CH_3---CH_2---X	Ethyl halide	−32	12.2	38.0	72.2
CH_3---CH_2---CH_2---X	n-Propyl halide	2	46.6	70.9	102.4
CH_3---CH---X | CH_3	Isopropyl halide	−11	36.5	59.6	89.5
CH_3---CH_2---CH_2---CH_2---X	n-Butyl halide	—	78.0	101.6	127
CHX_3 (an alkyl trihalide)	Haloform	126	61.2	149.5	119 (m.p.)

Name	Formula	Use
Trichloromethane (chloroform)	$CHCl_3$	Anesthetic, sedative, antiseptic
Triiodomethane (iodoform)	CHI_3	Antiseptic
Dichlorodifluoromethane (Freon)	CCl_2F_2	Refrigerants, aerosol, propellants
1,1,2-Trichloroethene	$CCl_2{=}CHCl$	Dry-cleaning solvent

Table 29.10 Some Polyhalogen Compounds and Their Uses

Alkanols or Alcohols, ROH

Compounds containing a hydroxyl group bonded to a carbon atom are known as alkanols. Alcohols include compounds containing one or more hydroxyl groups such as the alkanediols (two OH groups), the alkanetriols (three OH groups), and so on. Of great industrial importance, the alcohols are used as solvents for shellacs, varnishes, and lacquers; in plastics, explosives, cosmetics, drugs, and special fuels; and for many other purposes.

The formulas, IUPAC names, common names, and physical constants of some alcohols are given in Table 29.11.

Name	Formula	Melting Point (°C)	Boiling Point (°C)
Methanol (methyl alcohol)	$CH_3{-}OH$	-97.8	64.5
Ethanol (ethyl alcohol)	$CH_3{-}CH_2{-}OH$	-117.3	78.5
1-Propanol	$CH_3{-}CH_2{-}CH_2{-}OH$	-127	97.8
2-Propanol (isopropyl alcohol)	$CH_3{-}\underset{\underset{CH_3}{\|}}{CH}{-}OH$	-85.8	82.3
1-Butanol	$CH_3{-}CH_2{-}CH_2{-}CH_2{-}OH$	-89.8	117.7
2-Butanol	$CH_3{-}CH_2{-}\underset{\underset{OH}{\|}}{CH}{-}CH_3$	—	99.5
2-Methyl-1-propanol	$CH_3{-}\underset{\underset{CH_3}{\|}}{CH}{-}CH_2{-}OH$	-108	107.3

Table 29.11 Names, Formulas, and Physical Constants of Some Alcohols

An hydroxyl group may be bonded to any carbon atom in the chain. This gives rise to primary, secondary, and tertiary alcohols comparable to the primary, secondary, and tertiary alkyl halides:

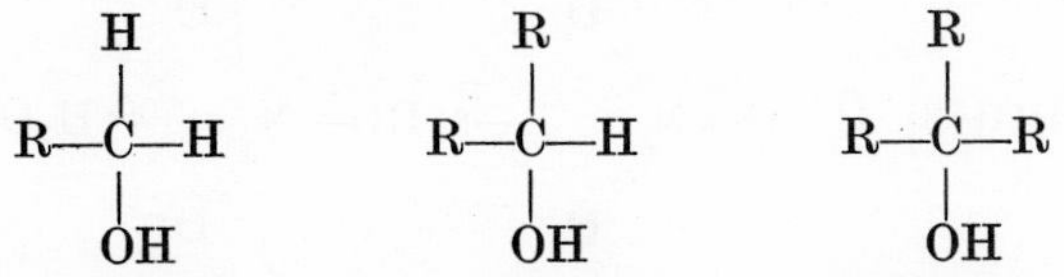

$$
\begin{array}{ccc}
\text{H} & \text{R} & \text{R} \\
| & | & | \\
\text{R}{-}\text{C}{-}\text{H} & \text{R}{-}\text{C}{-}\text{H} & \text{R}{-}\text{C}{-}\text{R} \\
| & | & | \\
\text{OH} & \text{OH} & \text{OH} \\
\text{A primary} & \text{A secondary} & \text{A tertiary} \\
\text{alcohol} & \text{alcohol} & \text{alcohol}
\end{array}
$$

Physical Properties of Alcohols. The boiling points of the alcohols are higher than those of the corresponding alkyl halides or alkanes, due largely to hydrogen bonding among alcohol molecules:

$$
\underset{\overset{\displaystyle |}{H}}{R—\ddot{O}\!:} \quad \underset{\overset{\displaystyle |}{R}}{H—\ddot{O}\!:} \quad \underset{\overset{\displaystyle |}{R}}{H—\ddot{O}\!:}
$$

That hydrogen bonding is responsible for the relatively high boiling points of alcohols is suggested by comparison of the boiling point of ethyl alcohol, 78.5°C, with that of its isomer dimethyl ether, $CH_3—O—CH_3$, which boils at -24°C. In the ether, no hydrogen bonding possibilities exist.

The lower alcohols are all highly soluble in water because in these compounds the hydroxyl group comprises an appreciable portion of the molecule and attraction between the water and alcohol dipoles is important. As the number of carbon atoms in the alcohol molecule increases, the water solubility decreases because the alcohol is becoming more like a hydrocarbon and less like water. For example, 1-hexanol is only slightly soluble in water but highly soluble in hexane.

Chemical Properties of Alcohols. The chemical properties of alcohols may be summarized under three headings: (1) reactions analogous to those of water; (2) reactions in which the hydroxyl group is replaced; and (3) dehydration reactions in which both a hydrogen atom and the hydroxyl group are removed.

1. Reactions analogous to those of water include the following.

(a) Alcohols, like water, show weak acid and base properties:

$$
\underset{\overset{\displaystyle |}{H}}{2R—O} \;\rightleftarrows\; \underset{\overset{\displaystyle |}{H}}{RO—H^+} + RO^-
$$

Oxonium   Alkoxide
ion   ion

(b) Alcohols, like water, react with active metals to liberate hydrogen:

$$
2ROH + 2Na \longrightarrow 2NaOR + H_2
$$

Sodium
alkoxide

2. Replacement of the hydroxyl group can be accomplished by several reagents including phosphorus trihalides and thionyl chloride, $SOCl_2$, nitric, and sulfuric acids.

$$
3ROH + PCl_3 \longrightarrow 3RCl + H_3PO_3
$$

$$
2ROH + SOCl_2 \longrightarrow 2RCl + H_2SO_3
$$

$$
ROH + H—O—N{\overset{\displaystyle O}{\underset{\displaystyle O}{}}} \longrightarrow RO—N{\overset{\displaystyle O}{\underset{\displaystyle O}{}}} + H_2O
$$

Alkyl nitrate

When glycerol is allowed to react with nitric acid, nitroglycerine (glyceryl trinitrate) is formed:

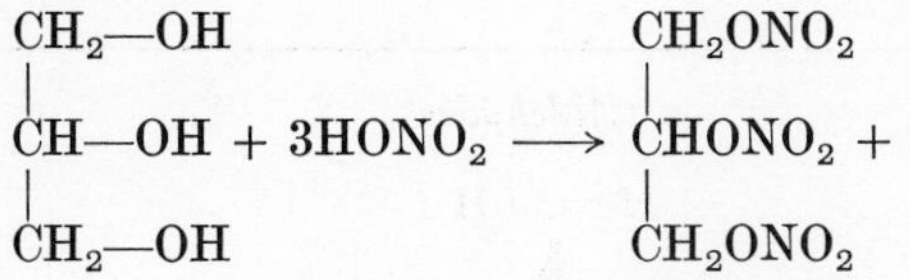

$$
\begin{array}{l}
CH_2\!-\!OH \\
|\\
CH\!-\!OH \ + \ 3HONO_2 \ \longrightarrow \\
|\\
CH_2\!-\!OH
\end{array}
\qquad
\begin{array}{l}
CH_2ONO_2 \\
|\\
CHONO_2 \ + \ 3H_2O \\
|\\
CH_2ONO_2 \\
\text{Nitroglycerine}
\end{array}
$$

When alcohols react with sulfuric acid, alkyl hydrogen sulfates are formed:

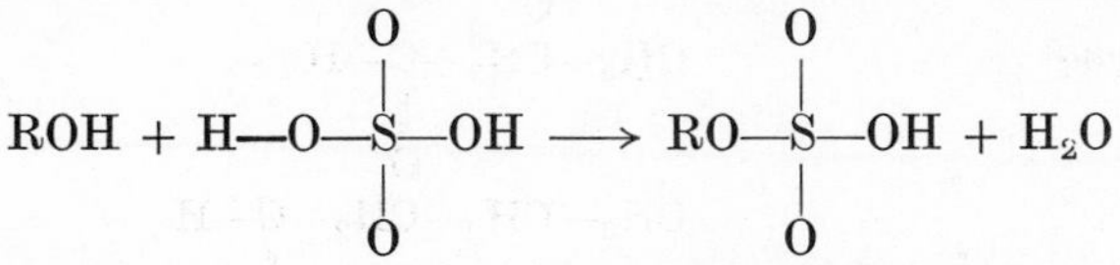

$$
\begin{array}{ccc}
& O & O \\
& \| & \| \\
ROH \ + \ H\!-\!O\!-\!S\!-\!OH & \longrightarrow & RO\!-\!S\!-\!OH \ + \ H_2O \\
& \| & \| \\
& O & O
\end{array}
$$

Alkyl hydrogen sulfate

The sodium salts of alkyl hydrogen sulfates made from long-chain alcohols (C_{12} to C_{14}) are detergents.

3. Dehydration of alcohols results in the formation of alkenes and may be accomplished using hot, concentrated sulfuric acid:

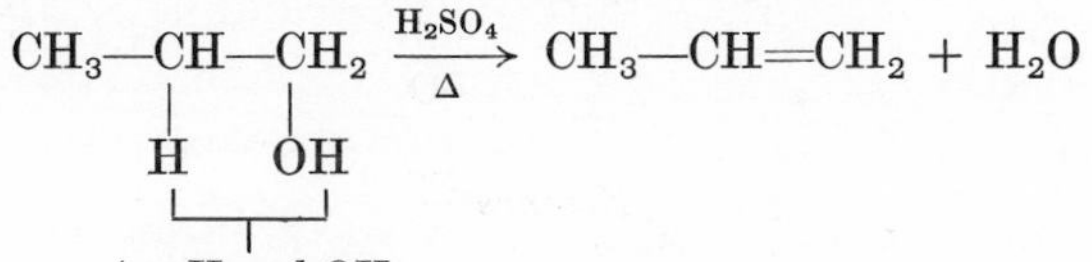

$$
\begin{array}{c}
CH_3\!-\!CH\!-\!CH_2 \ \xrightarrow[\Delta]{H_2SO_4} \ CH_3\!-\!CH\!=\!CH_2 \ + \ H_2O \\
| \qquad | \\
H \quad\ OH
\end{array}
$$

(an H and OH
on adjacent
carbon atoms
are removed)

$$
\begin{array}{cc}
O & O \\
\| & \| \\
\textit{Aldehydes (Alkanals), } RC\!-\!H; \ \textit{Ketones (Alkanones), } \ R\!-\!C\!-\!R
\end{array}
$$

Compounds containing the group

$$
\begin{array}{c}
-C\!-\!H \\
\| \\
O
\end{array}
$$

are known as aldehydes; compounds containing the group

$$
\begin{array}{c}
C\!-\!C\!-\!C \\
\| \\
O
\end{array}
$$

are called ketones. The group

$$
\begin{array}{c}
-C\!- \\
\| \\
O
\end{array}
$$

common to both aldehydes and ketones is known as a carbonyl group. The aldehyde group is always located at the end of a chain of carbon atoms; the carbonyl portion of the ketone group is located on nonterminal

Table 29.12 Names, Formulas, and Boiling Points for Some Aldehydes and Ketones

Name	Formula	Boiling Point (°C)
Aldehydes		
Formaldehyde (methanal)	$H-C-H$ $\underset{O}{\overset{\|}{}}$	-21
Acetaldehyde (ethanal)	CH_3-C-H $\underset{O}{\overset{\|}{}}$	20.2
Propionaldehyde (propanal)	CH_3-CH_2-C-H $\underset{O}{\overset{\|}{}}$	48.8
Butyraldehyde (butanal)	$CH_3-CH_2-CH_2-C-H$ $\underset{O}{\overset{\|}{}}$	61
Benzaldehyde	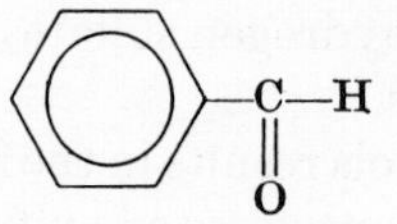 C₆H₅—C—H ‖ O	179.5
Acrolein (propenal)	$CH_2{=}CH-C-H$ $\underset{O}{\overset{\|}{}}$	52.5
Ketones		
Acetone (propanone)	CH_3-C-CH_3 $\underset{O}{\overset{\|}{}}$	56.1
Methyl ethyl ketone (butanone)	$CH_3-C-CH_2-CH_3$ $\underset{O}{\overset{\|}{}}$	79.6
Diethyl ketone (3-pentanone)	$CH_3-CH_2-C-CH_2-CH_3$ $\underset{O}{\overset{\|}{}}$	102.7
Methyl *n*-propyl ketone (2-pentanone)	$CH_3-C-CH_2-CH_2-CH_3$ $\underset{O}{\overset{\|}{}}$	101.7

Note: Common names are listed first here to emphasize their common usage for these compounds and to point out that the systematic names are not necessarily preferred.

carbon atoms. Table 29.12 gives names and formulas for some aldehydes and ketones.

The simplest aldehydes and ketones are known by their common names. The IUPAC nomenclature rules designate that the characteristic ending for aldehydes is -*al* and the ending for ketones is -*one*. The usual rule of selecting the longest continuous chain of carbon atoms containing the aldehyde or ketone group as the basis for the name is followed here as in the other homologous series. Thus the compound

$$CH_3-CH_2-\underset{O}{\overset{\|}{C}}-\underset{\underset{CH_3}{\overset{|}{CH_2}}}{CH}-CH_2-CH_3$$

is named 4-ethyl-3-hexanone, and

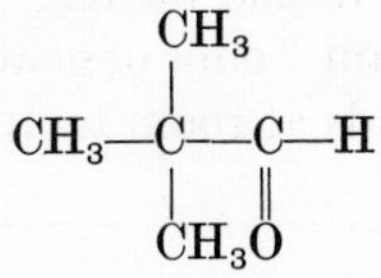

$$
\begin{array}{c}
CH_3 \\
| \\
CH_3-C-C-H \\
| \quad \parallel \\
CH_3 \quad O
\end{array}
$$

is 2,2-dimethylpropanal.

The simpler aldehydes and ketones, except formaldehyde, are liquids, and the C_1 to C_4 compounds are freely soluble in water. All the low molecular weight aldehydes and ketones have a penetrating odor, but as the carbon content increases, the odor becomes fragrant. As a result certain aldehydes and ketones are used in perfumes.

An aldehyde may be distinguished from a ketone by weak oxidizing agents. The aldehyde is very easily oxidized, the

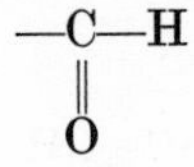

$$
\begin{array}{c}
-C-H \\
\parallel \\
O
\end{array}
$$

group being changed to a

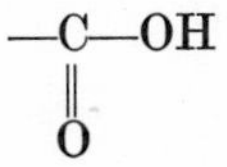

$$
\begin{array}{c}
-C-OH \\
\parallel \\
O
\end{array}
$$

group, while the ketone is oxidized only by strong oxidizing agents. Two special reagents, Fehling's solution (which contains Cu^{+2} ions) and Tollen's reagent (which contains Ag^+ ions), are weak oxidizing agents which will oxidize aldehydes but not ketones. In Fehling's solution an aldehyde reduces the copper(II) ion to copper(I) ion which precipitates as red copper(I) oxide, Cu_2O. An aldehyde also reduces the silver ion, Ag^+, in Tollen's reagent to metallic silver which forms a silver mirror on the walls of the glass test tube.

Reactions of aldehydes and ketones are of great importance. They will be discussed in Chap. 30.

Carboxylic Acids, $RC\overset{\displaystyle O}{\overset{\displaystyle \parallel}{-}}OH$

Compounds containing the carboxyl group

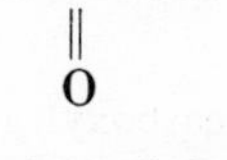

$$
\begin{array}{c}
-C-OH \\
\parallel \\
O
\end{array}
$$

(the name comes from *carbo*nyl and hydr*oxyl*) comprise the class of substances known as carboxylic acids. Many of these compounds are found in plants and animals either free or combined with alcohols. The members of this series are weak acids having ionization constants at 25°C of about 1×10^{-5}. The IUPAC nomenclature for these acids follows the pattern of the previously discussed series except that the ending *-oic* acid is employed as illustrated in Table 29.13.

The lower members of the series have disagreeable odors. Butanoic acid is responsible for the odor in rancid butter. The C_6, C_8, and C_{10} straight-chain acids have the unpleasant "odor of goats." The acids containing one to ten carbon atoms are liquids at room temperature, the higher members

Table 29.13 Names, Formulas, and Physical Constants of Some Carboxylic Acids

Name	Formula	Melting Point (°C)	Boiling Point (°C)	Ionization Constant at 25°C
Methanoic acid (formic acid)	H—C—OH ‖ O	8.4	100.5	2.1×10^{-4}
Ethanoic acid (acetic acid)	CH_3—C—OH ‖ O	16.6	118.1	1.8×10^{-5}
Propanoic acid (propionic acid)	CH_3—CH_2—C—OH ‖ O	−22	141.1	1.3×10^{-5}
Butanoic acid (butyric acid)	CH_3—CH_2—CH_2—C—OH ‖ O	−7.9	163.5	1.5×10^{-5}
2-Methylpropanoic acid (isobutyric acid)	CH_3—CH—C—OH | ‖ CH_3 O	−47.0	154.4	1.4×10^{-5}

Table 29.14 Reaction Sites in Carboxylic Acids and Possible Reaction Products

Site of Reaction	Description	Products
1. R—C—O—H ‖ O	Replacement of ionizable hydrogen by reaction with active metals or with base	R—C—O⁻M⁺ ‖ O salts
2. R—C—OH ‖ O	Replacement of the hydroxyl group—e.g., (a) by reaction with alcohols,	R—C—OR′ ‖ O esters
	(b) by reaction with PCl_3 or $SOCl_2$	R—C—X ‖ O acyl halides
3. R—C—OH ‖ O	Reaction at the carbonyl group—e.g., reaction with reducing agents	R—CH_2—OH alcohols
4. R—C—OH ‖ O	Removal of the carboxyl group—e.g., fusion with sodium or electrolysis of acid	RH alkane
5. R—C—OH ‖ O	Reactions with the alkyl group—e.g., Cl_2 will substitute for hydrogen atoms on alkyl portion of molecule	R′—CH—CO_2H | Cl 2-chloroalkanoic acid

are waxlike solids. All the acids have relatively high boiling points due in part to hydrogen bonding in the liquid and in part to relatively strong van der Waals forces. Acids containing one to four carbon atoms are completely miscible with water; those having six or more carbon atoms are almost insoluble in water. This reflects again the interplay between the polar and nonpolar portions of the molecules in determining the properties of the substance. The short-chain molecules have small nonpolar portions and are soluble in water; the long-chain molecules have large nonpolar portions and are not soluble in water but are soluble in hydrocarbons.

Chemical Reactions of Acids. The chemical reactions of carboxylic acids may be predicted from the structure of the molecule. Five different kinds of reactions are thus predicted, and all are experimentally observed. They are summarized in Table 29.14.

Carboxylic acids and their esters (compounds with alcohols) are found in all living things. Methanoic, or formic, acid is found in bees and in sea nettles and is responsible for the irritation following the sting from these organisms. Acetic acid and its derivatives are important in both carbohydrate and lipid (fat) metabolism. Esters of this acid have the pleasant odors associated with many fruits and flowers. Long-chain acids such as the C_{16} and C_{18} compounds are found in fats.

Some common polycarboxylic acids are illustrated below:

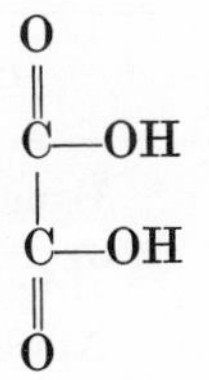

Oxalic acid
(ethanedioic acid)

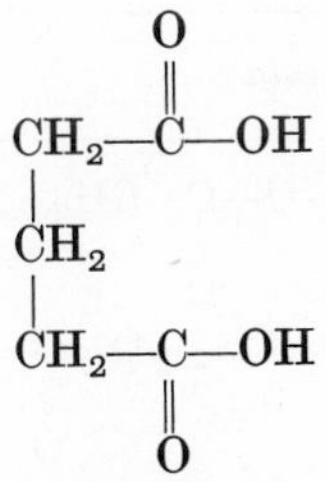

Glutaric acid
(pentanedioic
acid)

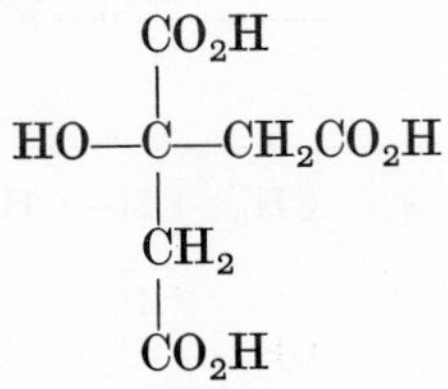

Citric acid
(3-carboxyl-3-hydroxy-
pentanedioic acid)

Derivatives of Carboxylic Acids

Important derivatives of carboxylic acids include esters,

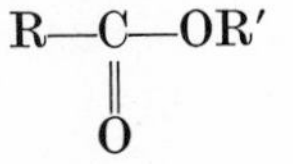

$$R—C—OR'$$
$$\|$$
$$O$$

metal salts, $RCO_2^-M^+$, acyl halides,

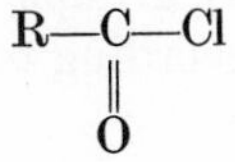

$$R—C—Cl$$
$$\|$$
$$O$$

acid anhydrides,

$$R—C—O—C—R$$
$$\|\quad\quad\|$$
$$O\quad\quad O$$

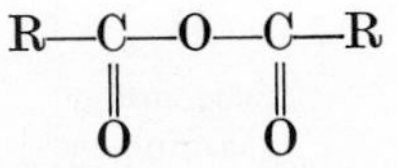

and amides,

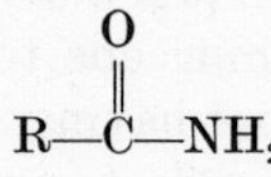

$$R—\overset{\overset{\displaystyle O}{\|}}{C}—NH_2$$

Esters. These compounds, many of which are liquids and have fragrant odors, are formed when carboxylic acids react with alcohols.

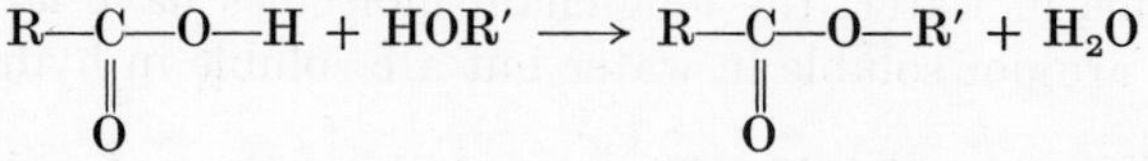

$$R—\underset{\underset{\displaystyle O}{\|}}{C}—O—H + HOR' \longrightarrow R—\underset{\underset{\displaystyle O}{\|}}{C}—O—R' + H_2O$$

Esters are named from the alkyl group of the alcohol and the anion of the acid. For example, the ester formed between ethyl alcohol and acetic acid

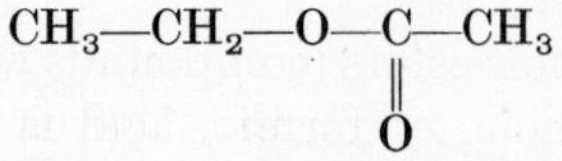

$$CH_3—CH_2—O—\underset{\underset{\displaystyle O}{\|}}{C}—CH_3$$

is ethyl acetate. Names, formulas and odors of various esters are given in Table 29.15.

The other derivatives of carboxylic acids will be discussed as needed in subsequent chapters. Nearly all are reactive substances and are used in many syntheses.

Table 29.15 Names, Formulas, and Odors of Various Esters

Name	Formula	Odor
Isoamyl acetate	$CH_3—\underset{\underset{\displaystyle CH_3}{\|}}{CH}—CH_2—CH_2—O—\underset{\underset{\displaystyle O}{\|}}{C}—CH_3$	Banana oil
Amyl acetate (*n*-pentyl ethanoate)	$CH_3—CH_2—CH_2—CH_2—CH_2—O—\underset{\underset{\displaystyle O}{\|}}{C}—CH_3$	Apricot, cider
Isoamyl isovalerate	$CH_3—\underset{\underset{\displaystyle CH_3}{\|}}{CH}—CH_2—CH_2—O—\underset{\underset{\displaystyle O}{\|}}{C}—CH_2—\underset{\underset{\displaystyle CH_3}{\|}}{CH}—CH_3$	Apple
Ethyl butyrate	$CH_3—CH_2—O—\underset{\underset{\displaystyle O}{\|}}{C}—CH_2—CH_2—CH_3$	Apricot, peach
Octyl acetate	$CH_3—(CH_2)_6—CH_2—O—\underset{\underset{\displaystyle O}{\|}}{C}—CH_3$	Orange

Amines

Amines are derivatives of ammonia in which one or more hydrogen atoms are replaced by alkyl (or aryl) groups, and they are called primary, secondary, or tertiary amines according to the number of hydrogen atoms replaced.

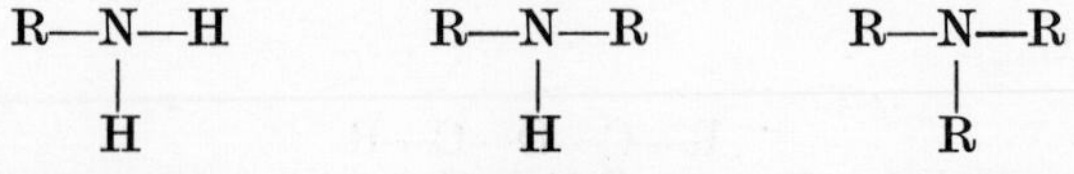

$$\underset{\underset{\displaystyle H}{\|}}{R—N—H} \qquad \underset{\underset{\displaystyle H}{\|}}{R—N—R} \qquad \underset{\underset{\displaystyle R}{\|}}{R—N—R}$$

A primary   A secondary   A tertiary
amine   amine   amine

The aliphatic amines resemble ammonia but are more basic than ammonia. The lower members of the series are gases and are soluble in water. Volatile amines have a fishlike odor with a hint of the ammonia odor. The aromatic amines are weaker bases than ammonia. Found in both plants and animals, amines are used to make medicinals, including sulfa drugs, local anesthetics, and anti-malarials. Table 29.16 gives names, formulas, and boiling points of a number of amines.

Name	Formula	Boiling Point (°C)
Methylamine	$CH_3—NH_2$	−6.5
Ethylamine	$CH_3—CH_2—NH_2$	16.6
n-Propylamine	$CH_3—CH_2—CH_2—NH_2$	48.7
n-Butylamine	$CH_3—CH_2—CH_2—CH_2—NH_2$	77.8
Dimethylamine	$CH_3—\overset{\displaystyle CH_3}{\overset{\displaystyle |}{N}}—H$	7.4
Trimethylamine	$CH_3—\underset{\underset{\displaystyle CH_3}{\displaystyle |}}{\overset{\displaystyle CH_3}{\overset{\displaystyle |}{N}}}—CH_3$	3.5
Ethylene diamine	$NH_2—CH_2—CH_2—NH_2$	117

Table 29.16 Names, Formulas, and Boiling Points of Some Aliphatic Amines

Aromatic Compounds

An introduction to the chemistry of aromatic compounds and their molecular structure was given in Chap. 10. Benzene, usually represented by the formula

is the parent compound of the entire class of aromatic substances.

Because of resonance stabilization, aromatic rings are relatively unreactive at room temperature. However the hydrogen atoms in these structures may be substituted by various monovalent groups. Examples are chlorobenzene,

and m-dinitrobenzene,

Such substitution gives rise to aromatic compounds containing nearly all the functional groups discussed in the preceding sections. Thus there are

aromatic amines such as aniline,

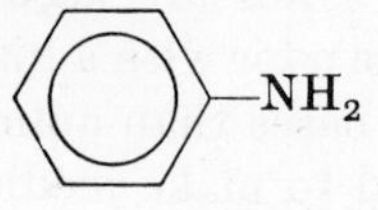

aromatic aldehydes and ketones such as benzaldehyde,

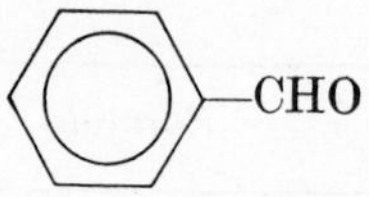

and benzophenone,

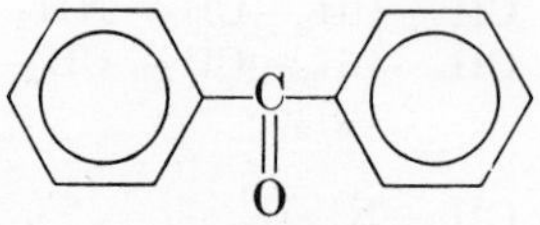

aromatic hydroxyl compounds, known as phenols and exemplified by phenol itself,

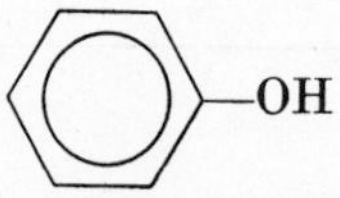

aromatic acids, $ArCO_2H$, etc.   Examples of some of these substances are given in Table 29.17.

If more than one hydrogen atom in benzene is replaced, numerous isomers can be formed, as shown in Chap. 10.

Aromatic compounds, many obtained from the distillation of coal tar, are used in pharmaceuticals, dyestuffs, explosives, plastics, fibers, perfumes, insecticides, lacquers, solvents, and many other materials. Benzene is an important fuel and solvent; phenol is a common disinfectant; substituted phenols are widely used to impregnate wood to protect it against decay and insects; naphthalene is used in "moth balls;" aniline is the base of the dye industry; chlorobenzene is used in the manufacture of DDT insecticide; styrene,

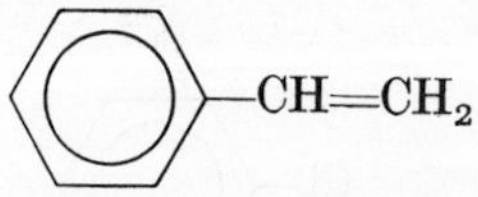

is a component of synthetic rubber and of plastics; trinitrotoluene and picric acid, (trinitrophenol) are high explosives; benzene sulfonic acid,

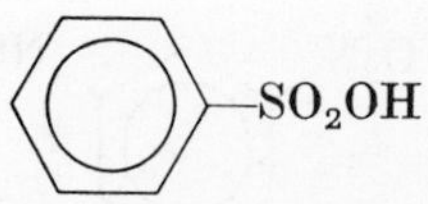

and its derivatives are used as detergents, sulfa drugs, and antiseptics.

The chemistry of aromatic compounds is some of the most interesting and highly developed in all of chemistry.

Formula	Name	Melting Point (°C)	Boiling Point (°C)
benzene ring	Benzene	5.5	80.1
naphthalene	Naphthalene	80.3	218
chlorobenzene —Cl	Chlorobenzene	−45.2	132.1
phenol —OH	Phenol	41	182
toluene —CH$_3$	Toluene	−95	110.6
benzoic acid —C—OH, O	Benzoic acid	121.4	—
aniline —NH$_2$	Aniline	−6.2	184.4
nitrobenzene —NO$_2$	Nitrobenzene	5.8	210

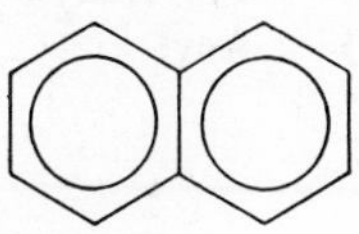

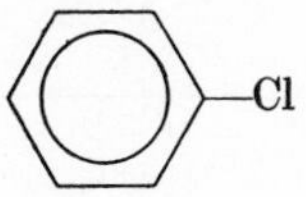

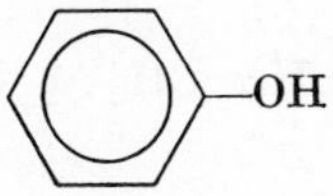

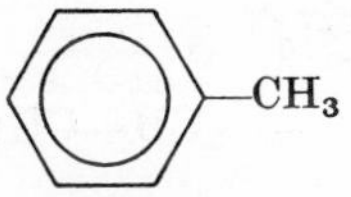

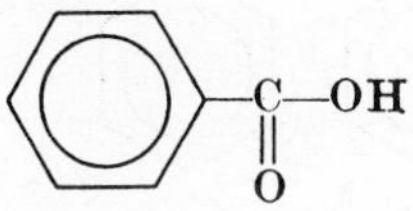

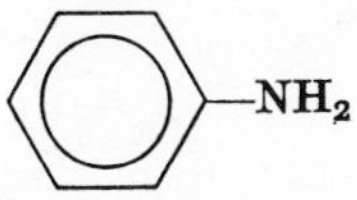

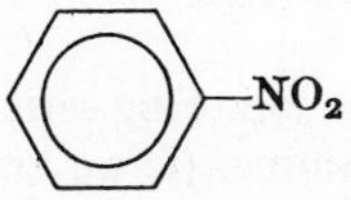

Table 29.17 Formulas, Names, and Physical Constants of Some Aromatic Compounds

SUMMARY

In this chapter we have sought to classify many of the more than two million known organic compounds, first into broad groups known as the aliphatic and aromatic divisions, and then into smaller families or series of compounds called homologous series. The compounds in each series are shown to possess certain similarities in properties and structure. Some important structural features and properties have been summarized for ten homologous series, and a system of nomenclature has been developed for members of these series.

SOME SPECIAL TERMS

Aliphatic	**Alkynes**	**Amines**	**Nitroalkyls**
Aromatic	**Alkanols**	**Alkyl halides**	**Esters**
Homologous series	**Alkanals**	**Aryl halides**	**Ethers**
Alkanes	**Alkanones**	**Phenols**	**Sulfonic acids**
Alkenes	**Alkanoic acids**	**Nitroaryls**	**Thiols**
	Alkanedioic acids		**Diols**

Methyl	**Phenyl**	**Trifluoromethyl**	**Cycloalkyl**
Ethyl	**Ethenyl**	**Amino**	**Acyl**
Propyl	**Ethnyl**	**Mercapto**	
tert-Butyl	**Methoxy**	**Halo**	
cis and trans isomers			
o, m, and p isomers			

QUESTIONS AND PROBLEMS

1. Name each of the following:

   (a) 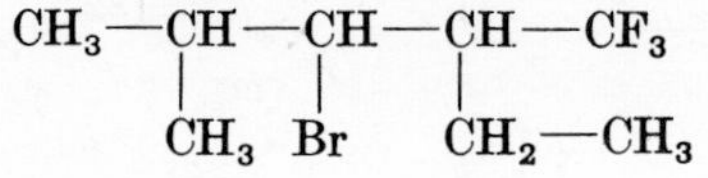 $CH_3-CH-CH-CH-CF_3$
   with CH_3, Br, CH_2-CH_3 substituents

   (d) 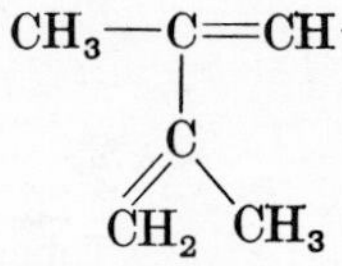 $CH_3-C=CH-CH_3$ with C / CH_2 CH_3

   (b) $CH_2=C-CH_2-CH-CH_3$ with CH_3 and phenyl

   (e) $CH_3-CH——CH-CHO$ with two phenyl groups

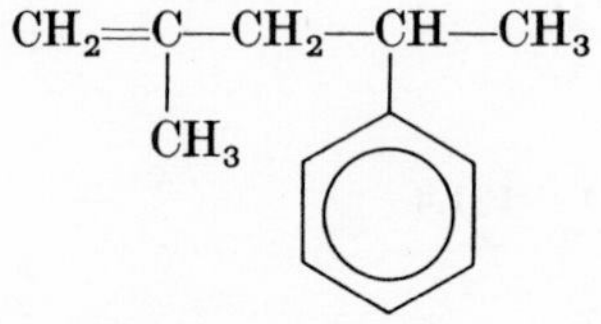

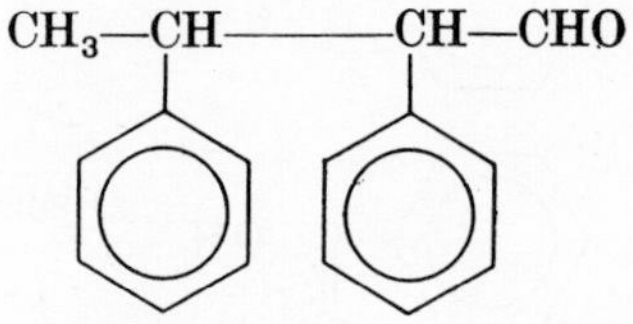

   (c) phenyl—$CH-CH_2-CO_2H$ with $CH=CH_2$

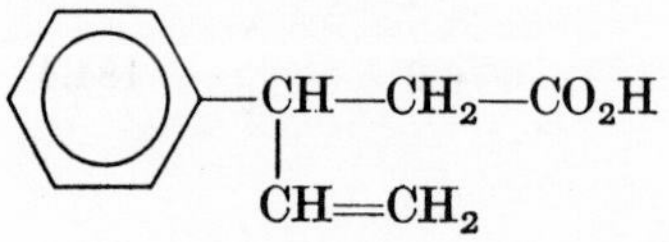

   (f) 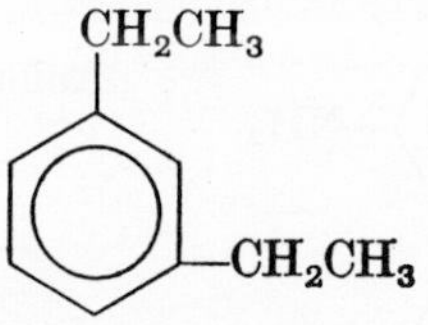 CH_2CH_3 ... CH_2CH_3 on benzene ring

2. Write a structural formula for one compound in each of the following series: (a) a diene, (b) a triol, (c) an ether, (d) an ester, (e) an amine, (f) an aryl bromide, (g) an aromatic ketone, (h) an acetylene, (i) an acid anhydride, (j) an acid halide, (k) a dicarboxylic acid.

3. Write structural formulas for each of the following: (a) o-nitrophenol, (b) 2,4,6-tribromotoluene, (c) cis-2-pentene, (d) trichloracetic acid, (e) ethylene glycol, (f) tert-butyl alcohol, (g) 2-aminopropanoic acid, (h) 3-ethenyl-1,3-pentadiene.

4. Write structural formulas for: (a) all isomers of heptane, (b) all alcohols having the formula $C_5H_{11}OH$, (c) all isomers of trichlorobenzene, (d) all possible dichloro-2-butenes.

5. Offer an explanation for the fact (a) that the boiling points of the isomeric pentanes decrease in the order

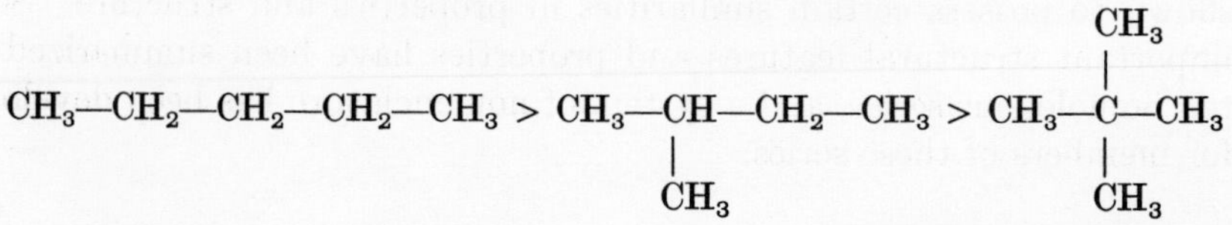

$$CH_3-CH_2-CH_2-CH_2-CH_3 > CH_3-CH-CH_2-CH_3 > CH_3-C-CH_3$$

with CH_3 substituent on the middle structure, and CH_3 (top and bottom) on the right structure.

and (b) that in general more highly branched isomers have lower boiling points than their straight-chain analogues.

6. On analysis a certain secondary alcohol was found to contain 60.0 per cent carbon, 13.3 per cent hydrogen, and 26.6 per cent oxygen. Write a structural formula for this alcohol.

7. Offer an explanation for the observation that the boiling points of alkyl halides generally increase in the order RF < RCl < RBr < RI more or less independently of the particular R group. (Table 29.9.)

8. Give examples of reactions in which alcohols act (a) as acids, (b) as bases.

9. Account for the variation in boiling point among the following two-carbon molecules.

Substance	Boiling Point (°C)
Ethyl chloride	12.2
Ethyl alcohol	78.5
Ethylamine	16.6
Propionic acid	141.1

10. It is said that amines are stronger bases than ammonia. Offer an explanation for (a) the fact that amines are basic and (b) the fact that in general they are stronger bases than ammonia.

REFERENCES

ALLINGER, N. L., and J. ALLINGER. *Structures of Organic Molecules.* Englewood Cliffs, N. J.: Prentice-Hall, 1965.

BORDWELL, F. *Organic Chemistry.* New York: Macmillan, 1963.

HART, H., and R. A. SCHUETZ. *A Short Course in Organic Chemistry*, 3rd ed. Boston: Houghton Mifflin, 1966.

HERZ, W. *The Shape of Carbon Compounds.* New York: Benjamin, 1963.

30

Organic Chemistry II: Reactivity of Some Organic Structures

The preparation of the organomagnesium ethers is, in general, extremely simple. The apparatus is just a round-bottomed flask connected with a good ascending condenser and with a dropping funnel with stopcock, but it is indispensable that everything be absolutely dry.   Victor Grignard (1871–1935)

Each functional group in organic compounds is associated with several chemical reactions unique to that group (Chap. 10). Nearly all members of the homologous series containing a given functional group will undergo the reactions associated with that group. For example, all alkanes react with chlorine, under the proper conditions, to give alkyl chlorides, and nearly all alkyl chlorides in the presence of aqueous sodium hydroxide will react to give alcohols. The existence of reactions associated with a specific functional group makes it possible to relate chemical reactivity to molecular structure, to predict the kinds of reactions a new substance may undergo, and to plan a sequence of chemical reactions for the synthesis of a substance.

While it is possible to summarize the reactions associated with each functional group, we shall find it useful and informative to look for broad classes of reactions which are common to a number of functional groups and which relate structure to reactivity in a most fundamental way. At least five broad classes of such reactions are recognized:

1. *Oxidation and Reduction Reactions.* Oxidation reactions in organic chemistry are those in which carbon-hydrogen bonds are broken and carbon-oxygen bonds are formed. An illustration of the scope of oxidation reactions is given by the following sequence in which an alkane is oxidized

first to an alcohol, then to an aldehyde, then to a carboxylic acid, and finally to carbon dioxide and water.

$$CH_4 \xrightarrow{[O]} CH_3OH \xrightarrow{[O]} HCHO \xrightarrow{[O]} HCO_2H \xrightarrow{[O]} CO_2 + H_2O$$

Alkane   Alcohol   Aldehyde   Carboxylic acid

Reduction reactions are those in which hydrogen atoms are added to an organic compound; this is sometimes accompanied by removal of oxygen atoms or atoms of other nonmetals.

Reductions may be illustrated by the equations

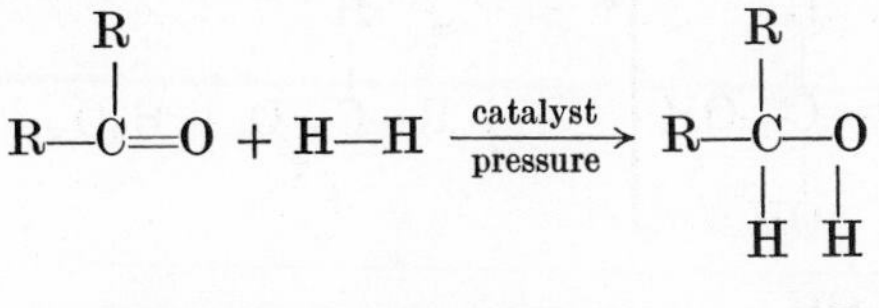

$$\underset{\displaystyle R}{R—\overset{\displaystyle R}{\underset{|}{C}}=O} + H—H \xrightarrow[\text{pressure}]{\text{catalyst}} R—\overset{\displaystyle R}{\underset{|}{\underset{\displaystyle H}{\underset{|}{C}}}}—\overset{}{\underset{\displaystyle H}{\underset{|}{O}}}$$

$$R—CH_2—X + \text{reducing agent} \longrightarrow R—CH_3 + \text{other products}$$
(X is a nonmetal)

2. *Condensation Reactions.* These are reactions in which two molecules join together (condense), often with the elimination of a small molecule such as water, ammonia, or hydrogen chloride, as illustrated below:

$$X—OH + Y—OH \longrightarrow X—O—Y + H_2O$$

3. *Addition Reactions.* In these reactions a small molecule, or molecules, adds or joins to another molecule. Such reactions occur at double or triple bonds and may be represented by the generalized equation

$$A—A + X{=}Y \longrightarrow \underset{\displaystyle A \quad A}{X—Y}$$

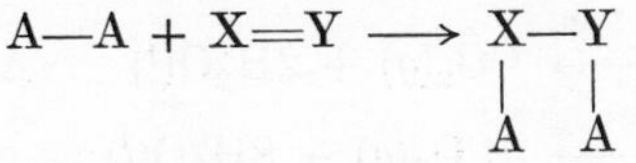

4. *Elimination Reactions.* In these reactions a small molecule such as water or hydrogen chloride is removed from an organic compound. Usually the portions of the small molecule are removed from adjacent carbon atoms in the organic compound as illustrated by the equation

$$\underset{\displaystyle X \quad Y}{R—CH—CH—R'} \longrightarrow RCH{=}CHR' + X—Y$$

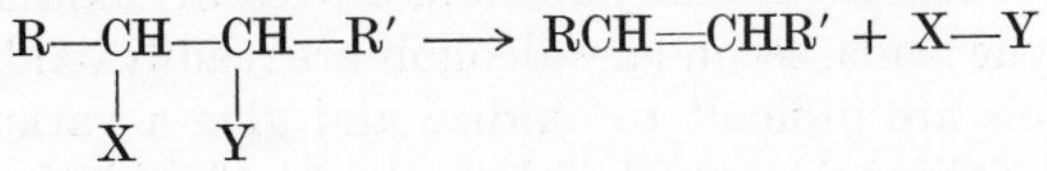

Eliminations usually result in the formation of double or triple bonds.

5. *Substitution Reactions.* In these reactions one atom or group displaces another atom or group as illustrated by the generalized equation

$$A + R—X \longrightarrow A—R + X$$

The entering and leaving groups include monovalent groups such as hydrogen, halogen, hydroxyl, amino, and many others.

Oxidation and Reduction Reactions

Oxidation and reduction reactions are among the most important and useful reactions of organic compounds, and because of the many possibilities for oxidation or reduction in the variety of organic structures known, these reactions are probably the most diverse in scope, conditions, and required reagents of any class of organic reactions.

Oxidations. The types of reactions involved in the oxidation of a saturated carbon atom appear to involve:

1. Replacement of —H by —OH,

$$R\text{—}H + [O]^* \longrightarrow R\text{—}OH$$

2. Successive oxidation on the carbon atom that is already partially oxidized,

$$R\text{—}\overset{\displaystyle H}{\underset{\displaystyle H}{\overset{\displaystyle |}{\underset{\displaystyle |}{C}}}}\text{—}OH \xrightarrow{[O]} \left[R\text{—}\overset{\displaystyle H}{\underset{\displaystyle OH}{\overset{\displaystyle |}{\underset{\displaystyle |}{C}}}}\text{—}OH \right]^* \longrightarrow R\text{—}\overset{\displaystyle H}{\overset{\displaystyle |}{C}}\text{=}O + H_2O$$

$$R\text{—}\overset{\displaystyle H}{\overset{\displaystyle |}{C}}\text{=}O \xrightarrow{[O]} R\text{—}\overset{\displaystyle OH}{\overset{\displaystyle |}{C}}\text{=}O$$

3. Complete oxidation to carbon dioxide and water.

Using these possible reactions, we discuss some typical oxidation reactions below.

Oxidation of Alkanes. Alkanes burn in air or oxygen with the formation of carbon dioxide and water, and with the liberation of large amounts of heat. As a result, hydrocarbons are among our most important fuels for heat and power.

$$CH_4(g) + 2O_2(g) \longrightarrow CO_2(g) + 2H_2O(l) \qquad \Delta H^\circ = -210,800 \text{ cal}$$

$$C_7H_{16}(l) + 11O_2(g) \longrightarrow 7CO_2(g) + 8H_2O(l) \qquad \Delta H^\circ = -1,146,000 \text{ cal}$$

In the presence of insufficient oxygen, carbon monoxide and carbon may form, resulting in less efficient heat or power production and in a safety hazard.

Oxidation of Alcohols. Primary alcohols are readily oxidized to aldehydes and to carboxylic acids; secondary alcohols are readily oxidized to ketones; tertiary alcohols are difficult to oxidize and give a variety of oxidation products. All of this is in accord with the types of oxidation reaction given above.

$$R\text{—}\overset{\displaystyle H}{\underset{\displaystyle H}{\overset{\displaystyle |}{\underset{\displaystyle |}{C}}}}\text{—}OH \xrightarrow{[O]} \left[R\text{—}\overset{\displaystyle H}{\underset{\displaystyle OH}{\overset{\displaystyle |}{\underset{\displaystyle |}{C}}}}\text{—}OH \right] \longrightarrow R\text{—}\overset{\displaystyle H}{\overset{\displaystyle |}{C}}\text{=}O \xrightarrow{[O]} R\text{—}\overset{\displaystyle OH}{\overset{\displaystyle |}{C}}\text{=}O$$

A primary   An aldehyde   A carboxylic acid
alcohol   (usually difficult
to isolate)

---

* Brackets in these cases represent an unstable or sometimes an assumed intermediate species.

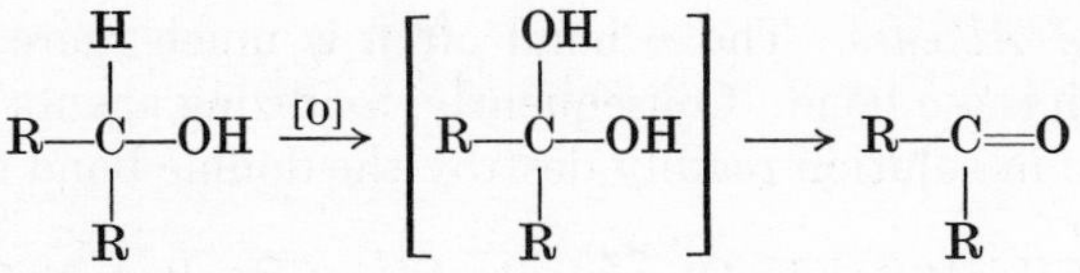

$$\underset{\substack{\text{A secondary}\\\text{alcohol}}}{R-\overset{\displaystyle H}{\underset{\displaystyle R}{\overset{|}{\underset{|}{C}}}}-OH} \xrightarrow{[O]} \left[R-\overset{\displaystyle OH}{\underset{\displaystyle R}{\overset{|}{\underset{|}{C}}}-OH} \right] \longrightarrow \underset{\text{A ketone}}{R-\overset{|}{\underset{\displaystyle R}{C}}=O}$$

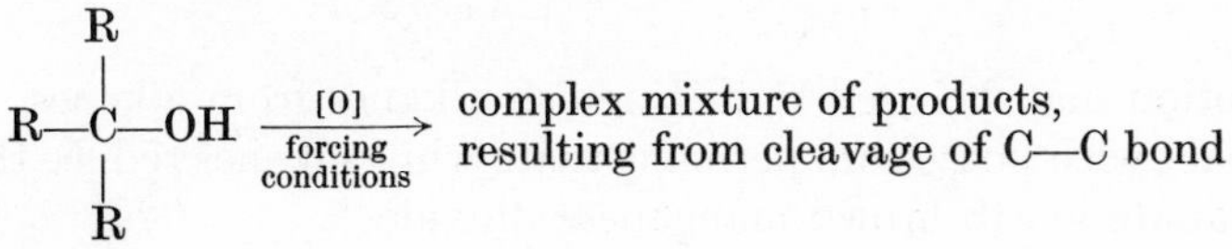

$$\underset{\substack{\text{A tertiary}\\\text{alcohol (no easily}\\\text{oxidized C—H bond)}}}{R-\overset{\displaystyle R}{\underset{\displaystyle R}{\overset{|}{\underset{|}{C}}}-OH}} \xrightarrow[\substack{\text{forcing}\\\text{conditions}}]{[O]} \substack{\text{complex mixture of products,}\\\text{resulting from cleavage of C—C bond}}$$

Oxidation of alcohols is used as a method of preparing a few aldehydes and a number of ketones and as a diagnostic test to ascertain if a given alcohol is primary, secondary, or tertiary. Oxidizing agents commonly used to oxidize alcohols are acidified solutions of potassium dichromate, $K_2Cr_2O_7$, or potassium permanganate, $KMnO_4$. Hot copper oxidizes (dehydrogenates) low molecular weight alcohols in the vapor state to aldehydes or ketones.

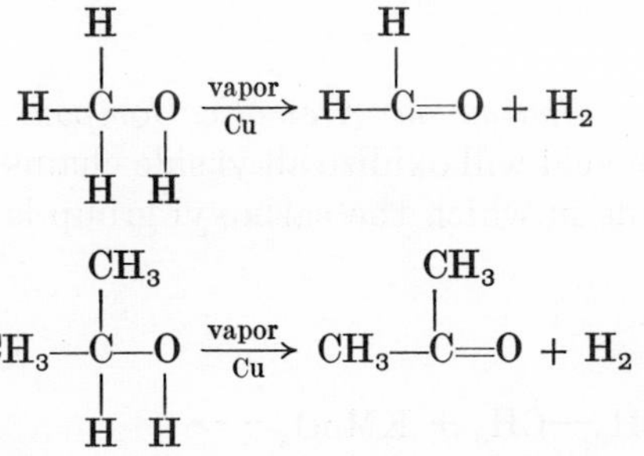

$$H-\overset{\displaystyle H}{\underset{\displaystyle H}{\overset{|}{\underset{|}{C}}}-\overset{\displaystyle }{\underset{\displaystyle H}{\overset{}{\underset{|}{O}}}} \xrightarrow[\text{Cu}]{\text{vapor}} H-\overset{\displaystyle H}{\overset{|}{C}}=O + H_2$$

$$CH_3-\overset{\displaystyle CH_3}{\underset{\displaystyle H}{\overset{|}{\underset{|}{C}}}-\overset{\displaystyle }{\underset{\displaystyle H}{\overset{}{\underset{|}{O}}}} \xrightarrow[\text{Cu}]{\text{vapor}} CH_3-\overset{\displaystyle CH_3}{\overset{|}{C}}=O + H_2$$

Oxidation of Aldehydes and Ketones. As indicated in Chap. 29, aldehydes are very readily oxidized to carboxylic acids and ketones are oxidized only with difficulty. The reason for this is the presence of the aldehydic hydrogen

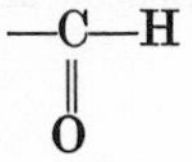

$$-\overset{\displaystyle }{\underset{\displaystyle O}{\overset{}{\underset{\|}{C}}}-H$$

in aldehydes and its absence in ketones.

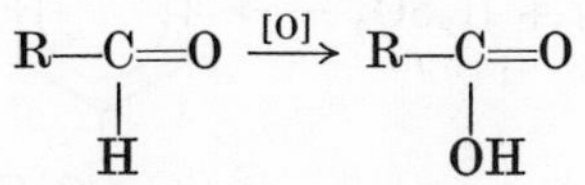

$$\underset{\text{An aldehyde}}{R-\overset{|}{\underset{\displaystyle H}{C}}=O} \xrightarrow{[O]} \underset{\text{A carboxylic acid}}{R-\overset{|}{\underset{\displaystyle OH}{C}}=O}$$

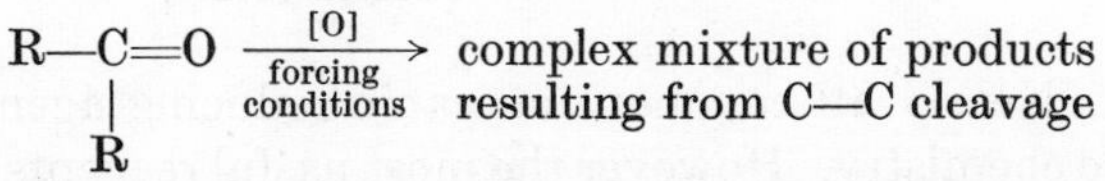

$$\underset{\text{A ketone}}{R-\overset{|}{\underset{\displaystyle R}{C}}=O} \xrightarrow[\substack{\text{forcing}\\\text{conditions}}]{[O]} \substack{\text{complex mixture of products}\\\text{resulting from C—C cleavage}}$$

Oxidation of Alkenes. The π bond often is much more susceptible to oxidation than is a σ bond. Consequently, oxidizing agents like potassium permanganate in solution readily destroy the double bond to give glycols:

$$R-CH{=}CH-R + KMnO_4 \xrightarrow{H_2O} \underset{\underset{\text{A glycol}}{\overset{\displaystyle ||}{OH\ \ OH}}}{R-CH-CH-R} + MnO_2 + KOH$$

This reaction may be used to distinguish alkanes from alkenes. Alkanes do not react with potassium permanganate while alkenes reduce the purple permanganate ion to brown manganese dioxide.

Further oxidation of the glycol brings about cleavage of the carbon-carbon bond between the two hydroxyl groups:

$$\underset{\underset{OH\ \ OH}{\overset{\displaystyle ||}{}}}{R-CH-CH-R} \xrightarrow[-H_2O]{[O]} \underset{\underset{O}{\overset{\displaystyle \|}{}}}{2R-C-OH}$$

The two fragments are isolated as the corresponding acids as indicated. Oxidation of an alkene is useful for locating the position of the double bond in a molecule. For example, oxidation of 2-pentene, $CH_3-CH{=}CH-CH_2-CH_3$, with potassium permanganate gives both acetic and propanoic acids, showing that the double bond was between the second and third carbon atoms.

Oxidation of Side Chains on Aromatic Compounds. Potassium permanganate or nitric acid will oxidize alkyl side chains on aromatic rings to give carboxylic acids in which the carboxyl group is bonded to a carbon atom in the ring.

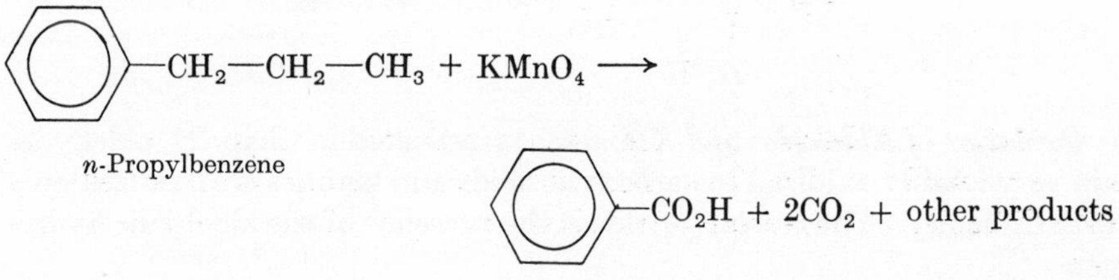

n-Propylbenzene

Benzoic acid

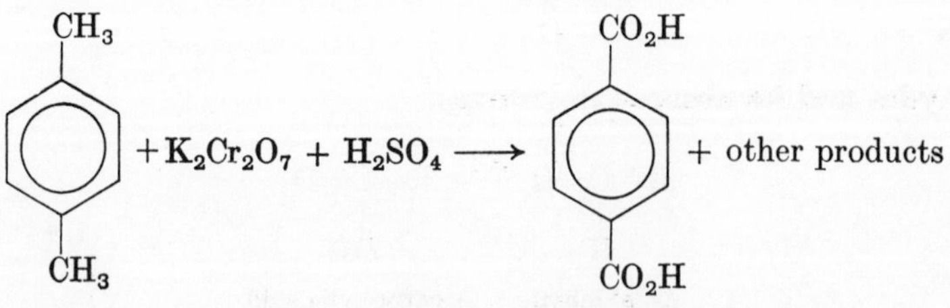

Phthalic acid

Reductions. Nearly all common inorganic reducing agents have been used in organic chemistry. However the most useful reagents are hydrogen with solid catalysts, metal hydrides such as lithium aluminum hydride, $LiAlH_4$, and active metals such as sodium and zinc.

Reduction of Carbon-Carbon Multiple Bonds. Catalytic hydrogenation is the most generally applicable procedure for reducing alkenes, alkynes, or aromatic compounds. The commonly used catalysts are the finely divided metals nickel, palladium, or platinum so prepared that the catalyst will present a large surface area. Hydrogen, at low pressures (25 to 40 lb/sq in.) or at high pressures (up to 5,000 lb/sq in.), is employed. Low-pressure hydrogenations are usually carried out at room temperature, while temperatures of 100°C or 200°C are common for high-pressure hydrogenations. Examples of reductions and their conditions for several types of unsaturated compounds are given below.

Alkenes:

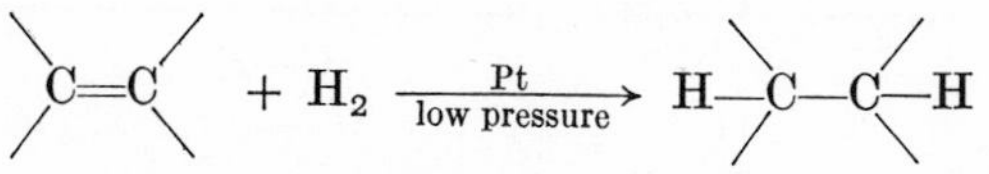

Alkynes:

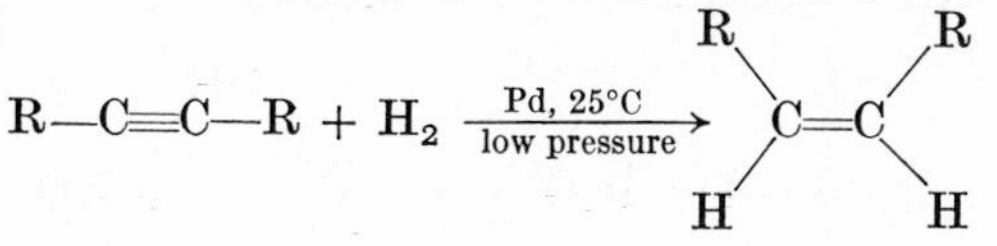

Cis product

Aromatics:

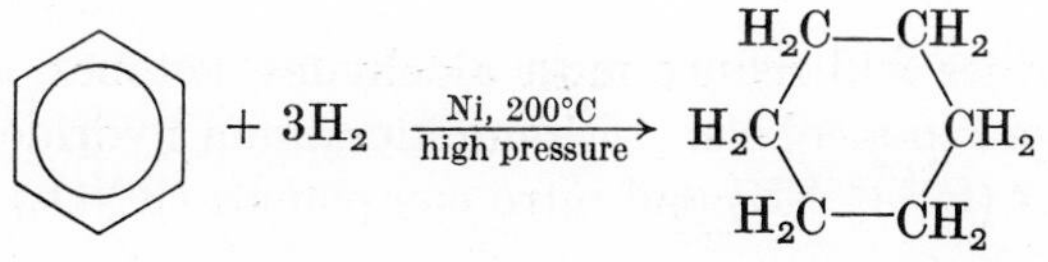

Cyclohexane

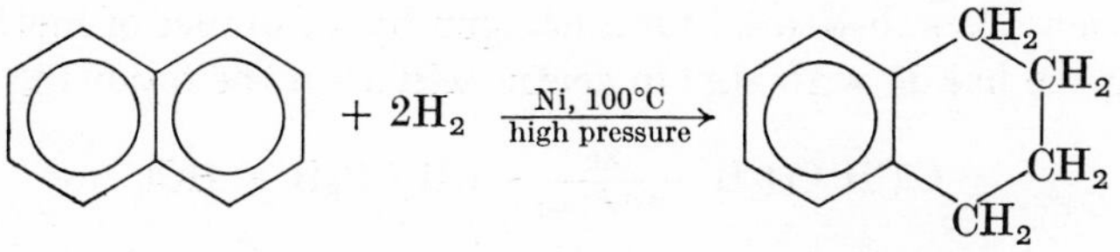

Tetralin
(tetrahydronaphthalene)

Reduction of Carbon-Oxygen and Carbon-Nitrogen Multiple Bonds. These may be reduced by catalytic hydrogenation but the reductions often are accomplished more easily with metal hydrides or active metals. Illustrations of the use of metal hydrides include:

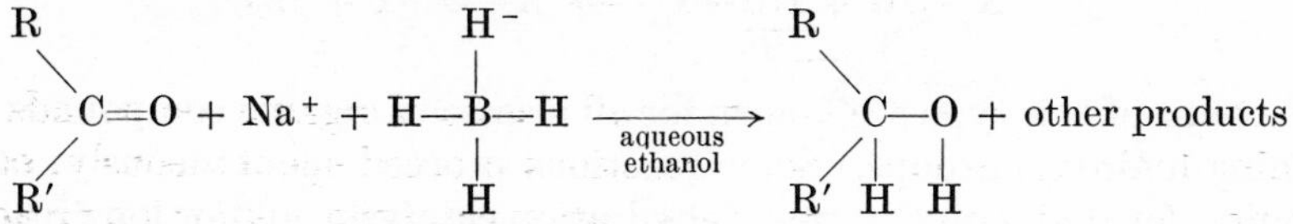

Sodium borohydride

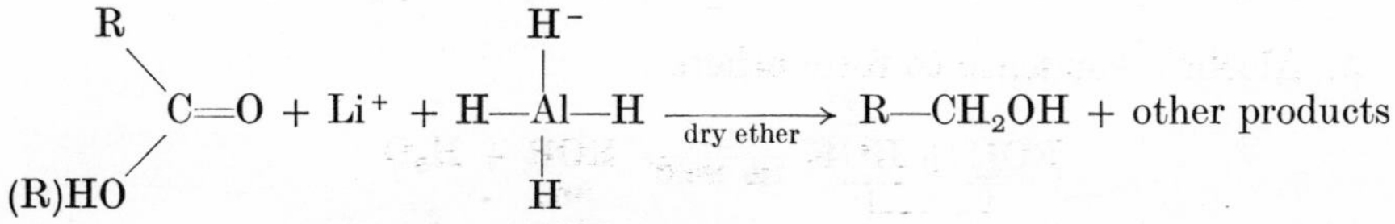

Lithium aluminum hydride

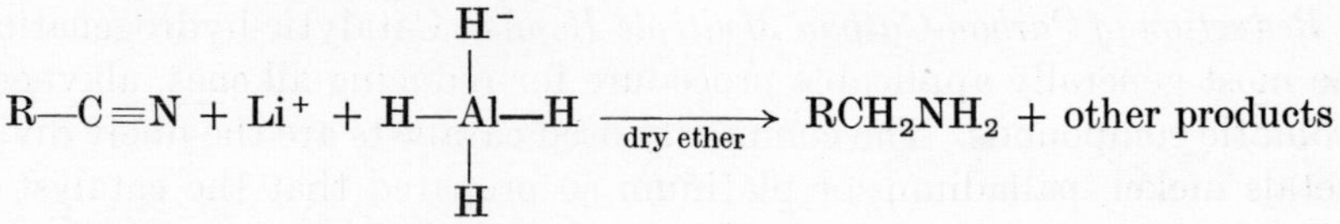

$$R—C\equiv N + Li^+ + H—\overset{\overset{\displaystyle H^-}{|}}{\underset{|}{Al}}—H \xrightarrow{\text{dry ether}} RCH_2NH_2 + \text{other products}$$

The first step in each of these reactions probably involves a transfer of the type

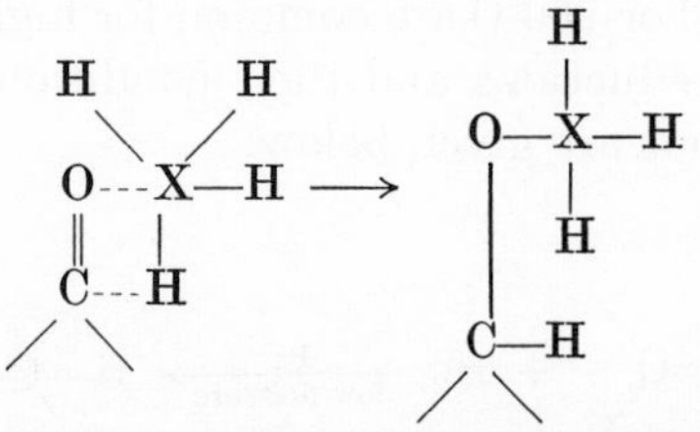

where X is boron or aluminum. This may be followed by reaction of the intermediate with water illustrated as follows:

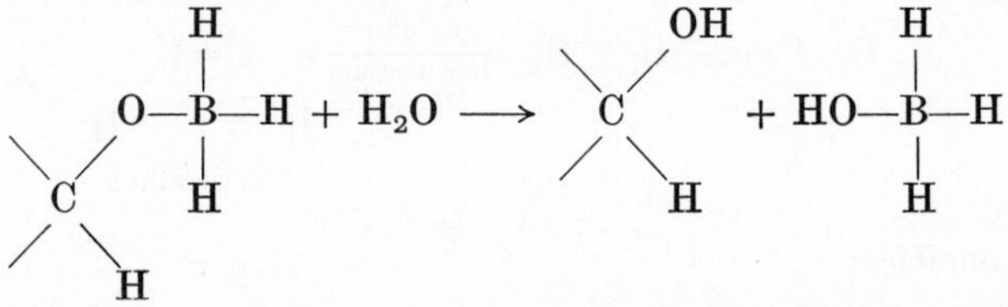

Metal hydrides will reduce most aldehydes, ketones, carboxylic acids, and their esters to alcohols. Lithium aluminum hydride may be used to reduce nitriles ($R—C\equiv N$) and nitro compounds (RNO_2) to amines:

$$RNO_2 + LiAlH_4 \longrightarrow RNH_2 + \text{other products}$$

Hydrogen may be substituted for a halogen by a number of methods such as treating the halide with zinc in acetic acid as in the following example:

$$ClCH_2CO_2H \xrightarrow[\text{HO}_2\text{CCH}_3]{\text{Zn}} CH_3CO_2H + HCl$$

Condensation Reactions

Condensation Reactions in Which Water Is Evolved. The general equation for condensations of this type is

$$X—OH + HO—Y \longrightarrow X—O—Y + H_2O$$

Reactions of this type are known for all classes of organic compounds containing hydroxyl groups. Some reactions proceed spontaneously; others require elevated temperatures, dehydration catalysts, and/or long reaction times. Examples of condensation reactions of this type include:

1. Alcohols condense to form ethers.

$$ROH + HOR \xrightarrow[240–280°C]{Al_2O_3} \underset{\substack{\text{An} \\ \text{ether}}}{ROR} + H_2O$$

2. Carboxylic acids condense to form acid anhydrides.

$$R-\overset{O}{\underset{\parallel}{C}}-OH + HO-\overset{O}{\underset{\parallel}{C}}-R \xrightarrow[\Delta]{P_4O_{10}} R-\overset{O}{\underset{\parallel}{C}}-O-\overset{O}{\underset{\parallel}{C}}-R + H_2O$$

An acid
anhydride

3. Alcohols condense with acids to give esters.

$$ROH + HO-\overset{O}{\underset{\parallel}{C}}-R' \longrightarrow R-O-\overset{O}{\underset{\parallel}{C}}-R' + H_2O$$

$$ROH + HONO_2 \longrightarrow R-O-NO_2 + H_2O$$

$$ROH + H-O-\overset{O}{\underset{\underset{OH}{\mid}}{\overset{\parallel}{P}}}-OH \longrightarrow RO-\overset{O}{\underset{\underset{OH}{\mid}}{\overset{\parallel}{P}}}-OH + H_2O$$

In the reactions of alcohols with carboxylic acids, it is known from oxygen isotope tracer studies that the hydroxyl group of the expelled water molecule comes from the carboxyl group and the hydrogen atom comes from the alcohol.

$$R-\overset{O}{\underset{\parallel}{C}}-O^{18}-H + HOR' \longrightarrow R-\overset{O}{\underset{\parallel}{C}}-OR' + H_2O^{18}$$

By preparing the carboxylic acid with a labeled oxygen atom, it was possible to show that the labeled atom was present in the water formed as a reaction product.

Condensation Reactions in Which Hydrogen Chloride Is Evolved. Many reactions of this type are known. Usually the chlorine atom of the liberated molecule comes from a compound having a reactive chlorine atom such as the acyl or aroyl halides,

$$R-\overset{O}{\underset{\parallel}{C}}-Cl \quad \text{or} \quad Ar-\overset{O}{\underset{\parallel}{C}}-Cl$$

and the hydrogen atom comes from a compound having reactive hydrogen atoms, usually those containing —OH or

$$\overset{\diagdown}{\underset{\diagup}{N}}H$$

groups. Sometimes a base is added to the reaction mixture to neutralize the hydrogen chloride as it is formed and to prevent reversal of the reaction. Examples of condensation reactions where hydrogen chloride is evolved are:

1. Alcohols and acyl halides give esters.

$$R-OH + Cl-\overset{O}{\underset{\parallel}{C}}-R' \longrightarrow R-O-\overset{O}{\underset{\parallel}{C}}-R' + HCl$$

2. Ammonia or amines and acyl halides give amides.

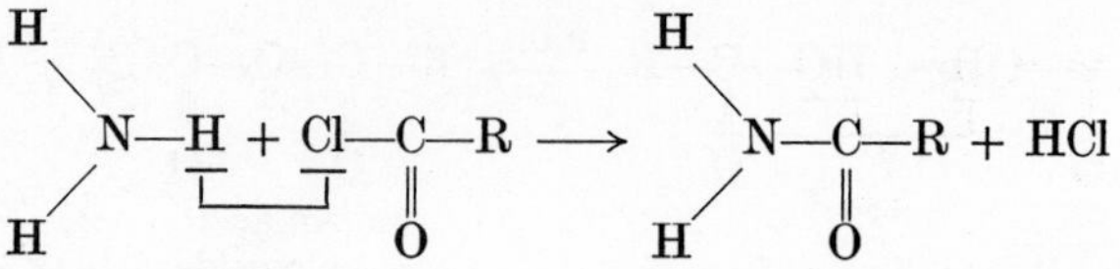

$$
\underset{H}{\overset{H}{N}}{-}H + Cl{-}\underset{O}{\overset{\|}{C}}{-}R \longrightarrow \underset{H}{\overset{H}{N}}{-}\underset{O}{\overset{\|}{C}}{-}R + HCl
$$

An amide

3. Alkyl halides react with ammonia or amines to give amines.

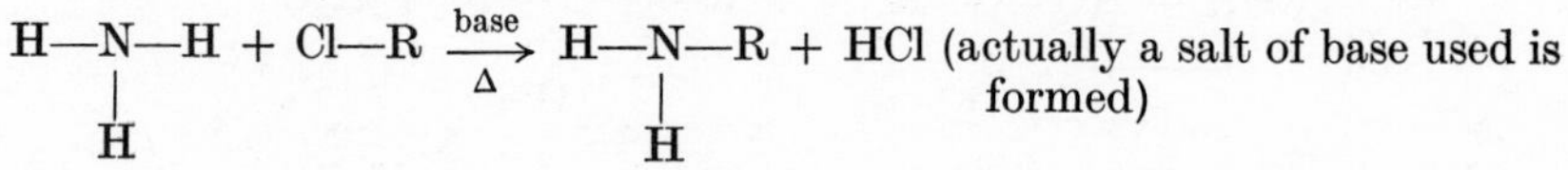

$$
H{-}\underset{H}{\overset{|}{N}}{-}H + Cl{-}R \xrightarrow[\Delta]{base} H{-}\underset{H}{\overset{|}{N}}{-}R + HCl \text{ (actually a salt of base used is formed)}
$$

Primary
amine

The product of this reaction may react with additional alkyl halide to produce secondary amines (R_2NH) and tertiary amines (R_3N).

PROBLEM. ■ Show by equations how N-ethylacetamide,

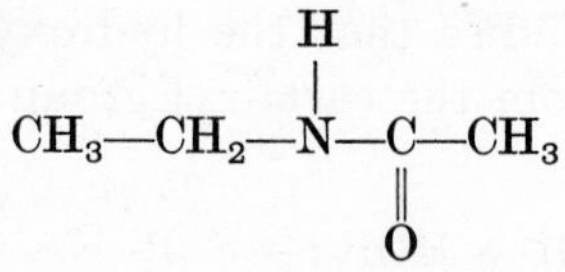

$$
CH_3{-}CH_2{-}\underset{O}{\overset{H}{\underset{\|}{N}}}{-}\overset{|}{C}{-}CH_3
$$

can be prepared from ethyl chloride, acetyl chloride,

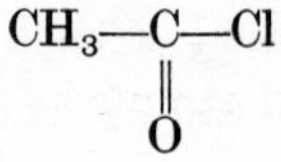

$$
CH_3{-}\underset{O}{\overset{\|}{C}}{-}Cl
$$

and ammonia.

SOLUTION

$$
CH_3{-}CH_2{-}Cl + H{-}\underset{H}{\overset{|}{N}}{-}H \xrightarrow[\Delta]{base} CH_3{-}CH_2{-}\underset{H}{\overset{|}{N}}{-}H + HCl \text{ (actually a salt of base used)}
$$

$$
CH_3{-}CH_2{-}\underset{H}{\overset{|}{N}}{-}H + Cl{-}\underset{O}{\overset{\|}{C}}{-}CH_3 \longrightarrow CH_3{-}CH_2{-}\underset{H}{\overset{|}{N}}{-}\underset{O}{\overset{\|}{C}}{-}CH_3 + HCl
$$

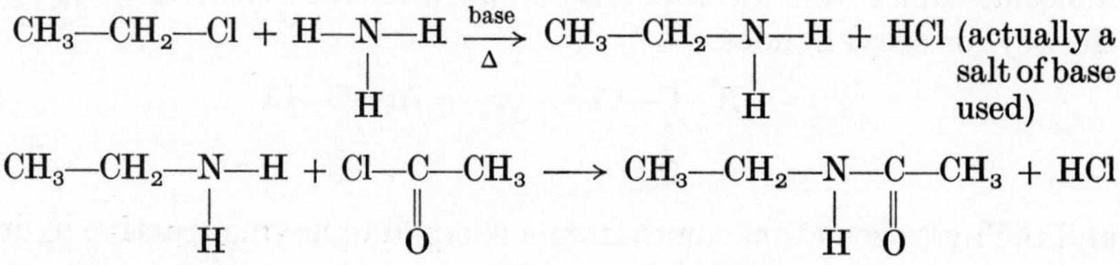

Condensation Reactions in Which a Carbon-Carbon Bond Is Formed.
These reactions, which might also be classed as addition reactions, occur with aldehydes, with some ketones, and with esters which have a hydrogen atom on the carbon atom adjacent to the carbonyl group:

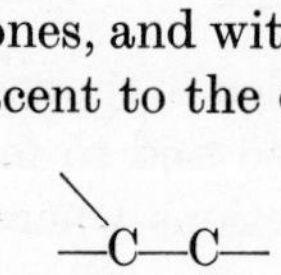

$$
{-}\underset{H}{\overset{\diagup}{C}}{-}\underset{O}{\overset{\|}{C}}{-}
$$

In the presence of base, most compounds having this structural feature undergo self-addition as illustrated in the generalized reaction:

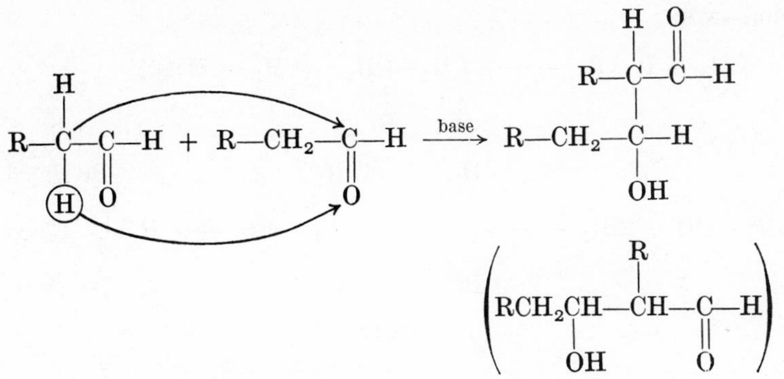

$$R-\underset{\underset{\text{(H)}}{\overset{\text{H}}{|}}}{C}-\underset{\text{O}}{\overset{\|}{C}}-H + R-CH_2-\underset{\text{O}}{\overset{\|}{C}}-H \xrightarrow{\text{base}} R-\underset{\underset{\text{OH}}{|}}{\overset{\overset{\displaystyle R-\underset{\text{H}}{\overset{\text{H}}{|}}C-\overset{O}{\overset{\|}{C}}-H}{}}{C}}-H$$

$$\left(RCH_2CH-\underset{OH}{\overset{|}{\underset{}{C}H}}-\underset{R}{\overset{|}{C}}-\underset{O}{\overset{\|}{C}}-H \right)$$

Such reactions, known as *aldol-type condensations*, belong to a very wide class of reactions which can be used to double the chain length and, in some cases, introduce several functional groups into a compound. Sometimes two aldehydes are used, one having no hydrogen atom on the carbon atom adjacent to the carbonyl group.

Addition Reactions

Addition to Alkenes or Alkynes. The characteristic reaction of alkenes and alkynes is addition. Such reactions usually proceed at a very rapid rate, even at low temperatures, whereas most substitution reactions in hydrocarbons proceed slowly, often requiring catalysts and elevated temperatures. Reagents which add to carbon-carbon multiple bonds include: chlorine, bromine, hydrogen; binary acids such as HCl, HBr, HI, and H_2O, sulfuric acid, and hypochlorous acid. Examples of some addition

---

● ● ●   MECHANISM OF AN ALDOL CONDENSATION

The reaction mechanism is believed to involve the following steps:

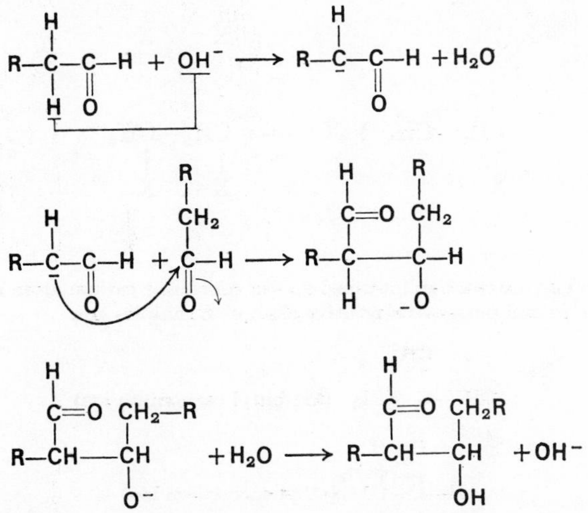

$$R-\underset{\underset{\text{H}}{\overset{\text{H}}{|}}}{\overset{\text{H}}{|}}{C}-\underset{\text{O}}{\overset{\|}{C}}-H + OH^- \longrightarrow R-\underset{\text{H}}{\overset{\text{H}}{|}}{C}-\underset{\text{O}}{\overset{\|}{C}}-H + H_2O$$

$$R-\underset{\underset{\text{O}}{\|}}{\overset{\text{H}}{|}}{C}-C-H + \underset{\underset{\text{O}}{\|}}{\overset{\overset{\text{R}}{|}}{\overset{CH_2}{|}}}{C}-H \longrightarrow R-\underset{\underset{\text{O}}{-}}{\overset{\overset{\text{H}}{|}}{\overset{C=O}{|}}}{C}-\underset{}{\overset{\overset{\text{R}}{|}}{\overset{CH_2}{|}}}{C}-H$$

$$R-\underset{\underset{\text{O}^-}{|}}{\overset{\overset{\text{H}}{|}}{\overset{C=O}{|}}}{CH}-\underset{}{\overset{CH_2-R}{|}}{CH} + H_2O \longrightarrow R-\underset{\underset{\text{OH}}{|}}{\overset{\overset{\text{H}}{|}}{\overset{C=O}{|}}}{CH}-\underset{}{\overset{CH_2R}{|}}{CH} + OH^-$$

reactions are:

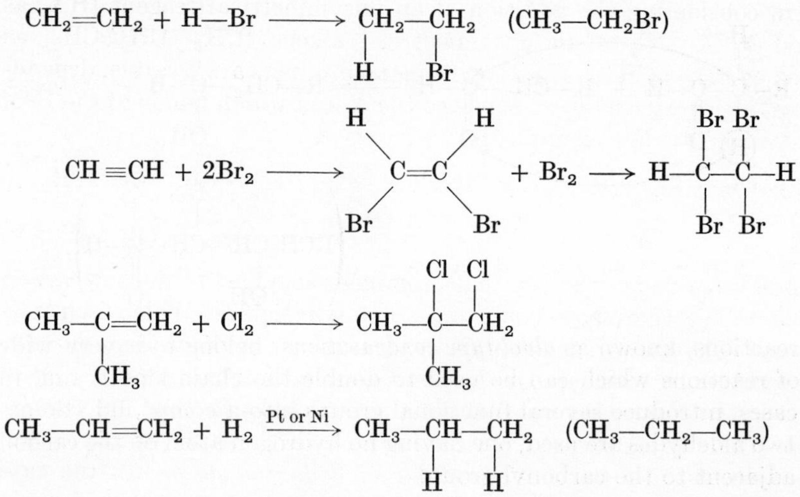

$$CH_2{=}CH_2 + H{-}Br \longrightarrow \underset{\underset{H}{|}\quad\underset{Br}{|}}{CH_2{-}CH_2} \quad (CH_3{-}CH_2Br)$$

$$CH{\equiv}CH + 2Br_2 \longrightarrow \underset{\underset{Br}{|}\quad\underset{Br}{|}}{\overset{\overset{H}{|}\quad\overset{H}{|}}{C{=}C}} + Br_2 \longrightarrow H{-}\underset{\underset{Br}{|}}{\overset{\overset{Br}{|}}{C}}{-}\underset{\underset{Br}{|}}{\overset{\overset{Br}{|}}{C}}{-}H$$

$$\underset{\underset{CH_3}{|}}{CH_3{-}C}{=}CH_2 + Cl_2 \longrightarrow CH_3{-}\underset{\underset{CH_3}{|}}{\overset{\overset{Cl}{|}}{C}}{-}\overset{\overset{Cl}{|}}{C}H_2$$

$$CH_3{-}CH{=}CH_2 + H_2 \xrightarrow{\text{Pt or Ni}} CH_3{-}\underset{\underset{H}{|}}{CH}{-}\underset{\underset{H}{|}}{CH_2} \quad (CH_3{-}CH_2{-}CH_3)$$

The mechanism of addition to carbon-carbon double bonds is believed to involve attack by an electron-seeking species such as the positive end of the HBr dipole or even a very reactive bromonium ion, Br^+ (formed by a dissociation of the type $:\!\overset{..}{Br}\!:\!\overset{..}{Br}\!: \rightarrow :\!\overset{..}{Br}^+ + :\!\overset{..}{Br}\!:^-$). The electron-seeking reagent attacks (and bonds to) the pair of electrons in the π bond of the alkene, creating a carbonium ion:*

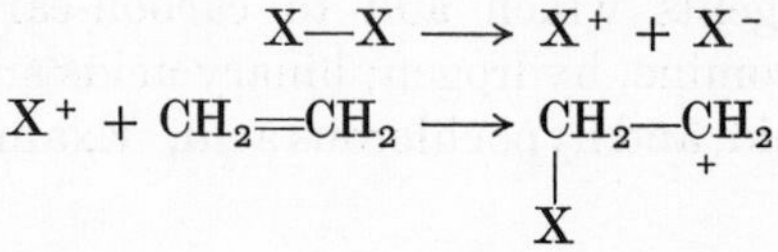

$$X{-}X \longrightarrow X^+ + X^-$$

$$X^+ + CH_2{=}CH_2 \longrightarrow \underset{\underset{X}{|}}{CH_2}{-}\underset{+}{CH_2}$$

Carbonium ion

The carbonium ion thus formed can then react with an anion or with another molecule of the adding reagent as in

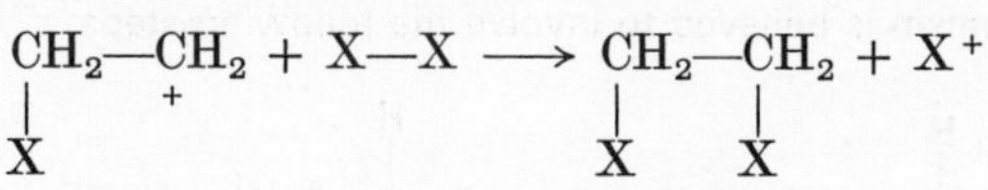

$$\underset{\underset{X}{|}\ +}{CH_2}{-}CH_2 + X{-}X \longrightarrow \underset{\underset{X}{|}}{CH_2}{-}\underset{\underset{X}{|}}{CH_2} + X^+$$

or

$$\underset{\underset{X}{|}\ +}{CH_2}{-}CH_2 + X^- \longrightarrow \underset{\underset{X}{|}}{CH_2}{-}\underset{\underset{X}{|}}{CH_2}$$

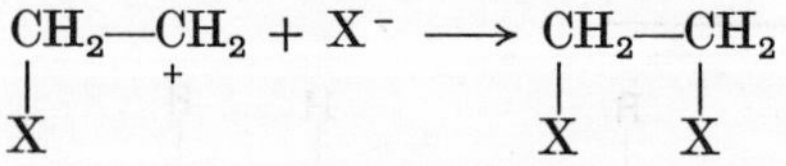

* Carbonium ions are reactive intermediates in which one carbon atom is bonded to only three other groups and possesses a positive charge. Examples are:

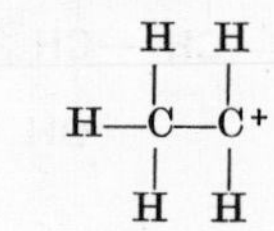

$$CH_3{-}\underset{+}{\overset{\overset{CH_3}{|}}{C}}{-}CH_3 \quad (\textit{tert}\text{-butyl carbonium ion})$$

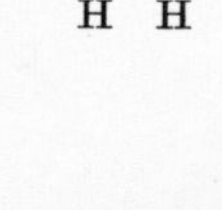

$$H{-}\underset{\underset{H}{|}}{\overset{\overset{H}{|}}{C}}{-}\overset{\overset{H}{|}}{C}{}^+ \quad (\text{ethyl carbonium ion})$$

Addition at Primary or Secondary Carbon Atoms. An interesting question arises in considering the addition of an unsymmetrical reagent (HX, as opposed to X—X) to an unsymmetrical alkene (CH_3—CH=CH_2, as opposed to CH_2=CH_2). Here two isomeric products are possible, depending upon which carbon atom bonds to the X and which bonds to the H of the HX reagent. For example, in the reaction

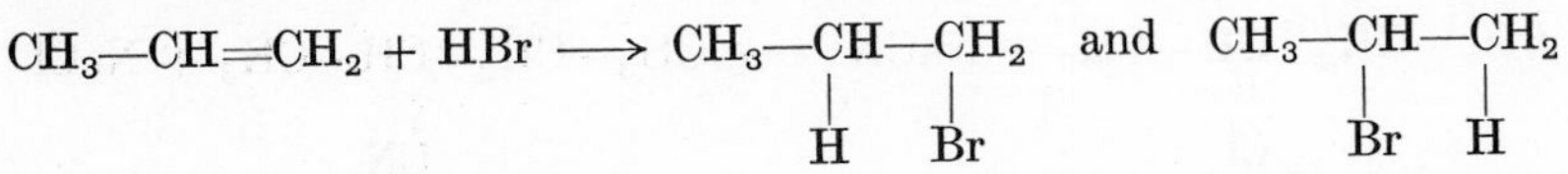

$$CH_3-CH=CH_2 + HBr \longrightarrow CH_3-\underset{\underset{H}{|}}{C}H-\underset{\underset{Br}{|}}{C}H_2 \quad \text{and} \quad CH_3-\underset{\underset{Br}{|}}{C}H-\underset{\underset{H}{|}}{C}H_2$$

hydrogen bromide may add so that bromine is attached to the end carbon atom or to the central carbon atom. The question is: Which isomer is preferred? The answer, determined by measuring the yields of products in many reactions of this type, is: *In general, when an unsymmetrical reagent molecule adds to an unsymmetrical molecule with a double bond, the positive portion of the unsymmetrical reagent molecule bonds to the double bonded carbon atom bearing the greater number of hydrogen atoms.* In the case shown, 2-bromopropane is obtained in high yield.

Other examples of unsymmetrical addition are:

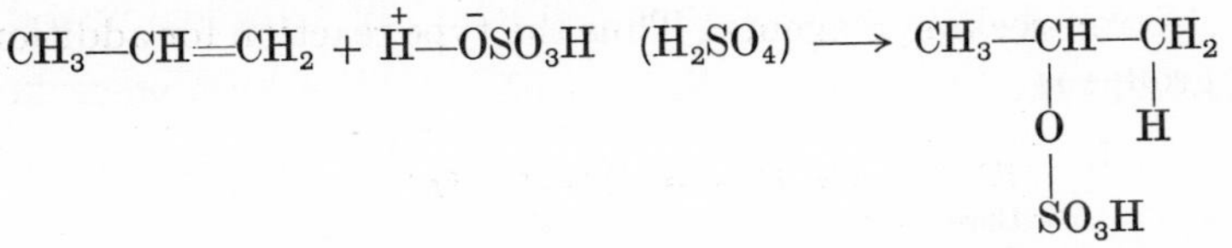

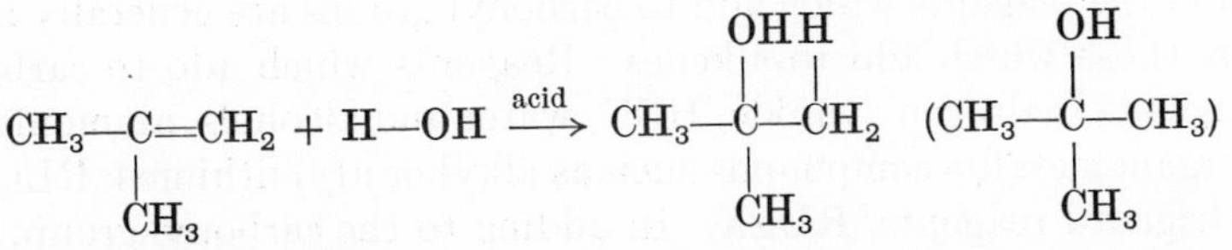

$$CH_3-CH=CH_2 + \overset{+}{H}-\overset{-}{O}SO_3H \quad (H_2SO_4) \longrightarrow CH_3-\underset{\underset{\underset{\underset{SO_3H}{|}}{O}}{|}}{C}H-\underset{\underset{H}{|}}{C}H_2$$

$$CH_3-\underset{\underset{CH_3}{|}}{C}=CH_2 + H-OH \xrightarrow{acid} CH_3-\underset{\underset{CH_3}{|}}{\overset{\overset{OH}{|}}{C}}-\overset{\overset{H}{|}}{C}H_2 \quad (CH_3-\underset{\underset{CH_3}{|}}{\overset{\overset{OH}{|}}{C}}-CH_3)$$

An interesting addition reaction has been developed by the petroleum industry to convert low-molecular-weight hydrocarbons (obtained from petroleum and from the cracking process) to high-octane gasolines. An illustration of this process is the reaction

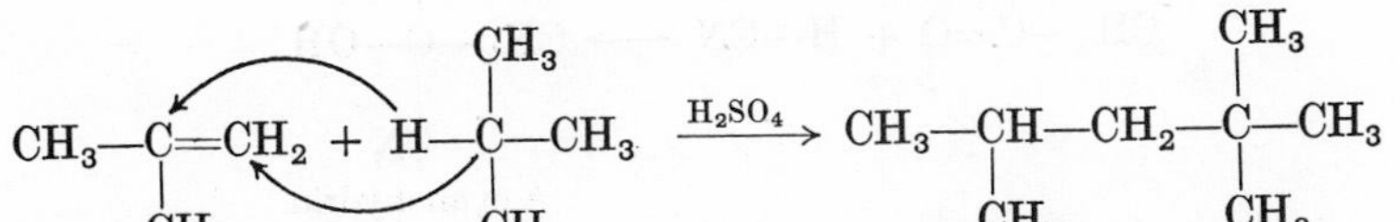

$$CH_3-\underset{\underset{CH_3}{|}}{C}=CH_2 + H-\underset{\underset{CH_3}{|}}{C}-CH_3 \xrightarrow{H_2SO_4} CH_3-\underset{\underset{CH_3}{|}}{C}H-CH_2-\underset{\underset{CH_3}{|}}{\overset{\overset{CH_3}{|}}{C}}-CH_3$$

2,2,4-Trimethylpentane
(a high-octane gasoline)

The mechanism of this reaction is complex but the products can be explained if the tertiary butyl group of isobutane acts like a positive group and the hydrogen atom of that molecule acts like a negative group.

PROBLEM. ■ Show by equations a method for converting 1-butene to 2-cyano-butane,

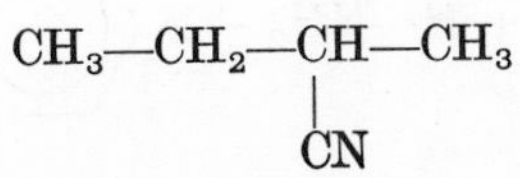

$$CH_3-CH_2-\underset{\underset{CN}{|}}{C}H-CH_3$$

SOLUTION

Recalling that HCN is not among the molecules that can be added to alkenes but that a CN group can be put into a molecule by displacing a halide ion, we might use the following reaction sequence:

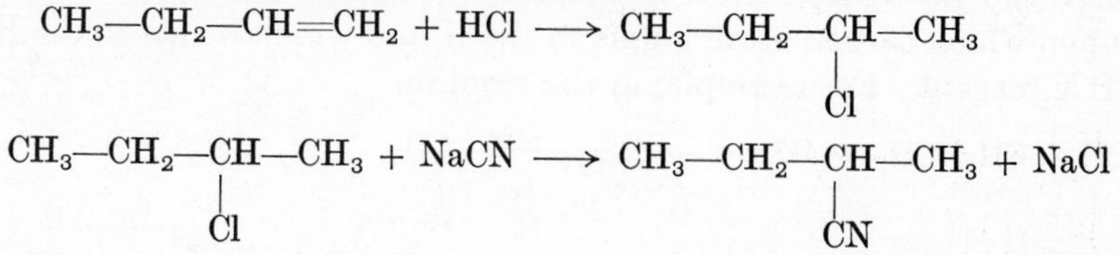

$$CH_3—CH_2—CH{=}CH_2 + HCl \longrightarrow CH_3—CH_2—\underset{\underset{Cl}{|}}{CH}—CH_3$$

$$CH_3—CH_2—\underset{\underset{Cl}{|}}{CH}—CH_3 + NaCN \longrightarrow CH_3—CH_2—\underset{\underset{CN}{|}}{CH}—CH_3 + NaCl$$

Addition to Carbonyl Groups. The π bond in the carbonyl group makes addition reactions possible at this site. However, the greater electronegativity of oxygen over carbon and the possibilities for resonance

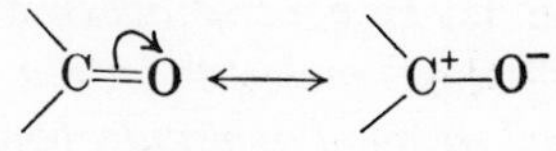

$$\diagup\!\!{C}{=}O \longleftrightarrow \diagup\!\!{C^+}{-}O^-$$

make the carbon atom more positive and the oxygen atom more negative than the carbon atoms sharing the π bond in alkenes. The positive than character of the carbonyl carbon atom makes this group sensitive to electron-donating reagents in contrast to the alkene double bond which is sensitive to electron-seeking reagents. Thus the type reaction for addition to carbonyl groups is

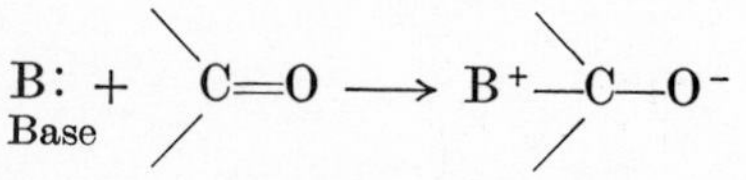

$$\underset{Base}{B:} + \diagup\!\!{C}{=}O \longrightarrow B^+{-}\diagup\!\!{C}{-}O^-$$

and the reagents which add to carbonyl groups are generally not the same as those which add to alkenes. Reagents which add to carbonyl groups include hydrogen cyanide, HCN, water and alcohols, ammonia, and many organometallic compounds such as alkyl or aryl lithiums, RLi or ArLi and Grignard reagents, RMgX. In adding to the carbonyl group, the positive portion of the reagent bonds to the oxygen atom, while the negative portion bonds to the carbon atom. Examples of carbonyl addition reactions include:

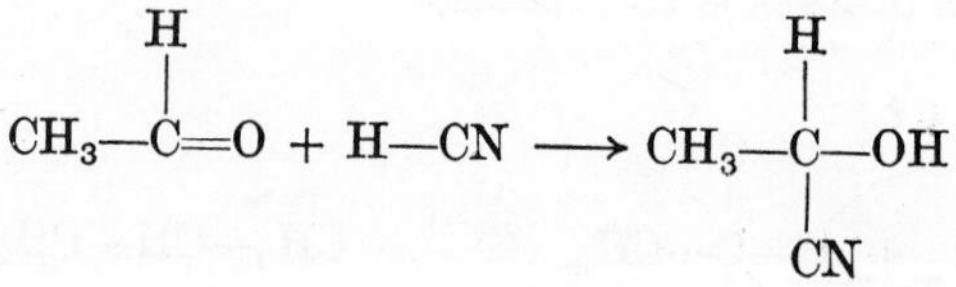

$$CH_3—\overset{\overset{H}{|}}{C}{=}O + H—CN \longrightarrow CH_3—\underset{\underset{CN}{|}}{\overset{\overset{H}{|}}{C}}—OH$$

A cyanohydrin

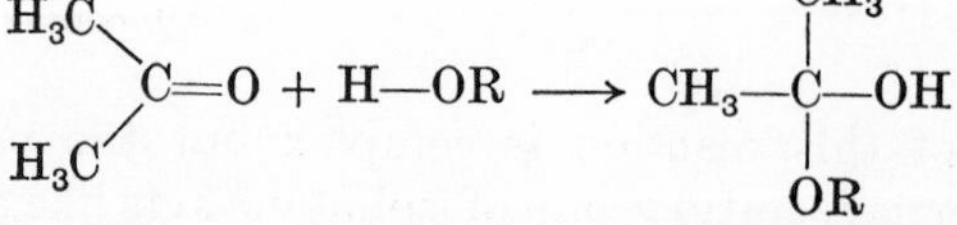

$$\underset{H_3C}{\overset{H_3C}{\diagup}}C{=}O + H—OR \longrightarrow CH_3—\underset{\underset{OR}{|}}{\overset{\overset{CH_3}{|}}{C}}—OH$$

A hemiacetal

$$\langle\!\!\bigcirc\!\!\rangle—\overset{\overset{H}{|}}{C}{=}O + H—NH_2 \longrightarrow \langle\!\!\bigcirc\!\!\rangle—\underset{\underset{NH_2\ H}{|}}{\overset{\overset{H}{|}}{C}}—O$$

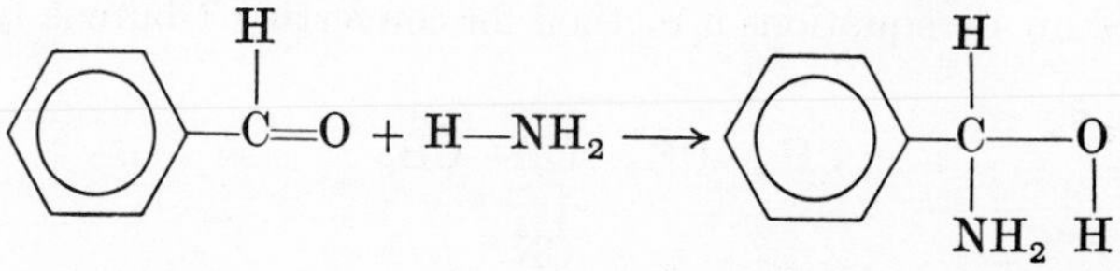

An aldehyde ammonia

$$
\underset{\text{An alcoholate}}{\langle\bigcirc\rangle\!\!-\!\!\overset{\overset{\displaystyle H}{|}}{C}\!\!=\!\!O + RLi \longrightarrow \langle\bigcirc\rangle\!\!-\!\!\overset{\overset{\displaystyle H}{|}}{\underset{\underset{\displaystyle R}{|}}{C}}\!\!-\!\!O^{-}Li^{+}}
$$

$$
CH_3\!\!-\!\!\overset{\overset{\displaystyle }{\|}}{\underset{\underset{\displaystyle O}{}}{C}}\!\!-\!\!CH_3 + RMgX \longrightarrow CH_3\!\!-\!\!\overset{\overset{\displaystyle R}{|}}{\underset{\underset{\displaystyle OMgBr}{|}}{C}}\!\!-\!\!CH_3
$$

Preparation of Secondary and Tertiary Alcohols from Aldehydes and Ketones. The last two reactions above are particularly useful for preparing secondary and tertiary alcohols, especially those containing different R groups in the same compound such as

$$
\langle\bigcirc\rangle\!\!\underset{CH_3CH_2}{\overset{}{\diagdown}}\!\!CHOH \quad \text{or} \quad CH_3\!\!-\!\!CH_2\!\!-\!\!\overset{\overset{\displaystyle CH_3}{|}}{\underset{\underset{\displaystyle CH}{|}}{C}}\!\!-\!\!OH
\;\;\underset{CH_3\;\;CH_3}{\diagup\diagdown}
$$

The aldehyde and the organometallic compound can be selected so as to prepare a secondary alcohol containing any two desired R groups. For example, the compound 2-butanol,

$$
CH_3\!\!-\!\!\underset{\underset{\displaystyle OH}{|}}{CH}\!\!-\!\!CH_2\!\!-\!\!CH_3
$$

can be prepared from ethanal and ethyllithium by the reaction sequence

Step 1
$$
CH_3\!\!-\!\!\overset{\overset{\displaystyle H}{|}}{C}\!\!=\!\!O + CH_3\!\!-\!\!CH_2\!\!-\!\!Li \longrightarrow CH_3\!\!-\!\!\overset{\overset{\displaystyle H}{|}}{\underset{\underset{\displaystyle CH_2CH_3}{|}}{C}}\!\!-\!\!OLi
$$

Step 2
$$
CH_3\!\!-\!\!\overset{\overset{\displaystyle H}{|}}{\underset{\underset{\displaystyle CH_2CH_3}{|}}{C}}\!\!-\!\!OLi \xrightarrow{\underset{H_2O}{HCl}} CH_3\!\!-\!\!\overset{\overset{\displaystyle H}{|}}{\underset{\underset{\displaystyle CH_2CH_3}{|}}{C}}\!\!-\!\!OH + LiCl
$$

The second step in the process, treatment of the reaction product from Step 1 with hydrochloric acid, is the replacement of the lithium ion by a hydrogen ion, thereby producing the desired alcohol.

Tertiary alcohols may be made from ketones and organolithium reagents by similar addition and replacement reactions.

Grignard reagents, similar in many ways to the organolithium reagents, are made by adding magnesium to an alkyl or aryl halide dissolved in anhydrous ether.

Certain derivatives of ammonia add to the double bond of the carbonyl group. This may be followed by a loss of water from adjacent atoms to form a double bond, as illustrated by the reaction sequence

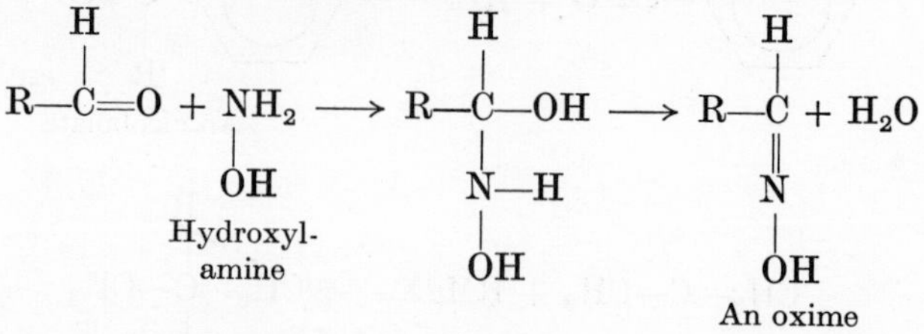

$$R-\overset{\overset{\displaystyle H}{|}}{C}=O + NH_2 \longrightarrow R-\overset{\overset{\displaystyle H}{|}}{\underset{\underset{\displaystyle N-H}{|}}{C}}-OH \longrightarrow R-\overset{\overset{\displaystyle H}{|}}{\underset{\underset{\displaystyle N}{|}}{C}} + H_2O$$

Hydroxyl-
amine

$$\overset{\displaystyle OH}{}$$ $$\overset{\displaystyle OH}{}$$

An oxime

Such reactions are much used in the laboratory in identifying aldehydes and ketones by the preparation of oximes or similar derivatives which are crystalline solids and which can in turn be identified by their melting points and X-ray diffraction patterns. In this case, examination of the crystalline oxime serves to identify the aldehyde from which it was derived.

Addition of Hydrogen to Carbonyl Groups: Reduction Reactions. While the addition reactions discussed here occur readily in aldehydes and ketones, they do not occur to any appreciable extent in carboxylic acids and their derivatives, even though these substances contain carbonyl groups. All types of carbonyl groups, however, will add hydrogen in the presence of appropriate reducing agents.

Addition to $-C\equiv N$. Nitriles, $R-C\equiv N$, add hydrogen to give amines or water to form carboxylic acids.

The second reaction is especially useful for preparing carboxylic acids having a particular R group. For example, phenylacetic acid

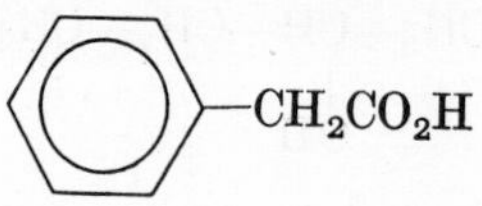

can be prepared from toluene by the reactions

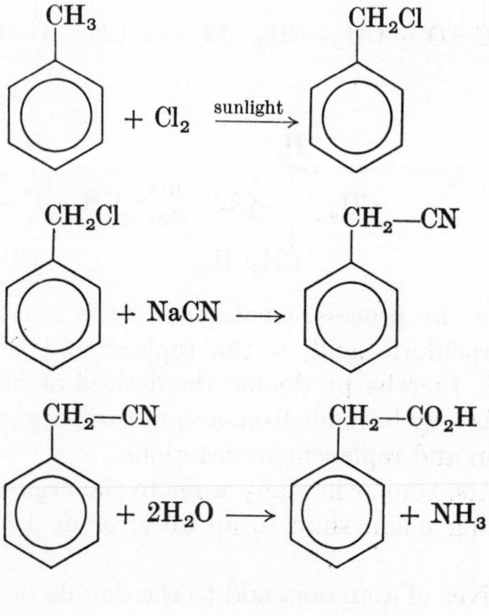

Elimination Reactions

Elimination of Water. When water is eliminated from adjacent carbon atoms in an alcohol as in

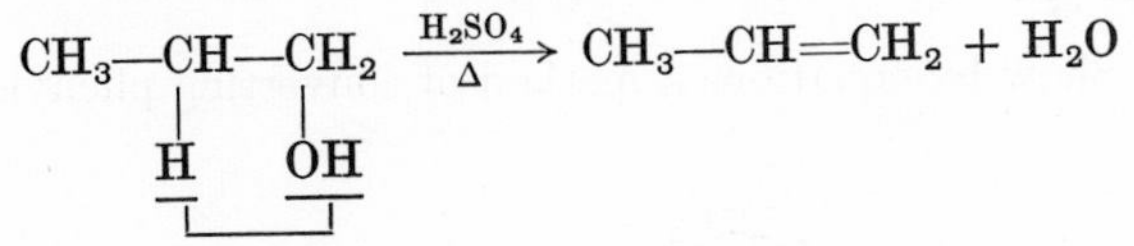

$$CH_3-CH-CH_2 \xrightarrow[\Delta]{H_2SO_4} CH_3-CH{=}CH_2 + H_2O$$
$$\quad\quad\;|\quad\;|$$
$$\quad\quad H\;\;OH$$

the process is called dehydration and the product is an alkene. Dehydrating agents for alcohols are substances which have a great affinity for water and include concentrated sulfuric or phosphoric acids or activated aluminum oxide, Al_2O_3, at high temperatures. Dehydration of alcohols is a commonly used reaction for the preparation of alkenes. Reaction conditions vary widely, depending on the reactivity of the alcohols. Primary alcohols are usually more difficult to dehydrate than are tertiary alcohols.

Some alcohols yield more than one alkene on dehydration. For example, 2-butanol gives both 1- and 2-butene as shown below:

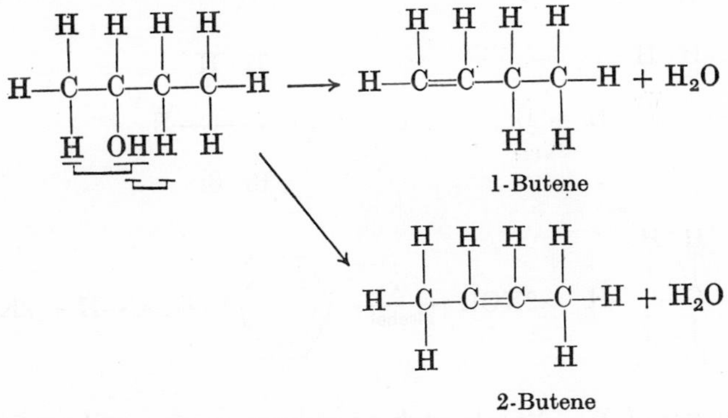

1-Butene

2-Butene

Elimination of HX. When a hydrogen halide molecule is eliminated from adjacent carbon atoms in an alkyl halide, the process is known as *dehydrohalogenation* and is often accomplished with a solution of potassium hydroxide dissolved in alcohol. Most alkyl halides undergo dehydrohalogenation.

Examples of these reactions are:

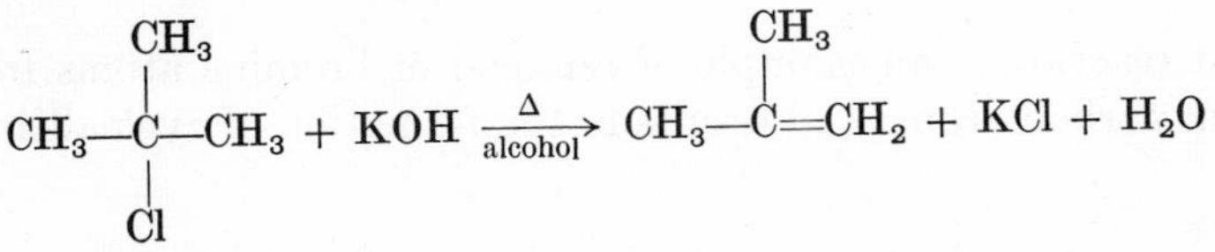

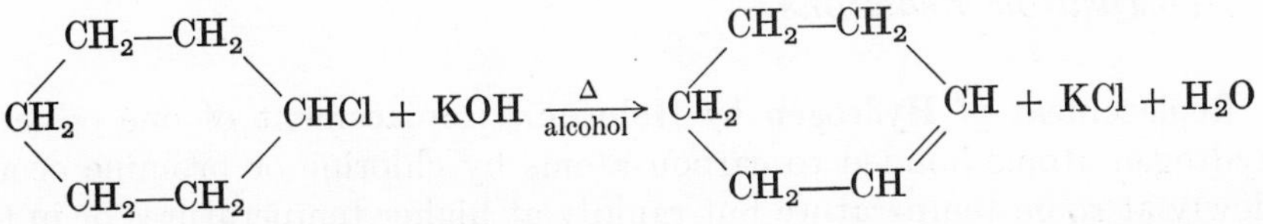

Alkynes can be prepared by the dehydrohalogenation of dihalides as in the reaction

$$CH_3-\underset{\underset{H}{|}}{\overset{\overset{H}{|}}{C}}-\underset{\underset{Br}{|}}{\overset{\overset{Br}{|}}{C}}-H + 2KOH \xrightarrow[\text{alcohol}]{\Delta} CH_3-C\equiv CH + 2KBr + 2H_2O$$

PROBLEM. ■ Show by equations a method of converting phenylethanol,

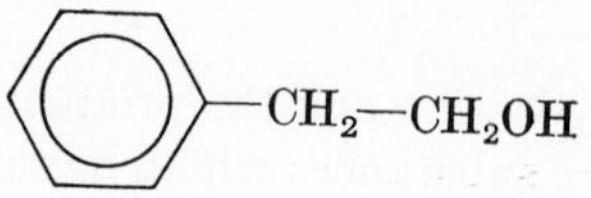

$$\bigcirc\!\!\!\!\bigcirc-CH_2-CH_2OH$$

to phenylethyne.

SOLUTION

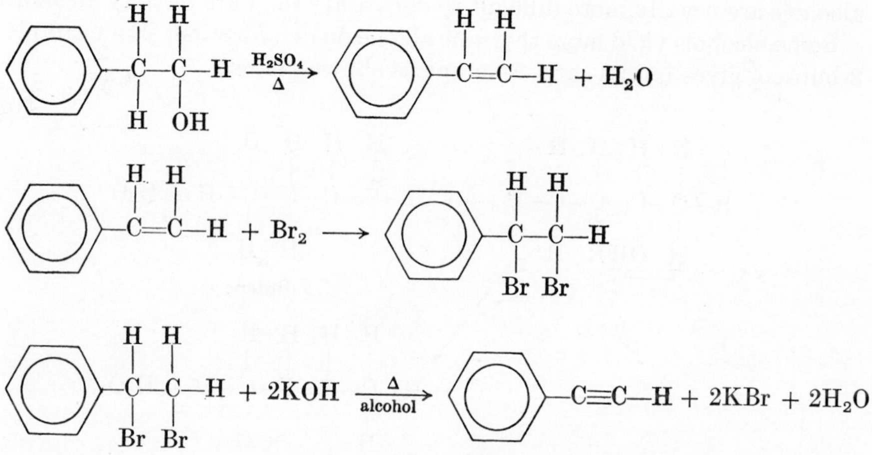

$$\bigcirc\!\!\!\!\bigcirc-\underset{\underset{H}{|}}{\overset{\overset{H}{|}}{C}}-\underset{\underset{OH}{|}}{\overset{\overset{H}{|}}{C}}-H \xrightarrow[\Delta]{H_2SO_4} \bigcirc\!\!\!\!\bigcirc-\overset{\overset{H}{|}}{C}=\overset{\overset{H}{|}}{C}-H + H_2O$$

$$\bigcirc\!\!\!\!\bigcirc-\overset{\overset{H}{|}}{C}=\overset{\overset{H}{|}}{C}-H + Br_2 \longrightarrow \bigcirc\!\!\!\!\bigcirc-\underset{\underset{Br}{|}}{\overset{\overset{H}{|}}{C}}-\underset{\underset{Br}{|}}{\overset{\overset{H}{|}}{C}}-H$$

$$\bigcirc\!\!\!\!\bigcirc-\underset{\underset{Br}{|}}{\overset{\overset{H}{|}}{C}}-\underset{\underset{Br}{|}}{\overset{\overset{H}{|}}{C}}-H + 2KOH \xrightarrow[\text{alcohol}]{\Delta} \bigcirc\!\!\!\!\bigcirc-C\equiv C-H + 2KBr + 2H_2O$$

Elimination of X_2. Metals such as sodium or zinc will remove halogen atoms from two carbon atoms in a molecule. Examples are:

$$CH_3-CH_2-\underset{\underset{Br}{|}}{CH}-\underset{\underset{Br}{|}}{CH_2} + Zn \longrightarrow CH_3-CH_2-CH=CH_2 + ZnBr_2$$

$$Br-CH_2-CH_2-CH_2-CH_2-Br + 2Na \longrightarrow \begin{matrix} CH_2-CH_2 \\ | \qquad | \\ CH_2-CH_2 \end{matrix} + 2NaBr$$

The last reaction is an example of removal of bromine atoms from non-adjacent carbon atoms and results in the formation of cycloalkanes.

Substitution Reactions

Replacement of Hydrogen by Halogen. Replacement of one or more hydrogen atoms bonded to carbon atoms by chlorine or bromine occurs slowly at room temperature but rapidly at higher temperatures or in the presence of sunlight. An example of this reaction is the chlorination of ethane:

$$Cl-Cl + H-\underset{\underset{H}{|}}{\overset{\overset{H}{|}}{C}}-\underset{\underset{H}{|}}{\overset{\overset{H}{|}}{C}}-H \longrightarrow H-\underset{\underset{H}{|}}{\overset{\overset{H}{|}}{C}}-\underset{\underset{H}{|}}{\overset{\overset{H}{|}}{C}}-Cl + HCl$$

Almost all carbon-hydrogen bonds can be made to undergo this reaction. Very often such reactions result in mixtures of products as illustrated by the reaction of methane with excess chlorine which gives all four possible chlorinated products:

$$H-\underset{\underset{H}{|}}{\overset{\overset{H}{|}}{C}}-H + Cl-Cl \longrightarrow H-\underset{\underset{H}{|}}{\overset{\overset{H}{|}}{C}}-Cl \; (+HCl) \xrightarrow{Cl_2} H-\underset{\underset{Cl}{|}}{\overset{\overset{H}{|}}{C}}-Cl \; (+HCl)$$

$$\Big\downarrow Cl_2$$

$$Cl-\underset{\underset{Cl}{|}}{\overset{\overset{Cl}{|}}{C}}-Cl \; (+HCl) \xleftarrow{Cl_2} Cl-\underset{\underset{Cl}{|}}{\overset{\overset{H}{|}}{C}}-Cl \; (+HCl)$$

However, it is possible to control reaction conditions so as to get good yields of one of several possible products.

The reaction pathway or *mechanism* for halogenation reactions accelerated by sunlight is known to be a *free-radical chain process* (Chap. 24). Halogenation reactions are fast and exothermic and may lead to explosions.

Reaction at Primary and Secondary Carbon Atoms. An interesting structural question arises when one considers the chlorination of propane and higher alkanes. If conditions are fixed so that only one hydrogen atom in each molecule of alkane is replaced, two isomers are possible—i.e., 1-chloropropane and 2-chloropropane:

$$H-\underset{\underset{H}{|}}{\overset{\overset{H}{|}}{C}}\!=\!\underset{\underset{H}{|}}{\overset{\overset{H}{|}}{C}}\!=\!\underset{\underset{H}{|}}{\overset{\overset{H}{|}}{C}}\!+\!H + Cl_2 \longrightarrow HCl + Cl-\underset{\underset{H}{|}}{\overset{\overset{H}{|}}{C}}-\underset{\underset{H}{|}}{\overset{\overset{H}{|}}{C}}-\underset{\underset{H}{|}}{\overset{\overset{H}{|}}{C}}-H \quad \text{or} \quad H-\underset{\underset{H}{|}}{\overset{\overset{H}{|}}{C}}-\underset{\underset{Cl}{|}}{\overset{\overset{H}{|}}{C}}-\underset{\underset{H}{|}}{\overset{\overset{H}{|}}{C}}-H$$

1-Chloropropane   2-Chloropropane

The 1-chloropropane arises when a hydrogen atom on either of the end carbon atoms in propane is replaced; 2-chloropropane arises when a hydrogen atom on the central carbon atom is replaced. The question then is: Do both isomers appear in the reaction products, and if so, what are the relative amounts of each? The answer to this question, found by experiment, is: Both isomers invariably appear. At temperatures of 400°C and above, the ratio of 1-chloropropane to 2-chloropropane is 3 to 1—consistent with statistical considerations. These are based on the fact that there are six hydrogen atoms on terminal carbon atoms and two hydrogen atoms on the central carbon atom in propane. Thus there are six chances to form 1-chloropropane for every two chances to form 2-chloropropane in this case. As the reaction temperature is lowered, the ratio of the two isomers approaches one. This suggests that attacking chlorine atoms are more selective in removing hydrogen atoms at lower temperatures and that they remove hydrogen atoms attached to the central carbon atom in propane (a secondary carbon atom) more readily than those attached to the end carbon atoms (primary carbon atoms).

Reaction at Tertiary Carbon Atoms. A similar situation obtains in the monochlorination of isobutane,

$$CH_3-CH-CH_3$$
$$|$$
$$CH_3$$

Here again two isomers are possible, and statistical considerations predict a 9 to 1 ratio of 1-chloro-2-methylpropane compared with 2-chloro-2-methylpropane. At high temperatures the product ratios approach this prediction, but at lower temperatures the substitution occurs preferentially on the tertiary carbon atom, and 2-chloro-2-methylpropane is present in largest amount.

These results are general for the chlorination of organic compounds and may be summarized as follows: high temperature chlorinations give nearly statistical isomer ratios; at lower temperatures substitution occurs most readily at tertiary carbon atoms and least readily at primary carbon atoms. At 300°C the relative rates of substitution are: primary, 1, secondary, 3.2, tertiary, 4.4.

Replacement of Halogen Bonded to Carbon. As indicated in Chap. 29, alkyl halides are used in synthesis of a number of kinds of organic compounds. These syntheses are possible because of the ease with which a halogen atom bonded to carbon is replaced by a base. Examples of such replacements and the kinds of compounds that can be synthesized from alkyl halides are given in Table 30.1.

Table 30.1 Replacement Reactions of Alkyl Halides

Reagent	Reaction	Organic Product
1. NaOH	$OH^- + RCl \longrightarrow Cl^- + ROH$	An alcohol
2. NaOR′	$OR'^- + RCl \longrightarrow Cl^- + ROR'$	An ether
3. NaSH	$SH^- + RCl \longrightarrow Cl^- + RSH$	A mercaptan
4. NaNH$_2$	$NH_2^- + RCl \longrightarrow Cl^- + RNH_2$	A primary amine
5. NaCN	$CN^- + RCl \longrightarrow Cl^- + RCN$	A nitrile
6. NaC≡C—R′	$C\equiv CR'^- + RCl \longrightarrow Cl^- + R-C\equiv C-R'$	An alkyne

In each of these reactions an anion replaces a chloride ion in the organic compound.

PROBLEM. ■ Starting with ethane, show by equations a method for preparing ethylamine, $CH_3CH_2-NH_2$.

SOLUTION

The amine can be made from sodamide, $NaNH_2$, and an alkyl halide (Reaction 4, Table 30.1). In this case the alkyl group must be an ethyl group so we need first to prepare ethyl chloride and then allow this to react with sodamide to give the amine. The reaction sequence then becomes

$$CH_3—CH_3 + Cl_2 \xrightarrow{\text{sunlight}} CH_3—CH_2—Cl + HCl$$

$$CH_3—CH_2—Cl + NaNH_2 \longrightarrow CH_3CH_2—NH_2 + NaCl$$

PROBLEM. ■ Starting with cyclohexane, show by equations a method for preparing methyl cyclohexyl ether,

$$
\begin{array}{c}
\quad\quad\quad CH_2—CH_2 \\
CH_3—O—CH \quad\quad\quad\quad CH_2 \\
\quad\quad\quad CH_2—CH_2
\end{array}
$$

SOLUTION

An ether is prepared from an alkyl halide and the sodium salt of an alcohol, NaOR (Reaction 2, Table 30.1). A methyl ether can be prepared from the sodium salt of methyl alcohol, $NaOCH_3$. The alkyl halide needed in this case is cyclohexyl chloride which can be made by chlorinating cyclohexane. Thus the sequence in this case becomes

$$
\begin{array}{c}
CH_2—CH_2 \\
CH_2 \quad\quad CH_2 + Cl_2 \longrightarrow \\
CH_2—CH_2
\end{array}
\begin{array}{c}
CH_2—CH_2 \\
CH_2 \quad\quad CH—Cl + HCl \\
CH_2—CH_2
\end{array}
$$

$$
\begin{array}{c}
CH_2—CH_2 \\
CH_2 \quad\quad CHCl + NaOCH_3 \longrightarrow \\
CH_2—CH_2
\end{array}
\begin{array}{c}
CH_2—CH_2 \\
CH_2 \quad\quad CH—O—CH_3 + NaCl \\
CH_2—CH_2
\end{array}
$$

Mechanism of Halogen Replacement. The mechanisms for halogen replacements involve *ions* as intermediates in contrast to the *free-radical* intermediates involved in replacement of hydrogen atoms attached to carbon atoms. Two important mechanisms for halogen replacement are recognized, and the mechanism dominant in a given case depends on the nature of the alkyl group in the alkyl halide. Primary halides undergo a one-step replacement in which the reaction rate is proportional to the concentration of each reactant. This can be called a *bimolecular mechanism*. Much evidence (Chap. 32) shows that in this mechanism, the attacking anion approaches the carbon atom to which it will become bonded from a side opposite to that occupied by the halide ion. As the attacking anion approaches, the halide ion leaves, as illustrated by the process

$$
Y^- + H—\overset{R}{\underset{H}{C}}—X \longrightarrow \left[Y\text{---}\overset{|}{C}\text{---}X \right]^- \longrightarrow Y—C{\diagup} + X^-
$$

Tertiary halides probably follow a two-step reaction sequence as illustrated below:

$$R—X \underset{\text{fast}}{\overset{\text{slow}}{\rightleftarrows}} R^+ + X^-$$

$$R^+ + Y^- \xrightarrow{\text{fast}} RY$$

In the first step the alkyl halide ionizes slowly to give the very reactive *carbonium ion*, R^+, which reacts very rapidly with the anion or even with the solvent. Since the first step is slow (rate-determining) and involves only the alkyl halide, the kinetics of this process are first order and we may call this a *unimolecular mechanism*. This mechanism is favored in polar solvents which assist the ionization step. Secondary halides follow both the first- and the second-order process, with the relative proportion of each depending on conditions and the nature of the alkyl group.

Replacement of Hydroxyl Bonded to Carbon. Direct displacement of an hydroxyl group by another anion,

$$ROH + X^- \longrightarrow RX + OH^-$$

seldom occurs because the anion X^- often shows a greater stability as an independent species than does the small, poorly polarizable OH^- ion. If the alcohol is placed in acid solution, however, the hydroxyl group is converted to the corresponding oxonium ion according to the reaction

$$ROH + H_3O^+ \rightleftarrows R—\overset{\overset{\displaystyle H}{|}}{O}—H^+ + H_2O$$

In oxonium ions, water is the leaving group, and the displacement reaction

$$X^- + R—\overset{\overset{\displaystyle H}{|}}{O}—H^+ \longrightarrow RX + H_2O$$

proceeds with relative ease. For this reason the displacement of hydroxyl groups is usually carried out in acid solutions.

Even in the presence of acids, primary alcohols are converted to alkyl chlorides very slowly. However, tertiary alcohols are rapidly converted to the corresponding chlorides under these conditions.

Aromatic Substitution Reactions. Replacement of hydrogen atoms bonded to an aromatic ring can be accomplished by the following reactions.

1. *Nitration:*

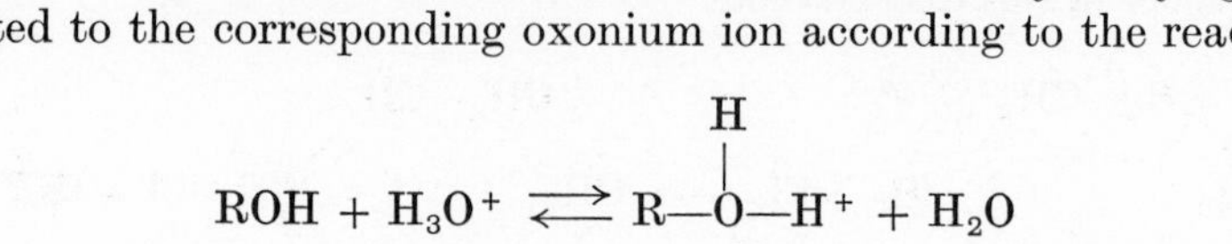

Nitrobenzene

2. *Sulfonation:*

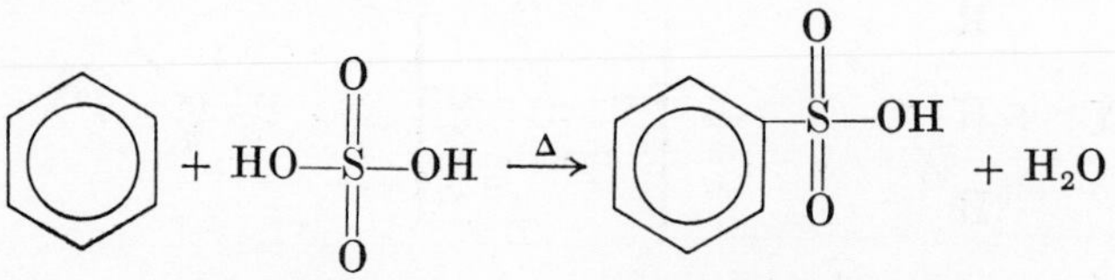

Benzene sulfonic acid

3. *Halogenation* using a Lewis acid catalyst:

$$C_6H_6 + Cl_2 \xrightarrow{FeCl_3} C_6H_5\text{-Cl} + HCl$$

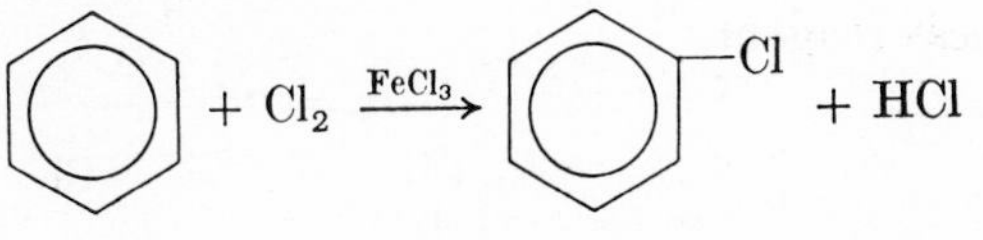

Sunlight does not catalyze this reaction.

4. *Alkylation* using a Lewis acid catalyst:

$$C_6H_6 + RCl \xrightarrow{AlCl_3} C_6H_5\text{-R} + HCl$$

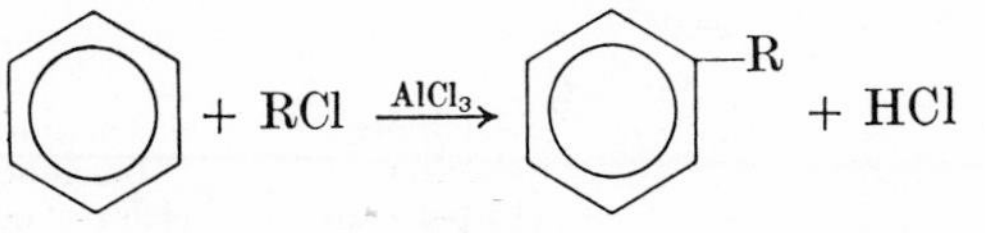

This reaction, known as the Friedel-Crafts reaction, is a method for obtaining aromatic structures having aliphatic side chains.

The mechanism of aromatic substitution usually involves attack by a reactive positive ion on the aromatic ring. This is in contrast to aliphatic substitution reactions which often involve attack by an electron-rich (often negative) species. In the aromatic reactions the ion, seeking a pair of electrons, adds to the ring. This is followed by expulsion of a proton:

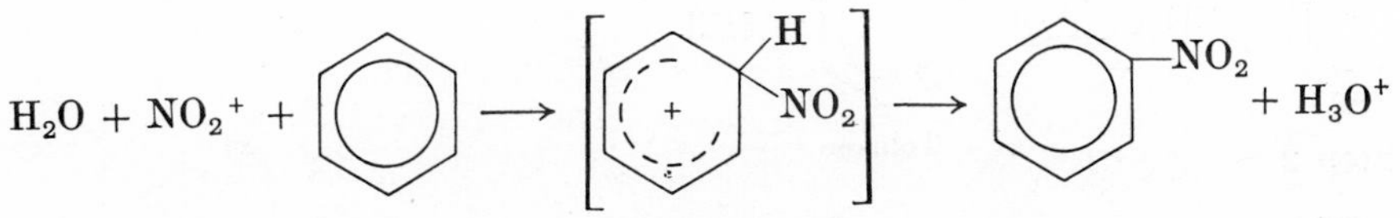

$$H_2O + NO_2^+ + C_6H_6 \longrightarrow \left[\text{transition state}\right] \longrightarrow C_6H_5\text{-}NO_2 + H_3O^+$$

Transition state

Other positive ions that will react are SO_3H^+, Cl^+, and R^+. The reactive positive ions are probably generated as follows:

$$H_2SO_4 + H\text{-}O\text{-}NO_2 \longrightarrow \left[H\text{-}\underset{|}{\overset{H}{O}}\text{-}NO_2\right]^+ + HSO_4^-$$

$$\left[H\text{-}\underset{|}{\overset{H}{O}}\text{-}NO_2\right]^+ \longrightarrow H_2O + NO_2^+$$

In nitration, the sulfuric acid catalyst donates a proton to nitric acid, giving a species which may lose water to give NO_2^+ (nitronium ion). In sulfonation, a similar reaction may occur:

$$H_2SO_4 + HO\text{-}SO_3H \longrightarrow \left[H\text{-}\underset{|}{\overset{H}{O}}\text{-}SO_3H\right]^+ + HSO_4^-$$

$$\left[H\text{-}\underset{|}{\overset{H}{O}}\text{-}SO_3H\right]^+ \longrightarrow H_2O + SO_3H^+$$

In alkylation, the aluminum chloride catalyst helps form the carbonium ion, R^+, according to the reaction

$$RCl + AlCl_3 \rightleftarrows R^+ + AlCl_4^-$$

It is possible to replace more than one hydrogen atom in a benzene ring by using an excess of the substituting reagent or by carrying out successive substitutions using different reagents. Examples of these possibilities are:

1. Use of excess reagent.

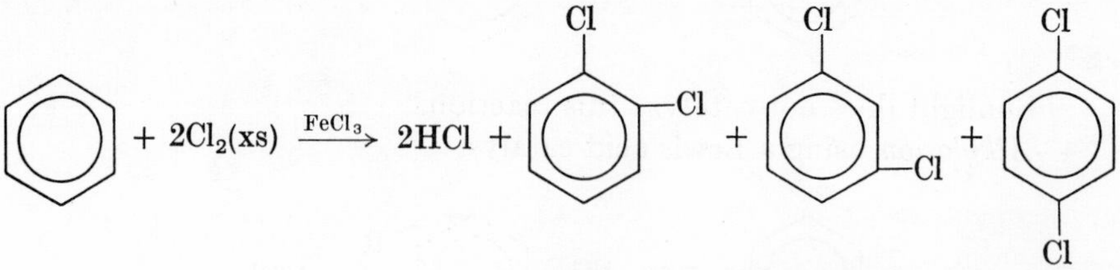

| o-Dichloro-
benzene
(11 per cent
of product) | m-Dichloro-
benzene
(1.6 per cent
of product) | p-Dichloro-
benzene
(87 per cent
of product) |

Here a mixture of all three disubstituted benzenes is obtained, but the yield of the 1,3-dichlorobenzene (or m-dichlorobenzene) is very poor —only 1.6 per cent of the product.

2. Successive substitutions.

Step 1

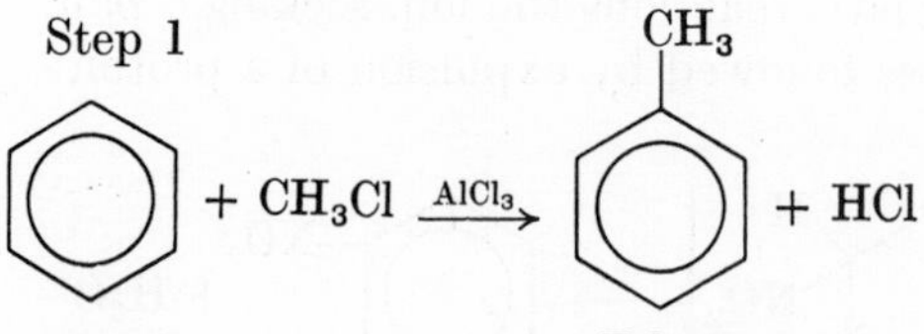

Toluene

Step 2

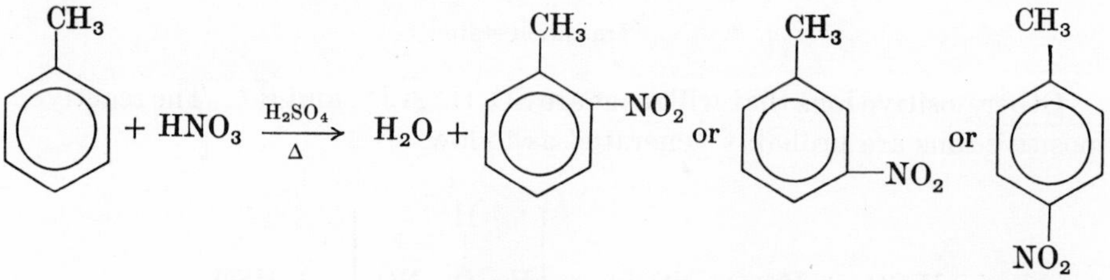

| o-Nitro-
toluene
(56 per cent
of product) | m-Nitro-
toluene
(3 per cent
of product) | p-Nitro-
toluene
(41 per cent
of product) |

In the second step a mixture of all three disubstituted benzenes is obtained, but here again the yield of the m-nitrotoluene is very low.

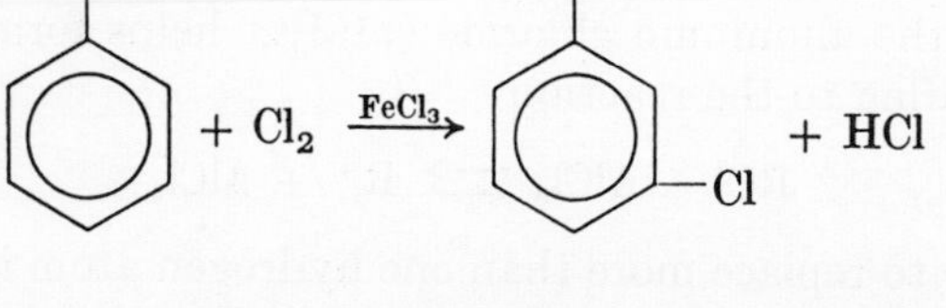

When a second substituent is introduced into a monosubstituted benzene, a mixture of the three isomeric disubstituted benzenes is usually obtained. However the yields of the three isomers vary greatly. In the two examples given above, good yields of the o- and p- isomers were obtained, but the yield of the m- isomer was very low. In the reaction the *m-* isomer is obtained in highest yields. From these and numerous similar results, chemists conclude that *the position taken by an entering substituent depends upon the substituent already present in the ring.* For example, in the first two examples given, the first substituents in the ring were a chloro and a methyl group respectively. These groups control the position taken by the second substituent (a chloro and a nitro group in the two cases in point). The yield of products clearly shows that both the methyl and chloro groups direct second substituents to the *o-* and *p-* positions but not to the *m-* position. On the other hand, the nitro group in nitrobenzene directs the second substituent to the *m-* position but not to the *o-* or *p-* positions. This behavior is rather general and it is possible to identify groups as being *ortho-para directing* or *meta-directing.*

Some ortho-para directing groups:

$$-NH_2, \; -OH, \; -N(CH_3)_2, \; -OCH_3, \; -CH_3, \; -Cl, \; -Br, \; -I$$

Some meta-directing groups (note the presence of multiple bonds in these groups):

Usually meta-directing groups decrease the activity of the ring toward further substitution. The ordering influence of substituents can be explained in terms of electronic structures. The entering group, a positive ion, seeks out the carbon atom which has the highest electron density. Substituents already present affect the electron density in the ring. Ortho-para directing groups tend to increase the electron density in the ring, and meta-directing groups tend to decrease the electron density in the ring. This is discussed in Chap. 32.

PROBLEM. ■ Show by equations a method for converting benzene (a) to *p-*bromonitrobenzene, and (b) to *m-*bromonitrobenzene.

SOLUTION

(a) To get the *p-* isomer we must first put an ortho-para directing group into the molecule, and then substitute the second group. Of the two, the bromo group is ortho-para directing so the sequence must be:

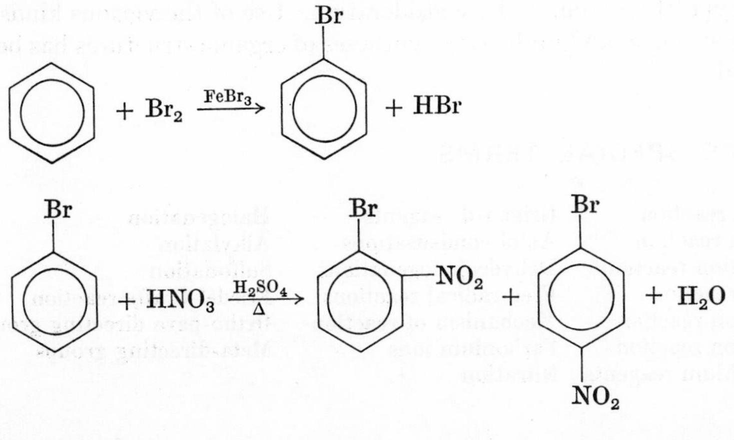

(b) To get the *m*- isomer, the meta-directing nitro group must be put in first, therefore the sequence becomes:

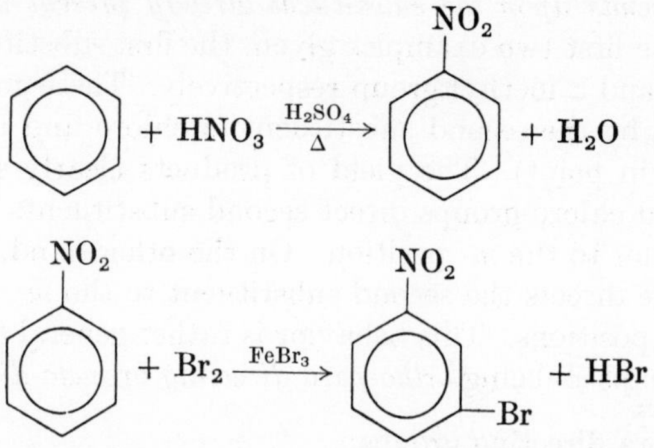

PROBLEM. ■ Devise a method for converting benzene to benzoic acid,

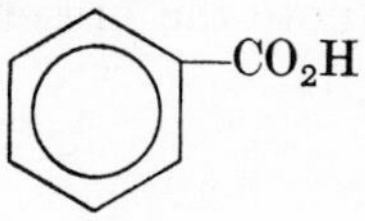

SOLUTION

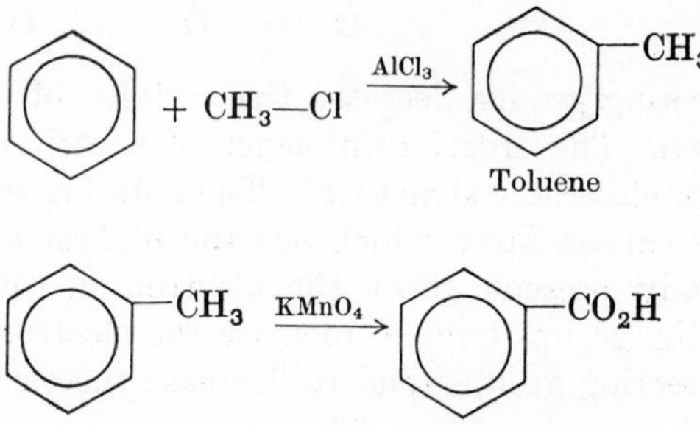

SUMMARY

Reactivity of organic structures has been discussed in terms of six types of reactions: (a) oxidations, (b) reductions, (c) condensations, (d) additions, (e) eliminations, and (f) substitutions. Emphasis has been placed on the relation between the structure and bonding in a given functional group and the type of reaction under consideration. Use of the various kinds of reactions in single- and multi-step syntheses of organic structures has been illustrated.

SOME SPECIAL TERMS

Oxidation reaction	**Grignard reagents**	**Halogenation**
Reduction reaction	**Aldol condensations**	**Alkylation**
Condensation reaction	**Dehydrohalogenations**	**Sulfonation**
Addition reaction	**Free-radical reactions**	**Friedel-Crafts reaction**
Elimination reaction	**Mechanism of reaction**	**Ortho-para directing groups**
Substitution reaction	**Carbonium ions**	**Meta-directing groups**
Organolithium reagents	**Nitration**	

QUESTIONS AND PROBLEMS

1. Name some oxidizing agents commonly used in organic chemistry and illustrate their use with a specific equation for each oxidizing agent.
2. Name some reducing agents commonly used in organic chemistry and illustrate their use with a specific equation for each reducing agent.
3. Using structural formulas and indicating the reagents needed, show how you could make each of the following conversions:

(a) 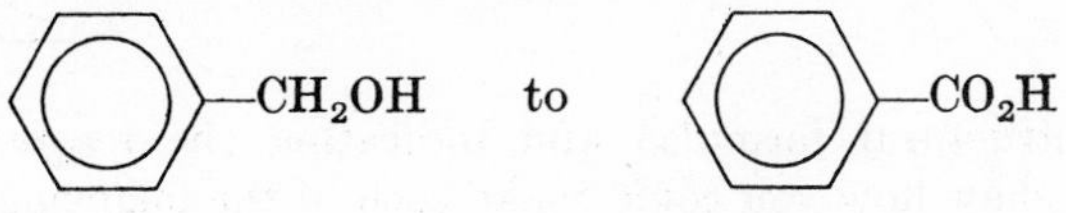 ⬡—CH_2OH to   ⬡—CO_2H

(b) 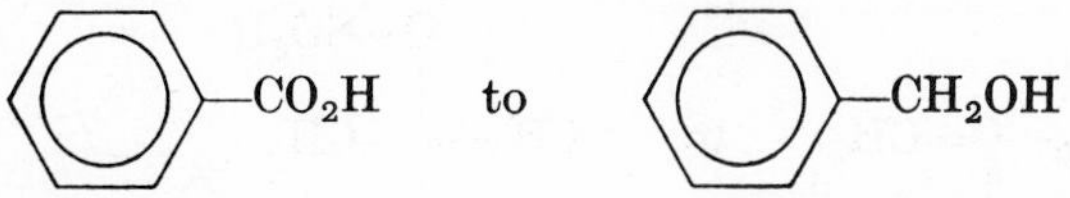 ⬡—CO_2H to   ⬡—CH_2OH

(c) $CH_3C{\equiv}N$ to $CH_3CH_2NH_2$

(d) 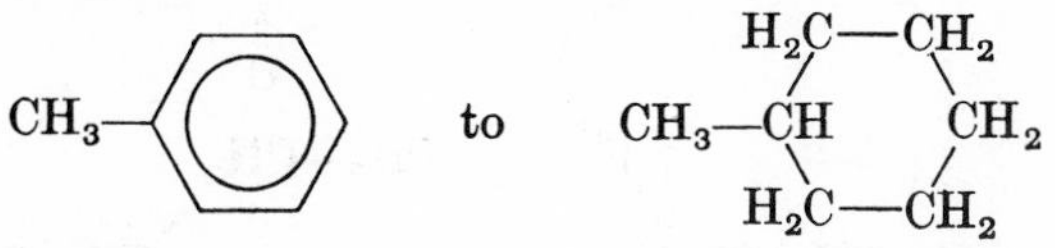 CH_3—⬡   to CH_3—CH⟨(cyclohexane ring: H_2C—CH_2 / CH_2 / H_2C—CH_2)⟩

(e) 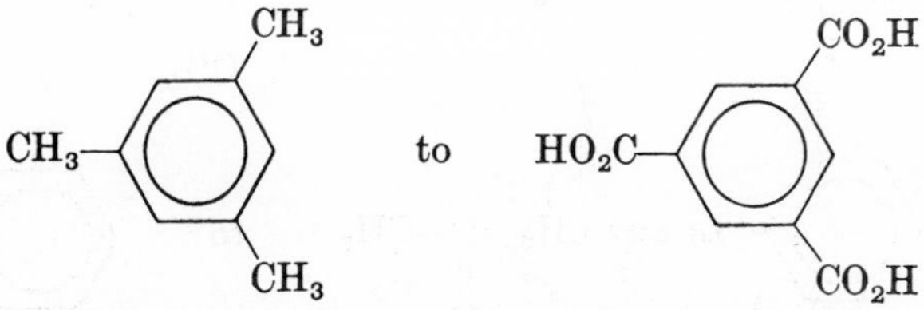 CH_3—⬡ (with CH_3 top and CH_3 bottom)   to HO_2C—⬡ (with CO_2H top and CO_2H bottom)

4. Give a simple chemical test which will distinguish: (a) an aldehyde from a ketone, (b) an alcohol from an aldehyde, (c) a primary alcohol from a secondary alcohol, (d) an alkane from an alkene, (e) a carboxylic acid from an alcohol, (f) an alcohol from an amine.
5. Upon heating with potassium permanganate an alkene having the formula C_6H_{12} gave propanoic acid as the only organic product. Write the structural formula for the alkene.
6. Upon treatment with lithium aluminum hydride a dione having the formula $C_6H_{10}O_2$ gave 3-methyl-2,4-pentanediol. Write the structural formula for the dione.
7. Using structural formulas and indicating the reagents and conditions needed, show how you could make each of the following conversions:

(a) CH_3—CH—CH_2OH to CH_3—CH—CH_2—O—CH_2—CH—CH_3
       | | |
      CH_3 CH_3 CH_3

(b) CH_3—CH—CH_2OH to CH_3—CH—C—O—C—CH_3—CH_3
       | | ‖   ‖ |
      CH_3 CH_3 O   O CH_3

(c) 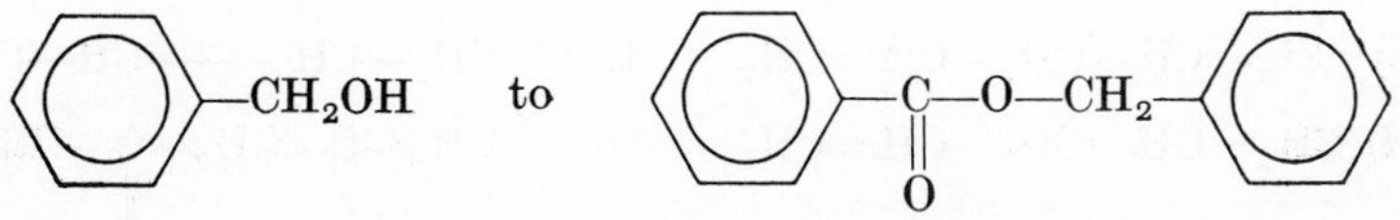 ⬡—CH_2OH to   ⬡—C—O—CH_2—⬡
                              ‖
                              O

(d) 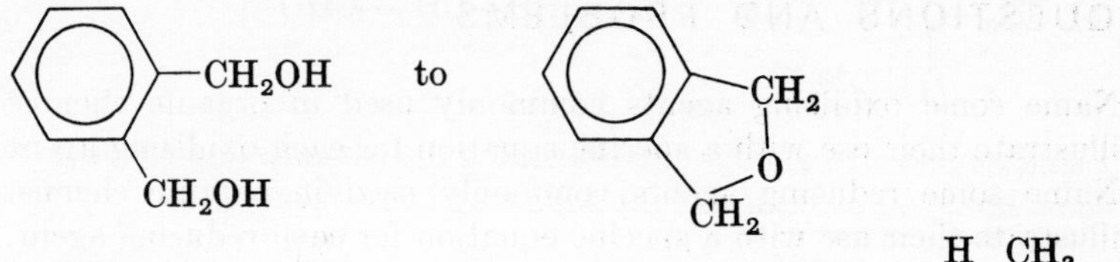 ⬡—CH₂OH   to   ⬡ with CH₂–O–CH₂ ring

(e) 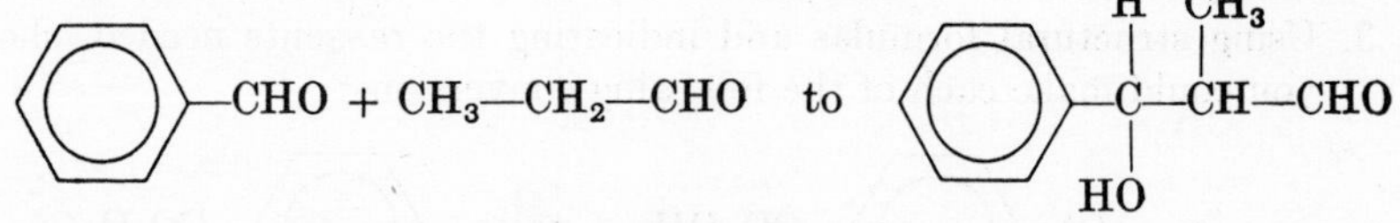 ⬡—CHO + CH₃—CH₂—CHO   to   ⬡—C(H)(OH)—CH(CH₃)—CHO

8. Using structural formulas and indicating the reagents and conditions needed, show how you could make each of the following conversions:

(a) 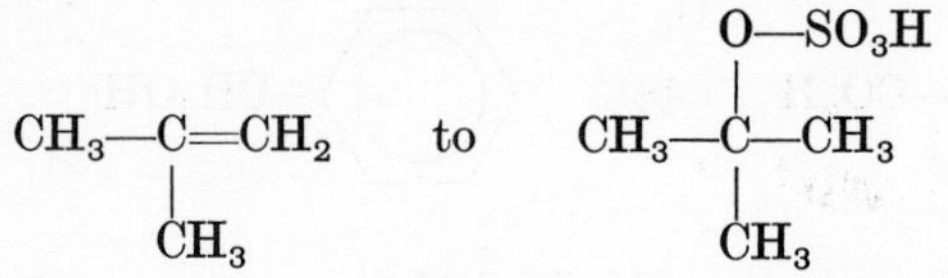 CH₃—C(CH₃)=CH₂   to   CH₃—C(O—SO₃H)(CH₃)—CH₃

(b) CH₃—CH=CH—CH₃   to   CH₃—C(=O)—CH₂—CH₃

(c) CH₃—CH=CH—CH₃   to   (CH₃—CH₂)(CH₃)CH—O—CH(CH₃)(CH₂—CH₃)

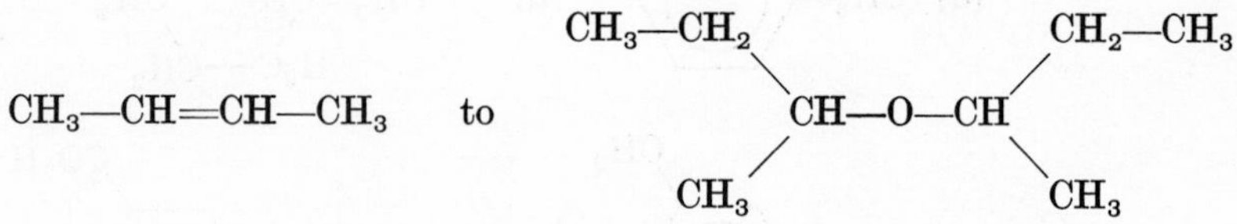

(d) 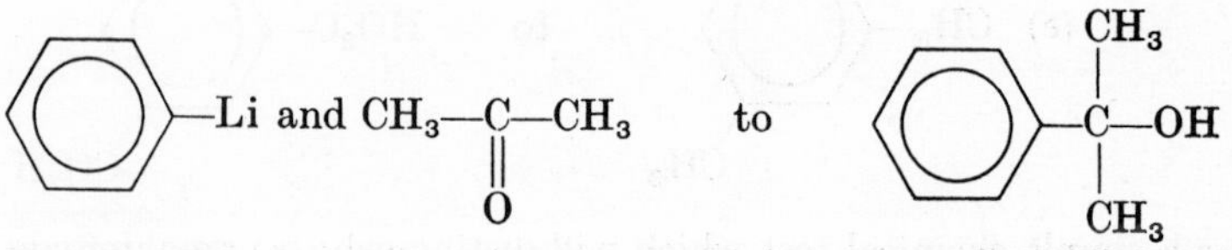 ⬡—Li and CH₃—C(=O)—CH₃   to   ⬡—C(CH₃)(CH₃)—OH

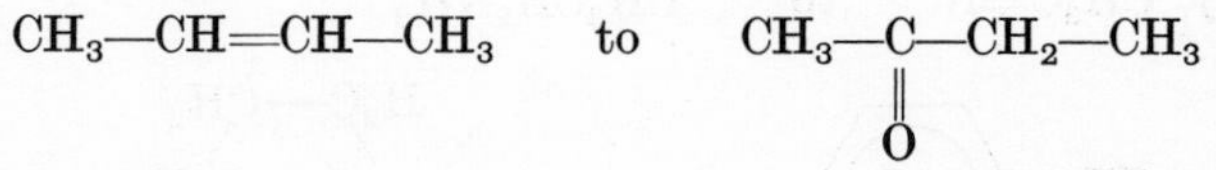

(e) 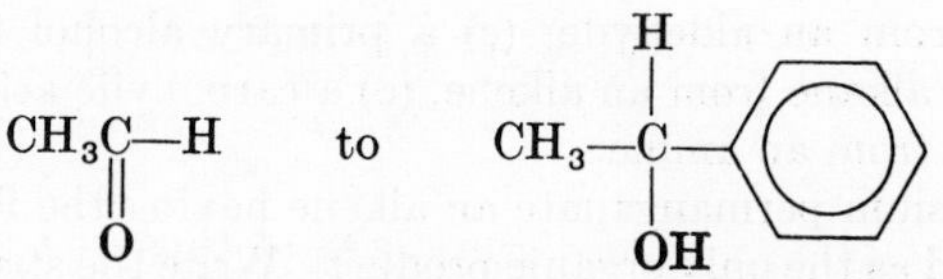 CH₃C(=O)—H   to   CH₃—C(H)(OH)—⬡

9. Using structural formulas and indicating the reagents and conditions needed, show how you could make the following conversions:

(a) 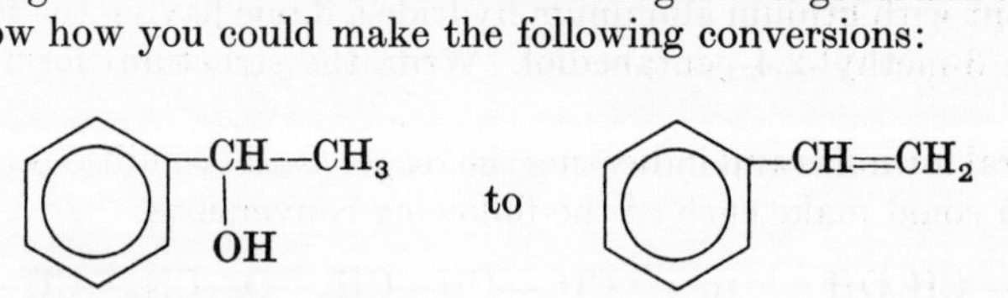 ⬡—CH(OH)—CH₃   to   ⬡—CH=CH₂

(b) 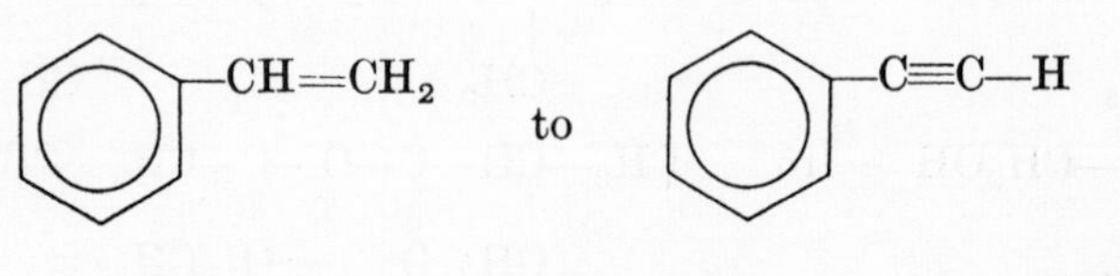 ⬡—CH=CH₂   to   ⬡—C≡C—H

(c) CH₂=CH—CH₂—CH=CH₂   to   CH₃—CH—CH—CH₃ (cyclopropane ring with CH₂)

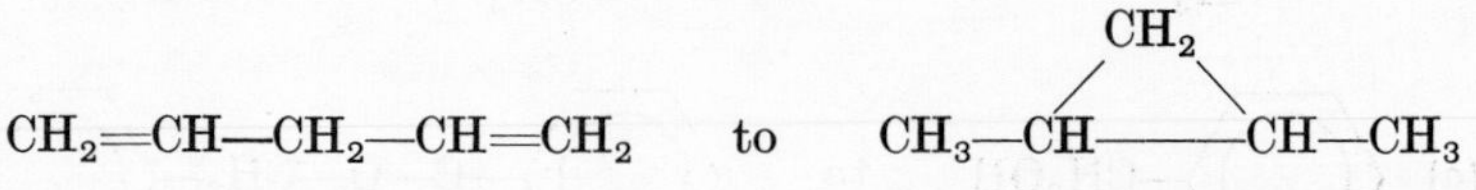

(d) 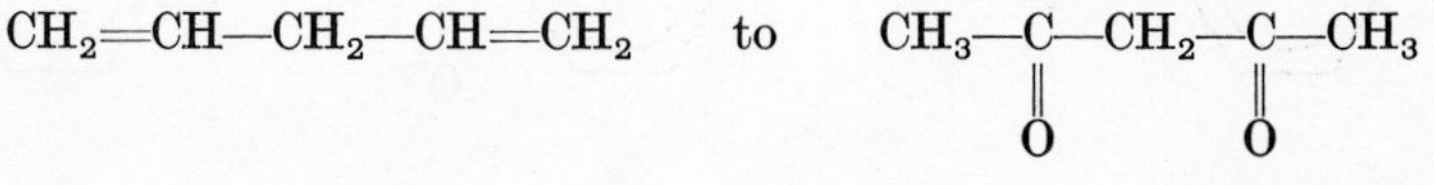 CH₂=CH—CH₂—CH=CH₂   to   CH₃—C(=O)—CH₂—C(=O)—CH₃

(e) $CH_3-\overset{\overset{\displaystyle O}{\|}}{C}-H$ to $CH_2=CH-CH_2-CHO$

10. Using structural formulas and indicating the reagents and conditions needed, show how you could make the following conversions:

(a) $CH_3-\underset{\underset{\displaystyle CH_3}{|}}{CH}-CH_3$ to $CH_3-\underset{\underset{\displaystyle CH_3}{|}}{\overset{\overset{\displaystyle Cl}{|}}{C}}-CH_3$

(b) $CH_3-\underset{\underset{\displaystyle CH_3}{|}}{CH}-Cl$ to $CH_3-\underset{\underset{\displaystyle CH_3}{|}}{CH}-C\equiv CH$

(c) $CH_3-\underset{\underset{\displaystyle CH_3}{|}}{C}=CH_2$ to $CH_3-\underset{\underset{\displaystyle CH_3}{|}}{\overset{\overset{\displaystyle CH_3}{|}}{C}}-NH_2$

(d) 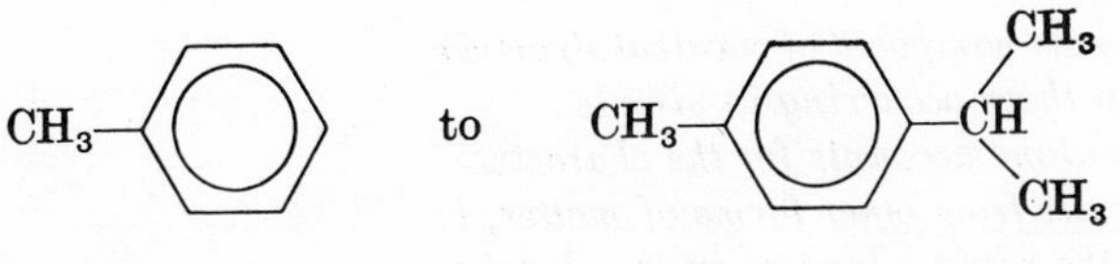 $CH_3-\bigcirc$ to $CH_3-\bigcirc-\overset{\overset{\displaystyle CH_3}{|}}{\underset{\underset{\displaystyle CH_3}{|}}{CH}}$

(e) 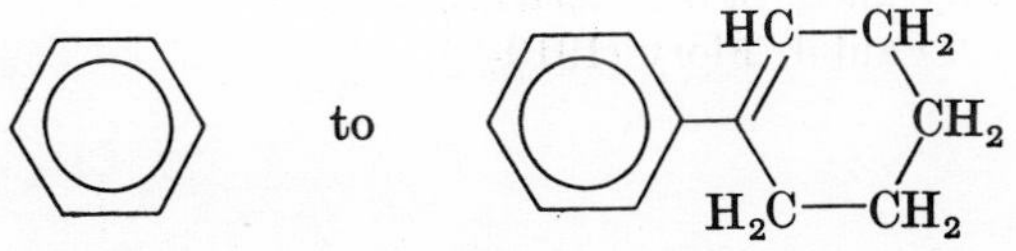 ⬡   to   (phenyl)−cyclobutene structure

REFERENCES

Bordwell, F. G. *Organic Chemistry.* New York: Macmillan, 1963.

Hart, H., and R. Schuetz. *A Short Course in Organic Chemistry*, 3rd ed. Boston: Houghton Mifflin, 1966.

Roberts, J. D., and M. C. Caserio. *Basic Principles of Organic Chemistry.* New York: Benjamin, 1964.

31

Polymers and Other Complex Molecules

The hypothesis that high polymers are composed of covalent structures many times greater in extent than those occurring in simple compounds, and that this feature alone accounts for the characteristic properties which set them apart from other forms of matter, is in large measure responsible for the rapid advances in the chemistry and physics of these substances.   Paul J. Flory (1910—)

For thousands of years man has used materials found in nature to provide himself with food, clothing, shelter, fertilizers, and drugs. Careful studies have revealed the structure and properties which characterize the materials used for these various purposes. With this information the chemist has synthesized products which are identical with, or, in many cases, better than, the materials found in nature. He has been able to duplicate or simulate many of the natural vitamins and drugs; he has made new anesthetics, new antiseptics, new fibers, and insecticides; he has learned to separate the molecules in petroleum and re-form them into improved gasolines, or to polymerize them into rubber, plastics, and textiles. Much of the luxury and improved standard of living in our modern life, as compared with that of ancient peoples, is the result of the work of the chemist. This chapter deals with the structure and properties of some natural products and some of the materials the chemist has helped to synthesize.

Polymers

Polymers are large molecules made up of many smaller molecules bonded together. The smaller molecules are called *monomers*. Naturally occurring polymers include rubber, cellulose (the structural material of plants), and the proteins of muscle and living cells. Synthetic polymers include many familiar products: (a) fibers such as nylon, Dacron, and Acrilan; (b) plastics for uses varying from brush handles to brush bristles and food wrappings, such as Bakelite, Styron, Plexiglas, Saran, and polypropylene; (c) elastomers such as synthetic rubber and Neoprene; and (d) resins, such as Glyptal, Duralon, or Lucite, for finishes on automobiles, boats, and other objects. More than half of the products of the chemical industries of the United States are based, to some degree, on the manufacture or use of polymers.

Chemically, polymers are classified according to the way in which the bonds are formed, as *addition* polymers and *condensation* polymers. In addition polymers the small molecules contain double bonds, and polymerization occurs by opening of the double bonds. Polymerized tetrafluoroethylene (commercial Teflon) is an example:

$$nCF_2{=}CF_2 \longrightarrow n[-CF_2-CF_2-] \longrightarrow$$
$$-CF_2-CF_2(-CF_2-CF_2-)_{n-2}CF_2-CF_2-$$

In condensation polymers, a small molecule such as water is eliminated between functional groups on two molecules. Polymerized terephthalic acid and ethylene glycol (commercial Dacron), in which bonding occurs through ester linkages, is an example:

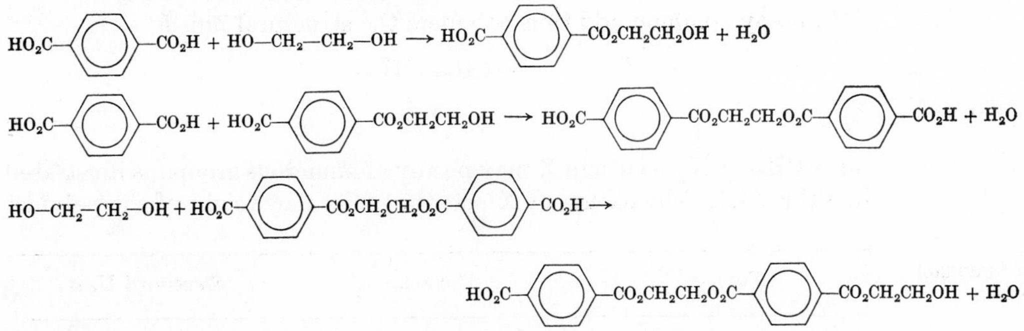

The size of the polymer molecules depends upon the conditions used in polymerization, and a sample of a given polymer will contain huge molecules of many different sizes. The average molecular weight of synthetic polymers may be as low as 5,000 or as high as several million. Of the naturally occurring polymers, rubber has molecular weights ranging from 60,000 to 350,000; cellulose has an average molecular weight of 300,000 to 500,000; some proteins have molecular weights as high as 15,000,000.

The Structure of Synthetic Polymers. Most polymers can be described in terms of their structural unit, or units. This unit usually is the monomer residue as it exists in the backbone of the polymer. For example, in polyvinyl chloride, the polymer made from vinyl chloride,

$$\underset{\underset{Cl}{|}}{CH_2{=}CH}$$

the structural unit is the group

$$\underset{\underset{Cl}{|}}{-CH_2-CH-}$$

In polystyrene, in which the monomer is styrene,

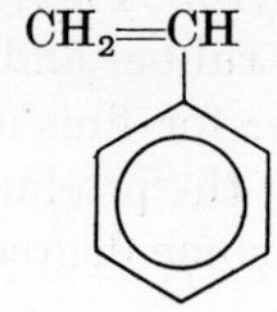

$$CH_2\!\!=\!\!CH$$

the structural unit is the group

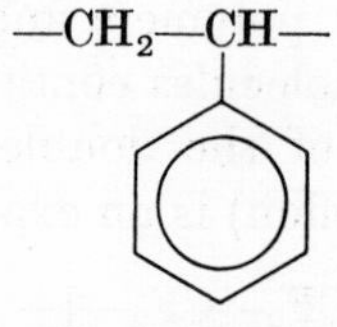

$$-CH_2\!-\!CH-$$

In the polyesters Dacron or Mylar it is the

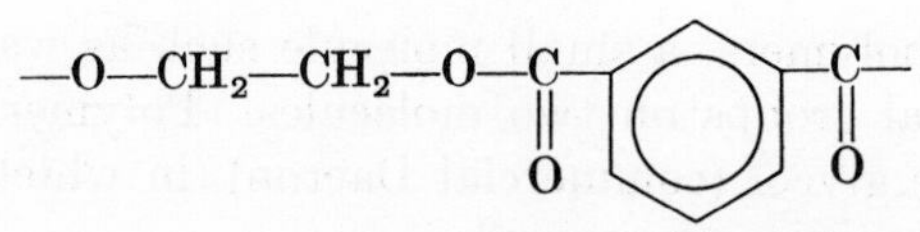

$$-O\!-\!CH_2\!-\!CH_2\!-\!O\!-\!\underset{O}{\overset{\|}{C}}\!\!-\!\!\bigcirc\!\!-\!\underset{O}{\overset{\|}{C}}\!-$$

unit, the residue of the two monomers used to make this polymer.

In many common addition polymers the structural unit is

$$-CH_2\!-\!\underset{X}{\overset{|}{C}}H-$$

(or $-CH_2\!-\!CX_2-$) where X may be any of numerous groups as illustrated in Table 31.1. The nature of X and the molecular weight of the polymer

Table 31.1 Monomers and Structural Units in Some Addition Polymers

Polymer	Monomer	Structural Unit
Polystyrene	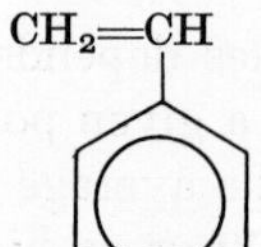 $CH_2\!\!=\!\!CH$	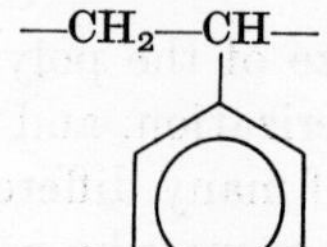 $-CH_2\!-\!CH-$
Polyacrylonitrile	$CH_2\!\!=\!\!\underset{CN}{\overset{\|}{C}}H$	$-CH_2\!-\!\underset{CN}{\overset{\|}{C}}H-$
Polyvinylidine chloride	$CH_2\!\!=\!\!CCl_2$	$-CH_2\!-\!\underset{Cl}{\overset{Cl}{\overset{\|}{C}}}-$
Polymethylmethacrylate	$CH_2\!\!=\!\!\underset{CO_2CH_3}{\overset{CH_3}{\overset{\|}{C}}}$	$-CH_2\!-\!\underset{CO_2CH_3}{\overset{CH_3}{\overset{\|}{C}}}-$
Polyisobutylene	$CH_2\!\!=\!\!\underset{CH_3}{\overset{CH_3}{\overset{\|}{C}}}$	$-CH_2\!-\!\underset{CH_3}{\overset{CH_3}{\overset{\|}{C}}}-$

determines to a great extent the properties of these polymers. For example, polyethylene (X is H) is used as tough, water impermeable films; poly-acrylonitrile (X is CN) is used as fibers; polystyrene is used as a moldable plastic (combs, brush handles) and as an insulating plastic foam; poly-isobutylene

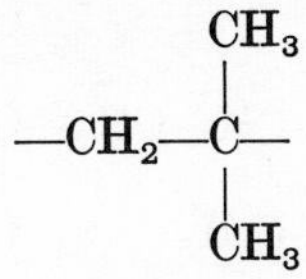

$$-CH_2-\underset{\underset{CH_3}{|}}{\overset{\overset{CH_3}{|}}{C}}-$$

is a synthetic rubber. Table 31.2 lists some commercial addition polymers and their uses. We shall discuss the relation between structure and properties in the next section.

In most addition polymers the monomers are aligned in the polymer in a head-to-tail arrangement—i.e.,

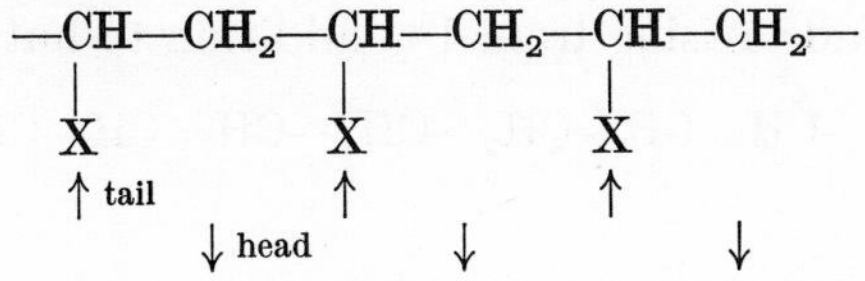

$$-\underset{\underset{\uparrow\text{ tail}}{X}}{CH}-CH_2-\underset{X}{CH}-CH_2-\underset{X}{CH}-CH_2-$$

Homopolymers are those containing a single repeating unit; copolymers contain two repeating units. Polypropylene is a homopolymer; Saran is a copolymer.

The structural units in the polymer may be arranged or connected in several ways. In linear polymers the units are connected to one another in a chain arrangement as X—M—M—M—M—M···Y where M is a bivalent structural unit and X and Y are the end groups which prevent the polymer chain from growing longer. Branched polymers have the general structure

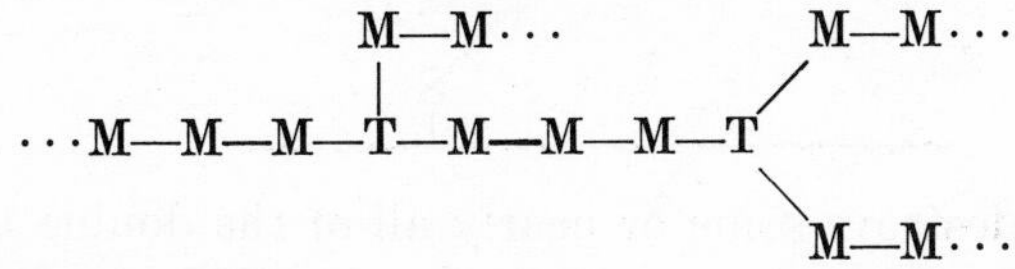

$$
\begin{array}{ccc}
M-M\cdots & & M-M\cdots \\
| & & / \\
\cdots M-M-M-T-M-M-M-T & \\
& & \backslash \\
& & M-M\cdots
\end{array}
$$

which arises when a monomer having three bonding sites is incorporated into the polymer.

Example: $-O-CH_2-\underset{\underset{O-}{|}}{CH}-CH_2-O-$

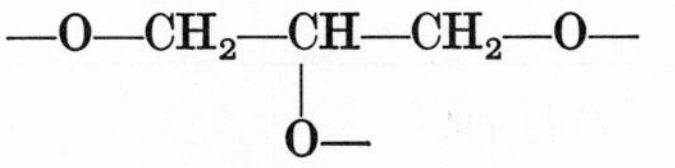

Network polymers are possible when a tetrafunctional monomer such as divinyl benzene

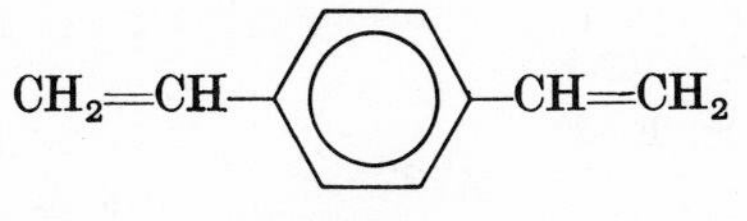

$$CH_2=CH-\hexagon-CH=CH_2$$

is used with a comonomer such as styrene. This is illustrated in Figure 31.1. The common phenol-formaldehyde resin known as Bakelite, one of the first synthetic polymers made, is a network polymer.

Much synthetic rubber is a copolymer of about 25 per cent styrene and 75 per cent butadiene ($CH_2=CH-CH=CH_2$). The polymer backbone

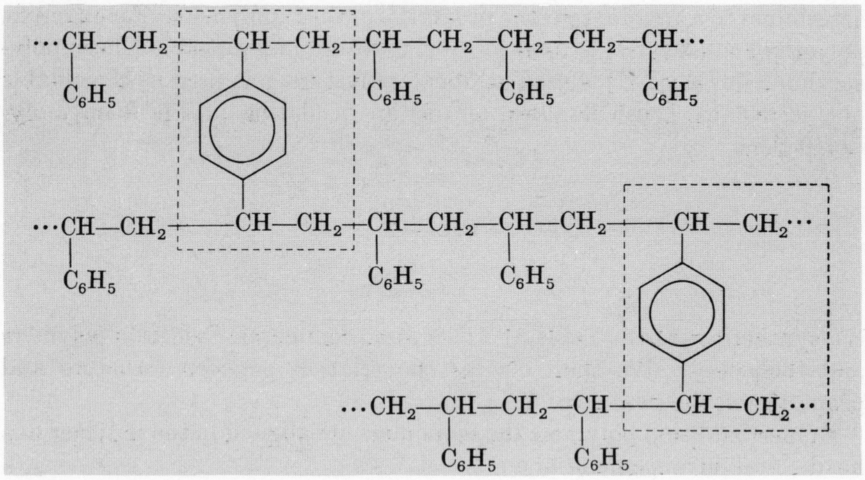

Figure 31.1 Portion of a network copolymer of styrene and divinyl benzene.

contains double bonds arising from 1–4 addition to butadiene:

$$\cdots CH-CH_2-CH_2-CH=CH-CH_2-CH_2-CH=CH-CH_2\cdots CH_2-CH\cdots$$
$$\ \ \ \ \ \ |\qquad\qquad\qquad\qquad\qquad\qquad\qquad\qquad\qquad\qquad\qquad |$$
$$\ \ \ \ \ C_6H_5\qquad\qquad\qquad\qquad\qquad\qquad\qquad\qquad\qquad\qquad C_6H_5$$

Vulcanization usually involves treating the polymer with sulfur which reacts with the double bonds to form cross-links between polymer chains illustrated as follows:

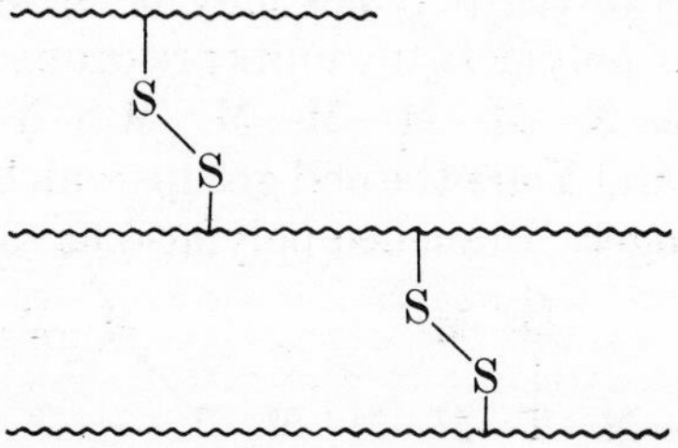

This cross-linking destroys some or nearly all of the double bonds. Soft rubber contains about 1 to 2 per cent sulfur and still has double bonds. Hard rubber may contain as much as 35 per cent sulfur. It has very few double bonds and very little elasticity.

Table 31.2 Some Commercial Addition Polymers

Name	Monomer	Polymer	Uses
Polyperfluoroethylene, Teflon	F F | | C=C | | F F Tetrafluoro-ethylene	F F F F | | | | —C—C—C—C— | | | | F F F F	Chemically resistant; electrical insulation, liner for laboratory ware, pumps, frying pans
Polystyrene Styron, Lustron	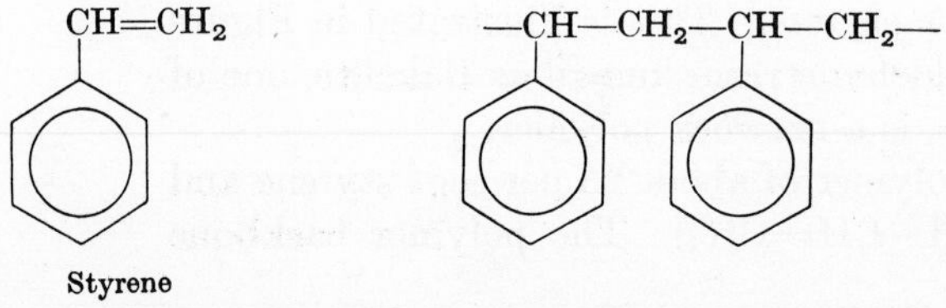 CH=CH₂ Styrene	—CH—CH₂—CH—CH₂—	Plastic foams, wrapping material, handles

Name	Monomer	Polymer	Uses
Polyacrylonitrile, Orlon, Acrilan	$CH\!=\!CH_2$ | CN Acrylonitrile	$-CH\!-\!CH_2\!-\!CH\!-\!CH_2-$ | | CN CN	Fibers
Polyvinylchloride, Koroseal, Geon	$CH\!=\!CH_2$ | Cl Vinyl chloride	$-CH\!-\!CH_2\!-\!CH\!-\!CH_2-$ | | Cl Cl	Raincoats, tank lining
Polypropylene	$CH\!=\!CH_2$ | CH_3 Propylene	$-CH\!-\!CH_2\!-\!CH\!-\!CH_2-$ | | CH_3 CH_3	Wool substitute, transparent films
Polymethylmethacrylate, Lucite, Plexiglas	CH_3 | $C\!=\!CH_2$ | CO_2CH_3 Methyl methacrylate	CH_3 CH_3 | | $-C\!-\!CH_2\!-\!C\!-\!CH_2-$ | | CO_2CH_3 CO_2CH_3	Plastic windows, handles
Polyvinylacetate, Gelva, Vinylite	$CH\!=\!CH_2$ | O_2CCH_3 Vinylacetate	$-CH\!-\!CH_2\!-\!CH\!-\!CH_2-$ | | O_2CCH_3 O_2CCH_3	Latex paints, adhesives
Poly-N-vinylpyrrolidone, Periston	$CH\!=\!CH_2$ | N CH_2 $C\!=\!O$ | | $CH_2\!-\!CH_2$ N-vinylpyrrolidone	$-CH\!-\!CH_2\!-\!CH\!-\!CH_2-$ | | N N CH_2 $C\!=\!O$ CH_2 $C\!=\!O$ | | | | $CH_2\!-\!CH_2$ $CH_2\!-\!CH_2$	Blood plasma substitute, hair sprays
Vinyl chloride, vinyl acetate copolymer, Tygon	—	$-CH\!-\!CH_2\!-\!CH\!-\!CH_2-$ | | Cl O_2CCH_3	Flexible tubing, sheets
Vinylidene chloride, acrylonitrile copolymer, Saran	Cl | $C\!=\!CH_2$ | Cl Vinylidene chloride	Cl | $-C\!-\!CH_2\!-\!CH\!-\!CH_2-$ | | Cl CN	Transparent film
Styrene, butadiene, copolymer	$CH_2\!=\!CH\!-\!CH\!=\!CH_2$ Butadiene	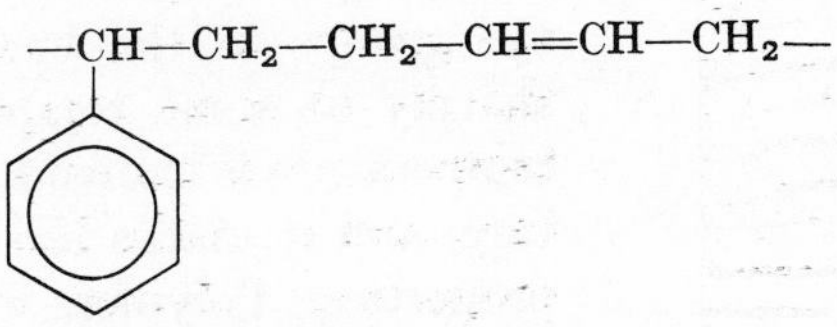 $-CH\!-\!CH_2\!-\!CH_2\!-\!CH\!=\!CH\!-\!CH_2-$	Synthetic rubber

Polyisoprene	$CH_2\!=\!C\!-\!CH\!=\!CH_2$
	  |
	  CH_3
	Isoprene
		$-CH_2\!-\!C\!=\!CH\!-\!CH_2-$
		   |
		   CH_3
			Synthetic rubber

Polychloroprene	$CH_2\!=\!C\!-\!CH\!=\!CH_2$
	  |
	  Cl
	Chloroprene
		$-CH_2\!-\!C\!=\!CH\!-\!CH_2-$
		   |
		   Cl
			Synthetic rubber

Relation of Polymer Structure to Properties. In this section we shall attempt to relate the structure of some linear polymers to the properties they exhibit in some of their commercial applications. We shall consider four types of properties: those suitable for (a) plastics, (b) rubber, (c) films, and (d) fibers.

The molecular weight and the molecular-weight distribution of a polymer has a profound effect on its physical properties. All synthetic polymers and many natural polymers consist of mixtures of molecules of various molecular weights. The softening point, the toughness, and the degree of crystallinity of polymers are related to this distribution. In general, a narrow range of molecular weights in a sample gives more useful polymers. Above a certain molecular weight for each substance small changes in molecular weight have only a negligible effect on the properties of the polymer. It is in this molecular-weight range that the following considerations apply.

Let us now consider the nature of the solid state in linear polymers. Here is a system composed of very long threadlike structures which have lost nearly all of their translational energy. As in other solids these molecules have a tendency to arrange themselves in an orderly way. However, because the threads are so long and so flexible, it is difficult to attain a high degree of order. Instead, with few exceptions, the situation may be described as a generally amorphous assembly of threads. Embedded in this assembly there may be small highly organized crystallites of about 100 A in length. The interior of these crystallites resembles that of ordinary crystals. In effect then, we view the solid polymer as composed of a matrix of threads which may contain stiff rod-like or disc-like crystallites embedded in it. The degree of crystallinity or the percent of the total matrix composed of crystallites varies with the temperature, the molecular weight, and the structure of the polymer (Figure 31.2). Very high molecular weight polyethylene is about 95 per cent crystalline; most polymers have much less crystallinity.

Considering now the energy and structure within the amorphous matrix of threads, the evidence—both experimental and theoretical—shows that this region consists of randomly arranged, coiled, uncoiled, knotted, entangled threads. At lower temperatures the atoms or groups in the threads have vibrational energy but neither the thread nor its parts undergo appreciable rotational motion. Rotational motion of threads involves twisting and writhing like a wounded snake. Such rotations of the groups in the backbones of linear polymers almost always begin sharply at some temperature in the range $-100°C$ to $+200°C$. This temperature is known to polymer chemists as the glass transition temperature, and it marks the separation between plastic properties and rubber properties. Polymers with glass transition temperatures well below room temperature will be rubbers (elastomers) at room temperature; those with glass transition temperatures well above room temperature are likely to find use as plastics. Some adhesives are polymers which make the transition near room temperature. Mechanical properties that are important for plastics include tensile strength at break (the resistance to longitudinal stress); impact strength; flexural strength. For rubbers the tensile strength, the per cent elongation, and the per cent rebound often are important.

(a)

(b)

Figure 31.2 Crystallites in a linear polymer. (a) Unoriented. (b) Oriented after stretching.

Just as rubber must be vulcanized for many uses, so many plastics require a plasticizer, often called an internal lubricant. For example, the addition of about 40 per cent of dioctyl phthalate to polyvinylchloride lowers the glass transition temperature to about 0°C thus turning it into the form used to make transparent raincoats.

The question now arises: What structural features tend to make a polymer act like a rubber or like a plastic at room temperature? Stating the question in another way, we are asking why rotational motion (and ease of mechanical distortion) sets in at lower temperatures for some polymers than for others. The answer seems to be related to the attractive forces between chains or to the bulk of the groups attached to the backbone, which must move as the polymer portions rotate. The three polymers on the left in Table 31.3 all are plastics at room temperature.

	Polymer	T_G (°C)	Polymer	T_G (°C)	
Plastics	Polystyrene	100	Styrene-butadiene polymer	−55	*Rubbers*
	Polymethylmethacrylate	110	Polyisobutylene	−65	
	Polyvinylchloride	80	*trans*-Polyisoprene	−53	

Table 31.3 Glass Transition Temperatures for Some Well-Known Polymers

Polystyrene and polymethylmethacrylate both have large groups attached to the backbone. These groups should retard rotation, thus increasing the glass transition temperature. In polyvinylchloride the polar chlorine atoms probably form hydrogen bonds with hydrogen atoms in adjacent molecules, again causing the glass transition temperature to be relatively high. By contrast, styrene-butadiene rubber, which contains 75 per cent butadiene and only 25 per cent styrene, has a glass transition temperature of −55°C. Since butadiene has only hydrogen atoms, these portions of the thread are expected to start rotating at relatively low temperatures.

Returning now to crystallinity in polymers, we raise the question: What properties are characteristic of polymers having a relatively high degree of crystallinity? Experience shows that such polymers are characterized by high tensile strength, stiffness, hardness, and low solubility. Further, if the crystallites can be oriented in a single direction within the matrix, the material increases considerably in tensile strength, and in toughness. Such properties are highly desirable for fibers and for films.

Most of the polyethylene manufactured is made into films for packaging. These films are permeable to atmospheric gases but are impermeable to water. They have low density, high flexibility, high tear strength. They can be sterilized without losing their shape. Polyethylene also can be molded into pipe, containers, etc.—objects which are inert to most inorganic materials.

At first thought one might expect polyethylene to be a rubber at room temperature; it has no polar forces between threads and no bulky groups to retard their rotation. Instead of forming a matrix of randomly oriented, freely rotating threads, it organizes into a solid having a large per cent of rodlike crystallites. Evidently it is easier for polyethylene molecules than for those of many other polymers to lie side by side in a well-organized crystallite. The suggested reason for this is illustrated in Figure 31.3.

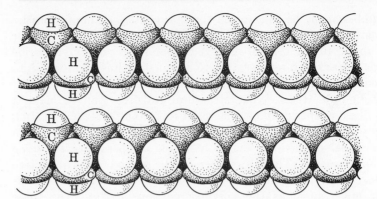

Figure 31.3 Illustrating the packing of polyethylene in a crystallite.

Here we see that the polyethylene threads can pack very efficiently in a crystal because the small hydrogen atoms do not disrupt the symmetry of the packing. By contrast, polyvinylchloride has very little crystallinity because the bulky chlorine atoms prevent efficient packing in the crystallite.

Polyacrylonitrile also shows a relatively high degree of crystallinity. This is believed to be due to the formation of a large number of hydrogen bonds between chains as illustrated below. Polyacrylonitrile is one of the best synthetic fibers.

$$
\begin{array}{c}
-CH_2-CH-CH_2-CH-CH_2-CH- \\
\mid \quad\quad\quad \mid \quad\quad\quad \mid \\
CN \quad\quad\quad CN \quad\quad\quad CN \\
\vdots \quad\quad\quad \vdots \quad\quad\quad \vdots \\
H \quad\quad\quad H \quad\quad\quad H \\
\mid \quad\quad\quad \mid \quad\quad\quad \mid \\
-C-CH_2-C-CH_2-C- \\
\mid \quad\quad\quad \mid \quad\quad\quad \mid \\
CN \quad\quad\quad CN \quad\quad\quad CN
\end{array}
$$

Stereoregular polymers (page 635) also are capable of giving solids having a high degree of crystallinity.

When fiber-forming polymers crystallize in the absence of external stresses, the crystallites orient at random. If an external stress is applied to the polymer, the crystallites tend to orient in the direction of the external stress. When this is done at temperatures below the melting point of the crystals, it is called cold drawing. Orientation greatly increases the hardness and tensile strength of the fiber.

Reactions of Addition Polymerization. The formation of synthetic addition polymers proceeds by a chain-reaction mechanism (Chap. 24). The chain carriers may be free radicals, ions, or organometallic compounds.

Figure 31.4 Showing how the molecules of a high polymer are aligned to form a filament when the matrix is stretched during drying or coagulation.

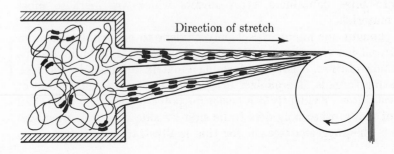

Direction of stretch

As in all chain reactions, the over-all process involves reactions of initiation, propagation, and termination.

Free-Radical Polymerization.   A small amount of substance is added to the monomer which, by (a) thermal or photochemical decomposition or by (b) a one-electron oxidation-reduction reaction, forms a free radical. This constitutes the initiation step. For (a), a peroxide is commonly used; (b) often uses an ion of a metal which can display more than one oxidation state.

Initiation reaction:

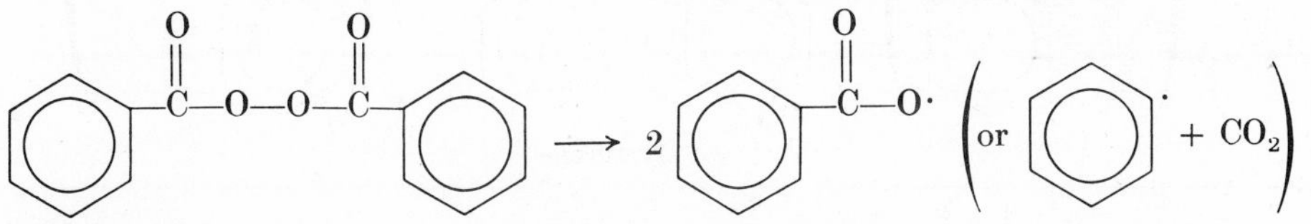

The free radicals (R·) thus formed react with monomer molecules containing double bonds. With styrene as monomer, the reaction would be

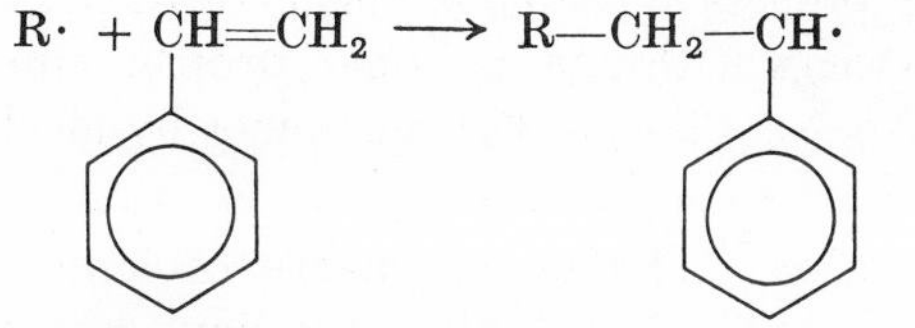

Styrene

The species formed from the ethylene derivative is still a free radical and can add additional olefinic molecules, forming always a free radical. These continue the chain reaction in *propagation steps*.

Propagation reactions:

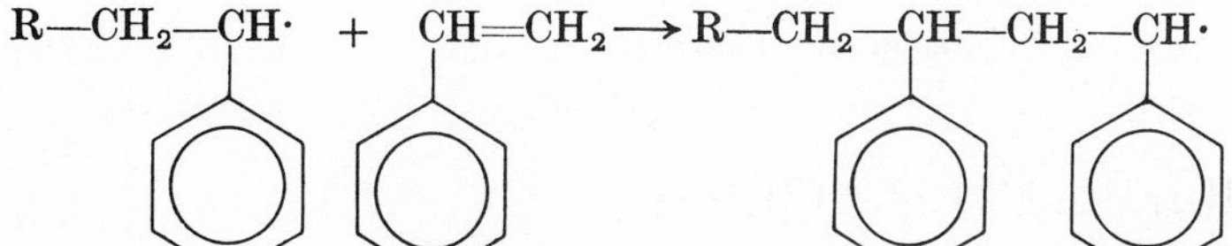

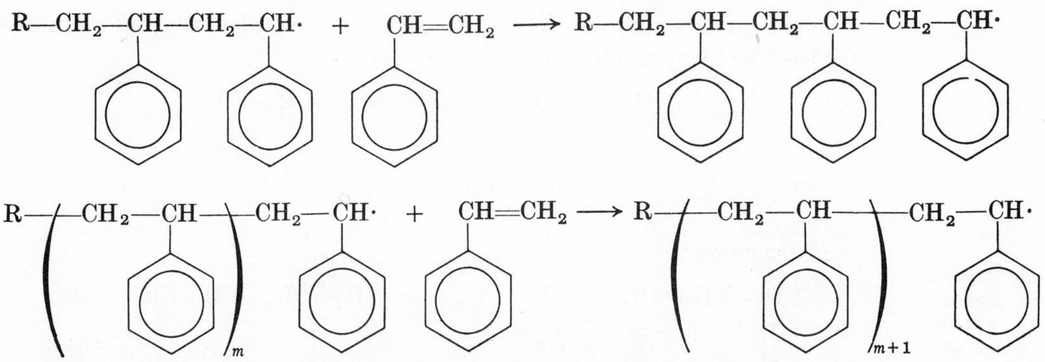

Finally, two of the growing free radicals meet and saturate the free valence on each, forming a stable molecule in the *termination* step.

Termination reaction:

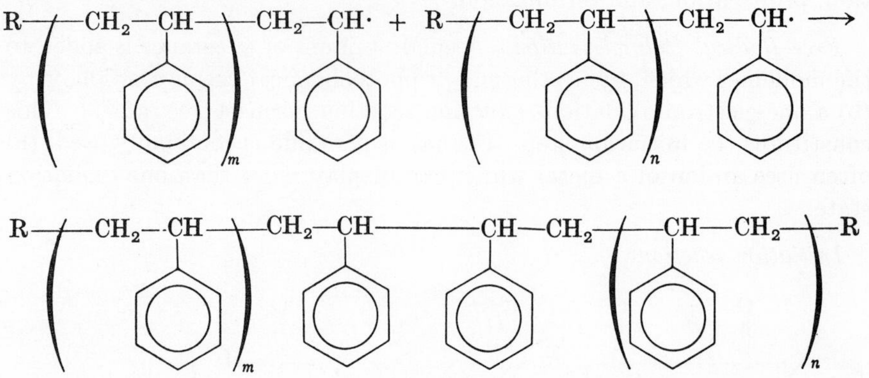

Polystyrene

Free-radical polymerizations show all the characteristics of free-radical reactions generally, and can be studied by methods similar to those discussed for other free-radical chain processes in Chap. 24. An important modification is the process of *emulsion polymerization*, in which the propagation reactions occur within a polymer droplet emulsified in a soap solution which is kept saturated with monomer by mechanical stirring.

Ionic Polymerization. The chain nature of ionic polymerization is similar to that of free-radical polymerization, but the reactions are usually much more rapid. The chain carriers may be cations, as when a Lewis acid such as boron trifluoride is used as initiator:

$$BF_3 + H_2O \longrightarrow HOBF_3{}^-, H^+$$

Initiation:

$$H^+ + (CH_3)_2C{=}CH_2 \longrightarrow (CH_3)_3C^+$$
Isobutene monomer

Propagation:

$$(CH_3)_3C^+ + (CH_3)_2C{=}CH_2 \longrightarrow$$

$$(CH_3)_3C{-}CH_2{-}\overset{+}{C}(CH_3)_2$$

Chain carriers may also be anions, as when a metal and liquid ammonia are used to form amide ion, $NH_2{}^-$,

$$NH_2{}^- + CH_2{=}\underset{\underset{CN}{|}}{CH} \longrightarrow NH_2{-}CH_2{-}\underset{\underset{CN}{|}}{CH}{}^-$$
Acrylonitrile
monomer

Propagation:

$$NH_2{-}CH_2{-}\underset{\underset{CN}{|}}{CH}{}^- + \underset{\underset{CN}{|}}{CH}{=}CH_2 \longrightarrow NH_2{-}CH_2{-}\underset{\underset{CN}{|}}{CH}{-}CH_2{-}\underset{\underset{CN}{|}}{CH}{}^-$$

In cationic polymerization, the termination step appears to be essentially a reversal of the initiation step, regenerating a double bond:

$$(CH_3)_3C(\!-\!CH_2\!-\!C(CH_3)_2\!-\!)_nCH_2\!-\!\overset{+}{C}(CH_3)_2, \ \bar{B}F_3OH \longrightarrow$$

$$(CH_3)_3C(\!-\!CH_2\!-\!C(CH_3)_2)_n\!-\!CH_2\!-\!C(CH_3)\!=\!CH_2 + BF_3\cdot H_2O$$

In anionic polymerization, no unsaturation appears in the stable polymer:

$$H_2N\!-\!\!\left(\!\!\begin{array}{c}CH_2\!-\!CH\\ \ \ \ \ |\\ \ \ \ CN\end{array}\!\!\right)_{\!\!n}\!\!-\!CH_2\!\cdot\!CH^- + NH_3 \longrightarrow H_2N\!-\!\!\left(\!\!\begin{array}{c}CH_2\!-\!CH\\ \ \ \ \ |\\ \ \ \ CN\end{array}\!\!\right)_{\!\!n}\!\!-\!CH_2\!-\!CH_2 + NH_2^-$$

Organometallic Polymerization. In this process a mixture of an aluminum alkyl and a transition metal chloride such as $TiCl_4$ is used as an initiator or "Ziegler catalyst." The mechanism of the reactions is not entirely clear, but the reaction system contains suspended solids, and it seems likely that the process is a heterogeneous ionic polymerization. The growing ionic chain carriers remain attached to the solid surface, and monomer molecules about to be added to the carrier approach this surface with a particular orientation with respect to the chain-carrier ion. In some cases the result of this orientation is that, if the polymer formed contains asymmetric carbon atoms (Chap. 32), these will be found to have always the same orientation at all points down the chain. Such a polymer is called an isotactic polymer. Isotactic polymers are more dense and more nearly crystalline than those which have random orientations. They belong to a class known as *stereoregular* polymers.

Reactions of Condensation Polymerization. In a condensation polymerization, all reactions are of the same type, repeated over and over again, rather than of the three types of initiation, propagation, and termination for addition polymerization. The common reactions are those of esterification, as in the example of Dacron given earlier, of amide formation, as in the formation of Nylon 6-6,

$$H_2N\!-\!CH_2\!-\!CH_2\!-\!CH_2\!-\!CH_2\!-\!CH_2\!-\!CH_2\!-\!NH_2$$
Hexamethylene diamine

$$+ \ HO_2C\!-\!CH_2\!-\!CH_2\!-\!CH_2\!-\!CH_2\!-\!CO_2H \longrightarrow$$
Adipic acid

$$HO_2C\!-\!CH_2\!-\!CH_2\!-\!CH_2\!-\!CH_2\!-\!C\!\!\begin{array}{c}\nearrow O\\ \searrow\\ \ \ \ HN\!-\!CH_2\!-\!CH_2\!-\!CH_2\!-\!CH_2\!-\!CH_2\!-\!CH_2 + H_2O\\ \ \ \ \ \ \ \ \ \ \ \ \ \ \ \ \ |\\ \ \ \ \ \ \ \ \ \ \ \ \ \ \ \ NH_2\end{array}$$

or of dehydration, as in the formation of the silicones (Chap. 20). The molecules in a condensation polymer are commonly more varied in size than those in an addition polymer.

Natural Polymers. The important naturally occurring polymers include rubber, cellulose, starch, glycogen, and proteins. The structural stability of plants depends to a great extent on cellulose. Starch and glycogen are essential sources of carbohydrates for plants and animals; and proteins seem to be the substances most intimately concerned with life itself. In short, natural polymers occur in all living things and play an essential role in life processes.

Polymers of Glucose: Cellulose, Starch, Glycogen. One formula for glucose* is

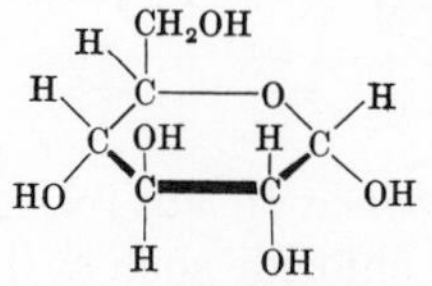

which can be simplified for present purposes to

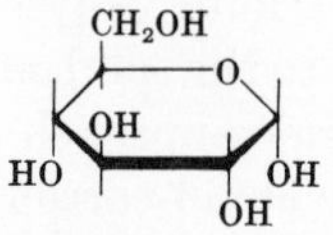

The presence of five hydroxyl groups in the molecule suggests immediately the possibility of condensation polymers of glucose—both linear and branched polymers as illustrated below.

A linear polymer of glucose:

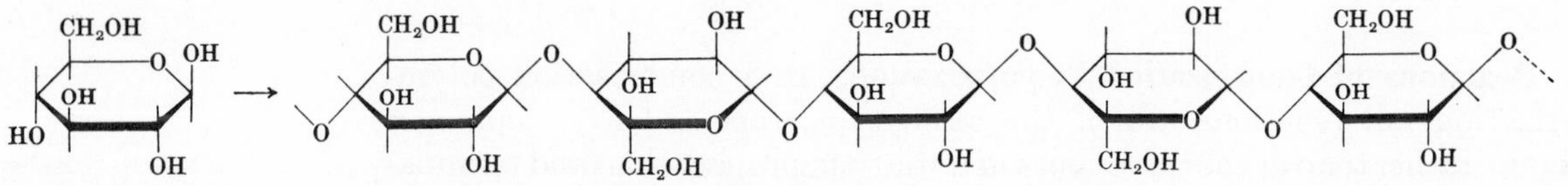

A branched polymer of glucose:

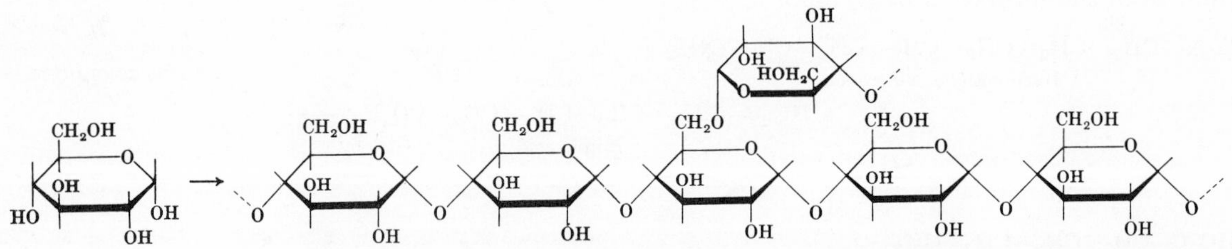

Both types of glucose polymers are known. Cellulose is a linear polymer, while starch and glycogen have considerable branching and a helical structure. In both starch and cellulose, the backbone of the polymer is formed by elimination of water between the first carbon atom on one glucose molecule and the fourth carbon atom on the second molecule as

---

* This formula and its significance is developed further in Chap. 32. The heavy lines are present to create the impression that the ring is tipped out of the plane of the paper.

illustrated below,

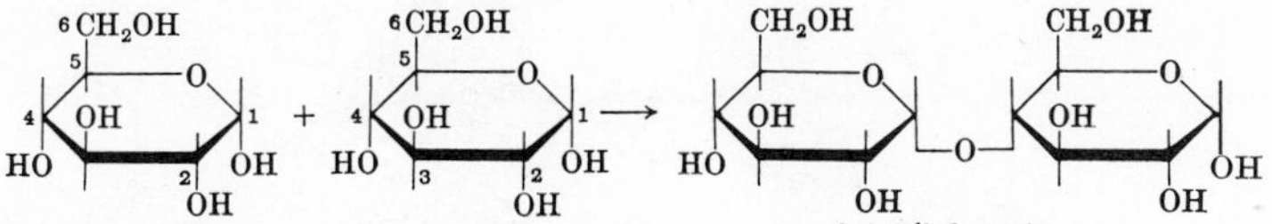

A 1,4 linkage in a
glucose polymer

The branch points in starch and glycogen appear to involve the first carbon atom on one glucose molecule and the sixth carbon atom in a glucose molecule in the backbone as illustrated in the branched polymer structure above. For reasons that will be discussed in Chap. 32, two spatial arrangements are possible for the distribution of the glucose units around the oxygen atoms which connect them. One of these arrangements is found in cellulose, the other in starch and glycogen.

Table 31.4 Some Commercial Condensation Polymers

Name	Monomer	Structural Unit	Uses
Dacron, Terylene	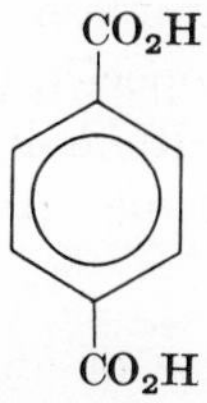 CO_2H (Terephthalic acid) / $HOCH_2CH_2OH$ Ethylene glycol	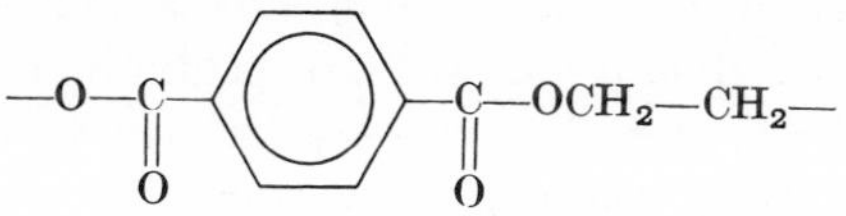	Textile fibers
Nylon 6-6	$HO_2C(CH_2)_4CO_2H$ Adipic acid / $H_2N(CH_2)_6NH_2$ Hexamethylene diamine		Textile fibers, bristles, sheets
Bakelite, Durez	$H_2C{=}O$ Formaldehyde 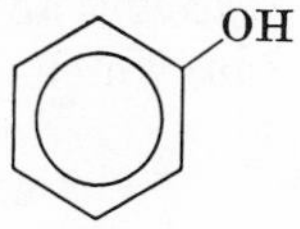 / Phenol	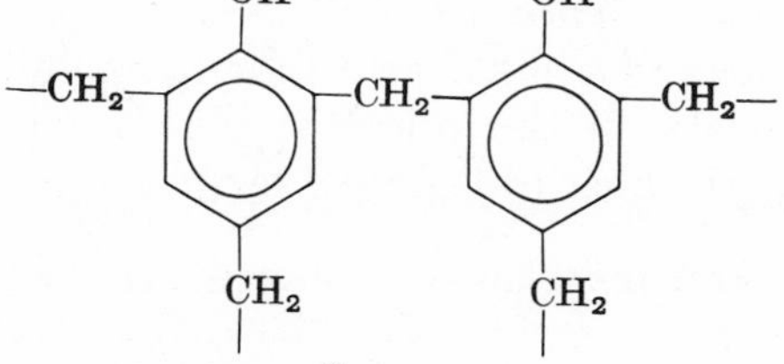	Records, telephone receivers
Beetle	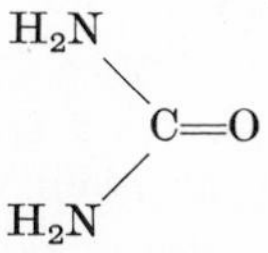 H_2N $C{=}O$ H_2N Urea / $H_2C{=}O$ Formaldehyde	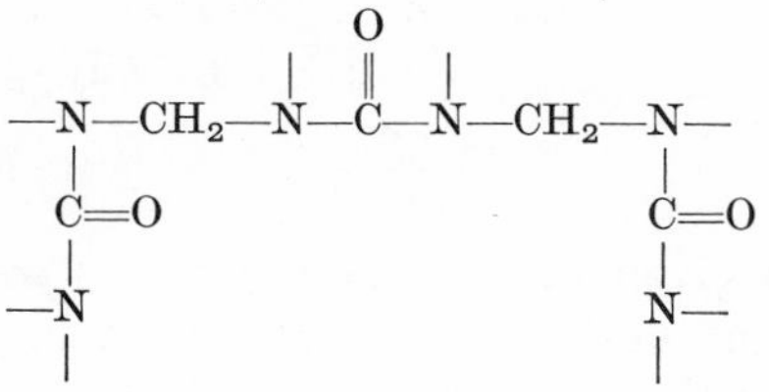	Molding powders, buttons, bottle caps

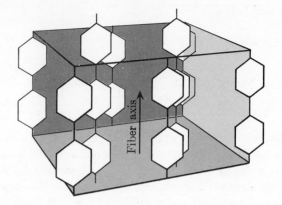

Figure 31.5 Diagram of crystalline cellulose showing that the polymer chains lie approximately parallel to the axis of the fiber.

Starch. This is the reserve carbohydrate of plants and it makes up large fractions of cereals, potatoes, and rice. Starch granules from different sources vary in appearance both in shape and size. The chemical content of all starches is similar—all are branched polymers of glucose and the differences in properties are related to the chain length and degree of branching. Starch contains a soluble component, amylose (10 to 20 per cent of sample), and an insoluble component, amylopectin (80 to 90 per cent). Amylose contains from 60 to 300 glucose units/molecule; amylopectin contains from 300 to 6,000 glucose units/molecule. Amylopectin is very highly branched; amylose is a linear polymer.

Glycogen. This is the energy-reserve carbohydrate of animals, found mainly in muscles and liver. Although it resembles starch in appearance, it has a lower molecular weight.

Cellulose. The structural material of plants, the principal component of cell walls, the chief constituent of cotton fiber (90 per cent), wood (50 per cent), and paper, cellulose is a linear polymer containing between 1,800 and 3,000 glucose units/molecule. X-ray studies show that the polymer chains lie approximately parallel to the axis of a cellulose fiber (Figure 31.5). This accounts for the strength of such fibers. Cellulose, because of its abundance, has found many uses in addition to those mentioned. It reacts with nitric acid to form explosives such as *guncotton* and cellulose nitrate. With acetic anhydride it gives cellulose acetate which is used as a textile fiber (rayon) and in motion picture film.

Proteins. These substances may be thought of as copolymers of α-amino acids,

$$
\begin{array}{c}
\text{R—CH—C—OH} \\
\quad | \quad \ \| \\
\quad \text{NH}_2\ \text{O}
\end{array}
$$

and a given protein molecule may contain as many as twenty or more different amino acids. The molecular weight of proteins ranges from several thousand to several million and proteins occur in all cells of all animals and plants.

The amino acids are linked in the polymer by peptide (amide) linkages resulting from the elimination of water between an amino group in one molecule and a carboxyl group in a second molecule.

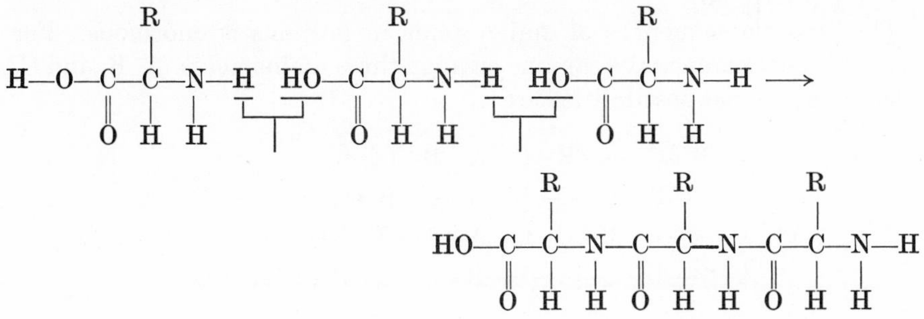

$$
\begin{array}{ccccccc}
 & R & & & R & & & R \\
 & | & & & | & & & | \\
H-O-C-C-N-H & HO-C-C-N-H & HO-C-C-N-H \longrightarrow \\
 & \| \; | \; | & & & \| \; | \; | & & & \| \; | \; | \\
 & O \; H \; H & & & O \; H \; H & & & O \; H \; H
\end{array}
$$

$$
\begin{array}{ccccc}
 & R & & R & & R \\
 & | & & | & & | \\
HO-C-C-N-C-C-N-C-C-N-H \\
 & \| \; | \; | \; \; \; \| \; | \; | \; \; \; \| \; | \; | \\
 & O \; H \; H \; O \; H \; H \; O \; H \; H
\end{array}
$$

The general formula for a polypeptide (a portion of a protein chain) is

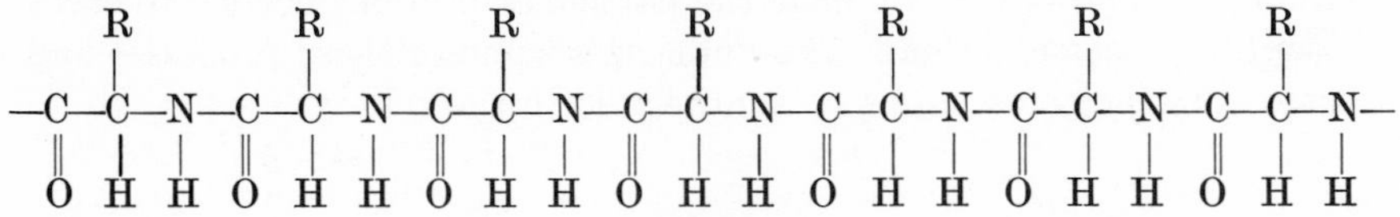

$$
\begin{array}{ccccccc}
R & R & R & R & R & R & R \\
| & | & | & | & | & | & | \\
-C-C-N-C-C-N-C-C-N-C-C-N-C-C-N-C-C-N-C-C-N- \\
\| \; | \; | \; \; \| \; | \; | \; \; \| \; | \; | \; \; \| \; | \; | \; \; \| \; | \; | \; \; \| \; | \; | \; \; \| \; | \; | \\
O \; H \; H \; O \; H \; H \; O \; H \; H \; O \; H \; H \; O \; H \; H \; O \; H \; H \; O \; H \; H
\end{array}
$$

A polypeptide

A protein molecule consists of one or more polypeptide chains which are often coiled and bonded to one another in a variety of ways.

The twenty or so amino acids found in proteins differ in the structure of the R group in the general α-amino acid formula

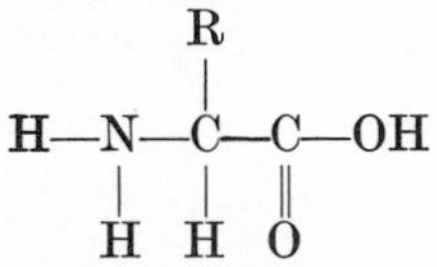

$$
\begin{array}{c}
R \\
| \\
H-N-C-C-OH \\
| \; | \; \| \\
H \; H \; O
\end{array}
$$

Examples of some common amino acids are given in Table 31.5. The distribution of amino acids in proteins varies widely. For example, about half of silk fibroin is glycine, whereas egg albumin is composed of 18 amino acids in amounts varying from 1.5 to 16.5 per cent.

The exact sequence of amino acids in a protein chain is very important for it determines, to a great extent, the properties of the protein molecule. Thus in the polypeptide illustrated below, the recurring sequence of amino acids is: alanine-glycine-phenylalanine-alanine-glycine-phenylalanine-alanine, etc.

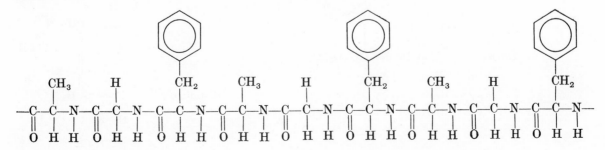

The sequence of amino acids in the protein may determine the shape of the coiled molecule. In the case of enzymes (one kind of protein molecule), the molecular geometry is believed to be intimately associated with the chemical activity (Chap. 33).

The possible sequences of amino acids in proteins is enormous. For example, how many ways can one arrange three amino acids, A, B, and C, in a chain? Some possibilities are

$$A—B—C—A—B—C—A—B—C, \text{ etc.}$$
$$A—C—B—A—C—B—A—C—B, \text{ etc.}$$
$$A—A—B—B—C—C—A—A—B—B—C—C, \text{ etc.}$$
$$A—B—B—C—A—B—B—C—A—B—B—C, \text{ etc.}$$

Since many proteins contain twenty or more amino acids, it is clear that the number of different kinds of proteins is almost unlimited. Fortunately, the living cell knows how to make the particular proteins needed to carry out the life processes. Chap. 33 summarizes some of these processes and indicates how proteins might be synthesized in the cell.

Table 31.5 Some Amino Acids Found in Proteins

Name	Formula	Name	Formula
Glycine	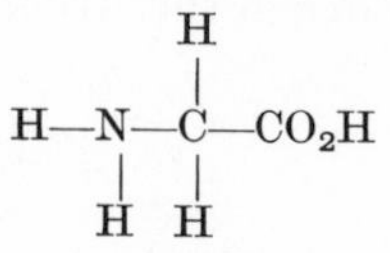 H—N—C—CO$_2$H (H, H, H)	Serine	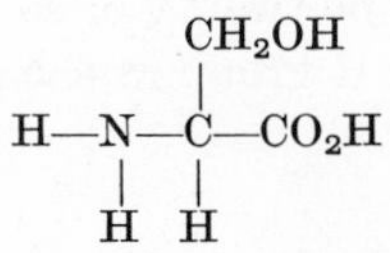 CH_2OH; H—N—C—CO$_2$H (H, H)
Alanine	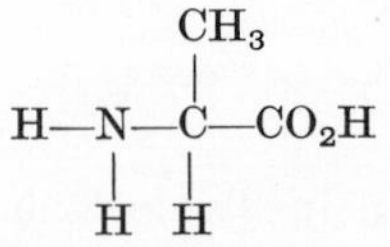 CH_3; H—N—C—CO$_2$H (H, H)	Threonine	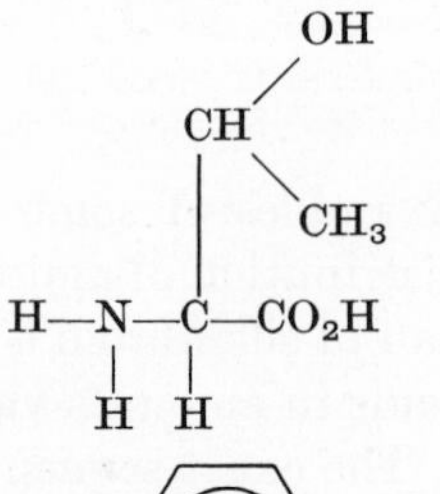 CH(OH)(CH$_3$); H—N—C—CO$_2$H (H, H)
Phenylalanine	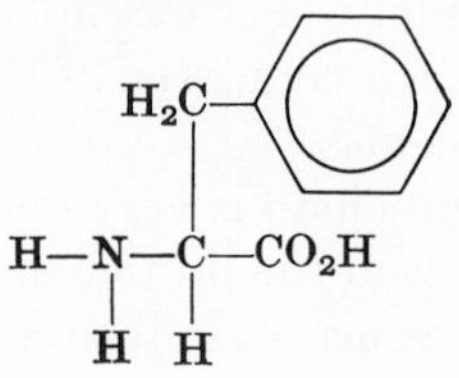 H$_2$C—C$_6$H$_5$; H—N—C—CO$_2$H (H, H)	Tyrosine	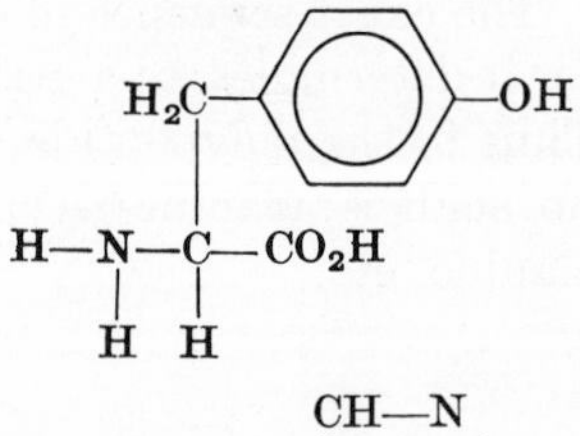 H$_2$C—C$_6$H$_4$—OH; H—N—C—CO$_2$H (H, H)
Leucine	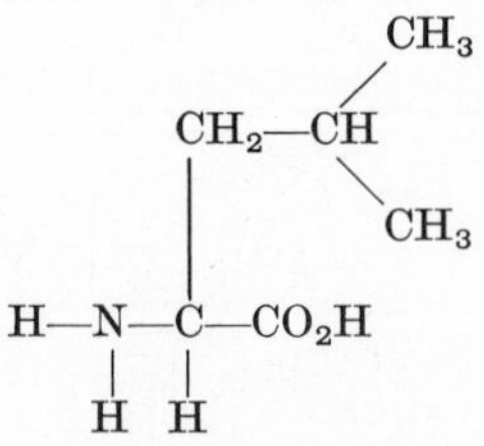 CH$_2$—CH(CH$_3$)$_2$; H—N—C—CO$_2$H (H, H)	Histidine	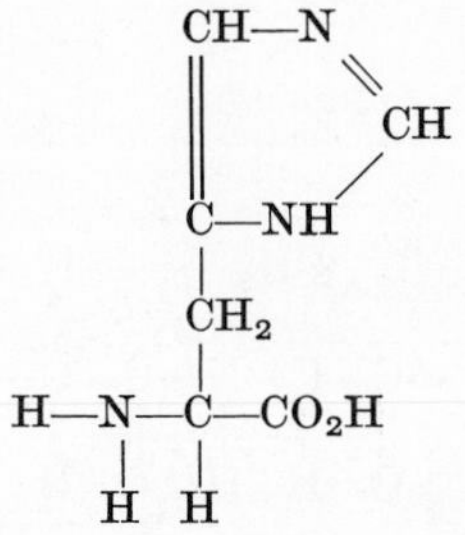 imidazole ring (CH—N=CH, C—NH); CH$_2$; H—N—C—CO$_2$H (H, H)

Other Important Complex Molecules

Alkaloids. These are a large group of nitrogen-containing bases having a marked physiological activity and usually obtained from plants by extraction with dilute acids. The acid reacts with the basic alkaloid to form a soluble salt of the base. Some common alkaloids, their formulas, and sources or uses are given in Table 31.6.

Steroids. These are a group of compounds containing the cyclopentanophenanthrene ring structure illustrated below:

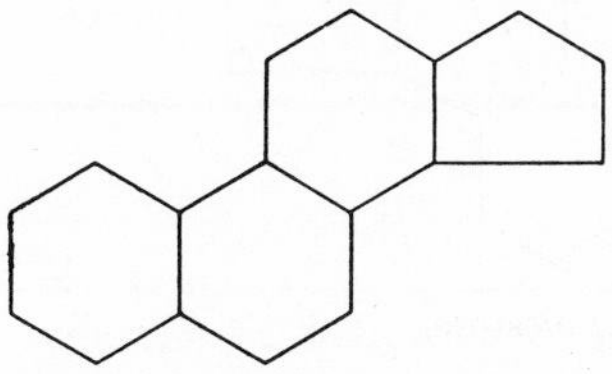

The steroids are widely distributed among plants and animals and are

Table 31.6 Some Common Alkaloids, Their Formulas, Sources, and Uses

Name	Formula	Source	Uses
Nicotine	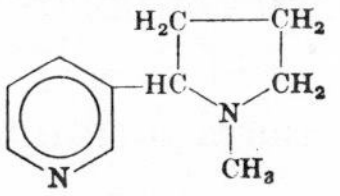	Tobacco (4–6 per cent of dry leaf)	Insecticide
Quinine	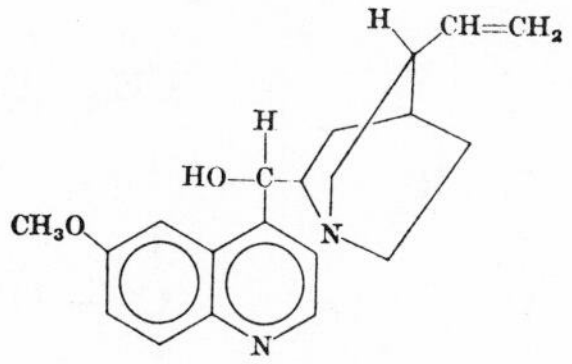	Bark of cinchona tree	Malaria cure
Morphine	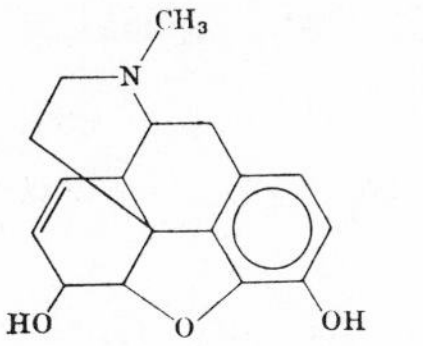	Opium poppy	Powerful analgesic
Strychnine	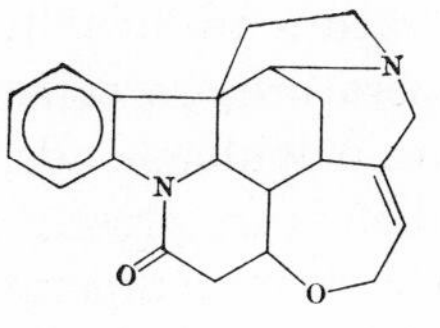	Seeds of *strychnos nux vomica*	Deadly poison, stimulant for nervous system
Reserpine (Newest group)	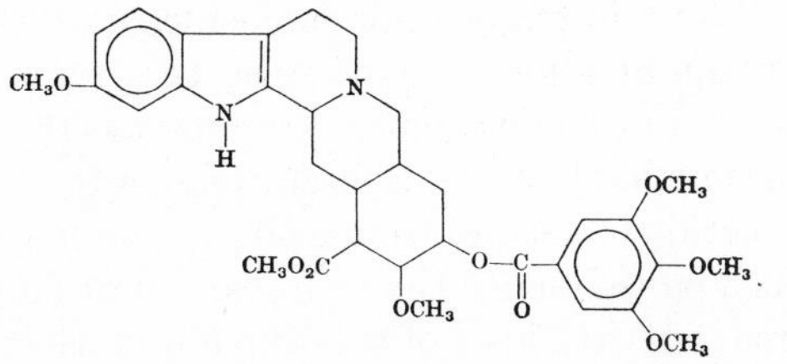	*Rauwolfia serpentina* (Indian snake root)	Tranquilizers, lower blood pressure

essential constituents of brain and spinal tissue, bile, sex hormones, the cardiac aglycones, and the hormones of the adrenal cortex.

A commonly occurring steroid is cholesterol, which is present in relatively large amounts in blood plasma and in the brain, and in smaller amounts in all animal cells. The structure of cholesterol is

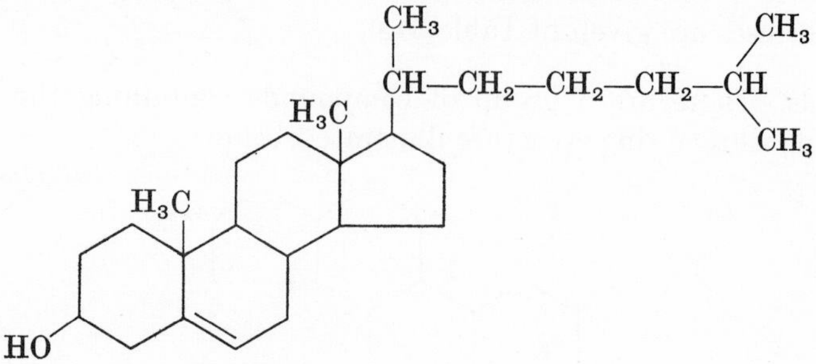

Cholesterol

It has been established that cholesterol can be synthesized in the cells of animals starting from acetic acid. Formulas for other steroids are given in Table 31.7.

Fats and Oils. These are the organic substances occurring in plant and animal tissue which are soluble in nonpolar or weakly polar solvents. Fats and oils are triesters of glycerol and long-chain carboxylic acids. They are known as *triglycerides*. The general formula for a fat or oil is

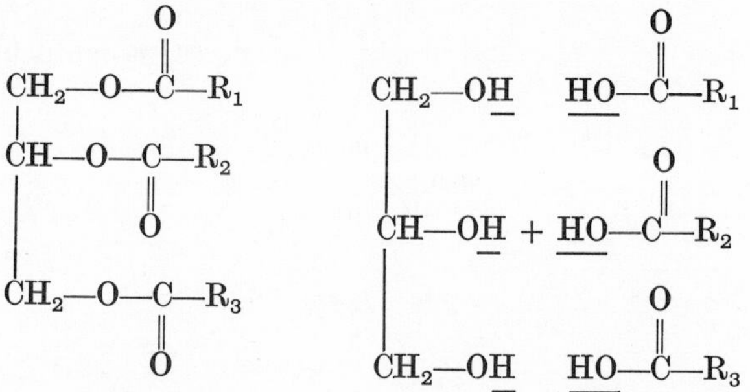

A triglyceride   Glycerol   Carboxylic acid
                      Components of a fat

The distinction between fats and oils is not sharp but triglycerides which are solids at room temperature are usually called fats while those which are liquids at room temperature are called oils. If the R groups in the triglyceride contain few or no double bonds, the substance will probably be a solid at 25°C; if double bonds are present in the R groups, the substance will probably be a liquid at room temperature.

The R groups found in triglyceride molecules vary widely depending on the species of plant or animal. However, the most common R groups found contain 15 or 17 carbon atoms. Not only are the R groups in a given triglyceride molecule likely to be different (e.g., a C_7, a C_{15}, and a C_{17}), but a group of triglyceride molecules from a single source will contain a variety of R groups. As a consequence the composition of fats is usually given in terms of the percent of each kind of R group found when the fat is analyzed. For example, an analysis of human fat was reported to contain the per cents of various R groups given in Table 31.8.

Table 31.7   Formulas for Some Steroids

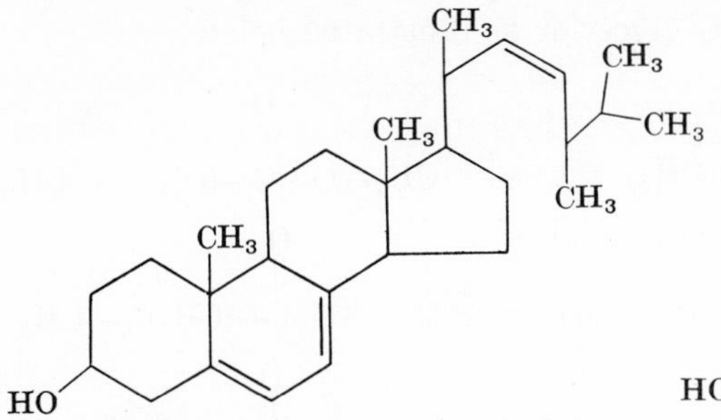

Ergosterol (precursor of vitamin D-2)

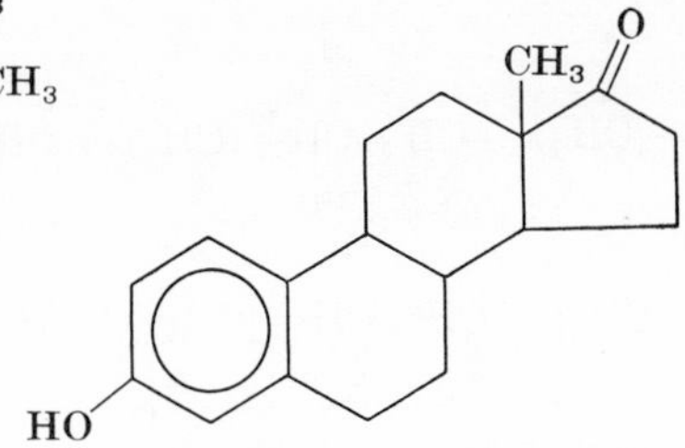

Estrone (a female hormone)

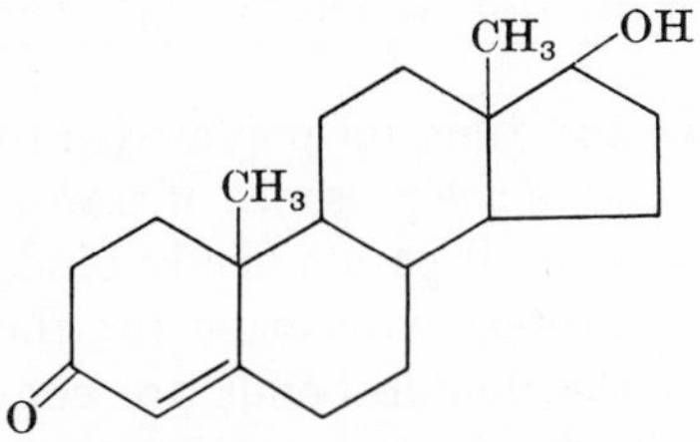

Testosterone (a male sex hormone)

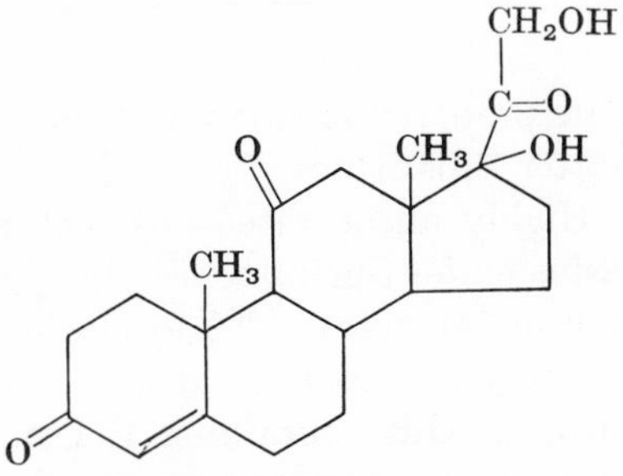

Cortisone (effective in treatment of rheumatoid arthritis)

The hydrolysis of fats with base is known as saponification (soap-making) because one product of the reaction is soap.

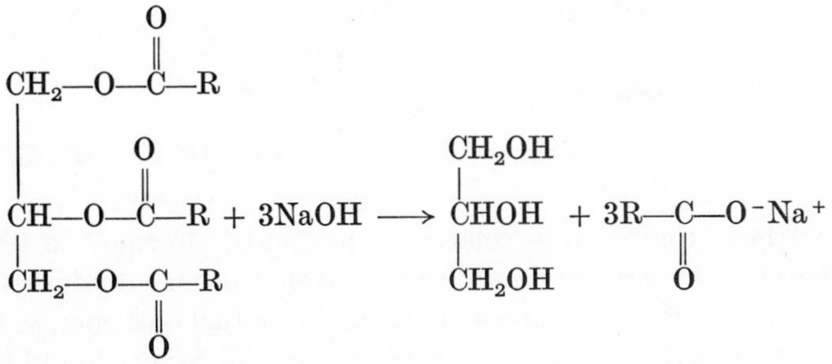

A soap

Most soaps are sodium or potassium salts of long-chain (C_{12}–C_{18}) carboxylic acids. The carboxylate end of the soap anion is water soluble while the hydrocarbon end is oil soluble. Thus one end of the soap anion acts to dissolve grease deposits while the other end "sticks" to the water. The result is that the soap carries with it, into the water, the grease and dirt that associates with the hydrocarbon end of the soap anion.

Table 31.8 Analysis of Human Fat (per cent)

Saturated R				Alkenyl R			Alkadienyl R	Alkatetraenyl
C_{11}	C_{13}	C_{15}	C_{17}	C_{13}	C_{15}	C_{17}	C_{17}	C_{19}
0.5	3.3	25.0	8.4	0.4	6.2	45.9	9.8	0.6

Vegetable oils may be converted to fats by hydrogenation of the double bonds in the R groups of the triglyceride as illustrated below:

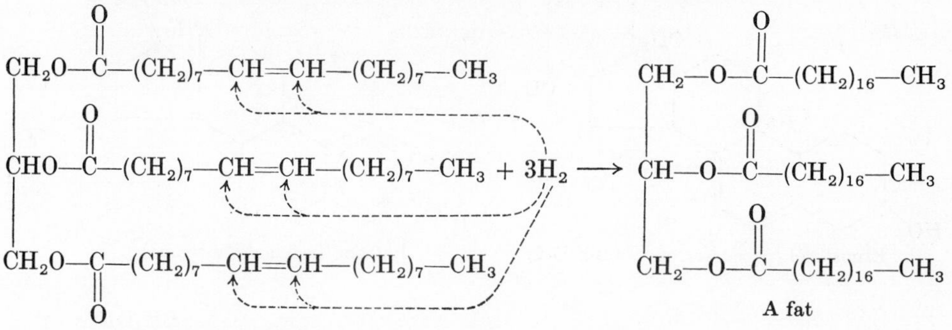

An oil → A fat

Fats prepared in this way from vegetable oils are used as shortening or as butter substitutes.

Highly unsaturated oils such as linseed oil and tung oil polymerize to resins under the influence of oxygen from air and in the presence of transition metal soaps. The formation of such resins in oil paints firmly binds the pigment to the surface and serves as a protective coating for the surface. Oils containing R groups in which the double bonds are conjugated polymerize more rapidly than others and paints containing these oils are fast drying. Highly unsaturated, resin-forming oils are known as *drying oils*.

Simple Carbohydrates. The simple carbohydrates are glucose and fructose,

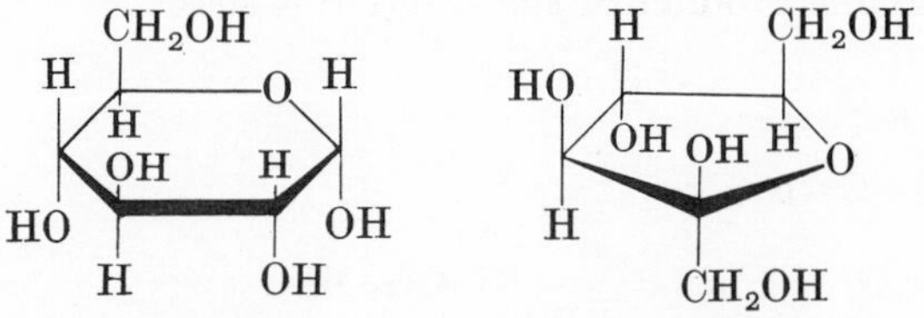

Glucose   Fructose (a common form)

their derivatives, and certain related compounds. Formed in plants by photosynthesis from carbon dioxide and water, the carbohydrates are not only the probable original sources of all our body fuel and energy, but also the starting materials for the synthesis of many substances found in plants and animals.

A Common Monosaccharide: Glucose (Dextrose) $(C_6H_{12}O_6)$. Pure glucose is a white crystalline solid which resembles cane sugar in its properties, but is only about half as sweet. It is an inexpensive and healthful food. A small percentage (about 0.1 per cent) is present in the blood of persons in good health, and a much larger percentage in the blood of persons afflicted with diabetes. Glucose will ferment, in the presence of certain enzymes, especially in the zymase of yeast, to form alcohol:

$$C_6H_{12}O_6 \xrightarrow{\text{enzyme}} 2C_2H_5OH + 2CO_2$$

Fructose (Fruit Sugar, Levulose) $(C_6H_{12}O_6)$. Fructose is a white solid which occurs, along with glucose, in fruits and honey.

Sucrose ($C_{12}H_{22}O_{11}$). Sucrose, a compound containing one glucose and one fructose molecule condensed together, is an example of the compounds containing two simple sugar molecules, known as disaccharides. Sucrose is obtained from sugar cane and sugar beets and is used principally for food.

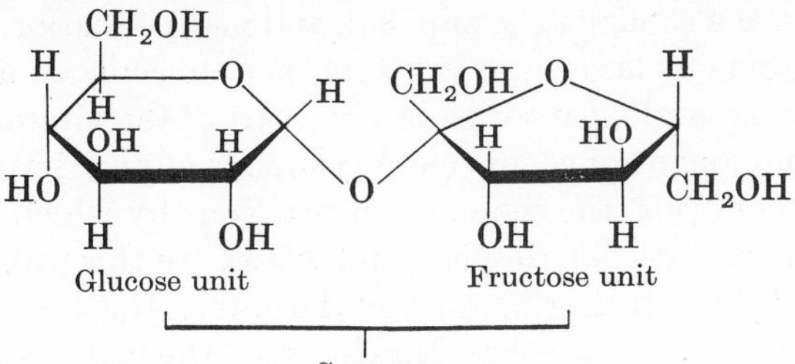

Glucose unit   Fructose unit

Sucrose

Lactose (*Milk Sugar*) ($C_{12}H_{22}O_{11}$). The disaccharide lactose occurs in the milk of all mammals. The average composition of cow's milk is as follows:

Component	Per Cent
Water	87.0
Casein	
(nitrogenous matter)	3.3
Butterfat	4.0
Lactose	5.0
Mineral matter	0.7

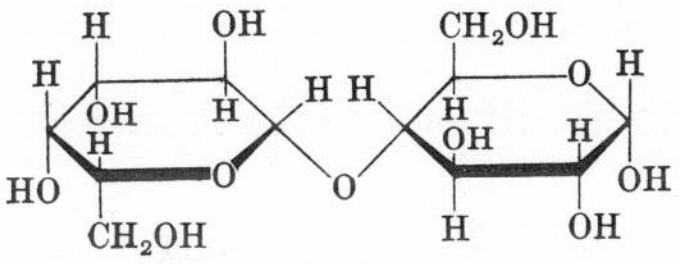

One form of lactose

Lactose resembles sucrose in appearance, but is not as soluble and is only about one-fourth as sweet. The souring of milk is the result of the conversion of milk sugar into lactic acid, a compound whose formula is

$$CH_3\text{---}CH\text{---}CO_2H$$
$$|$$
$$OH$$

This change is known as lactic fermentation, and is brought about by certain bacteria. These bacteria (or their spores) are everywhere present in the air and are associated especially with dust and dirt.

Maltose ($C_{12}H_{22}O_{11}$). This sugar, also a disaccharide, is only about half as sweet as sucrose. It is prepared by the action of malt upon starch; hence the name maltose. It is an isomer of lactose.

Malt is the name applied to barley which has been moistened, kept in a warm place until it has germinated, and then heated until the vitality of the grain has been destroyed. In the process of germination an enzyme is formed known as diastase, and it is this substance which gives malt its property of changing starch into maltose. Amylase, an enzyme in saliva, brings about a similar change in the starch present in our foods.

Vitamins. Systematic experimental studies have shown that the health of humans and other animals cannot be maintained on a diet consisting of only proteins, fats, carbohydrates, and minerals. Very small amounts of vitamins also are necessary for the proper functioning of the body. The body cannot synthesize vitamins; hence it must depend upon plants and other animals for them.

Because vitamins function in such small amounts, their role in life chemistry must be that of a catalyst. Generally a vitamin is the main or sole component of a coenzyme (Chap. 33), and many function in the transfer of hydrogen atoms or larger groups from one molecule to another in the living cell. For example, pantothenic acid, part of the vitamin-B complex, is the major component of coenzyme A, which is of vital importance in the tricarboxylic acid cycle, the sequence of reactions by which foodstuffs are converted to energy, carbon dioxide, and water. In this process coenzyme A is responsible for transferring an acetyl group, CH_3CO-, from pyruvic acid to oxalacetic acid. The connection between the biochemical role of the coenzyme and the clinically observable manifestations of vitamin deficiency—arrested growth, deficiency diseases—is now being established.

Some vitamins have simple formulas such as nicotinamide

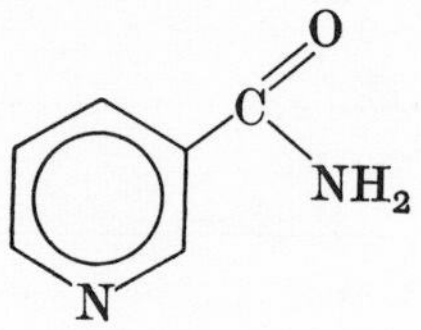

Others, like vitamin A, are more complex:

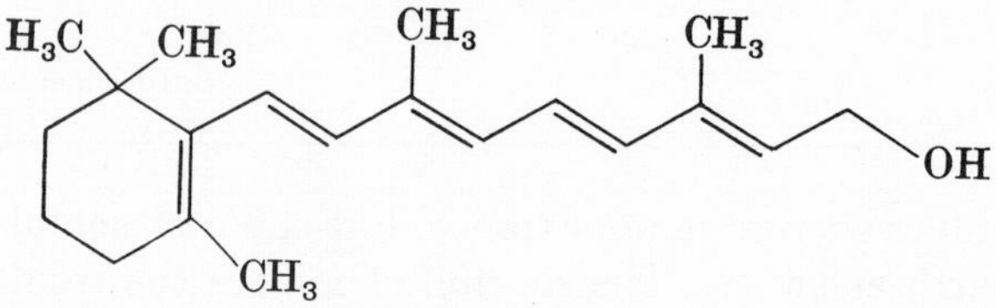

Table 31.9 summarizes the vitamins, their roles as coenzymes, and the deficiency diseases they prevent in humans.

Sulfa Drugs. These were found to be particularly useful in combating bacteria that produce pneumonia, gas gangrene, meningitis, and blood poisoning. The first of these compounds prepared was sulfanilamide (below), but it caused serious reactions in some patients. Chemists modified the properties of the sulfa drugs by replacing one of the hydrogen atoms on the $-SO_2-NH_2$ group of sulfanilamide with other groups, thus producing compounds that are more effective in combating bacteria, but less harmful to the patient. Some of the more common sulfa drugs are sulfadiazine, sulfathiazole, sulfaguanidine, sulfapyridine.

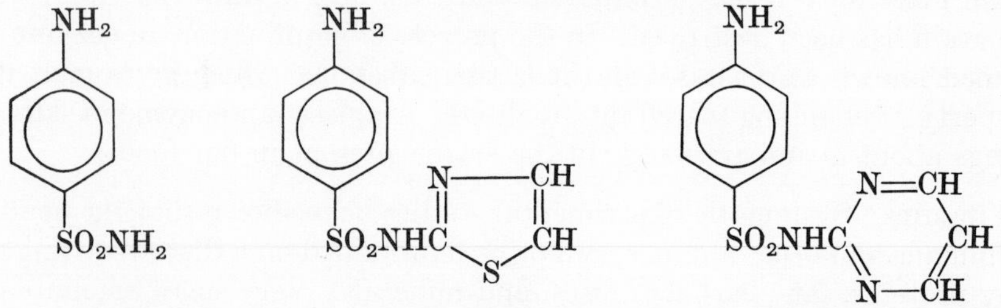

Sulfanilamide   Sulfathiazole   Sulfadiazine

Table 31.9 Vitamins

Vitamin	Name	Deficiency Disease of Man	Daily Requirement*
Fat-Soluble Vitamins			
A	(Axerophthol)	Night blindness, xerophthalmia	1.5–2.0 mg
D	Calciferol	Rachitis	0.025 mg
E	Tocopherol	Unknown (muscular dystrophy?)	[5 mg]
K	Phylloquinone	Delayed blood clotting	[0.001 mg]
Q	Ubiquinone	Unknown	
F	Essential fatty acids	Debated	Unknown
	Thioctic acid	Unknown	Unknown
Water-Soluble Vitamins			
B_1	Thiamine	Beriberi (polyneuritis)	0.5–1.0 mg
	Riboflavin	"Pellagra sine pellagra"	1 mg
B_2	Nicotinamide	Pellagra	
complex	Folic acid	Megaloblastic anemia	[1–2 mg]
	Pantothenic acid	Burning foot syndrome	[3–5 mg]
B_6	Pyridoxine	Unknown	[1.5 mg]
B_{12}	Cobalamin	Pernicious anemia	0.001 mg
C	Ascorbic acid	Scurvy	75 mg
H	Biotin	Very rare ("egg white injury," dermatitis)	[0.25 mg]

* Values in brackets indicate estimated amounts.

Antibiotics. Close upon the development of the sulfa drugs came the discovery of penicillin, which has proved to be extremely effective in the treatment of gonorrhea, pneumonia, meningitis, osteomyelitis, gas gangrene, and streptococcus and staphylococcus infections. Penicillin is called an antibiotic agent; it inhibits or kills microorganisms. It is produced by various strains of mold called *Penicillium notatum*, and is now prepared on a large scale. Penicillin has been synthesized. The general formula for penicillin is

R may be

$$-CH_2-CH=CH-CH_2-CH_3$$
$$-CH_2-C_6H_5$$
$$-CH_2-C_6H_4-OH(p)$$
$$-CH_2-(CH_2)_5-CH_3$$

Table 31.10 Uses of Some Antibiotics

Name	Effective Against
Penicillin	Pneumonia, peritonitis, diphtheria, gas gangrene, meningitis, syphilis, gonorrhea
Streptomycin	Dysentery, undulant fever, urinary tract infections, typhoid fever, human tuberculosis, certain gastric infections
Chloromycetin	Influenza, whooping cough, typhoid fever, typhus
Aureomycin } Terramycin }	Viral pneumonia, human tularemia, psittacosis, typhus, some urinary infections, peritonitis, skin lesions, syphilis

Some other antibiotics now used are streptomycin, chloromycetin, aureomycin, and terramycin.

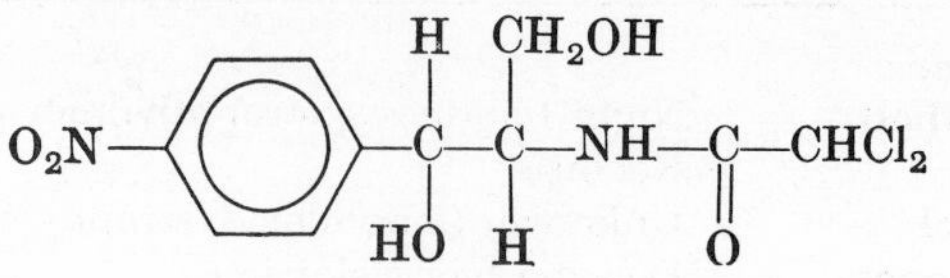

$$O_2N-\text{(ring)}-\underset{\underset{HO}{|}}{\overset{\overset{H}{|}}{C}}-\underset{\underset{H}{|}}{\overset{\overset{CH_2OH}{|}}{C}}-NH-\underset{\underset{O}{\|}}{C}-CHCl_2$$

Chloromycetin

Household Drugs. The formulas for some drugs commonly found in the home are given below.

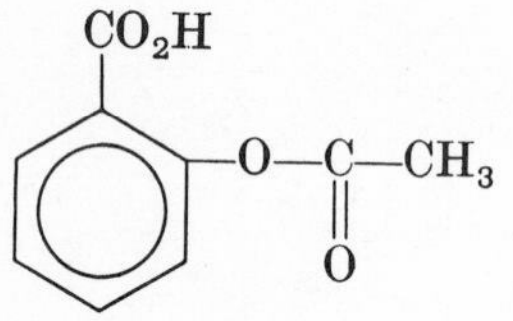

Aspirin
(acetylsalicylic acid
analgesic and antipyretic)

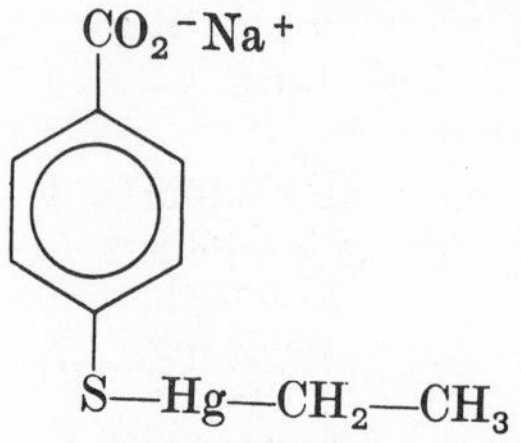

Merthiolate

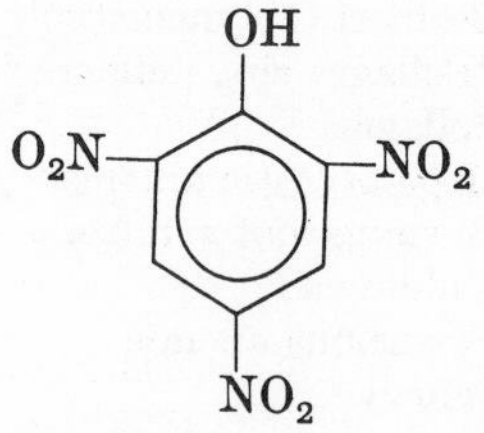

Picric acid (burns)

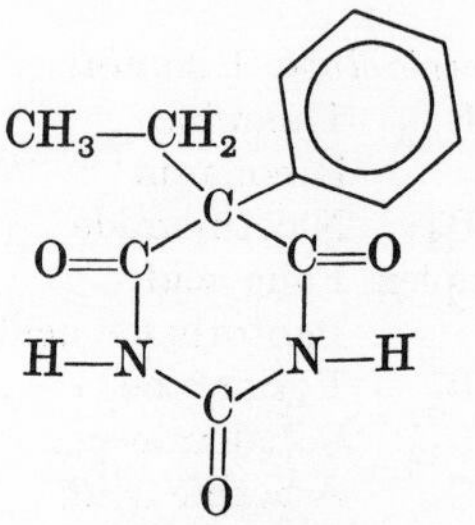

Phenobarbital
(sedative and hypnotic)

SUMMARY

In this chapter we have surveyed very briefly some of the large organic molecules that have importance in our lives. Starting with man-made polymers, we have examined the molecular structure, methods of synthesis, and properties of important plastics, fibers, films, and elastomers. We have attempted to relate properties to molecular structure and motion within the polymer. Naturally occurring polymers—starch, cellulose, proteins—were described briefly. This was followed by descriptions of the structure of alkaloids, steroids, fats and oils, simple carbohydrates, vitamins, sulfa drugs, and antibiotics.

SOME SPECIAL TERMS

Polymers
addition polymers
condensation polymers
monomers
plastics
fibers
films
elastomers
linear polymers
cross-linked polymers
homopolymers
copolymers
glass-transition temperature
crystallinity
polymer backbone

emulsion polymerization
free-radical polymerization
organometallic polymerization
cellulose
starch
polypeptides
amino acids
glucose

Alkaloids
nicotine
quinine
morphine
reserpine

Vitamins
A, B$_1$, B$_2$, B$_6$, B$_{12}$
C, D, E, F, H, K, Q
Steroids
cholesterol
ergosterol
estrone
cortisone
Sulfa drugs
sulfanilamide
sulfathiazole
sulfadiazine

Fats and oils
triglycerides
Simple carbohydrates
fructose
lactose
sucrose
maltose
Antibiotics
penicillin
streptomycin
chloromycetin

QUESTIONS AND PROBLEMS

1. Distinguish between addition and condensation polymers.
2. Give structural formulas for the monomers of six commercially important polymers and illustrate the reactions by which each of the monomers is converted into the polymer.
3. Draw structural units for specific polymers to illustrate each of the following: (a) a rigid plastic, (b) a flexible plastic, (c) a film, (d) a fiber, (e) an elastomer (rubber).
4. Discuss the relation of polymer structure to properties. Account for the fact that a given polymer may be used in several applications, for example, as a rubber in one application, as a flexible plastic in another.
5. Distinguish among free-radical, organometallic, and condensation polymerization reactions.
6. Emulsion polymerization was initiated because the monomers used were not sufficiently soluble in water to give high molecular weight polymers. How would the formation of an emulsion in the reaction mixture help eliminate this problem?
7. Contrast the starch and cellulose polymer structures.
8. Explain in terms of molecular structure why there are so many kinds of proteins.
9. What features do alkaloids have in common?
10. What structural unit is common to most steroids? What is the shape of this structure?
11. Distinguish structurally between a fat and an oil.
12. Compare the structures and properties of sucrose, lactose, and maltose.
13. What features—structurally or physiologically—do vitamins have in common?
14. Can you find any obvious structural similarities between the sulfa drugs and the antibiotics like penicillin?

REFERENCES

BILLMEYER, F. W. *Textbook of Polymer Chemistry*. New York: Wiley, 1962.
FIESER, L. F., and M. FIESER. *Steroids*. New York: Reinhold, 1959.
GORDON, M. *High Polymers*. London: Iliffe, 1963.
HENDRICKSON, J. B. *The Molecules of Nature*. New York: Benjamin, 1965.
KATRITZSKY, A. R., and J. M. LAGOWSKI. *Heterocyclic Chemistry*. New York: Wiley, 1960.
O'DRISCOLL, K. F. *The Nature and Chemistry of High Polymers*. New York: Reinhold, 1964.

32

Some Physical Organic Chemistry

When an interaction is transmitted through, and by means of, an electronic system, it alters the positions and motions of the intervening electrons. Thus theories of transmitted interactions are essentially theories of electron displacement.

Sir Christopher K. Ingold (1896—)

Modern organic chemistry is a complex blend of a systematic organization of information, a vast body of facts, and an emerging and exciting theory. Bits and pieces of this theory have been included whenever feasible during the preceding chapters on organic chemistry. In this chapter we shall examine in some detail three theoretical aspects of this branch of chemistry. The first is optical isomerism, a type of isomerism possible with dissymmetric (not symmetrical) molecules. The second deals with the area of reaction mechanisms and of the experimental and intellectual tools used in developing the theory in this field. The third has to do with the relative strengths of acids and bases and how the important and successful electronic theory of organic chemistry evolved from such studies.

Optical Isomerism

In Chaps. 10, 29, and 30 we encountered various types of isomeric organic compounds. These include:

1. Functional group isomers such as

    ethanol, $CH_3—CH_2—OH$, and dimethyl ether, $CH_3—O—CH_3$

2. Position isomers as exemplified by

    butane, $CH_3—CH_2—CH_2—CH_3$, and isobutane, $CH_3—CH—CH_3$
    with CH_3

    o- and p-xylene,

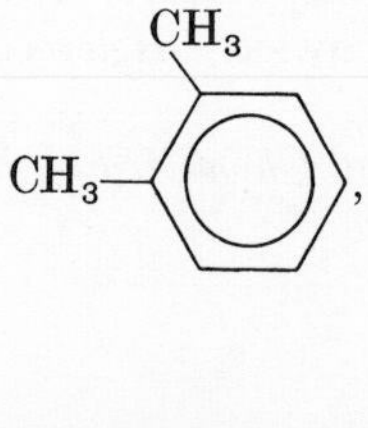

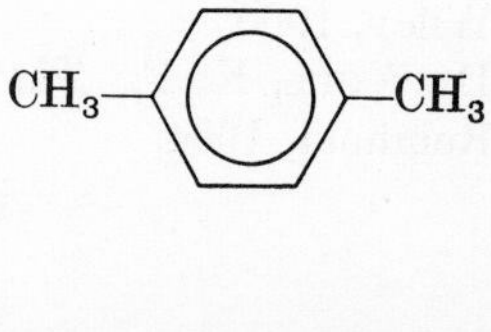

1- and 2-butene, $CH_2{=}CH{-}CH_2{-}CH_3$ and $CH_3{-}CH{=}CH{-}CH_3$

3. Geometrical isomers such as

cis- and trans-2-butene

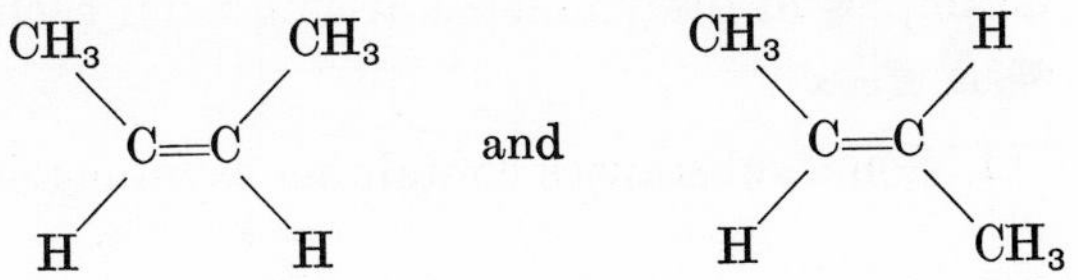

$$
\begin{array}{ccc}
CH_3 \quad CH_3 & & CH_3 \quad H \\
\diagdown \diagup & & \diagdown \diagup \\
C{=}C & \text{and} & C{=}C \\
\diagup \diagdown & & \diagup \diagdown \\
H \quad\quad H & & H \quad\quad CH_3
\end{array}
$$

We are now ready to consider still another type of isomerism known as optical isomerism.

Certain structures, such as that of lactic acid,

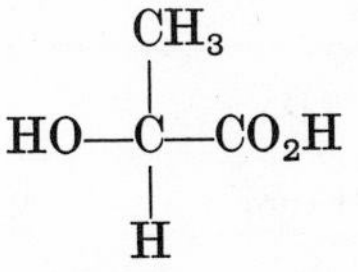

$$
\begin{array}{c}
CH_3 \\
| \\
HO{-}C{-}CO_2H \\
| \\
H
\end{array}
$$

may exist in two different forms differing only in the arrangement of the four groups around the central carbon atom. These two forms will be nonsuperimposable mirror images of one another, related to each other as a left hand is to a right. This situation might be visualized more clearly if one attempts to build models of the lactic acid structure using ball and stick models. If several lactic acid structures are constructed at random and compared, we will discover that not all of the structures are superimposable and hence all are not identical. In fact, two (and only two) different structures can be constructed. These are nonsuperimposable mirror images of one another, and they are one kind of optical isomers known as *enantiomorphs*.

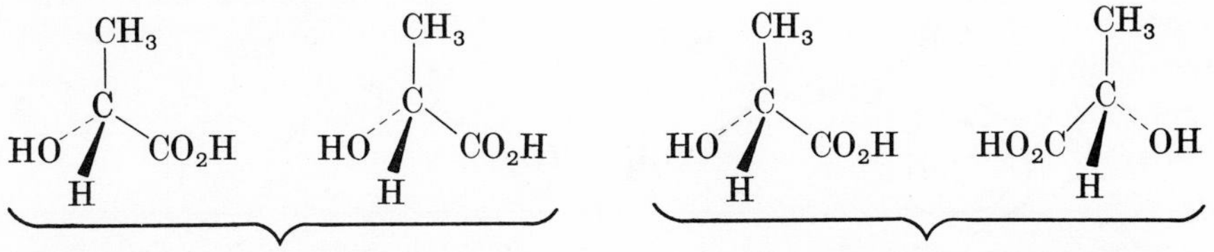

(These are superimposable and identical. The hydrogen atom lies above the plane of the page (━): the OH group lies below this plane (- - -).)

(These are nonsuperimposable mirror images. They are not identical but are enantiomorphs.)

In general, enantiomorphs are found whenever a molecular structure may be assembled in either of two forms which are nonsuperimposable mirror images of one another. Such structures are said to be dissymmetric—i.e., wanting in symmetry.

Dissymmetric Molecules. Dissymmetric organic molecules owe this property to either or both of the following structural features:

1. One or more carbon atoms bonded to four different groups (asymmetrically substituted, or asymmetric carbon atoms) which may be represented by the expression

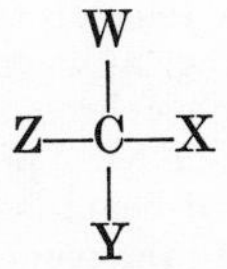

$$
\begin{array}{c}
W \\
| \\
Z{-}C{-}X \\
| \\
Y
\end{array}
$$

2. Rigid or semirigid structural elements which prevent the substance from assuming a symmetrical spatial arrangement.

Examples of dissymmetry arising from each of these structural features are:

1. Some substances containing asymmetric carbon atoms:

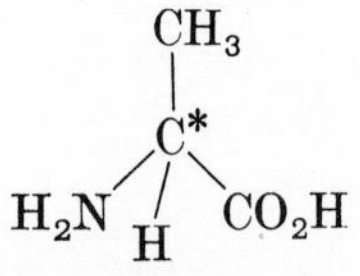

| Alanine | 2-Phenylethanol | Threose | Threonine |

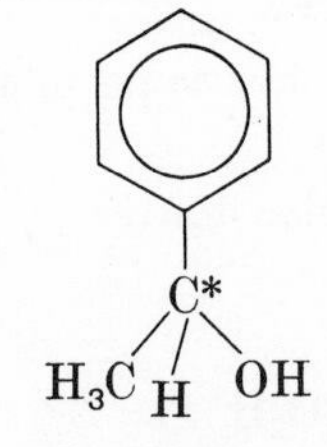

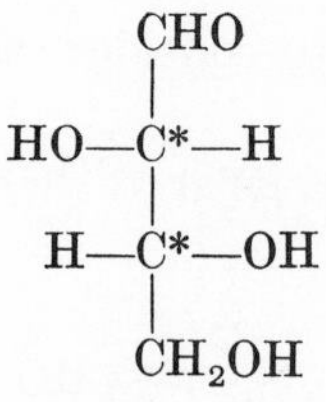

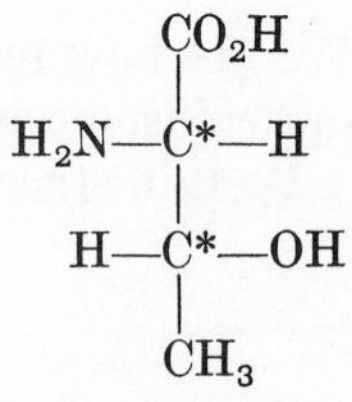

2. Some dissymmetric substances containing no asymmetric carbon atoms:

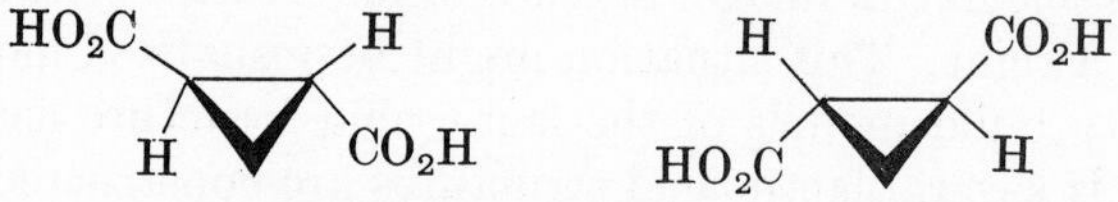

Trans-cyclopropane-1,2-dicarboxylic acid

(The cyclopropane ring is perpendicular to the plane of the page, and the H and CO_2H groups lie in the plane of the page.)

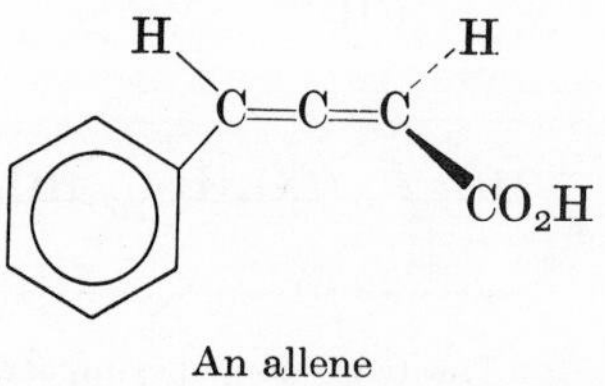

An allene 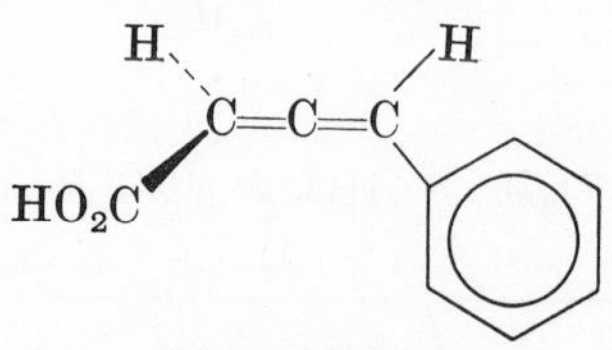   Mirror image

(The three carbon atoms lie in the plane of the paper as do the bonds connecting the phenyl groups and the hydrogen on the first carbon atom.)

Properties of Optical Isomers—Optical Activity. Enantiomorphs are identical in most physical properties—e.g., boiling point, solubility, infrared spectra (in solution)—but they rotate the plane of polarized light in opposite directions.† It is because of this effect on light that they are said to possess *optical activity* and are called optical isomers. The enantiomorph which rotates the beam of light to the right is said to be *dextrorotatory*; the optical isomer which rotates it to the left is *levorotatory*.

---

* Asymmetric carbon atoms.

† A beam of ordinary light may be thought of as a series of rays of various wavelengths vibrating in all possible planes perpendicular to the direction of propagation. Monochromatic light consists of a narrow range of wavelengths, with the rays usually vibrating in all possible planes. If a beam of monochromatic light is passed through a substance such as Polaroid, tourmaline crystals, or a Nicol prism, only those rays vibrating in a single plane are transmitted. This transmitted beam is said to consist of plane polarized light. An optically active substance can rotate the plane of vibration of the rays in such a beam.

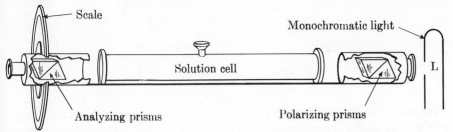

Figure 32.1 Diagram of a polarimeter.

Many naturally occurring substances, including all proteins, carbohydrates, alkaloids, and many vitamins and hormones, are optically active. The various enantiomorphs are often quite different in their biological properties. For example, the active principle secreted by the thyroid gland is one enantiomorph of the amino acid thyroxin; the other enantiomorph of this substance has several times less activity than its mirror image.

In order to understand more fully the meaning of "optical activity," it will be helpful to examine the manner in which it is measured. Optical activity is measured in a polarimeter (Figure 32.1), an instrument which converts ordinary light into plane polarized light, allows this to pass through a sample of the substance under consideration, and provides a technique for measuring the angle through which the original plane of the beam of polarized light is rotated by the sample.

The angle through which the plane of polarized light is rotated depends on the optically active substance, the temperature, the wavelength of the polarized light, and the length of the light path through the sample. However, at the same concentration, temperature, etc., a pair of enantiomorphs will rotate the beam by exactly the same extent but in opposite directions. Since one enantiomorph in a pair rotates the plane to the left and the other enantiomorph rotates it to the right, it is of importance to associate a certain arrangement of groups around an asymmetric carbon atom with the direction of rotation of the light beam.

Rotation and Configuration. The particular arrangement of groups around an asymmetric carbon atom is known as the *configuration* of the structure. For example, in glyceraldehyde

$$\begin{array}{c} CHO \\ | \\ H-C-OH \\ | \\ CH_2OH \end{array}$$

the groups —CHO, —OH, —CH₂OH, and —H may be thought of as being arranged around the asymmetric carbon atom in a clockwise sequence in one enantiomorph and in a counterclockwise sequence in the other enantiomorph as illustrated below.

Clockwise sequence
or configuration

Counterclockwise sequence
or configuration

Thyroxin

Projections of these formulas in the plane of the paper give the *projection formulas*:

Clockwise sequence   Counterclockwise sequence

Projection formulas are commonly used and can be interpreted in terms of the tetrahedral arrangement of the groups by constructing an imaginary tetrahedron around the projection formulas as follows:

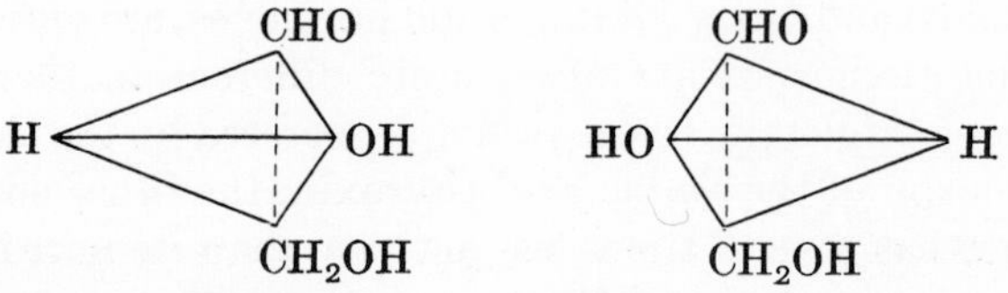

Clockwise sequence   Counterclockwise sequence

The problem now is to find out which sequence (the clockwise or the counterclockwise) is associated with rotation of the plane of light to the right (is dextrorotatory) and which sequence rotates the plane to the left (is levorotatory). This has been done using X-ray diffraction, and the result is that the glyceraldehyde structure with the clockwise sequence is dextrorotatory.

In the case of lactic acid, the sequence $-CO_2H$, $-OH$, $-H$, and $-CH_3$ is similar to that of glyceraldehyde. However, here the structure with the clockwise sequence is levorotatory, indicating that *the direction of rotation of the plane of light and the configuration around the asymmetric carbon atom need bear no obvious relationship*. However, such a relationship has been established using an advanced theory known as polarizability theory.

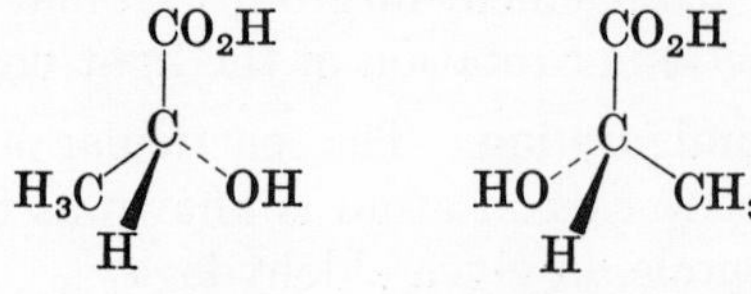

(is levorotatory)   (is dextrorotatory)

Because there is no obvious relation between configuration and direction of rotation, it has proved useful to relate all configurations to a single reference standard, and glyceraldehyde has been chosen. The enantiomorph with the clockwise sequence is called D-glyceraldehyde, and the enantiomorph with the counterclockwise sequence is known as L-glyceraldehyde.

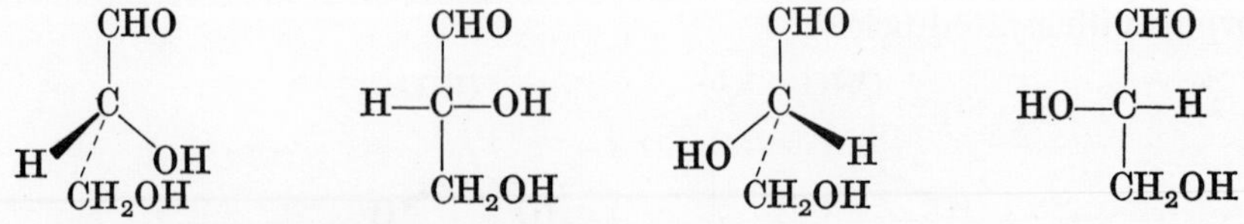

(perspective formula)   (projection formula)   (perspective formula)   (projection formula)
D-Glyceraldehyde   L-Glyceraldehyde

The configuration of the enantiomorphs of other optically active compounds can be specified by relating the configuration of the compound to that of one of the glyceraldehydes. For example, in alanine and lactic acid the configurations are specified as follows:

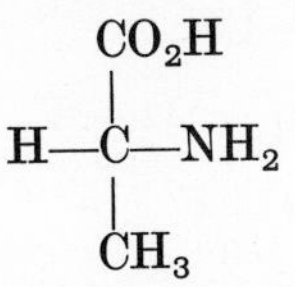

D-Alanine	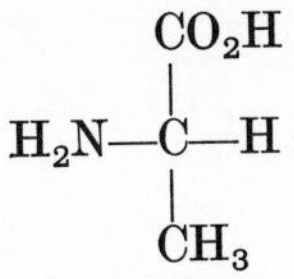 L-Alanine	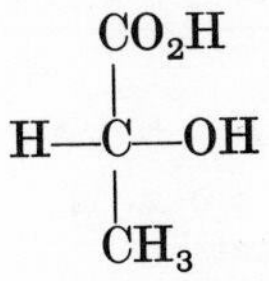 D-Lactic acid	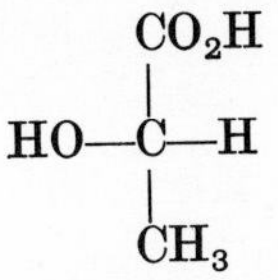 L-Lactic acid

It is well to remember that the letters D- and L- designate a configuration related to glyceraldehyde. They do not specify the direction of rotation of polarized light. The convention here is to write the formula as a vertical carbon chain with the most oxidized function at the top.

To indicate the direction of rotation of light by a given enantiomorph, the signs + for dextrorotatory and − for levorotatory are used. Thus the nomenclature for optically active compounds often includes D or L to specify configuration and (+) or (−) to indicate the direction of rotation. Examples of this are: D-(+)-glyceraldehyde, L-(+)-lactic acid, D-(−)-alanine.

Racemic Mixtures. If lactic acid is synthesized in the laboratory, the product has no optical activity; if lactic acid is taken from muscle tissue, dextrorotatory lactic acid is obtained. The explanation for these differences is that the laboratory preparations give a mixture containing equal parts of each enantiomorph. Such a mixture is called a *racemic mixture* or a *racemate* and is optically inactive since the dextrorotatory effect of the one isomer is exactly balanced by the levorotatory effect of the other. The separation of enantiomorphs from a racemic mixture is known as *resolution*. Muscle lactic acid is produced under the influence of specific enzymes present in muscles.

Molecules with Two Asymmetric Centers. Molecules with more than one asymmetric center, such as 2,3-dihydroxybutanoic acid,

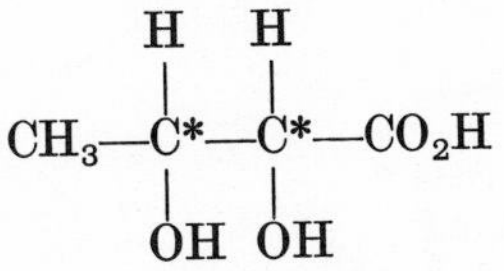

have more than two optical isomers. This is reasonable when one recalls that each asymmetric carbon atom may have two configurations. The number of optical isomers is related to the number of different combinations of these configurations that are possible. In 2,3-dihydroxybutanoic acid, for example, four combinations are possible—i.e.,

I			II	
	(both asymmetric carbon atoms in R-configuration)			(both asymmetric carbon atoms in S-configuration)

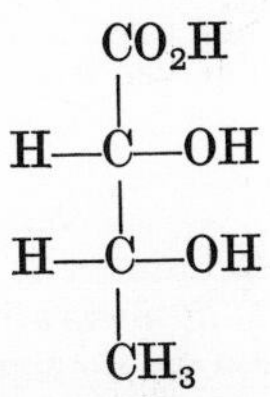

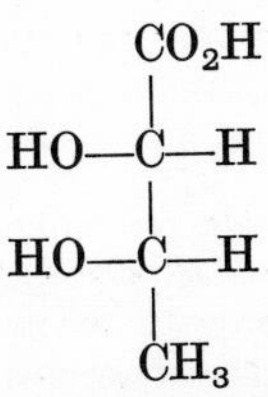

$$
\begin{array}{c}
\text{CO}_2\text{H}\\
|\\
\text{H---C---OH}\\
|\\
\text{HO---C---H}\\
|\\
\text{CH}_3
\end{array}
$$

III

(carbon 2 in R-
configuration;
carbon 3 in S-
configuration)

$$
\begin{array}{c}
\text{CO}_2\text{H}\\
|\\
\text{HO---C---H}\\
|\\
\text{H---C---OH}\\
|\\
\text{CH}_3
\end{array}
$$

IV

(carbon 2 in S-
configuration;
carbon 3 in R-
configuration)

Careful examination of the four optical isomers given above will reveal that I and II are enantiomorphs (mirror images) and that III and IV are enantiomorphs but that the similarity between I or II and III or IV is *not* a mirror image relationship. Optical isomers that are not mirror images are known as *diastereoisomers* or *diastereomers*.

A compound containing two *identical* asymmetric carbon atoms has only three optical isomers because the compounds corresponding to III and IV above are identical. An example of this is the tetraric (tartaric) acids.*

$$
\begin{array}{c}
\text{CO}_2\text{H}\\
|\\
\text{HO---C---H}\\
|\\
\text{H---C---OH}\\
|\\
\text{CO}_2\text{H}
\end{array}
$$

D-(−)-Tartaric acid
(both asymmetric
carbon atoms in
s-configuration)

$$
\begin{array}{c}
\text{CO}_2\text{H}\\
|\\
\text{H---C---OH}\\
|\\
\text{HO---C---H}\\
|\\
\text{CO}_2\text{H}
\end{array}
$$

L-(+)-Tartaric acid
(both asymmetric
carbon atoms in R-
configuration)

$$
\begin{array}{c}
\text{CO}_2\text{H}\\
|\\
\text{H---C---OH}\\
|\\
\text{H---C---OH}\\
|\\
\text{CO}_2\text{H}
\end{array}
$$

(carbon 2 in R-
configuration; carbon 3
in s-configuration)

$$
\begin{array}{c}
\text{CO}_2\text{H}\\
|\\
\text{HO---C---H}\\
|\\
\text{HO---C---H}\\
|\\
\text{CO}_2\text{H}
\end{array}
$$

(carbon 2 in
s-configuration;
carbon 3 in
R-configuration)

Identical and optically inactive
meso-tartaric acid

Meso-Tartaric acid is inactive because both asymmetric carbon atoms have the same groups attached but in opposite configurations; hence they have exactly the same rotating power but in opposite directions.

Alternative projection formulas for these acids are:

---

* It must be remembered in assigning configurations to the carbon atoms in the tartaric acids that the glyceraldehyde convention specifies that the formula be written as a vertical carbon chain with the most oxidized function at the top. Difficulties arise when a substance contains more than one asymmetric center. In such cases the configuration is expressed in an R or s notation which is analogous to, but more precise than, the DL system (see *J. Chem. Educ. 41* (1964), p. 116).

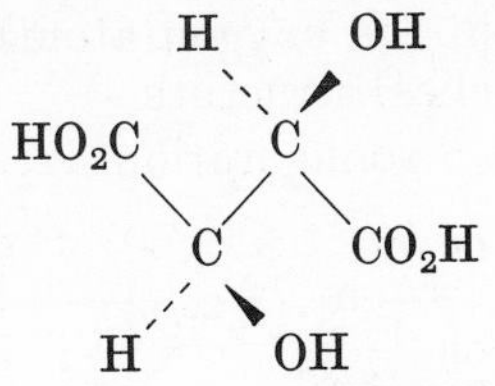

L-(+)-Tartaric acid 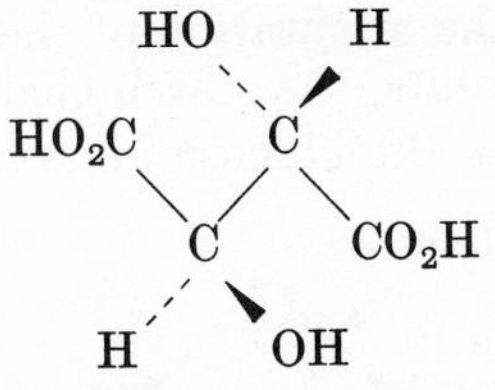   *meso*-Tartaric acid

Molecules with More Than Two Asymmetric Centers—Glucose. It can be shown that if a molecule has n different asymmetric centers, a total of 2^n optical isomers is possible, although certain symmetry elements may reduce this number. For example, the simple six-carbon sugars have the formula $C_6H_{12}O_6$ and a number of them contain five asymmetric carbon atoms as indicated by the structural formula

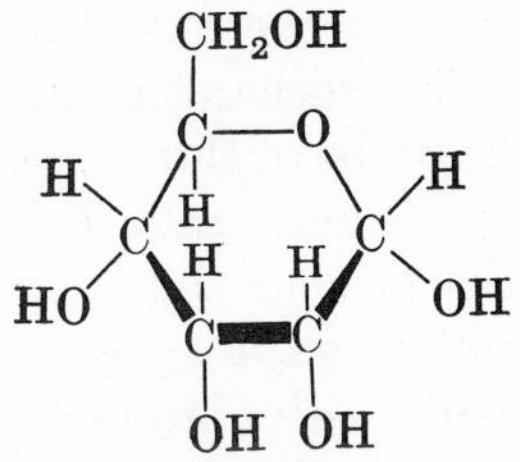

A six-carbon sugar showing the
five asymmetric carbon atoms

Consequently there are 32 optical isomers of the structure given above. These isomers differ in the configuration on one or more of the asymmetric carbon atoms. The most common naturally occurring isomers among the 32 are α-D-glucose and β-D-glucose whose formulas are given below.

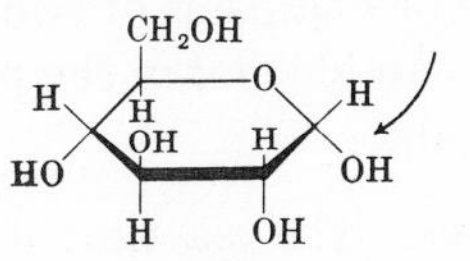

α-D-Glucose β-D-Glucose

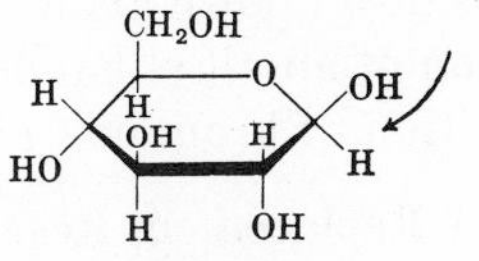

The configurations on the various asymmetric carbon atoms in these two glucose structures are identical except for that on the carbon atom marked by an arrow. This is known as the anomeric (or first) carbon atom. It is derived from an aldehyde group which has undergone a cyclization reaction with one of the hydroxyl groups on the glucose chain. Two forms are possible depending on the way the ring closes. The first is called the α-D-anomer; the second, the β-D-anomer.

Units of D-glucose are condensed into polymer chains in the biological macromolecules starch and cellulose. In starch the glucose units have the α-configuration:

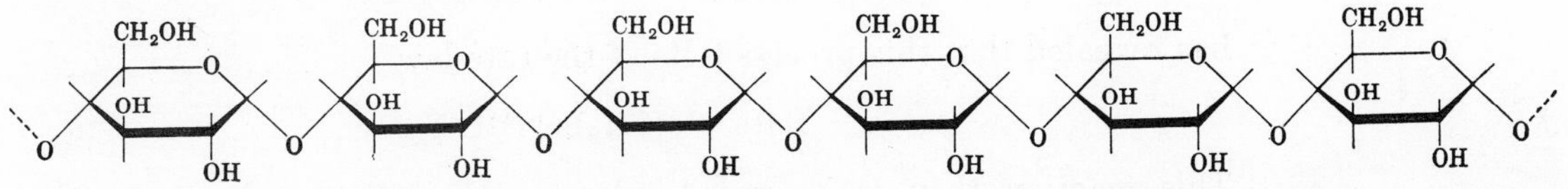

Because of the orientation of the bonds in the oxygen atoms connecting the glucose units, the starch chain is a helical structure.

In cellulose the glucose units have the β-configuration:

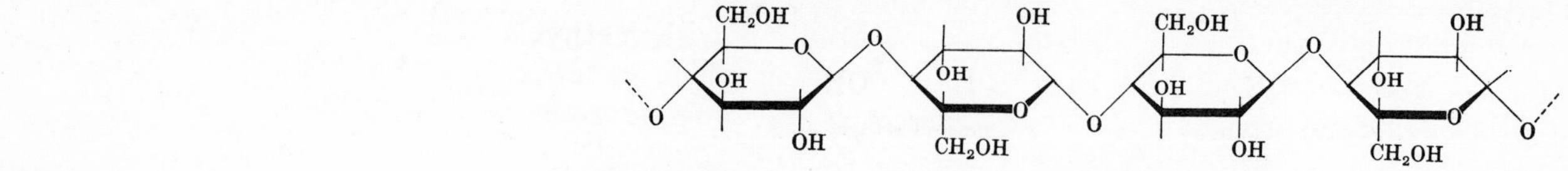

The geometry of the cellulose molecule is linear, appropriate for the structural material in plants.

Elucidation of Reaction Mechanisms

Both the development and the study of modern organic chemistry has been stimulated considerably by the elucidation of the mechanisms of many important reactions. The mechanism of a reaction in the ideal sense is a continuous picture of the paths of the atoms and electrons involved in the reaction from the time the reactants first come together until the products are formed. At the present time experimental techniques and tools are not adequate to obtain such a picture, and chemists have contented themselves, temporarily, with obtaining information that gives an indication of what is happening at one or more crucial periods during the course of the reaction.

In spite of their lack of sophistication, mechanistic studies have given greater insight into chemical reactions, and this in turn has led to the discovery of new reactions and to the design of entirely new experimental attacks on important problems in organic chemistry.

In this section we shall discuss as examples the studies which help elucidate what is now known about the mechanisms of two reactions—i.e., (a) the conversion of an alkyl halide to an alcohol in the presence of base, and (b) the addition of bromine to an alkene.

Mechanisms of Replacement Reactions. The reaction of an alkyl halide with a base is one of the most common and useful reactions in organic chemistry (Chap. 30). It is not surprising that the mechanism of this reaction has been the object of comprehensive studies for many years. Let us now examine the results of some of these studies and then use these results to develop the best picture we can of the pathway followed by this reaction.

Perhaps the most important tool in elucidating a mechanism is chemical kinetics. By studying the kinetics of a reaction we can often discover the rate-determining or slow step in the reaction sequence and we can sometimes discover the factors that control or change that step.

S_N2 *Reactions.* Investigation of the kinetics of the reaction

$$CH_3Br + OH^- \longrightarrow CH_3OH + Br^-$$

has revealed that this process follows the rate law

$$Rate = k[CH_3Br][OH^-]$$

This reaction then is a second-order reaction—first order in methyl bromide and first order in hydroxide ion. Evidently the slow step in this process involves the bringing together of hydroxide ions and methyl bromide molecules. What then is the nature of this collision between OH^- and CH_3Br?

One might guess that the hydroxide ion, on collision with methyl bromide, donates a pair of electrons to the carbon atom which in turn relinquishes control of the pair of electrons it shares with the bromine atom. This can be illustrated as follows:

$$H\colon\!\overset{..}{\underset{..}{O}}\colon^- \;+\; \overset{H}{\underset{\underset{H}{H}}{C}}\!-\!Br \longrightarrow HO\text{----}\overset{H}{\underset{\underset{H}{H}}{C}}\text{---}Br \longrightarrow HO\!-\!\overset{H}{\underset{\underset{H}{C}}{}}\overset{H}{}\;+\; \colon\!\overset{..}{\underset{..}{Br}}\colon^-$$

This view of the mechanism also suggests that the hydroxide ion attacks from the side opposite the bromine atom and that the configuration on the carbon atom is inverted (turned inside out) during the course of the reaction.

The first idea—opposite-side attack—seems reasonable because (a) the bromine atom is much larger than the hydrogen atoms so an attack from the bromine side would be hindered, and (b) there would be less repulsion between the entering negatively charged hydroxide ion and the leaving negatively charged bromide ion in an opposite-side attack than in an attack from any other direction.

The second idea—inversion of the configuration—is not as readily accepted, for it suggests that the three hydrogen atoms bonded to carbon must move from one side of the carbon atom to the other in a manner analogous to an umbrella turning inside out. However, this idea is so intriguing that we should consider designing an experiment to test it. What kind of experiment will do this?

Since an inversion of configuration may be involved, perhaps we could prepare an optically active alkyl halide which follows second-order kinetics in reaction with hydroxide ions, allow it to react, and see if the alcohol formed is also optically active and if it rotates polarized light in a direction consistent with an inversion. One classic experiment of this type was carried out with optically active 1-phenyl-2-chloropropane. The results are summarized in the equation

$$HO^- \;+\; \overset{H_3C}{\underset{\underset{CH_2-}{H}}{C}}\!-\!Cl\;\bigcirc \longrightarrow HO\!-\!\overset{CH_3}{\underset{\underset{CH_2-}{H}}{C}}\;\bigcirc \;+\; Cl^-$$

D-configuration   L-configuration

Here the active starting material was in the D-configuration, and the product isolated was found to be optically active and in the L-configuration. Similar results have been reported in a number of analogous cases. These, coupled with other quantitative studies on the reaction rate, have established beyond doubt that, in second-order reactions of this type, the hydroxide ion attacks the carbon atom from the side opposite the halogen atom and brings about an inversion of configuration. This process is known as a Walden inversion.

This mechanism has been shown to be operative with a wide variety of bases including other halide ions, alkoxide ions, ammonia and amines, sulfides, carboxylate anions, etc. Since all of these bases supply electrons in the reaction, they have been called *nucleophiles* (nucleus-loving reagents) and the second-order reaction of an alkyl halide with a base has been called an S_N2 reaction—*substitution* by a *nucleophilic* reagent in a *bimolecular* process.

S_N1 Reactions. Not all alkyl halides follow second-order kinetics in reactions with bases. For example *tert*-butyl chloride in the presence of base follows the rate law

$$\text{Rate} = k[(CH_3)_3CCl]$$

This is a first-order process, independent of the concentration of base, and is known as an S_N1 reaction (substitution, nucleophilic, unimolecular). Evidently the slow step in this process is the decomposition or dissociation of one molecule of *tert*-butyl chloride. What then is the nature of this decomposition or dissociation?

One suggestion is that a dissociation of the type

Step 1

$$CH_3-\underset{\underset{CH_3}{|}}{\overset{\overset{CH_3}{|}}{C}}-Cl \xrightarrow{\text{slow}} CH_3-\underset{\underset{CH_3}{|}}{\overset{\overset{CH_3}{|}}{C}}{}^+ + Cl^-$$

occurs, and this is followed by a very rapid step such as

Step 2a

$$CH_3-\underset{\underset{CH_3}{|}}{\overset{\overset{CH_3}{|}}{C}}{}^+ + OH^- \xrightarrow{\text{fast}} CH_3-\underset{\underset{CH_3}{|}}{\overset{\overset{CH_3}{|}}{C}}-OH$$

or by

Step 2b

$$CH_3-\underset{\underset{CH_3}{|}}{\overset{\overset{CH_3}{|}}{C}}{}^+ + H_2O \xrightarrow{\text{fast}} CH_3-\underset{\underset{CH_3}{|}}{\overset{\overset{CH_3}{|}}{C}}-OH + H^+$$

Since Steps 2a and 2b are rapid and occur after the slow step, they will have no influence on the reaction rate. The speed of the reaction will depend on how easily the halide can dissociate into carbonium ions and chloride ions. Again we might ask the question, What kind of experiment can one perform to ascertain if this postulate of dissociation is reasonable?

Remembering that positive and negative ions will not separate at ordinary temperatures unless a dipolar solvent or its equivalent is present to insulate the charges from one another, we might suggest that if dissociation is the slow step, then this step should be especially sensitive to the solvent used for the reaction. Strongly polar solvents should increase the reaction rate; weakly polar solvents should decrease the reaction rate. Table 32.1 summarizes the results of experiments in which the rate of the reaction of *tert*-butyl chloride with hydroxide ion was measured in the solvent ethanol to which various amounts of water was added.

The data in Table 32.1 clearly show that water—a good solvent for ions—has a remarkable accelerating effect on this reaction. Similar effects are noted with other solvent systems and in the presence of added ions which act to increase the ionizing power of the solvent. These facts and a number of others have convinced most chemists that the mechanism in the first-order reaction of alkyl halides with base involves a slow solvent-assisted ionization of the halide followed by rapid reaction of the carbonium ion formed in this step with the base or with the solvent.

S_N1 *vs.* S_N2. Since some alkyl halides follow the S_N1 and others the S_N2 route, the next important question is: What factors favor one route over the other? Extensive study was required to answer this question but the results are now known. While a complete summary of these results is too exhaustive for our present purposes, the following simple generalizations indicate some important factors which appear to control the reaction pathway:

1. In general, primary alkyl halides follow the S_N2 mechanism.
2. In general, tertiary alkyl halides follow the S_N1 mechanism.
3. In general, secondary alkyl halides follow both S_N1 and S_N2 routes.
4. As the polarity of the solvent increases, the S_N1 mechanism is favored; as the solvent polarity decreases, the S_N2 mechanism is favored.
5. The S_N1 mechanism is sometimes favored if the attacking nucleophile is an extremely weak base, such as fluoride ion, for example.

Mechanism of Addition Reactions. The addition of bromine to an alkene in the dark and in a polar solvent is usually a rapid reaction and its rate is difficult to follow. Without the reaction rate data, where can one start to investigate the mechanism? Perhaps we could first ask the question: Does the reaction occur in one or in several steps?

To decide on an experiment which might provide an answer to this question, let us imagine that the bromine molecule adds in two steps, possibly according to the scheme

Table 32.1 Effect of Solvent Polarity on Rate of *tert*-Butyl Chloride Hydrolysis

Per Cent of Water in Ethanol	Relative Rates
0	1
10	30
20	240
30	1,200
50	30,000
60	120,000

If this mechanism is operative, the bromide ion in Step 2 can be replaced—at least in some molecules—by some other ion such as chloride ion or nitrate ion. To check this, we need only add sodium chloride or sodium nitrate to the reaction mixture. If the products include compounds such as in appreciable amounts, then we can be reasonably certain that the mechanism is not a one-step addition of bromine to the double bond but involves at least two steps—one in which the bromine atom is bonded to the carbon atom and one in which the other anion is bonded. (The reaction is too fast to consider three-body collisions.) When the experiments using chloride or nitrate ions are performed, it is found that these ions are incorporated into the products in significant quantities. This suggests that one bromide atom adds at a time, as postulated. Perhaps it adds first as Br^+, leaving a bromine ion, Br^-, free.

Further information concerning this stepwise pathway comes from an examination of the products in reactions such as

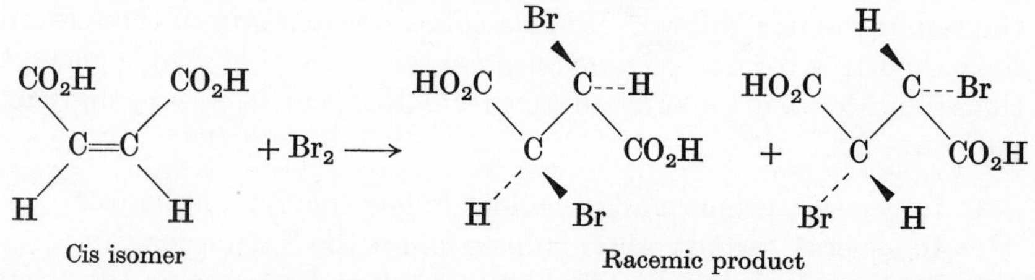

Here a cis alkene reacts with bromine. Noting that the product in this reaction contains two identical asymmetric carbon atoms, we realize that three optical isomers are possible—a pair of enantiomorphs and a meso (optically inactive) compound. Upon examining the product, however, we find that it is a racemic mixture of the enantiomorphs but that little of the meso compound is present. On the other hand, if one starts with the trans alkene, he finds only the meso isomer in the products.

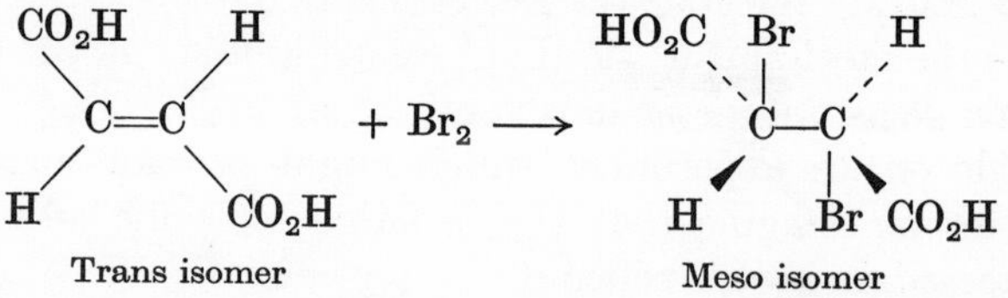

Similar results are found when bromine adds to the cis or trans isomers of other substances.

We can explain these results if we imagine that the alkene is a planar structure and the bromine atoms add, one from above the plane and one from below, as indicated in Figure 32.2.

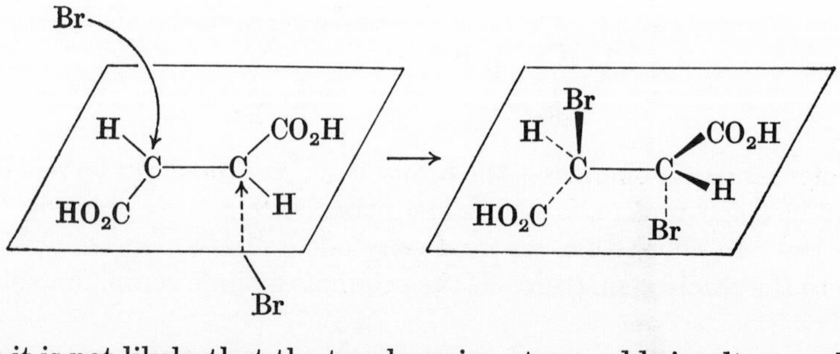

Figure 32.2 Addition of bromine to an olefinic double bond.

Since it is not likely that the two bromine atoms add simultaneously, it is necessary to consider just what it is that causes the planarity of the alkene structure to be retained during the period following addition of the first bromine atom and before the second bromine atom attacks. During this period one of the carbon atoms is bonded to bromine but the other carbon atom should be free to rotate, thereby moving the groups bonded to it out of the plane:

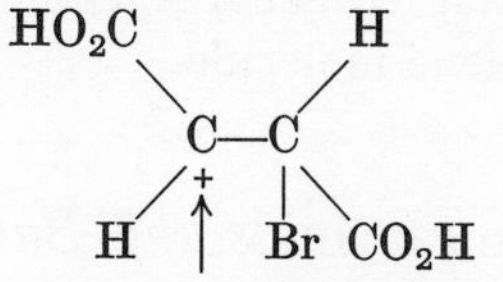

$$
\begin{array}{ccc}
HO_2C & & H \\
& C\text{—}C & \\
H & \overset{+}{Br} & CO_2H
\end{array}
$$

(This carbon atom should
be free to rotate with
its groups during the
period between Steps 1
and 2.)

If such rotation occurs, the products will include all three optical isomers. The facts are that the products do not contain all three optical isomers. These products can be explained only by assuming that the alkene remains planar during the interval between Steps 1 and 2.

To explain the retention of planarity during this period it has been postulated that the first bromine atom actually interacts with the π bond between the carbon atoms and forms a so-called bromonium ion having the structure*

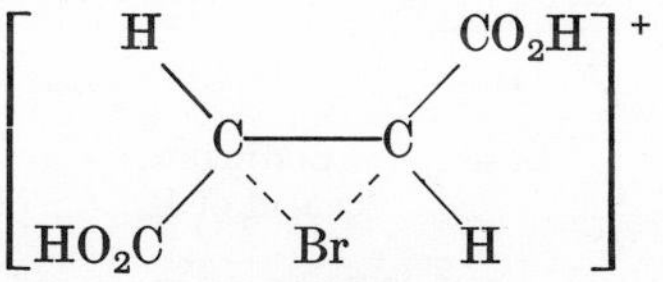

$$
\left[\begin{array}{ccc}
H & & CO_2H \\
& C\text{——}C & \\
HO_2C & Br & H
\end{array}\right]^+
$$

A bromonium ion
(This retains the stereochemistry
until the second bromine species
attacks.)

The bromonium ion could then maintain the stereochemistry of the alkene structure until the second bromine species, the bromide ion, attacks from above. The bromonium-ion picture accounts for the facts, and as a result it has been accepted as a working hypothesis by many chemists. However, the question cannot be considered settled.

In summary, the present view of the mechanism of addition of bromine to alkenes involves the following reaction sequence and intermediates:

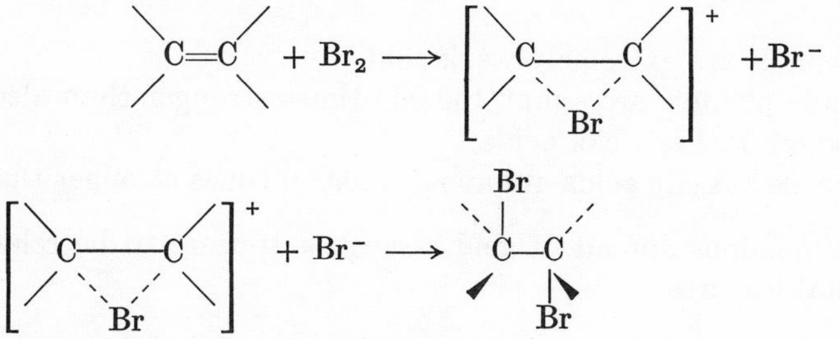

$$
C\text{=}C + Br_2 \longrightarrow \left[\ C\text{——}C \ \underset{Br}{}\right]^+ + Br^-
$$

$$
\left[\ C\text{——}C \ \underset{Br}{}\right]^+ + Br^- \longrightarrow \ \underset{Br}{\overset{Br}{C\text{—}C}}
$$

* In the diagram, the bromine atom lies below the plane of the page but the alkene structure lies in the plane of the page.

In the first step the complex known as a bromonium ion is formed. In the second step bromide ion attacks the bromonium ion from the side opposite the bromine atom in the bromonium ion. This results in what is known as *trans addition* to alkenes. In such processes Br_2 is known as an electrophile (electron-seeking reagent) since it attacks the center of high electron density in the alkene molecule.

The Strengths of Organic Acids and Bases

From studies of the relative strengths of organic acids and bases, the organic chemists have developed an elaborate and highly successful theory relating acid or base strength to the availability of electrons in particular bonds or at particular atoms in a compound. This is called the electronic theory of acids and bases, but its principles have been so widely and successfully applied to reaction mechanisms and to other facets of organic chemistry that it is fair to say that the electronic theory is second in importance only to the structural theory in the organic chemistry of the present day.

Acids: Structure and Acid Strength. Recalling that Brønsted defined acids as proton donors and bases as proton acceptors and has expressed the reactions of acids with bases in terms of the equilibrium

$$HA \quad + \quad B \quad \rightleftarrows \quad BH^+ \quad + \quad A^-$$

| Acid | Base | Conjugate acid of B | Conjugate base of HA |

we might raise the question: What is the origin of acidity in organic compounds? To answer this question we should examine the structures of organic acids of various acid strengths. Four important classes of organic compounds which have acid properties are

ROH	ArOH	RCO_2H	$ArCO_2H$
Alcohols	Phenols	Aliphatic carboxylic acids	Aromatic carboxylic acids
$K_I \sim 10^{-16}$	$K_I \sim 10^{-10}$	$K_I \sim 10^{-5}$	$K_I \sim 10^{-4}$

The ionization constants, K_I, for these acids (in water at 25°C) indicate that:

1. alcohols are extremely weak acids;
2. while phenols are about 100,000 times stronger than alcohols, they too are rather weak acids;
3. the carboxylic acids are about 100,000 times stronger than phenols.

This tremendous spread of acid strengths appears to be related to two structural features:

1. The apparent electronegativity of the group bonded to the hydrogen atom to be ionized—i.e., the RO, ArO, RCO_2, or $ArCO_2$ groups. This may account for differences in acid strength between members of the same family, as for example, between acetic acid, CH_3CO_2H, $K_I = 1.8 \times 10^{-5}$, and chloroacetic acid, $ClCH_2CO_2H$, $K_I = 1.3 \times 10^{-3}$.

2. The relative stability of the anion, X^- (formed when the proton is removed), compared with the stability of the unionized acid molecule, HX. This may account for the difference in acid strength between alcohols and phenols or between alcohols and carboxylic acids. When an alcohol ionizes, the RO^- has no structural feature to make it more stable than the unionized alcohol. Both the phenoxide, $C_6H_5O^-$, and carboxylate, RCO_2^-, anions are stabilized by resonance that is not likely in the unionized acids. Resonance hybrids for these anions include:*

Resonance hybrids of phenoxide ion

Resonance hybrids of carboxylate ion

Thus if upon ionization a stabilizing resonance effect comes into play, a proton may be removed more readily than would be possible without this stabilizing influence.

Effect of Substituents on Acid Strength. To see how the electronic theory of acids and bases developed and to illustrate some of its important principles, we shall now consider the effect on the strength of various acids of replacing hydrogen atoms attached to carbon atoms by other atoms or groups.

Let us consider first the effect of replacing one of the hydrogen atoms on the methyl group in acetic acid. Table 32.2 gives the pK_I† values for a group of substituted acetic acids. Examination of the data of this table reveals that of the eleven substituents listed, only the methyl group decreases the acid strength; the other substituents increase it to various degrees. Recalling that acid strength usually increases with an increase in the electron-withdrawing ability of substituents (cf., inorganic oxyacids, Chaps. 9, 16–19) we might attribute the differences in strength of the acids in Table 32.2 to differences in electron-withdrawing ability of the substituents present. On this premise we can arrange the various substituents in order of increasing *electron-withdrawing ability* as follows:

Table 32.2 pK_I Values for Some Substituted Acetic Acids, $Y-CH_2-CO_2H$ (in water at 25°C)

Acid Substituent, Y	pK_I
CH_3-	4.88
$H-$ (acetic acid)	4.76
(phenyl)	4.31
$HO-$	3.83
CH_3O-	3.53
$I-$	3.12
$Br-$	2.86
$Cl-$	2.86
HO_2C-	2.80
$F-$	2.66
$NC-$	2.47
O_2N-	1.68

$H-$, (phenyl), $HO-$, CH_3O-, $I-$, $Br- = Cl-$, HO_2C-, $F-$, $NC-$, O_2N-

———————Increasing electron-withdrawing ability———→
(based on strengths of substituted acetic acids)

---

* In these formulas pairs of electrons in p or in π orbitals are designated as dashes for convenience in representation.

† pK_I is defined as $-\log K_I$.

Using this series as a guide we might say, for example, that the nitro group ($-NO_2$) is much more electron-withdrawing than the phenyl or the methoxy (CH_3O-) group or that iodine atoms are less electron-withdrawing than fluorine atoms.

But what can be said of the methyl group which decreases the acid strength when it replaces a hydrogen atom in acetic acid? Can we call this an *electron-donating group*? This has become the custom, and not only this group but all other alkyl groups are considered electron-donating groups, in part because, when present, they decrease the strength of the acid.

What happens to the acid strength when more than one electron-withdrawing or electron-donating substituent is substituted into the acetic acid molecule? Table 32.3 gives the answer.

Table 32.3 Effect on Acid Strength of Successive Substitutions in Acetic Acid

Acid	pK_I	Acid	pK_I
CH_3CO_2H	4.76	CH_3CO_2H	4.76
$ClCH_2CO_2H$	2.86	$CH_3CH_2CO_2H$	4.88
Cl_2CHCO_2H	1.29	$(CH_3)_2CHCO_2H$	4.86
Cl_3CCO_2H	0.65	$(CH_3)_3CCO_2H$	5.05

Successive substitution of chlorine atoms (an electron-withdrawing group) increases the acid strength; successive substitution of methyl groups (an electron-donating group) generally decreases the acid strength.

Just what makes a given group stronger or weaker in its respective electronic tendencies is not completely understood. Present theories picture the electronic contribution of a group as a combination of at least two tendencies. The first, known as the *inductive effect*, is roughly analogous to electronegativity and is a measure of the tendency of the atom or group to attract and control the valence electrons. Groups which attract electrons more strongly than hydrogen atoms may be electron-withdrawing groups; those which attract electrons less strongly than hydrogen atoms may be electron-donating groups. The inductive effect is sometimes indicated in a formula as in $CH_3 \rightarrow -CH_2CO_2H$ or $O_2N \leftarrow -CH_2CO_2H$ where the electronic tendencies are specified.

The second factor, sometimes called the *resonance effect*, is a measure of the ability of the atom or group to enter into resonance with the system to which it is bonded. Some groups supply electrons and others withdraw electrons upon entering into resonance. The nitro group, $-NO_2$, for example withdraws electrons via resonance as illustrated with *p*-nitrophenol.

The methoxy group, CH_3O—, on the other hand supplies electrons in its resonance interaction as illustrated with p-methoxyphenol.

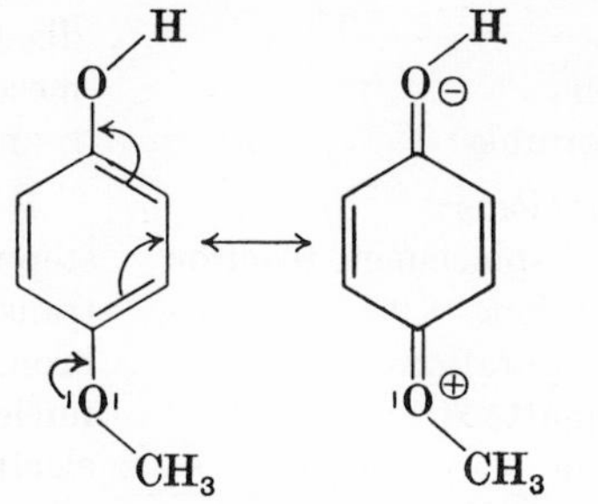

In its inductive effect the methoxy group is electron-withdrawing; in its resonance effect, it is electron-donating. Its over-all electronic contribution often depends upon the extent to which it can enter into resonance with the system to which it is bonded.

Bases: Structure and Base Strength. The important organic bases include the aliphatic and aromatic amines—RNH_2, R_2NH, R_3N, $ArNH_2$, Ar_2NH, and Ar_3N. The strength of a base is related to its ability to accept protons or to supply a pair of electrons to the molecule of an acid. The general reaction of an organic base might be written

$$R\ddot{N}H_2 + HX \rightleftharpoons \left[\begin{matrix} H \\ \underset{\cdot\cdot}{R}\ddot{N}H_2 \end{matrix} \right]^+ + X^-$$

Since base strength increases with the electron-supplying ability of the basic atom in the molecule, one would predict that electron-donating groups should *increase* and electron-withdrawing groups should *decrease* base strength. Measurement of the ionization constants of amines of varying structures corroborates this prediction.

SUMMARY

Three facets of theoretical organic chemistry have been introduced in this chapter. They are optical isomerism, reaction mechanisms, and the electronic theory of acids and bases. The concept of dissymmetric molecules and of the nonsuperimposability of molecular structures is seen to be manifested in optical isomerism. Various ramifications of this isomerism have been presented. In discussing the elucidation of reaction mechanisms, we have placed emphasis on the experimental evidence for the pathways of nucleophilic displacement reactions and of addition reactions at the π bond in alkenes. From studies of the relative strengths of acids and bases, an elementary form of the electronic theory of organic acids and bases has been developed.

SOME SPECIAL TERMS

Optical isomerism
  dissymmetric molecules   enantiomorphs
  nonsuperimposable mirror images   asymmetric carbon atoms

optical activity   racemic mixtures
rotation of polarized light   racemate
dextrorotatory   resolution
levorotatory   diastereoisomers
configuration   meso isomer
projection formula   D and L configurations

Reaction mechanisms
nucleophilic displacement reaction   stepwise addition
S_N1, S_N2 reactions   trans addition
inverted configuration   bromonium ion
opposite-side attack   nucleophile
solvent effects   electrophile

Electronic theory of acids and bases
ionization constants, pK_I inductive effect
electron-withdrawing groups   resonance effect
electron-donating groups

QUESTIONS AND PROBLEMS

1. Define each of the following terms: (a) dissymmetric molecule, (b) asymmetric carbon atom, (c) enantiomorph, (d) diasteroisomers, (e) dextrorotatory, and (f) racemization.

2. Draw configurational formulas for all the optical isomers of the following. Indicate the enantiomorphs and the diastereomers.

(a) CH_3—CH—CH—CH_3
           | |
           Br Br

(b) CH_2—CH_2
                  | |
     HO_2C—CH——CH
                      |
                   (phenyl ring)

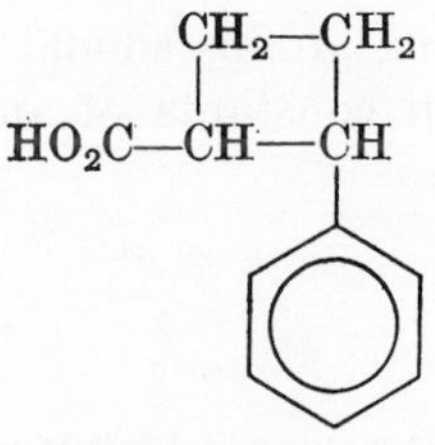

(c) CH_3—CH—CO_2H
           |
           NH_2

(d) CH_3—CH—CH—CO_2H
           | |
           OH NH_2

3. Draw configurational formulas for each of the following:
   (a) the L-configuration of

   CH_3—CH—CO_2H
          |
          NH_3

   (b) the L-configuration of

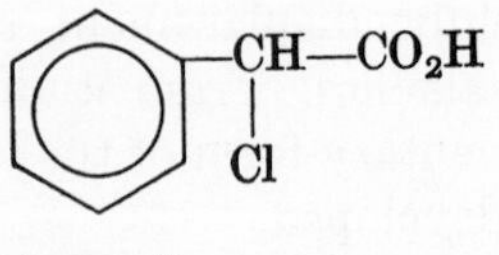

   (phenyl ring)—CH—CO_2H
                  |
                  Cl

   (c) all possible configurations of

   CH_3—CH—CH—CO_2—CH_3
          | |
          Cl Cl

4. Write configurational names for each of the following:

(a) 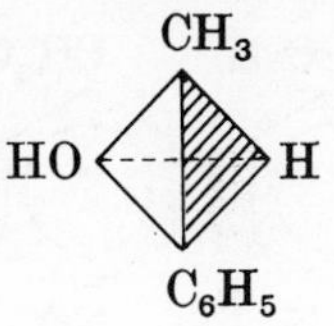 HO $\triangleleft$ —$\cdots\triangleright$ H   with CH_3 above and C_6H_5 below

(c)

$$CO_2H$$
$$H\text{—}\overset{|}{\underset{|}{C}}\text{—}OH$$
$$C_6H_5$$

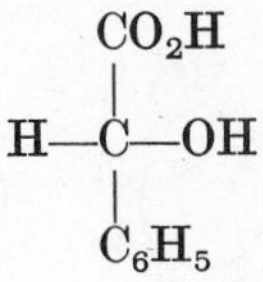

(b) 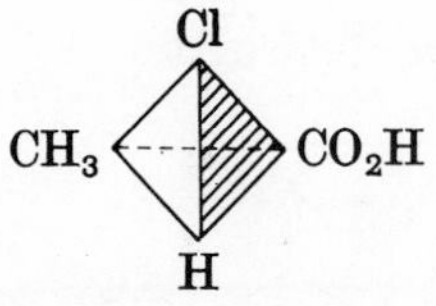 CH_3 $\triangleleft$ —$\cdots\triangleright$ CO_2H with Cl above and H below

(d)

$$CO_2H$$
$$H\text{—}\overset{|}{C}\text{—}NH_2$$
$$H_2N\text{—}\underset{|}{C}\text{—}H$$
$$CH_3$$

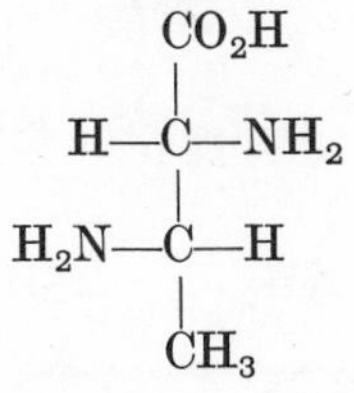

5. Distinguish between S_N1 and S_N2 reactions on the basis of chemical kinetics and optical activity.

6. Which of the following reactions would you expect to proceed most readily under conditions favorable to the S_N2 reaction? Explain your answer.

(a) CH_3O^- +
$$CH_3\ CH_2$$
$$\diagdown$$
$$CH\text{—}Cl \longrightarrow$$
$$\diagup$$
$$CH_3$$

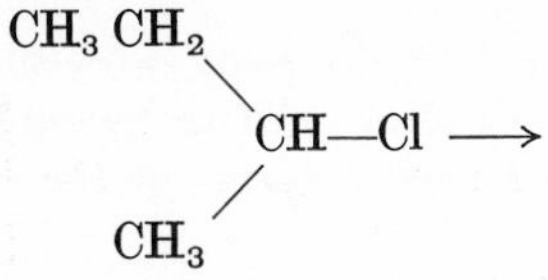

(b) HO^- +
$$CH_3\text{—}CH_2$$
$$\diagdown$$
$$CH\text{—}Cl \longrightarrow$$
$$\diagup$$
$$CH_3$$

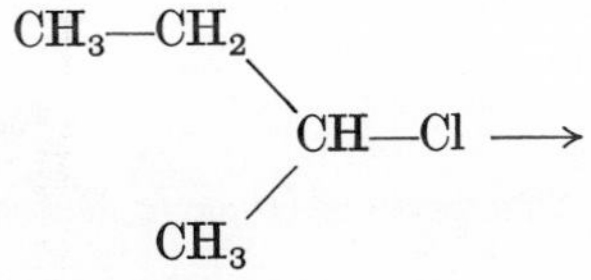

(c) Cl^- +
$$CH_3\text{—}CH_2$$
$$\diagdown$$
$$CH\text{—}Cl \longrightarrow$$
$$\diagup$$
$$CH_3$$

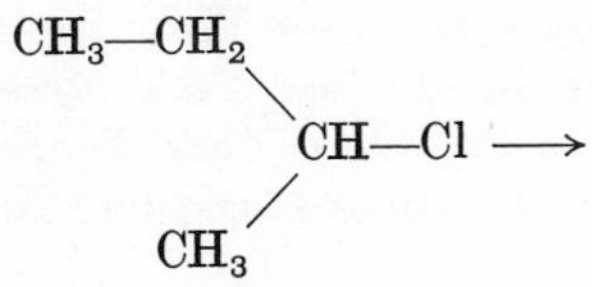

7. Draw the configurational formula for the organic product in each of the following reactions:

(a) Br_2 +
$$CH_3 \qquad CH_3$$
$$\diagdown \qquad \diagup$$
$$C\text{=}C \longrightarrow$$
$$\diagup \qquad \diagdown$$
$$H \qquad H$$

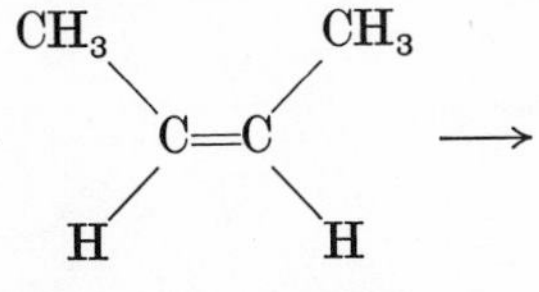

(b) Br_2 +
$$CH_3 \qquad H$$
$$\diagdown \qquad \diagup$$
$$C\text{=}C \longrightarrow$$
$$\diagup \qquad \diagdown$$
$$H \qquad CH_3$$

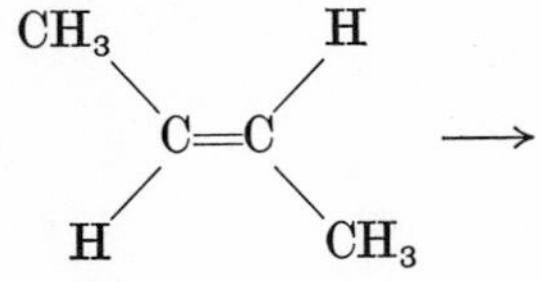

(c) HCl +
$$CH_3 \qquad CH_3$$
$$\diagdown \qquad \diagup$$
$$C\text{=}C \longrightarrow$$
$$\diagup \qquad \diagdown$$
$$H \qquad H$$

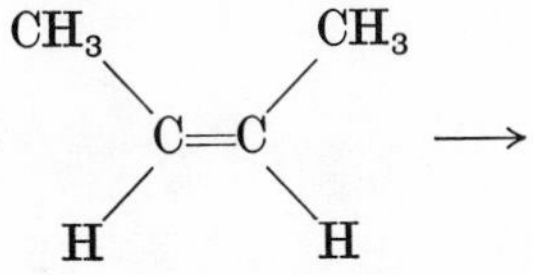

8. Arrange the following in order of *increasing* acid strength:

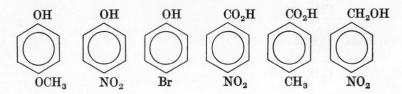

9. Arrange the following in order of increasing base strength:

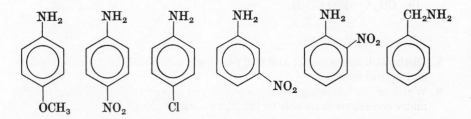

10. It is observed that, in general, electron-donating substituents on the benzene ring are ortho-para directing while electron-withdrawing substituents often are meta-directing. Account for this in terms of the electronic theory of organic chemistry.

REFERENCES

ALLINGER, N. L., and J. ALLINGER. *Structures of Organic Molecules.* Englewood Cliffs, N. J.: Prentice-Hall, 1965.

BRESLOW, R. *Organic Reaction Mechanisms.* New York: Benjamin, 1965.

HINE, J. *Physical Organic Chemistry,* 2d ed. New York: McGraw-Hill, 1962.

MISLOW, K. *Introduction to Stereochemistry.* New York: Benjamin, 1965.

SYKES, P. *A Guidebook to Mechanism in Organic Chemistry.* New York: Wiley, 1961.

33

Some Chemistry of Living Cells

Now our model for deoxyribonucleic acid is, in effect, a pair of templates each of which is complementary to the other. We imagine that prior to duplication the hydrogen bonds are broken and the two chains unwind and separate. Each chain then acts as a template for the formation on to itself of a new companion chain so that eventually we shall have two pairs of chains where we only had one before.*

James D. Watson (1928—) and F. H. C. Crick (1916—)

Biochemistry is the study of the chemistry of life processes. Today the major research effort in this science is the study of the chemical reactions that are taking place in living cells. Previously, the technique and knowledge in this area limited researchers to the isolation and identification of the substances present in the cell. But from such studies they were able to learn a tremendous amount about nutrition, blood chemistry, digestion, and many other processes that keep the organism alive and healthy. The persistent efforts of researchers to look into the cell and identify the chemical reactions occurring under life conditions led to the techniques and the know-how which in the last half of this century have revealed to us the secret of heredity and many other features of life processes.

The experiments that led to these revelations are themselves monuments to the intellect. Much of the work involved the use of radioactive tracers. Bacteria, because of their speed in reproduction, were the organisms used most often.

While the chemistry of the cell is extremely complicated, the underlying principles are not difficult to grasp—the chemical reactions of the cell are believed to be determined and controlled by template molecules which adsorb the reactants on their surfaces, catalyze the reactions, and release the products to the cell; energy conversion and utilization revolves largely around one molecule which absorbs energy in its formation and releases

---

* The quotation is from "Genetical Implications of the Structure of Deoxyribonucleic Acid," *Nature*, *171* (1953), p. 964.

energy when it decomposes, and heredity is controlled by threadlike molecules keyed to a four-unit code.

This chapter gives an overview of the chemistry of the living cell. While the picture presented is a simplified one, it represents the current view held by most biochemists.

The Living Cell. Biology students are accustomed to thinking of a cell as a drop of viscous liquid surrounded by a membrane. Inside the membrane is the cytoplasm—mostly water but containing numerous heterogeneous regions identified as mitochondria, ribosomes, lysosomes, etc. Toward the center of the cell is the nucleus where the genetic information is stored. While this is a familiar picture to biology students, the biochemist has a somewhat more penetrating view of the cell. He sees it as a highly organized chemical factory, capable of carrying out a myriad of very specific chemical reactions rapidly and efficiently, able to control these reactions to meet the needs of the cell and the organism, and so skillful in regulating its energy requirements that it captures 60 per cent of the energy of its fuel—a feat only a few man-made machines can claim.

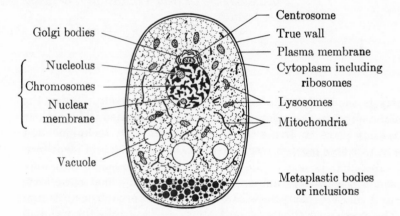

Figure 33.1 Diagram of a living cell.

Labels (left): Golgi bodies, Nucleolus, Chromosomes, Nuclear membrane, Vacuole

Labels (right): Centrosome, True wall, Plasma membrane, Cytoplasm including ribosomes, Lysosomes, Mitochondria, Metaplastic bodies or inclusions

Two of the most important questions concerning this complex chemical factory are:

1. How is it possible for the cell to carry out only certain chemical reactions when the materials needed for carrying out so many other reactions are present?
2. What is the chemical secret associated with efficient energy utilization of the cell?

We shall use these two questions as the basis for studying some chemistry of the cell.

Enzymes—The Reaction Controllers. Experiments have shown that nearly every reaction in the cell proceeds readily only in the presence of a specific enzyme. In the absence of appropriate enzymes most reactions would proceed so slowly that the cell would die. Enzymes are protein molecules often having molecular weights in the 50,000 range though many are larger than this (Figure 33.2). Almost all of these huge molecules are specific catalysts. This means that a given enzyme will speed up one

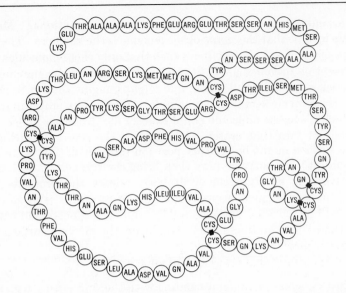

Figure 33.2 Model of an enzyme: bovine ribonuclease. Each circle represents an amino acid.

chemical reaction but not another, even though the second reaction may be very similar to but not exactly the same as the first. For example, the enzyme sucrase will catalyze the hydrolysis of sucrose into glucose and fructose, but it will not catalyze the hydrolysis of maltose into two glucose molecules. All of this means that the cell can carry out only those reactions for which an appropriate enzyme is present, and very few others. This also means the cell must contain a very large number of different types of enzyme molecules. It is estimated that there are about 1,700 enzyme units in one mitochondrion of a beef heart cell.

Not only is a specific enzyme required for nearly every reaction in the cell, but cellular reactions usually proceed through a number of steps each one of which requires an enzyme (Figure 33.3). For example, in the oxidation of glucose to carbon dioxide and water—a reaction every student can carry out in one operation using a test tube and a burner—the cell uses seventeen steps and seventeen enzymes. Eleven of these steps take place in the cytoplasm; six occur in the mitochondrion.

Perhaps the next logical question to ask is, Why are enzymes specific? What is there about these huge protein molecules that enables them to

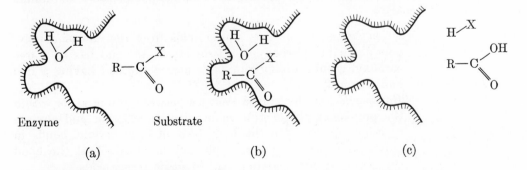

Figure 33.3 Enzyme specificity—enzyme catalysts bring reactants together in close contact and proper orientation for the reaction to proceed. (a) Enzyme and substrate approach each other. (b) Enzyme-substrate complex. (c) Enzyme and products separate.

catalyze only one of many possible chemical reactions? Many biochemists believe that the shape of the enzyme is the key here. They believe that the shape of a given enzyme is such that only those molecules involved in the reaction it controls will fit at the active site on the enzyme surface. At the risk of oversimplification, one might imagine that in terms of this theory, the enzyme sucrase, for example, might have a crater in its surface into which a sucrose molecule could exactly fit. No other molecule in the cell could fit into that crater. Adjacent to the sucrose position on the enzyme surface might be another position into which only a water molecule could fit. The enzyme may then bring sucrose and water together at the active site, catalyze the hydrolysis, release the products from its surface, proceed to pick up a second pair of reactants, and so on. This process will be repeated until the cell has sufficient glucose and fructose, at which time these products may remain on the enzyme surface, thereby temporarily inactivating it.

Other important characteristics of enzymes are:

1. Most enzymes have names ending with the suffix -ase—e.g., amylase, maltase, lipase, nuclease—although some, such as renin, pepsin, and trypsin, retain an earlier nomenclature.
2. To be effective, some enzymes require the presence of metal ions, such as zinc, or magnesium, or other molecules known as coenzymes. Often these coenzymes are vitamins or are related to vitamins.
3. The action of enzymes is influenced by pH and by temperature. Each enzyme has an optimum pH and an optimum temperature range where its activity is greatest. High temperatures will permanently destroy enzyme activity.
4. A very few enzymes catalyze more than one reaction.

Examples of some enzymes and the reactions they catalyze are:

1. *Carbohydrases*—enzymes which catalyze the hydrolysis of starch, starch fragments (dextrins), or disaccharides into simple sugars.

   Sucrase—hydrolysis of sucrose to glucose and fructose.
   Lactase—hydrolysis of lactose to glucose and galactose.

2. *Proteases*—enzymes which catalyze the conversion of proteins or protein fragments (polypeptides) to simple polypeptides and amino acids.

   Exopeptidases—hydrolyze amino acids from the end of a polypeptide chain. Carboxypeptidases attack the end having a free carboxyl group; amino peptidases attack the end having a free amino group.
   Endopeptidases—hydrolyze linkages between amino acids within the protein or polypeptide chain. Pepsin, trypsin, and chymotrypsin each catalyze the hydrolysis of only certain bonds in polypeptide chains. For example, pepsin functions at the bond connecting aromatic amino acids to acidic amino acids.

3. *Esterases*—enzymes which catalyze the conversion of esters to alcohols and acids.

   Lipases—hydrolysis of fats to glycerol and fatty acids.

Phosphatases—hydrolysis of phosphate esters

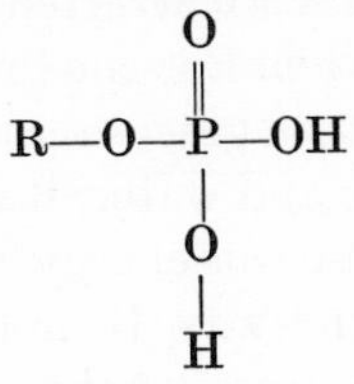

$$R-O-\overset{\overset{\displaystyle O}{\|}}{\underset{\underset{\displaystyle H}{|}}{P}}-OH$$

to phosphoric acid and alcohol—a key reaction in glucose metabolism.

4. *Transferases*—enzymes which catalyze the transfer of a group from one molecule to another. For example, the body is able to make certain amino acids by transferring an amino group from an amino acid in large supply to a structure capable of being converted to the desired amino acid as illustrated below.

Transaminases—transfer of amino group—e.g.,

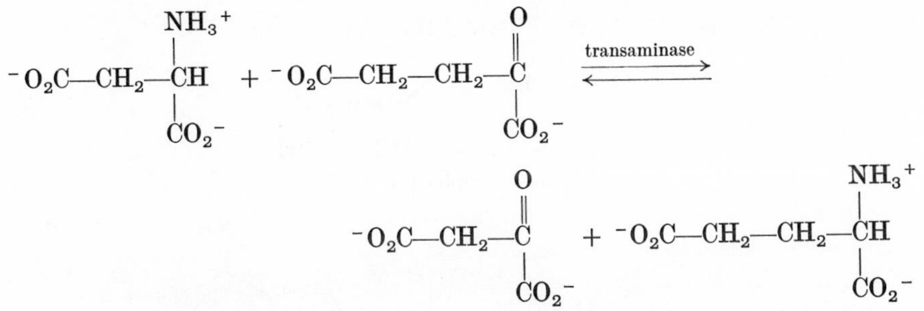

$$^-O_2C-CH_2-\overset{\overset{\displaystyle NH_3{}^+}{|}}{\underset{\underset{\displaystyle CO_2{}^-}{|}}{CH}} \;+\; {}^-O_2C-CH_2-CH_2-\overset{\overset{\displaystyle O}{\|}}{\underset{\underset{\displaystyle CO_2{}^-}{|}}{C}} \quad \overset{\text{transaminase}}{\underset{\longleftarrow}{\longrightarrow}}$$

$$^-O_2C-CH_2-\overset{\overset{\displaystyle O}{\|}}{\underset{\underset{\displaystyle CO_2{}^-}{|}}{C}} \;+\; {}^-O_2C-CH_2-CH_2-\overset{\overset{\displaystyle NH_3{}^+}{|}}{\underset{\underset{\displaystyle CO_2{}^-}{|}}{CH}}$$

Transmethylases—transfer of methyl groups.
Transphosphorylases—transfer of phosphate groups.
Oxidases—transfer of hydrogen atoms.

5. *Nucleases*—enzymes which catalyze the hydrolysis of nucleic acids ultimately to pentoses, phosphoric acid, pyrimidines and purines.

DNAases—degradation of DNA.
RNAases—degradation of RNA.

ATP-ADP—The Energy Converters. Like most other chemical factories, the cell requires relatively large quantities of fuel to sustain its operation. In normal operation a large fraction of the cell's reactions are endothermic or, more important, they are nonspontaneous. This is evidenced by the spontaneous decomposition of components of cells upon death. Living cells use glucose (and decomposition products from both fats and proteins) as a fuel source. While glucose, in being oxidized to carbon dioxide and water, can supply an adequate quantity of energy, the cell cannot always use that energy at the time the glucose is being oxidized. Neither can the cell allow too much energy to be released to the surroundings. If even half of the energy from oxidizing glucose were released to the cell, the temperature of the cell would rise so high that the enzymes would be inactivated. Thus the cell needs (a) a mechanism for capturing and storing the energy from its fuel; and (b) another mechanism for supplying this energy when and where it is needed.

The basis for these two mechanisms lies in some very elementary chemistry. When a compound A is converted to a compound B, energy may be released or absorbed, and when B is converted back to A the reverse will be true. Suppose, then, that as glucose goes through its seventeen-step degradation to carbon dioxide and water, it releases energy a bit at a time in many of these steps. Suppose this energy is used to convert compound A to compound B. All along the way B molecules are being formed and energy is being stored. Now, suppose the cell needs energy. Can it not obtain this by converting some B molecules back to A molecules?

This is believed to be the energy conversion mechanism of the cell. The molecules A and B are adenosine diphosphate, ADP, and adenosine triphosphate, ATP, although there are several other pairs of molecules which may serve the same function.

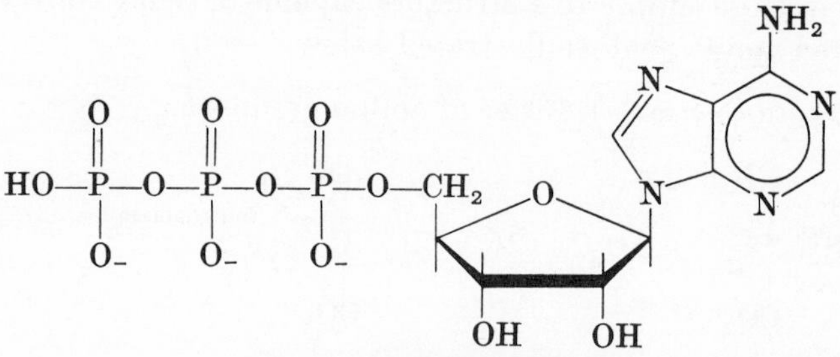

Adenosine triphosphate, ATP

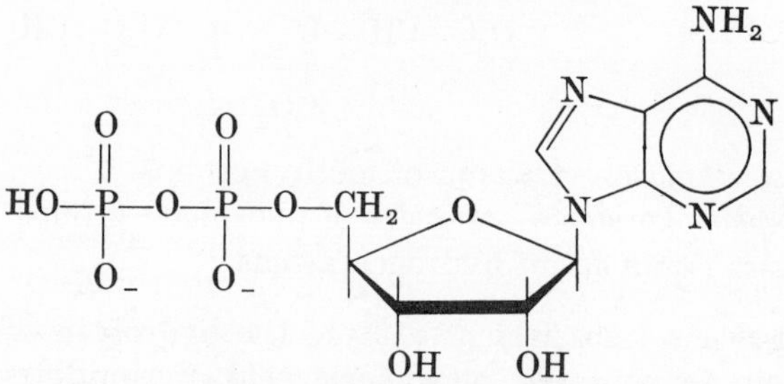

Adenosine diphosphate, ADP

In spite of the complicated structures of ATP and ADP, their energy conversion function lies in the phosphate portion of the molecule. In ADP there are two phosphate groups; in ATP there are three such groups. Addition of the third phosphate group to ADP requires considerable energy—four to five times as much as is needed to link a phosphate group to an alcohol, for example. Therefore when ADP is converted to ATP, energy is required and is stored in the ATP formed:

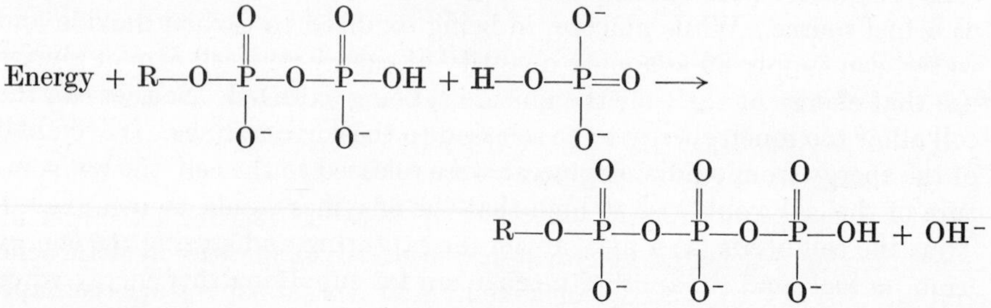

When energy is needed, ATP reacts with water to give ADP and energy.

$$\text{ATP} + H_2O \longrightarrow \text{ADP} + H_2PO_4^- + \text{energy}$$

The question often is asked: Why does it take so much energy to form the triphosphate bond? The answer seems to be related to the fact that in forming a covalent bond to the ADP molecule, the third phosphate unit must localize some of its delocalized (resonance-involved) electrons. Evidently the energy required to do this is appreciable.

ATP is the key compound in the cell as far as energy utilization is concerned. When the cell needs to carry out an endergonic (energy-absorbing) reaction, that energy is supplied by hydrolyzing ATP back to ADP. When the supply of ATP runs low, the cell produces more by oxidizing glucose or other energy-releasing molecules.

More than 90 per cent of the ATP is made in the mitochondria of the cell. Many cells contain from 50 to 5,000 mitochondria. Cells having high-energy requirements have more mitochondria than those having low-energy requirements.

Oxidation of Glucose. The actual sequence of reactions in which a glucose molecule in the cell is oxidized to carbon dioxide and water is given in Figure 33.4. The sequence may be divided into two main portions. The first consists of the breakdown of the glucose molecule into two three-carbon fragments—pyruvic and/or lactic acids. This portion of the oxidation sequence is called glycolysis. The second portion of the sequence is the conversion of the pyruvic (or lactic) acid to carbon dioxide and water which occurs via the tricarboxylic acid, or Krebs, cycle.

During glycolysis a glucose molecule first reacts with a molecule of ATP resulting in a transfer of a phosphate unit from ATP to carbon atom 6 on the glucose molecule (Figure 33.4). The glucose-6-phosphate then is transformed to an isomer, fructose-6-phosphate, which reacts with a second ATP molecule to produce fructose-1,6-diphosphate. The diphosphate decomposes to two molecules of glyceraldehyde-3-phosphate which proceed through a series of steps, some involving oxidation (or reduction) of the three-carbon fragments, and results finally in the formation of pyruvic or lactic acid. Two oxidation steps in this series each produce two ATP molecules (one for each three-carbon fragment oxidized) with the result that the over-all glycolysis sequence gives a net production of two ATP molecules (two ATP molecules were used in transferring phosphate units to glucose or fructose molecules, and four were produced in the oxidations). The ATP molecules, of course, have energy in storage.

Glycolysis is important in the muscular activity of the body. When the body calls on its muscles to perform continuous labor, the muscles must produce energy without the presence of sufficient oxygen for the complete oxidation of carbohydrate to carbon dioxide and water. In glycolysis the over-all reaction

$$C_6H_{12}O_6 \rightleftharpoons \underset{\text{Lactic acid}}{2CH_3CHOHCO_2H} + 2\text{ATP}$$

involves no oxygen. Under strenuous activity muscles show a decrease in their glycogen (reserve carbohydrate) content and an increase in lactic acid content. No oxygen need be consumed. However, at some stage (perhaps

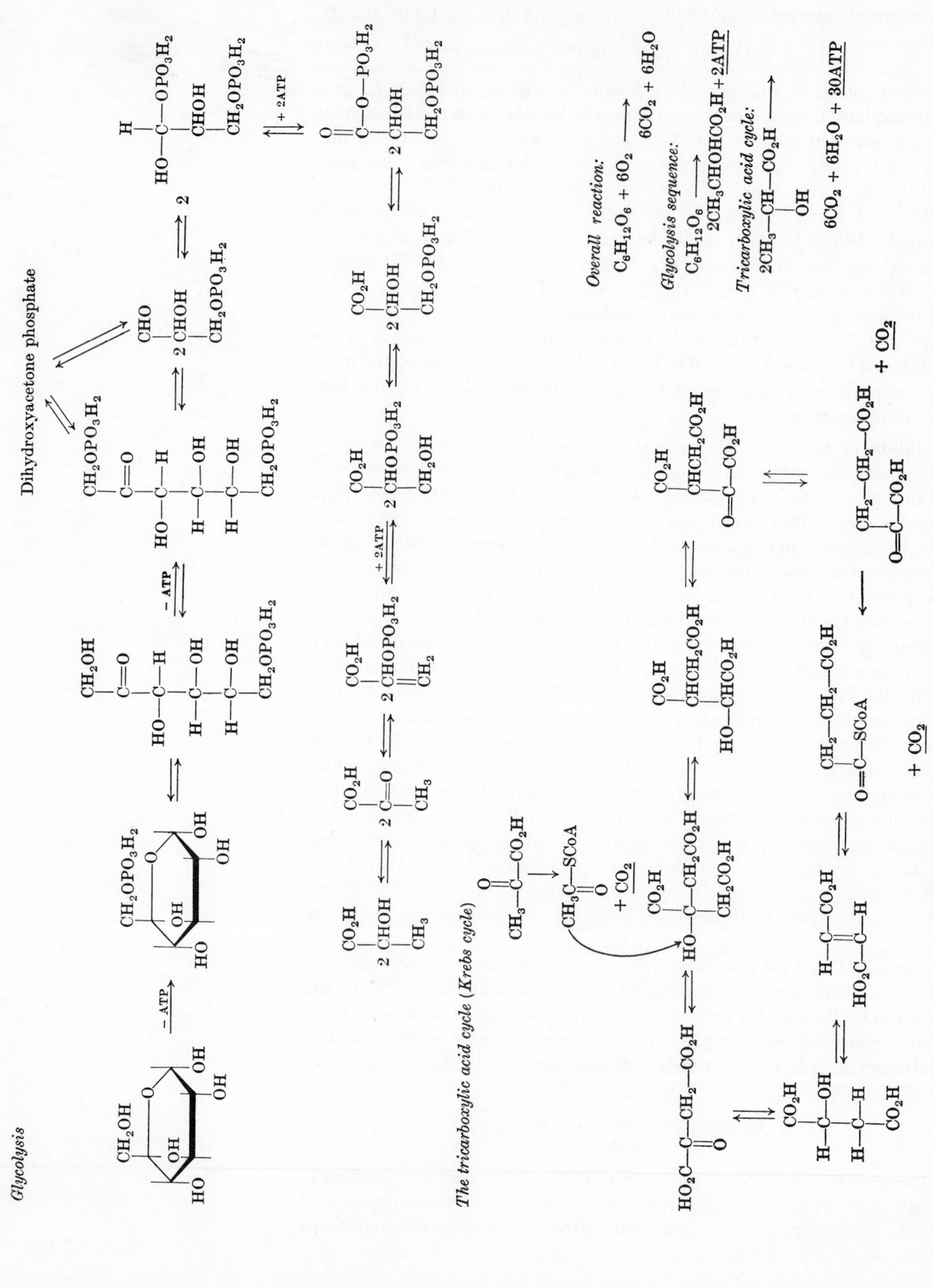

Figure 33.4 Sequence of steps by which glucose is oxidized to carbon dioxide and water in living animal cells.

after muscular activity is over), lactic acid must be reconverted to glycogen and the energy required to do this must come from the oxidation of some of the lactic acid—a process which does require oxygen (see discussion of the Krebs cycle). Panting and gasping for breath after a period of strenuous muscle activity is an indication of the body's demand for oxygen to do this job.

The Tricarboxylic Acid Cycle (Krebs Cycle). The second portion of the glucose oxidation sequence involves the oxidation of pyruvic (or lactic) acid to carbon dioxide and water by a series of reactions which form a cyclic process (Figure 33.4). The intermediates formed in the first steps of this cycle are tricarboxylic acids such as citric acid,

$$\begin{array}{c} CH_2CO_2H \\ | \\ HO-C-CO_2H \\ | \\ CH_2CO_2H \end{array}$$

hence the name tricarboxylic acid cycle.

This cycle is the only known reaction sequence by which a foodstuff can be completely oxidized in the body. Foodstuffs other than carbohydrates must be converted first to pyruvic acid or to some other intermediate in the cycle before they can be oxidized to carbon dioxide and water.

Pyruvic acid itself is not an intermediate in the tricarboxylic acid cycle. It is first converted to a substance known as acetyl-coenzyme A(CoA)

$$\underset{\underset{O}{\|}}{CH_3C}-SCoA$$

in one of the most complex and surely one of the most important reactions of the cell. This reaction may be written

$$CH_3-\underset{\underset{O}{\|}}{C}-CO_2H + CoA-SH \xrightarrow{[-2H]} CH_3-\underset{\underset{O}{\|}}{C}-SCoA + CO_2$$

$$\quad\; \text{Pyruvic acid} \qquad\qquad\qquad\qquad \text{Acetyl-coenzyme A}$$

and involves both oxidation and loss of carbon dioxide. Moreover, five cofactors are needed in addition to the enzyme. These cofactors include coenzyme A, magnesium ion, and compounds related to other vitamins in the B group.

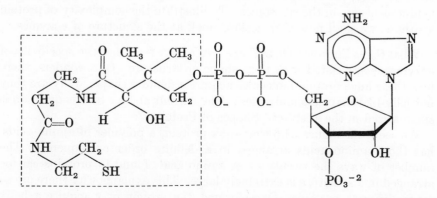

Figure 33.5 Coenzyme A. The portion on the left is from vitamin B_4 (pantothenic acid).

Acetyl-CoA enters the tricarboxylic acid cycle by reacting with oxalacetic acid

$$O{=}C{-}CO_2H$$
$$\mid$$
$$CH_2{-}CO_2H$$

to give citric acid which is transformed, by the series of steps shown in Figure 33.4, again to oxalacetic acid with a loss of two molecules of carbon dioxide along the way. In effect, then, the tricarboxylic cycle takes the two-carbon fragment left from the original glucose, attaches it to an oxalacetic acid molecule, and subjects this to a series of steps which result in the liberation of two molecules of carbon dioxide and regeneration of the starting material, oxalacetic acid. In addition, 15 molecules of ATP are produced as each molecule of lactic acid from glycolysis is converted first into pyruvic acid and then into carbon dioxide and water as the pyruvic acid passes through the tricarboxylic acid cycle.

The Fate of Food. When food enters the organism it must be transformed into useful form. This may mean breaking down molecules such as fats, starch, and proteins into smaller segments. In our bodies such reactions ordinarily take place in the alimentary tract under the influence of digestive enzymes secreted into various regions of the tract by digestive glands such as the pancreas. Before entering the blood stream, proteins are hydrolyzed to amino acids, and carbohydrates to glucose or other simple sugars which are able to pass through the cell membrane.

Inside the cell there also are large molecules which must be broken down into smaller segments before these parts can be utilized effectively. An example is glycogen, a polymer of glucose similar to starch, which the cell uses to store glucose until it is needed. Breakdown of large molecules in the cell usually takes place in the lysosomes, and a different team of enzymes is needed for each type of substance broken down.

If the food is to be used as fuel, it will be oxidized with the accompanying formation of ATP. As mentioned, most of the ATP is formed in the mitochondria, in the tricarboxylic acid cycle.

Much of the food material entering the cell is used to build new cell material—replacements for worn or damaged parts, or components for new cells. Since most of this material is protein in nature, the cell must first assemble the amino acids, making some if necessary, and then synthesize the extremely complicated proteins. A large fraction of the protein synthesis occurs in the ribosomes. To illustrate the complexity of protein synthesis we shall now take a closer look at the structure of enzymes.

What Gives Enzymes Their Shape? We have seen that the specificity of enzymes is associated with their shape or structure. One wonders, then, how these huge protein molecules acquire a definite shape. Why are they not jelly-like shapeless molecules? The current answer to this question is summarized in the abstract "Shapes of Proteins."

We see from Figure 33.6 that each protein, a polymer of amino acids, has those amino acids arranged in a definite order or sequence. The number of ways the twenty or so amino acids found in proteins can be arranged in a structure is extremely large. This explains why there are so many different proteins. Once formed, the protein may acquire a helix

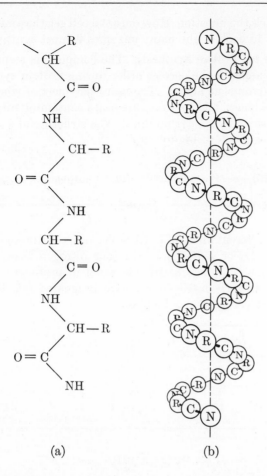

(a)   (b)

Figure 33.6 Polypeptide structure; portion of a protein molecule. (a) The structural formula. (b) A formula emphasizing the α-helix of the protein molecule.

structure stabilized by a large number of hydrogen bonds formed between portions of the same huge molecule, or it may form fibers or sheets where the hydrogen bonds are formed between parallel chains. The shape of the protein structure is maintained by the large number of hydrogen bonds and, in the case of enzymes, also by other attractive forces (van der Waals, dipole interaction).

Having established why enzymes have definite shapes or structures, we

● ● ●   SHAPES OF PROTEINS

The structure of a protein may be described in terms of four basic structural levels:

Primary structure—related to an amino acid sequence, R_1, R_2, R_3, etc. (see also Chap. 32), and illustrated as follows:

Secondary structure—due to hydrogen bonding. Long protein chains have thousands of H-bonds between various portions of the same chain or between adjacent chains.

are now ready to ask the question, How does the cell get the amino acids in the correct order* in each of the many enzymes it must synthesize?

RNA—Template for Protein Synthesis. The compounds responsible for getting the amino acids in the correct order during protein synthesis are known as RNA (ribonucleic acids). These are polymers of ribose (a five-carbon sugar), phosphate, and four organic bases containing nitrogen, two of which are purines and two, pyrimidines. The structure of a segment of an RNA molecule is given in Figure 33.7.

$$-\text{Ribose—Phosphate—Ribose—Phosphate—}$$
$$|\qquad\qquad\qquad\qquad |$$
$$\text{N-Base}\qquad\qquad\text{N-Base}$$

Pyrimidine   Purine

There are many different kinds of RNA molecules, the differences arising in the particular order or sequence of the four nitrogen bases along the polymer chain. This is similar to the situation in proteins and can be illustrated as follows. If the nitrogen bases are designated as I, II, III, and IV, some possible RNA structures include

I II III IV I II III IV

and

I I I IV II III I I I IV II III

• • •   SHAPES OF PROTEINS *cont.*

1. Internal hydrogen bonding gives helix structure in globular proteins (enzymes).
2. Hydrogen bonding between molecules gives sheet or fibrous structures (hair, skin).

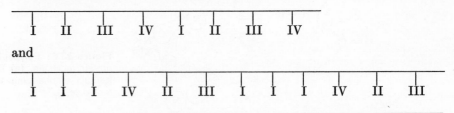

Tertiary structure—folding or coiling of helix on itself. This is the result of all types of intermolecular attractive forces: H-bonds, dipole interaction, van der Waals forces—even S—S bridges between segments of the chain form in some cases. The tertiary structure of a protein is related also to the sequence of amino acids, the size and properties of the R-groups in the chain being here of especial importance. The unique catalytic properties of enzymes presumably are closely related to the tertiary structure.

Quaternary structure—grouping of subunits to give a large, active structure. Some active proteins are believed to be clusters of several subunits, each of which is inactive separately, but if put together in appropriate order, become physiologically active.

---

* As an illustration of how important it is that this sequence of amino acids be correct, it is known that if one amino acid in the 574 that make up a hemoglobin molecule is placed incorrectly, an individual becomes sick and may die of sickle-cell anemia.

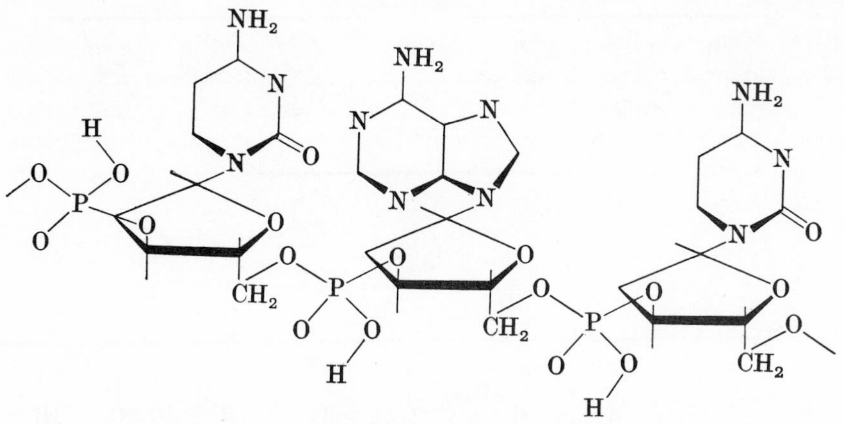

Figure 33.7 Representation of a segment of an RNA chain.

Two forms of RNA are needed in a protein synthesis. The first, known as *messenger-RNA*, has imprinted on it all the directions needed to make one kind of protein. There are at least as many different messenger-RNA molecules as there are different proteins. The second form of RNA is known as *transfer-RNA*. Its job is to pick up one particular amino acid and bring it to messenger-RNA. There are at least as many kinds of transfer-RNA molecules as there are amino acids.

Now let us consider an oversimplified but not unreasonable picture of protein synthesis as controlled by the two forms of RNA by using the following schematic diagrams.

1. This represents messenger-RNA. The four nitrogen bases are indicated by line formulas.

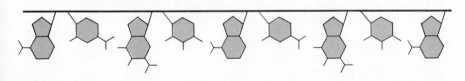

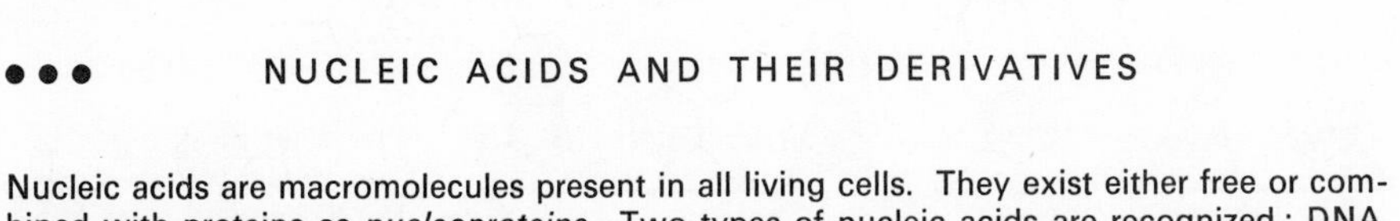

● ● ●   NUCLEIC ACIDS AND THEIR DERIVATIVES

Nucleic acids are macromolecules present in all living cells. They exist either free or combined with proteins as *nucleoproteins*. Two types of nucleic acids are recognized: DNA, *deoxyribonucleic* acids, and RNA, *ribonucleic* acids. The molecular weights of isolated DNA molecules range from 6 million to greater than 120 million. RNA molecules have molecular weights from 20,000 to 2 million or more.

DNA contains the purines *adenine* and *guanine* and pyrimidines *cytosine* and *thymine* suspended from *deoxyribose* (a sugar derivative) which, along with *phosphate*, forms the backbone of the DNA polymer.

RNA contains the purines *adenine* and *guanine* and pyrimidines *cytosine* and *uracil* suspended from *ribose* (a five-carbon sugar) which, along with *phosphate*, forms the backbone of the RNA polymer.

Nucleic acids may be considered to be repeating sequences of *nucleotides*. A nucleotide unit consists of a *base (purine or pyrimidine)-sugar-phosphate* complex. A *nucleoside* is a nucleotide without the phosphate member.

2. These represent three kinds of transfer-RNA.

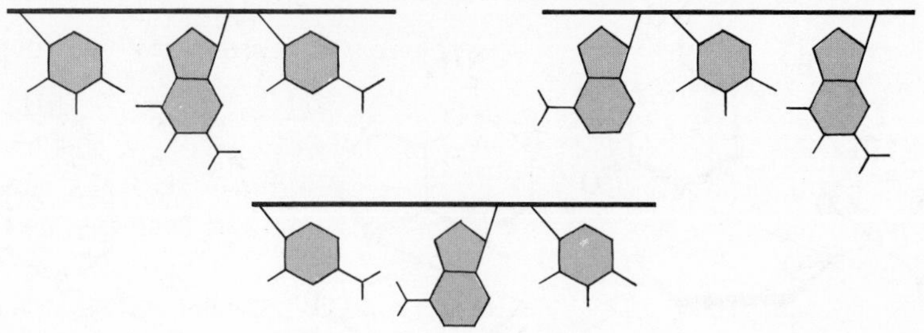

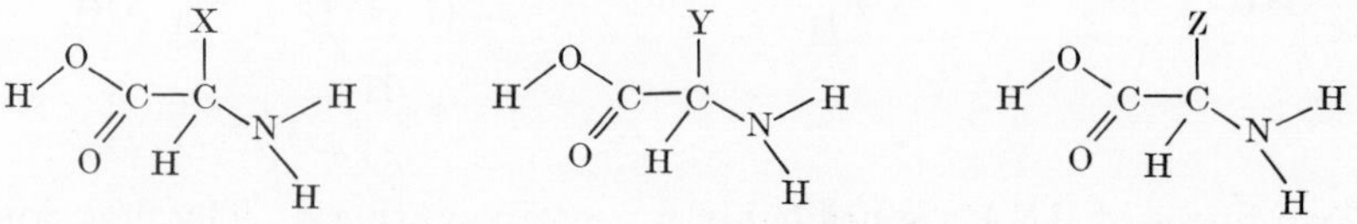

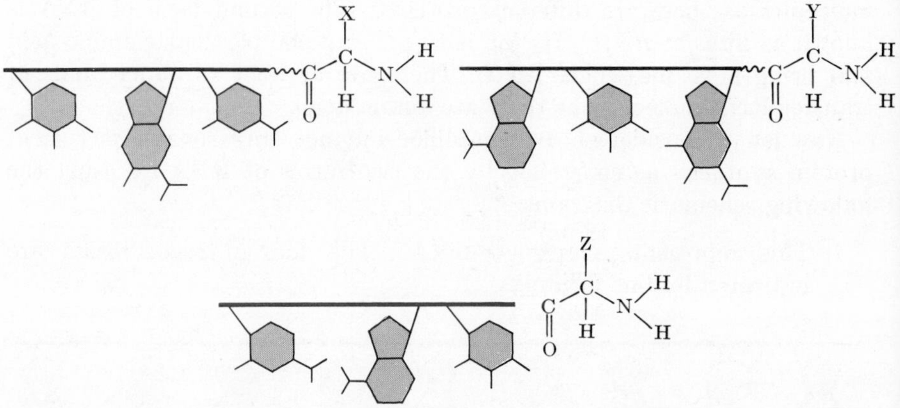

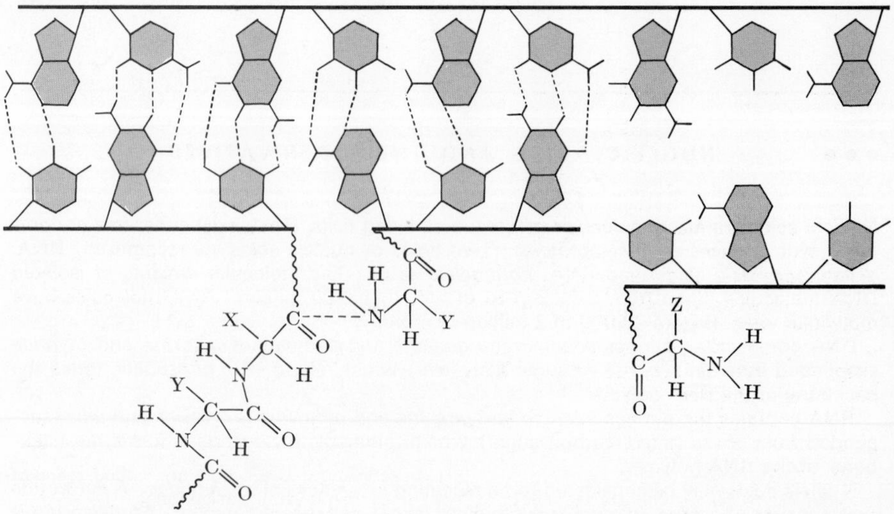

growing polypeptide chain

Note that the transfer-RNA can enter only at certain points. Once in position the amino acids can enter the polypeptide or protein chain.

The two new features which the schematic representation brings out are:

1. There is a complementary relation between pairs of the nitrogen bases. This is brought about by hydrogen bonding. In RNA the complementary pairs are adenine and uracil, guanine and cytosine, as shown in Figure 33.8.

When transfer-RNA brings an amino acid to messenger-RNA, a union between the two RNA molecules occurs only when cytosine is opposite guanine and adenine is opposite uracil at points of contact between the two RNA chains.

2. Transfer-RNA needs three nitrogen bases (known as code triplets) to fix an amino acid. For example, transfer-RNA with three adenine groups will pick up the amino acid phenylalanine,

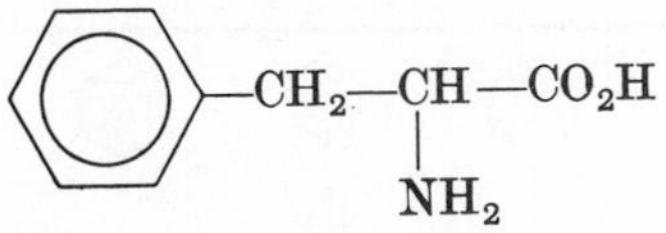

$$\text{C}_6\text{H}_5-\text{CH}_2-\text{CH}-\text{CO}_2\text{H}$$
$$\underset{\text{NH}_2}{|}$$

Code triplets for some other amino acids are given in Table 33.1. Most amino acids respond to more than one code triplet as indicated in the table. This means several different transfer-RNA molecules may be able to pick up a given amino acid.

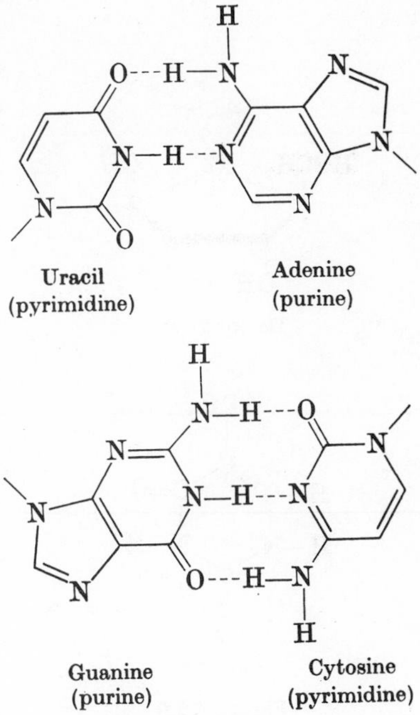

Figure 33.8 The matching pairs of nitrogen bases in RNA showing the alignment through hydrogen bonding.

Table 33.1 RNA Code Triplets Associated with Various Amino Acids

Amino Acids	Code Triplets (C, cytosine; G, guanine; U, uracil; A, adenine)
Alanine, $\text{CH}_3-\text{CH}-\text{CO}_2\text{H}$, NH_2	GCU, GCC, GCA, GCG
Serine, $\text{HOCH}_2-\text{CH}-\text{CO}_2\text{H}$, NH_2	AGU, AGC, UCC, UCU
Leucine, $\text{CH}_3-\text{CH}-\text{CH}_2-\text{CH}-\text{CO}_2\text{H}$, CH_2, NH_2	CUU, CUC, CUA, CUG, UUA, UUG
Tyrosine, 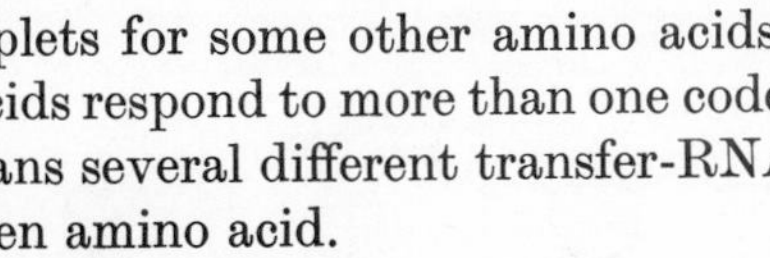 $\text{HO}-\text{C}_6\text{H}_4-\text{CH}_2-\text{CH}-\text{CO}_2\text{H}$, NH_2	UAU, UAC
Proline, 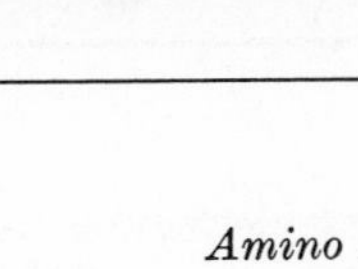 (pyrrolidine)—CO_2H	CCU, CCC, CCA, CCG

Note: These code triplets are associated with messenger-RNA and are called *codons.* Transfer-RNA for a given amino acid contains the corresponding anticodons.

HOCH$_2$ O   OH

OH

Deoxyribose

CH$_3$

H—C   C=O

H—N   N—H

O

Thymine

Figure 33.9

Where Does RNA Get Its Information ? Messenger-RNA is thought to be synthesized in the nucleus of the cell in a manner analogous to the synthesis of proteins just described. However, in this case the template is the gene, a material known as DNA—deoxyribonucleic acid. Chemically, DNA is similar to RNA with two exceptions: (a) DNA contains the sugar deoxyribose (similar to ribose but having one less oxygen atom) instead of ribose, and (b) it contains the pyrimidine thymine instead of uracil (Figure 33.9). A portion of a DNA chain can be represented

—Deoxyribose—Phosphate—Deoxyribose—Phosphate—Deoxyribose—Phosphate
    | | |
  Thymine   Adenine   Cytosine

Apparently DNA is able to line up the appropriate segments of RNA (the so-called nucleotides) along its chain, perhaps in a manner similar to that represented in the scheme

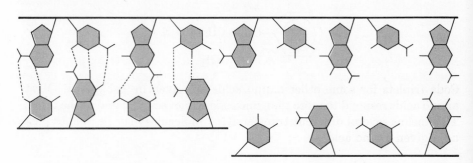

Once in position the nucleotides are linked together by enzymes known as RNA-DNA polymerases to give messenger-RNA. Messenger-RNA leaves the nucleus and finds its way to the ribosomes where it supervises the synthesis of proteins.

DNA—Key to All Life. Molecules of DNA not only carry the chemical code needed to manufacture the proteins which sustain the cell, but they also have the ability to split into two and make exact copies of themselves —a quality essential for cellular reproduction. In essence this means that they make the cell what it is and see to it that new cells are produced in the image of the parent. Evidently DNA molecules are the molecules of life— they define the life processes of the cell, and they go on faithfully reproducing themselves in exactly the same form and generating exactly the same enzymes time after time in immortal splendor.

The secret of DNA's ability to make exact copies of itself over and over again lies, of course, in its structure. Each DNA molecule is a helix composed of two strands of polynucleotides. The two strands are held together by hydrogen bonding between the nitrogen bases. Every adenine unit in one strand is hydrogen bonded to a thymine unit in the other strand, and every cytosine unit in one strand is bonded to a guanine unit in the other. The DNA molecule appears then like a spiral rope ladder, as illustrated in Figure 33.10.

When ready to replicate, the two strands unwind and separate. Each strand rebuilds its missing partner from the nucleotides present in the nucleus of the cell. In the rebuilding process the four nitrogen bases line up in the complementary relation described for RNA. When the rebuilding process is complete, there are two identical DNA molecules where one existed before. On cell division, one of these remains with each daughter cell to pass on the genetic information.

DNA molecules are present in every living cell. Apparently these molecules remain in the nucleus, well protected from potential dangers and shocks more likely in the cytoplasm. The molecular weight of DNA is about 6 million; one molecule may contain 20,000 nucleotides.

One DNA molecule may contain several genes—i.e., several coded sequences each able to make a different RNA molecule. In a complex organism such as man, all the genetic information (DNA) needed to make the full-grown adult is packed into the fertilized human egg and weighs approximately 6×10^{-12} g. The DNA in every human cell contains all the genetic information the fertilized egg contained. One problem now being solved is: Why are cells in a complex organism so different if all contain the same DNA?

Blue Eyes and DNA. The color of eyes, hair, and skin is determined by the amount of pigment called *melanin* (black) present in the pupil of the eye, the hair, or the skin. Melanin is formed from the amino acid tyrosine

$$HO-\bigcirc-CH_2-\underset{\underset{NH_2}{|}}{CH}CO_2H$$

in a series of steps. Each step requires an enzyme, and each enzyme is produced from a specific RNA template. The amount of melanin produced will depend upon the amount of one of the messenger-RNA molecules present. If much of this particular RNA is present, much melanin will be produced; if only a small amount is present, only a small quantity of melanin will result. A DNA molecule in the nucleus of the cell apparently controls the production of this RNA and hence controls the color of the eyes, hair, and skin of the subject. Since the DNA molecule is passed on to the progeny, they will resemble their parents in coloring. Should something happen to the gene responsible for melanin production, none of this pigment will be made and the individual will be an albino.

Viruses and Heredity. A virus is simply a DNA (or RNA) molecule surrounded by a protective protein. When injected into a cell the virus DNA directs the formation of enzymes not previously present in the cell. The cell can then perform chemical reactions not possible previously. Upon cell division the virus DNA will be transmitted to the daughter cells and will then become part of the cell's genetic characteristics. If the chemical process initiated by the virus DNA is harmful to the cell, it could destroy the cell or possibly produce a series of self-destroying cells. This may do great harm to the organism if the infection is not stopped.

If artificial and beneficial viruses could be made, they might be injected into cells and certain genetic defects might be corrected or memory might

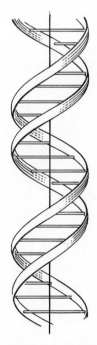

Figure 33.10 The Watson-Crick model of a molecule of DNA. The two ribbons denote the two complementary chains, and the horizontal bars represent the pairs of bases holding the chains together.

be improved. In effect, this is a mechanism for controlling heredity. Scientists everywhere hope that if and when such heredity control is possible, it will be used for the benefit of mankind and not for his derogation. Very recently viruses have been synthesized in the biochemical laboratory.

Evidence for the Role of DNA and RNA. The preceding picture of the chemistry of the cell was presented with no experimental evidence. Actually it would take several volumes to summarize the evidence for what has been condensed in this chapter. However, as an indication of the kind of experiments and reasoning employed by biochemists and microbiologists in this work, the following is presented.

In 1946 Wendell Stanley received a Nobel prize for demonstrating that a chemical substance he had crystallized could be stored indefinitely and on contact with a tobacco plant would produce a viral disease; indeed it would actually multiply in the plant and produce more virus. In effect he showed that a crystalline substance was *infective*, was able to reproduce or to stimulate reproduction of itself. The crystalline substance was found to contain a protein and a nucleic acid.

About 1952, A. D. Hershey and M. Chase grew bacteriophage (bacterial virus) in the presence of radioactive sulfur and radioactive phosphorus. They knew sulfur was present in some amino acids and would therefore be incorporated in the protein portion of the virus. Similarly, phosphorus is a component of nucleic acids so the radioactive phosphorus would be incorporated in the nucleic acid portion of the freshly made virus. They then infected the host cells with the doubly labeled virus and looked for the radioactive sulfur and phosphorus within the cells. They reasoned that if only the radioactive phosphorus were there, then only the nucleic acid penetrated the cell; if only the radioactive sulfur were found, then only the protein penetrated. They found much radioactive phosphorus and only a trace of radioactive sulfur in the contents of the cell; this showed that the nucleic acid DNA alone is the infective material.

Analysis of the purines and pyrimidines of the DNA from various sources, reported about 1952, gave some interesting results. A small sample of these are given in Table 33.2 While the ratios of the two purines or the two pyrimidines varied from source to source, the ratio of the purines to the pyrimidines remained constant at about 1.0.

This, of course, helped J. D. Watson and F. H. C. Crick, in 1953, make their famous postulate concerning the pairing of purines and pyrimidines and enabled them to construct the double-strand model for DNA given in Figure 33.10.

Table 33.2 Analysis of Individual Purines and Pyrimidines in DNA From Several Sources

| SOURCE | MOLAR RATIOS | | |
	Adenine: Guanine	*Thymine: Cytosine*	*Purines: Pyrimidines*
Man (liver)	1.42	1.80	1.09
Ox (thymus)	1.29	1.43	1.1
Sheep (spleen)	1.26	1.36	1.01
Hen (crythrocytes)	1.45	1.29	0.99
Trout (sperm)	1.32	1.36	1.1

M. Meselson and F. W. Stahl in 1958 supported the Watson-Crick postulate by some most ingenious experiments. They grew bacteria on a medium (food) containing a heavy isotope of nitrogen so that all proteins and nucleic acids in the cells became labeled with heavy nitrogen. Then they grew two generations of these bacteria on ordinary nitrogen and isolated the DNA. Using centrifugation, they determined how the heavy nitrogen was distributed among the DNA molecules. Results indicated that half of the DNA molecules had some heavy nitrogen; the other half had only natural nitrogen. This is exactly what Watson and Crick predicted, for as the bacteria with heavy nitrogen multiplied on the natural nitrogen medium, the DNA strands with heavy nitrogen separated and synthesized their complementary strands using natural nitrogen. On analysis their DNA contained strands of heavy nitrogen isotopes and strands containing natural nitrogen isotopes; the two kinds of strands could be separated in the ultracentrifuge.

Finally, we summarize the experiments of A. Kornberg and his group prior to 1957; they found an enzyme which catalyzes the formation of DNA molecules *in vitro* starting from a broth of nucleotides. The synthesis needs two things in order to proceed: (a) all four deoxyribonucleotides must be present, and (b) a pre-existing molecule of DNA must be present. With these available, new DNA molecules similar to the template DNA are synthesized. Even though the enzyme is isolated from bacteria, it will direct the synthesis of human or other DNA molecules, provided only that the appropriate DNA template is present. Evidently it is the DNA molecule that carries the information; the enzyme merely directs the linking together of the nucleotides after they are in the proper order. In 1967, Kornberg reported making the first synthetic virus.

While these are but a few of the many thousands of researches directed toward the chemistry of living cells, they provide some insight into the nature of this very exciting field of science.

SUMMARY

This chapter gives an overview of the chemistry of the living cell. It discusses the views held by most biochemists concerning the role of enzymes, the chemistry of energy conversion within the cell, the function and chemistry of nucleic acids, and the chemical nature of heredity. An indication of the kind of experimental evidence and reasoning employed in developing this picture is given also.

SOME SPECIAL TERMS

Biochemistry	Enzymes	ADP-ATP	Nucleic acids
Living cells	proteins	glycolysis	nucleotides
cytoplasm	carbohydrases	tricarboxylic	messenger-RNA
mitochondria	proteases	acid cycle	transfer-RNA
ribosomes	esterases	coenzyme A	DNA
lysosomes	transferases		ribose
nucleus	transaminases		pyrimidine
	nucleases		purine
			viruses

QUESTIONS AND PROBLEMS

1. Why are enzymes more specific than many other catalysts?
2. What is the substrate of an enzyme?
3. List the five groups of enzymes and summarize the chemistry of each group.
4. Explain why all enzymes are not equally specific.
5. Describe the molecular structure of an enzyme.
6. What is a coenzyme?
7. How can labeled compounds be used to study reactions in cells?
8. What is the importance of ATP in the cell? How is it formed?
9. For every molecule of glucose oxidized to carbon dioxide and water, how many ATP molecules have been used? How many have been formed?
10. When lactic acid is reconverted to glucose, why must some lactic acid be oxidized to carbon dioxide and water?
11. Why is the transformation of pyruvic acid to carbon dioxide and water known as a "cycle"?
12. Which are the energy-producing steps of the tricarboxylic acid cycle? Which steps involve reduction?
13. Which vitamins are involved in the tricarboxylic acid cycle?
14. How are proteins synthesized in the cell?
15. Distinguish between the roles of messenger-RNA and transfer-RNA.
16. In what ways does DNA differ from RNA?
17. What is a gene?
18. Describe the Watson-Crick model for DNA replication.
19. How might the injection of a virus into a living cell change the heredity characteristics of the cell?
20. Design an experimental approach that would establish the RNA code triplets for several amino acids.

REFERENCES

BENZER, S. "The Fine Structures of the Gene," *Scientific American*, vol. *206*, no. 1 (1962), pp. 70–84.

CHANGEUX, J. P. "The Control of Biochemical Reactions," *Scientific American*, vol. *212*, no. 4 (1965), pp. 36–54.

CONN, E. E., and P. K. STUMPF. *Outlines of Biochemistry*, 2nd ed. New York: Wiley, 1967.

CRICK, F. H. C. "The Genetic Code," *Scientific American*, vol. *207*, no. 4 (1962), pp. 66–74.

HOLUM, J. R. *Elements of General and Biological Chemistry*. New York: Wiley, 1962.

HURWITZ, J., and J. J. FURTH. "Messenger RNA," *Scientific American*, vol. *206*, no. 2 (1962), pp. 41–49.

Appendix A

Values of Important Constants

Avogadro's number	N	6.0225×10^{23} molecules mole^{-1}
Boltzmann's constant	k	1.3805×10^{-16} erg °K^{-1} molecule^{-1}
Charge on the electron	e	4.80298×10^{-10} esu
		1.60210×10^{-19} coul
Electron rest mass	m_e	9.1091×10^{-28} g
		0.00055 a.m.u.
Neutron rest mass	m_n	1.6748×10^{-24} g
		1.008665 a.m.u.
Proton rest mass	m_p	1.6725×10^{-24} g
		1.007825 a.m.u.
Planck's constant	h	6.6256×10^{-27} erg sec
Gas constant	R	0.0820541 atm °K^{-1} mole^{-1}
		8.3143 joule °K^{-1} mole^{-1}
		1.9872 cal °K^{-1} mole^{-1}
Faraday's constant	F	9.6487×10^4 coul equivalent^{-1}
Speed of light	c	2.997925×10^{10} cm sec^{-1}

Some Conversion Relationships

ELECTRIC CHARGE

One coulomb (coul) $= 2.778 \times 10^{-4}$ amp-hr
$= 1.036 \times 10^{-6}$ F
$= 2.998 \times 10^9$ statcoul

ELECTRIC DIPOLE MOMENT

One debye $= 1 \times 10^{-18}$ esu-cm
$= 3.33 \times 10^{-20}$ coul × A
$= 0.21$ electron × A

ENERGY AND WORK

(Mass units are included as energy equivalents.)

One erg
$$= 10^{-7} \text{ joule}$$
$$= 2.389 \times 10^{-8} \text{ cal}$$
$$= 6.242 \times 10^{11} \text{ ev}$$
$$= 1.113 \times 10^{-24} \text{ kg}$$
$$= 670.5 \text{ a.m.u.}$$

One calorie (cal)
$$= 4.1840 \times 10^{7} \text{ erg}$$
$$= 4.184 \text{ joule}$$
$$= 2.613 \times 10^{19} \text{ ev}$$
$$= 4.659 \times 10^{-17} \text{ kg}$$
$$= 2.807 \times 10^{10} \text{ a.m.u.}$$

One electron volt (ev)
$$= 1.602 \times 10^{-12} \text{ erg}$$
$$= 1.602 \times 10^{-19} \text{ joule}$$
$$= 3.827 \times 10^{-20} \text{ cal}$$
$$= 1.783 \times 10^{-36} \text{ kg}$$
$$= 1.074 \times 10^{-19} \text{ a.m.u.}$$

One kilogram (kg)
$$= 8.987 \times 10^{23} \text{ erg}$$
$$= 8.987 \times 10^{16} \text{ joule}$$
$$= 2.142 \times 10^{16} \text{ cal}$$
$$= 5.610 \times 10^{35} \text{ ev}$$
$$= 6.025 \times 10^{26} \text{ a.m.u.}$$

One atomic mass unit (a.m.u.)
$$= 1.492 \times 10^{-3} \text{ erg}$$
$$= 1.492 \times 10^{-10} \text{ joule}$$
$$= 3.564 \times 10^{-11} \text{ cal}$$
$$= 9.31 \times 10^{8} \text{ ev}$$
$$= 1.660 \times 10^{-27} \text{ kg}$$

FORCE

One newton (nt)
$$= 10^{5} \text{ dyne}$$
$$= 0.2248 \text{ lb}$$

One pound (lb)
$$= 4.448 \times 10^{5} \text{ dyne}$$
$$= 4.448 \text{ nt}$$

LENGTH

One meter (m)
$$= 39.37 \text{ in.}$$
$$= 3.281 \text{ ft}$$
$$= 6.214 \times 10^{-4} \text{ mi}$$

One inch (in.) $= 2.540 \text{ cm}$

One Angstrom (A) $= 10^{-10} \text{ m}$

One micron $= 10^{-6} \text{ m}$

One light-year $= 9.4600 \times 10^{12} \text{ km}$

Mass and Weight

(Mass-weight equivalents are valid for terrestrial use only.)

One gram (g)
$$= 6.852 \times 10^{-5} \text{ slug}$$
$$= 6.024 \times 10^{23} \text{ a.m.u.}$$
$$= 3.27 \times 10^{-2} \text{ oz}$$
$$= 2.205 \times 10^{-3} \text{ lb}$$

One atomic mass unit (a.m.u.) $= 1.6602 \times 10^{-24} \text{ g}$

One pound (lb) $= 453.6 \text{ g}$

One ton
$$= 2000 \text{ lb}$$
$$= 907.2 \text{ kg}$$

Pressure

One atmosphere (atm)
$$= 1.013 \times 10^6 \text{ dyne/cm}^2$$
$$= 76.0 \text{ cm Hg}$$
$$= 14.70 \text{ lb/in.}^2$$
$$= 2116 \text{ lb/ft}^2$$
$$= 760 \text{ torr}$$

One centimeter mercury (cm Hg)
$$= 1.316 \times 10^{-2} \text{ atm}$$
$$= 1.333 \times 10^4 \text{ dyne/cm}^2$$
$$= 5.353 \text{ in. H}_2\text{O}$$
$$= 0.1934 \text{ lb/in.}^2$$
$$= 27.85 \text{ lb/ft}^2$$

Appendix B

Name	Density*	Melting Point (°C)	Name	Density*	Melting Point (°C)
Aluminum	2.702	660	Mercury (liquid)	13.546	−38.87
Antimony	6.684	630.5	Molybdenum	10.2	2625
Arsenic (metallic)	5.7	814[36 atm]	Nickel	8.90	1452
Barium	3.5	850	Palladium	12.0	1555
Bismuth	9.80	271	Phosphorus (red)	2.20	590[43 atm]
Boron	2.5	2300	Phosphorus (yellow)	1.82	44.1
Bromine (liquid)	3.119	−7.2	Platinum	21.45	1755
Cadmium	8.6	320.9	Potassium	0.86	62.3
Calcium	1.55	810	Radium	5(?)	960(?)
Carbon (diamond)	3.51		Selenium (gray)	4.80	220
Carbon (graphite)	2.26	3500	Silicon	2.4	1420
Chromium	7.1	1615	Silver	10.5	960.5
Cobalt	8.9	1480	Sodium	0.97	97.5
Copper	8.92	1083	Strontium	2.6	800
Gallium	5.91	29.75	Sulfur (monoclinic)	1.96	119.0
Gold	19.3	1063	Sulfur (rhombic)	2.07	112.8
Iodine	4.93	113.5	Tantalum	16.6	2850
Iridium	22.4	2350	Tellurium (metallic)	6.24	452
Iron	7.86	1535	Tin (white, tetragonal)	7.31	231.85
Lead	11.34	327.5	Titanium	4.5	1800
Lithium	0.53	186	Tungsten	19.3	3370
Magnesium	1.74	651	Vanadium	5.96	1710
Manganese	7.2	1260	Zinc	7.14	419.43

* In g/cc at room temperature.

Table 2 Weight in Grams of 1 liter
of Various Gases Under Standard
Conditions ; Boiling Points Under
Pressure of 760 torr

Name	Weight of 1 Liter	Boiling Point (°C)	Name	Weight of 1 Liter	Boiling Point (°C)
Acetylene	1.1621	−83.6	Hydrogen chloride	1.6398	−85.0
Air	1.2930		Hydrogen sulfide	1.5392	−59.6
Ammonia	0.7708	−33.3	Methane	0.7168	−161.4
Argon	1.7824	−185.7	Nitric oxide	1.3402	−151.0
Carbon dioxide	1.9768	sublimes	Nitrogen	1.2506	−195.8
Carbon monoxide	1.2504	−192.0	Nitrous oxide	1.9777	−89.5
Chlorine	3.214	−34.6	Oxygen	1.4290	−183.0
Helium	0.1785	−268.9	Propane	2.0200	−45.0
Hydrogen	0.08987	−252.7	Sulfur dioxide	2.9266	−10.0

Table 3 Vapor Pressure of Water Expressed in Torr (Millimeters of Mercury) (International Critical Tables)

Temperature (°C)	Pressure	Temperature (°C)	Pressure	Temperature (°C)	Pressure
10	9.209	21	18.650	32	35.663
11	9.844	22	19.827	33	37.729
12	10.518	23	21.068	34	39.898
13	11.231	24	22.377	35	42.175
14	11.987	25	23.756	36	44.563
15	12.788	26	25.209	37	47.067
16	13.634	27	26.739	38	49.692
17	14.530	28	28.349	39	52.442
18	15.477	29	30.043	40	55.324
19	16.477	30	31.824	50	92.51
20	17.535	31	33.695	100	760.00

Table 4 The Natural Isotopes of the Elements

Atomic Number	Symbol and Atomic Weight	Natural Isotopes (Mass numbers)	Atomic Number	Symbol and Atomic Weight	Natural Isotopes (Mass Numbers)
1	H 1.0080	1, 2	50	Sn 118.70	120, 118, 116, 119, 117, 124, 122, 112, 114, 115
2	He 4.003	4, 3	51	Sb 121.76	121, 123
3	Li 6.940	7, 6	52	Te 127.61	130, 128, 126, 125, 124, 122, 123, 120
4	Be 9.02	9			
5	B 10.82	11, 10	53	I 126.92	127
6	C 12.010	12, 13	54	Xe 131.3	132, 129, 131, 134, 136, 130, 128, 124, 126
7	N 14.008	14, 15			
8	O 16.000	16, 18, 17	55	Cs 132.91	133
9	F 19.00	19	56	Ba 137.36	138, 137, 136, 135, 134, 130, 132
10	Ne 20.183	20, 22, 21			
11	Na 22.997	23	57	La 138.92	139, 138
12	Mg 24.32	24, 25, 26	58	Ce 140.13	140, 142, 138, 136
13	Al 26.97	27	59	Pr 140.92	141
14	Si 28.06	28, 29, 30	60	Nd 144.27	142, 144, 146, 143, 145, 148, 150
15	P 30.98	31			
16	S 32.06	32, 34, 33, 36	61	Pm	—
17	Cl 35.457	35, 37	62	Sm 150.43	152, 154, 147, 149, 148, 150, 144
18	Ar 39.944	40, 36, 38			
19	K 39.096	39, 41, 40	63	Eu 152.0	153, 151
20	Ca 40.08	40, 44, 42, 48, 43, 46	64	Gd 156.9	158, 160, 156, 157, 155, 154, 152
21	Sc 45.10	45			
22	Ti 47.90	48, 46, 47, 49, 50	65	Tb 159.2	159
23	V 50.95	51, 50	66	Dy 162.46	164, 162, 163, 161, 158, 160
24	Cr 52.01	52, 53, 50, 54	67	Ho 164.94	165
25	Mn 54.93	55			
26	Fe 55.85	56, 54, 57, 58	68	Er 167.2	166, 168, 167, 170, 164, 162
27	Co 58.94	59	69	Tm 169.4	169
28	Ni 58.69	58, 60, 62, 61, 64	70	Yb 173.04	174, 172, 173, 171, 176, 170, 168
29	Cu 63.57	63, 65			
30	Zn 65.38	64, 66, 68, 67, 70	71	La 174.99	175, 176
31	Ga 69.72	69, 71	72	Hf 178.6	180, 178, 177, 179, 176, 174
32	Ge 72.60	74, 72, 70, 73, 76	73	Ta 180.88	181
33	As 74.91	75	74	W 183.92	184, 186, 182, 180
34	Se 78.96	80, 78, 76, 82, 77, 74	75	Re 186.31	187, 185
35	Br 79.916	79, 81	76	Os 190.2	192, 190, 189, 188, 187, 186, 184
36	Kr 83.7	84, 86, 82, 83, 80, 78			
37	Rb 85.48	85, 87	77	Ir 193.1	193, 191
38	Sr 87.63	88, 86, 87, 84	78	Pt 195.23	195, 194, 196, 198, 192, 190
39	Y 88.92	89	79	Au 197.2	197
40	Zr 91.22	90, 94, 92, 91, 96	80	Hg 200.61	202, 200, 199, 201, 198, 204, 196
41	Nb 92.91	93			
42	Mo 95.95	98, 96, 95, 92, 94, 97, 100	81	Tl 204.39	205, 203, 206, 207, 208, 210
43	Tc	—	82	Pb 207.21	208, 206, 207, 204, 210, 211, 212, 214
44	Ru 101.7	102, 104, 101, 99, 100, 96, 98			
45	Rh 102.91	103	83	Bi 209.00	209, 210, 211, 212, 214
46	Pd 106.7	106, 108, 105, 110, 104, 102	84	Po	210, 211, 212, 214, 215, 216, 218
47	Ag 107.880	107, 109			
48	Cd 112.41	114, 112, 111, 110, 113, 116, 106, 108	85	At	218, 215
			86	Rn 222	222, 220, 219
49	In 114.76	115, 113	87	Fr	223

Note: The isotopes of each element are listed in the order of abundance (the most abundant being given first). A dash (—) signifies that the element has no natural isotopes. The table lists only natural isotopes. Approximately 292 natural isotopes and 1375 artificial isotopes are known today.

Table 4
(continued)

Atomic Number	Symbol and Atomic Weight		Natural Isotopes (Mass numbers)	Atomic Number	Symbol and Atomic Weight		Natural Isotopes (Mass Numbers)
88	Ra	226.05	223, 224, 226, 228	96	Cm		—
89	Ac		227, 228	97	Bk		—
90	Th	232.12	227, 228, 230, 231, 232, 234	98	Cf		—
91	Pa	231	231, 234	99	E		—
92	U	238.07	238, 235, 234	100	Fm		—
93	Np	—		101	Mv		—
94	Pu		239	102	No		—
95	Am		—	103	Lw		—

Table 5 Some Standard Oxidation Potentials in Basic Solution (Values in Acid Solution Are Given in Table 23.1)

Half-Reactions	E° Volts
$Ca(s) + 2OH^- \rightleftarrows Ca(OH)_2(s) + 2e^-$	3.03
$K(s) \rightleftarrows K^+ + e^-$	2.93
$Al(s) + 4OH^- \rightleftarrows Al(OH)_4^- + 3e^-$	2.35
$P(s) + 2OH^- \rightleftarrows H_2PO_2^- + e^-$	2.05
$H_2PO_2^- + 3OH^- \rightleftarrows HPO_3^{-2} + 2H_2O + 2e^-$	1.57
$Mn(s) + 2OH^- \rightleftarrows Mn(OH)_2(s) + 2e^-$	1.55
$Zn(s) + 4CN^- \rightleftarrows Zn(CN)_4^{-2} + 2e^-$	1.26
$Zn(s) + 4OH^- \rightleftarrows Zn(OH)_4^{-2} + 2e^-$	1.216
$HPO_3^{-2} + 3OH^- \rightleftarrows PO_4^{-3} + 2H_2O + 2e^-$	1.12
$S_2O_4^{-2} + 4OH^- \rightleftarrows 2SO_3^{-2} + 2H_2O + 2e^-$	1.12
$Zn(s) + 4NH_3 \rightleftarrows Zn(NH_3)_4^{+2} + 2e^-$	1.03
$SO_3^{-2} + 2OH^- \rightleftarrows SO_4^{-2} + H_2O + 2e^-$	0.93
$Sn(OH)_4^{-2} + 2OH^- \rightleftarrows Sn(OH)_6^{-2} + 2e^-$	0.90
$PH_3 + 3OH^- \rightleftarrows P(s) + 3H_2O + 3e^-$	0.89
$H_2 + 2OH^- \rightleftarrows 2H_2O + 2e^-$	0.828
$Ni(s) + 2OH^- \rightleftarrows Ni(OH)_2(s) + 2e^-$	0.72
$AsO_2^- + 4OH^- \rightleftarrows AsO_4^{-3} + 2H_2O + 2e^-$	0.67
$Fe(OH)_2(s) + OH^- \rightleftarrows Fe(OH)_3(s) + e^-$	0.56
$S^{-2} \rightleftarrows S + 2e^-$	0.48
$Cr(OH)_4^- + 4OH^- \rightleftarrows CrO_4^{-2} + 4H_2O + 3e^-$	0.13
$H_2O_2 + 2OH^- \rightleftarrows O_2 + 2H_2O + 2e^-$	0.076
$Mn(OH)_2(s) + 2OH^- \rightleftarrows MnO_2(s) + 2H_2O + 2e^-$	0.05
$Cu(NH_3)_2^+ + 2NH_3 \rightleftarrows Cu(NH_3)_4^{+2} + e^-$	0.0
$Mn(OH)_2(s) + OH^- \rightleftarrows Mn(OH)_3(s) + e^-$	−0.1
$Co(OH)_2(s) + OH^- \rightleftarrows Co(OH)_3(s) + e^-$	−0.17
$I^- + 6OH^- \rightleftarrows IO_3^- + 3H_2O + 6e^-$	−0.26
$ClO_2^- + 2OH^- \rightleftarrows ClO_3^- + H_2O + 2e^-$	−0.33
$ClO_3^- + 2OH^- \rightleftarrows ClO_4^- + H_2O + 2e^-$	−0.36
$4OH^- \rightleftarrows O_2 + 2H_2O + 4e^-$	−0.401
$I^- + 2OH^- \rightleftarrows IO^- + H_2O + 2e^-$	−0.49
$Ni(OH)_2(s) + 2OH^- \rightleftarrows NiO_2(s) + 2H_2O + 2e^-$	−0.49
$MnO_4^{-2} \rightleftarrows MnO_4^- + e^-$	−0.564
$MnO_2(s) + 4OH^- \rightleftarrows MnO_4^- + 2H_2O + 3e^-$	−0.588
$MnO_2(s) + 4OH^- \rightleftarrows MnO_4^{-2} + 2H_2O + 2e^-$	−0.60
$ClO^- + 2OH^- \rightleftarrows ClO_2^- + H_2O + 2e^-$	−0.66
$Br^- + 2OH^- \rightleftarrows BrO^- + H_2O + 2e^-$	−0.76
$2OH^- \rightleftarrows H_2O_2 + 2e^-$	−0.88
$Cl^- + 2OH^- \rightleftarrows ClO^- + H_2O + 2e^-$	−0.89

Ligand	Dissociation Equilibrium	K
NH_3	$Ag(NH_3)_2{}^+ \rightleftarrows Ag^+ + 2NH_3$	6×10^{-8}
	$Cd(NH_3)_4{}^{+2} \rightleftarrows Cd^{+2} + 4NH_3$	2.5×10^{-7}
	$Co(NH_3)_6{}^{+2} \rightleftarrows Co^{+2} + 6NH_3$	1.3×10^{-5}
	$Co(NH_3)_6{}^{+3} \rightleftarrows Co^{+3} + 6NH_3$	2.2×10^{-34}
	$Cu(NH_3)_4{}^{+2} \rightleftarrows Cu^{+2} + 4NH_3$	4.6×10^{-14}
	$Ni(NH_3)_6{}^{+2} \rightleftarrows Ni^{+2} + 6NH_3$	4.8×10^{-8}
	$Zn(NH_3)_4{}^{+2} \rightleftarrows Zn^{+2} + 4NH_3$	2.6×10^{-10}
F^-	$AlF_6{}^{-3} \rightleftarrows Al^{+3} + 6F^-$	1.5×10^{-20}
	$FeF_6{}^{-3} \rightleftarrows Fe^{+3} + 6F^-$	5×10^{-16}
Cl^-	$HgCl_4{}^- \rightleftarrows Hg^{+2} + 4Cl^-$	1.1×10^{-16}
	$SnCl_4{}^{-2} \rightleftarrows Sn^{+2} + 4Cl^-$	3.2×10^{-2}
I^-	$HgI_4{}^- \rightleftarrows Hg^{+2} + 4I^-$	5.3×10^{-21}
	$PbI_3{}^- \rightleftarrows Pb^{+2} + 3I^-$	3.6×10^{-6}
CN^-	$Ag(CN)_2{}^- \rightleftarrows Ag^+ + 2CN^-$	1×10^{-21}
	$Cd(CN)_4{}^{-2} \rightleftarrows Cd^{+2} + 4CN^-$	1.4×10^{-19}
	$Co(CN)_4{}^{-2} \rightleftarrows Co^{+2} + 4CN^-$	7.9×10^{-20}
	$Cu(CN)_2{}^- \rightleftarrows Cu^+ + 2CN^-$	5×10^{-28}
	$Fe(CN)_6{}^{-4} \rightleftarrows Fe^{+2} + 6CN^-$	1×10^{-35}
	$Fe(CN)_6{}^{-3} \rightleftarrows Fe^{+3} + 6CN^-$	1×10^{-42}
	$Hg(CN)_4{}^{-2} \rightleftarrows Hg^{+2} + 4CN^-$	4×10^{-42}
	$Pb(CN)_4{}^{-2} \rightleftarrows Pb^{+2} + 4CN^-$	5×10^{-11}
	$Ni(CN)_4{}^{-2} \rightleftarrows Ni^{+2} + 4CN^-$	1×10^{-22}
	$Zn(CN)_4{}^{-2} \rightleftarrows Zn^{+2} + 4CN^-$	1.3×10^{-17}
SCN^-	$FeSCN^{+2} \rightleftarrows Fe^{+3} + SCN^-$	1×10^{-3}
$SO_3{}^{-2}$	$Ag(SO_3)_2{}^{-3} \rightleftarrows Ag^+ + 2SO_3{}^{-2}$	3×10^{-9}
$S_2O_3{}^{-2}$	$Ag(S_2O_3)_2{}^{-3} \rightleftarrows Ag^+ + 2S_2O_3{}^{-2}$	6×10^{-14}

Table 6 Instability Constants of Complex Ions

Compound	Solubility Product	K_{sp}
Aluminum hydroxide	$[Al^{+3}] \times [OH^-]^3$	5×10^{-33}
Barium carbonate	$[Ba^{+2}] \times [CO_3{}^{-2}]$	1.6×10^{-9}
Barium chromate	$[Ba^{+2}] \times [CrO_4{}^{-2}]$	8.5×10^{-11}
Barium sulfate	$[Ba^{+2}] \times [SO_4{}^{-2}]$	1.0×10^{-10}
Barium oxalate	$[Ba^{+2}] \times [C_2O_4{}^{-2}]$	1.5×10^{-8}
Bismuth sulfide	$[Bi^{+3}]^2 \times [S^{-2}]^3$	1×10^{-70}
Cadmium hydroxide	$[Cd^{+2}] \times [OH^-]^2$	2×10^{-14}
Cadmium sulfide	$[Cd^{+2}] \times [S^{-2}]$	6×10^{-27}
Calcium carbonate	$[Ca^{+2}] \times [CO_3{}^{-2}]$	6.9×10^{-9}
Calcium oxalate	$[Ca^{+2}] \times [C_2O_4{}^{-2}]$	1.3×10^{-9}
Calcium sulfate	$[Ca^{+2}] \times [SO_4{}^{-2}]$	2.4×10^{-5}
Chromium hydroxide	$[Cr^{+3}] \times [OH^-]^3$	7×10^{-31}
Cobalt sulfide	$[Co^{+2}] \times [S^{-2}]$	5×10^{-22}
Cupric hydroxide	$[Cu^{+2}] \times [OH^-]^2$	1.6×10^{-19}
Cupric sulfide	$[Cu^{+2}] \times [S^{-2}]$	4×10^{-36}
Ferric hydroxide	$[Fe^{+3}] \times [OH^-]^3$	6×10^{-38}
Ferrous hydroxide	$[Fe^{+2}] \times [OH^-]^2$	2×10^{-15}
Ferrous sulfide	$[Fe^{+2}] \times [S^{-2}]$	4×10^{-17}
Lead carbonate	$[Pb^{+2}] \times [CO_3{}^{-2}]$	1.5×10^{-13}
Lead chromate	$[Pb^{+2}] \times [CrO_4{}^{-2}]$	2×10^{-16}
Lead iodide	$[Pb^{+2}] \times [I^-]^2$	8.3×10^{-9}
Lead sulfate	$[Pb^{+2}] \times [SO_4{}^{-2}]$	1.3×10^{-8}
Lead sulfide	$[Pb^{+2}] \times [S^{-2}]$	4×10^{-26}
Magnesium carbonate	$[Mg^{+2}] \times [CO_3{}^{-2}]$	4×10^{-5}

Table 7 Some Solubility Products at 20°C

Table 7 (continued)

Compound	Solubility Product	K_{sp}
Magnesium hydroxide	$[Mg^{+2}] \times [OH^-]^2$	8.9×10^{-12}
Magnesium oxalate	$[Mg^{+2}] \times [C_2O_4^{-2}]$	8.6×10^{-5}
Manganese hydroxide	$[Mn^{+2}] \times [OH^-]^2$	2×10^{-13}
Manganese sulfide	$[Mn^{+2}] \times [S^{-2}]$	8×10^{-14}
Mercurous chloride	$[Hg_2^{+2}] \times [Cl^-]^2$	1.1×10^{-18}
Mercuric sulfide	$[Hg^{+2}] \times [S^{-2}]$	1×10^{-50}
Nickel hydroxide	$[Ni^{+2}] \times [OH^-]^2$	1.6×10^{-16}
Nickel sulfide	$[Ni^{+2}] \times [S^{-2}]$	1×10^{-22}
Silver arsenate	$[Ag^+]^3 \times [AsO_4^{-3}]$	1×10^{-23}
Silver bromide	$[Ag^+] \times [Br^-]$	5×10^{-13}
Silver carbonate	$[Ag^+]^2 \times [CO_3^{-2}]$	8.2×10^{-12}
Silver chloride	$[Ag^+] \times [Cl^-]$	2.8×10^{-10}
Silver chromate	$[Ag^+]^2 \times [CrO_4^{-2}]$	1.9×10^{-12}
Silver iodate	$[Ag^+] \times [IO_3^-]$	3×10^{-8}
Silver iodide	$[Ag^+] \times [I^-]$	8.5×10^{-17}
Silver phosphate	$[Ag^+]^3 \times [PO_4^{-3}]$	1.8×10^{-18}
Silver sulfide	$[Ag^+]^2 \times [S^{-2}]$	1×10^{-50}
Stannous sulfide	$[Sn^{+2}] \times [S^{-2}]$	1×10^{-24}
Zinc hydroxide	$[Zn^{+2}] \times [OH^-]^2$	5×10^{-17}
Zinc sulfide	$[Zn^{+2}] \times [S^{-2}]$	1×10^{-20}

Appendix C

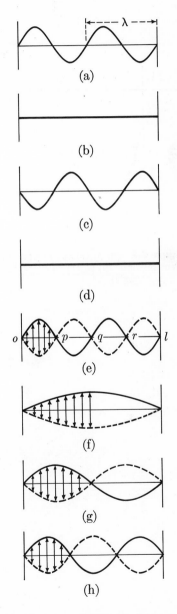

Wave Motion and Wave Functions

A string stretched between two points can undergo vibrations about its straight position. The motion is periodic in time, and also periodic with distance along the string. Parts (a), (b), (c), and (d) of Figure C.1 represent one type of motion—at the beginning of a cycle, one-fourth of the way through, one-half of the way through, and three-fourths of the way through. At $t = T$ the string will have completed a full cycle, and will look like (a) again. Part (e) shows the maximum displacements [from parts (a) and (c)] and illustrates the way in which individual particles of the string undergo a simple straight-line vibratory motion between these two extremes. The distance these particles travel in their up-and-down motion is known as the amplitude of their vibrations; the figure shows that the amplitude of a particle depends upon its position along the string; particles at the *nodes* o, p, q, r, and l do not move at all. Since the string is fixed at each end, points o and l must always be nodes; hence the vibrations must always be such that the wavelength λ is equal to $2l/n$, where n is an integer. Parts (a) to (e) correspond to $n = 4$; parts (f) to (h) show some other patterns.

The assumption of De Broglie that electrons can be represented as waves means that they can be described in terms of electromagnetic waves. The amplitudes corresponding to the particle motion of parts (e) to (h) correspond to values of the electric and magnetic components of the electron waves (see Figure 4.3). The forces of tension in the vibrating string are analogous, for electrons in atoms, to the forces between electrons and nucleus. The constraints exerted on the motion by tying the string at both ends are analogous to the requirement that these waves be standing waves, with nodes which are fixed in space and unchanging in time.

The mathematics requires the solution of a complex differential equation known as the Schrödinger equation, which relates the amplitude of the electric and magnetic field to the distance and direction from the nucleus, just as the amplitudes of the string particles' motion are a function of the distance along the string. The wave function, denoted by ψ, is the solution to the Schrödinger equation, and is itself a mathematical equation which describes how the amplitude of the wave varies with distance (and direction). Just as the string can vibrate only for integral values of n, so the

Figure C.1 (a) at $t = 0$; (b) at $t = \frac{1}{4}T$; (c) at $t = \frac{1}{2}T$; (d) at $t = \frac{3}{4}T$; (e) vibratory motion of particles in the string; (f) $n = 1$; (g) $n = 2$; (h) $n = 3$.

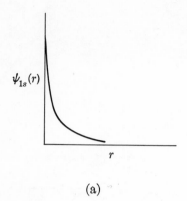

(a)

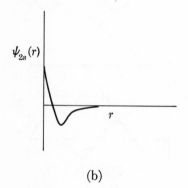

(b)

Figure C.2 (a) $\psi_{1s}(r)$ as a function of r (schematic). (b) $\psi_{2s}(r)$ as a function of r (schematic).

wave equation has solutions, for electrons as waves in atoms, only for integral values of three quantum numbers—three because the amplitudes vary in three dimensions, rather than in the one dimension from o to l.

The results of the calculations are simplest for the case of the hydrogen atom, with its single electron, and, for this atom, the simplest wave functions are those for quantum numbers l and m equal to zero. Then ψ is a function only of r, the distance from the nucleus, and of the principal quantum number, n. We find for

$$n = 1, l = 0, m = 0: \qquad \psi_{1s} = \left(\frac{1}{\sqrt{\pi}}\right)\left(\frac{1}{a_o}\right)^{3/2} e^{-r/a_o}$$

For

$$n = 2, l = 0, m = 0: \qquad \psi_{2s} = \left(\frac{1}{4\sqrt{2\pi}}\right)\left(\frac{1}{a_o}\right)^{3/2}\left(2 - \frac{r}{a_o}\right)e^{-r/2a_o}$$

where a_o is the constant representing the radius of the first Bohr orbit. These two functions are plotted in Figure C.2 (a) and (b); ψ_{1s} shows no node (except at $r = \infty$); ψ_{2s} shows one node, at $r = 2a_o$.

The general expression for the wave function for the s states ($l = 0$) of hydrogen is

$$\psi_{ns}(r) = -\frac{1}{2\sqrt{\pi}}\sqrt{\left(\frac{2}{na_o}\right)^3 \frac{(n-1)!}{2n[n!]^3}}\, e^{-r/na_o}\, \mathrm{L}_n^1\left(\frac{2r}{na_o}\right)$$

where

$$\mathrm{L}_n^1\left(\frac{2r}{na_o}\right)$$

is the abbreviation for a polynomial of the form

$$\mathrm{L}_n^1\left(\frac{2r}{na_o}\right) = (-1)^n n\left\{\left(\frac{2r}{na_o}\right)^{n-1} - n(n-1)\left(\frac{2r}{na_o}\right)^{n-2}\right.$$
$$+ \frac{n(n-1)(n-1)(n-2)}{2!}\left(\frac{2r}{na_o}\right)^{n-3}$$
$$\left. - \frac{n(n-1)(n-2)(n-1)(n-2)(n-3)}{3!}\left(\frac{2r}{na_o}\right)^{n-4} + \cdots\right\}$$

Neither of these expressions is important for the student except to show the specific dependence of the hydrogen wave function upon the quantum number n. The energies for these states are given by

$$E = -\frac{2\pi^2 me^4}{n^2 h^2}$$

The quantum numbers n (and l and m) thus appear naturally in the solutions of the wave equation, and determine the energy levels and the forms of the wave function appropriate to those levels.

Appendix D

Band Theory of Metals

Previous discussion has suggested that the valence electrons in metals are free to move and that this freedom explains the high conductivity of metals. The amount of current carried increases with increase in the potential difference across the ends of the conductor, so that, to make the explanation consistent, it must be assumed that the electrons move faster, permitting more charge to reach the end of the conductor in unit time. Continuing the argument, we note that this requires that the electrons have translational energies, and that these translational energies can increase continuously as the potential difference across the ends increases. Quantum theory predicts, however, that the energy of a system can only increase in quantum jumps from one energy level to another, and we know, from our experience with light absorption by atoms, that the energy separation between one electron level and another is quite large. How then can the electrons in metals change their energies so readily and by continuous increments?

The answer is given by the band theory of metals. Consider as an example sodium atoms each with its single 3s valence electron. When the atoms are far apart, the energy of the 3s electrons can be considered to be the same for all atoms. As the atoms approach each other, moving toward the final internuclear distances of the sodium crystal, these levels split, so that some 3s levels are higher and some lower than in the isolated atom. The situation is somewhat similar to that envisioned in the molecular orbital theory discussion (Figure 6.18) in which two identical levels, one on each atom, separate into bonding σ orbitals and antibonding σ^* orbitals as the nuclei of two atoms approach to form a diatomic molecule. Note that there still appear, in the diatomic molecule, as many levels (two, σ and σ^*) as there were levels (two) in the two isolated atoms. In a metal crystal there are many more than two atoms, and the number of energy levels is increased correspondingly, so that in a small bit of sodium weighing a milligram or so there will be as many as 10^{19} levels of different energy which can be traced back to the 3s levels of the same energy in the

701

10^{19} isolated atoms which have come together to form the crystal. The spacing between these levels is very small, so that very small increments of energy—corresponding to very small changes in potential difference, for example—can push the electron from one level to the next.

The group of closely spaced levels in the metal, derived from a single level in the isolated atom, is known as an energy band. Each energy level within the band can contain two electrons, but not more than two, and, if two, they must, according to the Pauli principle, have opposite spins. As usual in filling energy levels, those of lowest energy fill first, so that, in the sodium crystal, the single $3s$ electrons contributed by each atom are just sufficient to fill the lower half of the levels in the $3s$ band. This fact is important, because it means that there are many empty levels available in the band for one of the valence electrons to move to, by absorption of small amounts of energy; an electron cannot move into a level already filled with its quota of two.

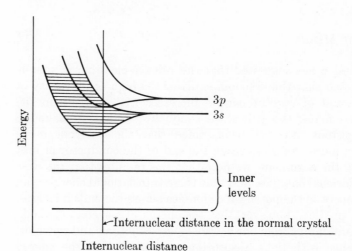

Figure D.1 Energy bands in a metal.

The $3s$ levels of sodium atoms produce one band in the crystal; the $3p$ levels produce other bands, and similarly for other energy levels within the atoms. The separation of the highest and the lowest levels in the bands, and the separation between bands, depend upon the nature of the elements in the crystal, the structure and directions in the crystal, and the internuclear distances. The situation for sodium is sketched diagrammatically in Figure D.1. One imagines that the nuclei of all the atoms in the crystal, originally at large distances from each other, are brought closer and closer together. The highest and the lowest levels at each distance are marked by the heavy lines, and the closeness of spacing of the individual levels is suggested by the horizontal lines in the $3s$ band. At the distances shown, the $1s$, $2s$, and $2p$ levels have not separated into bands; the inner electrons occupying those levels are still under the control only of their own nuclei. To use an earlier wording, they have not been contributed to the community.

Note that, in sodium, there is considerable overlapping of the bands at the internuclear distance. This means that electrons occupying either s or p levels in this overlapping region may easily transfer from one band to

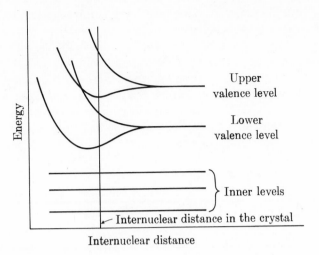

Figure D.2 Energy bands in an insulator.

another. For other substances, this is not necessarily the case. The corresponding figure for a typical insulator, for example, might look like Figure D.2. Here, at the internuclear distance in the crystal, there is still an appreciable energy separation between the highest level of the lower band and the lowest level of the upper. Even though the levels of the upper band were empty, and receptive to electrons from below, the energy requirement to lift electrons across the "forbidden" zone from the lower band to the higher band is so large that practically no electrons make the transition. If the substance has just enough valence electrons to fill all the levels of the lower band, so that no easy transfer of electrons from filled to empty levels within that band is possible, then the substance acts as an insulator, since no electrons can make the large jump from the lower band to the free spaces of the upper band.

In a few cases, the height of the forbidden zone, although large with respect to separation between levels within the band, is still not so large that some electrons, perhaps thermally excited, cannot move into the upper band. Once there, they are free to accept small amounts of energy and become conduction electrons. This is an explanation of the behavior of one of the types of semi-conductors, which show an increase in conductivity with increase in temperature. As more electrons are thermally excited, they cross the forbidden zone and contribute to the conduction.

Appendix E

Balancing Oxidation-Reduction Equations

The Oxidation-State Method. Having discovered what element is oxidized and what element reduced, we may write and balance the equation for an oxidation-reduction reaction. The rule is that *the total change in the oxidation state of one element must be equal and opposite to the total change in the oxidation state of another*. This corresponds to the statement that for any oxidation there must be an equal amount of reduction and to the statement that the number of electrons gained in the reduction must equal the number lost in the oxidation. The same rule is followed in balancing net ionic equations.

Example. Balance the equation for the reaction

$$\overset{\text{change of } -V}{\overbrace{KMnO_4 + NaCl + H_2SO_4 \longrightarrow Cl_2 + K_2SO_4 + MnSO_4 + H_2O + Na_2SO_4}} \quad (1)$$

$$\underset{\text{change of I}}{\underbrace{}}$$

The changes in oxidation state of manganese and chlorine are indicated. The total change for chlorine must be V to equal the total change for manganese; this will require five chlorine atoms, or 5NaCl. However, chlorine appears as Cl_2 in the products, so that 5NaCl could form only $2\frac{1}{2} Cl_2$. In order to balance the equation, therefore, we can multiply by two, so that we have 10NaCl and $5Cl_2$. This makes a total oxidation-state change for chlorine of 10; so we must also multiply $KMnO_4$ by two to give $2KMnO_4 \rightarrow 2MnSO_4$, with a total oxidation-state change of -10. With these figures the equation is

$$2KMnO_4 + 10NaCl + H_2SO_4 \longrightarrow$$
$$5Cl_2 + K_2SO_4 + 2MnSO_4 + H_2O + Na_2SO_4 \quad (2)$$

The remainder of the equation may now be balanced by inspection. There are eight oxygen atoms in the $2KMnO_4$, which evidently appear as H_2O, so there must be $8H_2O$ in the products. To supply the sixteen hydrogen atoms (in $8H_2O$) we need $8H_2SO_4$. When three of the eight sulfate ions have been used for $K_2SO_4 + 2MnSO_4$, the other five appear in $5Na_2SO_4$, which includes the ten sodium atoms from $10NaCl$, and the equation is balanced.

$$2KMnO_4 + 10NaCl + 8H_2SO_4 \longrightarrow$$
$$5Cl_2 + K_2SO_4 + 2MnSO_4 + 8H_2O + 5Na_2SO_4 \quad (3)$$

Balancing Net Ionic Equations. It has been pointed out (Chap. 3) that there is a great advantage in writing equations in ionic form where ions are involved. For example, the equation just shown is equally—in fact, more nearly—correct when written

$$2MnO_4^- + 10Cl^- + 16H_3O^+ \longrightarrow 5Cl_2 + 2Mn^{+2} + 24H_2O \qquad (4)$$

since the K^+, Na^+, and SO_4^{-2} ions take no actual part in the reaction. The question now arises, Can we write this equation directly without going through the molecular form? The answer is yes, and the process we use is less complicated than the other form, provided we keep track of the charges on the ions. The steps are as follows:

1. Write down the correct symbols or formulas for the reactants and products (without regard to water or its ions). For this reaction we would have

$$MnO_4^- + Cl^- \longrightarrow Mn^{+2} + Cl_2 \qquad (5)$$

This much must be known, namely, that the MnO_4^- ion, when it acts as an oxidizing agent in acid solution, yields Mn^{+2}, and that the chloride ion, when oxidized, yields Cl_2. From this point the equation may be balanced by a systematic procedure.

2. Check oxidation states. Manganese is VII in MnO_4^-, II in Mn^{+2}; chlorine is $-I$ in Cl^-, 0 in Cl_2; there is a change of $-V$ for manganese and I for chlorine.

3. Balance oxidation against reduction. This requires a ratio of $5Cl^-$ to $1MnO_4^-$. So we write

$$2MnO_4^- + 10Cl^- \longrightarrow 2Mn^{+2} + 5Cl_2 \qquad (6)$$

4. Balance charges. An ionic equation must balance electrically as well as chemically. Since this reaction takes place in aqueous solution, we may assume that water and its ions are involved. Note that, as the equation now stands, there are twelve minus charges on the left and four plus charges on the right. We can balance charges either by adding $16H_3O^+$ on the left or $16OH^-$ on the right. Since the reaction takes place in the presence of acid, the former balancing is preferred, and the equation becomes

$$2MnO_4^- + 10Cl^- + 16H_3O^+ \longrightarrow 2Mn^{+2} + 5Cl_2 \qquad (7)$$

5. Complete the material balance. A final examination now shows an excess of 48 hydrogen atoms and 24 oxygen atoms on the left. Presumably 24 molecules of water are formed, and the equation is complete.

$$2MnO_4^- + 10Cl^- + 16H_3O^+ \longrightarrow 2Mn^{+2} + 5Cl_2 + 24H_2O \qquad (8)$$

The Half-Reaction Method. A useful plan to follow is first to write the half-reaction equations, showing the gain or loss of electrons, and then adjust the number of molecules or ions involved so that the number of electrons gained by the oxidizing agent is equal to the number lost by the reducing agent. In writing the half-reaction equations for reactions which take place in solution, water and its ions (the hydronium ion and the hydroxyl ion) may be used at will as reagents, since they are always present. Of course, as with any reaction, the products of the reaction must be known before the equation can be written.

Example. When hydrochloric acid is added to potassium permanganate, chlorine is formed.

Step 1. The products of the reaction are the manganese ion (Mn^{+2}), chlorine, and perhaps water; the reactants are the permanganate ion (MnO_4^-), the hydronium ion, and the chloride ion.

Step 2. The half-reaction equation for the oxidation is simply

$$2Cl^- \longrightarrow Cl_2 + 2e^- \tag{9}$$

The reduction involves the addition of electrons to permanganate ion

$$5e^- + MnO_4^- \longrightarrow Mn^{+2} \tag{10}$$

This is not balanced with respect to the atoms present, since no oxygen-containing substance appears on the right. To correct this, add hydronium ions to the left and water to the right, and balance materially:

$$5e^- + MnO_4^- + 8H_3O^+ \longrightarrow Mn^{+2} + 12H_2O \tag{11}$$

Step 3. The balanced half-reaction equations must now be made to correspond with each other. Since two electrons appear as products and five as reactants, it is evident that a total of ten electrons (least common multiple) must be transferred, or

$$10Cl^- \longrightarrow 5Cl_2 + 10e^- \tag{12}$$

$$10e^- + 2MnO_4^- + 16H_3O^+ \longrightarrow 2Mn^{+2} + 24H_2O \tag{13}$$

and adding,

$$10Cl^- + 2MnO_4^- + 16H_3O^+ \longrightarrow 5Cl_2 + 2Mn^{+2} + 24H_2O \tag{14}$$

Equation (14) is the balanced ionic equation for the oxidation of chloride ions by permanganate ions in an acid solution.

Appendix F

Answers to Odd-Numbered Problems

Chapter 1

Problem 19	(a) 1.06 qt
	(b) 4.72 cc
	(c) 28.35 g
Problem 21	(a) 2.0 cm
	(b) 1.5×10^2 g
Problem 23	3.21×10^3 tons

Chapter 2

Problem 7	6.41×10^{-9} erg	
	or 4×10^3 ev (hint $\rightarrow$ 1 volt $\cdot$ coul = 1 joule)	
Problem 9	$_1^2$H	3.4×10^{-24} g = 2.0 a.m.u
	$_1^3$H	5.2×10^{-24} g = 3.1 a.m.u
Problem 11	Bi	3.47×10^{-22} g
	Au	3.27×10^{-22} g
	Tm	2.81×10^{-22} g
	Pr	2.34×10^{-22} g
	Cs	2.21×10^{-22} g
	I	2.11×10^{-22} g

Chapter 3

Problem 3	(a) 2×10^{23}
	(b) 2.4×10^{24}
	(c) 1.5×10^{23}
	(d) 5.97×10^{22}
	(e) 4.5×10^{23}
	(f) 6.0×10^{24}

Problem 5	(a) 8.0 g
	(b) 14 g
	(c) 28 g
	(d) 40 g
	(e) 1.1×10^2 g
	(f) 4.1×10^2 g

Problem 7	(a) 2×10^1 g
	(b) 4.1×10^3 g
	(c) 7×10^2 g
	(d) 6×10^2 g
	(e) 2×10^{-4} g

Problem 9	(a) N_2O
	(b) CuO
	(c) CO
	(d) $KClO_3$
	(e) HCN

Problem 11	$CHCl_3$

Problem 13	(a) 1 mole NH_3 = 17 g
	(b) 2/7 mole and 10 g H_2O
	(c) 3 moles NH_3 and 6 moles H_2O
	(d) 1.63×10^3 g NO_2
	249 g H_2

Problem 15	$2C_2H_6 + 7O_2 \rightarrow 4CO_2 + 6H_2O$

Problem 17	5.00 moles Na_2CO_3 = 530 g Na_2CO_3

Problem 19	(a) 616 g CO_2
	288 g H_2O
	(b) O_2, 8 moles

Chapter 4

Problem 3	(a) 1.79×10^5 joules
	(b) 2.07×10^5 joules
	(c) 2.67×10^5 joules
	(d) 7.79×10^8 joules

Problem 11	(a) 32
	(b) 14
	(c) 18

Problem 15	(a) Be
	(b) B
	(c) P

Chapter 6

Problem 15	1.5 A

Chapter 7

Problem 11	(a) $+6$
	(b) $+5$
	(c) -3
	(d) $+4$
	(e) $+5$
	(f) $+4$
	(g) $+5$
	(h) 0
Problem 15	0.31 g
Problem 19	3.2×10^2

Chapter 8

Problem 9	35 g
Problem 15	(a) 43.38%
	(b) 38.27%

Chapter 9

Problem 9	10 g

Chapter 10

Problem 9	(a) 20.1%
	(b) 14.4%
	(c) 7.76%

Chapter 12

Problem 7	O_2	4.82×10^4 cm/sec
	H_2	1.93×10^5 cm/sec
	SO_2	3.41×10^4 cm/sec
Problem 13	175 cc	
Problem 15	6.19 liters	
Problem 17	$970°K = 697°C$	
Problem 19	1.20×10^{23}	

Chapter 13

Problem 9	650 g

Chapter 14

Problem 3	181.5 kcal/mole	
Problem 7	(a)(i)	$P_A = 20$ torr
		$P_B = 90$ torr
		$P_T = 110$ torr
	(a)(ii)	$P_A = 60$ torr
		$P_B = 30$ torr
		$P_T = 90$ torr

Problem 13	KCl	0.2
	$CaCl_2$	0.1
	K^+	0.2
	Ca^{+2}	0.1
	Cl^-	0.4

Problem 15   (b)

Problem 17   76

Problem 19 O_2 .992 cm³
N_2 1.864 cm³
$\dfrac{[O_2] \text{ in normal air}}{[O_2] \text{ in dissolved air}}$ $\dfrac{8.93 \times 10^{-3}}{4.43 \times 10^{-4}}$
O_2/N_2, dissolved air 0.53; normal air 0.25

Chapter 15

Problem 9 $18°6'$

Chapter 20

Problem 5 7.8×10^3 cal/g°C

Problem 7 -32.74 kcal/mole

Problem 9 -196 kcal/mole

Problem 11 159.5 kcal/mole

Problem 15 $+42.6$ kcal/mole

Chapter 21

Problem 3 $K_{Aver.} = 54.7$

Problem 7 $K = 1 \times 10^{-21}$ and $[S^{-2}] = 1 \times 10^{-22}\ M$

Problem 9 4×10^{-5}

Problem 11 10^{-14}

Problem 19 3.6×10^{-9}

Problem 21 3.0×10^{-6}

Problem 23 $1.0 \times 10^{-2}\ M$

Problem 25   (a) $3 \leq pH \leq 6$
(b) $3 \leq pH \leq 7$

Problem 29 11.7

Chapter 22

Problem 11 $-22,768$ cal

Problem 13 -10.6 kcal

Problem 15	ΔH	7.37 kcal
	ΔE	6.67 kcal
	ΔS	20.9 cal

Problem 19   (a) *at 450°C*:

P_{O_2} = 270 torr
P_{Hg} = 540 torr
K_p = 1.79 × 10⁻¹

at 420°C:

P_{O_2} = 129 torr
P_{Hg} = 258 torr
K_p = 1.96 × 10⁻²

(b) 7.4 g

Chapter 23

Problem 7	6.02 × 10²³
Problem 13	1.13 volt
Problem 15	5.0 × 10²⁵

Chapter 24

Problem 5	1020 min
	17 hr
Problem 15	1st

Chapter 25

Problem 7	V_{He}/V_U = 1.7 × 10⁻²
	r_{He}/r_U = 2.6 × 10⁻¹
Problem 15	333

Chapter 26

Problem 7	3

Chapter 27

Problem 7	9.30°C
	3.72
	5.58
	7.44
	7.44
	7.44

Index

Index

D E F G H I J 5 4 3 2 1 7 0 6 9

TABLE OF RELATIVE ATOMIC WEIGHTS (Based on the Atomic Mass of $^{12}C = 12$)

Name	Symbol	Atomic Number	Atomic Weight	Name	Symbol	Atomic Number	Atomic Weight
Actinium	Ac	89	....	Mercury	Hg	80	200.59
Aluminum	Al	13	26.9815	Molybdenum	Mo	42	95.94
Americium	Am	95	....	Neodymium	Nd	60	144.24
Antimony	Sb	51	121.75	Neon	Ne	10	20.183
Argon	Ar	18	39.948	Neptunium	Np	93	....
Arsenic	As	33	74.9216	Nickel	Ni	28	58.71
Astatine	At	85	....	Niobium	Nb	41	92.906
Barium	Ba	56	137.34	Nitrogen	N	7	14.0067
Berkelium	Bk	97	....	Nobelium	No	102	....
Beryllium	Be	4	9.0122	Osmium	Os	76	190.2
Bismuth	Bi	83	208.980	Oxygen	O	8	15.9994*
Boron	B	5	10.811*	Palladium	Pd	46	106.4
Bromine	Br	35	79.909†	Phosphorus	P	15	30.9738
Cadmium	Cd	48	112.40	Platinum	Pt	78	195.09
Calcium	Ca	20	40.08	Plutonium	Pu	94	....
Californium	Cf	98	....	Polonium	Po	84	....
Carbon	C	6	12.01115*	Potassium	K	19	39.102
Cerium	Ce	58	140.12	Praseodymium	Pr	59	140.907
Cesium	Cs	55	132.905	Promethium	Pm	61	....
Chlorine	Cl	17	35.453†	Protactinium	Pa	91	....
Chromium	Cr	24	51.996†	Radium	Ra	88	....
Cobalt	Co	27	58.9332	Radon	Rn	86	....
Copper	Cu	29	63.54	Rhenium	Re	75	186.2
Curium	Cm	96	....	Rhodium	Rh	45	102.905
Dysprosium	Dy	66	162.50	Rubidium	Rb	37	85.47
Einsteinium	Es	99	....	Ruthenium	Ru	44	101.07
Erbium	Er	68	167.26	Samarium	Sm	62	150.35
Europium	Eu	63	151.96	Scandium	Sc	21	44.956
Fermium	Fm	100	....	Selenium	Se	34	78.96
Fluorine	F	9	18.9984	Silicon	Si	14	28.086*
Francium	Fr	87	....	Silver	Ag	47	107.870†
Gadolinium	Gd	64	157.25	Sodium	Na	11	22.9898
Gallium	Ga	31	69.72	Strontium	Sr	38	87.62
Germanium	Ge	32	72.59	Sulfur	S	16	32.064*
Gold	Au	79	196.967	Tantalum	Ta	73	180.948
Hafnium	Hf	72	178.49	Technetium	Tc	43	....
Helium	He	2	4.0026	Tellurium	Te	52	127.60
Holmium	Ho	67	164.930	Terbium	Tb	65	158.924
Hydrogen	H	1	1.00797*	Thallium	Tl	81	204.37
Indium	In	49	114.82	Thorium	Th	90	232.038
Iodine	I	53	126.9044	Thulium	Tm	69	168.934
Iridium	Ir	77	192.2	Tin	Sn	50	118.69
Iron	Fe	26	55.847†	Titanium	Ti	22	47.90
Krypton	Kr	36	83.80	Tungsten	W	74	183.85
Lanthanum	La	57	138.91	Uranium	U	92	238.03
Lawrencium	Lw	103	257	Vanadium	V	23	50.942
Lead	Pb	82	207.19	Xenon	Xe	54	131.30
Lithium	Li	3	6.939	Ytterbium	Yb	70	173.04
Lutetium	Lu	71	174.97	Yttrium	Y	39	88.905
Magnesium	Mg	12	24.312	Zinc	Zn	30	65.37
Manganese	Mn	25	54.9380	Zirconium	Zr	40	91.22
Mendelevium	Md	101	....				

Note: The values for atomic weights given in the table apply to elements as they exist in nature, without artificial alteration of their isotopic composition, and, further, to natural mixtures that do not include isotopes of radiogenic origin. (Table adopted by the International Commission on Atomic Weights of IUPAC, 1965.)

 * Atomic weights so designated are known to be variable because of natural variations in isotopic composition. The observed ranges are: hydrogen, ± 0.00001; boron, ± 0.003; carbon, ± 0.00005; oxygen, ± 0.0001; silicon, ± 0.001; sulfur, ± 0.003.

 † Atomic weights so designated are believed to have the following experimental uncertainties: chlorine, ± 0.001; chromium, ± 0.001; iron, ± 0.003; bromine, ± 0.002; silver, ± 0.003.